GOOD BEER GUIDE 1992

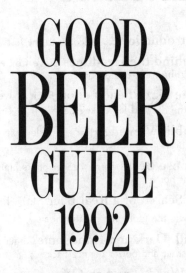

EDITED BY JEFF EVANS

Campaign for Real Ale

34 Alma Road, St Albans,
Herts, AL1 3BW

CONTENTS

Editor: Jeff Evans. **Deputy Editor:** Jill Adam. **Leg Work:** Iain Dobson, Iain Loe, Steve Cox, Malcolm Harding, Roger Protz, Andrew Sangster, Jo Bates, Catherine Dale, Su Tilley, Clare Stevens, Iljoesja Lowinsky. **Maps:** David Perrott. **Cover Design:** Rob Howells **Cover Photograph:** Tom Dobbie. **Cartoons** on pages 39, 65, 276, 282, 293, 367 and 383 first appeared in *Punch*.

Published by: Campaign for Real Ale Ltd., 34 Alma Road, St Albans, Herts, AL1 3BW. Tel. (0727) 867201 **Typeset and Printed by:** Cambridge University Press. Thanks to Philip Lunn and Richard Jacobs.

ISBN 1 85249 004 7 © Campaign for Real Ale Ltd. 1991/92

30,000 CAMRA members make this guide possible. Particular thanks go to those involved with surveying and providing vital information on beers, breweries and pubs.

INTRODUCTION

Welcome to the festivities.

We in the Campaign for Real Ale are delighted that you have decided to join us in this informal celebration of 21 years of campaigning. But in taking time out to commemorate the anniversary of the founding of this hugely successful consumer movement, we shall be sure to avoid giving ourselves a self-gratifying pat on the back, for there is still much to be done.

Yes, CAMRA has wrought memorable changes in the British brewing industry: one only has to cast one's mind back to the dark days of 1971 to realise just what has been achieved. When four beer-lovers from the North West of England put together the foundations of the movement on a holiday in Ireland, it was against a background of a rolling Red Barrel in a Britain where giant brewers were crushing smaller enterprises in their clumsy iron fists.

Beer had become gassy, cold, stale-tasting and characterless, and the big brewers were forcing unpleasant national brands down the throats of drinkers, at the expense of flavoursome, local brews.

So when the Campaign for the Revitalisation of Ale was born 21 years ago, it was in response to a mean, gluttonous beer industry that cared little for the drinkers who had made it rich and powerful. Now the drinkers were fighting back.

Interest in the movement grew rapidly. Meetings and demonstrations were well attended and branches were initiated all over the country. It seemed the beer-drinking public was not as stupid as the brewers thought it was. Soon a national consumer organisation was in full swing, and its name was changed to coin a new phrase which has become synonymous with quality in the brewing industry: it became the Campaign for *Real Ale*.

Real Ale as a term was invented to describe beer brewed in traditional style, from traditional ingredients, by traditional processes, and served in traditional ways. In other words, a beer quite unlike the keg substitutes of the time. Keg beers were processed: pasteurised, chilled and filtered at the brewery to make them easy to manage and transport, and then chilled once more at the pub to annual their stale, metallic flavour, at the same time injected with a surfeit of gas to give them some life. Real ale, in contrast, was not tampered with in any of these ways. It was allowed to leave the brewery still fermenting in its cask — unfiltered and unpasteurised, living, breathing and maturing. Its natural carbonation meant that carbon dioxide canisters were not required and the beer could be drawn to the bar by a simple handpump, electric pump or an air pressure pump, arriving there with its own gentle effervescence, not some artificial gassiness. And it was not chilled to death, but comfortably cool and refreshing, full of rich flavour.

Throughout the seventies the Campaign for Real Ale grew in prominence, taking on the brewers head to head and, whilst not always winning the battles, keeping ahead in the war. Keg beer was overwhelmingly rejected by the beer drinker and small, independent breweries found that they had an ally in their fight against the bully boys.

But, as the seventies became the eighties, some perceived the conflict to be over, with real ale now readily available in most parts of the country and even the national brewers now reinstalling handpumps on their bar counters. However, here in the nineties, new challenges keep arising and CAMRA has as much on its plate today as ever.

We are still vigilant about quality: there's no victory in being able to drink cask-conditioned beer in every pub if it's of a poor standard. And the take-over spree is still with us. Small breweries remain under threat and local brews are still being lost at the expense of national brands. Some brewers are leaving the industry, being enticed into operating simply as pub owners, their beer supplied by a distant, national beer factory. Prices continue to rise at ridiculous rates and the future of our much-abused national treasure, the pub, is being clouded by a new emphasis on retailing and profit which is destroying its greatest asset, the dedicated, genial tenant licensee.

CAMRA may have earned some laurels, but it certainly will not rest on them. Its 21st year is as important as its first and so we urge those who take an interest in what they drink to join the 30,000 of us who currently form CAMRA's highest-ever membership total. The form on page 480 outlines the benefits of membership of what is also a great social club.

Throughout CAMRA's 21 years, the *Good Beer Guide* has been the movement's flagship: drawing attention to the rights and wrongs in the industry, offering praise where due and slamming those who seek to manipulate the industry for their own ends. This year's *Guide* is no exception. The Breweries Section is once again your comprehensive listing of all Britain's traditional beers and the brewers who produce them, and the Pubs Section ensures that you are aware of nearly 5,000 outlets where these beers can be sampled. Yet these pubs are more than mere watering holes. They are listed with all the facilities they provide, from accommodation and meals to family rooms and real fires. We're also celebrating a new arrival this year, though please don't pass the cigars around on this occasion. For new amongst the symbols is one for pubs which offer no-smoking rooms or areas. In recognition of the desire of many pub-users for a smoke-free environment, we are pleased to introduce this symbol.

We have achieved much, but there's plenty more to do. Lift your glasses and let's drink to the next 21 years!

Jeff Evans: Editor

BEHIND THE HEADLINES

There have been two big stories in the news recently. One has involved companies giving up brewing to become pub-owning chains, signing supply deals with national brewers to produce their beer for them. The other has featured the decision of several major companies to move from the traditional tenancy to longer leases. What's this all about? **Steve Cox** has been eavesdropping.

Supply and Demand

The boardroom of Greed & Sons plc, a slightly ailing regional brewer. Lord Charles Greed, company Chairman, is talking to Sir Hugo Price-Wright, Group Finance Director....

Price-Wright ...So, Charles, NatBrew can brew our beer for £60 a barrel less than we can do it ourselves! All we have to do is agree a seven-year supply deal.

Greed A very tempting offer, Hugo. (*scribbles furiously*) That's about 20 pence a pint isn't it? I suppose with those big beer factories not running to capacity they must want the business pretty badly... Their over-capacity is our opportunity. (*sighs*) But I'm not sure I want to go down the Greenalls/Devenish/Boddingtons route really.

Price-Wright But it's brilliant Charles. No more production problems – you know what trouble we've had recently. No more TV campaigns persuading people to buy our frankly mediocre beer, and the national brewers are taking us apart in the free trade anyway. NatBrew will brew something more or less the same as our existing product .... (*sounds of a gin and tonic being sipped*) ... while we pocket the cash.

Greed £60 a barrel ... We won't cut prices of course.

Price-Wright Of course not. We'll claim we're investing more in our pubs.

Greed But can we sell this to the Board? It's a bit of a major change of tack, isn't it? Brewers for 170 years and all that.

Price-Wright Of course. Retailing is the buzz word for the eighties. OK, it's 1992, but it still sounds up to date. Concentrating on retail. Core activity. Getting out of manufacturing ... We'll rename the company Greed Leisure Group – GLUG. That'll impress the brewery analysts. And of course, if the replacement beer isn't up to scratch, we can always bring in one or two national brewers' beers and claim we are offering a wider choice. What the hell, the big brewers will line up to sell to us.

Greed Well, what are we going to do with our breweries? Can't imagine anyone will want to buy breweries without pubs to take the beer, after all.

5

Price-Wright	We'll close them, and blame the MMC report. Everyone else does.
Greed	But we've only got 800 pubs. What's the MMC report got to do with it?
Price-Wright	Nothing, but it sounds like a good excuse.
Greed	Fine. You've convinced me. *Eerie howl. There is a pause.*
Greed	(*quavering*) Ah, who are you?
Third Voice	(*sternly*) I am the ghost of Roger Greed, your great-great-great grand-uncle and founder of this company. You recognise me from the portrait in the sample room, no doubt.
Greed	I haven't been in the sample room recently …
Third Voice	(*sharply*) That much is obvious from anyone who has drunk the beer this year. (*more kindly*) I have returned to warn you that you are making a terrible mistake.
Greed	But … £60 a barrel … retailing … concentrating on our core activity.
Third Voice	Oh, a nice argument now, maybe. But what makes you think that you'll get the same prices in five years' time, when the nationals have finished merging and closing their breweries? When there are only three national brewers, you'll stock what they want, and at the prices they demand. They'll have you over a barrel. Besides which, whatever happened to pride in this company? You're proposing to end a fine history, to quit brewing just as cask beer sales are starting to rise. Just as people are starting to appreciate local and individual brews again. And you're signing a supply deal that makes you an annexe of the NatBrew empire. Not to mention what you're doing to the pubs. It's enough to make me turn in my grave ….

Lease Said, Soonest Mended

Meanwhile, in the offices of NatBrew Retail, the pubs division of a national brewer ….

Director	So this, gentlemen, is 'Onslaught', our new 20-year lease which will replace the traditional tenancy. Twenty years offers genuine security for the lease-holder, and, because it is 'assignable', he can sell it on to someone else. For the first time the tenant can actually benefit from the business he builds up.
1st recruit	Sounds like a good deal, sir.
2nd recruit	Yes, but I saw something in the paper the other day. It said that rents for these leases are three times those for an ordinary tenancy. Plus the lease-holder becomes responsible for repairs. Doesn't that make the lease rather expensive?
Director	(*cheerfully*) Not at all. Leases represent a much better deal for the entrepreneurial tenant.

2nd recruit I'm not sure I get this. The business won't change, will it? So how can a tenant pay three times the rent, and pay for repairs to the pub as well? The amount of beer and food they sell isn't likely to treble because they've got a new agreement, is it?

Director Well, if tenants are going to get security under the Landlord and Tenant Act, they're going to have to pay for it.

2nd recruit But surely this is going to put up prices? I mean, the lease-holder's got to try and make a living. They've got to raise the money somewhere. But if beer prices rise any further, people will stay out of pubs. And then there are all these penalties if the lease-holder doesn't sell the amount of beer we require ....

Director Look, the public may moan about beer prices but, up until now, they've always paid them.

2nd recruit I still don't see how small pubs are going to cope with these enormous rents. There's a limit to the prices people will pay. What happens if the lease-holder goes bankrupt?

Director We repossess the pub and put another lease-holder in of course.

2nd recruit At the same rent?

Director (*annoyed*) Of course. If we lowered it, it would prove we'd got it wrong the first time. And we never do that.

2nd recruit So you could say – not that I am saying so – that this security business is a bit double-edged. I mean, bankruptcy isn't terribly secure, is it?

Director Look, all these questions are quite irrelevant. This is the agreement we are asking our tenants to sign. The decision has already been taken at Board level, and that's it.

2nd recruit But we've given all the tenants notice to quit. So if they don't take on a trebled rent, you put them out on the streets by July 1992. And my local landlady is 55. What does she want with a 20-year lease?

Director Don't blame us, blame the Government. Things worked fine before we had tenant security. Anytime anyone made a real success of a pub, we could get rid of them and put in a manager. And these small pubs are a problem anyway. Backstreet locals are worth more as sites for offices. Village pubs are worth more as sites for housing. If we can't make more money out of these pubs, they'll have to close. We can't go on pouring money into repairing them. It's sink or swim, I'm afraid.

2nd recruit Hence the 'Onslaught', lease?

Director Yes, perhaps we need a better name for it.

Steve Cox is CAMRA's Campaigns and Communications Manager.

THE FIZZ PHENOMENON: The Rise and Fall of Keg Beer

Brian Glover

How are the mighty fallen. The woman at Courage's central office had never heard of it. 'Tavern? Are you sure we used to brew it?' The beer – 'it's what your right arm's for' – no longer flexed any memory muscle, let alone a distant drinker's wrist. Yet for over 20 years it had been one of the brewing giant's major products, heavily promoted in a crowd of commercials.

'Tavern Time' stopped ticking in 1984, the brand consigned to a great metal dustbin in the sky. But its legacy lives on. For the fizzical exercise left behind not only a series of slick slogans and a heap of unwanted plastic bar cowls – but also a thriving consumer campaign.

Tavern and its main keg rivals – Double Diamond (Allied Breweries), Worthington E (Bass), Tartan (Scottish & Newcastle), Tankard (Whitbread) and, brashest of all, Watney's Red – had pressurised disillusioned drinkers into striking back. Fed up with processed national blands replacing traditional local beers, they supported the Campaign for Real Ale.

The highest profile – and biggest red rag target – was provided by Watney, which replaced its earlier Red Barrel with an aggressive campaign for Watney's Red in 1971. A million pounds was spent on the Red Revolution, using a variety of left-wing leaders like Castro and Khrushchev to promote the darker, sweeter and weaker new brew. Lookalikes were found for revolutionary figures like Chairman Mao for a storm of posters, and television commercials showed counter-espionage agents trying to stop the spread of Red, by exploding road tankers. Unfortunately they failed. The thick Red line got through – and then blew up in Watney's face. Within months it was the drinkers who were revolting, and by the end of the decade Red was dead.

Little did the first brewers who tinkered with container beer imagine the bar-room battles their experiments were to unleash. And it can all be blamed on a few thirsty tennis players in East Sheen.

In 1929, Watney had bought a German pasteuriser, primarily to stabilise the bulk beer it was selling to the Far East. Sealed in five-gallon stainless steel drums, the chilled, filtered and pasteurised ale proved better able to survive the long sea voyage and high

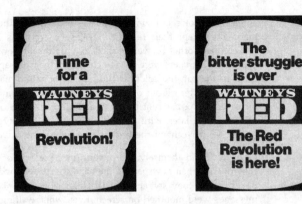

temperatures. One of Watney's brewers responsible was a member of a Surrey tennis club, and when players complained that their ale, chiefly drunk at the weekend, was going off during the week, the pasteurised beer was installed. Soon this Red Barrel brew spread to more sporting clubs and other outlets unable to handle cask ale.

Flowers of Stratford-upon-Avon, the other pioneer of container beer, introducing it in 1935, was the first to use the term 'keg'. However, it was unable to register the name and other brewers were allowed to adopt the explosive title.

But sales were still small beer; the dispense equipment, involving compressed carbon-dioxide to give the dead liquid a semblance of life, was expensive, and the poor stainless steel of the time gave an unpleasant, metallic taste. In addition, the war meant there were restrictions on the use of metals.

Keg only took off in the late fifties and early sixties, thanks to two parallel developments. On the one side were technical advances: stainless steel fabrication greatly improved; aluminium was introduced as an alternative material and inert resins were created to coat the interior of the kegs to reduce the metallic tang – but not the cooked, pasteurised taste. Most significantly, in 1958 a new design of keg was introduced where the coupling device to the dispense system was an integral part of the container. Prior to this, the beer could easily become infected through poor handling of this device in the pub cellar. Now it could be cleaned at the brewery.

The second development was the rapid growth of a handful of national combines. Frantic take-over activity saw the emergence of colossal conglomerates under Allied Breweries, Bass Charrington, Courage, Watney, Whitbread and Scottish & Newcastle. And wherever these giants trod, they left in their wake a trail of closed breweries and lost local beers. Above all, the logic of these giant groups meant national brands that could be promoted across the country from Aberdeen to Penzance; beers that would taste the same in Carlisle and Kent, and could be easily handled by any fool with a spanner – keg beers.

Already, the long, hot summer of 1959 had exposed the poor way many pubs kept their cask beer; sales of Watney's Red Barrel rocketed and other brewers rushed to jump on the cool new dray waggon. (Keg beers were usually chilled on their passage from the cellar to the bar, the coldness and high carbonation masking their lack of character.) From one per cent of the market in 1959, keg increased to six per cent by 1965 and then fizzed to over 20 per cent a decade later, with lager frothing up on the outside with a further 10 per cent of the trade. The catalyst was advertising.

Drinkers found themselves drowning in a sea of slogans. When they opened their newspapers, the names were splashed across the pages; when they switched on the television, the million-pound messages were mouthed on screen. Even while waiting at the bus stop, the brands were spread across the billboard opposite – and then on the side of the bus when it eventually arrived.

King of the kegs was Double Diamond. Once a premium bottled pale ale, a weaker keg version was introduced late in 1962 with memorable lines like 'I'm only here for the beer' and a 'Double Diamond works wonders'. By 1971, when CAMRA was born, it accounted for 27 per cent of Allied's total beer sales, and was said to be Britain's best selling beer, reaching a peak of two million barrels a year. Allied spent £500,000 advertising DD alone in 1971 – and next to nothing on traditional draught beer. Courage devoted the whole of their TV advertising budget that year to Tavern. Bass put their LSD behind Worthington E, while Whitbread tried to persuade drinkers: 'It's Tankard that helps you excel, after one you'll do anything well.'

Regional and local breweries inevitably followed the nationals in producing their own keg beers. Some, like Gibbs Mew of Salisbury, went over entirely to keg. Their main brand, in a colour clash with Watney's Red, was Blue Keg. The blue brew even fostered its own promotional menagerie of zoo animals, like the Kegopotomus, the Keglican and the Kegaroo. Others appealed to more basic instincts. Nationally, Whitbread threw down the Gauntlet to the advertising standards authorities, with a beer blatantly aimed at the young through its barely veiled image of violence and aggression. With a counter mounting of a clenched mailed fist, Gauntlet – 'It'll grab you!' – was the toast of the early soccer hooligans.

What your right arm's for.

But drinkers soon saw through the froth, helped by a series of hard-hitting exposés. 'Keg beers, gassy, highly-priced and much-loved by the husky manhood of the TV commercial are, in fact, among the worst value. Some brews are so weak they could have been sold legally in America during part of the Prohibition era,' reported the *Sunday Mirror* in 1971. Ansells of Birmingham were so embarrassed by the revelation that their Kingpin Keg contained only 2.96 per cent alcohol, that they withdrew the brew. Devenish of Cornwall were so embarrassed by the revelation that their Saxon came bottom of the keg bitter league table with 2.7 per cent that they increased its strength.

Now such beers are no more, killed off by the consumer campaign they helped create. Even the towering national brands have toppled into oblivion or a quiet corner. Tavern and Red are dead: Red is not even openly discussed. 'Whenever I ask about the beer,' explained a new employee, 'people raise their eyebrows and change the subject.' Draught Double Diamond has ceased to sparkle. 'It's still well received in a few pockets,' said a spokesman for Allied. Bass thought Worthington E had been withdrawn, but then discovered a few outlets in the North East of England. Tankard is down to a few tipplers in the South: 'Just those who still insist on it.' Only Tartan continues to flow strongly.

Some of the names have reverted to their original role — as the labels of strong export pale ales. Double Diamond is the best-selling bottled beer import in Canada; Red Barrel still rolls in the United States and Europe. But the kingdom of the keg ales in Britain has blown away, with sales of traditional cask bitter overtaking keg. Real ale has shown that there is taste and life after dead beer.

*Brian Glover is a freelance journalist, former Editor of the CAMRA newspaper, **What's Brewing**, and author of several specialist beer publications.*

PUBLIC VIEWING:
TV Locals Exposed

Hilary Kingsley

Watching as much television as I have to frequently drives me to drink. But when I was asked to consider the television pub, I began to wonder how it is I'm not teetotal.

My idea of the perfect pub is genuine oak beams, an open log fire, a friendly, but quiet, atmosphere and good food, so that if I can't be bothered to cook, I can eat well without feeling I've been reckless. What I can't abide are space invaders, warm white wine, plastic beams and coal-effect fires.

So how does the TV local rate? The most famous is the Rovers Return in *Coronation Street*, meeting place and drinking hole for the good folk of Weatherfield for over 30 years. A typical back-street pub, the Rovers seems to be the social mecca for the area; the characters rarely talk about going anywhere else. Even if they're conducting a secret affair or want to impress a new girlfriend, the first thing they do is call in at the Rovers. Wow!

Many pints ago, when it was run by Jack and Annie Walker (the woman who put the vinegar into salt 'n' vinegar crisps), the Rovers was a basic but homely pub. It had its own snug bar where, in 1964, Martha Longhurst slumped dead over a glass of milk stout.

The hub of Weatherfield life

Stout in the snug: Minnie Cawldwell (*Margot Bryant*), Ena Sharples (*Violet Carson*) and Martha Longhurst (*Lynne Carol*)

But since Newton & Ridley refurbished it, the Rovers has gone downhill. True, something had to be done (particularly when it was discovered that anyone using the gents' toilet would have ended up in Albert Tatlock's kitchen), but the new Rovers is as unimaginative as its menu. Can Betty Turpin not cook anything other than hotpot? I know her recipe is supposed to be one of the seven wonders of the catering world but it's a bit much day in day out, especially in the middle of June.

Still, unremarkable though the Rovers is, we must be grateful that old Cec Newton put the block on Nigel Ridley's plans to turn it into an American theme pub. Surely such an unsuitable setting would have spelt financial disaster for the brewery. One other point: usually in a pub, darts players are the noisiest customers. Yet the ones in the Rovers never speak. Perhaps Betty's hotpot has burned their tongues.

More to my liking is the Woolpack in *Emmerdale*, a fine traditional Yorkshire stone pub (the exterior is the Commercial Inn at Esholt near Bradford), even though I'm not sure I would want to be sitting at the same table as Joe and Jack Sugden if they had just come from the sheep dip. And I have my doubts about new licensee Alan Turner. His switch from Ephraim Monks to Skipdale Brewery immediately proved unpopular with the regulars who defected to Ernie Shuttleworth's Maltshovel. Mind you, I'm amazed they put up with Turner's predecessor, whiskery, whinging Amos Brearly, being rude to them for so long.

Most importantly, they serve real beer at the Woolpack, unlike at the Rovers, where the keg beer served up is not only unappetising but totally out of keeping with its North Western location where so many traditional breweries thrive. Ironically though, actor Stan Richards, who plays *Emmerdale's* boozer-in-chief Seth Armstrong, is not a lover of beer, much preferring scotch, but downs real ale on set in the course of duty.

13

The other famous British soap pub is the Queen Vic from *EastEnders* which sells Luxford & Copley. If the sign of a good pub is that you can eat off the floor, the Queen Vic would be a winner because it invariably looks as if someone has done just that. Certainly no palace, its clientele is rough and the bar staff are usually conducting an internal feud.

But if I survived a pint of Churchill's, I doubt if I could digest it watching Ethel's Willy slobbering over a glass or hearing Dot Cotton describe her latest health problem, though they do make efforts at the Queen Vic. Even in the days when Angie drank most of the profits and the world's slowest barman, Lofty, moved at the pace of a caterpillar (making him the original 'pub grub'), Wicksy used to entertain, if that's the right word, at the piano. The advantage, I suppose, was that there was no need to apply for a music licence and it saved having to ring the bell at chucking-out time. They've also had strippers (male and female), talent nights, karaoke, quizzes and darts matches. The Queen Vic, in fact, is a real community pub, it's just a shame about the community.

If the Queen Vic looks a bit tatty, think how preferable it is to its one-time rival, the awful Dagmar, with its potted palms, tuxedos and smarmy landlord, Wilmott-Brown. Yet the Dagmar was not the worst TV pub. That dubious honour goes to the Waterhole in *Neighbours*. Of all the bars in the world, this has to be the most boring. It has neither atmosphere nor customers. And anyone brave enough to go in should check their change. For three weeks once, the till was fixed at $3.30 – and Madge had only served mineral water.

The Woolpack's new landlord, Alan Turner (Richard Thorp), in confrontation with its boozer-in-chief, Seth Armstrong (Stan Richards)

Sam Malone (Ted Danson) mine host at Boston's Cheers

Very few television shows have actually been set in pubs, although they are regularly featured in almost all the successful series. *Only Fools and Horses* has its Nag's Head, where Del Boy knows he can order his Drambuie and grapefruit or Beaujolais Nouveau 1976 without fear of ridicule; *All Creatures Great and Small* has the Drovers and *Minder* has its Winchester Club. Back in the fifties, David Kossoff and Peggy Mount were *The Larkins*, a cockney couple running a country pub, and Jimmy Hanley ran the TV advertising magazine *Jim's Inn*. But the most successful TV drinking place of all must be *Cheers*, the American sit-com modelled on the Bull & Finch in Boston's Beacon Street. It's clean, friendly and the service, even from Woody, is quick. One word of warning though – the 'beer' is not even the gassy keg lager it is supposed to be, rather a coloured mixture laced with salt to make it foam. George Wendt, who plays big Norm, describes it as 'revolting'.

Long-running series often sprout pubs, almost begrudgingly in the case of *Brookside*, the show that hoped to break the soap mould. The rougher elements of *Brookside* pop down to the Swan (fine if you don't mind the odd murder) and Sheila Grant actually served there for a while, the equivalent of Mavis Wilton working at a strip club. The Crossroads Motel once boasted one of the smallest bars in history where Amy Turtle served a clear-coloured liquid even if the customer asked for a scotch, but probably the best public houses on TV are those in *Inspector Morse*, although John Thaw admits that he is not a beer drinker. Not all actors are like John and Stan Richards though. When James Bolam and Rodney Bewes played *The Likely Lads*, it was not uncommon for them to knock back nine pints of bitter during a recording. And they managed to remember their lines.

So, rather like beer itself, TV pubs are a matter of taste. The Waterhole is weak and watery, Cheers is lively and fruity, the Rovers is flat with a hint of sourness, the Queen Vic is a bit gassy and the Woolpack is full-bodied with a distinctive aroma. If you don't mind, though, I think I'd rather stay at home with a mug of Ovaltine.

*Hilary Kingsley is television critic of the **Daily Mirror**.*

HOUSE BEERS:
Enjoying Beer at Home

Barrie Pepper

Having turned on the word processor, please excuse me while I draw myself a pint of mild from the cask under the stairs. OK? Then let's begin.

I suppose I was the only kid in England who went to the South Yorkshire coalfield for his summer holidays. It was part of an exchange deal with a cousin of similar age who would spend his holidays with my family. As we lived in the boisterous seaside resort of Blackpool, there was some sort of perverse logic about it. Apart from the timeless cricket test matches on Darfield recreation ground, my most pleasant memories are those of visiting Mr Durdy's off-licence shop to fetch a quart of Barnsley Bitter for my uncle. It was carried in a jug that held just the correct amount and my instructions were specific: 'Sup rather than spill!' The reward was a glass of shandy.

The corner off-licence is now, with a handful of exceptions, part of the folk history of drinking at home. It has been submerged in a sea of supermarkets and mini-markets in the retail rape of the last three decades. Only those shops able to offer specialist opportunities to the home drinker can compete. Even then there are problems. My attempt to follow the television programmes of Beer Hunter Michael Jackson around the world with an appropriate beer for each country met defeat in the episode on the United States. That I should drink the awful Budweiser after sampling the superb Budvar from Czechoslovakia was unthinkable.

Drinking at home is as old as drinking in the pub, possibly older. From the late 18th century and into the present one, urban pubs had jug and bottle departments from where respectable widows and spinsters would carry home their pint of stout covered by a cloth. Common brewers would offer for sale a tempting list of beers in pins, firkins and kilderkins or in imperial pint bottles by the dozen. Every big house or farm would have a tapped barrel in the kitchen and working class homes would take in a case or two of the bottled local brew, if only at Christmas.

Within recent memory, the sadly missed Davenports brewery sent its vans around the streets of midland and northern towns selling its 'Beer at Home', and breweries produced 'Family' and 'Dinner' ales specially for the take-home trade. They lacked real character but did little harm.

Price list from Stansfeld & Co.'s brewery, showing Dinner Ale from 4/6d

Then along came beer in cans. Its nascence in Britain was in 1936 but its real emergence was in the fifties and sixties. There was Long Life, a near beer from Ind Coope, and party cans from Watney, which were all the rage for a while (though the likelihood of you being invited to another party was left in question). They tasted like metal polish and had all the charisma of BO in a space suit.

Many people brewed at home and many still do. Up to the 1950s it was illegal to produce home brews beyond a rather limited gravity. It was one of those stupid laws that could never be policed and, like dog licences at seven and a tanner, was universally ignored. Eventually it was revoked and home brewing had a birthday.

Of course there is home brewing and home brewing. Some of the materials for this activity come in a can. Malt extract and hop extract are supplied along with dried yeast; all the home brewer needs to add is water and sugar. Tastes vary but generally the end product is cloying and sweet. The true exponents crush their own barley for a full mash, add appropriate hops and ferment by using yeast begged, borrowed or stolen from the local brewery. Again styles vary according to taste, but many amateur brewers produce beers of quality and character. The canard that all home-brew is of great strength is usually passed on after someone has suffered on the day after a pint or two of something from a kit. But the accolade for the worst home-brew must go to a Yorkshire 'inventor' who came up with a brew bag – simply add water, wait for two weeks and drink. Ugh.

Alongside the real ale revolution in the mid-seventies, there was a minor but significant turn around in the take-home beer trade. It developed with the arrival in Britain of specialist foreign beers,

17

including some excellent ones from Belgium and Germany. Then, in 1978, a number of CAMRA members in Leeds formed a co-operative to open a real ale off-licence shop – the Ale House – strategically situated close to the city's university and bed-sitter land. From a bank of handpulls it sold cask-conditioned beer in quantities from half a pint in your own bottle to a polypin, and casks from a pin to a hogshead. There were wines, spirits and bottle beers as well, but the dreaded cans were eschewed. It was an idea that was copied in Liverpool, Bradford, York and other towns. Then the big brewers, fearful perhaps of the move breaking into their profits, encouraged their licensees to promote outsales of draught beer in plastic 'carry kegs'.

The Ale House, pioneer of take-away draught beer

There was encouragement from several quarters for these moves, not least from the police who saw drinking at home as a positive move to safer roads. CAMRA had spawned CART – the Campaign for Real Take-home – to combat the advance of bright beer in quart-sized PET bottles, developed first, appropriately enough, for Davenports.

In 1979 Guinness promoted its 'draught Guinness in a bottle', an incongruity that never really took off. With each six pack was a twizzle stick that enabled you to create the famous creamy head so beloved by drinkers of that classic Dublin drink. It was several years later before others were to copy. Guinness came back with 'canned draught Guinness', using a more sophisticated method to create the head. Now some of the bigger brewers – Courage, Ind Coope, Bass and Whitbread – are following suit and putting some of their top-selling 'draught' ales into cans. The difference between these beers and other straightforward beers in a can is that some of them contain a special thingummyjig which releases nitrogen to create a head not unlike that from a handpull sparkler. Others have the gas inserted before canning.

The latest take-home trend: 'draught' beers in a can

Whilst these beers probably start their life as the same brew as real draught ale, they are then filtered and pasteurised and they have an aroma of metal that all the sophisticated technology of coating can interiors has been unable to remove. Ironically Guinness, which won a Queen's Award for Technological Achievement for its new device, has come up with a brand new, new brand called Guinness Draught Bitter, brewed solely for the home trade.

Bottled beers may be heavier and bulkier to carry but they have the advantage of being better tasting than the canned varieties and are regarded as more ecologically sound. And bottled specialist beers and lagers from the Continent are now widely available thanks to the enlightened buying policies of the larger supermarket chains. Tesco, in particular, has extended its selection to include such excellent beers as Pilsner Urquell and Budweiser Budvar from Czechoslovakia, some Rauchbier and Weisse from Germany and the Lambic and Trappist beers of Belgium. Some of these beers are difficult to find in pubs and in any case are often best appreciated at home.

In the way that wine drinkers lay down a stock for their personal consumption, beer drinkers should be encouraged to do the same. A case of Worthington White Shield might just last through a couple of dinner parties, and a half a dozen corked bottles of the splendid Chimay Red can take their place alongside the '82 Chateau Lafite in the cellar.

Drinking at home can often be a much more personal and satisfying activity than a visit to the pub, particularly on wet winter evenings with Beethoven on the turntable and a roaring fire in the grate. So, with an empty glass, I bid my farewells and repair to the cask for replenishment. Paradise enough.

A freelance writer, broadcaster and journalist, Barrie Pepper is also Chairman of the British Guild of Beer Writers.

19

IN SEARCH OF A REAL BEER: Why Go Ale-Less Abroad?

Michael Jackson

Britishers visiting that other place, commonly known as Abroad, frequently observe that there is nothing to drink but lager. In some countries, the lager may be very good, but that can still fail to satisfy the craving for the more complex flavours of an ale. The answer to this requirement is to travel, where possible, in countries which do brew some ales (or, often, porters or stouts). As CAMRA members may be aware, but perhaps not other readers of this guide, there are more such countries than might be expected.

In some instances, their brews will even meet the definition of real ale, in that they will be 'naturally conditioned', though their secondary fermentation is often in the bottle rather than the cask.

THE LOW COUNTRIES Britain's best pubs cannot offer the selection of bottle-conditioned ales available in some other countries. Two of my favourite beer-bars anywhere in the world are in Amsterdam. Their names translate easily: Het Laatste Oordeel (Raadhuis Straat) and In De Wildeman (Nieuwezijds Kolk, near the main street called the Damrak). The 'Wild Man' is closed on Sundays, and so are several of the Continent's best-known specialist beer cafés; phone before you visit. Both of these Amsterdam bars have the best of beers from The Netherlands as well as a great selection of well-kept Belgian brews (many unpasteurised or bottle-conditioned).

Several countries well known for their lagers also make ales. This is true of The Netherlands, but Belgium is the outstanding example: noted by unschooled drinkers for its not-bad lager but by connoisseurs for its tradition of colourful ales. One of those most readily recognizable as an ale is the robust, spicy brew identified simply as De Koninck, and made in Antwerp. Like many brews, this is far better on draught than in the bottle. From the tap, it is filtered but not pasteurised. Drinkers are offered a shot-glass of the yeast to tip back into their De Koninck at the characterful pub opposite the brewery (Café Pelgrim, on Boomgaard Straat). Or try De Koninck in the student café Den Engel, on the Grote Markt, or Quinten Matsijs, at the corner of Moriaan Straat and Hoofdkerk Straat).

None of these three cafés has a large selection of beers. For that, try Kulminator, at 32 Vleminckveld, which has a huge range. Every city in Belgium has specialist beer cafés, and among those I have

20

One of the Low Countries' many specialist beer bars

enjoyed are De Hopduvel, Rokerel Straat, Ghent; 't Brugs Beertje, Kemel Straat, Bruges; Chez Moeder Lambic, Boendaalse Steeweg, Elsene, Brussels; and Taverne Botteltje, Louisa Straat, Ostend.

Lambic is a style of beer: arguably the most 'real' of all, in that it is fermented with wild yeasts. These impart a winey character. Natural Lambic, very low in carbonation, and often tart, is rarely found outside the region of production: the villages on the western periphery of Brussels. A blend of young and old Lambics creates a more carbonated product called Gueuze. A sweetened version is known as Faro. Sometimes cherries are added, to make a beer called Kriek; or raspberries, to make Frambozen or Framboise, depending upon your choice of language.

Two famous Brussels cafés specialising in this style, albeit in relatively tame versions, are nonetheless worth a visit: Becasse, at Rue Tabora, just behind Grand' Place; and Mort Subite, at Rue de Montagne-aux-Herbes Potagères. In the producing district, I strongly recommend In De Rare Vos, in the village of Schepdaal, and the various cafés in Beersel.

Even the most unambitious of Belgian cafés is likely to offer a tempting beer-list. The most fashionable style at the moment is 'White Beer' such as Hoegaarden, made with wheat, seasoned with coriander and Curaçao orange peels, and fermented with an ale yeast, which leaves a heavy sediment.

Although it is not bottle-conditioned, Rodenbach Grand Cru is an ale which should be sampled by any visitor to Belgium. With an intentional sourness imparted by two years' maturation in ceiling-high wooden casks, it is surely the most quenching beer in the world.

21

Beers labelled as Saisons are summer-seasonal quenchers of a more obviously ale-like character, and usually come in wine bottles, with a yeast sediment. Five Trappist monasteries make bottle-conditioned strong ales, and several other abbeys give their name to similar products made in commercial breweries. The Trappist monastery of Westmalle is famous for a strong golden ale called Tripel, which is another Belgian classic, as is the strong golden ale called Duvel, which means devil.

FRANCE Belgian brews are popular in France, which also has its own ales, called Bières de Garde. Most of them are brewed in the area between Lille and Boulogne, and they are readily available in the cafés and supermarkets of the Channel ports. Jenlain, La Choulette and Trois Monts are all good examples: spicy, malty, and full of flavour.

Both Belgian and French ales are widely available in the speciality beer cafés of Paris. If you have time to visit only one, I would suggest Au Général La Fayette. This is at 52 Rue La Fayette, and closes on Sundays.

Lorraine and Alsace have the reputation, but in the reality the less interesting brews, though it does not hurt to try Aldelscott, made with a dash of smoked whisky malt. In Strasbourg, visit the beer café Aux 12 Apôtres, at Rue Mercière, near the Cathedral.

IN THE ALPS Across the border in Switzerland, you might just find an Altbier (the usual term for an ale), or Weizenbier (a spicy, fruity, wheat beer, made with an ale yeast, and often unfiltered). Try the tiny house brewery at the Fischerstube, at 45 Rheingasse, Basel, noted for its Weizenbier. In Austria, a very malty Altbier called St Thomas Bräu is made by Baron Bachofen von Echte in the cellars of his schloss (chateau) at Nüssdorf, on the edge of Vienna. Take the Nüssdorf tram to the end of the line, and ask for the brauhaus.

A choice of ales from San Francisco's Anchor Steam brewery

GERMANY Altbier and Weizenbier are known in many parts of the German-speaking world. In Germany itself, Düsseldorf is especially known for its Altbier (the best is at Zum Uerige, at Berger Strasse, in the Old Town); Cologne makes a very pale, golden, style of ale called Kölschbier (try Päffgen, Friesen Strasse or Malzmühle, at Heumarkt); and Weizenbier is especially associated with Bavaria. Try the example called Aventinus at the Schneider tavern, on Tal Strasse, in Munich. In recent years, almost every German city has sprouted new 'house breweries', most of them specialising in unfiltered beers, and, wherever you travel throughout the developed world, it is worth asking your hosts, guides or friendly beer-lovers if there is a 'house brewery', 'brew pub' or 'micro-brewery' in town. There are too many to list here.

In the absence of any of the treats promised thus far, you may have to settle for a damned fine lager. Germany and Czechoslovakia have the best. In Germany especially, watch out for immensely strong lagers described as Bock. These are regarded as historical specialities in Munich and Kulmbach, Franconia. Germany, and particularly Franconia, offer several unfiltered variations; look out for signs saying: kellerbier, kräusenbier, zwickelbier or ungespunderd. In Franconia, the town of Bamberg specialises in Rauchbier (smoked lager). In Czechoslovakia, Prague has a wonderful dark lager at U Fleků (11 Kremencova, in the New Town).

USA Throughout Eastern Europe, the Mediterranean, Asia and Australasia, it never hurts to ask for ale, porter, stout, dark lager or wheat beer. You may be pleasantly surprised, especially in Japan and Australia. But the biggest surprises in the New World are in North America, where the number of new small breweries runs into hundreds. If you are in Los Angeles, make sure to sample the range of small-brewery beers at a bar called Father's Office (1018 Montana Ave, Santa Monica). In San Francisco, call 863-8350 to arrange a visit to the Anchor Steam brewery and, while you are there, pick up a copy of *The Celebrator*, a newspaper listing beer-bars and the 70-odd breweries in the state. Several US states now have such papers, however the North West is the beer capital. Sample beer on the premises at the Bridgeport, Widmer and Portland breweries (all in Portland) and at Red Hook in Seattle. My favourite pub in Seattle is the Red Door, in Fremont, and I would recommend a one-day trip to Grant's brew pub in Yakima.

In Middle America, visit Sherlock's Home, in Minneapolis, and Goose Island, in Chicago. On the East Coast, head for the Commonwealth brew pub and Doyle's Bar, in Boston; the Manhattan Brewing Company, Brewksy's and the Peculier Pub, in New York; Dock Street and Sam Adams, in Philadelphia; Sissons and Baltimore Brewing in that city; and The Brickskeller in Washington, DC.

That is no more than a taste but, as they say in America, enjoy!

*'Beer Hunter' Michael Jackson is author of **The Pocket Beer Book** (Mitchell Beazley).*

23

TALL, DARK AND HANDSOME: Stout and Porter Bounce Back

Roger Protz

Benjamin Disraeli, after a late-night sitting in parliament, repaired to a restaurant and supped well on oysters and Guinness. As early as the mid-19th century, with a plethora of brewers producing dark porters and stouts, the leader of the Tory Party saw fit to ask for one brand of beer by name. Even then, Guinness had set down its marker as the greatest stout brewer in the world. It had become a legend in its own mealtime.

Today people ask for 'a Guinness' as casually as others speak of 'Hoovering the carpet' when they are using a vacuum cleaner made by a different company. 'Guinness' and 'stout' have become synonymous, to the chagrin of the handful of brewers who still walk in its giant shadow with their own dark beers.

Such is Guinness's dominance – its beers are available in 120 countries and are brewed under licence in 34 – that stout is considered to be quintessentially Irish. But at the risk of rousing nationalist feeling, it must be said for the record that the origins of porter and stout lie not in Ireland but at the heart of the old imperial nation: they are, in short, London inventions.

The Anglo-Irish poet and satirist Jonathan Swift mentioned stout in one of his works as early as 1720. He was undoubtedly referring to a strong beer, probably brown in colour as was the London style, but almost certainly not black. For it was the habit of brewers of the time to call the strongest beer they produced 'Stout Butt Beer' or 'Stout' for short.

Within a few years, stout was to become a more definitive brewing term when, just two years after Swift had penned his lines, a publican in East London started to brew a new type of beer that was to revolutionise the brewing industry.

Ralph Harwood was the owner of the Bell Brewhouse in Shoreditch. As the name of the tavern implies, he brewed his own ale, in common with most of his contemporaries. He served a mainly working-class clientele, including many market porters. They had acquired a taste for a beer called 'Three Threads' – a mix of three ales: pale ale, young brown ale and 'Twopenny', a mature old ale. The name of the mix came from the fact that the beers were poured from spiggots threaded into three different casks.

Disraeli's supper of oysters and Guinness, as viewed by Rex Whistler (reprinted by kind permission of Guinness PLC)

Harwood decided to brew one beer that would replicate all three. He called his new brew 'Entire Butt', as it came from just the one cask, but such was the insatiable demand for it among his customers that it quickly acquired the nickname of 'Porter'.

The demand for porter became so vast that by 1758 a writer described it as 'the universal cordial of the populace'. Publican brewers such as Harwood could not keep pace with it and commercial or 'common' brewers switched from ale to porter brewing.

The young Samuel Whitbread moved from his first, small, ale brewery at Old Street to new premises in Chiswell Street where he produced only porter, with the aid of all the new technologies made possible by the industrial revolution, such as steam power and, later, yeast cultivation and refrigeration. By the early 19th century porter had provided the springboard for a modern commercial brewing industry dominated by companies with the capital to build great brewhouses capable of producing vast amounts of beer. In 1812 Whitbread's Chiswell Street plant brewed 122,000 barrels of porter a year, Barclay Perkins 270,000, Meux Reid 180,000 and Truman Hanbury 150,000.

Porter and stout – and stout now meant the strongest porter brewed – were exported far and wide: to Imperial Russia, the American colonies... and Ireland. In Dublin, in 1759, a young brewer named Arthur Guinness had bought a semi-derelict brewery

25

in St James's Gate and, in common with the other brewers of the Irish capital, produced ale. He tasted the dark beers from London and in 1799 took the fateful decision to emulate Sam Whitbread and convert his brewhouse solely for porter and stout production.

He bequeathed to his heirs the foundations for one of the greatest brewing dynasties ever known. Today Guinness no longer brews porter (the last batches were produced in the 1970s) but its Extra Stout, foreign Extra Stout and the bottle-conditioned Original Stout continue to delight millions. The group accounts for 83 per cent of stout production in the Irish republic but, with sales growing, there is sufficient slack for the two Cork brewers, Beamish and Murphy, to also ride the black tide.

These Irish stouts, weighing in at less than 4 per cent alcohol by volume, are less than half the strength of their illustrious forebears. The ingredients may be used more sparingly, especially hops, but the recipes are largely unchanged. At the heart of porter and stout lies black malt, either in the form of malt that has been kilned and roasted to extreme, or unmalted roasted barley which looks and tastes like roasted coffee beans. It is these dark malts that not only give the finished beers their ruby-black colour but also the rich and tempting aromas and flavours of roasted grain, black chocolate and coffee.

The London Porter brewed by Pitfield Brewery (now part of Premier Ales) uses an 1850s Whitbread recipe that comprises pale, crystal and black malt. At 5.5 per cent alcohol, it is close to the strength of the everyday sipping porters brewed at that time. Nethergate Brewery's Old Growler in Suffolk, with an even more impressive 5.8 per cent ABV, is based on an older recipe, a 1750 London one for mild. Mild is not a true member of the porter family but with that alcoholic strength and a recipe that includes pale, crystal and black malt, it must be close to the type of beer first perfected by Ralph Harwood. Nethergate no longer adds coriander and bog myrtle, though, part of the original ingredients list, indicating that hops in the 18th century were still joined in the copper by plants that had added bitterness to beer for centuries, long before the hop arrived in England from the Low Countries.

(*Reprinted by kind permission of Guinness PLC*)

(Reprinted by kind permission of Guinness PLC)

Among the many fascinating attempts to recreate British, as opposed to Irish, versions of porter and stout, Burton Bridge brews a bottle- and cask-conditioned porter that uses chocolate malt rather than black. It has a delectable biscuity flavour and dry, bitter finish with strong chocolate notes.

It is good to see the porter revival reaching Burton on Trent, for it was here that pale ales developed in the 19th century and, once their popularity was established, sent dark beers into rapid decline. Porter and stout had all but vanished from the scene in Britain by 1914 though variations on the theme, such as sweet, milk and even oyster stouts, lingered on and Mackeson, an underrated beer, is with us still.

The Irish stouts dominate the market. The 'draught' versions are now all keg – filtered, pasteurised and served by a mixed gas system of nitrogen and carbon dioxide. Only a churl would deny that they are good, rich and tasty beers, even though they are pressurised. But it is good to see – and the Breweries Section of the *Guide* is testimony to the fact – that a growing number of British brewers are returning to the dark fold with true, cask versions of the style.

I am tempted to call this new breed the real McCoy but I might raise eyebrows among my good friends in Cork and Dublin. Let's just say that Mr Disraeli would have enjoyed them with his oysters.

*Roger Protz is a former Editor of the **Good Beer Guide** and a regular contributor to **The Guardian**, the **Morning Advertiser** and Radio 4's **Food Programme**. He is now Editor of the CAMRA newspaper, **What's Brewing** and author of many books on beer and pubs.*

A WORD – AND A SPECIAL OFFER – FROM THE *GBG* SPONSORS

The link between real ale and real fires is undisputed. More than 1,000 of the pubs in this year's *Guide* already appreciate the true value of a real coal fire and its unique ability to draw in customers, especially on a cold winter's night.

All those publicans, customers and lovers of everything genuine know the warm welcome that only an open fire can give to a pub's bar or lounge. What better way to escape the everyday pressures of life?

But as sponsors for the ninth time of the ever popular *Good Beer Guide*, that is all we have to say to extol the virtues of coal. Instead, this year we're backing up our claims by making it even easier for *Good Beer Guide* readers to return to a real fire.

British Coal has produced a new video guide, *Opening Up Your Fireplace*, to help meet an ever growing public demand, as more and more people re-open disused fireplaces and put the life back into the room. The step-by-step video guide was originally produced to help professional fireplace installers, but we feel that it's so easy to follow that the guide will benefit any enthusiastic DIYer looking to bring a coal fire back into their life. Priced at £4.99, we are giving them away free by post to the first 500 *Good Beer Guide* readers who write asking for a copy!

OPENING UP YOUR FIREPLACE

Fortunately, most houses – and pubs – do still have chimneys or class one flues and for them a return to the traditional values of an open fire can be surprisingly simple. Just watch this video and see for yourself.

All you have to do is write, with your name and address to:

> The *GBG* Video Offer,
> The Cosyhome Sales Office,
> British Coal,
> Freepost,
> Eastwood,
> Nottingham,
> NG16 3BR

and it won't even cost you a stamp!

British Coal will send you a free copy of the video guide and a covering letter offering you ten per cent discount on a selected range of attractive fireplaces. Open up your fireplace to solid fuel and we'll automatically make you a member of the *Coal Customer Club*, complete with all the special offers and privileges that entails. As a member you'll be sent regular copies of *Club News*, with up to date information about the fires, roomheaters, central heating systems and services available from British Coal.

Don't you think it's time for *you* to rediscover the pleasures of a real coal fire?

PS If your local doesn't have a real coal fire, why not have a quiet word with your landlord. In fact, why not lend him your copy of the video after you have opened up your own fireplace?

USING THE
GOOD BEER GUIDE

**PUB
ENTRIES**

Pubs are arranged in counties and then in alphabetical order of towns and villages. English counties come first, then Welsh. Scottish regions, Northern Ireland and the remaining British Islands follow. East and West Sussex fall under S; North, South and West Yorkshire under Y, and the Glamorgans under G.

**TYPES
OF PUB**

All pubs are selected by CAMRA branches; they are pubs used and visited regularly by CAMRA members all year round. Primary qualification for entry is the quality of the beer served, in conjunction with the selection available and the service provided. But such is the variety of pubs serving good ale these days that you will find all kinds of hostelry, from a basic back-street boozer to a graceful country inn, and from a lively, young persons' haunt to a relaxing pub where conversation is the only entertainment. There are pubs for everyone, offering accommodation, meals, real fires, gardens, traditional games, children's facilities and, now, no-smoking areas – and all with great beer.

**OPENING
HOURS**

Pubs in England and Wales can now open between 11am and 11pm, though some may choose to be more restrictive. The hours provided are correct at the time of surveying, but licensees may vary their opening times according to trade. Sunday hours are standard, 12–3 and 7–10.30, unless otherwise stated. For Scotland and other areas, see the appropriate section of the *Guide*.

BEERS

Beers are listed in alphabetical order of brewery and then in increasing gravity order – as a rule of thumb, the weakest first. Only real ales are listed. Tenants of national breweries now have the right to stock a 'guest' beer, a real ale of their own choosing, not brewed by the brewery which owns their pub. Whilst the big breweries have worked hard to undermine this prerogative, many tenants now take the opportunity to stock a guest, and this is indicated in the text. The term 'guest' has also been used in other pubs where extra beers are occasionally introduced alongside regular offerings. Seasonal beers, such as winter ales, are clearly not always available. Check the Breweries Section for detailed information on all beers.

**MAPS
AND
SYMBOLS**

Each county is accompanied by a map indicating the location of pub entries and the independent breweries which brew there. Don't forget to check neighbouring counties for even more pubs, if you are near the county boundary. A full explanation of the symbols used is provided on the inside front cover.

Happy Drinking!

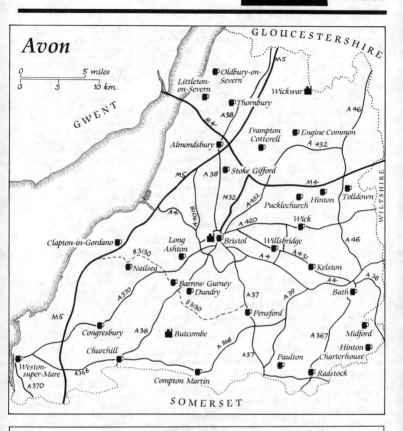

Avon

GLOUCESTERSHIRE

GWENT

WILTSHIRE

0 5 miles
0 5 10 km

Littleton-on-Severn · Oldbury-on-Severn · Wickwar · Thornbury · Engine Common · Frampton Cotterell · Almondsbury · Stoke Gifford · Pucklechurch · Hinton · Tolldown · Clapton-in-Gordano · Long Ashton · Bristol · Willsbridge · Kelston · Nailsea · Barrow Gurney · Dundry · Pensford · Bath · Congresbury · Butcombe · Midford · Hinton Charterhouse · Churchill · Paulton · Radstock · Weston-super-Mare · Compton Martin

SOMERSET

Butcombe, Butcombe; **Hardington, Ross, Smiles**, Bristol; **Wickwar**, Wickwar

---

Almondsbury

Bowl
16 Church Road, Lower Almondsbury (off A38)
☎ (0454) 612757
11–3, 6 (5.30 Fri)–11
Courage Bitter Ale, Best Bitter, Directors; John Smith's Bitter; Wadworth 6X *or* **Eldridge Pope Royal Oak** Ⓗ
Comfortable, old village pub next to the church.
🏠 Q ⑧ ⌶ ◖ ◗ ♣ P

Barrow Gurney

Princes Motto
Barrow Street
☎ (0272) 472282
11–2.30, 6–11 (12–2, 7–10.30 Sun)
Draught Bass Ⓖ; **Butcombe Bitter** Ⓗ; **Marston's Pedigree** Ⓗ; **Wadworth 6X** Ⓖ; **Whitbread Boddingtons Bitter** Ⓗ
Friendly, unassuming, well-run free house with a good fire in winter. Restricted parking. Use

roadside, carefully. Large garden. 🏠 Q ⑧ ♣ P

Bath

Bell Inn
103 Walcot Street
☎ (0225) 460426
11.30–11
Courage Best Bitter, Directors; Eldridge Pope Royal Oak; Smiles Best Bitter Ⓗ
A lively boozer, locally renowned for its jazz and soul music on Mon and Wed eves and Sun lunchtimes. Bar billiards. 🏠 ♣ ♣

Belvedere Wine Vaults
25 Belvedere, Lansdown Road
☎ (0225) 330264
11–3, 5.30–11
Draught Bass; Charrington IPA Ⓗ
Welcoming, unpretentious local with a quiet lounge bar. Q ⊕ ♣

Coeur de Lion
17 Northumberland Place (in passageway opp. Guildhall)

☎ (0225) 465371
11.30–11
Cornish Original, Steam Bitter, Royal Wessex Ⓗ
Generally reckoned to be the smallest pub in Bath; has survived two attempts by the brewery to close it down. The frontage features superb stained-glass windows from the now defunct Devenish brewery.
≈ (Spa)

Devonshire Arms
139 Wellsway (A367)
☎ (0225) 428837
11–2.30 (3 Sat), 6–11
Draught Bass; Wadworth 6X; Welsh Brewers Worthington BB Ⓗ
Refurbished local with a skittle alley as part of the public bar. Live music Thu and Sat nights. Eve meals served Mon–Thu.
◖ ◗ ⊕ ♣ P

Fairfield Arms
1 Fairfield Park Road, Fairfield Park ☎ (0225) 310594
11–2.30 (3 Sat), 6–11
Courage Best Bitter; John Smith's Bitter Ⓗ

31

Avon

Welcoming local on the north-eastern outskirts of the city.
🏠 🍴 ♣

Golden Fleece
1–3 Avon Buildings, Lower Bristol Road (A36)
☎ (0225) 429572
11–2.30, 5.30–11
Courage Bitter Ale, Best Bitter; John Smith's Bitter 🅷
Traditional, corner pub within easy walking distance of Twerton Park football ground. Interesting guest beer programme. No food Sun.
🍴 🍺 ♣ P

Hatchets
6–7 Queen Street (off Queen Sq) ☎ (0225) 425045
11–11
Beer range varies 🅷
Pleasant surroundings for good food at lunchtimes; lively in the evenings, when the upstairs bar is popular with younger drinkers. Three regular guest beers, plus house beer, Hatchets Best, brewed by Mole's. 🍴 ⇄ (Spa)

King William
36 Thomas Street, London Road (A4) ☎ (0225) 428096
11–11
Archers Village, Best Bitter; Marston's Pedigree 🅷
Lively, street-corner boozer. Guest beer. 🍺 ♣

Larkhall Inn
St Saviours Road, Larkhall
☎ (0225) 425710
11–2.30, 6–10.30 (11 Fri & Sat)
Courage Best Bitter, Directors 🅷
Distinctive pub with unusual brass beer engines. No entry after 10.30pm Fri and Sat.
🏠 Q 🏠 🍺 ♣

Midland Hotel
14 James Street West
☎ (0225) 425029
11–3, 5.30–11 (11–11 Sat in summer)
Courage Bitter Ale, Best Bitter, Directors 🅷
Large, central pub opposite the old Green Park railway station (now a supermarket). No food Sun. 🍴 🍺 ♣

New Westhall
Upper Bristol Road (A4)
☎ (0225) 425432
11–2.30, 5.30–11 (11–11 Sat)
Marston's Border Mild, Border Bitter, Pedigree 🅷
Popular, main road local, opposite Royal Victoria Park. Small car park. 🏠 🍴 🍺 ♣ P

Olde Farmhouse
1 Lansdown Road
☎ (0225) 316162
12–3, 6–11 (12–11 Fri & Sat)
Draught Bass; Butcombe Bitter; Hall & Woodhouse Tanglefoot; Wadworth 6X 🅷

Lively local of great character. Bar billiards played. Eve meals Fri and Sat only. Small car park.
🏠 ♦ P

Pig & Fiddle
2 Saracen Street
☎ (0225) 460868
12–3, 5 (6 Sat)–11
Ash Vine Bitter, Challenger, Tanker 🅷
A former fish restaurant: Bath's first new pub in many years and Ash Vine's only tied house, apart from the original brew pub in Somerset. Two regular guest beers and Thatcher's cider. No food Sun. 🏠 🍴 ⇄ ⏷

Porter Butt
York Place, London Road (A4)
☎ (0225) 425084
12–3, 5–11 (12–11 Sat)
Draught Bass; Courage Bitter Ale, Best Bitter, Directors 🅷
Two-bar local with upstairs function and meeting rooms; next to local bus depot. Live music. No food Sun. 🏠 🍴 🍺 ♣ P

Rose & Crown
6 Brougham Place, Larkhall (400 yds NW of A4/A46 jct)
☎ (0225) 425700
11–2.30, 5–11 (11–11 Sat)
Butcombe Bitter; Marston's Pedigree; Wickwar Brand Oak 🅷
Friendly, out of town local, worth seeking out. Thatcher's cider. 🍺 ♣ ⏷

Smith Brothers
11–12 Westgate Buildings
☎ (0225) 330470
11–11 (11–3, 5.30–11 winter)
Eldridge Pope Hardy Country, Royal Oak 🅷
Spacious, central, one-room pub with a public bar section. Regular guest beer. Small car park. 🍴 ♦ ⇄ ♣ P

Star
23 The Vineyards (A4)
☎ (0225) 425072
11–2.30, 5.30–11
Draught Bass 🅶**; Charrington IPA; Wadworth 6X, Old Timer** 🅷
Enjoy the atmosphere in this classic town pub, where Bass is still served from the jug.
🏠 Q 🍺 ♣

Bristol

Brewery Tap
8 Upper Maudlin Street (next to Smiles brewery)
☎ (0272) 297350
11–11 (closed Sun)
Smiles Brewery Bitter, Best Bitter, Exhibition 🅷
Small, intimate and imaginatively designed with wood panelling inset with hop sack, an attractive slate horseshoe bar and a chequered-tiled floor. Guest beers and specialist

Belgian bottled beers available, incl. Chimay and Duval. Opens at 8am for breakfasts. Q 🍴

Brown Jug, Real Ale Off-Licence
77 Garnet Street, Bedminster (off the Chessells)
☎ (0272) 635145
5–10.30 (11–2, 6–10.30 Sat; 12–2, 7–10 Sun)
Beer range varies
Real ale off-licence run by a CAMRA member. Two real ales usually available, offering an imaginative choice at very competitive prices.

Cadbury House
68 Richmond Road, Montpelier (off Cheltenham Road, A38)
☎ (0272) 247874
12–11
Courage Best Bitter; Wadworth 6X; Wickwar Brand Oak, Olde Merryford 🅷
A no-frills, one-bar pub, serving a local, predominantly young clientele. Music can be loud in the eve. Meals available any time until early eve.
🏠 🏠 🍴 ♦ ⇄ (Montpelier)

Cambridge Arms
Coldharbour Road, Redland
☎ (0272) 735754
11–11
Courage Bitter Ale, Best Bitter, Directors 🅷
Comfortable, well-run pub with a large garden at the rear. Attracts a good mix of clientele and can get busy. Interesting meals. Guest beer. 🏠 🍴 P

Greyhound
32 Princess Victoria Street, Clifton ☎ (0272) 734187
11–11
Draught Bass; Courage Best Bitter, Directors; John Smith's Bitter 🅷
Small, two-bar pub: a busy, narrow front bar and a food-oriented back bar, offering a wide choice of meals. Popular with the business community in historic Clifton 'Village'. Fine old facade. 🏠 🍴 🍺

Highbury Vaults
164 St Michaels Hill, Kingsdown (off B4051)
☎ (0272) 733203
12–11
Brains SA; Smiles Brewery Bitter, Best Bitter, Exhibition 🅷
Smiles' first tied house, successfully expanded and refurbished in Victorian style; only the front bar is original. Popular with university students and very busy during term-time. At least one guest beer always available. Good value food (no eve meals Sat or Sun).
Q 🏠 🍴 ♦ 🍺 ⇄ (Clifton Down) ♣

Humpers Off-Licence

26 Soundwell Road, Staple Hill
☎ (0272) 565525
12–2, 4.30–10.30 (12–2, 7–10.30 Sun)
**Draught Bass Ⓗ; Butcombe
Bitter Ⓖ; Smiles Best Bitter,
Exhibition Ⓗ; Wadworth
6X Ⓖ&Ⓗ**
A friendly, well run off-licence:
an oasis for good real ale with
interesting guest beers from far
and wide. Beers are available in
any quantity from a half pint
upwards. ○

Kellaway Arms

140 Kellaway Avenue, Horfield
☎ (0272) 246694
11–3, 6–11 (12–2.30, 7–10.30 Sun)
**Courage Bitter Ale, Best
Bitter; Wadworth 6X Ⓗ**
Large, friendly pub with a small
lounge and a large, lounge-style
public bar. Situated near
Horfield Common. No weekend
food. Q ⑧ Ⓒ ⊟

Kings Head

60 Victoria Street (B4053, 250
yds NW of A4)
☎ (0272) 277860
11 (12 Sat)–3.30, 5.30 (7.30 Sat)–11
**Courage Bitter Ale, Best
Bitter Ⓗ**
Small, Victorian gem, restored
but unspoilt, next to a church
with a leaning tower. Full of
original character, with a lovely
snug. Four-pint jug discount
beer at off-peak times, Mon–Fri.
Excellent and reasonably priced
bar snacks (not available
weekends).
Q ⇌ (Temple Meads)

Kings Head

Whitehall Road
☎ (0272) 517174
11–3, 6–11
**Courage Bitter Ale, Best
Bitter, Directors Ⓗ**
Popular, suburban local with a
skittle alley incorporated in the
public bar. Live jazz every Tue.
♨ ⑧ Ⓒ ♣ P

Knowle Hotel

Leighton Road, Knowle
☎ (0272) 777019
11.30–2.30, 5.30–11 (11–3, 6–11 Sat)
**Ind Coope Burton Ale; Smiles
Best Bitter; Tetley Bitter Ⓗ**
Large, friendly, two-bar pub
with good views from the
lounge. Quiz night. Good value
food. ⑧ Ⓒ ⊟ ♣

Old Castle Green

46 Gloucester Lane, Old
Market (off A420, on one-way
system)
☎ (0272) 550925
11.30–11 (12–3, 7–11 Sat)
**Marston's Border Mild,
Burton Best Bitter, Pedigree,
Owd Rodger Ⓗ**
Small and successful hostelry
with a cosmopolitan clientele
and an old public bar

atmosphere: suits all tastes.
Good quality, fresh food with
vegetarian options.
⑧ Ⓒ ▶ ⇌ (Temple Meads) ♣

Old Duke

45 King Street (off A4044, near
'Welsh Back' quay)
☎ (0272) 277137
12–2, 7–11
**Courage Best Bitter,
Directors Ⓗ**
This world-renowned jazz
centre is a must for lovers of
trad jazz (admission charged on
jazz nights). Lunches served
Mon–Fri. Historic King Street
has a good choice of real ale
pubs. Ⓒ ⇌ (Temple Meads)

Park House

154 St John's Lane, Bedminster
☎ (0272) 663905
11–3, 6.30–11
**Courage Bitter Ale, Best
Bitter Ⓗ**
A small, regulars' pub. Morland
Old Speckled Hen and Bitter
alternate as guest beers.
Q ⊟ ♿ ♣

Phoenix

15 Wellington Road (next to
Parkway multi-storey car park)
☎ (0272) 558327
11.30–11
**Draught Bass; Oakhill
Bitter Ⓗ, Yeoman Ⓖ; Smiles
Best Bitter Ⓗ; Wadworth
6X Ⓖ**
Small, corner local close to
Broadmead shopping centre and
St Judes flats. Friendly, and
popular with all age groups.
Collection of bottles and old
Bristol photos. Snacks; guest
beers; good value.
⑧ ⇌ (Temple Meads) ♣

Plough & Windmill

194 West Street, Bedminster
☎ (0272) 663460
10.30–11
**Draught Bass; Courage Best
Bitter; Wadworth 6X Ⓗ**
Several traditional rooms with
sporting themes and a friendly
atmosphere. Bar snacks
available. ⑧ ♣

Prince of Wales

84 Stoke Lane, Westbury on
Trym (500 yds from village
centre)
☎ (0272) 623715
11–3, 5.30–11 (11–11 Sat)
**Courage Bitter Ale,
Directors Ⓗ**
Traditional and friendly pub in a
residential area: a single, good-
sized bar. Guest beer.
♿ ⑧ Ⓒ ♣

Seven Ways

23 New Street (off A420)
☎ (0272) 556862
11.15–3, 6.30–11
**Courage Best Bitter; John
Smith's Bitter; Wadworth
6X Ⓗ**

Friendly, two-bar local near the
popular drinking area of Old
Market, with an entrance
fronting St Matthias Park. The
lounge is preferred by older
customers; also a sporty bar and
a skittle alley. Imaginative guest
beers change regularly. Lunches
served Mon–Fri. Ⓒ ♣

Sportsmans Arms

20 Wade Street, St Judes (off
B4050)
☎ (0272) 559323
11–3, 6.15–11
**Courage Bitter Ale, Best
Bitter, Directors** (winter) Ⓗ
Homely, L-shaped, open-plan
local with a pleasing, tiled
frontage. Snack-type, 'with-
chips' meals available (not Sun).
Whist played. The garden is a
haven for wild birds. ⑧ Ⓒ ♣

Star

4–6 North Street, Bedminster
☎ (0272) 663588
11–2.30, 5.30–11
**Ansells Bitter; Ind Coope
Burton Ale; Smiles Best
Bitter Ⓗ**
Spacious and comfortable, one-
bar pub in the heart of
Bedminster. Two dartboards.
Vegetarian meals available.
⑧ Ⓒ ♣ ♣

Victoria

20 Chock Lane, Westbury on
Trym
☎ (0272) 500441
12–2.30, 5 (6 Sat, 7 Wed)–11
**Adnams Broadside; Draught
Bass; Hall & Woodhouse
Tanglefoot** (summer)**;
Wadworth IPA, 6X, Old
Timer Ⓗ**
Popular, busy pub, comfortably
furnished and out of the way,
down a quiet lane. Live music
first Sun lunchtime each month.
No food at weekends.
Tanglefoot alternates with
Wadworth Farmer's Glory.
⑧ Ⓒ ♣

White Lion

Quay Head, Colston Avenue
(opp. Cenotaph)
☎ (0272) 254819
11.30–3 (2.30 Sat), 5–10.30 (11 Fri &
Sat; closed Sun)
**Draught Bass; Ind Coope
Burton Ale; Smiles Best
Bitter Ⓗ**
Small, friendly pub in the city
centre. Gents beware of the
18th-century, cast iron, spiral
staircase – originally from the
old Bristol prison – probably
the narrowest ever! Good value
snacks. Management is a little
sensitive to style of dress.
⇌ (Temple Meads)

Try also: Barley Mow, Barton
Rd, St Philips (Wadworth);
Swan, Midland Rd (Free)

Avon

Churchill

Crown Inn
The Batch, Skinners Lane (off A38) OS447598
☎ (0934) 852995
11–3, 5.30–11
Draught Bass; Butcombe Bitter; Eldridge Pope Hardy Country; Palmers IPA 🅶
Cottage-style, stone-built pub in a quiet lane. Busy, it offers the best range of beers in the area and specialises in guest beers. House ale, Batch Bitter, is Cotleigh Harrier. No food Sun.
🏠 Q 🅰 🍴 🖤 Å

Clapton-in-Gordano

Black Horse
Clevedon Lane
OS474741 ☎ (0272) 842105
11–3 (2.30 Mon–Fri in winter), 6–11 (11–11 Fri & Sat in summer)
Courage Best Bitter Ale, Best Bitter, Directors 🅶
600 year-old, stone-built pub, formerly the village lock-up, now the very friendly centre of village life. The history of pub and village is shown in photos on the walls. Live music and quiz nights alternate on Mon. No food Sun.
🏠 Q 🍴 🍴 🥗 🖤 ❤ P

Compton Martin

Ring O' Bells
On A368 ☎ (0761) 221284
11.30–3, 7–11
Draught Bass 🅶; **Butcombe Bitter; Wadworth 6X** 🅷
Almost the perfect pub: first-class food and beer; a large family room with all facilities; a safe garden with plenty of children's amenities; and a separate bar with pub games. Guest beers.
🏠 Q 🥗 🍴 🍴 🥗 🖤 ❤ P

Congresbury

White Hart
Wrington Road (off A370)
☎ (0934) 833303
11.30–3, 6–11
Butcombe Bitter; Hall & Woodhouse Badger Best Bitter; Wadworth 6X 🅷
Suburban pub, highly recommended for its food. The family room at the back leads out onto the patio. Children's play area in the garden.
🏠 Q 🥗 🍴 🍴 🥗 P

Dundry

Winford Arms
Bridgwater Road (A38)
☎ (0272) 392178
11–2.30 (3 Sat), 5.30 (7 Sat)–11
Courage Best Bitter,

Directors; **Wadworth 6X** 🅷
A half-timbered, stone cottage: clean and comfortable. It has a large, separate family room and an outside play area for children. Q 🥗 🍴 🍴 🥗 ❤ P

Engine Common

Cross Keys
North Road, Yate (just N of A482) ☎ (0454) 228314
11.45–2.30, 5.45–11
Courage Best Bitter; John Smith's Bitter; Wadworth 6X 🅷
Pleasant, old country local with two bars; the public bar has a stone-flagged floor. The lively clientele raise money for charities. Plenty of pub games available. No food Sun.
🏠 Q 🍴 🍴 🥗 ❤ P

Frampton Cotterell

Golden Lion
Beesmoor Road
☎ (0454) 773348
11–11
Draught Bass; Ind Coope Burton Ale 🅶
Large, family pub recently refurbished and extended to provide a single bar with a separate family area. Food always available. A new restaurant and accommodation opened in 1991. 🥗 🍴 🍴 P

Rising Sun
43 Ryecroft Road
☎ (0454) 772330
11.30–3, 7–11
Draught Bass; Hall & Woodhouse Tanglefoot; Marston's Pedigree; Smiles Best Bitter; Wadworth 6X 🅷
A real free house: a small pub with a single bar and a separate skittle alley. Refurbishment has not changed its character and it is usually busy with locals.
🍴 🍴 ❤ P

Hinton

Bull
Off A46, 1 mile SW of M4 jct 18 ☎ (027 582) 2332
11.30–2.30, 6 (7 winter)–11
Draught Bass; Wadworth IPA, 6X, Old Timer 🅷
A country local with a splendid garden for children. Full meals (incl. vegetarian option) are served in the lounge.
🏠 🥗 🍴 🍴 🥗 ❤ P

Hinton Charterhouse

Rose & Crown
High Street (B3110)
☎ (022 122) 722153
11.30 (11 Sat)–3, 6–11
Draught Bass; Charrington IPA; Marston's Pedigree;

Wadworth 6X 🅶
A comfortable, wood-panelled lounge bar and a separate restaurant. Skittles, darts and dominoes played.
🏠 🅰 🍴 🍴 🥗 ❤

Kelston

Old Crown
On A431
☎ (0225) 423032
11.30–2.30, 6.30–11 (12–2, 7–10.30 Sun)
Draught Bass; Butcombe Bitter; Smiles Best Bitter; Wadworth 6X, Old Timer 🅷
Traditional, 18th-century coaching inn with a flagstone floor and an original beer engine. Lunchtime food available Mon–Sat; eve meals served Thu–Sat in the restaurant. Large garden. Occasional guest beers.
🏠 Q 🍴 🍴 Å ❤ P

Littleton-on-Severn

White Hart
1½ miles off B4461 at Elberton
OS596900
☎ (0454) 412275
11.30–2.30, 6–11 (11–11 Sat)
Smiles Brewery Bitter, Best Bitter, Exhibition; Wadworth 6X 🅷
Very popular pub, dating from the 16th century: good food and a good atmosphere. Petanque played in the summer. Winner of Avon CAMRA *Pub of the Year* 1990 and national *Pub Refurbishment* Award. Regular guest beers.
🏠 Q 🥗 🍴 🛏 🍴 ❤ P

Long Ashton

Angel Inn
172 Long Ashton Road (near B3128 jct)
☎ (0275) 392244
11–2.30, 5.30–11 (11–3, 6.30–11 Sat)
Courage Best Bitter, Directors; Oakhill Bitter; John Smith's Bitter; Wadworth 6X 🅷
Lovely, old, unspoilt village pub with a large courtyard seating area for summer and a big log fire in winter. Note the priest hole in the corner of the fireplace. A cosy bar, a snug and a dining room.
🏠 Q 🍴 🍴 🥗

Bird in Hand
17 Weston Road
☎ (0275) 392329
11–2.30 (3 Sat), 6.30–11
Draught Bass; Charrington IPA 🅷
A friendly, two-bar, regulars' pub on the main road. 🍴 🥗 P

Try also: **Robin Hood's Retreat** (Courage)

Midford

Hope & Anchor
On B3110
☎ (0225) 832296
11.30–2.30, 6.30–11
Draught Bass; Butcombe Bitter; Marston's Pedigree; Wadworth 6X Ⓗ
Nestling between the old Somerset and Dorset railway line and the disused Somerset coal canal; a 300 year-old pub with a restaurant and a small family room. ⌂ ⌘ ⌗ ◖ ▶ P

Nailsea

Blue Flame
West End (off A370)
OS449690 ☎ (0275) 856910
11–3, 6–11
Draught Bass; Marston's Pedigree (summer); **Smiles Best Bitter** Ⓖ
An unpretentious, friendly rural pub with a small public bar and a lounge. Often busy with locals and visitors alike. Occasional guest beers.
⌂ Q ⌘ ⌗ ⒽⒹ ◖ ♣ ○ P

Sawyers Arms
3 High Street
☎ (0275) 853798
11–3.30, 5.30–11
Courage Best Bitter, Directors; Eldridge Pope Hardy Country, Royal Oak; John Smith's Bitter Ⓗ
Popular, friendly two-roomer on the edge of the village. No food Sun. ⌘ ◖ ▶ P

Oldbury-on-Severn

Anchor Inn
Church Road
☎ (0454) 413331
11.30–2.30 (3 Sat), 6.30 (6 Sat)–11
Draught Bass Ⓖ; **Butcombe Bitter; Marston's Pedigree; Theakston Best Bitter** Ⓗ; **Old Peculier** Ⓖ
Fine, very popular, old local. Note the well-worn steps at the entrance. People travel miles for its good range of beers and excellent food.
⌂ Q ⌘ ◖ ▶ Ⓗ Ⓗ ♣ P

Paulton

Somerset Inn
Bath Road (½ mile NE of Paulton) OS660571
☎ (0761) 412828
12–2.30 (3 Fri & Sat), 7–11
Courage Bitter Ale, Best Bitter; Wadworth 6X Ⓗ
One-bar, village pub, renowned for its food. Fine views over the Cam Valley. ⌂ ⌘ ◖ ▶ ♣ ○ P

Pensford

Rising Sun
Church Street (off A37)

☎ (0761) 490402
11.30–2.30, 7–11
Ind Coope Burton Ale; Tetley Bitter; Wadworth 6X Ⓗ
15th-century, stone-built cottage in a superb setting, beside the River Chew: cosy, comfortable and friendly. Enclosed garden for children. Try the home-made soup – it's filling. ⌂ ⌘ ◖ ▶ ⒽⒹ P

Try also: Travellers Rest (Courage)

Pucklechurch

Rose & Crown
Parkfield Road (N off B4465)
☎ (027 582) 2351
11–2.30, 6.30–11
Draught Bass; Hall & Woodhouse Tanglefoot; Wadworth IPA, 6X Ⓗ
A large, village local with two bars, plus a hatch. A horse brass decor, but a good atmosphere; popular with the locals. The separate restaurant does not intrude on the pub. Large car park, and a garden with slides. ⌂ Q ⌘ ◖ ▶ Ⓗ Ⓖ ♣ P

Radstock

Waldegrave Arms
Market Place (A367)
☎ (0761) 34359
11–2.30 (3.30 Fri & Sat), 6–11
Courage Best Bitter; John Smith's Bitter; Wadworth 6X Ⓗ
Large, old, roadside hotel in the town centre. Two bars which both enjoy a friendly, local pub atmosphere. Live music weekends. No eve meals Sun.
⋈ ◖ ▶ Ⓗ ♣ P

Stoke Gifford

Parkway Tavern
43 North Road (2 mins' walk from Parkway station)
☎ (0272) 690329
11.30–2.30, 5–11 (11–11 Fri & Sat)
Banks's Mild, Bitter Ⓔ
A large, modern, open-plan pub with a split-level area for the dartboard. Reasonably-priced bar food, and some of the cheapest beer in Bristol. Separate function room. No food Sun.
⌘ ◖ Ⓗ ⇌ (Parkway) ♣ P

Thornbury

Knot of Rope
59 High Street
☎ (0454) 412147
11–11
Banks's Mild, Bitter Ⓔ
A well-appointed pub, reputedly haunted by the ghost of a young girl. Secret tunnels, too, and a good atmosphere.
⌂ Q ⌘ ◖ ▶ Ⓗ Ⓗ ♣ P

Tolldown

Crown
On A46, ½ mile S of M4 jct 18
☎ (0225) 891231
11–2.30, 6 (7 Sat)–11
Wadworth IPA, 6X, Old Timer Ⓗ
16th-century, Cotswold-stone, roadside inn, handy for visiting nearby Durham House and deer park. No eve meals Sun or Mon.
⌂ ⌘ ◖ ▶ P

Weston-super-Mare

Major From Glengarry
10–14 Upper Church Road
☎ (0934) 629594
11.30–3, 6–11
Draught Bass; Butcombe Bitter; Wadworth 6X Ⓗ
A large, open-plan inn tucked away opposite the Knightstone Theatre. Large, well-defined eating area; play area for children. Busy in summer. Guest beer changes monthly. ◖ ▶ ♣

Wick

Rose & Crown
High Street (A420)
☎ (027 582) 2198
11–2.30, 5.30 (6 Sat)–11
Courage Best Bitter, Directors; John Smith's Bitter; Wadworth 6X Ⓗ
Comfortable and spacious old inn (c.1640). Old photographs of the area and bric-a-brac depict a bygone era. The splendid, period restaurant has a varied, reasonably-priced menu.
⌂ Q ⌘ ◖ ▶ Ⓗ Ⓗ P

Willsbridge

Queens Head
Willsbridge Hill, Bath Road (A431, 150 yds NW of A4175 jct)
☎ (0272) 322233
11–2.30, 6.30–11
Courage Bitter Ale, Best Bitter Ⓗ
Don't be fooled by the dusty exterior; this is a delightfully tidy, unspoilt, multi-roomed, wood-panelled, 17th-century local. Convenient for Bitton Steam Railway and Willsbridge Mill. Snacks only. The car park is 25 yards down the road.
Q ⌘ Ⓗ ♣ P

Join CAMRA —
see page 480!

Bedfordshire

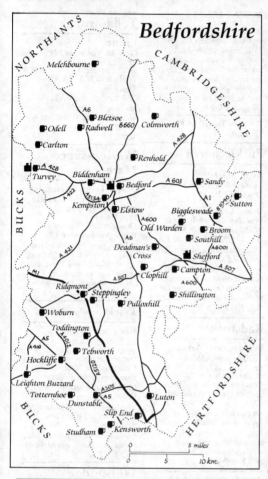

Bedfordshire

ship's beam. Coaching stables at the rear, plus a garden. Good food available (no meals Fri–Sun eves). 🏠 🍺 🍴 ♣

Biddenham

Three Tuns
Main Road (S of A428)
OS022499 ☎ (0234) 354847
11.30–2.30, 6–11
Greene King IPA, Rayments Special, Abbot Ⓗ
Delightful, village inn with an excellent range of home-cooked food. Children permitted in the dining area. Skittles played. No food Sun. 🏠 🍺 🍴 ♣ P

Biggleswade

Crown
34 High Street
☎ (0767) 312228
11–3, 5.30–11
Greene King IPA, Abbot Ⓗ
Friendly town-centre hotel with a spacious main bar, a small back bar and comfortable restaurant in which children are welcome. No food Sun eve.
🛏 🍺 🍴 ⇌ P

Bletsoe

Falcon
Rushden Road (A6)
☎ (0234) 781222
11–2.30, 5.30–11
Wells Eagle, Bombardier Ⓗ
17th-century coaching inn with a large, riverside garden and play area. Skittles in the public bar; families welcome. The landlord flies the flag outside and hates plastic! No eve meals Sun or Mon.
🏠 Q 🛏 🍺 🍴 🍴 ♣ P

Broom

Cock
High Street (100 yds N of B658)
☎ (0767) 314411
12–3, 6–11
Greene King IPA, Abbot Ⓖ
Multi-roomed, village local with beer served direct from the cellar. Separate skittles room.
🏠 🛏 🍺 🍴 ♣ P

Campton

White Hart
Mill Lane (off A507)
☎ (0462) 812657
11.30–3, 7–11 (11–11 Sat)
Mansfield Riding Bitter; Wells Eagle Ⓗ
Popular, three-bar, open-plan, village pub with a comfortable lounge and dining area. Games dominate the public bar, which has a flagstone floor and an inglenook. Petanque played all year. Guest beers. No lunches Sun. 🏠 🍺 🍴 🍴 ♣ P

🏭 **Banks & Taylor**, Shefford; **Nix Wincott**, Turvey; **Wells**, Bedford

---

Bedford

Anchor
397 Goldington Road (A428)
☎ (0234) 353606
11–3, 6–11
Greene King IPA, Abbot Ⓗ
Large pub with a nautical theme on Goldington Green, providing a good range of meals at all times. Children are welcome in the conservatory, and the garden is popular in the summer. Q 🛏 🏠 🍺 🍴 🍴 🍴 ♣ P

Clarence
13 St Johns Street (A6)
☎ (0234) 352781
11–11
Ind Coope Benskins Best Bitter Ⓗ
Large, town pub with a quiet lounge and a games-oriented public bar. Good value bar meals (not served Sun). It may be necessary to use the back door between 3 and 5.30pm.
🏠 🍺 ⇌ (St Johns) ♣ P

Fleur de Lis
12 Mill Street (off A6)
☎ (0234) 211004
10.30–2.30 (3 Sat), 5.30 (7 Sat)–11 (12–2, 7–10.30 Sun)
Wells Eagle Ⓗ
A well-run, town pub with an excellent social mix. Parking difficult at lunchtime. Upstairs meeting room. No food Sun. 🍴

Flower Pot
25 Tavistock Street (A6/A428 jct) ☎ (0234) 353049
11–11
Greene King IPA, Abbot Ⓗ
The oldest pub in Bedford (1595), featuring an original

Carlton

Fox
35 High Street (3 miles N of
A428 at Turvey) OS953553
☎ (0234) 720235
10.30–2.30, 6–11
**Adnams Broadside; Wells
Eagle** Ⓗ
18th-century, friendly, thatched,
village inn with excellent
restaurant and bar food. Near
Harrold Country Wildlife Park.
No food Sun, or Mon eve.
Children welcome before 8pm.
Q ❀ ◑ ▶ P

Try also: Royal Oak (Banks &
Taylor)

Clophill

Stone Jug
Back Street (N of A6/A507
roundabout)
☎ (0525) 60526
11–3, 6–11
**Banks & Taylor Shefford
Bitter; Courage Directors;
John Smith's Bitter;
Theakston Best Bitter** Ⓗ
Deservedly popular free house
with an amiable atmosphere and
competitive prices. Check before
taking children (not admitted
after 8pm). No lunch Sun; book
for eve meals at weekends.
Guest beers. ⊱ ❀ ◑ ♣ P

Colmworth

Wheatsheaf
Wilden Road (1 mile E of B660)
OS101574 ☎ (023 062) 370
11–2.30, 6–11
**Adnams Bitter, Broadside;
Draught Bass; Marston's
Pedigree** Ⓗ
17th-century, country inn to
the south of the village. Low
beams – mind your head!
Children's play area in the
garden. Varied bar food and full
menu in the restaurant. Guest
beers. ⚓ Q ❀ ◑ ▶ ⊕ ♣ P

Deadman's Cross

White Horse
On A600
☎ (023 066) 634
11–3, 6 (7 Sat)–11
**Banks & Taylor Shefford
Bitter, SOS, Black Bat** Ⓗ
Friendly, roadside pub with
excellent food in the restaurant
and the attractive, book-lined
bar, which has an inglenook. Bar
billiards played. ⚓ ⊱ ❀ ◑ ▶ ♣ P

Dunstable

Highwayman Hotel
London Road (A5)
☎ (0582) 661999
11–2.30, 6–11 (12–2, 7–10.30 Sun)
Wells Eagle, Bombardier Ⓗ

Spacious, comfortable lounge
bar attached to a hotel on the
southern edge of town. A locals'
public bar and a separate
restaurant (no meals Sun).
❀ ⋈ ◑ ⊕ ⊕ ♣ P

Elstow

Swan
Bedford Road
☎ (0234) 352066
11–3, 7–11
Greene King IPA, Abbot Ⓗ
Old, village pub near Elstow
Abbey and Moot Hall Museum;
in John Bunyan country.
❀ ◑ ♣ P

Hockliffe

Red Lion
Watling Street (A5)
☎ (0525) 210240
11–2.30 (3 Sat), 5.30 (6 Sat)–11
**Ind Coope Benskins Best
Bitter; Tetley Bitter;
Wadworth 6X** Ⓗ
Friendly, roadside pub with one
long bar where one end is
oriented towards games, and
the other towards food. The
sizeable garden has barbecues in
summer. Mah-jong played.
❀ ⋈ ◑ ▶ ⅙ ♣ P

Kempston

Wellington
16 Bedford Road (B531)
☎ (0234) 350975
12–3, 6 (7 Sat)–11
Wells Eagle, Bombardier Ⓗ
Traditional, corner local on the
main road. Comfortably
furnished, with a small
restaurant in which children are
welcome. No eve meals Sun or
Tue. ❀ ◑ ▶ ⊕

Kensworth

Farmers Boy
216 Common Road
☎ (0582) 872207
11–11
**Fuller's Chiswick, London
Pride, ESB** Ⓗ
Well renovated, ex-Watney's,
village pub which has reverted
to two bars. Note the original
Mann, Crossman & Paulin
leaded windows. Comfortable
lounge with a separate dining
area. Good range of good value
food, lunchtime and eves.
⚓ ❀ ◑ ▶ ⊕ ♣ P

Leighton Buzzard

Ashwell Arms
Ashwell Street (off A418)
☎ (0525) 372080
11–2.30, 5.30–11 (11–11 Sat)
**Adnams Broadside; Wells
Eagle, Bombardier** Ⓗ
Solid-looking pub with red
paintwork, carpets, curtains, soft

furnishings and even a pool
table! The soporific saloon bar
contrasts well with the lively
games-oriented public.
Broadside and Bombardier
alternate. Q ⊕ ♣

Stag
Heath Road (A418, N of centre)
☎ (0525) 372710
12 (11 Fri & Sat)–2.30, 6 (7 Sat)–11
Fuller's London Pride, ESB Ⓗ
V-shaped pub whose tiny public
bar has a room for a dartboard,
pool table and little else. The
large saloon bar is plain but
comfortable. Stands in a fork in
the road. Q ⊕ ♣ P

Star
Heath Road (A418, 1½ miles N
of centre) ☎ (0525) 377294
11–2.30 (3 Sat), 5.30–11 (6 Sat)–11
**Adnams Bitter; Draught
Bass; Ind Coope ABC Best
Bitter; Wadworth 6X** Ⓗ
Smart pub inside and out, on
the northern edge of town. The
L-shaped bar is furnished with
sewing machine tables; note the
interesting cricket, aircraft and
sewing machine artefacts – also
a seismograph! Home-cooked
food, but above-average prices
(no meals Sun). Q ❀ ◑ ▶ P

Luton

Gardeners Call
151 Hightown Road
☎ (0582) 29037
11–3, 5.30–11
**Greene King IPA, Rayments
Special, Abbot** Ⓗ
Two-bar, town pub with a
strong local following. TV in
the public and a fish tank in the
lounge. No food at weekends.
❀ ◑ ▶ ⋈ ♣ P

Two Brewers
43 Dumfries Street
☎ (0582) 23777
11.30–3, 5.30–11 (12–4, 7–11 Sat)
**Banks & Taylor Shefford
Bitter, SPA, Edwin Taylor's
Stout, SOS, Black Bat**
(winter) Ⓗ
Lively locals' pub, just off the
town centre, with a back yard
for outside drinking. No food at
weekends. ❀ ◑ ♣

Melchbourne

St John's Arms
Knotting Road OS030663
☎ (0234) 708238
11–4, 6–11
Greene King IPA, Abbot Ⓗ
Former gamekeeper's lodge
with a fine tankard collection
and a warm welcome. Flexible
about afternoon closing – knock
if pub seems closed. Function
room in a converted barn
(available for families);
occasional garden barbecues in
summer. ⚓ ⊱ ❀ ◑ ▶ ♣ ♣ P

Bedfordshire

Odell

Mad Dog
Little Odell (W end of village)
OS955575 ☎ (0234) 720221
11–2.30, 6–11
Greene King IPA, Rayments Special, Abbot Ⓗ
Thatched pub near the Harrold-Odell Country Park. A ghost may be spotted near the inglenook. Children's roundabout in the garden. Home-cooked food, incl. vegetarian dishes. Q ⑧ ◖ ▶ P

Try also: Bell (Greene King)

Old Warden

Hare & Hounds
High Street
☎ (076 727) 225
11–2.30, 6–11
Wells Eagle, Bombardier Ⓗ
Welcoming, two-bar country pub in a picturesque village near the Shuttleworth Aircraft Collection and the Swiss Gardens. Children welcome in the restaurant which specialises in fresh fish. Guest beers.
🏚 ❧ ⑧ ◖ ▶ ⊞ ♣ P

Pulloxhill

Cross Keys
High Street
☎ (0525) 712442
11–2.30, 6–11
Adnams Broadside; Wells Eagle Ⓗ
15th-century pub with a small bar at the front and a large restaurant of more recent construction to the rear. The food offers good value but can dominate. Large grounds entertain some unusual activities. 🏚 Q ⑧ ◖ ▶ ◖ ▲ P

Radwell

Swan
Felmersham Road (1 mile off A6) OS004575
☎ (0234) 781351
12–2.30, 6.30–11 (closed Sun eve)
Wells Eagle, Bombardier Ⓗ
17th-century, thatched, country inn with a restaurant and a quiet bar. High quality food includes a vegetarian choice (no food Tue eve or Sun). Garden with children's play area.
🏚 Q ⑧ ◖ ▶ P

Renhold

Three Horseshoes
42 Top End (1 mile from A428)
☎ (0234) 870218
11–2.30, 6–11 (11–11 Sat)
Greene King XX Mild, IPA, Abbot Ⓗ
Friendly, village pub with a children's play area in the garden. One of the few outlets for mild, this pub also provides home-cooked food (no meals Tue eves or Sun).
🏚 Q ⑧ ◖ ▶ ⊞ ♣ P

Ridgmont

Rose & Crown
89 High Street (A418, near M1 jct 13)
☎ (052 528) 245
10.30–3, 6–11
Adnams Broadside; Mansfield Riding Mild, Bitter; Wells Eagle Ⓗ
Popular, welcoming pub and restaurant (booking advised). The refurbished public bar has a separate games area; the large grounds offer facilities for camping/caravanning and barbecues in summer.
🏚 ⑧ ◖ ▶ ⊞ ▲ ♣ P

Sandy

Bell
Station Road (50 yds S of B1042)
☎ (0767) 680267
12–3 (4 Sat), 5.30–11
Greene King IPA Ⓗ
Friendly, one-bar local, opposite the station. Handy for the RSPB HQ at Sandy Lodge. No food Sun lunch or Mon.
🏚 ⑧ ◖ ▶ ⇌ ♣ P

Try also: Lord Nelson (Whitbread)

Shillington

Musgrave Arms
Apsley End Road
☎ (0462) 711286
11–3, 5.30–11
Greene King IPA, Rayments Special, Abbot Ⓖ
Unspoilt, country local, successfully brought into the 20th century: a cosy, low-beamed lounge and a clay-tiled public bar. The wide range of home-cooked food includes curry, game and vegetarian dishes. Barbecues in summer. Regular live music (jazz Mon, folk Wed). 🏚 ⑧ ◖ ▶ ⊞ ⬥ ♣ P

Slip End

Frog & Rhubarb
Church Road
☎ (0582) 452722
12–3, 5.30–11
Adnams Bitter; Draught Bass; Greene King IPA, Abbot Ⓗ
Large, friendly, split-level pub. Live music Sat eves. Good quality food. ⑧ ◖ ▶ ♣ P

Southill

White Horse
High Road (1 mile W of B658)
☎ (0462) 813364

11–3, 6–11 (supper licence)
Whitbread Wethered Bitter, Flowers IPA Ⓗ
Large, country inn and restaurant (children welcome in latter) which boasts a miniature (diesel) railway in its extensive garden. Two function rooms, incl. a banqueting suite. A brief walk from Southill Park cricket ground. Shove-ha'penny board. No food Sun eve, but a supper licence extension at other times (one hour lunchtime and eve).
🏚 ⑧ ◖ ▶ ⊞ ♣ P

Steppingley

French Horn
5 Church Road
☎ (0525) 712051
12–3, 6–11
Adnams Bitter; Draught Bass; Ind Coope ABC Best Bitter; Tetley Bitter Ⓗ
Old inn, dating in part from the 14th century, with a public bar somewhat dominated by a pool table. Larger, L-shaped lounge bar and a separate restaurant, too (booking advised; closed Sun eve and Mon). No bar meals weekend eves, though the food is highly recommended. Occasional guest beer.
🏚 Q ⑧ ◖ ▶ ⊞ ♣ P

Try also: Drovers Arms (Wells)

Studham

Red Lion
Church Road
☎ (0582) 872530
11 (12 winter)–3, 5.30–11
Adnams Bitter; Draught Bass; Courage Directors; Ruddles Best Bitter; Theakston Best Bitter Ⓗ
Comfortable and friendly, one-bar pub overlooking the common. Bar billiards and monthly quiz eves. Good range of home-cooked, good value food (no meals Sun eve). Guest beer. 🏚 Q ⑧ ◖ ▶ ♣ P

Sutton

John O'Gaunt
High Street
☎ (0767) 260377
12–3, 7–11
Greene King IPA, Abbot Ⓗ
Attractive pub in a picturesque village where a ford crosses the High Street. Good range of bar food (not served Sun). Skittles played; boules court in the garden. ⑧ ◖ ▶ ⊞ ♣ P

Tebworth

Queens Head
The Lane ☎ (052 55) 4101
11–3, 6 (7 Sat)–11
Adnams Broadside; Wells Eagle Ⓗ

Two small bars, popular with locals and visitors alike. A very hospitable and entertaining pub with weekly sing-songs. No meals Sun. ⚏ ⊛ ◖ ⊟ ♣ P

Toddington

Bedford Arms
64 High Street
☎ (052 55) 2401
11.30–3, 6.30–11
Wells Eagle Ⓗ
Attractive pub both outside and in, with a magnificent rambling garden to the rear. Two warm and comfortable lounge bars. A new kitchen is being built, so check for meals. ⚏ ⊛ ◖ ⊟ ♣ P

Oddfellows Arms
Conger Lane (village green)
☎ (052 55) 2021
11–3, 6–11
Courage Best Bitter, Directors; John Smith's Bitter; Wadworth 6X Ⓗ
Attractive, 15th-century pub with hanging baskets. The three bars range from the two-tabled public to the immaculate Croft Bar, with its gallery and huge open fire. Pavement tables for summer drinking. Varied food. ⚏ ⊛ ◖ ♣

Sow & Pigs
19 Church Square
☎ (052 55) 3089
11–11
Greene King IPA, Rayments Special, Abbot Ⓗ

A village institution: rich in atmosphere and full of colourful characters. The appealingly chaotic interior is somewhat haphazardly furnished and features church pews, a piano and a harmonium. Pigs abound ('Pig Snout' played)! No food Sun. Parking is via Park Lane and St George's Close.
⚏ Q ◖ ♣ P

Totternhoe

Old Bell
29 Church Road
☎ (0582) 662633
11–2.30 (3 Sat), 6 (7 Sat)–11
Adnams Bitter; Bateman Mild; Greene King IPA; Palmers BB; Samuel Smith OBB Ⓗ
Comfortable, L-shaped bar with a low-beamed ceiling and exposed brickwork. The beer range is liable to alter but always includes two guest beers, generally 'exotics'.
⚏ ⊛ ◖ ♣ P

Old Farm Inn
Church Road
☎ (0582) 661294
11–3.30, 6–11
Fuller's Chiswick, London Pride Ⓗ
Popular, friendly, old, village pub with a large fireplace in each bar; traditional public and cosy lounge. Garden to the side of the pub. No meals Sun.
⚏ Q ⊛ ◖ ⊟ ♣ P

Turvey

Three Cranes
High Street (off A428)
☎ (023 064) 305
11–3, 6–11
Adnams Bitter; Fuller's London Pride, ESB; Hook Norton Best Bitter Ⓗ
17th-century coaching inn with an excellent range of food, including vegetarian and pizza dishes, in both the pub and the separate restaurant. Guest beers in summer. ⚏ Q ⊛ ◖ ◖ P

Woburn

Magpies
Bedford Street (A418)
☎ (0525) 290219
12–3, 6–11
Ruddles Best Bitter, County; Webster's Yorkshire Bitter Ⓗ
Coaching inn with bags of character in the centre of the village. Courtyard for summer drinking. Beware of the narrow entrance to the car park.
Q ⊛ ⋈ ◖ ▶ ⊟ P

Royal Oak
George Street ☎ (0525) 290610
11–3, 5.30–11 (11–11 Sat)
Greene King IPA, Rayments Special, Abbot Ⓗ
Multi-roomed, low-ceilinged pub, recently extended but still packed in the eve, although quieter at lunchtime. Food recommended (eve meals Tue only). ⚏ ⋛ ⊛ ◖ ♣ P

'It's so refreshing to have a drink without having to listen to the pub machines paying out every five minutes'

Berkshire

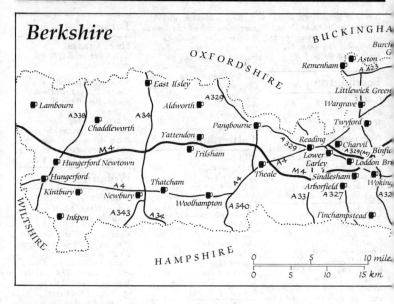

Aldworth

Bell
Off B4009 OS555797
☎ (0635) 578272
11–3, 6–11 (closed Mon)
Arkell's 3B, Kingsdown; Hall & Woodhouse Badger Best Bitter; Morrells Dark Ⓗ
Excellent atmosphere in a haven for traditionalists. This pub has been in the same family for over 200 years and hasn't changed much during this period. Splendid, one-handed clock monitors the passage of time in the tranquil tap room. Hot rolls only to eat. National CAMRA *Pub of the Year* 1990.
🏚 Q 🕮 🍽 ♣ P

Try also: Four Points (Free)

Arborfield

Swan
Eversley Road, Arborfield Cross (A327) ☎ (0734) 760475
11–3, 6–11
Courage Best Bitter, Directors Ⓗ
Attractive old country pub with two pleasant, intimate bars. Very friendly, with 'chatty' landlord. Separate, well-furnished function room. No meals Sun eve. 🕮 🍺 P

Aston

Flower Pot
Aston Lane (off A423 down Ferry Lane) ☎ (0491) 574721
11–3, 5.30–11 (11–11 Sat)
Brakspear XXX Mild (summer), **Bitter, Special, Old** (winter) Ⓗ
Wonderful old inn near River Thames. Lounge with armchairs; traditional public bar. Has own landing stage. No eve meals Sun/Mon.
🏚 Q 🕮 🍽 🍺 🐕 🛏 Å ♣ P

Binfield

Stag & Hounds
Forest Road (B3018/ B3034 jct) OS711851
☎ (0344) 483553
11–3, 5.30–11
Courage Best Bitter, Directors Ⓗ
Friendly, two-bar pub with separate wine bar/bistro at side. Old oak beams; interesting nick-nacks; alcoves with seating. The lovely saloon has three open fires. Family room eves and weekends only. Garden is close to road and not suitable for children. Eve meals in bistro (not Sun). 🏚 Q 🍽 🕮 🍺 P

Bracknell

Blue Lion
Broad Lane (100 yds from 'Horse & Groom' roundabout on A322) ☎ (0344) 425875
11.30–3, 5–11 (11.30–11 Sat)
Draught Bass; Charrington IPA Ⓗ
Recently-refurbished, providing comfortable surroundings for drinking, eating and talking. Eve meals on request. 🍽 🍺 P

Green Man
Crowthorne Road, Easthampstead (bus-only exit off A322/A329 link, Downshire Way) ☎ (0344) 423667
11–3, 6–11 (11–11 Sat)
Courage Best Bitter, Directors Ⓗ
Well-run pub providing a range of facilities. Little passing trade but popular locally. No meals Sun. 🍽 🍺 ♣ P

Burchett's Green

Red Lion
Applehouse Hill, Hurley (A423, 200 yds N of A404 jct)
☎ (062 882) 4433
11–11
Brakspear Bitter, Special, Old Ⓗ
Country pub with a friendly, intimate atmosphere. Bar area was doubled in 1990. Occasional live music on Sat. Spacious front terrace with plentiful log fires; glorious log fires in winter. Has been a pub since 1750. 🏚 Q 🍽 🕮 🛏 P

Chaddleworth

Ibex
☎ (04882) 311
11–2.30 (3 Sat), 6.30–11
Courage Best Bitter, Directors Ⓗ
Splendid country inn with three bars on the edge of a downland village. Landlord rode Desert Orchid to 17 wins. Good varied food: try the Ibex Pie (not goat!). Large car park and pretty walled garden. 🏚 🕮 🍽 🛏 ♣ P

Charvil

Lands End
Lands End Lane (off A3032, 1 mile along Park Lane)
OS781748 ☎ (0734) 340700
11–2.30, 6–11

Brakspear Bitter, Special, Old Ⓗ
Excellent pre-war pub surrounded by narrow lanes. Large patio and garden lead down to river. Small family room. No meals Sun. Interesting collection of bottles.
⌇ ✤ ◖◗ ⊟ ♣ P

Cippenham

Swan
140 Lower Cippenham Lane
☎ (0628) 604676
11–11
Ind Coope Benskins Best Bitter; Tetley Bitter Ⓗ
Friendly, two-bar local with a spacious feel, especially in the public bar. No jukebox or fruit machines in the saloon. One of a triangle of pubs opposite the village pond.
⌂ Q ✤ ◖◗ ⊟ ♣ P

East Ilsley

Crown & Horns
Off A34
☎ (063 528) 205
11–3, 6–11
Draught Bass; Fuller's London Pride; Morland Bitter, Old Speckled Hen; Theakston Old Peculier; Wadworth 6X Ⓗ
Historic 300 year-old free house in village centre. Fine all-round pub with good food, accommodation and TV/children's room. 160 whiskies behind the bar. Used for filming BBC series *Trainer*. Skittle alley.
⌂ ⌇ ✤ ◖◗ ⊟ ⚲ ✤ ♣ P

Finchampstead

Queens Oak
Church Lane (opp. parish church) OS639794
☎ (0734) 734855
11.30–2.30, 6–11
Brakspear Bitter, Special, Old Ⓗ
Good, all-round friendly pub for walkers (near open countryside and NT area). Has had a pleasant no-smoking bar for over a decade. Friendly landlord. The only pub of this name in Britain. No food Sun.
⌂ Q ✤ ◖◗ ⚲ ⚲ ♣ P 🕱

Frilsham

Pot Kiln
On Yattendon-Bucklebury road OS793639 ☎ (0635) 201366
12–2.30, 6.30–11
Arkell's 3B; Morland Bitter, Old Speckled Hen; Ringwood Fortyniner Ⓗ
Pub with the best views in Berkshire; not another building in sight. Dates in part from 15th century; bricks were made here in the 1700s; has been a pub for over 200 years. Rolls only to eat Sun, and Mon eve. Live folk music Sun eve.
⌂ Q ✤ ✤ ◖◗ ⊟ ♣ P

Holyport

Belgian Arms
Holyport Street
☎ (0628) 34468
11–2.30, 5.30 (7.30 winter)–11
Brakspear Bitter, Special, Old Ⓗ
Old, wisteria-clad local just off the green. The village pond is at the end of the garden. Formerly known as 'the Eagle' or 'Prussian Eagle', it was renamed during WW1 to avoid suggestion of Prussian support. Dining area is small and intimate. No food Sun.
⌂ Q ✤ ◖◗ ⚲ P

Hungerford

Plume
High Street (opp. Town Hall)
☎ (0488) 682154
11–3, 6–11 (11–11 Fri & Sat)
Courage Best Bitter, Directors Ⓗ
Two-bar town local with a friendly welcome for all. Games in public bar; dining area off lounge bar. Guest beer.
⌂ ✤ ◖◗ ⚲ ♣

Hungerford Newtown

Tally Ho
On A338, 1 mile S of M4 jct 14
☎ (0488) 682312
11–3, 5.30–11

Wadworth IPA, 6X Ⓗ
Comfortable, friendly, late-Victorian pub. Good, varied food (incl. vegetarian).
⌂ ◖◗ ♣ P

Inkpen

Swan
Craven Road, Lower Inkpen, (Hungerford-Combe road) OS359643 ☎ (048 84) 326
11.30–2.30 (not Tue), 6.30–11 (closed Mon)
Brakspear Bitter; Hook Norton Best Bitter; Mitchell's ESB or **Greene King Abbot** Ⓗ
Popular, large, 16th-century, beamed country pub near famous Combe Gibbet. The excellent menu features English and Singaporean dishes (no food Sun eve). Three open fires. Guest beers. ⌂ Q ✤ ◖◗ ♣ P

Kintbury

Blue Ball
High Street ☎ (0488) 58515
11–2.30, 6–11 (11–11 Sat)
Courage Best Bitter Ⓗ
Beams, brick, wood panels, a warm welcome and a fire to match in this typical, busy village pub. Dogs permitted on lead, but no children inside. Small car park. Guest beers.
⌂ Q ✤ ◖◗ ⊟ ⚲ ♣ P

Try also: **Dundas Arms** (Free)

Lambourn

George Hotel
Market Place ☎ (0488) 71889
11–3, 6–11
Arkell's 3B Ⓗ
Smart, friendly pub in the centre of a famous racing village. Much frequented by stable lads. Opens at 8.30am for breakfasts. Excellent plain food: home-cooked ham, egg and chips a speciality. ✤ ⚲ ◖◗ ⚲ P

Try also: **Wheelwrights Arms** (Morland)

Littlewick Green

Cricketers
☎ (0628) 822888
11–3, 5.30–11
Eldridge Pope Hardy Country; Fuller's London Pride; Morland Bitter, Old Speckled Hen; Wadworth 6X Ⓗ
Popular village local on the edge of the cricket green. Originally cottages and probably a blacksmith's, it now has three separate drinking areas. Its history can be traced back over 400 years. Old Speckled Hen and Hardy alternate. No food Sun eve.
Q ⌇ ✤ ◖◗ ⚲ P

Berkshire

Loddon Bridge

George
Loddon Bridge Road (A329, near A329M, between Reading and Wokingham)
☎ (0734) 61844
11–2.30 (3 Sat), 5.30 (5 Thu & Fri)–11
Courage Best Bitter, Directors; John Smith's Bitter H
Pleasantly-furnished riverside pub, now surrounded by new housing and trading estates. Contrasting trade: business people lunchtimes; young people eves. A well-known local landmark.
🛏 ◖ ⇌ (Winnersh Triangle) P

Lower Earley

Seven Red Roses
Maiden Place (near shopping centre on Kilnsea Drive)
☎ (0734) 351781
11–3, 5.30–11
Draught Bass; Charrington IPA H
Busy, modern pub with interesting Bass Breweriana, incl. model of a Burton union square. No-smoking area at lunchtime.
🛏 ◖ ▶ ⟁ ♣ ⊠

Maidenhead

Ark
20 Ray Street (off A4 between bridge and town)
11–2.30, 5.30–11
Courage Best Bitter H
Small, Victorian, back-street local with tiny patio garden and separate games room for pool. The pub was built above ground level in the flood-plain – hence the name. Plain decor, but good, homely atmosphere. Lunchtime snacks. 🛏 ⟁ ♣

North Star
Westborough Road (off A4 at W end of town; left after Pond House)
☎ (0628) 22711
11–2.30, 6–11
Courage Best Bitter H
Small, two-bar pub. Public has been enlarged without spoiling the character. Note old Nicholson price list. The pub's name recalls the first loco to reach Maidenhead in 1835, (driven by IK Brunel). 🛏 ⟁ ♣

Vine
20 Market Street
10.30–11
Brakspear XXX Mild (summer), **Bitter, Special, Old** (winter) H
Town-centre pub with one bar. Runs its own darts (men and ladies), football and crib teams. Reasonably-priced by local standards. Busy lunchtimes with

business clientele; home-made food on a varied menu (no food Sat/Sun). ◖ ⇌ ♣

Newbury

Plough Inn
Greenham Road (opp. Stroud Green) ☎ (0635) 47269
12–11 (10.30–11 Sat)
Courage Directors; John Smith's Bitter; Wadworth 6X H
Newbury's smallest pub: all bare bricks and old timbers. Has the best outside drinking of any pub in town. 🛏 ◖ ⇌ ♣ P

Red House
12 Hampton Road (first turning off Pound Street, off Bartholomew Street)
☎ (0635) 30584
12–3, 7.30–11 (12–3, 7.30–10.30 Sun)
Archers Golden; Marston's Pedigree H
Very small, friendly local near centre but off the beaten track. Bar billiards and darts. Q ⇌ ♣

Try also: Catherine Wheel, Cheap Street (Courage); **Dolphin**, Bartholomew Street (Courage)

Oakley Green

Old Red Lion
Oakley Green Road (B3024, off A308 Windsor–Maidenhead road) ☎ (0753) 863892
11–3, 5.30–11
Brakspear Bitter; Ind Coope Friary Meux Best Bitter, Burton Ale H
Traditional country pub with loads of character. Separate dining area: good food. The original building is 16th-century. Aunt Sally in back garden. Q 🛏 ◖ ▶ ♣ P

Old Windsor

Oxford Blue
Crimp Hill (off A308 Slough-Windsor road, right before Wheatsheaf)
☎ (0753) 861954
11–11
Brakspear Bitter; Ind Coope Burton Ale; Tetley Bitter H
Pub over 300 years old and fronted by a verandah over-looking fields. Back bar is full of airline memorabilia. Adventure-type garden for children and a popular restaurant with home-cooked food. Q 🛏 🛏 ◖ ▶ P

Pangbourne

Cross Keys
Church Road (near A329)
☎ (0734) 843268
11–3, 6–11
Courage Best Bitter,

Directors; Eldridge Pope Hardy Country H
Unspoilt, 17th-century pub. Patio garden backs on to the River Pang. Small aviary on patio. 🛏 ⟁ ⟁ ⋈ ◖ ▶ ⟁ ⇌ ♣ P

Star
Reading Road (A329)
OS636765 ☎ (0734) 842566
11–3, 6 (7 Sat)–11
Courage Best Bitter, Directors H
Village local, the lounge bar of which was a bottling factory for H Levers ginger beer for 107 years. Live music occasionally. No food Mon eve or Sun.
🛏 ◖ ▶ ⇌ ♣ P

Reading

Blagrave Arms
35 Blagrave Street (100 yds from station)
☎ (0734) 590920
11–11 (11–2.30, 7–11 Sat; closed Sun)
Courage Best Bitter, Directors; John Smith's Bitter H
Valiant attempt at re-creating a Victorian alehouse: wood-block floor, marble-topped tables, etched glass and gas lighting. Usually heaving at lunchtime and pleasantly quieter in the eve. Cheery bar staff. ◖ ▶ ⇌

Butler
Chatham Street (off ring road near swimming pool)
☎ (0734) 576289
11.30–3, 5.30–11 (11.30–11 Fri & Sat)
Fuller's Chiswick, London Pride, ESB H
Efficiently-run town pub retaining mementoes of Butler & Son who bottled their own Guinness and wines on the premises. Intimate atmosphere with colourful clientele. Folk music Thu. No food Sun. Parking limited. 🛏 🛏 ◖ ▶ P

Horn
St Mary's Butts
☎ (0734) 574794
11–3, 5.30–10.30 (11–10.30 Wed & Thu; 11–11 Fri & Sat)
Courage Best Bitter, Directors H
Sit and watch the world go by from this traditional, town-centre pub which is popular with shoppers, traders and business people. No meals Sun.
🛏 ◖

Sweeney & Todd
10 Castle Street (near civic centre) ☎ (0734) 586466
11–11 (closed Sun eve)
Adnams Bitter; Eldridge Pope Hardy Country, Royal Oak; Wadworth 6X H
Splendid little bar at the rear of a pie shop. Cellar restaurant and patio area (covered in winter). Always a cheery atmosphere

here where diners mix easily with drinkers. House wines and port are recommended, as are the home-made pies. Q ❀ ◐ ▶

Wallingford Arms

2 Caroline Street/Charles Street (off ring road near swimming pool)
☎ (0734) 575272
11–3, 5.30–11 (12–11 Fri; 11–11 Sat)
Morland Bitter, Old Masters, Old Speckled Hen Ⓗ
Good, solid local with comfortable bars and a congenial atmosphere. Not easy to find, but worth the effort. No food Sun. ❀ ◐ ⊟ P

Warwick Arms

77 Kings Road
☎ (0734) 500412
11–11 (11–3, 7–11 Sat)
Morland Bitter, Old Speckled Hen; Thwaites Bitter; Young's Special Ⓗ
Open-plan pub with split-level seating areas and efficient service. Very popular with the business sector. Near the Kennet and Avon Canal. No food Sat eve or Sun. Guest beers from around the country. Skittle alley. ❀ ◐ ▶ ⬠ ⇌ ♣

Remenham

Five Horseshoes

Remenham Hill (A423)
☎ (0491) 574881
11–3, 5–11
Brakspear XXX Mild, Bitter, Special, Old Ⓗ
Comfortable, friendly, two-bar, roadside inn.
⚏ Q ❀ ⊨ ◐ ▶ ⊟ ▲
⇌ (Henley: not winter Sun) ♣ P

Try also: Two Brewers
(Brakspear)

Sindlesham

Walter Arms

Bearwood Road (off B3030/A329, near Bearwood House and College)
☎ (0734) 780260
11–2.30 (3 Sat), 5–11
Courage Best Bitter, Directors Ⓗ
Striking country pub just out of suburbia. Built by John Walter, the then owner of *The Times*. Always popular, efficient and friendly; well-known for excellent, imaginative food. Quality accommodation.
⚏ Q ❀ ⊨ ◐ ▶ P

Slough

Alpha Arms

26 Alpha Street (off High Street)
☎ (0753) 22727
11.30–3, 5.30–11 (12–2.30, 7–10.30 Sun)
Courage Best Bitter, Directors Ⓗ

Small, back-street local with friendly landlady and customers. One bar only, with an intimate atmosphere. Parking difficult but a car park is nearby. Lunchtime snacks and simple meals (Mon–Fri only). Try the roast beef sandwich. Q ◐ ⇌ ♣

Herschel Arms

22 Park Street (50 yds from High Street behind Boots)
☎ (0753) 24089
11–11
Courage Best Bitter Ⓗ
Rough and ready, back-street pub. Inimitable Irish atmosphere. Quiet back bar is small but plush. Good food (eves till 7.30). Q ◐ ▶ ⊟ ⇌

Thatcham

White Hart

2 High Street
☎ (0635) 63251
11–11 (11–3, 5.30–11 Sat)
Courage Best Bitter, Directors Ⓗ
Smart, comfortable, town-centre pub, run in tandem with the excellent King's Head across the road. Well-known for food (no eve meals Tue, Thu or Sun). Guest beers. ❀ ◐ ▶ P

Theale

Falcon

High Street (old A4)
☎ (0734) 302523
11–11
Courage Best Bitter, Directors Ⓗ
Old coaching inn, near site of former Blatch's brewery. No lunches Sun. Guest beers.
❀ ◐ ⊟ ⇌ ♣ P

Lamb at Theale

Church Street (old A4)
☎ (0734) 302216
11–2.30 (3 Fri & Sat), 5.30 (6 Sat)–11
Courage Best Bitter, Directors Ⓖ
Beer kept on stillage behind bar and cooled with water jackets in summer. Function room with part-time skittle alley; garden with children's play frame, trees, etc. Regular guest beers. No food Sun. ⚏ Q ⚘ ❀ ◐ ⊟ ⇌ ♣ P

Red Lion

Church Street (old A4)
☎ (0734) 302394
11–3, 5.30–11
Ind Coope Burton Ale Ⓗ
Popular village pub with well-appointed skittle alley. Sun lunch served. ❀ ◐ ▶ ♣ P

Twyford

Duke of Wellington

High Street ☎ (0734) 340456
11–2.30 (3 Fri & Sat), 5 (6 Sat)–11
Brakspear XXX Mild, Bitter, Special, Old Ⓗ

Friendly, 16th-century village pub: popular public bar and quieter lounge, with occasional visitations by a ghostly highwayman. Sheltered garden. No food at weekends.
❀ ◐ ⊟ ⇌ ♣ P

Try also: Kings Arms
(Brakspear)

Wargrave

Bull

High Street (A321 crossroads)
☎ (0734) 403120
11–2.30, 6–11
Brakspear Bitter, Special Ⓗ
17th-century village pub with beams and a huge open fire. Well-deserved reputation for food (no meals Sun eve).
⚏ Q ❀ ⊨ ◐ ▶ ⇌ (not winter Sun)

Greyhound

High Street (A321, School Lane jct) ☎ (0734) 402556
11–3, 5.30–11 (11–11 Sat)
Courage Best Bitter Ⓗ
Friendly, two-bar, basic pub: busy public bar, cosy snug. Always one guest beer. Family room lunchtime only.
⚏ Q ⚘ ❀ ◐ ⊟ ⇌ (not winter Sun) ♣ P

Windsor

Court Jester

Church Lane
☎ (0753) 864257
11–11
Ind Coope Friary Meux Best Bitter, Burton Ale; Tetley Bitter Ⓗ
Imposing, old pub set in cobbled streets facing the main gate of the castle (150 yards away). One bar with a separate dining area. Eve meals in summer only.
◐ ▶ ⬠ ⇌ (Central & Riverside) ♣

Prince Christian

11 Kings Road
☎ (0753) 860980
11–3, 5–11 (11–11 Fri & Sat)
Brakspear Bitter; Fuller's London Pride Ⓗ
Windsor's only free house, five mins' walk (down Sheet Street) from town centre. One guest beer in addition to above. No food weekends. ◐ ⇌ (Central)

Winkfield

Old Hatchet

Hatchet Lane
☎ (0344) 882303
11–3, 6–11 (11–11 Fri & Sat)
Draught Bass; Charrington IPA; Fuller's London Pride Ⓗ
Attractive pub converted from three woodcutter's cottages. Popular for drink and food. Worth seeking out. ⚏ ❀ ◐ ▶ P

Berkshire

Wokingham

Crooked Billet
Honey Hill (off B3430, 2 miles SE of town) OS826667
☎ (0734) 780438
11–11
Brakspear Bitter, Special, Old Ⓗ
Excellent, extended country pub with chiming clock. Wide food range ensures busy lunchtime trade. Ramp access for wheelchair to bar. Well worth finding. ⬔ Q ⓫ ⓘ ◗ ♣ P

Queens Head
23 The Terrace (A329, top of Station Road)
☎ (0734) 781221
11–3, 5.30–11
Morland Bitter, Old Masters, Old Speckled Hen Ⓗ
Charming, single-bar pub, retaining much olde worlde character. Popular with locals and business people. Garden (at rear through pub) has Aunt Sally. No food Sat/Sun.
⬔ ◗ ♣ ♣

Try also: Ship, Peach Street (Fuller's)

Woolhampton

Rising Sun
Bath Road (A4 towards Reading) ☎ (0734) 712717
11.15–2.30 (11–3 Sat), 6–11 (12–2.30, 7–10.30 Sun)
Arkell's 3B; Fuller's London Pride; Hook Norton Best Bitter; Morland Bitter; Ringwood Old Thumper; Theakston Best Bitter; Younger IPA Ⓗ
Small public bar with bar billiards; lounge splits into eating and drinking areas. Reasonably quiet, with music kept very low. Decor is standard but unpretentious. Popular at Sun lunchtime. Can be very crowded because of size. ⬔ ⓫ ◗ ⓘ ◗ ♣ P

Try also: Falmouth Arms, A4 (Eldridge Pope)

Wraysbury

Green Man
28 Station Road (off B376)
☎ (0753) 812404
11–2.30, 6–11
Ind Coope Friary Meux Best Bitter, Burton Ale Ⓗ
Two-bar pub near station. Lounge is slightly plush and predominantly used by diners. Small, boisterous public (used mostly by locals) has the remains of a Ring the Bull pitch, last used in the late 1940s.
⬔ ◗ ⓘ ◗ ⓔ ⬀ ♣ P

Yattendon

Royal Oak
The Square OS552745
☎ (0635) 201325
12–3, 6.30–11
Adnams Bitter; Hall & Woodhouse Tanglefoot; Wadworth 6X Ⓗ
Award-winning, 16th-century inn, still retaining its character. Very high standard of food, using only the freshest ingredients.
⬔ Q ⬀ ⬔ ⊠ ◗ ◗

Join CAMRA —
see page 480!

TRADITIONAL BEER – WHICHEVER WAY YOU LIKE IT

You pays your money and you takes your choice. Traditional beer comes in many shapes and forms, each with its own individual character and fan club. Bitter is the most common in Britain – a low to mid strength hoppy beverage, occasionally called pale ale and sometimes misleadingly labelled 'Best Bitter', which should mean a more full-bodied beer of higher gravity. Degrees of hoppiness, bitterness, maltiness and strength, hand in hand with regional preferences, are what mark out one brew from another.

Then there is Mild, the butt of humorists whose imagination reaches no further than the old man sipping a half in the corner of the pub. How wrong could they be. Light or dark in colour, full-flavoured and refreshing, yet pleasantly low in alcohol, mild has less hops and therefore less bitterness than Bitter and is good value at its cheaper price.

When winter comes, respectfully sip an Old or Winter Ale in front of the fire; these rich, potent warmers are not for gulping. At any time, try a Stout with its heavy hoppiness and complex flavours of dark and roasted malts, as Roger Protz recommends earlier in this book.

Sadly, the other widely available types of beer in Britain are mostly in processed form: bottled brown ales (sweetish milds, sometimes high in gravity) and barley wines (very strong, all-malt brews). As for lager, that's a case unto itself (see page 181).

Buckinghamshire

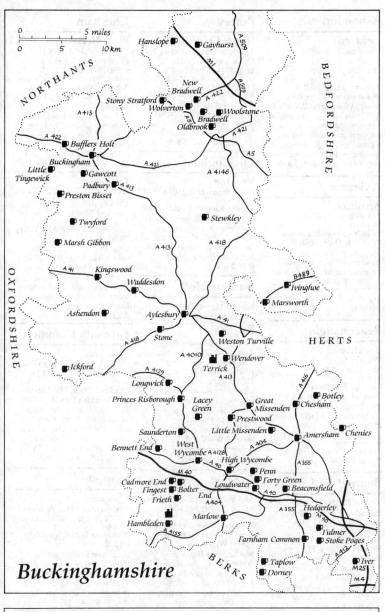

🏭 **Chiltern**, *Terrick*; **Old Luxters**, *Hambleden*

Amersham

Eagle
145 High Street (W end, in old town) ☎ (0494) 725262
11–3, 6–11 (12–2.30, 7–10.30 Sun)
Adnams Bitter; Ind Coope Benskins Best Bitter; Tetley Bitter Ⓗ

Traditional, town local which is larger inside than its exterior implies. More adventurous customers can approach by the footbridge at the rear. Eve meals Sat only; no food Sun.
🏨 Q 🕸 ◑ ◗ ♣

Kings Arms
30 High Street (old town)
☎ (0494) 726333
11–11
Greene King IPA; Ind Coope Benskins Best Bitter Ⓗ, **Burton Ale** Ⓖ

Magnificent, 15th-century coaching inn which offers cream teas. The many rooms are beautifully furnished. Separate award-winning restaurant.
🏨 Q 🕸 ◑ ◗ ♣ P

Buckinghamshire

Ashendon

Red Lion
Lower End (lane off road by church) OS704143
☎ (0296) 651296
12–2.30, 7–11
Adnams Bitter; Hall & Woodhouse Badger Best Bitter; Wadworth IPA, 6X Ⓗ
400 years old and once used as a local magistrates court, a small, but comfortable pub with a separate dining area offering imaginative food (no food Sun eve). Guest beers. ♨ ⛺ ◖ ♣

Aylesbury

Aristocrat
1 Wendover Road
11–3, 5–11
Fuller's Chiswick, London Pride, Mr Harry, ESB Ⓗ
Busy pub with a good atmosphere. Bar meals incl. vegetarian dishes. Happy hour 5–7. ⛺ ◖ ▮ ⅆ ⇌

Try also: Bell Hotel, Market Sq (Free)

Beaconsfield

Greyhound
Windsor End
☎ (0494) 673823
11–2.30, 5.30–11
Courage Best Bitter Ⓗ
Small saloon bar with a small snug bar attached; large public bar behind, and a function room upstairs. No food Mon eve or Sun. Guest beers. Q ⛺ ◖ ▮ ⅋

Try also: Prince of Wales, Wycombe End (Free)

Bennett End

Three Horseshoes
Horseshoe Road OS783973
☎ (0494) 483273
12–2.30, 7–11
Brakspear Bitter; Whitbread Flowers Original Ⓗ
Unspoilt, 18th-century inn with a view to match. Not easy to find but well worth the effort. Accommodation includes a water bed. Eve meals Tue–Sat.
♨ Q ⛺ ⇥ ▮ ⅋ ♣ P

Bolter End

Peacock
On B482 ☎ (0494) 881417
11–2.30, 6–11
Draught Bass; Ind Coope ABC Best Bitter Ⓗ
Popular, country pub with cosy corners. The emphasis is on home-cooked bar meals, especially steak and kidney pie (no food Sun eve).
♨ Q ⛺ ◖ ▮ ⅆ ♣

Botley

Hen & Chickens
119 Botley Road (1½ miles E of Chesham) OS977022
☎ (0494) 783303
11–2.30 (3 Sat), 6–11 (12–2.30, 7–10.30 Sun)
Ind Coope Benskins Best Bitter; Tetley Bitter Ⓗ
Fine, old pub with a beamed interior and a large beer garden. Two guest beers from Allied. No food Sun. ♨ ⛺ ◖ ▮ ♣ P

Buckingham

New Inn
Bridge Street ☎ (0280) 815713
10–11
Greene King IPA, Abbot Ⓗ
Former ABC pub, recently sold to independent brewers, and offering a big welcome, with full family facilities in the cellar bar. Sri Lankan cuisine a speciality.
♨ ⛺ ✂ ◖ ▮

Bufflers Holt

Robin Hood Inn
On A422 W of Buckingham
☎ (0280) 813387
11–2.30, 6.30–11
Hall & Woodhouse Badger Best Bitter; Hook Norton Best Bitter, Old Hooky; Wadworth 6X Ⓗ
18th-century, roadside inn with a friendly welcome. Boasts a fine selection of malt whiskies and country wines, plus an exciting and varied menu (no food Sun/Mon eves). Guest beers. ♨ ⛺ ⇥ ◖ ▮ ♣ P

Cadmore End

Blue Flag
On B482 3 miles S of M40; between Stokenchurch and Lane End ☎ (0494) 881183
11–2.30, 6–11
Morland Bitter, Old Speckled Hen; Webster's Yorkshire Bitter; Whitbread Boddingtons Bitter Ⓗ
Warm, friendly pub offering impeccable service. Strong emphasis on food, incl. fish specialities. Separate restaurant. Occasional guest beers.
Q ⇥ ◖ ▮ ⅆ P

Chenies

Red Lion
Off A404 OS022980
☎ (0923) 282722
11–3, 5.30–11
Ind Coope Benskins Best Bitter, Burton Ale; Tetley Bitter Ⓗ
Comfortable and friendly, village pub which caters for drinkers and diners alike. One guest beer from Allied. Q ◖ ▮ P

Chesham

Black Horse
Chesham Vale (2 miles N of Chesham, on Cholesbury road) OS964046 ☎ (0494) 784656
11–2.30, 6–11 (12–2.30, 7–10.30 Sun)
Adnams Bitter; Ind Coope Benskins Best Bitter, Burton Ale Ⓗ
Old inn with low beams and an enormous garden. The large menu and many diners do not detract from the good, pub atmosphere. Comfortable and friendly. Guest beer. ⛺ ◖ ▮ ⅆ P

Dorney

Pineapple
Lake End Road
11–3, 5–11
Ind Coope Burton Ale; Tetley Bitter Ⓗ
Originally two cottages, the saloon side dating from 1743 and fronted by a picturesque porch with its own post box. Small darts room just behind the Victorian fireplace in the public bar. No food Sun.
♨ Q ⛺ ◖ ▮ ⅋ ♣ P

Farnham Common

Yew Tree
Collins Wood Road (A355 N of village) ☎ (0753) 643723
11–11
Morland Bitter, Old Masters, Old Speckled Hen Ⓗ
Pub named after a magnificent yew tree which burnt down in 1972. Two small bars: a lounge given over to food and a very active public bar, with a TV for sports. ♨ ⛺ ◖ ▮ ⅋ ⅆ ♠ P

Fingest

Chequers
1½ miles off B482 at Bolter End OS778991 ☎ (0491) 63335
11–3, 6–11
Brakspear Bitter, Special, Old Ⓗ
Smart, comfortable pub with distinct areas, incl. no-smoking. The spacious garden is a feature. Outstanding bar food and restaurant (no food Sun eve).
♨ Q ✂ ⛺ ◖ ▮ P ✗

Forty Green

Royal Standard of England
Forty Green Road, Knotty Green (off B474 at Knotty Green garage) OS923919
☎ (0494) 673328
11–3, 5.30–11
Brakspear Special; Eldridge Pope Hardy Country, Royal Oak; Marston's Pedigree; Owd Rodger; Webster's Yorkshire Bitter Ⓗ

Ancient and historic free house, very popular at all times, despite being difficult to find. Good food bar; house bitter.
🏛 Q ⌂ ▬ ⏧ ◐ ← P

Frieth

Prince Albert
Moor End OS798906
11–2.30 (3 Sat), 5.30–11
Brakspear XXX Mild, Bitter, Special, Old Ⓗ
Small and exceptionally cosy pub with a dog and an intimate atmosphere. No chips! Not to be missed. 🏛 Q ▬ ⏧

Fulmer

Black Horse
Windmill Road
11–2.30, 6–11
Courage Best Bitter, Directors Ⓗ
One of the few three-bar pubs in the area. It dates from the early 17th-century, when it lodged the masons building the church next door. The central bar is plain and simple; the public bar can get crowded when the darts team are playing. No food Sun.
🏛 Q ▬ ⏧ ◐ ← P

Gawcott

Cuckoos Nest
New Inn Lane
10.30–3 (not Mon), 6–11
Hook Norton Best Bitter; Marston's Pedigree Ⓗ
Two-bar, village free house with an enthusiastic landlord. Live music every Sun lunch; guest beer in summer. 🏛 ▬ ⏧ ← ♣

Gayhurst

Sir Francis Drake
11–3, 6–11
Mansfield Riding Bitter; Wells Eagle, Bombardier Ⓗ
Small, village pub near the village; a former gatehouse of the manor where the Gunpowder Plot was conceived.
🏛 ▬ ⏧ ◐ ♣ P

Great Missenden

White Lion
High Street ☎ (024 06) 2114
11–2.30, 5.30–11 (11–11 Sat)
Greene King Abbot; Ind Coope Benskins Best Bitter Ⓗ
Solid, Victorian pub with a strong accent on games; it has five darts teams, plus crib, dominoes and pool teams. The regular Allied guest beer may include Ansells Mild. Aviary in the garden. No food Sun.
▬ ⏧ ← ▲ ⇌ ♣ P

Hambleden

Stag & Huntsman
1 mile N of Henley–Marlow road (A4155)
☎ (0491) 571227
11–2.30, 6–11
Brakspear Bitter, Special; Old Luxters Barn Ale; Wadworth 6X, Farmer's Glory Ⓗ
Unspoilt, three-bar pub in a picturesque brick and flint NT village. Splendid garden and extensive menu (seafood). No food Sun eve. Guest beers.
🏛 ▬ ⇥ ◐ ← ▬ ←

Hanslope

Globe
Hartwell Road (½ mile N of village) ☎ (0908) 510336
11–3, 6–11
Banks's Bitter Ⓔ
Smart, roadside, village pub with a comfortable lounge and a small public bar. Children's play area in garden with a small menagerie. No meals Mon eve.
▬ ⏧ ◐ ← ← P

Hedgerley

One Pin
One Pin Lane, Farnham Common ☎ (0753) 643035
11–4, 5.30–11
Courage Best Bitter, Directors Ⓗ
Traditional, two-bar pub at a crossroads south of the village: a comfortable lounge and a cosy public. Landlord has been in residence for 27 years and the lounge is still furnished in the Courage style of the late 60s (dark wood). No food Sun.
🏛 Q ▬ ⏧ ← ← ♣ P

High Wycombe

Bell
Frogmoor (A4128, 100 yds off Oxford St) ☎ (0494) 21317
11–2.30, 5.30–11
Fuller's Chiswick, London Pride, ESB Ⓗ
Cosy, busy, town-centre pub, close to the railway viaduct. Low ceilings and beams are features. Eve meals Mon–Thu till 9pm; Sun lunch by reservation only. ⇥ ⏧ ◐

General Havelock
114 Kingsmead Road (parallel to A40, 1m E of centre)
11–2.30 (3 Fri & Sat), 5.30 (5 Fri)–11
Fuller's Chiswick, London Pride, ESB Ⓗ
Comfortable, smart and friendly; a popular lunchtime venue with home-cooked 'specials' (no food Sun).
🏛 ▬ ⏧ P

Wendover Arms
180a Desborough Avenue (½ mile S of A40, W of centre)
11–2.30, 5 (6 Sat)–11 (11–11 Fri)
Brakspear XXX Mild, Bitter, Special, Old Ⓗ
On a hill south of the town centre; worth a walk for Wycombe's only mild. A spacious pub with a games-cum-function room. No eve meals Tue. ▬ ⏧ ◐ ♣ P

Ickford

Royal Oak
Bridge Road ☎ (0844) 339633
11–11 (11.30–3.30, 6–11 winter)
Morrells Dark, Bitter Ⓗ
Old-style English bar with a good, friendly, country atmosphere. 🏛 ▬ ⏧ ♣ P

Iver

Bull
High Street ☎ (0753) 651115
11–3, 5.30–11
Ind Coope Benskins Best Bitter, Burton Ale Ⓗ
Dates back to 1778, and was rebuilt by 1817 after a fire. Now leaded windows, with bull motif panes, front the building. The plush saloon has wood panelling and a Victorian character. No food Sun.
⇥ ⏧ ◐ ← P

Ivinghoe

Rose & Crown
Vicarage Lane (turning opp. church, then first right)
OS945163 ☎ (0296) 668472
12–2.30 (11–3 Sat), 6–11
Adnams Bitter; Greene King IPA; Morrells Dark Ⓗ
Hard to find, but worth the effort, this ex-Allied pub is now a thriving, village local. A stronger, guest beer is also available. No food Sun. Parking difficult. 🏛 Q ⏧ ◐ ← ▲ ♣

Kingswood

Crooked Billet
Ham Green ☎ (0296) 770239
11–3, 6–11 (11–11 summer)
Greene King Abbot; Ind Coope Burton Ale; Tetley Bitter; Wadworth 6X Ⓗ
Large, roadside establishment, comprising a comfortable bar, a separate restaurant and a substantial function room.
🏛 ▬ ⏧ ← ▲ ♣ P

Lacey Green

Pink & Lily
Pink Road, Parslow's Hillock (1 mile E of village) OS826019
☎ (024 028) 308
11.45 (11 Sat)–3, 6–11
Brakspear Bitter; Glenny Dr Thirsty's Draught,

47

Buckinghamshire

Hobgoblin; Ind Coope Burton Ale; Wadworth 6X; Whitbread Boddingtons Bitter ⊞
Popular, country pub with a varied clientele. The 'Brooke Bar' is an original snug dedicated to Rupert, the poet. Excellent bar food (no chips; no meals Sun eve). Large garden. Up to eight beers available. ⌂ Q ⊕ ◖ ♣ P

Little Missenden

Crown
Off A413 ☎ (024 06) 2571
11–2.30, 6–11 (12–2.30, 7–10.30 Sun)
Hook Norton Best Bitter; Marston's Pedigree; Morrells Varsity ⊞
Totally unspoilt, old, village pub with a warm welcome. The one small bar manages to create a two-bar atmosphere. A credit to the family who have run it since 1923. No food Sun. ⌂ Q ⊕ ◖ ♣ ○ P

Red Lion
Off A413 ☎ (024 06) 2876
11–2.30, 5.30 (6 Sat)–11 (12–2, 7–10.30 Sun)
Ind Coope Benskins Best Bitter, Burton Ale ⊞
Classic, village local which remains completely unspoilt; the fireplace dates from 1649. Children are welcome in the separate family and games room. Likely to become a free house. Two guest beers. Eve meals from at 7.30. ⌂ Q ⇆ ⊕ ◖ ♣ P

Little Tingewick

Red Lion
Mere Road ☎ (0280) 847836
11–11
Fuller's Chiswick, London Pride, ESB ⊞
Lively, village local with Civil War connections – ask the landlord. Traditional Sun lunch a speciality. ⌂ ⇆ ⊕ ◖ ◗ P

Longwick

Red Lion
Thame Road (A4129)
☎ (084 44) 4980
12–2.30, 6–11
Fuller's London Pride; Hook Norton Best Bitter; Ind Coope ABC Best Bitter ⊞
Substantial, roadside inn, spacious and comfortable with a separate dining area (no eve meals Sun). Q ⋈ ◖ ◗ ♣ P

Loudwater

Derehams Inn
Derehams Lane (off A40)
OS903908 ☎ (0494) 30965
11–2.30, 5.30–11
Brakspear Bitter; Fuller's London Pride; Greene King

Abbot; Whitbread Wethered Bitter, Boddingtons Bitter ⊞
Formerly the 'Bricklayers' in its Wethered days; a cosy, locals' pub, unspoilt by progress. Beers may vary. Lunches weekdays only. ⌂ ⊕ ◖ ♣ P

Marlow

Chequers
High Street ☎ (0628) 482053
11–11
Brakspear Bitter, Special ⊞
Rambling, 16th-century inn with two lively bars and a restaurant. Opposite the late Wethereds brewery. Over-21s only in the bars. ⌂ Q ⊕ ⋈ ◖ ◗ ⇌

Clayton Arms
Quoiting Square, Oxford Road (off West St, A4155)
10.30–2.30 (3 Fri & Sat), 6–11
Brakspear XXX Mild, Bitter, Old ⊞
Totally original, a gem: two small bars with bare boards. A genuine local where the landlord has lived for over 60 years. ⌂ Q ⋈ ⊕ ⇌ ♣

Marsh Gibbon

Plough
Church Street ☎ (0869) 277305
11–3, 6–11
Draught Bass; Morrells Dark, Bitter ⊞
Pleasant, two-bar, 16th-century pub, catering for all ages. Separate dining room with extensive menu. Live music alternate Sats. ⌂ ⊕ ◖ ⊟ ▲ ♣ ○ P

Marsworth

Red Lion
Vicarage Road (off B489, near GU Canal bridge 130)
OS919147 ☎ (0296) 668366
11–2.30, 6–11
Banks & Taylor Shefford Bitter; Draught Bass; Hook Norton Best Bitter; Wadworth 6X ⊞
Superb, village local with contrasting bars on two levels. The long public bar displays a noticeboard full of local information and has a bar-billiards table. Home-made curries are specialities (no food Sun). ⌂ Q ⊕ ◖ ◗ ⊟ ♣ ○ P

Milton Keynes: Bradwell

Prince Albert
17 Vicarage Road
☎ (0908) 312080
11–2.30 (5 Sat), 5.30 (7 Sat)–11
Adnams Broadside; Mansfield Riding Mild; Theakston XB; Wells Eagle, Bombardier ⊞

Popular, village local with a single, comfortable lounge bar and a children's play area in the garden. Draught mild is rare for the area; beers may vary. No eve meals Sun/Mon. ⌂ ⊕ ◖ ♣ P

New Bradwell

Foresters Arms
Newport Road
11–11 (11–4, 6–11 Sat)
Wells Eagle ⊞
Honest, down-to-earth, no-frills, two-bar local. ⊕ ⊟ ⇌ (Wolverton)

New Inn
2 Bradwell Road
11–11
Adnams Broadside; Wells Eagle, Bombardier ⊞
Lively, canalside inn. Good value bar food and a separate restaurant upstairs. ⊕ ◖ ⊟ ⇌ (Wolverton) P

Oldbrook

Cricketers
Oldbrook Boulevard
☎ (0908) 678844
11–3, 4.30–11 (11–11 Sat)
Greene King XX Mild, IPA, Abbot ⊞
Splendid, estate pub with a cricketing theme. The autographed bats should keep any buff busy! No eve meals Sun. ⊕ ◖ ◗ ⇌ (Central) P

Woolstone

Cross Keys
34 Newport Road, Great Woolstone (1 mile from M1 jct 14) ☎ (0908) 679404
11–2.30, 5.30–11
Wells Eagle, Bombardier ⊞
Splendid, country thatch, now encircled by the new city, without having lost a real village atmosphere. Guest beer. ⊕ ◖ ◗ ⊟ ♣ P

Padbury

New Inn (& Petrol Station)
Aylesbury Road (A413)
10–2.30, 5.30–11
Hook Norton Best Bitter; Ind Coope ABC Best Bitter ⊞
Ex-ABC pub of great charm, recently sold to the tenant. Its small, cosy bars are a step back in time. ⌂ Q ⊕ ⊟ ♣ P

Penn

Horse & Jockey
Church Road, Tylers Green
☎ (0494) 815963
11–2.30, 5.30–11
Ansells Mild; Brakspear Bitter; Ind Coope Benskins Best Bitter, Burton Ale ⊞

Spacious and comfortable pub, serving food throughout the opening hours. Guest beers.
🏠 ◖ 🕭 ♣ P

Preston Bisset

Old Hat
Main Street ☎ (028 04) 355
11–2.30, 7 (6 Sat)–11
Hook Norton Best Bitter 🅷
Listed free house with a great welcome. The small bar has a splendid wooden settle. A fixed point in an ever-changing world. 🏠 Q ♣

Prestwood

Kings Head
Wycombe Road (A4128)
11–11
Brakspear XXX Mild, Bitter, Special, Old; Greene King Abbot; Marston's Pedigree 🅶
A permanent beer festival in two bars with real fires. Always at least eight beers from independent brewers. Guest beers. Snacks always available.
🏠 Q 🕭 ♣ ⌂ P

Princes Risborough

Bird in Hand
47 Station Road (off A4010)
☎ (084 44) 5602
11–3, 6–11
Greene King IPA, Abbot 🅷
Flourishing under new ownership, a smart but cosy locals' pub, near the station. Fine selection of single malts.
🏠 ◖ 🕭 ⇌ ♣

Try also: **George & Dragon**, High St (Ind Coope)

Saunderton

Golden Cross
Wycombe Road (A4010)
☎ (024 024) 2293
12–2.30, 5.30–11
Ind Coope ABC Best Bitter, Burton Ale 🅷
Comfortable, roadside pub with a secluded garden. Imaginative home-cooked meals (not served Sun/Mon eves).
Q 🏠 ◖ ▶ 🕭 ⇌ ♣ P

Try also: **Rose & Crown** (Free)

Stewkley

Swan
High Street North
☎ (0525) 240285
11–2.30 (3 Sat), 6–11
Courage Best Bitter, Directors; John Smith's Bitter 🅷
Excellent, Georgian pub in the centre of the village. Always a good atmosphere. No food Sun and no eve meals Mon.
🏠 🏠 ◖ ▶ ♣ P

Stoke Poges

Plough
Wexham Street (400 yds N of hospital) ☎ (0753) 662663
11–3, 5–11
Ind Coope Benskins Best Bitter, Burton Ale; Tetley Bitter 🅷
Traditional, low-ceilinged, wayside pub, very much a locals' haunt but strangers are made welcome. One end of the bar is a shrine to rugby league. Popular for food (no meals Sat eve, or Sun). 🏠 Q 🏠 ◖ ▶ ♣ P

Stone

Waggon & Horses
39 Oxford Road (A418)
☎ (0296) 748740
11–2.30 (3 Sat), 6–11
Ind Coope ABC Best Bitter, Burton Ale 🅷
Pleasant, roadside pub with two separate bars. Landlord has the cellarmanship award for Burton Ale. Good value food at all times. 🏠 ◖ ▶ 🕭 ♣ P

Stony Stratford

Bull Hotel (Vaults Bar)
High Street ☎ (0908) 567104
12–11
Draught Bass; Eldridge Pope Royal Oak; Ind Coope ABC Best Bitter; Theakston XB; Wadworth 6X; Younger IPA 🅷
Small, Victorian bar adjoining a famous, old coaching inn (involved in the original 'cock and bull story'). Folk club every Sun lunch. Ever-changing range of beers. 🏠 🏠 ◖ ▶ 🕭 ♣ P

Taplow

Horse & Groom
735 Bath Road (A4)
11–11
Draught Bass; Charrington IPA 🅷
17th-century, listed building, originally a post house on the first mail route to Ireland. Its origins could date back to the 1500s. The 19th-century extensions are also listed, with the Gothic windows in keeping with the original building. Under threat of closure to become offices. The old stables and part of the garden have already been saved from the bulldozer. 🏠 🕭 ⇌ ♣ P

Twyford

Red Lion
Church End ☎ (0296) 730339
12–2.30, 6–11
Ind Coope ABC Best Bitter, Burton Ale 🅷
Tiny, unspoilt, 17th-century

pub across a long front garden. Wonderful, cosy atmosphere.
🏠 Q 🏠 P

Waddesdon

Five Arrows
High Street (A41, close to manor) ☎ (0296) 651727
10–3, 5 (6 Sat)–11
Hook Norton Best Bitter 🅷
Ornate, grandiose, Rothschild building, bearing the family emblem. The unpretentious lounge bar is home to Owlswick Morrismen. Restaurant and regular guest beers (no food Sun eve).
🏠 ⇌ ◖ ▶ 🅰 ♣ P

Wendover

Red Lion
High Street ☎ (0296) 622266
11–11
Brakspear Bitter; Fuller's London Pride; Greene King Abbot; Marston's Pedigree; Morland Bitter, Old Speckled Hen 🅷
Large and comfortable, old coaching inn and centre of village life. Table service in all bars; separate restaurant. The range of beers sometimes changes. 🏠 ⇌ ◖ ▶ ⇌ P ⅄

Weston Turville

Plough
Brook End ☎ (0296) 612546
11–2.30, 6–11
Fuller's Chiswick, London Pride, ESB 🅷
Friendly, one-bar, village local with a goat and guinea fowl in the garden. Bar food includes real German sausages (no meals Sun). 🏠 ◖ ♣ P

West Wycombe

George & Dragon Hotel
High Street
☎ (0494) 464414
11–2.30, 5.30–11 (11–11 Sat)
Courage Best Bitter, Directors 🅷
19th-century coaching inn in a National Trust village. The original-timbered bar is reputed to be haunted. Excellent garden. Guest beers. 🏠 Q ⏱ 🏠 ⇌ ◖ ▶ P

Wolverton

Crauford Arms
Stratford Road
11–2.30, 5–11 (11–11 Fri & Sat)
Adnams Bitter; Charrington IPA 🅷
Imposing building opposite the BR works, with a Victoriana theme in the large and comfortable lounge. The public bar doubles as games room. No food Sun or Mon. ◖ 🕭 ⇌ ♣ P

Cambridgeshire

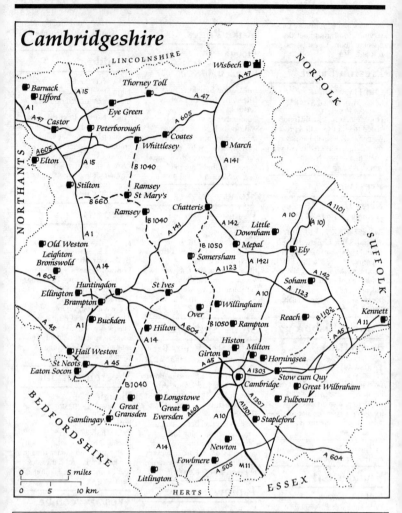

Cambridgeshire

(Map showing towns including Barnack, Ufford, Castor, Peterborough, Elton, Stilton, Thorney Toll, Eye Green, Coates, Whittlesey, March, Ramsey, Ramsey St Mary's, Chatteris, Little Downham, Mepal, Somersham, Ely, Old Weston, Leighton Bromswold, Ellington, Huntingdon, Brampton, St Ives, Willingham, Soham, Reach, Kennett, Buckden, Hilton, Over, Rampton, Histon, Milton, Horningsea, Hail Weston, Girton, Stow cum Quy, St Neots, Eaton Socon, Cambridge, Great Wilbraham, Longstowe, Great Eversden, Great Gransden, Fulbourn, Gamlingay, Stapleford, Newton, Fowlmere, Litlington, bordered by LINCOLNSHIRE, NORFOLK, SUFFOLK, ESSEX, HERTS, BEDFORDSHIRE, NORTHANTS)

🏠 **Elgood's**, Wisbech

Barnack

Millstone
Millstone Lane
☎ (0780) 740296
11–3, 6–11
**Adnams Bitter; Everards
Tiger, Old Original** Ⓗ
Stone-built, village local close to
the 'Hills and Holes' – a former
quarry for churches. Separate
restaurant and function suite.
No eve meals Sun or Mon.
Guest beer. ☞ 🍴 ◖ ◗ ♿ P

Brampton

Dragoon
Buckden Road
☎ (0480) 53510
11–2.30, 6–11
Wells Eagle, Bombardier Ⓗ

Comfortable, well-appointed
pub with a locals' public bar and
a food-oriented lounge.
🍴 ◖ 🍴 ♣ P

Buckden

Falcon
Mill Road
☎ (0480) 811612
11–2.30, 6.30–11
**Mansfield Riding Mild; Wells
Eagle** Ⓗ
Situated just outside the main
village on the road to Offords.
A single lounge bar with a
separate games room at the rear.
Traditional games include
Northants skittles, now sadly
rare this far east. Two gardens:
one enclosed with a patio and
barbecue for summer. 🍴 ♣ P

Cambridge

Ancient Druids
Napier Street
☎ (0223) 324514
11–2.30 (4 Sat), 5.30 (5 Sat)–11
**Adnams Broadside; Ancient
Druids Kite Bitter, Druid's
Special, Merlin; Wells
Eagle** Ⓗ
Modern, open-plan pub with its
own micro-brewery. Excellent
food, especially curries (no
meals Sun eve). Adjoins Grafton
Centre shops and car park.
🍴 ◖ ◗

Cambridge Blue
85–87 Gwydir Street
☎ (0223) 61382
12–2.30 (3.30 Sat), 6–11
Banks & Taylor Shefford

Mild (occasional), **Shefford Bitter, SPA, Edwin Taylor's Stout** (occasional), **SOS, SOD** [H]
Busy, friendly little pub with a no-smoking bar and snug. Petanque pitch in the surprisingly large garden. Excellent home-cooked food. Guest beers, with always a mild available. Public car park opposite former Dale & Co. brewery. No food Sun eve.
⛫ Q ❀ ◐ ◑ ⊕ ✗

Cow & Calf
St Peters Street
☎ (0223) 311919
12–3, 5 (7 Sat)–11
Banks & Taylor Shefford Bitter; Courage Best Bitter; Nethergate Bitter; Samuel Smith OBB; Theakston Best Bitter [H]
Splendid, street-corner local. Cambridge CAMRA *Pub of the Year* 1990. Use Shire Hall car park in the evenings. Guest beers. No food at weekend.
⛫ ❀ ◐ ♣ ⊕

Elm Tree
Orchard Street
☎ (0223) 63005
11–11
Adnams Broadside; Wells Eagle [H]
Small, very friendly, one-bar pub, popular with FE students.
◐ ◑

Empress
72 Thoday Street
☎ (0223) 247236
11–2.30, 6.30–11 (12–2.30, 7–10.30 Sun)
Fuller's Chiswick; Marston's Pedigree; Whitbread Castle Eden Ale, Flowers Original [H]
There's always something going on at this friendly, lively, community pub. Courtyard for outdoor drinking. Weston's Old Rosie cider. ❀ ⊟ ♣ ⊕

Free Press
Prospect Row
☎ (0223) 68337
12–3, 6–11
Greene King IPA, Rayments Special, Abbot [H]
Hearty little pub packed with interesting features. No music, no pool and no fruit machines. Imaginative, high quality food. Rabbits roam free in the patio garden. ⛫ Q ❀ ◐ ◑ ✗

Green Dragon
5 Water Street, Chesterton
☎ (0223) 355182
11–2.30, 6–11
Greene King XX Mild, IPA, Rayments Special, Abbot [E]
Very old, heavily-beamed pub, opened-out inside but retaining distinct drinking areas. Folk music Mon nights. Top-notch, home-cooked food (Mon–Fri).
❀ ◐ ♣

Live & Let Live
40 Mawson Road
☎ (0223) 460261
12–2.30, 6–11
Marston's Border Bitter, Burton Best Bitter, Merrie Monk, Pedigree; Nethergate Bitter, Old Growler [H]
Wood panelling, exposed floorboards and solid furnishings create a warm, traditional atmosphere; characterful landlord. Eve meals finish at 8.30pm. ⛫ ◐ ◑ ♿ ⇌

Panton Arms
Panton Street
☎ (0223) 355733
11–2.30, 6–11 (11–11 Fri & Sat)
Greene King XX Mild, IPA, Rayments Special, Abbot [H]
A superbly straightforward public bar and a plusher lounge; once the brewery tap of the now-demolished Panton brewery – hence the gates to the patio. Bar billiards played.
❀ ◐ ◑ ⊟ ♣

Salisbury Arms
76 Tenison Road
☎ (0223) 60363
11–3, 6–11
Mansfield Riding Mild; Wadworth 6X; Wells Eagle, Bombardier [H]
Large, bustling pub, owned by Charles Wells, but offering a wide selection of guest beers. Ring the Bull played. No smoke-free area Fri/Sat eves.
◐ ♿ ⇌ ♣ ⊕ ✗

Seven Stars
249 Newmarket Road
☎ (0223) 354430
11–3, 6–11
Greene King XX Mild, IPA, Abbot [H]
Friendly, busy locals' pub, the haunt of volunteers from the nearby Cambridge Museum of Technology. No food Sun lunch. ◐ ◑ ⊟ ♣ P

Tap & Spile (Mill)
13–14 Mill Lane
☎ (0223) 357026
11–11
Beer range varies [H]
Always eight different ales are available at this busy, riverside pub, where much exposed brick and woodwork create a warm, traditional atmosphere. Homely food at lunchtime. ◐ ⊕

Tram Depot
5 Dover Street (off East Road, opp. Anglia HE college)
☎ (0223) 324553
11–3, 5–11 (11.30–11 Sat)
Earl Soham Gannet Mild, Victoria, Albert Ale, Old Cyril [H]
Once the stables of the Cambridge Street Tramway Co., now superbly converted into a characterful, lively pub.
Exceptional food (quality and value), with a good vegetarian selection. Public car park at the rear. Q ❀ ◐ ◑ ♿

White Swan
109 Mill Road
☎ (0223) 357144
11–3.30, 5.30–11
Greene King IPA, Abbot [H]
Friendly, street-corner local: one bar with a straightforward public bar area and smarter lounge section. Games room at the rear. Public car park in Gwydir Street. ❀ ⇌ ♣

Castor

Royal Oak
24 Peterborough Road
☎ (0733) 380217
11–2.30, 6–11
Ind Coope Burton Ale; Tetley Bitter [H]
Listed building with a thatched roof and considerable charm. The cosy atmosphere is enhanced by a low-beamed ceiling. Small area at the front of the pub for summer drinking.
⛫ Q ❀ ◐ ♣ P

Chatteris

Cock
41 London Road
☎ (035 43) 2026
11–3, 6–11
Webster's Yorkshire Bitter [H]
Large, converted house with ornate ceilings. Popular with all ages. Petanque played.
❀ ◐ ◑ ♣ P

Coates

Vine
4 South Green
☎ (073 120) 343
10.30–2.30, 6–11 (11–11 Sat)
Mansfield Riding Mild; Wells Eagle, Bombardier [H]
1950s-style lounge with an open fire. The large, enclosed garden is ideal for children, with swings and a climbing frame.
⛫ Q ❀ ⊟ ♣ P

Eaton Socon

Crown
Great North Road (A45, St Neots bypass)
☎ (0480) 212232
11–2.30, 5.30–11 (11–11 Sat)
Tetley Bitter [H]
Ivy-clad free house – often crowded. At least six real ales on offer. Booking advised for the restaurant. ❀ ◐ ◑ ⛺ P

Millers Arms
Ackerman Street (off Great North Road)
☎ (0480) 405965
12–2.30 (4 Sat), 6 (7 Sat)–11
Greene King XX Mild, IPA, Abbot [H]

Cambridgeshire

Small, 'village' pub on the larger of Eaton Socon's two greens. Large garden with many children's facilities and a boules pitch; summer barbecues. Popular with boat owners from the nearby river moorings. Children welcome until 8pm.
🏠 🛏 🏮 🍺 ♣

Ellington

Mermaid
Off A604, on village loop road
☎ (0480) 891450
12–2.30 (5 Sat), 7–11
Draught Bass Ⓗ
Friendly, one-bar, village free house, split into two areas by seating. Low ceiling with beams and a wood burning stove.
🏠 🛏 ♣

Elton

Crown
8 Duck Street
☎ (0832) 280232
11.30–2.30, 6–11
Greene King IPA; Marston's Pedigree Ⓗ
Grade II listed building on the village green, rebuilt in 1985 after a major fire. Features a large, comfortable bar and a separate restaurant. Games include shove-ha'penny, 'Pope Joan' and mini-skittles. Winner of local CAMRA *Pub of the Season* award. Guest beers.
🏠 🛏 🍺 ♣ P

Ely

Prince Albert
62 Silver Street
☎ (0353) 663494
11.30 (11 Fri)–2.30 (11–3.30 Sat), 6.30–11
Greene King XX Mild, IPA, Rayments Special, Abbot Ⓗ
The emphasis is firmly on good ale and good company in this friendly little pub. Delightful beer garden. Public car park across the street (entrance in Barton Road). 🏠 Q 🛏 ♣

Eye Green

Greyhound
41 Crowland Road (A1073, 800 yds from A47 jct)
☎ (0733) 222487
11–2.30, 7–11
Mansfield Riding Mild; Wells Eagle, Bombardier Ⓗ
Basic, popular, village local with a lounge and a public bar. Winner of local CAMRA *Pub of the Month* award. Large garden.
🏠 Q 🛏 ♣ P

Fowlmere

Queens Head
Long Lane
☎ (076 382) 288

12–3 (4 Sat), 6 (7 Sat)–11
Greene King IPA, Abbot Ⓗ
Excellent, village local: darts, dominoes and Shut the Box played in the comfy public bar. Wide selection of real cheeses and real breads at lunchtimes.
🏠 Q 🛏 ♣ P

Fulbourn

Bakers Arms
Hinton Road
☎ (0223) 880606
11–2.30, 5–11 (11–11 Wed–Sat)
Greene King XX Mild, IPA, Rayments Special, Abbot Ⓗ
Popular, village local; the outstanding garden includes a children's play area and animals. No food Sun. 🏠 🛏 🍺 🗡 ♣

Gamlingay

Cock
Church Street
☎ (0767) 502255
11–2.30, 6–11
Greene King IPA, Rayments Special, Abbot Ⓗ
Timber-framed pub of some character, with a wood-panelled interior and a large inglenook in the lounge bar. Garden and car park at the rear. 🏠 🛏 🍺 P

Girton

George Inn
71 High Street
☎ (0223) 276069
11–3, 6–11
Courage Best Bitter, Directors; John Smith's Bitter; Tolly Cobbold Mild, Bitter Ⓗ
Popular, village local. A full menu offers a lunchtime special and a vegetarian option (booking advisable for Sun lunch). No eve meals Sun or Mon. Q 🛏 🍺 🍺 ♣ P

Try also: Black Horse, Impington (Brent Walker)

Great Eversden

Hoops
High Street
☎ (0223) 262185
12–2.30 (may vary in summer), 7–11
Adnams Broadside; Wells Eagle Ⓗ, **Bombardier** Ⓖ
17th-century, village inn with a heavily timbered seating area separated from the public bar area by a conversational lobby. No food Mon. 🏠 🛏 🍺 🍺 ♣ P

Great Gransden

Crown & Cushion
☎ (076 77) 214
12–11 (12–2.30, 6–11 Mon)
Adnams Broadside Ⓗ;
Mansfield Riding Mild Ⓖ;
Wells Eagle, Bombardier Ⓗ
Split-level pub divided into

areas. Good, home-cooked food. Outdoor pool table and a small menagerie in the garden. Regular live music. 🏠 🛏 🍺 P

Great Wilbraham

Carpenters Arms
10 High Street
☎ (0223) 880202
11–2.30, 6.30 (7 winter)–11 (12–2, 7–10.30 Sun)
Greene King XX Mild, IPA, Rayments Special, Abbot Ⓗ
Idyllic, village local in a 17th-century listed building. The landlord is noted for his ribald ripostes. XX Mild and Rayments alternate. Home-made bar meals (eves Wed–Sat only).
🏠 Q 🛏 🍺 🍺 ♣ P

Hail Weston

Royal Oak
High Street (off A45)
☎ (0480) 72527
11–2.30, 6–11
Adnams Broadside; Mansfield Riding Bitter; Wells Eagle, Bombardier Ⓗ
Picturesque, thatched, village pub which has a large children's playground and pleasant family room with games. No eve meals Sun or Mon. 🏠 🛏 🛏 🍺 ♣ P

Hilton

Prince of Wales
Potton Road (B1040)
☎ (0480) 830257
11–2.30, 6–11 (11–11 Sat)
Adnams Bitter; Banks & Taylor Shefford Bitter; Draught Bass Ⓗ
Friendly, village free house with a small public bar and larger, well-furnished lounge. Good range of guest beers.
🏠 🛏 🍺 🍺 P

Histon

Red Lion
27 High Street
☎ (0223) 232288
11.30–2.30 (4 Sat), 5.30 (6 Sat)–11
Adnams Bitter; Draught Bass; Greene King IPA; Samuel Smith OBB; Taylor Landlord; Tetley Bitter Ⓗ
Relaxed surroundings with subdued red lighting, beams and brasses. Original home cooking (no chips) Mon–Fri.
🏠 🛏 🍺 ♣ P

Try also: All pubs in the village sell real ale

Horningsea

Plough & Fleece
High Street
☎ (0223) 860795
11.30–2.30, 7–11 (12–2, 7–10.30 Sun)
Greene King IPA, Abbot Ⓗ
Pub where the public bar is a

gem. Superb food based on old English recipes; try the chocolate pudding. No eve meals Sun or Mon.
🏛 Q 🍴 🌑 🍴 🔌 P

Huntingdon

Victoria
Ouse Walk ☎ (0480) 53899
11–2.30, 6–11
Courage Directors; Tolly Cobbold Bitter, Old Strong Ⓗ
Hard-to-find, back-street pub, but well worth the effort. One long bar is divided into distinct areas. Good choice of food.
🏛 🍴 🍴 ♣ ⏱

Kennett

Bell Inn
Bury Road
☎ (0638) 750286
11.30–2.30, 6–11
Adnams Bitter, Broadside; Nethergate Bitter Ⓗ
Fine, old inn with a food-oriented main bar and a pleasant, tile-floored, drinkers' area. Four guest beers. No eve meals Sun in winter.
🏛 🍴 🛏 🍴 🍴 P

Leighton Bromswold

Green Man
Off A604
☎ (0480) 890238
12–2.30 (not Tue), 6–11 (closed Mon)
Taylor Landlord; Theakston Old Peculier Ⓗ
Comfortable, rural free house with a collection of brewery memorabilia. Wide and ever-changing range of guest beers. Hood skittles played.
Q 🛋 🍴 🍴 ♣

Litlington

Crown
Silver Street
☎ (0763) 852439
11.30–3, 5.30–11
Greene King IPA, Rayments Special, Abbot Ⓗ
Enlarged, village pub, retaining two bars; the lounge bar has memorabilia from the nearby WWII American airbase. Don't be confused by the village one-way system. 🍴 🍴 🔌

Little Downham

Anchor
25 Main Street
☎ (0353) 699494
11–3, 6–11
Greene King IPA; Tolly Cobbold Mild, Original Ⓗ
Popular and welcoming, village local. Meals served Wed–Sat; the varied menu caters well for vegetarians. 🏛 Q 🍴 🍴 P

Longstowe

Golden Miller
High Street
11.30–2.30, 7–11
Adnams Bitter Ⓗ
One-bar free house named after a famous racehorse which was stabled nearby. Guest beers.
🍴 🍴 P

March

Ship
11 Nene Parade
☎ (0354) 56999
11–3, 7–11 (10.30–11 Sat)
Greene King XX Mild, IPA, Abbot Ⓗ, **Winter Ale** Ⓖ
17th-century, thatched, riverside pub with unusual carved ceiling beams. Extensive boat moorings. 🛏 🍴 ♣

Mepal

Three Pickerels
19 Bridge Road (far end of village from main road)
☎ (0353) 777891
12–3, 6–11
Marston's Border Bitter, Border Exhibition, Burton Best Bitter, Pedigree Ⓗ
Pub in an idyllic, riverside location, serving excellent, home-cooked food (book Sun lunch; no meals Sun eve).
🏛 🛏 🍴 🍴 P

Try also: Kings Head, Wilburton (Free)

Milton

Waggon & Horses
39 High Street
☎ (0223) 860313
12–2.30, 5 (7 Sat)–11
Bateman XB; Nethergate Bitter Ⓗ
Comfortable pub offering a varied range of guest beers. Lunches Mon–Fri. Weston's ciders. Limited parking.
🏛 🍴 ⏱ P

Newton

Queens Head
Fowlmere Road
☎ (0223) 870436
11.30 (11 Sat)–2.30, 6–11
Adnams Bitter, Old, Broadside (summer) Ⓖ
Wonderfully unspoilt, village pub. Freshly-made sandwiches, home-baked soup and real baked potatoes complement the ale.
🏛 Q 🛏 🍴 ♣ ⏱ P

Old Weston

Swan
☎ (083 23) 400
12–3 (4 Sat), 7–11
Adnams Bitter, Greene King Abbot; Marston's Pedigree Ⓗ
Olde-worlde free house, with beams and a low ceiling. Separate restaurant.
🏛 🍴 🍴 🔌 ♣ P

Over

Exhibition
2 King Street
☎ (0954) 30790
Courage Directors; Tolly Cobbold Bitter Ⓗ
Former beer-house expertly renovated and extended. Features a swimming pool for children. Good value food (lunches Mon–Fri; eve meals Fri and Sat). Guest beer.
🏛 🍴 🍴 ♣ P

Peterborough

Beacon
The Cresset, Rightwell, Bretton
☎ (0733) 265705
11–3 (4 Fri & Sat), 6–11
Home Bitter; Theakston Best Bitter; Thwaites Best Mild Ⓗ
Modern, refurbished lounge bar and carvery, located inside the Cresset Centre. Guest beers.
Q 🍴 🍴 ♿ P

Bogart's
17 North Street
☎ (0733) 349995
11–3 (4 Sat), 5.30 (7 Sat)–11
Adnams Broadside; Draught Bass; Bateman XB; Hook Norton Best Bitter; Taylor Landlord; Welsh Brewers Worthington BB Ⓗ
Very popular real ale oasis in the city centre. Interesting lunchtime food. Guest beers.
🍴 ≈

Boy's Head
Oundle Road, Woodston
☎ (0733) 65021
11–11
Courage Best Bitter, Directors; John Smith's Bitter Ⓗ
Lively pub built on a Saxon graveyard. Large, well-used public bar; live music in the lounge at weekends.
🛏 🍴 ♣ P

Crown
749 Lincoln Road, New England (old A15, 300 yds S of A15/A47 jct)
☎ (0733) 341366
11–3, 5–11 (11–11 Fri & Sat)
Adnams Bitter; Draught Bass; Charrington IPA; Theakston Old Peculier Ⓗ
Large and lively, corner pub with an imposing 1920s, mock Tudor facade; two separate bars and a function room with a midnight licence. Diverse clientele and entertainment. Excellent, home-made pizzas.
🏛 🍴 🍴 🔌 P

Cambridgeshire

Dragon
Hodson Avenue, Werrington
☎ (0733) 322675
11–2.30 (3.30 Fri & Sat), 5.30–11
Wells Eagle, Bombardier Ⓗ
Modern pub on a recently developed estate. A popular local catering well for family visits with a purpose-built children's room (plenty of toys). Guest beers. ♨ ⊛ ◖ ◗ ₺ ♣ P

Fenman
Whittlesey Road, Stanground
☎ (0733) 69460
11.30–3, 6–11 (12–2.30, 7–10.30 Sun)
Courage Best Bitter, Directors; John Smith's Bitter Ⓗ
Large, estate pub with a bar and lounge, on the eastern outskirts of Peterborough. Q ⊛ ⊟ ♣ P

Hand & Heart
12 Highbury Street, Millfield
☎ (0733) 69463
10.30–2.30 (3 Sat), 6–11
Courage Directors; John Smith's Magnet Ⓗ
Original Warwicks brewery windows remain on this gem of a pub in a quiet back street, away from the hubbub. A very friendly, lively public bar and a comfy, quiet lounge. Interesting whisky collection in the bar. ⚗ Q ⊟ ♣

Swiss Cottage
2 Grove Street, Woodston (100 yds off A604, near Marshall's garage) ☎ (0733) 68734
10.30–11
Courage Directors; John Smith's Bitter Ⓗ
Back-street local with an Irish flavour, built in the style of an Alpine chalet. ⊛ ◖ ⇌ ♣

Woolpack
29 North Street, Stanground
☎ (0733) 54417
11.30–3, 7–11
Brakspear Special; Fuller's Chiswick; Whitbread Boddingtons Bitter, Castle Eden Ale Ⓗ
Refurbished, village pub, two miles south east of the city centre. Notable stone fireplace, and a collection of militaria in the rear bar. The garden leads to the river (boat moorings). Guest beers. Q ⊛ ♣

Rampton

Black Horse
6 High Street
☎ (0954) 51296
11–3, 5–11 (11.30–11 Sat)
Greene King XX Mild, IPA, Abbot Ⓗ
Cheerful, village inn. The prints in the lounge have an interesting history – ask the landlord. Growing reputation for food, especially steaks (eve meals Thu–Sat). ⚗ ⊛ ◖ ◗ ⊟ ♣ P

Ramsey

Jolly Sailor
Great Whyte
☎ (0487) 813388
11–2.30, 6.30–11
Camerons Bitter; Courage Directors Ⓗ
Town-centre pub with a timeless feel; in the same family for many years. Display of local photographs. Q ⊛ ⊟

Three Horseshoes
Little Whyte
☎ (0487) 812452
11–2.30, 6–11
Courage Directors; John Smith's Bitter, Magnet Ⓗ
Busy, back-street pub with a distinct northern flavour. The back bar has been converted into a restaurant. Directors alternates with Magnet. ⋈ ◖ ◗ ⊟

Ramsey St Mary's

White Lion
201 Hurn Road
☎ (073 120) 386
12–2.30 (3 Sat; not Wed), 7–11
Adnams Broadside; Mansfield Riding Mild; Wells Eagle, Bombardier Ⓗ
Isolated pub in a long, Fenland village. Old photos in the lounge show local flooding. The garden has children's play equipment. No eve meals Tue. ⚗ Q ⊛ ◖ ◗ ⊟ ♣ P

Reach

Kings
8 Fair Green
☎ (0638) 741745
12–2.30, 7–11
Adnams Bitter; Greene King IPA; Mauldons Bitter; Nethergate Bitter Ⓗ
Well restored and comfortable pub with beams and subdued lighting. Conversation takes precedence in the split-level, compact bar. The front lawn extends down to the historic village green, famous for its May Bank Holiday fair. No meals Sun eve, or Mon. ⚗ ⊛ ◖ ◗ ⊟ ♣ P

St Ives

Oliver Cromwell
Wellington Street
☎ (0480) 65601
10.30–2.30, 6–11
Adnams Broadside; Greene King IPA Ⓗ
Busy lounge bar, largely unchanged in recent years; near the riverside quay and historic bridge. Note the unusually ornate sign. Pub clock keeps to GMT. Q ⊛

St Neots

Wheatsheaf
Church Street
☎ (0480) 77435
11–2.30, 6.30–11
Greene King XX Mild, IPA, Rayments Special, Abbot Ⓗ, **Winter Ale** Ⓖ
Cheerful locals' pub; a rare outlet in the area for the excellent XX Mild. ⚗ ⊛ ♣

Soham

Carpenters Arms
72 Brook Street (down Staples Lane, off Fordham Road, then right) ☎ (0353) 720869
11–11
Adnams Bitter; Bateman XB; Greene King IPA Ⓗ
Lively local, somewhat hidden away but well worth finding. Basic snacks available most times. ⚗ ♣ P

Somersham

Windmill
St Ives Road
☎ (0487) 840328
11–2.30, 6.30–11
Greene King IPA, Abbot Ⓗ
Cottage-style pub, one mile west of Somersham, with two contrasting bars. ⊛ ◖ ◗ ⊟ ♣ P

Stapleford

Tree
Bar Lane ☎ (0223) 843472
11.30–3, 6–11
Greene King XX Mild, IPA, Rayments Special, Abbot Ⓗ
Compact, cheerful, village local. 'Tree-stump' sandwiches are a speciality. No food Sun. ⊛ ◖ ◗ ♣ P

Stilton

Bell
Old Great North Road
☎ (0733) 242626
11–2.30, 6–11
Ind Coope Burton Ale; Marston's Pedigree; Ruddles County; Tetley Bitter Ⓗ
17th-century, stone-built coaching inn with a splendid, wrought iron sign. Stilton cheese was first sold here. James I, Oliver Cromwell and Dick Turpin have been visitors. Guest beers. ⚗ ⊛ ⋈ ◖ ◗ P ⨉

Stow cum Quy

Prince Albert
Newmarket Road
☎ (0223) 811294
11.30–3, 5–11
Bateman Mild; Greene King IPA Ⓗ

Lively pub which has offered more than 400 different beers in the last four years — invariably something exotic is available. 🏠 🍴 ◖ ▶ ♣ P

Thorney Toll

Black Horse
Wisbech Road
☎ (073 128) 218
11–2.30, 6 (7 winter)–11
Elgood's Bitter, Winter Warmer Ⓗ
Two-roomed pub with pool in one room and a collection of miniatures in the other; a popular stop for east coast traffic. Coaches welcome. May stay open summer afternoons.
🏠 ⬚ 🍴 ◖ ▶ ⬚ ♣ P

Ufford

White Hart
Main Street ☎ (0780) 740250
11–2.30 (4 Sat), 6–11
Home Bitter; Theakston Best Bitter, XB, Old Peculier Ⓗ
Stone-built, village pub with a friendly atmosphere. Folk nights alternate Suns; jazz Sun lunch in summer. No meals Sun eve, or Mon. 🏠 Q 🍴 ◖ ▶ ⬚ ▲ ♣ P

Whittlesey

Boat
2 Ramsey Road
☎ (0733) 202488
11–2.30 (5 Sat), 7–11
Elgood's Bitter, GSB Ⓗ
Traditional, small, town pub, with an unusual, boat-shaped bar front in the lounge. Popular with anglers.
🏠 Q 🍴 ⬚ ◖ ▶ ⬚ ♣ P

Bricklayers Arms
2 Station Road
☎ (0733) 202593
11–3, 6–11
Ruddles Best Bitter; Webster's Yorkshire Bitter Ⓗ
Popular, town local with a large, basic bar and a modernised lounge. Bar skittles played. Eve meals Sat only, unless booked.
🏠 🍴 ▶ ⬚ ⬚ ♣ P

Willingham

Three Tuns
Church Street
☎ (0954) 60437
11–2.30, 6–11 (12–2.30, 7–10.30 Sun)
Greene King XX Mild, IPA, Abbot Ⓗ

Village local in the classic mould — no frills, no fuss, just good ale and good company. Basic snacks at lunchtimes. Parking is not a problem. 🍴 ⬚ ♣

Wisbech

Red Lion
32 North Brink
☎ (0945) 582022
11.30–2.30, 6 (7 Sat)–11
Elgood's Bitter, Winter Warmer Ⓗ
Popular pub near Elgood's brewery; it stands amongst classical Georgian buildings, overlooking the tidal River Nene. Smart lounge bar and a separate restaurant (no eve meals Mon). 🍴 ◖ ▶ P

Three Tuns
76 Norwich Road
☎ (0945) 583502
11–2.30 (4 Sat), 6.30 (7 Sat)–11
Elgood's Bitter Ⓗ
Tidy, 160 year-old, locals' pub: a busy public bar with a games area and a quiet lounge with soft lighting. No food Sun.
🍴 ◖ ⬚ ♣

Try also: Wisbech Arms (John Smith's)

OGs AND ABVs

To hear beer enthusiasts discussing their pints in terms of OGs and ABVs must be confusing for those who simply enjoy good beer. But these technical abbreviations can help you choose the right beer for the right occasion.

OG stands for Original Gravity. This is the reading taken by hydrometer of the amount of fermentable sugars in the wort before fermentation commences (see page 62). Water has a gravity of 1000 degrees, so a beer with an OG of 1040 would have 40 parts of fermentable material in its volume before fermentation. This system is employed by Customs and Excise officials to gauge the amount of duty payable on the beer: the higher the OG the more duty to be paid. It is also useful for drinkers in assessing the approximate strength of the beer. A beer with a gravity of 1040 usually turns out to have a strength of about four per cent alcohol; one with an OG of 1050 is about five per cent. This is only a rule of thumb guide though, as some beers are fermented for longer to allow even more of the sugars to become alcohol. Morland Original Bitter, for instance, has an OG of 1035 but is four per cent alcohol when fermented.

More accurate is the Alcohol by Volume rating (ABV), which specifically tells you the percentage of alcohol in the beer on sale. Though some brewers do not comply, a glance at the pump clip or fount for the OG/ABV should now tell you how strong your beer is and, therefore, which best suits the occasion.

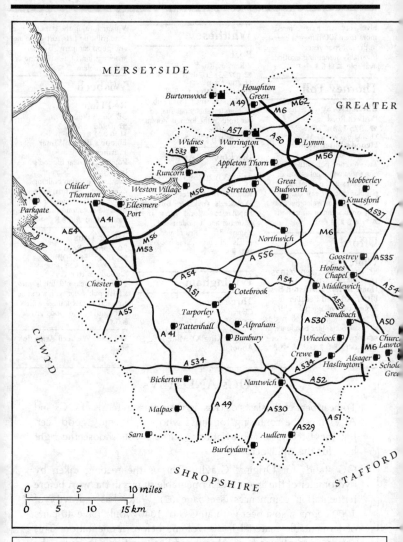

MERSEYSIDE

GREATER

Burtonwood

Houghton Green

A 49

M6 M62

M57

A 50

Warrington

Lymm

Widnes

A 533

M56

Appleton Thorn

Runcorn

Weston Village

Great Budworth

Mobberley

Childer Thornton

M56

Stretton

Knutsford

Parkgate

Ellesmere Port

A 537

A 41

A 54

M56

M53

Northwich

M6

A 556

Goostrey

A 535

Holmes Chapel

Chester

A 54

Cotebrook

A 54

Middlewich

A 54

A 51

A 53

A 55

Tarporley

Sandbach

A 50

Tattenhall

Alpraham

A 530

Wheelock

Churc Lawto

A 41

Bunbury

M6

A 534

Crewe

Alsager

Schol Gree

Bickerton

Nantwich

Haslington

A 52

Malpas

A 49

A 530

A 51

Sarn

Audlem

A 529

Burleydam

SHROPSHIRE

STAFFORD

| 0 | | 5 | | 10 *miles* |
| 0 | 5 | | 10 | 15 *km* |

🏠 **Burtonwood**, Burtonwood; **Coach House**, Warrington

Alpraham

Travellers Rest
Chester Road
☎ (0829) 260523
12–3 (not Mon–Fri), 6–11
McEwan 70/-; Tetley Walker Bitter Ⓗ
Award-winning locals' pub; quiet and friendly, though prone to the occasional sing-songs. Bowling green. 🏠 Q 🏢 ⊞ ♣ P

Alsager

Yeoman
Audley Road (½ mile from centre near station) ☎ (0270) 877995

11–3, 7–11
Ind Coope Burton Ale; Marston's Pedigree; Tetley Walker Bitter Ⓗ
Small, noisy bar and even smaller lounge. 🏠 ⊞ ≷ ♣ P

Try also: Wilbraham Arms (Robinson's)

Appleton Thorn

Village Hall
Stretton Road (B5159)
☎ (0925) 61187
8.30–11 (not Mon–Wed; 8.30–10.30 Sun)
Beer range varies Ⓗ
Cosy, quiet lounge attached to a

village hall which was once the local school. Non-members welcome. Hours restricted as shown; evenings only. Two guest beers always available. Q 🏢 ♣ P

Audlem

Bridge
Shropshire Street
☎ (0270) 811267
11–3, 7 (5.30 Fri & Sat)–11
Marston's Burton Best Bitter, Merrie Monk, Pedigree Ⓗ
A locals' and boaters' pub: a refreshment stop at the bottom of the Audlem flight of locks.
🏠 ≷ 🏢 ◖ ▶ ♣ P

castles. The pub bistro menu includes game. Skittle alley; games room bar closes at lunchtime to accommodate families. Guest beer at Christmas.
🏠 🕿 🍴 ⇌ ◖ 🍽 🅰 ♣ P

Bollington

Holly Bush
Palmerston Street
🕿 (0625) 573073
11–2 (3 Sat), 5 (5.30 Sat)–11 (12–2, 7–10.30 Sun)
Robinson's Mild, Best Bitter Ⓗ
Known as the 'Shoulder of Mutton' until the 1840s; today's pub, acquired by Robinson's in 1919, is pleasant and comfortable. 🍴 ◖ ♣ ♠

Vale
Adlington Road
🕿 (0625) 575147
11.30–3, 7–11
Taylor Landlord; Thwaites Best Mild, Bitter Ⓗ
Once three terraced houses, now a comfortable, one room pub. Live jazz Mon nights. No food Mon. 🏠 Q ◖ P

Bosley

Queens Arms
Leek Road 🕿 (0260) 223267
12–3, 5.30–11
Whitbread Boddingtons Bitter Ⓗ
Large, detached, 17th-century inn set in beautiful surroundings, with a pleasant garden to the rear. An attractive, open bar area has a small side room for families. No food Mon eves. 🏠 Q 🥤 🍴 ◖ P

Buglawton

Church House
Buxton Road 🕿 (0260) 272466
12–3, 6–11
Robinson's Mild, Best Bitter Ⓗ
Roomy pub with excellent bar meals and a restaurant (closed Sat eves). The unusual pub sign is combined with a pigeon cote.
🏠 🥤 🍴 ◖ 🍽 Ⓧ (lunchtime only)

Try also: Robin Hood (Marston's)

Bunbury

Dysart Arms
College Lane
🕿 (0829) 260183
12–3, 5.30–11 (11–11 Sat)
Thwaites Bitter Ⓗ
Olde-worlde village local in an olde-worlde village, opposite the church and a short walk from the canal.
🏠 🍴 ◖ 🍽 ⇌ ♣ P

Burleydam

Combermere Arms
On A525 🕿 (094 870) 223
11.30–3.30, 7–11
Draught Bass; Marston's Pedigree; Younger Scotch Ⓗ
17th-century pub; also serves as a polling station. Reputedly haunted – perhaps by failed candidates! Carpet skittles played. Guest beers.
🏠 🍴 ◖ 🍽 ♣ P

Burtonwood

Bridge Inn
Phipps Lane 🕿 (0925) 225709
11.30–11
Burtonwood Mild, Best Bitter, Forshaw's Ⓗ
Busy pub, listed in the *Guinness Book of Records* for the longest pint ever pulled (from the brewery one mile away). Bar is festooned with memorabilia from the landlord's illustrious rugby (union and league) career. Rugby league shown live on satellite TV in season. Bowling green. 🍴 🍽 🅰 ♣ P

Try also: Elm Tree (Burtonwood)

Chester

Albion
Park Street
11.30–3, 5.30–11
Stones Best Bitter Ⓗ
Unspoilt, street-corner pub; its unusual decor features WWI memorabilia. Good lunches (no fried food). No eve meals Fri or Sat. 🏠 Q ◖ 🍽 ♣

Boathouse
The Groves (road access via Dee Lane in Boughton)
🕿 (0244) 328709
11.30–11 (may close winter afternoons)
McEwan 70/-; Theakston Best Bitter, XB; Younger IPA Ⓗ
Pleasant riverside pub that can be very busy at weekends. Good range of imported beers. New 'Ale-taster' bar opened in summer 1991. No-smoking in the family room – the only family room in the city. Wheelchair ramp to Riverside bar. 🥤 ◖ 🍽 ﴾ ⇌ P Ⓧ

Centurion
Oldfield Drive, Vicars Cross (off A54, 1 mile from Chester)
🕿 (0244) 347623
11.30–3, 6–11 (11.30–11 Fri & Sat)
Jennings Bitter; Robinson's Best Bitter; Tetley Walker Bitter Ⓗ
Fairly modern pub with comfortable seating. Live music Wed. Sometimes has its own beer festival. Guest beer.
🍴 🍽 ♣ P

MANCHESTER

Disley

Poynton

Wilmslow

DERBYSHIRE

Bollington
A523 *Rainow*

Henbury
A537

Macclesfield
A34 A523 *Sutton*

A54

Eaton *Wincle*

Bosley

Buglawton
Congleton
Timbersbrook
Newbold

SHIRE

Cheshire

Lord Combermere
The Square 🕿 (0270) 811316
11–3.30 (5 Sat), 6–11
Courage Directors; John Smith's Bitter Ⓗ
Spacious, low-ceilinged, village local. The garden is home to rabbits and guinea pigs and families will also appreciate the children's menu.
🏠 🍴 ◖ ♣ P

Bickerton

Bickerton Poacher
Wrexham Road (A543)
🕿 (0829) 720226/720313
11.30–3, 6.30–11
Bass Special; Burtonwood Mild, Best Bitter, Forshaw's; Stones Best Bitter Ⓗ
15th-century coaching house on the Sandstone Trail footpath, near Peckforton and Beeston

Cheshire

Cherry Orchard
5 Chapel Lane, Boughton (at
A41 jct) ☎ (0244) 324013
11–11
**Courage Directors; John
Smith's Bitter** Ⓗ
A lively local: a single, large
room partitioned into smaller
areas to give a cosy feel. A
working red telephone box
stands next to the bar. 🏠 Q ♣ P

Clavertons
Lower Bridge Street
☎ (0244) 312320
11.30–4, 6–11 (11–11 Fri & Sat)
Lees Bitter, Moonraker Ⓗ
Low-ceilinged basement pub –
more like a wine bar – popular
with young people. Pleasant
atmosphere but liable to be
crowded and boisterous at
weekends. Ⓒ Ⓓ

Olde Custom House
Watergate Street
☎ (0244) 324335
11–3, 5–11
**Marston's Border Mild,
Border Exhibition, Border
Bitter, Pedigree** Ⓗ
A pleasant, friendly pub with an
interesting history. Three
separate bars are all decorated
with ornate carvings. CAMRA's
home in the city; also the base
for numerous (largely
unsuccessful) sports teams.
🏠 Q Ⓒ Ⓔ ♣

Old Harkers Arms
1 Russell Street
☎ (0244) 344525
11.30–3, 5–11 (11–11 Sat)
**Oak Best Bitter; Taylor
Landlord; Thwaites Bitter;
Whitbread Boddingtons
Bitter** Ⓗ
This welcome addition to the
Chester pub scene is housed in
the recently-converted ground
floor of a canalside warehouse.
Often crowded and not always
easy to get in at weekends.
Guest beers. Ⓒ Ⓓ ⇌

Childer Thornton

Half Way House
New Chester Road
11.30–3, 5.30–11
John Smith's Bitter Ⓗ
Old coaching inn between
Birkenhead and Chester. Small
rooms abound in this compact,
friendly local. ⑧ Ⓔ ♣ P

White Lion
New Road (200 yds off A41)
☎ (051) 339 3402
11.30–3, 5–11 (11.30–11 Fri & Sat)
Thwaites Best Mild, Bitter Ⓗ
Small, busy, friendly country
local. Two rooms cater for all
sections of the community;
one room is used by families
(lunchtimes only) but gets
crowded. No food Sun. 1990

CAMRA *Regional Pub of the
Year*. Excellent. 🏠 Q ⑧ Ⓒ P

Church Lawton

Lawton Arms
Liverpool Road West (A50,
near B5078 jct)
☎ (0270) 873743
11–3, 5.30–11
**Robinson's Mild, Best
Bitter** Ⓔ
A locals' pub: mainly a lounge
with a separate snug and games
room. Near a busy crossroads.
🏠 Q Ⓔ ♣ P

Congleton

Rams Head
Rood Hill ☎ (0260) 273992
12–2.30 (3 Fri & Sat), 7–11
**Marston's Pedigree; Tetley
Walker Bitter** Ⓗ
Small, cosy pub with a tiny
snug hidden at the rear.
Function room upstairs.
🏠 Ⓔ ♣ P

Cotebrook

Alvanley Arms
On A49, at B5152 jct
☎ (0829) 760200
11–3, 5.30–11
**Robinson's Mild, Best
Bitter** Ⓗ, **Old Tom** (winter) Ⓖ
Well-proportioned, attractive,
brick and sandstone pub. Two
small lounges can be fully
occupied by diners which may
offend the purist. Other features
include a babbling brook and a
gaggle of geese. Imaginative
menus and gourmet eves.
🏠 ⑧ ⋈ Ⓒ Ⓓ P

Crewe

Albion
1 Pedley Street (Mill Street)
☎ (0270) 256234
12–3 (4 Sat), 7–11 (may vary Sat;
12–11 Fri)
**Tetley Walker Dark Mild,
Bitter** Ⓗ
Small, busy, town pub. Beware
of sliding door giving access to
the bar. Guest beers.
⑧ Ⓔ Ⓖ ⇌ ♣

British Lion
58 Nantwich Road (A534, 200
yds from the station)
☎ (0270) 214379
12–4 (3 Tue), 7–11
**Ind Coope Burton Ale; Tetley
Walker Dark Mild, Bitter** Ⓗ
Small, very busy, town pub
mainly used by locals. Known
as 'the Pig'. 🏠 Ⓒ Ⓖ ⇌ ♣

Crown
25 Earle Street
☎ (0270) 257295
11–4, 7.30–11 (all day if busy)
**Robinson's Mild, Best
Bitter** Ⓗ

Old-fashioned town pub: one of
a dying breed of multi-roomed
pubs. Ⓔ ♣

Horseshoe
26 North Street
☎ (0270) 584265
12–3 (4 Sat), 7–11
**Robinson's Mild, Best
Bitter** Ⓗ
Old, high-ceilinged pub with
separate rooms for darts and
cards. 🏠 Ⓔ ♣ P

Kings Arms Hotel
56 Earle Street
☎ (0270) 584134
11–4, 7–11 (may vary)
**Whitbread Chester's Mild,
Best Bitter, Boddingtons
Bitter, Trophy Bitter** Ⓗ
Town-centre pub (near banger
racing track) with four rooms,
each with its own character and
regulars. Mild is deservedly the
most popular pint. Q Ⓔ Ⓖ ♣

Disley

Dandy Cock
Market Street (A6)
☎ (0663) 763712
11–11
**Robinson's Mild, Best
Bitter** Ⓗ
Small, comfortable, tasteful
lounge and separate *à la carte*
restaurant. Bar meals also
served. A very homely, village
pub. Small front terrace for
summer drinking.
🏠 Q ⑧ Ⓒ Ⓓ ⇌ P

Try also: **Crescent** (Robinson's)

Eaton

Plough
Macclesfield Road (A536, 2
miles from Congleton)
☎ (0260) 280207
12–3, 7–11
Banks's Mild, Bitter Ⓗ
Village green pub, revitalised in
recent years by ex-brewer
landlord Clive Wincle. Much
emphasis on food and can get
busy as a consequence. This
does not detract from the
welcoming atmosphere. No
meals Mon eve. 🏠 Ⓒ Ⓓ P

Waggon & Horses
Manchester Road (A34)
☎ (0260) 224229
11.30–4, 5.30 (6 Sat)–11
**Robinson's Mild, Best
Bitter** Ⓗ
Pleasant roadside pub with a
vast car park. Separate dining
room. 🏠 Q ⛄ ⑧ Ⓒ Ⓓ ♣ P

Ellesmere Port

Straw Hat
Hode Farm Road
12–10.45
**Courage Directors; John
Smith's Bitter** Ⓗ

Modern estate pub which has few frills but is nonetheless comfortable. Little difference in decor between the bar and lounge. 🝔 ♣

Goostrey

Crown
111 Main Road
☎ (0477) 32128
11–3, 5.30–11
Marston's Burton Best Bitter, Pedigree Ⓗ
Imposing, 16th-century pub in a sought after dormitory village. Homely lounge and traditional tap room. Wide range of food (not Sun eve or Mon). Nearest pub to Jodrell Bank radio telescope.
🝔 Q 🝔 🝔 🝔 🝔 🝔 ♣ P

Great Budworth

George & Dragon
High Street ☎ (0606) 891317
12–3, 7–11
Ind Coope Burton Ale; Tetley Walker Bitter Ⓗ
Holds centre stage in Cheshire's arguably most picturesque village: classic Tetley's interior but none the worse for that. Cosy, dimly-lit, warm colours; masses of copper and brass. Close to Marbury Country Park and the unique Anderton Lift. No-smoking family room open when busy. 🝔 🝔 🝔 🝔 🝔 ♣ P Ⓧ

Haslington

Hawk Inn
137 Crewe Road
☎ (0270) 582181
11–11
Robinson's Mild, Best Bitter Ⓗ
15th-century roadside inn with a separate restaurant. An exposed panel inside reveals the original wattle wall. Eve meals available Wed–Sat. 🝔 🝔 🝔 P

Henbury

Cock Inn
Chelford Road (A537)
☎ (0625) 423186
11–3, 5.30–11
Robinson's Mild, Best Bitter, Old Tom (winter) Ⓗ
Comfortable, main road pub, serving both local and passing trades; situated just outside Macclesfield. Children welcome in the restaurant. Q 🝔 🝔 🝔 🝔 P

Holmes Chapel

Swan
29 Station Road
☎ (0477) 32259
11–3, 4.30–11 (11–11 Fri & Sat)
Samuel Smith OBB, Museum Ⓗ
Former coaching inn with good food (try the pizzas). Interesting old black stove on display.
🝔 🝔 🝔 🝔 🝔 🝔 ♣ P

Houghton Green

Millhouse
Ballater Drive, Cinnamon Brow (off A574) ☎ (0925) 811405
12–3.30, 5.30–11
Holt Mild, Bitter Ⓗ
Large, spacious, estate pub built in the late 1980s to cater for new residential areas. The basic bar and plush lounge both have a popular local following. Quiz night Mon. 🝔 🝔 🝔 ♣ P

Knutsford

Builders Arms
Mobberley Road (off A537)
☎ (0565) 634528
11.30–3, 5.30–11 (12–2, 7–10.30 Sun)
Marston's Mercian Mild, Burton Best Bitter, Pedigree Ⓗ
Small and busy local with a keen games emphasis.
Q 🝔 🝔 🝔 ♣

White Lion
94 King Street
☎ (0565) 632018
11.30–11
Tetley Walker Bitter Ⓗ
Tasteful pub with extensive range of cheese and pâté lunches, Mon–Sat (doggie bags provided). Guest beer available each week: either Robinson's, Jennings or Hydes.
🝔 Q 🝔 🝔 ♣ ♣

Lymm

Bulls Head
32 The Cross (A6144)
☎ (092 575) 2831
11.30–11 (11.30–3, 5.30–11 winter)
Hydes' Anvil Mild, Bitter Ⓔ
Welcoming lounge and large public bar. Handy for visitors to the popular village centre. Early eve hot snacks for homeward-bound workers. 🝔 🝔 🝔 ♣

Spread Eagle
Eagle Brow (A6144)
☎ (092 575) 3139
11.30–11
Lees GB Mild, Bitter Ⓗ, **Moonraker** Ⓔ
Ornate, old pub near Lymm village cross and 200 yards from canal moorings. Three varying rooms: a basic bar, a small, cosy snug and a large, plush lounge on two levels. The snug is popular with locals, particularly early eve. 🝔 🝔 🝔

Wheatsheaf
Higher Lane, Broomedge (Agden Brow, A56)
☎ (092 575) 2567
11.30–3 (4 Sat), 5.30–11
Hydes' Anvil Mild, Bitter Ⓔ
Roadside pub dating back over

200 years. Recently extended into an open-plan layout with a central bar, but retains a strong following in the public bar area.
🝔 🝔 🝔 ♣ P

Macclesfield

Albion
London Road (A523)
☎ (0625) 425339
11–11
Robinson's Mild, Bitter, Best Bitter Ⓗ
Known as the 'Flying Horse' until 1855, this small, busy pub retains a beautiful vestibule window, evidence of its former identity. Handy for Macclesfield Town football matches. 🝔 ♣

Barnfield
22 Catherine Street
☎ (0625) 423194
11.30–3, 5.30–11
Robinson's Mild, Best Bitter Ⓗ
Recently modernised, one-room pub, previously called the 'Red Lion'. 🝔 🝔 ♣

Baths Hotel
40 Green Street (behind station)
6.30–11 (11–11 Sat)
Whitbread Boddingtons Mild, Bitter Ⓗ
Thriving pub named after the now-defunct public baths. Basic and friendly. 🝔 🝔 ♣

Evening Star
87–89 James Street (400 yds from A536/A523 jct)
☎ (0625) 424093
11–3, 5.30–11 (12–2, 7–10.30 Sun)
Marston's Mercian Mild, Burton Best Bitter, Pedigree Ⓔ
A friendly, little, tucked-away local. Difficult to find by car due to a maze of blocked streets. Quiet at lunchtimes but busier eves and weekends. Q 🝔 ♣

George & Dragon
23 Sunderland Street
☎ (0625) 421898
11–4 (3 Tue & Wed), 5.30 (7 Sat)–11
Robinson's Mild, Best Bitter Ⓔ
Friendly pub with good value food. Pool, darts and skittles played. Close to both bus and railway stations. Eve meals finish at 6.45 and are not served Sun. Q 🝔 🝔 🝔 🝔 ♣

Mulberry Bush
2 Carisbrook Avenue
☎ (0625) 421277
11.30–3, 5.30–11 (11–11 Thu–Sat)
Theakston Best Bitter; Whitbread Boddingtons Mild, Bitter Ⓗ
Pleasant, recently-refurbished, estate pub; a little difficult to find (hidden amongst tower blocks). 🝔 🝔 🝔 ♣ P

Cheshire

Puss in Boots
198 Buxton Road
☎ (0625) 423261
11–11
Whitbread Boddingtons Mild, Bitter Ⓗ
Large, stone pub, built shortly after the canal which it overlooks. The large mill opposite was once the home of 'Hovis'. The pub has been pleasantly refurbished and has good moorings for canal users.
ᵭ ⑧ ◖ ⊕ ♣ ♣

Malpas

Red Lion
1 Old Hall Street
☎ (0948) 860368
11–11
Draught Bass; Hanby Drawwell Ⓗ
Well-kept village inn which has its own sauna and solarium. Try also the pub's own special malt whisky. Restored cottages next to the pub provide accommodation. Wholesome country fare. ᵭ Q ᵭ ⑧ ▭ ◖ ◗ ♣ P

Middlewich

Boars Head
Kinderton Street (A54)
☎ (0606) 843191
12–3.30, 5.30–11
Robinson's Mild, Best Bitter Ⓔ
Large, multi-roomed pub on the edge of town. Spacious lounge, small tap room, games room and TV lounge.
Q ᵭ ▭ ◖ ♣ P

Mobberley

Bird in Hand
Knolls Green ☎ (0565) 873149
11.30–3, 5.30–11
Samuel Smith OBB, Museum Ⓗ
Pleasant, multi-roomed, roadside pub, serving good food (no meals Mon eve or Sun).
ᵭ Q ⑧ ◖ ◗ ♿ P

Try also: Chapel House (Boddingtons Pub Co.)

Nantwich

Bowling Green
The Gullet (behind church)
☎ (0270) 626001
11–11
Hanby Drawwell; Webster's Yorkshire Bitter, Choice, Wilson's Bitter Ⓗ
Smart pub, popular with young people but not overrun by them. Dates from the 15th-century and is one of the few buildings to survive the great fire of 1583. The restaurant is a recent addition.
⑧ ◖ ◗ ⊕ ♿ ⇌ ♣

Rifleman
68 James Hall Street (by playing fields)
☎ (0270) 629977
12–4, 6–11 (11–11 Fri & Sat)
Robinson's Mild, Best Bitter Ⓔ, **Old Tom** (winter) Ⓖ
Back-street local which can be difficult to find. Comfortable, open-plan layout. ᵭ ⑧ ◖ ♣ P

Newbold

Horseshoe
Fence Lane (left off A34 at Astbury church, right after ½ mile, follow bends for 1½ miles)
OS863602 ☎ (0260) 272205
11–3, 6–11
Robinson's Mild, Best Bitter Ⓗ
Isolated country pub, formerly part of a farmhouse. Difficult to find but worth the effort.
ᵭ ᵭ ⑧ ◖ ♣ P

Try also: Egerton (Robinson's)

Northwich

Freemasons
Castle Street (A559)
☎ (0606) 79310
11–11
Ruddles Best Bitter; Webster's Yorkshire Bitter, Wilson's Mild, Bitter Ⓗ
Small, cosy, busy and friendly pub at the top of Castle Hill.
⊕ ♣

Parkgate

Ship Hotel
The Parade (off A540, down to Parkgate Promenade)
☎ (051) 336 3931
10.30–3, 5–11
Oak Old Oak; Theakston XB, Old Peculier; Thwaites Bitter; Webster's Yorkshire Bitter Ⓗ
Stone-fronted hotel, overlooking River Dee and Welsh hills. Regular guest beers.
Q ▭ ◖ ◗ P

Poynton

Boars Head
Shrigley Road North, Higher Poynton
☎ (0625) 876676
11.30–3, 5.30–11 (11.30–11 Sat)
Whitbread Boddingtons Bitter Ⓗ
Unpretentious pub, convenient for outdoor activities. Close to Macclesfield Canal and the west entrance to Lyme Park. Adjacent to the Middlewood Way. Eve meals in summer.
Q ⑧ ◖ ◗ Å ⇌ (Middlewood)
♣ P

Rainow

Highwayman
On A5002, N of Rainow
☎ (0625) 573245
11.30–3, 7–11
Thwaites Bitter Ⓗ
400 year-old country pub with magnificent views.
ᵭ Q ⇌ ⑧ ◖ ◗ ⊕ ♣ P

Runcorn

Barley Mow
56 Church Street (Old Town)
☎ (092 85) 75235
11–3, 5 (7 Sat)–11
Walker Mild, Bitter Ⓗ
Smart, recently-extended, town-centre pub, overlooked by Runcorn-Widnes road bridge.
ᵭ ⑧ ◖ ⊕ ♿ ⇌ ♣

Windmill
Windmill Hill (off A558, 1 mile from A56 jct)
☎ (0928) 710957
11.30–3, 5–11 (11.30–11 Fri & Sat)
Hydes' Anvil Light, Bitter Ⓔ
Modern, octagonal-shaped pub: a split-level lounge with several pieces of antique furniture. Quiz night Tue.
ᵭ ⑧ ◖ ⊕ ♿ ♣ P

Sandbach

Iron Grey
49 Middlewich Road
☎ (0270) 765988
11–3 (4 Fri, 3.30 Sat), 5.30 (7 Sat)–11
Robinson's Mild, Best Bitter Ⓗ
Pub refurbished in line with the modern idiom. Rear patio for summer days. ᵭ ⑧ ♣

Sarn

Queens Head
Off B5069 OS440447
☎ (094 881) 244
11–3, 5–11
Marston's Border Mild, Burton Best Bitter Ⓗ
Small pub by a stream in the heart of South Cheshire. Meals in separate bistro.
ᵭ Q ⑧ ▭ ◖ ◗ ⊕ ♣ P

Scholar Green

Globe
Drumber Lane
12–3 (Mon & Sat only), 7–11
Marston's Burton Best Bitter, Pedigree Ⓗ
Very much a locals' pub: a tiny bar, a lounge and a games room. Strong darts following. Parking difficult. Q ⊕ ◖ P

Try also: Travellers Rest, Main Rd (Marston's)

Stretton

Hollow Tree
Tarporley Road (A49)
☎ (0925) 73733
11–11
Theakston Best Bitter, XB, Old Peculier Ⓗ
Renovated Georgian farmhouse with restaurant and large garden. Vegetarians and children catered for.
🏠 Q ☺ ◑ ▯ ▶ P

Sutton

Lamb
13 Hollin Lane OS932713
☎ (026 05) 2000
11.30–3, 5.30–11
Tetley Walker Bitter; Wells Bombardier Ⓗ
Pleasant village pub set slightly back from the road. Built in 1938 in local stone to replace a former pub of same name. A good place to start or finish a ramble in the nearby hills. No separate public bar but a good basic tap/games area. Guest beers. Eve meals Fri–Sun.
🏠 ▧ ◑ ▯ ✦ P

Tarporley

Crown Hotel
78 High Street
☎ (0829) 732416
11–11
Bass Mild XXXX; Burtonwood Best Bitter, Forshaw's Ⓗ
Excellent renovation of a run-down local which now provides meals and accommodation. Public bar and pool room; spacious lounges and a conservatory with views of Beeston Castle. Attractive watercolours of Cheshire. Beer range may be extended.
🏠 ▧ ⇥ ◑ ▯ ▢ ✦ P

Rising Sun
High Street (A49, near A51 jct)
☎ (0829) 732423
11–3, 5.30–11
Robinson's Mild, Best Bitter Ⓗ
Rambling, old inn of authentic character. A good range of excellent value food predominates, but one bar is usually reserved for drinkers. The dining room is bookable; children allowed. Pity about the fake fires! No food Sun eve.
◑ ▯ P

Tattenhall

Sportsmans Arms
On main street
☎ (0829) 70233
11–11
Thwaites Mild, Bitter Ⓗ
Busy, village local with a

bowling green and outdoor attractions for children, incl. pigs! Inside, this is a comfortable, friendly hostelry serving the best Thwaites for miles. 🏠 Q ▧ ◑ ▯ ✦ P

Timbersbrook

Coach & Horses
Dane in Shaw Bank (1 mile N of Congleton, off A527, on Rushton Spencer road)
OS890619 ☎ (0260) 273019
11–3, 6–11
Robinson's Mild, Best Bitter Ⓔ
A pleasant hostelry: a through-lounge with a small tap room behind the fireplace. Popular with locals.
🏠 ▧ ▧ ◑ ▯ ▢ ▵ ☖ P

Warrington

Lower Angel
27 Buttermarket Street (next to Odeon cinema)
☎ (0925) 33299
11–4, 7–11
Ind Coope Burton Ale; Walker Mild, Bitter, Best Bitter, Winter Warmer Ⓗ
A mecca for a decent choice of ales with about ten guest beers a week. A small, friendly, busy, two-roomed, town-centre pub. Basic bar and comfortable lounge, which even boasts its own ghost. Very busy Fri and Sat nights. ▢ ⇥ (Central) ✦

Penny Ferry
271 Thelwall Lane, Latchford (off A50) ☎ (0925) 38487
11.30–4.30, 7–11
Burtonwood Best Bitter, Forshaw's Ⓗ
Near Latchford Locks and the Manchester Ship Canal ferry service, this one-roomed, modern pub has walls adorned with nautical photos. Sandwiches available lunchtime. Rear patio. ▧ ✦ P

Try also: **Old Town House**, Buttermarket St (Courage)

Weston Village

Royal Oak
Heath Road South
☎ (0928) 565839
12–3, 7–11 (11–11 Fri)
Marston's Burton Best Bitter Ⓗ
Friendly, village pub overlooking the Mersey and the ICI Rocksavage works. Small, cosy lounge; larger bar. Back rooms are now occupied by two pool tables. Meeting room available upstairs. Quiz night Tue. ▧ ◑ ▯ ▢ ✦

Wheelock

Commercial
Crewe Road (off A534 at Canal Bridge) ☎ (0270) 760122
8–11 (12–2, 7–10.30 Sun)
Marston's Burton Best Bitter, Pedigree: Thwaites Bitter; Whitbread Boddingtons Bitter Ⓗ
Large, back-street local, with high ceilings, wooden partitions and wicker furniture. Here it is normal to serve the cider (Bulmers) with a slice of lemon.
🏠 Q ▢ ✦ ☖ P

Widnes

Victoria
20 Ann Street West (off A562, near B&Q) ☎ (051) 495 1495
11.30–11
Tetley Walker Mild, Bitter Ⓗ
Traditional, three-roomed pub: large lounge and bar, plus pool room. Live entertainment most Wed (country and western), Fri and Sat (60s music). Four real fires. Regular guest beers.
🏠 ▧ ▢ ✦

Try also: **Bradley** (Walker)

Wilmslow

Farmers Arms
Chapel Lane ☎ (0625) 532443
11–11
Whitbread Boddingtons Mild, Bitter Ⓗ
Traditional and thriving town local with excellent bar lunches and a busy tap room. No food Sun. 🏠 Q ▧ ▧ ◑ ✦

New Inn
Alderley Road
☎ (0625) 523123
11.30–3 (3.30 Fri & Sat), 5.30–11
Hydes' Anvil Light, Bitter Ⓔ
Large, extensive modernisation of a much smaller pub, aiming almost exclusively to cater for the appetites of shoppers trooping from the even larger, Sainsbury's supermarket next door. Eve meals Tue–Sat.
◑ ▯ ✦ P

Try also: **Riflemans** (Whitbread)

Wincle

Ship
☎ (0260) 227217
12–2 (3 Sat), 7–11 (closed Mon Nov–Mar)
Marston's Pedigree; Whitbread Boddingtons Bitter Ⓗ
Excellent, remote pub near a trout farm. Good for hikers and walkers. Guest beers.
Q ▧ ▧ ◑ ▯ ▢ ▵ ✦ P

BREWING *REAL* BEER

What follows is probably enough to make a master brewer wince. Come to that, any self-respecting home-brewer will gasp at the simplicity of this guide to brewing techniques. For the brewing of beer can be a crusade for perfection, with each ingredient considered, each step carefully monitored and the mechanics of brewing raised to the level of a fine art. And it is this personal involvement of the brewer which makes beer so diverse and appealing.

But let's start at square one. To brew beer you need a few basics: water (known as liquor in the trade), malted barley, hops and yeast. Some brewers add other ingredients, but these are the essentials. The malt is ground into a fine powder called grist and mixed in the mash tun (a giant teapot) with hot water. As the mash develops, so the fermentable sugars seep from the malt into the water, which is then drained off ready for the next stage. Meanwhile, the spent grist is sprayed (sparged) with hot water to wash out any extra sugars that would otherwise be wasted.

The new sugary liquid, known as wort, is then ferried to another boiler, the copper, where it is seasoned with hops, which add bitterness and act as a preservative. When the full flavour of the hops has been absorbed (a couple of hours), they are strained off in what is known as a hop back. The cooled wort is then sent off on its road towards becoming alcohol.

It is poured into fermenting vessels and yeast is added (pitched). This greedy little fungus soon runs amuck amongst the lovely, thick wort and, revelling in the sugars, it multiplies furiously, creating alcohol and carbon dioxide at the same time. After a day or two, the yeast has expanded in volume so much that most is scooped off and recycled for further use. A few days later, the new young beer takes another trip, this time to the conditioning tanks. Here any remaining sugars continue to be developed into alcohol by the remaining yeast. It is usually at this stage that a substance called finings (an unappetising-sounding derivative of fish bladders) is added. As unpleasant as it seems, this process has wondrous consequences, clearing the beer by dragging yeast to the bottom of the tank. After this, the beer is racked (poured into casks, without being filtered, and therefore taking some yeast with it) and a few dry hops or some fresh sugar may be added, to give the beer more aroma or to encourage a stronger fermentation in the cask.

The beer is now left to mature for a few more days, even after arrival in the pub cellar. Properly vented, the cask releases excess, newly created carbon dioxide, and time removes the sweetish, appley taste found in beers which are served too young. Poured straight from the cask, or drawn to the bar by a handpump or electric or air pumps, the result is usually a flavoursome, fresh, mouthfilling drink, quite unlike the nasty, processed pint of keg beer which set the CAMRA ball rolling 21 years ago (see *The Fizz Phenomenon*, page 8).

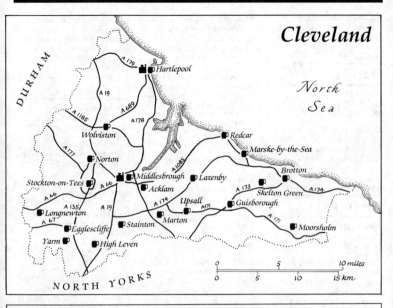

Cleveland

North Sea

DURHAM

A 179 *Hartlepool*

A 19 · A 689 · A 178

Wolviston

A 1185 · A 177 · A 178

Norton

A 1085 · *Redcar*

Marske-by-the-Sea

Stockton-on-Tees · *Middlesbrough* · *Lazenby* · *Brotton*

Acklam · A 173 · *Skelton Green* · A 174

A 66 · A 135 · A 19 · A 174 · *Upsall* · A171 · *Guisborough*

Longnewton · A 67 · *Stainton* · *Marton* · A 171

Egglescliffe · *Moorsholm*

Yarm · *High Leven*

NORTH YORKS

0 · 5 · 10 miles
0 · 5 · 10 · 15 km

🏭 **Camerons**, *Hartlepool*; **North Yorkshire**, *Middlesbrough*

Acklam

Master Cooper
291 Acklam Road
☎ (0642) 819429
11–11
Samuel Smith OBB, Museum Ⓗ
Listed building, an ex-fish and chip shop and restaurant with one L-shaped room. Original beams and ceilings are being revealed in current renovation. Eve meals on request.
🏛 ⊛ ⋈ ◑ ♣ P

Brotton

Green Tree
90 High Street
☎ (0287) 76377
12–4, 7.30–11
Camerons Strongarm Ⓗ
Former manor house, in part dating back to the 1300s, and an inn for over 400 years. A cosy and welcoming village pub with a deserved reputation for good beer and food. Unusual pub games. Two rooms for families. 🏛 Q ⌒ ◑ 🍴 ⌂ 🏠 ♣

Egglescliffe

Pot & Glass
Church Road
☎ (0642) 780145
11–3, 5.30–11 (12–3, 7.30–10.30 Sun)
Draught Bass Ⓗ
Charming, whitewashed village pub in the heart of Teesside with two bars and a separate

family/function room. The ornate bar fronts were carved from old furniture by a previous licensee. Resident ghostly nuns! Eve meals on request.
Q ⌒ ⊛ ◑ ⌂ ♣ P

Guisborough

Ship
Westgate ☎ (0287) 632233
11.30–11
Draught Bass Ⓗ
Terraced, town-centre pub, basic but cosy, and with a large, enclosed rear garden. Decorated with maritime relics. A popular pub with locals. 🏛 ⊛ Å ♣

Tap & Spile
Westgate ☎ (0287) 632983
11–11
Camerons Bitter, Strongarm Ⓗ
Old town-centre pub, formerly the 'Mermaid', now refurbished in typical Tap & Spile traditional fashion. Separate small function room at rear. Wide range of guest beers always available; occasional ciders. No food Sun.
⊛ ◑ ⌂ ⌂

Hartlepool

Jacksons Arms
Tower Street
☎ (0429) 862413
12–4, 7–11 (11–3, 5–11 Wed; 11–11 Thu–Sat)
Draught Bass; Taylor Landlord; Theakston XB, Old Peculier Ⓗ

Traditionally-styled old pub which has seen several changes of ownership in the last ten years. A comfortable lounge with a more basic bar.
◑ ◑ ⌂ 🍴 ⌂ ♣

New Inn
Durham Street
☎ (0429) 267797
11–4, 7–11 (11–11 Fri & Sat)
Camerons Strongarm Ⓗ
Small but busy local on the road to the headland. Well worth seeking out. Q ⌂ ♣

Tap & Spile
Vicarage Gardens
☎ (0429) 273954
11–11
Camerons Strongarm Ⓗ
Excellent Victorian, red-brick pub, renovated without losing its character. The focus of many community activities and charity fundraising events. Wide range of guest beers always available. Holds occasional mini beer festivals. Weston's cider.
Q ⌒ ◑ 🍴 ⌂ ♣ ⌂

High Leven

Fox Covert
Low Lane (between Yarm and Thornaby on A1044)
☎ (0642) 760033
11–3, 5–11
Vaux Samson, Double Maxim Ⓗ
Recently-altered pub, a cluster of whitewashed buildings at a

Cleveland

crossroads. Originally a farmhouse, it now has a warm, open-plan interior and a large, upstairs function room.
🏠 🍴 ◗ ♣ P

Lazenby

Nag's Head
High Street
☎ (0642) 440149
11.30–4 (4.30 Sat), 7–11
Draught Bass Ⓗ
Cosy pub, tastefully decorated, with numerous pictures and old photographs on the walls. Deceptively spacious, and deservedly popular for lunchtime meals (Mon–Fri). ◗ ♣

Longnewton

Vane Arms
Darlington Road
☎ (0642) 580404
11.30–3, 7–11
Draught Bass; Stones Best Bitter Ⓗ
Simple, two-roomed pub with a good reputation for food (incl. vegetarian). Lounge recently extended. 🏠 Q 🍴 ◗ 🍽 ♣ P

Marske-by-the-Sea

Clarendon
High Street
☎ (0642) 490005
11.30–3, 5.30–11 (11–11 Fri & Sat)
John Smith's Magnet; Theakston Best Bitter, Old Peculier Ⓗ
Old, town-centre pub with a friendly atmosphere and a long tradition of serving real ale.
Q 占 ≠ P

Frigate
Hummershill Lane (250 yds from square along Windy Hill Lane) ☎ (0642) 484302
12–3, 7–11
John Smith's Magnet Ⓗ
Pleasant estate pub with a large lounge and a separate bar with pool table. Another, quiet room is also available. ◗ ◖ ≠ ♣ P

Marton

Apple Tree
38 The Derby (Gainsborough Road, off Marton Road)
☎ (0642) 310564
11–4, 6–11 (11–11 Sat)
Draught Bass Ⓗ
Classy, modern pub on a private housing estate. The large lounge is cleverly divided to create a cosy atmosphere. Good food at lunchtimes. Family room till 7pm. 🍽 🍴 ◗ ◖ 占 ♣ P

Middlesbrough

Empire Hotel
Linthorpe Road
☎ (0642) 242589
11–11

Marston's Pedigree; Whitbread Trophy, Castle Eden Ale Ⓗ
Large, imposing building, recently redecorated in Art Deco style. One large room with other function rooms. Busy and popular with young people. Music can be very loud on occasions. 🍴 ◗ ◗ 占 ≠

Speedway Hotel
74 West Lane
☎ (0642) 243015
11.30–4, 5.30–11
John Smith's Magnet Ⓗ
A 1930s suburban pub with three rooms: a spacious bar, a cosy lounge and a function room. Frequent quiz nights.
🍽 🍴 ◖ 占 ♣ P

Tap & Barrel
86 Newport Road
☎ (0642) 219995
11–11
North Yorkshire Best Bitter, IPA, Erimus Dark, Flying Herbert, Dizzy Dick Ⓗ
Cosy, Victorian-style pub, converted from a shop near the town centre. Large upstairs dining/function room (used for families). Wide range of guest beers. Q 🍴 ◗ 占 ≠ ♣ ○

Westminster Hotel
Parliament Road
☎ (0642) 424171
11–3.30 (4.30 Fri & Sat), 7–11
John Smith's Magnet Ⓗ
A local built in 1938 and virtually unchanged. Three rooms include an atmospheric snug with a feature fireplace. Look out for the 'demon drink head' and individual animal carvings. Popular with football fans. 🏠 Q 🍽 ◖ 占 ♣ P

Try also: Southfield, Southfield Rd (Camerons); **Star & Garter**, Southfield Rd (Free)

Moorsholm

Toad Hall Arms
High Street (off A171, Guisborough-Whitby road)
☎ (0287) 60155
12–2.30, 7–11 (12–2, 7–10.30 Sun)
Tetley Mild, Bitter Ⓗ
Family-run pub with an interesting mix of locals and visitors. Enjoys a village setting, with views over moorland to the sea. No eve meals Mon.
🏠 🍴 ◗ 占 🅰 ♣ P

Norton

Unicorn
High Street ☎ (0642) 553888
11.45–3, 5.30–11 (11.45–11 Fri; 11–11 Sat)
John Smith's Magnet Ⓗ
Tiny three-roomed local beside the village green. Known locally

---

as 'Nellie's'. The dartboard was removed from the bar many years ago for health reasons! Occasional piano player in residence. No food Sun.
Q 🍽 🍴 ◖ 占

Redcar

Yorkshire Coble
West Dyke Road (S end of racecourse) ☎ (0642) 482071
11–3 (4 Fri & Sat), 6–11
Samuel Smith OBB Ⓗ
Large, modern, estate pub with a strong local clientele. Comfortable lounge with a more functional bar and games room. 🍴 ◗ 占 ♣ P

Skelton Green

Green Inn
Boosbeck Road
☎ (0287) 50475
11–3, 7–11
Camerons Strongarm Ⓗ
Busy, terraced local with several rooms. Bar snacks on request. Monthly barbecues in summer.
🏠 Q 占 ♣

Stainton

Stainton Inn
Meldyke Lane
☎ (0642) 599902
11.30–3, 6–11
Camerons Strongarm; Everards Old Original Ⓗ
Imposing, Victorian, red-brick pub in the village centre. Extended in 1987 into adjacent cottages. Strong emphasis on food (incl. vegetarian).
🍴 ◗ 占 ♣ P

Stockton-on-Tees

Cricketers Arms
Portrack Lane
☎ (0642) 675468
11–11 (11–4.30, 7–11 Sat)
Marston's Pedigree; Theakston Old Peculier; Whitbread Trophy, Castle Eden Ale Ⓗ
Comfortable and friendly, one-roomed pub with a separate games area. ◗ ♣ P

Dovecot Arts Centre
Dovecot Street
☎ (0642) 611625
12–2 (not Mon), 7–10.30 (7.30–11 Fri & Sat)
Camerons Strongarm; Tolly Cobbold Original Ⓗ
Arts centre bar open to the public. Hosts live music, theatre, exhibitions and regular mini beer festivals. No lunches Sun.
◗ ≠

Elm Tree
Elm Tree Avenue, Fairfield
☎ (0642) 677942
11.30–3 (3.30 Thu, 4 Fri, 4.30 Sat), 6–11

Courage Directors; John Smith's Bitter Ⓗ
Modern estate pub built in 1985. Several separate rooms are decorated in Art Deco style.
🛏 🏮 ◖ 🌓 🍴 🍺 ⚅ ♣ P

Fitzgerald's
9–10 High Street
☎ (0642) 678220
11.30–3.30 (11–11 Sat)
Draught Bass; McEwan 80/-; Taylor Landlord; Theakston Old Peculier Ⓗ
Open-plan, split-level pub with an imposing imposing facade. Very much a pub for the younger patron; rarely quiet in eve. ◖ ≈ ♣

Stockton Arms
Darlington Road, Hartburn
☎ (0642) 580104
11–11
Draught Bass Ⓗ
Imposing, red-brick, corner pub in a leafy suburb; warm and friendly interior. A traditional pub catering for all tastes. Imaginative home cooking (incl. vegetarian). 🏮 🍴 🛏 ◖ 🌓 🍺 ♣ P

Sun
Knowles Street
☎ (0642) 615676
11–4, 5–11 (11–11 Wed, Fri & Sat)
Draught Bass Ⓗ
An unspoilt drinkers' pub, one of Britain's great drinking establishments. Claims to sell more Draught Bass than any

other pub in the country. Local CAMRA *Pub of the Year* 1990.
🏮 🍺 ≈ ♣

Trader Jack's
Blue Post Yard (off High Street)
☎ (0642) 675718
11–11
Whitbread Trophy, Castle Eden Ale Ⓗ
The oldest pub in Stockton; formerly the Blue Post Hotel, now completely refurbished. The best jukebox in town. ◖

Upsall

Cross Keys
On A171, midway between Middlesbrough and Guisborough ☎ (0287) 610035
11–11
Theakston Best Bitter, Old Peculier Ⓗ
A 19th-century pub cleverly extended in a low-beamed, farmhouse style. Families are especially welcome. Handpulls are not visible from all parts of the pub, so please ask.
🛏 🍺 ◖ 🌓 🍴 P

Wolviston

Wellington
31–33 High Street
☎ (0642) 644439
11–3.30, 5.30–11
Draught Bass Ⓗ

Friendly, traditional
village pub with a we...
atmosphere. No food S...
Q ◖ ♣ P

Yarm

Harvester
Davenport Road, Layfield Farm (off A1044, Kirklevington-Worsall road)
☎ (0642) 785841
11.45–3, 6–11
Ruddles Best Bitter or **Webster's Choice; Ruddles County** Ⓗ
Smart, modern, estate pub with a separate games area and a lounge alcove in which children are welcome. Eve meals Thu–Sat only. 🛏 🍺 ◖ 🌓 🍴 ♣ P

Ketton Ox
100 High Street
☎ (0642) 788311
11–2.30, 5.30–11 (11–11 Sat & summer)
Vaux Samson, Double Maxim Ⓗ
Impressive former coaching inn in a village conservation area. Blocked-in oval windows on the facade betray the site of former cock-fighting rooms. A warm, open-plan pub with a long and interesting history. Meals Thu–Sat (booking advised). Family room lunchtime and early eve. 🛏 🍺 ◖ 🌓 ♣

'I'm the lager waiter, chief!'

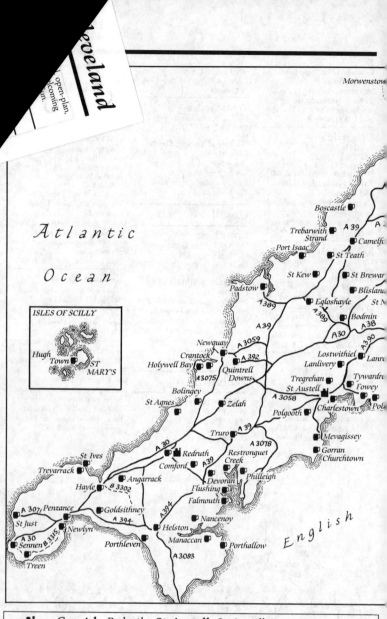

Morwenstow

Atlantic

Ocean

Boscastle

Trebarwith Strand

Port Isaac

St Teath

St Kew

Padstow

Egloshayle

St Brewar

Blislan

Camelfo

St N

Bodmin

ISLES OF SCILLY

Hugh Town

ST MARY'S

Newquay

Crantock

Holywell Bay

Quintrell Downs

Lostwithiel

Lanre

Lanlivery

Tregrehan

St Austell

Tywardre

Fowey

Bolingey

St Agnes

Zelah

Polgooth

Charlestown

Pol

Truro

Mevagissey

Gorran Churchtown

St Ives

Trevarrack

Redruth

Comford

Restronguet Creek

Angarrack

Devoran

Philleigh

Hayle

Flushing

Penzance

Goldsithney

Falmouth

St Just

Newlyn

Helston

Nancenoy

Sennen

Manaccan

Porthallow

Treen

Porthleven

English

🏭 *Cornish*, Redruth; **St Austell**, St Austell

Albaston

Queens Head
½ mile S of A390
☎ (0822) 832482
11–2.30 (3 Sat), 6–11
Courage Best Bitter, Directors; Eldridge Pope Royal Oak Ⓗ
Excellent village local on the edge of the spectacular Tamar Valley. An unspoilt pub which has had the same, well-respected landlord for many years. Good value bar snacks and Cornish pasties (non-microwaved).
🏚 Q 🏢 ⓓ ▲ ≄ ⌂ P

Altarnun

Rising Sun
Off A30, on Camelford road, 1 mile N of village OS825215
☎ (0566) 86636
11–3, 5.30–11
Draught Bass; Ruddles Best Bitter; Whitbread Best Bitter, Flowers Original Ⓗ
A lively, 16th-century, country pub, popular with both locals and visitors. It enjoys an unspoilt rural setting on the edge of Bodmin Moor. Ever-changing range of guest beers.
🏚 ⅍ 🏢 ⊨ ⓓ ▲ ♣ P

Angarrack

Angarrack Inn
Off A30 ☎ (0736) 752380
11–2.30, 6–11 (12–2, 7–10.30 Sun)
St Austell Bosun's, HSD Ⓗ
Very comfortable and welcoming, village pub, offering an extensive, good-value menu of home-cooked food (vegetarian option).
🏚 🏢 ⓓ ▲ P

Blisland

Royal Oak
Village Green ☎ (0208) 850739

66

Historic, town pub built before the Napoleonic Wars and reputed to hold the oldest continuous licence in Cornwall. The lounge is quiet. Good value food. Q ⌖ ❀ ⋈ ◖ ▶ ⬚ ♣ P

Bolingey

Bolingey Inn
Penwartha Road (near B3284)
☎ (0872) 572794
11–3, 6.30–11
Cornish Steam Bitter, Royal Wessex Ⓗ
A truly rural, 17th-century, compact and bijou, country pub which is only a short distance from the touristy, golden sandy beaches of Perranporth.
⌂ Q ⌖ ❀ ◖ ▶ ⋈ Å ⬚ P

Boscastle

Cobweb
☎ (084 05) 278
11–11 (11–2.30, 6–11 winter)
Draught Bass; Exmoor Gold; St Austell Tinners, HSD Ⓗ
An imposing, four-storey building which houses a bustling, lively local. Near the harbour of an attractive village. Guest beers.
⌂ Q ⌖ ❀ ◖ ▶ ⬚ ♣ P

Botus Fleming

Rising Sun
Off A388, 4 miles from Tamar Bridge ☎ (0752) 842792
12–3 (may vary), 6–11
Ruddles County; Ushers Best Bitter Ⓗ
Unspoilt and unpretentious, country pub with 12th-century origins, tucked away in a quiet village on the outskirts of Saltash. A happy, friendly pub now in the third generation of family ownership. Village-brewed cider. Raucous euchre sessions. ⌂ Q ❀ ⬚ ♣ ⬚ P

Callington

Coachmakers Arms
Newport Square (A388)
☎ (0579) 82567
11.30–2.30 (3 Sat), 6.30–11
Draught Bass Ⓗ
300 year-old coaching inn with all the character of a typical West Country pub: friendly atmosphere, good food and en suite accommodation. An ideal base for visiting West Devon and East Cornwall. Always two guest ales available from a wide range; ciders in summer.
Q ⋈ ◖ ▶ ♣ ⬚ P

Camelford

Masons Arms
Market Place
☎ (0840) 213309
11–11 (11–2.30, 6–11 winter)
St Austell Tinners, HSD Ⓗ

A comfortable, old pub in a busy town. The beer garden overlooks the River Camel, which has flooded the pub in the past. ⌂ ❀ ⋈ ◖ ▶ ⬚ ♣

Cargreen

Spaniards Inn
OS437627 ☎ (0752) 842830
11–3, 6–11
St Austell HSD; Wadworth 6X Ⓗ
Excellent, rambling inn, overlooking the River Tamar, with a verandah, restaurant and several other rooms.
⌂ Q ⌖ ❀ ⋈ ◖ ▶ ⬚ ♣ ♣ P

Charlestown

Rashleigh Arms
On main road ☎ (0726) 73635
11–11
Draught Bass; Greene King Abbot; Ruddles County; St Austell Tinners; Wadworth 6X Ⓗ
Large and friendly inn overlooking the famous port of Charlestown. Recently re-furbished, there are two large bars, a restaurant and a family room. At least two guest beers available. AA three-star accommodation.
⌖ ❀ ⋈ ◖ ▶ ⬚ Å ♣ P

Comford

Fox & Hounds
A393, Falmouth-Redruth road
☎ (0209) 820251
11–3, 6–11
Draught Bass; St Austell Bosun's, HSD Ⓖ
Comfortable, country pub with restaurant; a prize-winner in a flower and garden competition.
⌂ ❀ ◖ ▶ ⬚ Å ♣ P

Crantock

Old Albion
Langurroc Road
☎ (0637) 830243
11–3, 6.30–11 (11–11 Fri, Sat & summer)
Courage Best Bitter, Directors Ⓗ
Pub with a quaint-looking exterior and therefore popular with summer visitors; situated by the church lychgate, and convenient for the smooth, sandy beach or the coastal path. Food not always available in winter. ⌂ Q ❀ ◖ ▶ ♣ P

Devoran

Old Quay Inn
St Johns Terrace (off A39)
☎X (0872) 863142
11.30–3, 6–11
Cornish JD, Original Ⓗ
Friendly, welcoming pub with fine views over Devoran Quay and Devoran Creek.
⌂ ❀ ⋈ ◖ ▶ ♣ P

12–3, 6–11
Draught Bass; Cotleigh Tawny; Greene King Abbot Ⓗ
Friendly inn by the only true village green in Cornwall. Popular with locals and tourists alike. Separate lounge. Menu features excellent value daily specials. Spacious family room. Regular guest beers.
⌂ Q ⌖ ❀ ◖ ▶ ♣ ⬚ P

Bodmin

Masons Arms
5–9 Higher Bore Street (A389)
☎ (0208) 72607
11–3, 5–11 (11–11 Fri & Sat)
Draught Bass; Ushers Best Bitter Ⓗ

Cornwall

Egloshayle

Earl of St Vincent
Behind church, then first right
☎ (0208) 814807
11–3, 6.30–11
St Austell Tinners, HSD 🅗
Pub dating from the 15th
century, which originally
housed the builders of the
nearby church. Very smartly
refurbished with a fine collection
of old clocks. No meals Sun eve.
🏚 🏮 🍺 ▶ P

Falmouth

Seven Stars
The Moor ☎ (0326) 312111
11–3, 6–11
**Draught Bass; Courage
Directors; Cornish JD;**
Unspoilt by 'progress', this pub
has remained in the same family
for five generations. A lively tap
room, with barrels on display,
and a quiet snug to the rear,
together with a number of
benches on the forecourt, cater
for all tastes. Regular guest
beers. Q 🏮 🍺 🄰

Flushing

Royal Standard
Off A393 at Penryn
☎ (0326) 74250
11–2.30 (3 Fri & Sat), 6.30–11 (12–2,
7–10.30 Sun)
**Draught Bass; Cornish JD;
Whitbread Flowers IPA** 🅗
Friendly local near the entrance
to the village: beware of swans
in the road nearby. 🏚 🏮 🍺 ♣

Fowey

Ship Inn
3 Trafalgar Square
☎ (072 683) 2230
11–3, 6–11 (11–11 summer)
St Austell Tinners, HSD 🅗
Comfortable and friendly, 16th-
century inn which has historical
connections with the Rashleigh
family and Sir Francis Drake.
Separate games room.
🏚 🏮 🛏 🍺 ♣

Goldsithney

Crown
Fore Street (B3280)
☎ (0736) 710494
11–3 (5 summer), 6.30–11
**St Austell XXXX Mild,
Bosun's, HSD** 🅗
Attractive and comfortable,
village pub with a warm
atmosphere. Very popular
restaurant (bookings advisable),
also excellent, home-cooked bar
meals. St Austell Tinners may
be available in summer.
🏚 Q 🏮 🍺 🏮 ▶ 🄰

Try also: **Trevelyan Arms**
(Cornish)

Gorran Churchtown

Barley Sheaf
☎ (0726) 843330
12–3, 7 (6 Sat)–11
**Draught Bass; St Austell
Tinners** 🅗
A real country pub which serves
up to three guest beers, plus
cider, in summer.
🏚 🛏 🏮 ▶ 🄰 🄰 ♣ 🔄 P

Try also: **Llawnroc** (Free)

Hayle

Bird in Hand
Paradise Park, Trelissick Road
☎ (0736) 753974/753365
12–2.30, 6–11 (12–11 summer)
**Courage Directors; Paradise
Bitter, Artists Ale, Victory** 🅗
Set in a former coach house,
with an excellent range of beer
from its own brewery. Lies next
to Paradise Park, an
internationally renowned bird
garden. Meals and occasional
live music in summer. Children
welcome in the dining area.
Usually two guest beers.
🏮 🏮 ▶ 🄰 🄰 ⇶ P

Helston

Blue Anchor
50 Coinagehall Street
☎ (0326) 562821
10.30–3 (may extend), 6–11
**Blue Anchor Medium, Best,
Special, Extra Special** 🅗
Superb, 15th-century, thatched
pub, once a monks' resting place
and, last century, a tin-miners'
pay office. Splendidly strong
beer is brewed in the old
brewhouse in the rear yard.
Simple bar snacks. 🏚 Q 🛏 🄰

Holywell Bay

Treguth Inn
Off A3075
☎ (0637) 830248
11.30–11 (11.30–3, 7–11 winter)
**Courage Best Bitter,
Directors; John Smith's
Bitter; Wadworth 6X** 🅗
A traditional, thatched pub in a
delightful holiday retreat within a
superb sandy beach within
walking distance, plus a leisure
park also nearby. Guest beers.
🏚 Q 🛏 🏮 🏮 ▶ 🄰 ♣ P

Hugh Town, St Mary's, Isles of Scilly

Bishop & Wolf
Main Street ☎ (0720) 22790
11–11
St Austell Tinners, HSD 🅗,
Winter Warmer 🄶
Lively pub with a large bar

downstairs and snug/restaurant
above. Named after the two
famous Scillies lighthouses;
several maritime items on
display. Beer is fined at the pub
after the sometimes arduous
crossing! 🏮 ▶ 🄰 ♣

Try also: **Atlantic Hotel** (St
Austell)

Lanlivery

Crown Inn
Off A390, between Lostwithiel
and St Blazey
☎ (0208) 872707
11–3, 6–11
**Draught Bass; Welsh
Brewers Worthington BB** 🅗
Picturesque, 12th-century inn
with a slate-floor bar, a snug
and a separate restaurant. Well-
known locally for its good food.
Worth finding. Good facilities
for wheelchair visitors.
🏚 Q 🏮 🛏 🏮 ▶ 🄰 🄰 ♣ P

Lanreath

Famous Punch Bowl
Left off B3359, Looe–Liskeard
road ☎ (050 36) 218
11–3, 6–11
**Draught Bass; Charrington
IPA** 🅗
Magnificent, velveteen chaise
longues in the lounge and an
enormous flagstoned, farmer's
kitchen as the public bar in this
17th-century coach house with
enough room to swing a horse!
Guest beers in summer.
🏚 Q 🛏 🏮 🛏 🏮 ▶ 🄰 🄰 🄰 ♣ P

Launceston

White Horse Inn
14 Newport Square, St
Stephens (Bude road)
☎ (0566) 772084
11–11
**Ruddles Best Bitter, County;
Ushers Best Bitter; Webster's
Yorkshire Bitter** 🅗
Friendly, 18th-century coaching
inn with two large bars (regular
live music in the stable bar).
Wide selection of food available
all day. 🏚 Q 🏮 🛏 🏮 ▶ 🏮 ♣ 🔄 P

Try also: **Westgate** (Courage)

Looe

Jolly Sailor
Princes Square, West Looe (opp.
river passenger ferry)
☎ (050 36) 3387
12 (11 summer)–11
**Marston's Pedigree; Ruddles
Best Bitter; Ushers Best
Bitter** 🅗
'Jolly Japes' in one of Britain's
oldest pubs; the folk group has
sung for over 500 years every
Sat night in this low-beamed,
Cornish, shark fishing local.
Beware of generous portions of

good food. Fresh flowers on the bar. Q ✠ 🏠 ( ) 🍽 🚲 🅐 ⇆ ♣

Lostwithiel

Royal Oak
Duke Street (off A390)
☎ (0208) 872552
11–3, 5.30–11
Draught Bass; Marston's Pedigree; Whitbread Flowers IPA, Original 🅗
Busy and friendly, 13th-century inn with good accommodation and a restaurant. Guest beers always available.
Q ✠ 🏠 ( ) 🍽 🅐 ⇆ ♣ P

Manaccan

New Inn
☎ (032 623) 323
11–3, 6–11
Cornish Original, Royal Wessex
Very traditional, thatched pub in the village centre. Prides itself on good, home-cooked food. No jukebox or fruit machines. Tiny car park. 🏠 Q 🍽 ( ) 🅐 P

Menheniot

White Hart
1¼ miles off A38
☎ (0579) 42245/44946
12–2.30, 6 (5.30 Sat)–11
Draught Bass; Whitbread Boddingtons Bitter 🅗
Well-appointed, 16th-century, family-run hotel with a friendly, village atmosphere in the public bar. Varied menu with probably the best value Sunday roasts (eves) in the county. Pool room and small patio.
🏠 Q 🍽 ( ) 🍽 ♣ P

Mevagissey

Fountain Inn
St Georges Square (near harbour)
☎ (0726) 842320
11–11 (11.30–3, 6–11 winter)
St Austell Tinners 🅗
Friendly, local drinking house: two bars and an upstairs restaurant. Traditional decor, with excellent slate floors. Fish is a speciality in the restaurant.
🏠 Q ✠ 🍽 ( ) 🍽 🅐 ♣

Morval

Snooty Fox
☎ (050 34) 233
11–2.30, 6–11
Marston's Pedigree; Whitbread Best Bitter, Flowers Original 🅗
Large, single-bar pub with a converted stable as a family/games room and additional bar. Guest beers in summer. Excellent food; separate restaurant. The large garden has an adventure play

area and a campsite is also in the grounds.
🏠 Q ✠ 🍽 🏠 ( ) 🍽 🅐 P

Morwenstow

Bush Inn
OS151208 ☎ (028 883) 242
12–2.30, 7–11 (closed Mon in winter)
St Austell Tinners, HSD 🅗
Ancient pub with monastic origins, set high on the North Cornwall coast, near the church where Rev Hawker preached. A quiet pub with stone floors, simple wooden furniture and a friendly welcome. Guest beers.
🏠 Q 🍽 🅗 ♣ P

Nancenoy

Trengilly Wartha
Off B3291 OS731282
☎ (0326) 40332
11–2.30, 6–11 (may vary)
Courage Directors 🅖
Delightful, remote, country pub with beer-loving owners who ring the changes with a variety of guest beers. Also renowned for its food. Excellent walks nearby.
🏠 Q ✠ 🍽 ( ) 🅐 ♣ ⊙ P

Newlyn

Fishermans Arms
Fore Street ☎ (0736) 63399
10.30–2.30, 6–11
St Austell Tinners, HSD 🅗
Popular local with superb views over the harbour and Mount's Bay. Interesting inglenook and display of maritime memorabilia. Good value simple food. Limited parking. 🏠 Q ( ) 🍽 🏠 ♣ P

Newquay

Buccaneer
29 Mount Wise
☎ (0637) 874470
12–3, 7–11
Marston's Pedigree; Whitbread Boddingtons Bitter 🅗
The ground-floor bar of Hotel Sutherland, conveniently located a short walk from the town centre and surfing. No less than three guest beers, changed regularly. Beer festival first week in July (Newquay 1900 Week).
🏠 ✠ 🍽 ⇆ P

Padstow

Golden Lion
19 Lanadwell Street
☎ (0841) 532797
11–11 (11–2.30, 6–11 winter)
Cornish JD, Original 🅗
An old pub with a low-ceilinged public bar and a comfortable lounge; the stable for the 'Old Oss', used in the May Day celebrations. 🏠 🍽 🏠 ( ) 🅐 ♣

Penzance

Fountain Tavern
St Clare Street
☎ (0736) 62673
11–2.30, 5.30–11 (11–11 summer)
St Austell Bosun's, HSD 🅗
Unpretentious local with a real community spirit and a warm friendly atmosphere. Off the beaten track, but worth the effort to find it. Bar snacks available. 🏠 🍽 ✠ ⇆ ♣

Mount's Bay Inn
The Promenade, Werrytown
☎ (0736) 63027
11–2.30, 5.30–11
Draught Bass 🅗
Friendly free house on the promenade offering three guest ales, all on handpump. One stone-walled bar with a restaurant to one side.
🏠 Q ( ) 🅐

Philleigh

Roseland Inn
Off A3078, on King Harry Ferry road ☎ (087 258) 254
11–2.30, 6–11
Cornish JD, Original 🅗
Superb, unspoilt village inn with slate floors, beams and a locals' snug. Excellent, home-cooked food. Look out for the local rugby club in winter.
🏠 Q 🍽 ( ) 🅐 P

Polbathic

Halfway House
On A387 ☎ (0503) 30202
11–3, 5.30–11 (may vary summer)
Courage Best Bitter, Directors 🅗
Large, roadside inn with several bars, boasting a collection of rosettes for equestrian activities. Comprehensive menu.
🏠 Q ✠ 🍽 🏠 ( ) 🍽 🅐 ⇆
(St Germans) ♣ P

Polgooth

Polgooth Inn
Off A390 ☎ (0726) 74089
11–3, 5.30–11
St Austell Bosun's, Tinners, HSD 🅗
Re-styled on traditional lines, a pub which remains popular with visitors and locals.
🏠 ✠ 🍽 ( ) 🅐 P

Polperro

Three Pilchards Inn
Quay Road (on harbour)
☎ (0503) 72233
11–3, 7–11 (11–11 summer)
Courage Best Bitter, Directors 🅗
Friendly pub in a picturesque, small fishing port. Popular with ramblers and tourists; interesting menu. 🍽 ( ) 🅐 ♣ ⊙

Cornwall

Polruan

Lugger Inn
The Quay ☎ (072 687) 364
11–3, 6–11 (11–11 summer)
St Austell Tinners, HSD 🅗
Squiffy-roofed pub with a split-level bar and a riverview restaurant. A welcome port of call when catching the foot ferry to Fowey. 🏚 Q 🏵 🌀 🛏 ♣

Porthallow

Five Pilchards
☎ (0326) 280256
12–2.30, 6.30–11
Cornish Original; Greene King Abbot 🅗
Attractive, rural pub, situated on the beach with views over to Falmouth. Fine collection of brass ships' lamps, model ships and wreck histories. Guest beers in summer. Self-catering accommodation available.
🏚 Q 🏵🛏 🌀 🛒 ♣ 🅐

Porthleven *2/4/14 SHUT*

Ship Inn
Mount Pleasant Road
☎ (0326) 572841
11–11 (11.30–2.30, 7–11 winter)
Courage Best Bitter, Directors; John Smith's Bitter 🅗
Old, harbourside, 16th-century, fishermen's pub, with superb views and good, home-made food. 🏚 🛒 🏵 🌀 🅐 ♣ P

Port Isaac

Golden Lion
Fore Street ☎ (0208) 880336
11–11 (11–2.30, 6–11)
St Austell Tinners, HSD 🅗
Originally known as the Red Lion, this small pub overlooks the busy fishing harbour. Frequented by smugglers in days of old, now it is popular with locals and visitors. Mind the slightly uneven floor.
🏚 🛒 🌀 🔲 ♣

Quintrell Downs

Two Clomes
East Road (A392)
☎ (0637) 873485
12–2.30, 7–11
Beer range varies
Pub with thick stone walls; the clome ovens by the log fire give rise to its name. Chalet accommodation and nearby campsites are convenient for Newquay. The beer range is regularly changed. No eve meals winter Mons.
🏚 Q 🛒 🏵 🛏 🌀 🅐 🛒 ♣ P

Redruth

Tricky Dickys Wine Bar
Tolgus ☎ (0209) 219292

11–3, 5–11
Courage Directors; Greene King Abbot 🅗
Friendly wine bar, well-frequented by locals. Jazz band once a week. Guest beers and good value food always available. 🌀 🌀 P

Restronguet Creek

Pandora Inn
End of Passage Hill, Mylor (near A39) OS814371
☎ (0326) 72678
11–11 (11–3, 6.30–11 winter)
Draught Bass; St Austell Bosun's, Tinners, HSD 🅗
13th-century, thatched pub at the waterside, reachable by both road and water. Snacks in the bar and a restaurant upstairs (*à la carte*). Outside drinking on the quay and pontoon.
🏚 Q 🏵 🌀 🅐 P

St Agnes

Driftwood Spars
Trevaunance Cove (100 yds from beach)
☎ (087 255) 2428/3323
11.30–11
Ind Coope Burton Ale; Tetley Bitter 🅗
17th-century inn with a nautical theme. Cosy, quiet bar with a relaxed atmosphere and a fine collection of whiskies. Restaurant upstairs offers an extensive menu; live music at weekends. One guest beer. Children welcome in the lounge.
🏚 Q 🏵 🛏 🌀 🌀 🅐 P

St Breward

Old Inn
OS773098 ☎ (0208) 850711
12–3, 6–11
Draught Bass; Ushers Best Bitter 🅗
Built from locally quarried granite, this fine pub is said to date from the 11th century. Slate floors and beamed ceilings; large, single slabs of granite form the bar fronts.
🏚 🛒 🏵 🌀 ♣ P

St Cleer

Stag Inn
Fore Street (2 miles N of Liskeard) ☎ (0579) 42305
11–3, 6.30–11
Draught Bass; St Austell XXXX Mild, HSD; Whitbread Boddingtons Bitter, Flowers Original 🅗
Friendly, traditional inn with a warm, cosy atmosphere. Popular with both locals and tourists. Close to many features of historic interest on the fringe of Bodmin Moor. Excellent good value food. One guest beer and house ale: 'Antler' (Whitbread).
Q 🏵 🌀 🔲 ♣ P

St Ives

Cornish Arms
Trelyon (road to Carbis Bay)
☎ (0736) 796112
11–3, 5.30–11
Cornish JD, Original 🅗
Cosy pub with a friendly atmosphere and a fine collection of old photographs.
🏚 Q 🏵 🌀 🅐

St Just

Star
Fore Street ☎ (0736) 788767
11–3, 6–11
St Austell Tinners, HSD 🅖
Friendly pub at the village centre. A fine granite building.
🏚 Q 🛒 🏵 🛏 🌀 🅐

St Kew

St Kew Inn
☎ (0208) 84259
11–3, 6–11 (11–11 summer)
St Austell Tinners, HSD 🅖
Pub with a public bar in the old kitchen, with a large open fire, meat hooks in the ceiling and a worn, slate floor. Very popular in summer with visitors, but a quiet haven in winter. Steaks a speciality. 🏚 Q 🏵 🌀 🔲 P

St Neot

London Inn
☎ (0579) 20263
11–3, 6–11
Ruddles Best Bitter, County; Ushers Best Bitter 🅗
16th-century coaching inn with a flagstoned floor and open beams. Next to a church famed for its stained-glass windows. Skittle alley. No meals Sun eve.
🏚 🏵 🌀 🅐 ♣ P

St Teath

White Hart Hotel
☎ (0208) 850281
11–2.30, 6–11
Ruddles County; Ushers Best Bitter 🅗
Situated opposite the village clock tower, an old pub, dating from the 1700s and housing three bars, ranging from the quiet comfort of the snug to a boisterous, noisy games area.
🏚 🛒 🏵 🌀 🔲 ♣ P

Sennen

First & Last
On A30, ½ mile from Lands End
☎ (0736) 871680
11–2.30, 5.30–11 (may vary)
Wadworth 6X 🅗
Spacious, well-kept pub, popular with both locals and holidaymakers. Good value food; one, varied guest beer in summer. 🏚 Q 🛒 🏵 🌀 🅐 ♣ P

Stratton

Tree Inn
Fore Street ☎ (0288) 352038
11–11
Draught Bass; St Austell Tinners Ⓗ
Four bars set around the courtyard of a 16th-century coaching inn. Read the history of the pub and the nearby battle of Stamford Hill (1643) in the archway. Regular live music; skittle alley.
🔥 🐴 🍺 🍴 ▶ 🍺 ♣ P

Trebarwith Strand

Port William
OS864048 ☎ (0840) 770230
11–11
St Austell Tinners, HSD Ⓗ
Fine pub overlooking the beach and handy for families. Originally a harbour master's cottage and stables, when slate was brought down the valley to be loaded onto waiting ships. Two guest beers. Self-contained flat available.
🔥 🐴 🍺 🍴 ▶ Å ♣ P

Tregrehan

Britannia
On A390, 3 miles E of St Austell ☎ (0726) 812889
11–11
Draught Bass; Courage Best Bitter; St Austell Tinners Ⓗ
16th-century inn on the main road. Well known for food (available all day), it has a separate restaurant and a large, safe garden with a children's play area. Q 🐴 🍺 🍴 🍺 ♣ ☙ P

Treen 22/4/94

Logan Rock Inn
Off B3315 ☎ (0736) 810495
10.30–3, 5.30–11
St Austell Tinners, HSD Ⓗ
Outstanding, small, country pub near a beautiful coastal area with the famous Logan Rock nearby. Good food and a welcoming family room.
🔥 🐴 🍺 🍴 ▶ 🍺 Å ♣ P

Trematon

Crooked Inn
Signed on A38
☎ (0752) 848177
11–3, 6–11
Fergusons Dartmoor Best Bitter; Ruddles County; St Austell XXXX Mild, HSD Ⓗ
A good selection of traditional ales in an 18th-century farmhouse. Accommodation in the converted stable. Homely bar meals. 🔥 🐴 🍺 🛏 🍴 ▶ & Å P

Try also: Rod & Line, Tideford (Courage)

Trevarrack

Tyringham Arms
Off A3074 ☎ (0736) 740195
11–3, 5.30–11
Draught Bass; Ruddles County Ⓗ
Comfortable free house in an imposing, converted school. Very good value meals.
🔥 🐴 🍺 🛏 🍴 ▶ & Å P

Truro

City Inn
Pydar Street (up from cathedral, under viaduct) ☎ (0872) 72623
11–11
Courage Best Bitter, Directors; John Smith's Bitter; Wadworth 6X Ⓗ
Excellent community pub with a large collection of local pictures on the walls and jugs hanging from the ceiling. Family garden with aviary. Regular guest ale and good pub grub.
🍺 🍴 ▶ ≠ ⊕

Old Ale House
Quay Street ☎ (0872) 71122
11–2.30, 5.30 (6.30 Sat)–11
Draught Bass; Greene King

Abbot; Whitbread Boddingtons OB Bitter Ⓖ
Old ale house with a 'spit and sawdust' atmosphere. A happy, drinkers' pub, normally carrying up to ten real ales. Twice weekly jazz; excellent food. Cosmopolitan clientele. 🍴

Tywardreath

New Inn
Fore Street ☎ (072 681) 2901
11–2.30 (3 Fri & Sat; 4 Fri & Sat in summer), 6–11
Draught Bass; St Austell Tinners Ⓖ
Popular, village local near the coast, with a secluded garden leading off the lounge. No food Sun. 🍺 🍴 ▶ Å ≠ (Par) ♣ ☙

Upton Cross

Caradon Inn
On B3254, Liskeard–Launceston road ☎ (0579) 62391
11–3, 5.30–11
Marston's Pedigree; St Austell HSD; Whitbread Flowers Original Ⓗ
Friendly and welcoming, 17th-century, country inn, popular with both locals and visitors. Pool table in the bar and a jukebox with 1960s records. Local farm cider in summer; good value food.
🔥 Q 🍺 🍴 ▶ & ☙ P

Zelah

Hawkins Arms
On old A30
☎ (0872) 54339
11–3, 6–11
Ind Coope Burton Ale; Tetley Bitter Ⓗ
Although the village is now bypassed, this pub remains a good reason for finding the old road. Weekly-changed guest beers are popular with locals and holiday trade alike. Garden play area for children.
🔥 Q 🐴 🍺 🛏 🍴 ▶ Å ♣ P

The Symbols

🔥	real fire	&	easy wheelchair access
Q	quiet pub (at least one bar)	Å	camping facilities at the pub or nearby
🐴	indoor room for children	≠	near British Rail station
🍺	garden or other outdoor drinking area	⊕	near Underground station
🛏	accommodation	♣	pub games
🍴	lunchtime meals	☙	real cider
▶	evening meals	P	pub car park
🍺	public bar	✗	no-smoking room or area

Cumbria

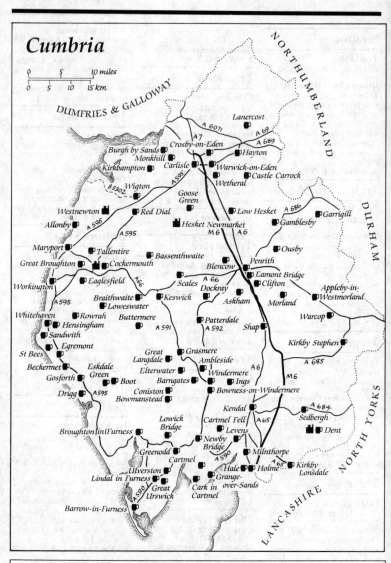

Cumbria

0   5   10 miles
0 5 10 15 km

DUMFRIES & GALLOWAY
NORTHUMBERLAND
DURHAM
NORTH YORKS
LANCASHIRE

Lanercost
Crosby-on-Eden
A7 A607 A689 A69
Hayton
Burgh by Sands
Monkhill
Kirkbampton
Carlisle
Warwick-on-Eden
Castle Carrock
Wetheral
B5302
Wigton
A595
Goose Green
Low Hesket
A686
Garrigill
Westnewton
Red Dial
Hesket Newmarket
M6 A6
Gamblesby
Allonby
A596
A595
Ousby
Maryport
Tallentire
Bassenthwaite
Blencow
Penrith
Great Broughton
Cockermouth
A66
Scales
A66
Eamont Bridge
Clifton
Appleby-in-Westmorland
Workington
Eaglesfield
Dockray
Askham
Morland
Warcop
Braithwaite
Keswick
Whitehaven
Rowrah
Loweswater
Patterdale
Shap
A595
Hensingham
Buttermere
A591
A592
Kirkby Stephen
Sandwith
Egremont
Great Langdale
Grasmere
Ambleside
St Bees
Eskdale Green
Elterwater
Windermere
A6
M6
Beckermet
Boot
Barngates
Ings
A685
Gosforth
Coniston
Bowmanstead
Bowness-on-Windermere
Drigg
A595
Kendal
A684
Sedbergh
Lowick Bridge
Cartmel Fell
Dent
Broughton in Furness
Levens
A65
Greenodd
Newby Bridge
Milnthorpe
Cartmel
A590
Holme
Kirkby Lonsdale
Ulverston
Hale
Lindal in Furness
A590
Grange-over-Sands
Great Urswick
Cark in Cartmel
Barrow-in-Furness

Dent, Dent; **Hesket Newmarket**, Hesket Newmarket; **Jennings**, Cockermouth; **Yates**, Westnewton

---

Allonby

Ship Hotel
Main Street ☎ (0900) 84462
12–3, 7–11 (11–11 summer)
Yates Bitter H
Pleasant, seaside hotel facing a
green area and the Solway.
Q ✿ ⌂ ◖ ❶ ♿ ⚲ Å ♣ P

Ambleside

Golden Rule
Smithy Brow (off A591,
towards Kirkstone)
☎ (053 94) 32257
11–11
Hartleys Mild, Bitter, XB H
A gem; virtually unspoilt beer
drinker's pub – simply a bar,
three rooms and a friendly
atmosphere. Mixed clientele,
including climbers and
paragliders (ask the landlord for
details). No pool; no jukebox.
Can get noisy – with
conversation! Eve meals finish
at 8pm. Limited parking.
⌂ Q ✿ ◖ ❶ ♣ P

White Lion Hotel
Market Place
☎ (053 94) 33140
11–3, 5.30–11 (11–11 Thu–Sat)
**Bass Special, Draught
Bass** H
Two-bar pub in the town
centre. Efficient friendly service;
good value food – especially
the roast beef lunch on Sun. The
low-geared handpumps are
unusual. Q ✿ ⌂ ◖ ❶ ♣ P

Try also: Stringers Bar,
Waterhead Hotel (Free)

72

Appleby-in-Westmorland

Royal Oak
Bongate ☎ (076 83) 51463
11.30–3, 6.30–11
Draught Bass; Theakston Best Bitter; Yates Bitter, Premium; Younger Scotch Ⓗ
Attractive, 17th-century coaching inn with a friendly, welcoming atmosphere. Excellent tap room.
🏚 Q 🍴 ⌂ ◖ ♣ P

Try also: **Grapes** (Marston's)

Askham

Queens Head
☎ (093 12) 225
11–3, 6–11
Vaux Samson (summer);
Wards Sheffield Best Bitter Ⓗ
17th-century, village-centre inn; cosy and friendly. Good food.
🏚 Q 🐕 🍴 ⌂ ◖ Å ♣ P

Barngates

Drunken Duck
Off B5286, 2 miles NW of Hawkshead OS351012
☎ (096 66) 347
11.30–3, 6–11
Jennings Bitter; Marston's Pedigree; Theakston XB, Old Peculier; Yates Bitter Ⓗ
One of the county's most famous pubs, reputed to be 400 years old. The amusing legend about the pub's name can be read inside. Two car parks and a beer garden. Guest beers. En suite accommodation.
🏚 Q 🐕 🍴 ⌂ ◖ Å ♣ P

Try also: **Queens Head**, Hawkshead

Barrow-in-Furness

Wheatsheaf
Anson Street (main road past rugby ground)
☎ (0229) 837515
11–3, 7–11
John Smith's Bitter Ⓗ
Friendly, comfortable local with views of the infamous Devonshire Dock Hall to disturb your contemplation of a good pint. Popular with Navy personnel, shipyard workers, rugby supporters and the average drinker (male and female). Q 🍴 ⌂ ◖ ♣

Try also: **Blue Lamp** (Thwaites)

Bassenthwaite

Pheasant Inn
Peel Wyke, Bassenthwaite Lake (signed from A66)
☎ (076 87) 76234

11.30–2.30 (10.30–3 Fri & Sat),
5.30–10.30 (11 Fri & Sat)
Draught Bass; Theakston Best Bitter Ⓗ
Typical, country inn in a delightful setting by Thornthwaite Forest and Bassenthwaite Lake: a snug bar with oak settles. Bar meals served; extensive menu in the hotel restaurant.
Q 🍴 ⌬ ⌂ Å P

Sun Inn
☎ (076 87) 76439
11–3, 6–11 (12–2.30, 7–10.30 Sun)
Jennings Bitter Ⓗ
Friendly, open-plan, village pub. Wide selection of bar meals (not Sun eve). Tables for outside drinking. 🏚 🐕 🍴 ◖ Å P

Beckermet

White Mare
☎ (0946) 841246
11–5, 5.30–11
Theakston Best Bitter, XB, Old Peculier; Younger Scotch, No. 3 Ⓗ
Large, attractive, village pub with several connecting rooms on different levels. Very popular for meals, especially Sun lunches. Weekly quizzes. Garden play area.
🏚 Q 🍴 ◖ ⌂ Å P

Try also: **Royal Oak** (Jennings)

Blencow

Clickham Inn
On B5288, 3 miles W of Penrith ☎ (076 84) 83406
Marston's Burton Best Bitter, Merrie Monk, Pedigree Ⓗ
Attractive, roadside inn on the old main road to Keswick. Good bar food, specialising in local and vegetarian dishes. Pool room. 🏚 Q 🍴 ◖ Å ♣ P

Boot

Burnmoor Inn
☎ (094 03) 224
11–3, 5–11
Jennings Bitter, Cumberland Ale Ⓗ
Traditional, Lakeland inn, dating from 1578 in parts. Meals include many authentic Austrian dishes. Scafell, La'al Ratty, waterfalls and superb walks are all nearby. 🏚 🐕 🍴 ⌂ ◖ Å P

Try also: **Woolpack Inn** (Free)

Bowmanstead

Ship Inn
½ mile S of Coniston, off A593
☎ (053 94) 41224
12–3, 7–10.30 (11–11 summer)
Hartleys XB Ⓗ
Friendly, village local, quiet in winter. Family room and games room. 🏚 Q 🐕 🍴 ⌂ ◖ Å ♣ P

Bowness-on-Windermere

Hole in T'Wall (New Hall Inn)
Lowside ☎ (096 62) 3488
11–11
Hartleys Mild, XB; Robinson's Best Bitter Ⓗ
Former blacksmith's, now a busy pub whose customers have included Dickens and Wordsworth. The patio (the ex-horse shoeing area) is a delight in summer. Upstairs family room/restaurant/function room. No eve meals Jan–Easter.
🏚 🐕 🍴 ◖ ♣

Braithwaite

Coledale Inn
Off A66, Cockermouth–Keswick road ☎ (059 682) 272
11–11
Yates Bitter Ⓗ
Pub built on the site of an old pencil factory. Good view of Skiddaw from the garden, which has play facilities for children (dogs and children welcome). House beer, Coledale XXPS, is in fact Younger Scotch.
🏚 🍴 ⌂ ◖ ◖ Å P

Broughton in Furness

Manor Arms
The Square ☎ (0229) 716286
12 (2 winter)–11
Taylor Landlord; Theakston Best Bitter; Yates Bitter Ⓗ
Welcoming local in the village centre. Several guest beers always available in excellent condition. Two real fires. Toasties and pies available for those who wish to complement their beer with a light snack. Park in The Square. 🏚 Q 🍴 ♣

Burgh by Sands

Greyhound
Off B5307, 6 miles W of Carlisle ☎ (022 876) 76579
Hours vary
Greenalls Thomas Greenall's Bitter Ⓗ
18th-century house converted into a pub by State Management in 1936. Extensive renovations have created an open-plan layout. Children's play area in the garden. 🍴 ◖ Å ♣ P

Buttermere

Bridge Hotel
OS175170 ☎ (059 685) 252
11–3, 6–11 (11–11 summer)
McEwan 80/–; Theakston Old Peculier; Younger No. 3 Ⓗ

Cumbria

Converted cornmill, first licensed in 1735, which has had various names, including the 'Victoria', after the monarch who stayed here. Popular with walkers; interesting memorabilia around the bar area. Q ✪ ⋈ ◖◗ ⊕ ▲ P

Cark in Cartmel

Rose & Crown Inn
☎ (053 95) 58501
11 (12 winter)–3, 6 (6.30 winter)–11 (11–11 Mon, Fri & Sat)
Hartleys XB H
Newly refurbished, village local, close to Holker Hall, which houses the Lakeland Motor Museum. Work is in progress to upgrade the kitchen and dining area. Benches and tables outside. ⚏ ✪ ⋈ ◖◗ ▲ ♣ P

Carlisle

Beehive Inn
Warwick Road (A69, ¾ mile E of centre) ☎ (0228) 32923
11–3, 7–11
Theakston Best Bitter H
Comfortable, two-roomed pub, handy for the soccer and rugby union grounds. Pub quizzes most Tue eves. ✪ ◖ ⊕ ♣

Howard Arms
Lowther Street
☎ (0228) 32926
11–11
Theakston Best Bitter, XB H
Very popular, city-centre pub with an impressive, tiled frontage. The large collection of State Management bottles is a reminder of Carlisle's brewing past. ✪ ◖ ≉

Kings Head
Fisher Street (behind town hall)
☎ (0228) 33797
11–11
McEwan 80/-; S&N Matthew Brown Mild; Theakston Best Bitter, XB H
Large, single-roomed pub on two levels. Reportedly the oldest surviving pub in the city. ✪ ◖ ≉ ⋈

Mary's Chambers
Mary Street (first left off Botchergate) ☎ (0228) 31316
11–11
Theakston Best Bitter H
Carlisle's newest pub, part of the refurbished County Hotel. Boasts a 60s-style interior and attractive, wooden furnishings. Guest beer. ⋈ ◖◗ ≉ ♣ P

Turf Inn
Newmarket Road
☎ (0228) 515367
11–2.30, 5.30–11 (11–11 Sat)
Marston's Pedigree; Whitbread Boddingtons Bitter, Castle Eden Ale H
Inn in a former racecourse grandstand; superbly restored

from a ruin. Not surprisingly, the bar has a horseracing theme. Excellent service in a comfortable, relaxing atmosphere. Free, informal quiz every Wed. ✪ ◖◗ ⅃ P

Woolpack Inn
Milbourne Street (off A595, opp. former brewery)
☎ (0228) 32459
11–3, 5.15–11 (11–11 Sat & occasional weekdays)
Jennings Mild, Bitter, Cumberland Ale, Sneck Lifter (occasional)
Large local with an extraordinary welcome: large lounge, snug bar and games room. A mural depicts Carlisle's history. After a short time you'll feel you've been a regular for years! Large selection of malt whiskies. Live jazz Thu and second Sun of month; other live music on Fri. ✪ ⋈ ◖◗ ≽ ♣ P

Cartmel

Cavendish Arms
☎ (053 95) 36240
11.30–3, 6–11
Draught Bass H
Large, comfortable and friendly pub in the centre of the village. Well known for its Aberdeen Angus steaks grilled over charcoal. Packed during bank hols, especially on racedays. The oldest pub in the village. ⚏ Q ✪ ⋈ ◖◗ ▲ ♣ P

Cartmel Fell

Masons Arms
Between Gummers How and Bowland Bridge OS413895
☎ (044 88) 486
11.30–3, 6–11
Bateman XB; Lakeland Amazon Bitter, Great Northern H
Very popular, roadside inn at the heart of the Lake District. Carries an enormous selection of bottled beers from all over the world, and is home to the Lakeland Brewery Co. (also brews a damson beer). Wide range of meals; guest beers. Busy at all times and large parties are discouraged. ⚏ Q ≽ ✪ ⋈ ◖◗ P

Castle Carrock

Duke of Cumberland
☎ (0228) 70341
7–11 (lunchtime opening summer only)
Marston's Burton Best Bitter, Pedigree H
Comfortable pub with a roaring fire and tasteful decor. Pool table and jukebox in the back room. ⚏ ✪ ◖◗ ▲ ♣ P

Try also: Hare & Hounds, Talkin (Hartleys)

Clifton

George & Dragon
On A6, 3 miles S of Penrith
☎ (0768) 65381
11–3, 7–11
Tetley Bitter H
Excellent example of a traditional Cumbrian inn, stone-built and set back from the main road in the middle of a cottage terrace. Modernisation – including the addition of a pool room – hasn't detracted from its cosy-cottage feel. ⚏ Q ⋈ ◖◗ ▲ ♣ P

Cockermouth

Swan Inn
56 Kirkgate ☎ (0900) 822425
11–3, 7–11
Jennings Bitter, Cumberland Ale H
400 year-old pub off a cobbled, Georgian square. Popular with locals; friendly welcome for visitors. Selection of over 170 whiskies. ⊕ ♣

Trout Hotel
Crown Street ☎ (0900) 823591
10.30–3, 5.30–11 (11–3, 7–10.30 Sun)
Draught Bass H
Well-established hotel in a prime, town-centre position near Wordsworth House. Pleasant bar; award-winning, riverside gardens. Children welcome. No-smoking area at lunchtime only. ✪ ⋈ ▲ P ✗

Coniston

Crown Hotel
Opp. main car park
☎ (053 94) 41243
11–11
Hartleys XB; Robinson's Bitter H
Busy, small hotel in the centre of the village. Meals all day. ⚏ ✪ ⋈ ◖◗ ▲ ♣ ⌣ P

Crosby-on-Eden

Stag Inn
Main Street ☎ (022 873) 210
12–3, 6–11
Jennings Mild, Bitter H
Lovely, olde-worlde pub with superb stonework and low beams. The restaurant upstairs has an excellent choice of real food. ◖◗ ♣ P

Dent

Sun Inn
Main Street (near church)
☎ (058 75) 208
11–3, 6–11 (11–11 summer, depending on trade)
Dent Bitter, Ramsbottom; Theakston XB H; **Younger Scotch** E
17th-century, beamed inn at the top of the cobbled main street.

The 'old' doms table is played on every night. A convenient place for cyclists and hikers to break their journey. Eve meals till 8.30. The Settle–Carlisle railway is four miles away.
🏰 Q 🍴 🛏 ◖◗ 🛅 Å ♣ P

Try also: George & Dragon (Free)

Dockray

Royal Hotel
☎ (076 84) 82356
Hours vary
Marston's Pedigree (summer); Whitbread Castle Eden Ale ⊞
Pub with a warming fire and welcome: a great place to rest after a hard day's walk. Guest beers in summer.
🏰 Q ざ 🍴 ◖◗ 🛅 占 Å ♣ P

Drigg

Victoria Hotel
☎ (094 04) 231
11–3, 6–11
Jennings Bitter ⊞
Friendly hotel with collection of knots and jugs. Separate dining room; beer garden; fishing rights on nearby River Irt.
🏰 🍴 🛏 ◖◗ ≽ P

Eaglesfield

Black Cock
2 miles from Cockermouth
☎ (0900) 822989
11–3, 6–11
Jennings Bitter ⊞
Cosy, village-centre pub, with the same landlady in residence for many years. Darts, dominoes and quizzes.
🏰 Q 🍴 占 ♣ P

Eamont Bridge

Beehive Inn
On A6, just S of Penrith
☎ (0768) 62081
11–3, 6–11 (11–11 summer)
Whitbread Boddingtons Bitter, Castle Eden Ale *or* Hartleys XB ⊞
Busy, roadside inn with a noteworthy sign, on the edge of the Lake District. Good, wholesome food; unusual, hexagonal pool table.
ざ 🍴 ◖◗ 占 Å ♣ P

Egremont

Blue Bell
6 Market Place
☎ (0946) 820581
11–3, 6–11 (12–2, 7–10.30 Sun)
Hartleys XB; Robinson's Best Bitter ⊞
Friendly, welcoming, homely and well-run pub at the heart of the town. Egremont is the home of the world gurning championship (taking place at the annual Crab Fair).
🏰 🍴 ♣ P

Elterwater

Britannia Inn
Off B5343 OS285061
☎ (096 67) 210
11–11
Hartleys XB; Jennings Mild, Bitter; Marston's Pedigree ⊞
Welcoming pub with good views in peaceful surroundings. Large dining area; very small snug. Spacious outdoor drinking area.
🏰 Q 🍴 🛏 ◖◗ 🛅 ♣ ⏻

Eskdale Green

George IV
☎ (094 03) 23262
11–3, 6 (4 summer)–11
Bass Special, Draught Bass; Theakston Best Bitter ⊞
Interesting pub with several interlinked rooms on different levels; a short walk from the miniature railway station. Occasional guest beer. Children welcomed. Formerly known as the 'Prince of Prussia.'
🏰 Q ざ 🍴 ◖◗ 🛅 Å P

Gamblesby

Red Lion
Off A686, 1½ miles from Melmerby OS393612
☎ (0768) 881316
11–2.30, 6–11 (closed Mon, except bank hols)
Whitbread Flowers IPA ⊞
Well-used, village local nestling at foot of the Pennines. Good, home-cooked food, good beer and 'crack'. Large selection of unusual pub games, incl. Tiger and Goats, Nine Men's Morris, chess and bar skittles.
🏰 Q ざ 🍴 ◖◗ ♣ P

Garrigill

George & Dragon
☎ (0434) 381293
12–3, 7–11
McEwan 70/-; Theakston Best Bitter, XB ⊞
Pub situated on the Pennine Way with cheap bunk house accommodation, two real fires and a good welcome. Guest beer. 🏰 Q ざ 🛏 ◖◗ 占 Å ♣ P

Goose Green

String of Horses
At B5299/B5305 jct
☎ (096 96) 358
11.30 (12 winter)–3, 7–11
Marston's Burton Best Bitter, Pedigree ⊞
Two-roomed, warm and cosy pub, at the gateway to Caldbeck Fells, on the old geese drovers' route from Whitehaven to Carlisle. Very friendly and family-run. In winter, the menu may not be as varied as in summer. 🏰 🍴 ◖◗ Å ♣ P

Gosforth

Gosforth Hall Hotel
On road to Wasdale Head
☎ (094 67) 25322
11–3, 5.30–11
Jennings Cumberland Ale; Stones Best Bitter ⊞
17th-century manor house converted into a pub and including many original features, such as a 1673 fireplace, beams, ceiling hooks and an inglenook. Outdoor swimming pool.
🏰 Q ざ 🍴 ◖◗ 🛅 Å P

Try also: All five pubs in Gosforth sell real ale

Grange-over-Sands

Hardcragg Hall
Grange Fell Road (off B5277)
☎ (053 95) 33353
11–3, 6–11
Thwaites Mild, Bitter ⊞
Elegant, 16th-century manor house with wood-panelled bars and dining rooms, and large, open fireplaces. Ever-changing guest beers. Bar billiards.
🏰 Q ざ 🍴 🛏 ◖◗ 占 Å ≽ ♣ P

Grasmere

Traveller's Rest
☎ (096 65) 604
11–11
Jennings Bitter, Cumberland Ale ⊞
Pleasant, roadside (A591) inn, at the foot of Dunmail Raise (the frontier between the former counties of Westmorland and Cumberland). Separate rooms for games and dining. A good start/finish for walks.
🏰 Q ざ 🛏 ◖◗ ♣ P

Great Broughton

Punch Bowl
19 Main Street (just off A66)
☎ (0900) 824708
6.30–11 (11.30–11 Thu–Sat & summer)
Jennings Bitter ⊞
Cosy pub with a pleasant atmosphere in the centre of the village. Children welcomed.
🏰 Q 🍴 ◖◗ 占 ♣ P

Great Langdale

Old Dungeon Ghyll
On B5343 at head of valley
OS285061 ☎ (096 67) 272
11–11
Marston's Merrie Monk, Pedigree; Theakston XB, Old Peculier; Yates Bitter ⊞
Popular walkers' and climbers' bar in an idyllic setting below the Langdale Pikes. Finalist in the 1990 CAMRA national *Pub of the Year* competition.
🏰 Q 🍴 ◖◗ Å ⏻ P

Cumbria

Great Urswick

Derby Arms
☎ (0229) 56348
12–2 (3 Fri), 5.30–11 (11–11 Sat)
Hartleys Mild, Bitter, XB ⊞
Village pub, the centre of local life. Good crack; a pukka beer house. Children welcome.
⌂ ⊛ ♣ P

Try also: General Burgoyne (Hartleys); **Swan** (Hartleys)

Greenodd

Machells Arms
Off A590 ☎ (0229) 861246
11–3, 6–11
Ind Coope Burton Ale; Tetley Bitter ⊞
Small, friendly, village-centre local, an ideal base for a holiday in the Lakes. ⌂ ⋈ (▌ ♣ P

Hale

Kings Arms
On A6, ½ mile S of Beetham
☎ (053 95) 63203
11–3, 6–11
Mitchell's Best Bitter ⊞
An L-shaped bar with settles and a smaller room off; a popular lunchtime halt. Family room upstairs. Bowling green.
⌂ ⋈ ⊛ (▌ P

Hayton

Stone Inn
2 miles W of Brampton on A69; ½ mile from A69
☎ (0228) 70498
11–3, 5.30–11
Draught Bass; Mitchell's Best Bitter; Theakston Best Bitter; Younger Scotch ⊞
Attractive and cosy, village local with a comfortable atmosphere. Serves a range of unusual toasties. ⌂ Q ⋈ ♣ P

Try also: Scotch Arms, Brampton (S&N)

Hensingham

Sun Inn
Hensingham Square
☎ (0946) 695149
12–4, 6.30–11
Jennings Bitter ⊞
Busy, unpretentious local, popular with all ages.

Try also: Richmond (S&N)

Holme

Smithy
Milnthorpe Road
☎ (0524) 781302
11.45–2.30, 6 (7 Fri & Sat)–11
Thwaites Best Mild, Bitter Ⓔ
Pub with a large main bar, which can still be crowded on summer weekends. Outdoor play area. ⊛ (▌ ⊛ ♣ P

Ings

Watermill Inn
On A591, near Ings church
☎ (0539) 821309
12–3 (2.30 winter; may extend summer), 6–11
Lees Moonraker; Theakston Best Bitter, XB, Old Peculier ⊞
Over 250 year-old converted timber mill, next to the River Gowan: a must for anyone visiting the area. A warm welcome and good food in a friendly, family-run hotel. Guest beers (from all over the UK) change frequently. No real cider in winter.
⌂ Q ⊛ ⋈ (▌ ⊛ ⚲ ♣ ⚲ P

Kendal

Castle
Castle Street (just off A6, at the N end of town)
☎ (0539) 729983
11–11
Tetley Walker Bitter ⊞
Pleasant, quietly-situated, two-roomed local, just off the tourist routes and near St George's church and the River Kent. Relax with the fish in the lounge or admire the framed, original Duttons window in the public bar. Guest beers. Home-cooked food. (▌ ⇌ ♣

Sawyers Arms
137 Stricklandgate (100 yds from A6/A591 jct, in NW part of town) ☎ (0539) 729737
11.30–4, 6.30–11 (11–11 Fri, Sat & summer)
Hartleys XB; Robinson's Best Bitter ⊞, **Old Tom** (winter) Ⓖ
A Kendalian hostelry full of local characters who ensure a warm welcome. Old Hartleys window on the frontage; Gaskell & Chambers Dalex pumps (c. 1936) still serve the beer. Large selection of 50s and 60s music on the jukebox. Food April–Oct only. ⋈ (▌ ⇌ ♣

Keswick

George Hotel
St John Street (top of market place) ☎ (076 87) 72076
11–11
Theakston Best Bitter, Old Peculier; Yates Bitter ⊞
Old coaching inn, now a smart hotel. Popular with climbers.
⌂ Q ⋈ ⋈ (▌ ⚲ ♣ P

Try also: Twa Dogs (Jennings)

Kirkbampton

Rose & Crown
On B5307 ☎ (0228) 576492
12–(varied closing; not winter), 7–11
Wilson's Mild ⊞

Unspoilt, busy, two-roomed local, very much a dominoes pub. Guest bitter.
⌂ Q ⋈ ⊛ (▌ ♣ ⚲

Kirkby Lonsdale

Sun
Market Street
☎ (052 42) 71965
11–11
Dent Bitter; Whitbread Boddingtons Bitter; Younger Scotch, No. 3 ⊞
Pub with a 17th-century, colonnaded facade; the interior is completely modern, but contrives an olde-worlde atmosphere with some nice touches. Food all day – even Sun – and recommended.
⌂ ⋈ (▌ ♣

Try also: Red Dragon (Jennings)

Kirkby Stephen

Kings Arms
Market Square
☎ (076 83) 71378
11–3, 6–11
Whitbread Boddingtons Bitter, Trophy ⊞
Weary and wet walkers are very welcome here, in the little snug at the side. Good quality food.
Q ⋈ ⋈ (▌ ⊛ ⚲ ⚲ ♣ P

Try also: White Lion (Marston's)

Lanercost

Abbey Bridge Inn (Blacksmiths Bar)
Off A69 ☎ (069 77) 2224
12–2.30, 7–11 (12–2.30, 7–10.30 Sun)
Wadworth 6X; Yates Bitter ⊞
17th-century smithy, converted into a beautiful, split-level bar and lounge. An attractive spiral staircase leads to the restaurant above. Frequently-changed guest beers. ⌂ Q ⊛ ⋈ (▌ ♣ P

Levens

Hare & Hounds
400 yds off A590
☎ (053 95) 60408/60783
11–3, 6–11
Vaux Samson; Wards Sheffield Best Bitter ⊞
Historic pub, c. 1714, with low ceilings, original beams and cosy settles. Excellent lunches all year but no eve meals Sun–Tue in winter. Dedicated landlord. Q ⊛ (▌ ♣ P

Lindal in Furness

Railway Inn
London Road (off A590)
☎ (0229) 62889
7/7.30–11 (12–11 Sat if custom demands)

Jennings Bitter, Cumberland Ale Ⓗ
Friendly, village local with a warm welcome (children included). Small play area at the rear in the beer garden. Varied guest beers. ▦ ⬛ ◖ ◗ ♣

Loweswater

Kirkstile Inn
OS209141 ☎ (090 085) 219
11–11
Jennings Bitter Ⓗ
Country inn next to the village church in an attractive walking area. Pleasant gardens with a view of Mellbreak. The restaurant has a good reputation (vegetarian dishes in the bar and restaurant). ▦ Q ⬛ ⋈ ◖ ◗ ♣ P

Low Hesket

Rose & Crown
On A6 ☎ (069 74) 73346
11–3, 6–11
Marston's Mercian Mild, Burton Best Bitter, Pedigree Ⓗ
Traditional, two-roomed, roadside pub with timber beams. Well worth a detour off the motorway. Camping 1½ miles away. ▦ ⬛ ◖ ◗ ⊟ ↺ P

Try also: **Lowther Arms**, Cumwhinton (Jennings)

Lowick Bridge

Red Lion
Off A5084 ☎ (022 985) 366
11–3.30, 6 (6.30 winter)–11
Hartleys Mild, XB; Robinson's Best Bitter Ⓗ
Friendly, country local, with a patio at the rear. Parking for eight cars only. ▦ Q ⬛ ◖ ◗ Å ♣ ↺ P

Maryport

Captain Nelson Tavern
Irish Street, South Quay
11–11
Whitbread Castle Eden Ale Ⓗ
New pub with a nautical theme. The one large, comfortable room resembles 'below deck' on a ship. Live music Wed nights and bank hols. Eve meals to order only. ◖ ≋

Milnthorpe

Coach & Horses
Haverflatts Lane
☎ (053 95) 63210
11–11 (may vary in winter)
Mitchell's Mild, Best Bitter Ⓗ
Open-plan, one-bar, locals' pub which manages to retain a two-bar atmosphere. Strong darts teams make for lively eves when playing at home. Eve meals Easter–Nov only. ▦ ⬛ ◖ ◗ ♣ P

Monkhill

Drovers Rest
400 yds W of Kirkandrews-on-Eden OS343587
☎ (0228) 76591
Hours vary
Jennings Mild, Bitter Ⓗ
Traditional pub with friendly locals. Skilfully enlarged and refurbished to retain its character. Family room lunchtimes only. ▦ ⛧ ৬ ♣ P

Morland

Kings Arms
Ware Street
☎ (093 14) 328
11–3, 6–11
Marston's Burton Best Bitter, Pedigree Ⓗ
Excellent pub with the friendliest licensees you could wish to meet. A resting place on the Cumberland Way, with camping close by. Meals most of the day. ⛧ ◖ ◗ Å ♣

Newby Bridge

Newby Bridge Hotel
☎ (053 95) 31222
11–11 (12–2.30, 7–10.30 Sun)
Ind Coope Burton Ale; Jennings Bitter; Tetley Bitter Ⓗ
Welcoming pub on the edge of the Lakes; an ideally situated watering hole on the southern tip of Lake Windermere. Marvellous open fire. ▦ ◖ ◗ ৬ Å P

Ousby

Fox Inn
Off A686, Penrith–Melmerby road ☎ (0768) 881374
12–3 (not Mon–Fri in winter), 6–11
Theakston Best Bitter, XB Ⓗ
Tastefully modernised, village inn, slightly off the beaten track but worth the effort to find. Large selection of home-cooked meals available; camping and caravan site at rear; large car park and two donkeys! ▦ Q ⬛ ⋈ ◖ ◗ Å ♣ P

Patterdale

White Lion Hotel
☎ (076 84) 82214
11–11
Whitbread Boddingtons Bitter, Castle Eden Ale Ⓗ
Pub situated near Lake Ullswater: walkers welcome. Excellent food. ⋈ ◖ ◗ Å ♣ ↺

Penrith

Lowther Arms
Queen Street ☎ (0768) 62792
11–2.30, 7–11
Theakston Best Bitter, XB Ⓗ
Cosy, country-style pub in the town centre. Good lunchtime food (eve meals 7–8pm summer only). ▦ Q ◖ ◗ ৬ Å ≋ ♣

Red Dial

Sun Inn
On A595, halfway between Carlisle and Cockermouth
☎ (069 73) 42167
12–2 (not Mon), 6–11
Jennings Bitter; Tetley Bitter Ⓗ
Excellent, roadside inn which has been tastefully extended. The food is highly recommended and is very good value, freshly cooked and served in the restaurant or bar. Beware of the real coal fire in the middle of a heat wave! Separate pool room. The guest beer varies. ▦ ⬛ ⋈ ◖ ◗ Å ♣ P

Rowrah

Stork Hotel
Rowrah Road (A5086)
☎ (0946) 861213
11–3, 6–11
Jennings Mild, Bitter, Cumberland Ale Ⓗ
Traditional, country pub with a field sports theme. Quiz league. ▦ ⬛ ⋈ ♣ P

St Bees

Queens Hotel
Main Street ☎ (0946) 822287
11–3, 5.30–11
McEwan 80/-; Theakston Best Bitter; Whitbread Boddingtons Bitter Ⓗ
Pub with a garden to the rear and a solarium and gymnasium in the basement. ⬛ ⋈ ◖ ◗ Å ≋ P

Sandwith

Dog & Partridge
☎ (0946) 692671
11–3, 6.30–11
Yates Bitter Ⓗ
Cosy, village pub over 250 years old, with several small rooms on different levels. The ghost of a bygone landlady, who banned all women, is reputed to jangle coins in her purse. Occasional guest beers. ▦ Q ⛧ ⬛ ◖ ◗ P

Scales

White Horse Inn
Set back from A66, Penrith–Keswick road
☎ (059 683) 241
11.30–2.30, 6.30–11 (11–3, 6–11 summer)
Jennings Bitter Ⓗ
Low, whitewashed building tucked neatly under the foot of Blencathra. A real fire burns at either end of the narrow, low-ceilinged lounge bar and a

warm, informal atmosphere prevails. Good, well-presented bar food (eve meals all week in summer; Fri–Sun in winter).
⛫ Q ◖ ◗ ♣ P

Try also: Mill Inn, Mungrisdale (Theakston)

Sedbergh

Dalesman
Main Street ☎ (053 96) 21183
11–11 (11–3, 6–11 winter)
Ind Coope Burton Ale; Tetley Walker Mild, Bitter Ⓗ
Popular, friendly, country inn, near the centre of this Dales market town. The Dales Way and Cumbria Cycleway pass nearby. A 16th-century building with original oak beams in evidence. Excellent value meals. Guest beer and a Tetley Walker house beer (Dalesman Bitter).
Q ❀ ⛟ ◖ ◗ ⛺ ♣ P

Red Lion
Finkle Street (near town centre)
☎ (053 96) 20433
11.30–3, 6.30–11
Marston's Mercian Mild, Burton Best Bitter, Pedigree Ⓗ
17th-century pub, popular with everybody. The absence of a jukebox makes for good conversation. An L-shaped bar and a covered beer garden at the rear. Q ❀ ◖ ◗ ⛺ ♣

Shap

Kings Arms
Main Street ☎ (097 16) 227
11–3, 6–11
Stones Best Bitter; Webster's Yorkshire Bitter, Wilson's Mild Ⓗ
Friendly local with a keen landlord and regular live music.
⛫ ⛟ ◗ P

Tallentire

Bush Inn
☎ (0900) 823707
11 (12 winter)–3, 6 (6.30 winter)–11
Theakston XB Ⓗ
Typical, rural village pub. No meals Tue. ⛫ ❀ ◖ ◗ ♿ ♣ P

Ulverston

Kings Head
Queens Street
☎ (0229) 52892
11–3 (5.30 Sat), 6 (6.30 Sat)–11 (11–11 Mon, Thu & Fri)
Theakston Best Bitter Ⓗ
Very popular pub, offering various guest beers, in the town which was the birthplace of Stan Laurel and which houses the only Stan Laurel museum.
⛫ ❀ ⛟ ◖ ⇌

Warcop

Chamley Arms
1 mile off A66, 7 miles E of Appleby ☎ (076 83) 41237
11–11
Marston's Burton Best Bitter, Pedigree Ⓗ
Pub busy with locals and visitors to the nearby military training area. A large collection of crests of visiting regiments adorns the public bar.
⛫ Q ♘ ❀ ◖ ◗ ⊟ ⛺ ♣

Warwick-on-Eden

Queens Arms Inn & Motel
☎ (0228) 60699
11–3, 5–11 (11–11 Sat)
Marston's Pedigree; Whitbread Boddingtons Bitter, Trophy, Castle Eden Ale Ⓗ
Attractive, 18th-century, roadside inn where a very warm, friendly welcome is assured. The open log fires and traditional furnishings contrive a perfect atmosphere for a convivial chat, whilst the children enjoy themselves in the adventure playground in the gardens. Separate restaurant.
⛫ Q ❀ ⛟ ◖ ◗ ♣ P

Wetheral

Crown Hotel
Station Road
☎ (0228) 61888
12–2, 5.30–11
Thwaites Bitter Ⓗ
Very comfortable hotel with excellent amenities, incl. a leisure club (with pool, squash, gym, etc.) and conference facilities. Tastefully decorated, the homely bar is popular with locals. Eve meals in the restaurant only.
❀ ⛟ ◖ ♿ ⇌ ♣ P

Whitehaven

Strand
37 New Lowther Street
☎ (0946) 65770
11–3, 7–11 (closed Sun lunch)
Whitbread Boddingtons Bitter, Castle Eden Ale; Younger Scotch Ⓗ
Busy, town-centre pub, popular with young people. Quizzes Tue eve at 9pm.
◖ ⇌ (Bransty) ♣

Try also: Central (S&N); **Welsh Arms** (Hartleys)

Wigton

Victoria
King Street
☎ (069 73) 42672
11–11
Jennings Mild, Bitter Ⓗ
Friendly and comfortable, two-roomed, town-centre pub, almost opposite the bus station.
♿ ⇌ ♣

Windermere

Grey Walls Hotel (Greys Inn)
Elleray Road (50 yds from A591) ☎ (096 62) 3741
11–11
Theakston Best Bitter, XB Ⓗ
Popular, village-centre pub noted for its jumbo-sized mixed grills. Food all day Sat; good value Sun lunch. Guest beer usually available.
⛫ ♘ ❀ ⛟ ◖ ◗ ⇌ ♣ P

Workington

Miners Arms
Guard Street ☎ (0900) 67216
11–3, 6–11 (12–3, 7.30–10.30 Sun)
S&N Matthew Brown Mild; Theakston Best Bitter, XB Ⓗ
Bustling, town-centre pub.
◖ ⇌ ♣ P

HARTLEYS RIP

In June 1991, Robinson's of Stockport announced that its Cumbrian subsidiary, Hartleys, was to close in November the same year. The Hartleys brewery, well known for its 'Beers from the Wood', was established in 1819 and fell under Robinson's control in 1982. The Hartleys beers available in the pubs above will now be brewed in Greater Manchester, rather than their true home of Ulverston, though how long they will survive is open to question.

Derbyshire

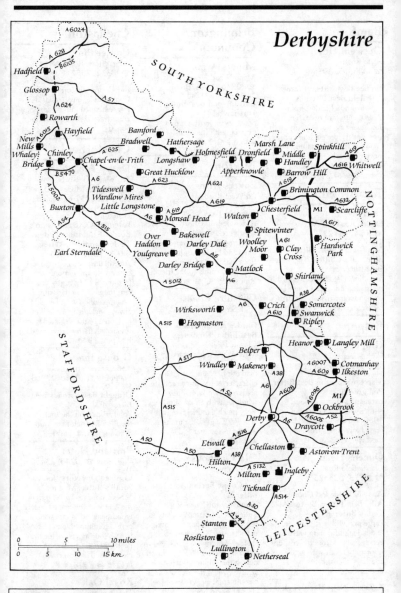

🏰 **Lloyds**, *Ingleby*

Apperknowle

Yellow Lion
High Street ☎ (0246) 413181
12–2 (3 Sat), 5–11
**Adnams Bitter; Stones Best
Bitter; Tetley Bitter** Ⓗ
Busy, stone-built, village free
house with a comfortable
lounge and a separate
restaurant. The extensive menu
includes vegetarian dishes.
Winner of several CAMRA

awards. Usually two guest
beers. Q 🕮 🍴 🍺 P

Try also: Barrack (John Smith's)

Aston-on-Trent

Malt Shovel
The Green ☎ (0332) 792256
11.30–3, 6–11
**Ansells Bitter; Ind Coope
Burton Ale; Marston's
Pedigree** Ⓗ
Busy pub with a friendly

lounge. Good food every day.
Patio. 🕮 🍴 ♣ P

Bakewell

Manners
Haddon Road
☎ (0629) 812756
11–11
Robinson's Best Bitter Ⓔ
Friendly local a short distance
from the centre of this busy
market town.
🏠 🕮 🛏 🍴 🕮 Å ♣ P

79

Derbyshire

Bamford

Derwent Hotel
Main Road
☎ (0433) 51395
11–11
Stones Best Bitter; Wards Sheffield Best Bitter ⊞
Country hotel dating from 1890, with tap room, two lounge areas and a dining room (reasonably-priced, home-made food). A friendly and unspoilt haven in the heart of the Peak District tourist area. Guest beers. ⏳ ⑧ ⇔ ◖ ▮ ⊞ Å ≉ ♣ P

Barrow Hill

Barrow
Station Road (off A619)
☎ (0246) 472277
11–11
Mansfield Riding Bitter; Stones Best Bitter; Theakston Best Bitter ⊞
Traditional, Victorian local with unusual graffiti. Four guest beers on handpump. Meals for parties by arrangement. ⏳ ⊟ ♣ ○ P

Belper

Grapes
High Street
☎ (0773) 826928
11–3, 5.30–11 (11–11 Fri)
Marston's Burton Best Bitter, Pedigree ⊞
Excellent, stone-built local, attractively modernised in 1980. An unusual collection of brass blow lamps features. No food weekends. ▦ ◖ P

Queens Head
Chesterfield Road
☎ (0773) 825525
11.30–11
Ansells Mild; Ind Coope ABC Best Bitter, Burton Ale; Tetley Bitter ⊞
Large pub with a roomy lounge and a delightful snug with bench seats. Across the corridor is a family room with a jukebox and toys. Guest beers.
▦ ⏳ ⑧ ◖ ♣

Try also: Nags Head, High Pavement (Mansfield)

Bradwell

New Bath Hotel
Stretfield Road (B6049)
☎ (0433) 20431
12–4, 7–11 (11–11 Sat)
Marston's Burton Best Bitter, Pedigree; Stones Best Bitter ⊞
Attractive country pub in a pleasant setting, with a view of Bradwell Edge. Homely bar with adjacent pool room and cosy lounge. Regular live music.
▦ ⑧ ⇔ ◖ ▮ Å ♣ P

Brimington Common

Miners Arms
Manor Road
☎ (0246) 234870
11–3, 7–11 (11–11 Sat)
Burtonwood Best Bitter, Forshaw's ⊞
Small, clean, well-run pub, popular with the locals.
⑧ ⇔ ◖ ▮ ⊟ ♣ P

Buxton

Bakers Arms
26 West Road
12–3, 6 (7 Sat)–11
Draught Bass ⒠
A double-fronted, stone cottage, worth seeking out. The two small rooms are cramped when busy and the lack of interference from machines of any description adds to the friendly atmosphere. Q ⊟ ≉ ♣ P

Cheshire Cheese
High Street ☎ (0298) 25371
11–11
Hardys & Hansons Best Mild, Best Bitter, Kimberley Classic ⊞
Refurbished some years ago, this stone-built pub, close to the market place, still has great character. It has three separate areas and two seated bay windows with an air of privacy. Very much a music pub, with jazz, R&B and skiffle in the garden in summer.
▦ ⑧ ◖ ▮ ≉ ♣ P

Old Clubhouse
Water Street
11–11
Ind Coope Burton Ale; Tetley Bitter ⊞
Originally the Duke of Rutland's Gentlemen's Club, as reflected in the spacious lounge with its easy chairs and book shelves. Impressive stairs lead to the snug. Water Street is closed during the summer Buxton Festival, when the area assumes a continental air. Views of the elegant opera house.
▦ ⑧ ◖ ▮ ≉ ♣

Chapel-en-le-Frith

Roebuck
Market Place
☎ (0298) 812274
11–3, 5–11
Tetley Mild, Bitter ⊞
Lounge with separate games room and eating area. Full of character, with oak beams and an unusual wooden bar. No music ensures good local gossip. The old Chapel stocks are opposite on the market place.
▦ Q ◖ ⊟ ♣

Chellaston

Corner Pin
Swarkestone Road (A514)
☎ (0332) 705715
11–11
Ind Coope Burton Ale ⊞
Comfortable, busy, roadside pub, extended into an adjoining cruck-framed cottage. No food Sun. ◖ P

Chesterfield

Derby Tup
387 Sheffield Road, Whittington Moor (400 yds S of A61/B6052 roundabout)
☎ (0246) 454316
11.30–3, 5–11
Bateman XXXB; Marston's Border Exhibition, Pedigree; Taylor Landlord; Tetley Bitter; Theakston XB ⊞
Superb, unspoilt, corner free house with three rooms. The landlord is a big rugby union fan; the pub dog (Hoskins) is very friendly. Guest beers always include a mild. All meats and most of the vegetables are organically farmed. Eve meals till 8pm. ◖ ▮ ♣ ○

Grouse Inn
136 Chatsworth Road, Brampton ☎ (0246) 279632
12–3, 6.30–11
Draught Bass; Stones Best Bitter ⊞
Popular local on the route to the Peak District. Rear yard drinking area. ⑧ ◖ ♣ ♣ P

Portland Hotel
West Bars ☎ (0246) 234502
11–3, 5.30–11
Courage Directors; John Smith's Bitter, Magnet ⊞
Mock Tudor (c. 1899) pub in the centre of the market square; wood-panelled lounges and period furniture. No lunches Sun. A touring centre for the Peak District, Chatsworth House and Haddon Hall.
▦ Q ⑧ ⇔ ◖ ▮ ⊟ ≉ P

Royal Oak
The Shambles (by market place)
☎ (0246) 205508
11–3, 7–11
Stones Best Bitter ⊞
One of the oldest buildings in the town, this remarkable 13th-century, half-timbered inn has an interesting bar, entered by the higher door. ◖ ⊟ ♣ ♣

Victoria Inn
Victoria Street West, Brampton (off A619, Chatsworth Road)
☎ (0246) 273832
12–4, 7–11
Vaux Samson; Wards Thorne Best Bitter, Sheffield Best Bitter, Kirby ⊞
Two-roomed, traditional local

with a warm welcome. A real fire burns in the best room. Guest beers from the Vaux group. ▲ 🏠 🍴 ♣ P

Chinley

Squirrels
Green Lane ☎ (0663) 750001
11–11
**Ind Coope Burton Ale;
Lloyds Derby Bitter; Tetley
Mild, Bitter** 🅗
Impressive, three-storey, stone-built hotel, imposing at first but with a warm welcome inside. Recently enlarged, with a comfortable lounge bar/dining area, leaving the original bar to take on the role of a vault. Two guest beers.
🏠 ⚲ ◖ 🍴 🅔 ⚘ Å ♣ ♣ 🕒 P

Clay Cross

Cannon
4 Thanet Street (off A61)
☎ (0246) 250078
12–3, 7–11
**Courage Directors; John
Smith's Magnet** 🅗
Mock Tudor pub and restaurant, taken over as a family concern in 1988 and well refurbished under the supervision of the landlord, a former master builder. Live music some nights, with quiz every Tue. 🏠 ◖ 🍴 P

Queens
113 Thanet Street (300 yds E of A61 traffic lights)
☎ (0246) 862348
12–3, 7–11
**Stones Best Bitter; Tetley
Bitter** 🅔
Typical local with a friendly atmosphere. Comfortable lounge; lively public bar; children's room leading onto a patio. Attractive hanging baskets in summer. 🕒 🏠 🍴 ♣ P

Cotmanhay

Bridge Inn
Bridge Street (off A6007)
☎ (0602) 322589
11–11
**Hardys & Hansons Best Mild,
Best Bitter** 🅔
Traditional, village local adjacent to the Erewash Canal; popular with fishermen and locals alike. The landlord is a real character who permits no swearing in the bar – a rare find indeed. Q 🏠 🅔 ♣ P

Crich

Cliff Inn
Cromford Road OS350545
☎ (077 385) 2444
11–3, 6–11
**Hardys & Hansons Best Mild,
Best Bitter, Kimberley
Classic** 🅗

Popular, stone-built local with two small rooms. Not far from the National Tramway Museum. 🏠 ◖ 🅔 P

Darley Bridge

Three Stags Heads
Main Road
☎ (0629) 732358
12–3, 6–11 (12–11 Sat)
**Hardys & Hansons Best Mild,
Best Bitter, Kimberley
Classic** 🅗
Olde-worlde pub with traditional decor, a homely atmosphere and a friendly welcome. The interesting initials over the side door – GOG (apparently meaning 'Go out quietly') date from the 18th-century, when the local hunt met here. East Midlands *Landlady of Year 1990*.
▲ Q 🏠 ◖ Å ♣ P

Darley Dale

Grouse Inn
Dale Road North (A6)
☎ (0629) 732297
12–3, 7–11
**Hardys & Hansons Best Mild,
Best Bitter, Kimberley
Classic** 🅗
Roadside local recently renovated by the brewery but still in keeping with a traditional pub. Good selection of lunchtime meals. Popular with all ages and handy for tourists with its large car park on the A6. Darts, dominoes played: a sporting pub. ▲ 🏠 ◖ ♣ P

Derby

Alexandra Hotel
203 Siddals Road
☎ (0332) 293993
11–3, 4.30–11
**Bateman Mild, XB, XXXB,
Victory; Marston's
Pedigree** 🅗
Pub with very pleasing, subtle decor, wooden floors and a friendly atmosphere. Bottled beer collection in the bar. Guest beers and ciders. No food Sun.
🏠 ◖ 🍴 ⚲ ♣ 🕒 P

Baseball Hotel
Shaftsbury Crescent (next to football ground)
☎ (0332) 44080
12–3, 7–11 (11–11 Sat match days)
**Adnams Bitter; Draught
Bass; M&B Highgate Mild;
Marston's Pedigree; Stones
Best Bitter** 🅗
Two-roomed pub with an unusual Victorian bar area in a very long front bar; large, smart, comfortable lounge. Function room available. Guest beers. ⚲ ◖ 🍴 ♣ P

Bell & Castle
Burton Road ☎ (0332) 42548
11–3, 6–11 (11–11 Sat)
**Banks's Mild; Draught
Bass** 🅗
Terrace of three stockingers cottages, built in the late 18th century and now converted into a public house. A Grade II listed building. Q 🅔 ♣

Boaters Bar &
Restaurant
17 Friargate
☎ (0332) 40581
11–2.30, 7–11
**Taylor Landlord; Wards
Thorne Best Bitter, Kirby** 🅗
Former restaurant now converted into a bar and dining room. Built c. 1650.

Brick & Tile
1 Brick Street (off Friargate)
☎ (0332) 45076
11–2.30, 7–11
**Ind Coope Burton Ale;
Marston's Pedigree** 🅗
Old, beamed building, dating from the 17th century. Exposed hand-made-brickwork, both inside and out. 🏠 ♣

Brunswick Inn
1 Railway Terrace
☎ (0332) 290677
11–11
Hook Norton Old Hooky 🅖;
**Marston's Pedigree; Taylor
Landlord** 🅗; **Theakston Old
Peculier** 🅗; **Wards Sheffield
Best Bitter, Kirby** 🅗
The oldest (1842) purpose-build railway pub in the world which retains its stone-flagged floor. No-smoking room always open. CAMRA East Midlands *Pub of the Year 1989 and 1990*. Various guest beers and draught cider always available.
Q 🕒 ◖ ⚲ ♣ 🕒 ✗

Crompton Tavern
43 Crompton Street
☎ (0332) 292259
11–11
**Wards Thorne Best Bitter,
Sheffield Best Bitter** 🅗
U-shaped room, catering for young people. Regular live music and entertainment. Guest beers in rotation. ◖ ♣

Dolphin Inn
Queen Street (200 yds from cathedral) ☎ (0332) 49115
11–11
**Draught Bass; M&B Mild,
Springfield Bitter; Stones
Best Bitter; Welsh Brewers
Worthington BB** 🅗
The most picturesque and oldest surviving pub in the city. Built in the same year as the cathedral tower (1530) in whose shadow it stands. One of the four rooms is devoted to memorabilia of a former local brewery. Guest beers. Q 🏠 ◖ 🍴 🅔 ♣ P

81

Derbyshire

Exeter Arms
Exeter Place ☎ (0332) 46679
11–3, 6–11
Marston's Pedigree Ⓗ
Small, basic, locals' pub which
was extensively altered and
enlarged in 1985. The last
Derby pub to cease brewing.
No food Sun. ▦ Q ⑧ ◖

Furnace
Duke Street ☎ (0332) 31563
11–3, 6–11
**Hardys & Hansons Best
Mild** Ⓗ, **Best Bitter** Ⓔ,
Kimberley Classic Ⓗ
Popular pub with an open-plan
interior and photographs of
bygone Derby. Close to St
Mary's Bridge and the historic
Bridge Chapel. ⑧ ♣

Strutts
73 London Road
☎ (0332) 44421
11–11
**Mansfield Riding Mild,
Riding Bitter, Old Baily** Ⓗ
One large lounge with 1920s
style decor, catering for the
youngest clientele. ⑧ ◖ ⇌ P

Vine Inn
37 Whittaker Street (off
Normanton Road, via Rose Hill
Street) ☎ (0332) 41473
11–3 (4 Fri & Sat), 7–11
**Draught Bass; M&B
Highgate Mild** Ⓗ
Long-established, back-street
local in a redeveloped area;
popular with all sections of a
mixed community. Offiler's
brewery started here in 1886.
Ⓔ ♣

Woodlark
80 Bridge Street (off Friargate)
☎ (0332) 32910
11.30–2.30, 6 (7.30 Sat)–11
**Draught Bass; M&B
Highgate Mild** Ⓗ
Former home-brew pub, built in
the early 19th century. Small
bar and large lounge, with
highly polished, brass-topped
tables. ♣

Try also: Great Northern,
Junction St (Ansells)

Draycott

Travellers Rest
Derby Road ☎ (033 17) 2332
11–2.30, 6–11
Marston's Pedigree Ⓗ
Modernised, double-fronted,
Victorian local with a separate
games room and skittle alley.
Ⓔ ♣ P

Dronfield

Old Sidings
91 Chesterfield Road
☎ (0246) 410023
12–11
**Vaux Samson; Wards Thorne
Best Bitter, Sheffield Best
Bitter** Ⓗ

Lively pub with an L-shaped
lounge on two levels;
comfortably furnished with a
railway theme. Eve meals in the
basement restaurant. Guest
beers. ◖ ⇌ ♣ P

Earl Sterndale

Quiet Woman
☎ (029 883) 211
11–3, 5.30–11
**Marston's Mercian Mild,
Burton Best Bitter,
Pedigree** Ⓗ
A superb example of a village
local, overlooking the village
green. Situated on the White
Peak Way. ▦ Ⓔ ♣ P

Etwall

Hawk & Buckle
Main Street ☎ (0283) 733471
11.30–2.30, 7–11
Marston's Pedigree Ⓗ
Smart, modernised village local
with a comfortable lounge and a
bar with a games area. Easier
parking opposite. ▦ ⑧ Ⓔ ♣ P

Glossop

Crown Inn
142 Victoria Street
☎ (0457) 862824
12–3, 5–11 (12–11 Fri & Sat)
Samuel Smith OBB Ⓗ
A true local with two small
'snugs', an active games room
and an attractive central bar.
▦ Q ⛴ ⑧ ♣

Fleece Inn
1 Bernard Street
☎ (0457) 865203
12–3, 6–11 (12–11 Fri & Sat)
**Taylor Landlord; Tetley
Bitter; Wadworth 6X** Ⓗ
Red-brick free house with an
original black and white tiled
floor and a red GPO phone box
in the corner. Two bar areas and
a games room. Very popular
live R&B/rock music on
Thu/Fri nights. Guest beers at
weekends. ▦ ⑧ ⇌

Surrey Arms
133 Victoria Street
☎ (0457) 853192
11.30–11
**Theakston Best Bitter;
Whitbread Boddingtons
Bitter** Ⓗ
Comfortably furnished lounge
with a small, thriving tap room.
Very friendly with a strong
local atmosphere. Ⓔ ⇌ ♣

Great Hucklow

Queen Anne
On B6049 ☎ (0298) 871246
12–3 (Sat only), 7–11
**Bass Mild XXXX; Stones Best
Bitter** Ⓗ
Warm, friendly, village local
with a tiny tap room. The

lounge is on two levels and
doubles as a dining room. Note:
closed Mon–Fri lunchtime.
▦ Q ⑧ ◖ ◗ Ⓔ ♣ P

Hadfield

Palatine Hotel
133 Station Road
☎ (0457) 852459
1 (12 Sat)–11
**Robinson's Mild, Best Bitter,
Old Tom** Ⓗ
Pub with a wooden-clad interior
and a warm and welcoming
atmosphere. Its proximity to
Hadfield railway station and bus
terminus ensures steady custom
all day. Old Tom is sold all year
round. ▦ ⛴ Ⓔ ⇌ ♣ P

Hardwick Park

Hardwick Inn
1 mile S of M1 jct 29
☎ (0246) 850245
11.30–3, 6.30–11
**Theakston XB; Younger
Scotch** Ⓗ
17th-century inn owned by the
National Trust. At the gates to
Hardwick Hall. No meals Sun
eve. ▦ ⛴ ⑧ ◖ ◗ P

Hathersage

Plough Inn
Leadmill Bridge (B6001, 1 mile
from village) ☎ (0433) 50319
11.45–3, 7–11 (11.45–11 Sat)
Stones Best Bitter Ⓔ
Comfortable pub converted
from a farmhouse on the banks
of the River Derwent. Strong
local trade but visitors are
always welcomed. Spacious,
split-level lounge and small,
intimate tap room.
▦ Q ⑧ ◖ ◗ Ⓔ Ⓐ ⇌ ♣ P

Hayfield

George
Church Street ☎ (0663) 43691
11–3, 5.30–11
Burtonwood Best Bitter Ⓗ
Quaint, old, stone pub with
stained-glass, and beamed
ceilings. An ideal base for
walking in the Kinder Scout area
of High Peak. ▦ ◖ P

Sportsman
Kinder Road (½ mile from
centre; follow campsite signs)
☎ (0663) 742118
6–11 (may extend Sat & summer)
Thwaites Best Mild, Bitter Ⓗ
Pleasant, spacious pub on the
road to Kinder Scout. A good
selection of food is available and
there is an upstairs room for
families. ▦ ⛴ ⇔ ◖ ◗ Ⓐ ♣ P

Heanor

Crown Inn
Church Street
☎ (0773) 712006

11–3, 7–11
Hardys & Hansons Best Mild, Best Bitter, Kimberley Classic [H]
Original, homely, roadside pub, built in 1909: a friendly public bar and a cosy, intimate lounge. Separate upstairs dining room. Limited parking. ❀ ⊨ ◐ ⊟ ♣

New Inn
107 Derby Road
☎ (0773) 719609
11–4, 7–11
Home Mild, Bitter [E]
Popular and friendly, compact local on Tag Hill. ❀ ◐ ⊟ ♣ P

Try also: Derby Arms, High St (Home)

Hilton

Old Talbot
Main Street ☎ (028 373) 3728
12–2.30, 7–11
Draught Bass [H]
Friendly, two-roomed, village local with a good atmosphere. Garden for summer drinking.
⌂ Q ❀ ◐ ⊟ ♣ P

Hognaston

Red Lion
Main Street ☎ (0335) 370396
11–3, 6–11
Marston's Pedigree [H]
Typical, upland village pub; one U-shaped room, warm and friendly. Also sells eggs and cheese. Families welcome in the pool room. ⌂ ◐ ◑ ♣ P

Holmesfield

Travellers Rest
20 Main Road
☎ (0742) 890446
12–4, 7–11
Home Bitter; Younger No. 3 [H]
Pleasant, two-room pub with pool in the tap room and a comfortable, if somewhat spartan, lounge. Occasional live music. ❀ ⊟ ⅄ ♣ P

Ilkeston

Durham Ox
Durham Street (off A6007/B6096)
☎ (0602) 324570
11–4, 6–11 (11–11 Sat)
Wards Mild, Thorne Best Bitter, Sheffield Best Bitter [E]&[H]
Busy, popular, back-street pub with an open-plan interior and a separate pool area. Cheap B&B. Real ale beef casserole is always available. Sun night quiz; occasional guest beer. Has been in every edition of this guide. Knock on side window if not open on time. ⌂ ❀ ⊨ ◐ ♣ P

Poplar
117 Bath Street (A6007)
☎ (0602) 324574
12–4, 7–11
Mansfield Riding Bitter; Tetley Bitter [H]
Deceptively large, town pub with front and rear snugs, and two pool tables. Some nice ornamental features. Loud disco Fri–Sat eves. ⌂ ◐ ⊟ ♣ P

Langley Mill

Railway Tavern
188 Station Road
☎ (0773) 764711
11–4, 6 (7 Sat)–11
Home Mild, Bitter [E]
Popular, roadside inn; efficiently run to a high standard. Displays a collection of ornamental cats. Regular weekend organist; steak night every Thu (eve meals Tue, Thu and Fri only).
❀ ◐ ◑ ⊟ ⇌ ♣ P

Little Longstone

Packhorse
Main Street ☎ (0629) 640471
11–3, 5 (6 Sat)–11
Marston's Burton Best Bitter, Pedigree [H]
Ancient, unspoilt, village local which has been a pub since 1787. Small, comfortable lounge and a tap room well used by ramblers.
⌂ Q ❀ ◐ ◑ ⅄ ♣

Longshaw

Grouse
On B6054 ☎ (0433) 30423
12–3, 7–11
Vaux Lorimers Best Scotch; Wards Sheffield Best Bitter, Kirby [H]
Originally built as a farmhouse in 1804 and the hayloft, barn doors and stone trough survive. A comfortable lounge at the front leads to a conservatory overhung with vines, and an adjoining tap room. No food Mon/Tue. ⌂ Q ❀ ◐ ◑ ⊟ ♣ P

Lullington

Colvile Arms
Coton Road ☎ (082 786) 212
7–11 (11–3, 7–11 Sat)
Draught Bass; Marston's Pedigree [H]
18th-century, village pub, the most southerly in the county; a basic, wood-panelled bar, a smart lounge and a separate games/meetings room. Bowling green in the garden. ⌂ ❀ ⊟ ♣ P

Makeney

Holly Bush Inn
Holly Bush Lane OS352447
☎ (0332) 841729
12–3, 6–11 (11–11 Sat)
Marston's Pedigree, Owd Rodger; Ruddles County; Theakston Old Peculier [H]&[G]
Old pub with many rooms, housed in Grade II listed buildings. Beer is brought up from the cellar in jugs. Guest beers. ⌂ Q ⛀ ❀ ⊨ ◐ ◑ ♣ P

Marsh Lane

Fox & Hounds
Main Road (B6056)
☎ (0246) 432974
12–3, 7–11
Burtonwood Best Bitter, Forshaw's [H]
Comfortable lounge and traditional tap room. Large beer garden and play area, alongside a good-sized car park.
⌂ ❀ ◐ ◑ ⊟ ♣ P

Matlock

Sycamore
9 Sycamore Road (up hill from Crown Square, left by county offices, 400 yds)
☎ (0629) 57585
11–3.30, 6 (7 Sat)–11
Draught Bass [H]
Comfortable, traditional pub away from the bustle of the town. No food Sun.
Q ❀ ◐ ⊟ ♣ P

Thorn Tree
48 Jackson Road (hill behind county offices)
☎ (0629) 582923
11.30–3, 7–11
Draught Bass; Mansfield Old Baily [H]
Small, unspoilt local, popular with office workers and darts players. Fine atmosphere and a friendly welcome. Worth searching out. No food Sun.
Q ❀ ◐ ⊟ ♣

White Lion
Starkholmes Road
☎ (0629) 582511
11.45 (11.30 Sat)–3, 6.30–11
Home Bitter; Theakston XB [H]
Olde-English pub, part of which used to be a cottage and still retains character. Just off the tourist routes with an excellent view of Matlock Bath and near playing fields. A keen sporting pub, also offering a good variety of meals, incl. specials.
Q ⛀ ❀ ◐ ♣ P

Middle Handley

Devonshire Arms
Westfield Lane (off B6052)
☎ (0246) 432189
11–3, 7–11
Stones Best Bitter [H]
Friendly and popular, village local with a central bar.
Q ❀ ♣ P

Derbyshire

Milton

Swan Inn
Main Street ☎ (0283) 703188
12–3, 7–11
Marston's Pedigree Ⓗ
Popular, village pub with a
smart lounge and a locals' bar.
No food Sun eve or Mon.
🏠 ◖ ▶ ◓ ♣ P

Monsal Head

Monsal Head Hotel
☎ (062 987) 250
11–11
**John Smith's Bitter;
Theakston Old Peculier** Ⓗ
150 year-old, country hotel
with an elegant, genteel lounge
in the main building. Most of
the real ales are in the rear bar,
which was once stables for the
long-gone Bulls Head. It now
features an inglenook, stall
seating and a manger. The
house beer is brewed by Lloyds.
Guest beers.
🏠 Q 🕯 ⋈ ◖ ◗ ◓ Å ♣ ⌂ P

Netherseal

Hollybush Inn
15 Main Street
☎ (0283) 760390
11–2.30 (3 Sat), 6–11
Marston's Pedigree Ⓗ
Village pub dating back to the
17th century or earlier.
Modified internally with a small
extension retaining the original,
beamed features. Meals served
in the lounge and separate
restaurant. ◖ ▶ ◓ ♣ P

New Mills

Crescent
Market Street
☎ (0663) 743889
11–3, 5.30–11
Tetley Mild, Bitter Ⓗ
Attractive, stone-fronted, town-
centre pub, handy for the Sett
Valley Trail and the Torrs.
◖ ▶ ◓ ⇌ (Central) ♣

Fox Inn
Brookbottom (end of High Lea
Road, off St Marys Road)
11–3, 5.30–11 (may vary)
**Robinson's Mild, Best
Bitter** Ⓗ
Old, white pub in a small
hamlet: a comfortable, beamed
lounge and a basic games room.
Enjoys an isolated location
along a single-track road.
Access (on foot only) from
Strines station.
🏠 🕯 ◖ ▶ ⇌ (Strines) ♣ P

Ockbrook

Royal Oak
Green Lane ☎ (0332) 662378
11–3, 6–11
Draught Bass Ⓗ

Characterful, village meeting
place with four small rooms. No
food Sun. 🏠 Q 🕯 ◖ ◓ ♣ P

Over Haddon

Lathkill Hotel
½ mile SW of B5055
☎ (0629) 812501
11.30–3, 6–11
**Wards Mild, Thorne Best
Bitter, Sheffield Best Bitter** Ⓗ
Free house in an idyllic setting,
overlooking one of the Peak's
most picturesque dales; a fine,
oak-panelled bar with
traditional-style leather and
wood furnishings. Excellent
food. Children welcome at
lunchtimes. 🏠 🕯 ⋈ ◖ ▶ ◓ Å P

Ripley

Three Horseshoes
Market Place ☎ (0773) 743113
11–3 (4 Sat), 5 (7 Sat)–11
Vaux Samson Ⓗ**; Wards
Mild** Ⓔ**, Sheffield Best
Bitter** Ⓗ
Market town-centre pub in
open-plan style. Guest beers.
Parking on the market place.
◖ ♣

Rosliston

Plough Inn
Main Street ☎ (0283) 761354
11.30–2.30, 6.30–11
**Marston's Pedigree, Owd
Rodger** Ⓗ
18th-century, village pub with
attractive black and white
exterior, adorned with hanging
baskets and flower-filled
troughs. An H-shaped drinking
area, with low ceilings, provides
a cosy atmosphere. Car parking
at the front and at the rear. No
food Sun. 🏠 ⍢ 🕯 ◖ ♣ P

Rowarth

Little Mill Inn
Signed off Siloh Road
OS011891 ☎ (0663) 743178
11–3, 5.30–11
**Banks's Bitter; Hanson's
Bitter; Robinson's Best
Bitter** Ⓗ
Busy, convivial pub serving
good, home-made food. A
veritable adventure park for
children. Separate restaurant.
Belgian bottled beers and one
guest ale. 🏠 Q ⍢ 🕯 ◖ ▶ Å P

Scarcliffe

Horse & Groom
Mansfield Road
☎ (0246) 823152
12–3.30, 7–11
Home Bitter Ⓗ
Beamed coaching inn with a
children's play area to the rear.
Eve meals by arrangement only.
🏠 Q 🕯 ◖ ◓ ♣ P

Shirland

Duke of Wellington
Main Road ☎ (0773) 833256
12–3, 7–11
Home Bitter Ⓔ
Busy, roadside pub with a cosy
lounge and a large tap room.
🏠 Q 🕯 ◓ ♣ P

Somercotes

Horse & Jockey
Leabrooks Road
☎ (0773) 602179
11–3, 7–11
Home Bitter, Mild Ⓗ
Popular, unspoilt local with
many rooms. Parking can be
difficult. 🏠 Q 🕯 ◓ ♣

Spinkhill

Angel Hotel
26 College Road
☎ (0246) 432315
12–3, 7–11
Tetley Bitter Ⓗ
Large, rambling, village local
and country inn; a comfortable,
L-shaped lounge with a separate
restaurant/function room.
Games room with snooker table
in the basement. Guest beers.
🏠 Q 🕯 ⋈ ◖ ▶ ♣ P

Spitewinter

Three Horse Shoes
Matlock Road (A632)
☎ (0246) 568034
11.30–11 (11–4, 7–11 Sat)
**Mansfield Riding Mild,
Riding Bitter, Old Baily** Ⓗ.
A quaint, country hostelry with
two rooms and a separate
dining room which serves
excellent value-for-money food
(incl. vegetarian).
🏠 Q 🕯 ◖ ▶ ◓ P

Stanton

Gate Inn
Woodlands Road
☎ (0283) 216818
11–3, 6–11
Marston's Pedigree Ⓗ
Comfortable and popular pub
where the landlord makes you
very welcome. The beer garden
has a children's play area. Good
food (no meals Sun).
🕯 ◖ ▶ ◓ ♣ P

Swanwick

Boot & Slipper
The Green ☎ (0773) 606052
11–3, 7–11
**Mansfield Riding Mild,
Riding Bitter** Ⓗ
Friendly, one-roomed, old-
fashioned local. Food Tue–Sat
only. 🏠 ◖ ♣ P

Gate Inn

The Delves (E of A61, via The
Green) ☎ (0773) 602039
11.30–3, 7–11
**Courage Best Bitter,
Directors; John Smith's
Bitter** Ⓗ
Smart, open-plan pub with bar,
lounge and restaurant areas. No
food Mon eve or Sun.
⊛ ◖ ♣ P

Ticknall

Chequers

27 High Street
☎ (0332) 864392
12–2.30, 6–11
**Marston's Pedigree; Ruddles
County** Ⓗ
Small and friendly local offering
many games, incl. bar billiards.
⊛ ♣ P

Tideswell

Anchor Inn

Four Lane Ends (A623/B6049)
☎ (0298) 871371
11–3, 6–11
**Hartleys Mild, XB;
Robinson's Mild, Best
Bitter** Ⓗ&Ⓔ
500 year-old pub on a crossroads: a traditional tap room
with a dartboard, and a
spacious, oak-panelled lounge
with a dining room at the rear.
🏚 Q ⊛ ◖ 🖛 Ⓖ ⚶ ♣ P

George Hotel

Commercial Road (next to
church) ☎ (0298) 871382
11–3, 7–11
**Hardys & Hansons Best Mild,
Best Bitter** Ⓗ
Stone-built, country hotel in the
centre of the village: a
comfortable lounge, with a
dining room off, and small snug,
leading to a tap room, which
has a dartboard and pool table.
🏚 Q ⊛ 🖛 ◖ 🖜 Ⓖ ♣ P

Try also: Horse & Jockey
(Tetley)

Walton

White Hart Inn

Matlock Road (B6015)
☎ (0246) 566392
11–3, 5–11
**Courage Directors; John
Smith's Bitter** Ⓗ
Pleasantly-situated, roadside inn
with a vast outdoor drinking
and children's play area, ideal
for summer eves. Noted for its
food (not available Sun eve).
Welcoming fire in winter.
🏚 ⊛ ◖ ♣ P

Wardlow Mires

Three Stags Head

At A623/B6465 jct
☎ (0298) 872268

5.30 (7 Mon)–11 (11–11 Sat &
summer; 7–11 summer Mon)
**Theakston Old Peculier;
Younger Scotch, No. 3** Ⓗ
Carefully restored, 17th-century
farmhouse pub. Two rooms: the
bar is heated by an ancient
cooking range, which is still
used for meals. Popular with
hikers; dogs welcome. Live
music occasionally. Note
restricted opening in winter.
🏚 Q ⊛ ◖ ⚶ ♣ P

Whaley Bridge

Navigation

Johnson Street
☎ (0663) 732308
11–11 (11–3, 5.30–11 winter)
**Whitbread Chester's Mild,
Boddingtons Bitter** Ⓗ
Double-fronted, stone pub,
tucked away amongst rows of
terraced houses. Close to the
terminus of the Peak Forest
Canal and a short walk from the
station. No food Sun.
⊛ ◖ Ⓐ ≠ ♣ P

Shepherds Arms

7 Old Road ☎ (0663) 732384
11–3, 7–11
**Marston's Mercian Mild,
Burton Best Bitter,
Pedigree** Ⓗ
Excellent, ageless local, perched
above the main road through
Whaley Bridge. The lounge is
dimly lit and quiet, in stark
contrast with the excellent
vault, with its stone-flagged
floor, unvarnished tables and
settle seats and stools. Food
Wed–Sun. 🏚 ⊛ ◖ Ⓐ ≠ ♣ P

Whitwell

Jug & Glass

Portland Street
☎ (0909) 720289
11–3, 6.30–11
**John Smith's Bitter,
Magnet** Ⓗ
Compact pub in the village
centre. Garden for summer
drinking. 🏚 ⊛ ⚶ ♣ P

Windley

Puss in Boots

Nether Lane OS294464
☎ (0773) 89316
11–3, 6–11
**Draught Bass; Marston's
Pedigree** Ⓗ
Isolated, characterful pub with a
low, beamed ceiling and a large
beer garden. No food Sun.
🏚 ⊛ ◖ ◗ ♣ P

Wirksworth

Blacks Head

Market Place ☎ (0629) 823257
11–3, 6–11 (11–11 Sat)
**Hardys & Hansons Best Mild,
Best Bitter, Kimberley
Classic** Ⓗ

One-roomed pub in the market
place. Children admitted.
Parking in the square.

George

8 Coldwell Street
☎ (0629) 822215
11–2.30, 7–11 (closed Sun lunchtime)
**Ind Coope Burton Ale; Tetley
Bitter** Ⓗ
Olde-worlde, two-roomed pub
off the market place. Busy and
very friendly. ◖ 🖜 ♣ P

Hope & Anchor

Market Place
☎ (062 982) 4620
11–4, 7–11
Home Bitter Ⓔ
Old, stone-built pub with a
large bar and a small lounge,
dominated by a 17th-century
chimneypiece. A pub of great
historic interest. Parking in the
market place.
🏚 Q 🖛 ◖ 🖜 🖜 ♣

Wheatsheaf

60 St Johns Street
☎ (0629) 825299
11–11 (6.30–11 Mon & Wed in winter)
**Mansfield Riding Bitter;
Marston's Pedigree** Ⓗ
Typical, market town, locals'
pub with two rooms of
different proportions.
🏚 ⊛ ◖ ♣ P

Woolley Moor

White Horse Inn

White Horse Lane (400 yds off
B6014) ☎ (0246) 590319
11.30–2.30 (3 Sat), 6.30–11
Draught Bass Ⓗ
Almost legendary for its fine ale
and food. Set in excellent
walking country, where the less
active can enjoy a beautiful
view of the rolling Derbyshire
hills. Ogston Reservoir is
nearby. Regular guest beer;
inventive menu (no food Sun
eve). Not to be missed.
Q ⊛ ◖ 🖜 Ⓐ ♣ P

Youlgreave

George Inn

Church Street
☎ (0629) 636292
11–3, 6–11
Home Mild, Bitter Ⓗ
Large, lively local across from
the village church. Haddon Hall
is nearby. Rear yard drinking
area. 🖜 ⊛ ◖ 🖜 🖜 ♣ P

Try also: Bulls Head
(Marston's)

Join CAMRA —
see page 480!

Devon

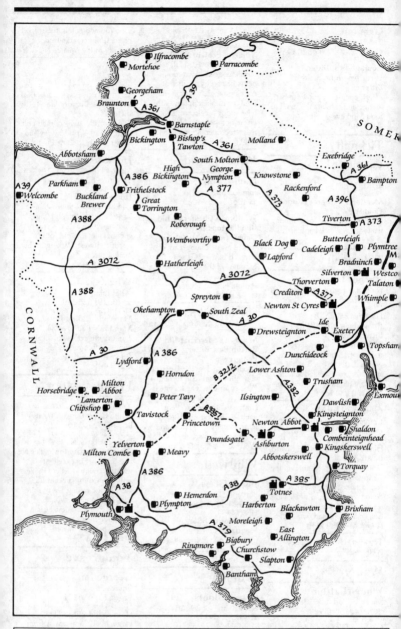

Beer Engine, Newton St Cyres; **Blackawton**, Totnes; **Exe Valley**, Silverton; **Mill**, Newton Abbot; **Otter**, Mathayes, Luppitt; **Summerskills**, Plymouth; **Thompson's**, Ashburton

Abbotsham

Thatched House
The Square
☎ (0237) 472334

12–3, 6–11
Draught Bass; Butcombe Bitter; Fuller's London Pride Ⓗ
Old pub in the centre of an attractive village. A basic local

which is popular in summer. Guest beers.
⌂ ◑ ▶ ♣ P

Try also: Pig on the Hill, Puse Hill

Devon

```
0        5       10 miles
0                15 km
```

S E T

Holcombe Rogus
Burlescombe
Clayhidon
Broadhembury
Mathayes
Honiton
Feniton
A35
A30
Kilmington
Axminster
Ottery St Mary
Sidford
Seaton
Axmouth
Sidmouth
Beer
A3052

Abbotskerswell

Two Mile Oak
Totnes Road
☎ (0803) 812411
11–2.30, 5–11 (11–11 Sat & summer)
**Draught Bass; Eldridge Pope
Royal Oak** G; **Whitbread
Flowers IPA** H
15th-century coaching house
with a food-dominated lounge,
though the public bar retains an
old-fashioned atmosphere.
🏚 🕃 🍴 🍺 P

Ashburton

London Inn
West Street ☎ (0364) 52478
11–2.30, 5–11
Thompson's Best Bitter, IPA H
Comfortable coaching house
with an enormous, rambling
lounge. The home of
Thompson's brewery. 🏚 🍴 P

Axminster

Axminster
Silver Street ☎ (0297) 34947
11–11
Palmers BB, IPA H
Pleasant, town pub, behind the
church. 🏚 🕃 🍴 🍺 ⏰ P

Millwey
Off Chard Road (A358)
11–2.30, 7–11
Palmers BB, IPA H
Friendly, suburban pub. Families
welcome in the skittle alley. No
food Sun lunch or Mon.
Q 🍴 🍺 P

Axmouth

Ship Inn
☎ (0297) 21838
11–2.30 (2 Fri & Sat), 6–11 (12–2.30,
7–10.30 Sun)
**Cornish Original, Royal
Wessex** H
Village pub famed for its food.
Bird sanctuary in the garden.
Cider in summer.
🏚 Q 🕃 🍴 🍺 👶 ⏰ P

Bampton

Exeter Inn
Tiverton Road (A396, just S of
Bampton) ☎ (0398) 331345
11–2.30, 6–11
Exmoor Ale H
Friendly pub though in summer
the Bermuda shorts brigade
tends to intrude. Basically old,
but altered and extended. NRA
fishing licences available.
🏚 Q 🕃 🍴 🍺 ⏰ P

Bantham

Sloop Inn
☎ (0348) 560215
11–3, 6–11
**Draught Bass; Ushers Best
Bitter** H
Large pub, very busy in
summer. Near a popular beach.
Bar skittles. 🏚 Q 🍴 🍺 P

Barnstaple

Corner House
108 Boutport Street
11–2.30, 5.30–11
Draught Bass H
Genuine, town ale house, with
an unspoilt wood-panelled and
wood-floored interior, appealing
to drinkers from all walks of life.
Guest beers. 🍺 👶

Beer

Anchor
Fore Street ☎ (0297) 20386
11–2.30, 5.30–11
**Draught Bass; Hall &
Woodhouse Badger Best
Bitter; Wadworth 6X** H
Warm, friendly pub with
pleasant staff, large bar areas
and an excellent restaurant,
offering fresh local produce,
especially fish. Cider in summer.
🏚 🕃 🍴 🍺 ⏰ ⏰

Bickington

Old Barn Inn
Bideford Road
☎ (0271) 72195
11.30–2.30, 6.30 (5 Fri & Sat)–11
(12–2, 7–10.30 Sun)
**Draught Bass; Fuller's
London Pride** H
Pub converted from a village
barn. Unobtrusive entertainment
Wed and Sun. Guest beers.
Children welcome. 🍴 P

Bigbury

Royal Oak
Off A379 ☎ (0548) 810313
11.30–3, 5.30–11
**Draught Bass; Furgusons
Dartmoor Strong** H
Village local near the sea. No
food Mon eves in winter.
🏚 Q 🕃 🍴 🍺 P

Bishop's Tawton

Three Pigeons
On A377 ☎ (0271) 72269
11–3, 6–11
Whitbread Flowers IPA H
15th-century village pub where
all pub sports are played in a
happy, family atmosphere. Bar
snacks served. Q 👶 🍺 P

Blackawton

Normandy Arms
Chapel Street
☎ (080 421) 316
12–2.30, 7 (6 summer)–11
**Draught Bass; Blackawton
Bitter, 44 Special; Ruddles
County** H
Engaging, 15th-century, village
pub with a reputation for good
food. A quietly impressive pub.
No meals winter Sun.
🏚 👶 🍴 🍺 👶 P

Black Dog

Black Dog
Village centre, 2 miles S of
B3042 ☎ (0884) 860336
11.30–2.30 (not Mon), 6.30–11
**Draught Bass; Whitbread
Boddingtons Bitter, Flowers
IPA** H
Rural inn at a crossroads. Good
value food (restaurant). Skittle
alley. 🏚 👶 🍴 🍺 P

Devon

Bradninch

Castle Inn
Fore Street ☎ (0392) 881378
11–2.30, 5.30–11
Ind Coope Burton Ale Ⓗ
Friendly, family-run free house,
refurbished to a high standard
and offering a wide range of
good food and beer. Landlord
holds the prestigious *Guild of
Master Cellarmen* award. Castle
Ale house beer from Allied.
🏠 🅲 ▮ Å ♣ P

Braunton

New Inn
Silver Street ☎ (0271) 812254
11–2.30, 5–11
**Draught Bass; Ushers Best
Bitter** Ⓗ
16th-century coaching inn
which, although altered, still
retains a warm welcome.
Situated in the old village
conservation area.
🏠 Q ⛄ 🛏 🅲 ▮ ⊞ ○ P

Try also: Black Horse

Brixham

Burton
32 Burton Street
11–3, 5.30 (6 winter)–11 (11–11 Fri &
Sat)
Courage Best Bitter Ⓗ,
Directors Ⓖ
Busy local, off the main street.
A sporty pub with two pool
tables and football table.
⛄ ⊞ 🅲 ⊞ ♣ P

Broadhembury

Drewe Arms
☎ (040 484) 267
11–11 (11–2.30, 6–11 winter)
**Draught Bass; Cotleigh
Tawny; Otter Ale** Ⓖ
Largely unspoilt, country pub in
a picture-book village of
whitewashed, thatched cottages.
Children admitted if well
behaved. Guest beers.
🏠 Q ⊞ 🅲 ▮ ⊞ ♣ ○ P

Buckland Brewer

Coach & Horses
OS419208 ☎ (0237) 451395
11.30–2.30, 5–11
**Whitbread Flowers IPA,
Original** Ⓗ
Old, village-centre, coaching inn
with a low ceiling – mind your
head when entering the lounge.
Whitbread guest beers.
🏠 Q ⛄ 🛏 🅲 ▮ ⊞ ♣ P

Burlescombe

Ayshford Arms
By railway ☎ (0823) 672429
12–3, 7–11
**Draught Bass; Brains Bitter;
Marston's Pedigree;**

**Whitbread Boddingtons
Bitter** Ⓗ
Spacious, lively pub serving
good food (separate restaurant).
🏠 Q ⛄ 🅲 ▮ ⊞ 🅲 P

Butterleigh

Butterleigh Inn
☎ (0884) 50407
12–3, 6 (5 Fri)–11
**Cotleigh Harrier SPA,
Tawny, Old Buzzard** Ⓗ
Friendly, village inn with a
stained-glass porch. Popular for
food and ales. Guest beers.
🏠 Q ⛄ 🛏 🅲 ▮ ⊞ 🅲 ♣ ○ P

Cadeleigh

Cadeleigh Arms
☎ (088 45) 238
12 (11 Wed & Sat)–2.30, 6–11
**Draught Bass; Butcombe
Bitter; Cotleigh Tawny** Ⓗ
Homely, traditional, country
pub. Live music at least once a
month on Fri. All food is home
cooked – even the bread. Guest
beers. ⛄ ⊞ 🅲 ▮ ⊞ ♣ P

Chipshop

Chipshop Inn
2½ miles off A384, W of
Tavistock ☎ (0822) 832322
12–2.30, 7 (6.30 Fri & Sat)–11
**Draught Bass; Exmoor Ale;
Marston's Pedigree** Ⓗ
One-bar country pub with a
mirror collection. Skittle alley.
Guest beers. ⊞ 🅲 ▮ ♣ P

Churchstow

Church House Inn
☎ (0548) 852237
11–2.30, 6–11
**Draught Bass; Ushers Best
Bitter** Ⓗ
Pub popular for food, especially
the carvery. 🏠 Q ⛄ ⊞ 🅲 ▮ Å P

Clayhidon

Half Moon
4½ miles S of Wellington
☎ (0823) 680291
12–2.30, 7–11 (12–2.30, 7–10.30 Sun)
**Draught Bass; Cotleigh
Tawny, Old Buzzard** Ⓗ
Old, but well cared for village
local with nice views across the
Culm Valley.
🏠 Q ⛄ ⊞ 🅲 ▮ ⊞ Å ♣ ○ P

Combeinteignhead

Wild Goose Inn
11.30–2.30, 6.30–11 (12–2.30, 7–10.30
Sun)
**Exmoor Gold; Mill Janner's
Ale; Wadworth 6X** Ⓗ
17th-century farmhouse, full of
character and pleasantly
eccentric. Jazz nights popular
Mon; good range of food;
guest beers. 🏠 ⊞ 🅲 ▮ P

Crediton

Crediton Inn
Mill Street ☎ (0363) 772882
11–11 (12–2.30, 7–10.30 Sun)
Beer range varies Ⓗ
Lively local built in 1852, its
sign depicting St Boniface. No
regular beers; all guests.
🅲 ▮ ⇌ P

Exchange
High Street ☎ (0363) 775833
11–3, 5–11 (11–11 Sat & summer)
**Courage Best Bitter,
Directors** Ⓗ
A comfortable, open-plan
lounge area, plus a basement
steak and wine bar. Guest beers.
Q ⛄ ⊞ 🅲 ▮ ⇌

Dawlish

Prince Albert
The Strand ☎ (0626) 862132
11–11
**Draught Bass; Whitbread
Flowers IPA** Ⓗ
Cosy and convivial house also
known as the 'Hole in the
Wall'. Eve meals served summer
only. 🏠 🅲 ▮ ⇌

Drewsteignton

Drewe Arms
The Square ☎ (0647) 21224
10.30–2.30, 6–11 (12–2, 7–10.30 Sun)
Whitbread Flowers IPA Ⓖ
Unspoilt, village pub with the
oldest and longest serving
landlady in the country. Close
to Fingle Bridge beauty spot
and Castle Drogo. 🏠 Q ⊞ ♣ ○

**Try also: Anglers Rest, Fingle
Bridge**

Dunchideock

Lord Haldon Hotel
Approach from Ide (off A30)
☎ (0392) 832483
10.30–2.30, 7–11
Draught Bass; Tetley Bitter Ⓗ
Large hotel with conference
facilities and superb views.
'Treacle mines' nearby. Guest
beer. Q ⛄ 🛏 🅲 ▮ Å P

East Allington

Fortescue Arms
Off A381 ☎ (054 852) 215
12–2, 6.30–11
Palmers IPA Ⓗ
Village local with bar and food
areas split (no meals Mon, or
lunches Tue, in winter).
🏠 Q ⊞ 🅲 ▮ ⊞ ○ P

Exebridge

Anchor Inn
On B3222 ☎ (0398) 23433
11–2.30, 6.30–11
**Ruddles County; Ushers Best
Bitter** Ⓗ

Pleasant, riverside inn with a children's garden and good food. Also serves Doone Bitter, brewed by Webster's.
🏛 Q ⌛ 🕏 🕭 ◖ ▮ 🕭 ⟿ ♣ ○ P

Exeter

Chaucers
High Street ☎ (0392) 422365
11–11 (closed Sun)
Draught Bass; Tetley Bitter 🄷
Busy pub underneath C&A's. Popular with office workers at lunchtime; the emphasis is generally on good value, interesting food. Guest beers.
◖ ▮ ⇌ (Central)

Cowick Barton
Cowick Lane ☎ (0392) 70411
11–2.30, 6–11
Courage Best Bitter, Directors; John Smith's Bitter 🄷
Comfortable, E-shaped, monastery-style pub, supposedly haunted by a friendly ghost. Large selection of country wines. John Smith's is sold as 'Monk's Ale'. No food Sun eve. 🏛 🕏 ◖ ▮ 🕭 P

Double Locks
Canal Banks, Marsh Barton
OS933900 ☎ (0392) 56947
11–11
Adnams Broadside; Eldridge Pope Royal Oak; Everards Old Original; Exmoor Ale; Greene King Abbot; Marston's Pedigree; Wadworth 6X 🄷
Lively, canalside pub with a huge garden. Excellent value bar meals; barbecues in summer. Very popular with students and families alike. Guest beers.
🏛 Q ⌛ 🕏 🕏 ◖ ▮ 🕭 🕭 🅰 ♣ ○ P

Exeter Community Centre
St Davids Hill
5–10.30 (10 Sat; closed Sun)
Ruddles County 🄷
An oasis for beers from independent breweries, where an annual Winter Ale Festival is held by the local CAMRA branch. Guest beers.
◖ ⇌ (Central/St Davids) ⚥

Great Western
Station Approach
☎ (0392) 74039
11–3, 5–11
Draught Bass; Charrington IPA 🄷
Busy pub/hotel opposite St Davids station. Comfortable lounge bars; good value food in a separate restaurant.
Q 🕭 🕭 ⇌ (St Davids) P

Hole in the Wall
Little Caste Street
11–3, 5.30–11 (closed Sun)
Eldridge Pope Hardy

Country, Royal Oak 🄷
Pub with an oak-beamed interior. Quiz night Tue. Guest beers. 🏛 ◖ 🕭 ⇌ (Central) ♣

Victoria Inn
Union Road ☎ (0392) 54176
11–2.30, 5.30–11 (11–11 Sat)
Cornish Steam Bitter; Greene King Abbot; Ruddles Best Bitter; Wadworth 6X 🄷
One-bar pub close to the university. Live groups on Tue.
◖ ▮

Well House
Cathedral Close
☎ (0392) 58464
11–2.30, 5–11
Draught Bass; Whitbread Flowers IPA 🄷
Popular bar next to the cathedral. Busy with office workers at lunchtime and everyone else in the eve. One, varying beer is sold as a house brew. The cellar is worth a visit. Guest beer. 🕏 ◖ ▮ ⇌ (Central)

Exmouth

Grove
The Esplanade
☎ (0395) 272101
11–2.30, 6–11
Beer range varies 🄷
Warm, friendly and popular, seafront pub, offering five continuously-changed beers. Regular mini beer festivals (not summer). Excellent, home-cooked food. 🕏 ◖ ▮ 🕭 ⇌ P

Feniton

Nog Inn
Ottery Road ☎ (0404) 850210
11–3, 6–11
Cotleigh Tawny 🄷
Cheerful, village local with a possessive cat. Work up a thirst in the squash court. Extensive range of guest beers from all parts of the UK. Runs to Zulu time! 🏛 🕭 🕭 ⇌ ♣ ○ P

Frithelstock

Clinton Arms
Off Bideford Road, 2 miles from Torrington ☎ (0805) 23279
12–2.30 (3 summer), 7 (6 summer)–11
Draught Bass 🄶
Pleasant, roadside pub in an attractive, rural setting, but with an unimaginative interior featuring an open lounge. The landlord possesses local fishing rights. Occasional guest beers.
🕏 🕭 ◖ ♣ P

Georgeham

Rock Inn
Rock Hill ☎ (0271) 890322
11–3, 5–11 (11–11 Fri, Sat & summer)
Draught Bass; Ruddles Best Bitter, County; Ushers Best Bitter 🄷

Traditional, unspoilt, village pub offering a good range of pub games, incl. shove-ha'penny and 'Pig's Head'. Occasional guest beers. Cider in summer.
🏛 ⌛ 🕭 ◖ ▮ 🕭 ♣ ○ P

George Nympton

Castle Inn
☎ (076 95) 2633
11.30–2.30, 6.30–11 (supper licence)
Whitbread Flowers IPA, Original 🄷
Pub run by the same family since it was built 100 years ago. Tastefully refurbished in 1990 to provide a lounge, a bar and a restaurant. 🏛 Q 🕏 ◖ ▮ ♣ ○ P

Great Torrington

Hunters Inn
Wells Street ☎ (0805) 23832
11–11
Whitbread Flowers IPA, Original 🄷
Popular, town house.
🏛 🕏 🕭 ♣

Puffing Billy
Old Station House (A386)
11–3, 5.30 (6 winter)–11
Greene King Abbot; Wadworth 6X 🄷
Former railway station converted to a pub, concentrating on food and the tourist trade. 🏛 🕏 ◖ ▮ ♣ P

Harberton

Church House Inn
11.30–2.30, 6–11
Draught Bass; Courage Best Bitter, Directors 🄷
An enormous, heavily beamed lounge and a good-size family room. Real antique furnishings and lots of real food. Guest beers. 🏛 Q 🕏 ◖ ▮ ○ P

Hatherleigh

Tally Ho
14 Market Street (A386)
☎ (0837) 810306
11–2.30, 6–11
Eldridge Pope Royal Oak; Tally Ho Potboiler's Brew, Tarka's Tipple, Janni Jollop 🄷
Ancient, market town pub with an accent on Italian home cooking and a fully operative brewery. 🏛 🕏 ◖ ▮ ♣ P

Hemerdon

Miners Arms
Off A38 ☎ (0752) 343252
11–2.30 (3 Fri), 5.30–11
Draught Bass 🄷&🄶**; Furgusons Dartmoor Best; Ruddles County; Ushers Best Bitter** 🄷
Former tin-miners' pub on the fringe of Dartmoor, near Plympton. Large garden.
🏛 🕏 ◖ ▮ 🕭 ♣ P

Devon

High Bickington

Old George Inn
Popular Terrace (B3217)
11–3, 6–11
Butcombe Bitter; Ind Coope Burton Ale Ⓖ
16th-century, village-centre inn displaying blacksmith's tools on the walls. A quiet room is sometimes used as a restaurant. No meals winter weekdays.
🏚 Q ⌂ 🍴 ◑ ◐ ♣ P

Holcombe Rogus

Prince of Wales
12–2.30, 7 (6 Fri & Sat)–11 (12–2.30, 7–10.30 Sun)
Draught Bass; Cotleigh Harrier, Tawny, Old Buzzard Ⓗ
Pleasant, country pub with interesting, cash register handpumps. The first pub to be part-owned by Cotleigh Brewery. Excellent food. Guest beers. 🏚 Q ⌂ 🍴 ◑ ♣ ◔ P

Honiton

Volunteer
High Street ☎ (0404) 42145
11–3, 6.30–11
Cotleigh Tawny Ⓗ
Friendly local with table skittles and pool. ⌂ 🍴 🅰 ⥲ ♣ ◔

White Lion
High Street ☎ (0404) 42066
11–2.30, 6–11 (11–11 Fri & Sat)
Archers Best Bitter; Cornish Original; Greene King Abbot; Wadworth 6X Ⓗ
The original White Lion across the road burned down twice before it was moved to its present site around the turn of the century. A comfortable, one-bar local with friendly staff.
🏚 Q 🍴 ◑ ◐ 🅰 ⥲ ♣ P

Horndon

Elephant's Nest
Off A386 ☎ (0822) 810273
11–2.30, 6–11
Palmers BB; Ruddles County; St Austell HSD; Webster's Yorkshire Bitter; Whitbread Boddingtons Bitter, Flowers IPA Ⓗ
Popular, moorland pub offering an extensive range of meals.
🏚 Q 🍴 ◑ ◐ ◔ P

Horsebridge

Royal Inn
6 miles W of Tavistock
12–2.30, 7–11 (12–2.30, 7–10.30 Sun)
Draught Bass; Greene King Abbot; Marston's Pedigree; Royal Inn Tamar, Horsebridge Best, Heller Ⓗ
15th-century, riverside brew pub, once a nunnery. No

children admitted. Excellent menu (not served Sun eve).
🏚 Q 🍴 ◑ ◐ ◔ P

Ide   18/4/94

Huntsman Inn
High Street ☎ (0392) 72779
11–3, 6–11
Cornish JD; Ruddles Best Bitter Ⓗ
Unspoilt, village pub; one bar with two open fires and a country atmosphere. Bar billiards. 🏚 🍴 ◑ ♣ ◔ P

Ilfracombe

Wellington Arms
High Street ☎ (0271) 862206
11–3.30, 5–11
Courage Best Bitter, Directors Ⓗ
Beamed, town pub with an Iron Duke theme and an aviary. Snooker; occasional guest beer; good value food.
🏚 Q ⌂ 🍴 ◑ ◐ ♣

Ilsington

Carpenters Arms
☎ (0364) 661215
11–2.30, 6–11
Whitbread Flowers IPA Ⓖ
Timeless, one-bar, village local frequented by serious darts and cards players. Experienced, friendly hosts. 🏚 🍴 ◑ ◐ ♣ ◔

Kilmington

New Inn
The Hill (200 yds S of A35)
11–2.30, 7 (6.30 Sat)–11
Palmers BB, IPA Ⓗ
Traditional, village local. Families welcome in the skittle alley. No food Mon.
🍴 ◑ ◐ ◔ ♣ P

Kingskerswell

Bickley Mill
Stoneycombe (1 mile W of village)
11–2.30, 6–11
Draught Bass; Eldridge Pope Royal Oak; Wadworth 6X Ⓗ
Very large, lounge-style, 13th-century, converted mill with terraced gardens. Good food.
🏚 ⌂ 🍴 ⥲ ◑ ◐ P

Kingsteignton

Old Rydon
Rydon Lane ☎ (0626) 54626
11–3, 6–11
Draught Bass; Wadworth 6X Ⓗ
Substantial, very old pub/restaurant with a new conservatory. Guest beers; house beer from Mill.
🏚 Q 🍴 ◑ ◐ P

Knowstone

Masons Arms
☎ (039 84) 231/582
11–3, 7–11
Cotleigh Tawny; Hall & Woodhouse Badger Best Bitter Ⓖ
Charming, ancient, thatched inn with beams and a stone floor. Excellent food. Camping in the garden for walkers on the Two Moors Way. Occasional cider.
🏚 Q ⌂ 🍴 ⥲ ◑ 🅰 ♣ ◔ P

Lamerton

Blacksmiths Arms
Off B3362, 4 miles from Tavistock ☎ (0822) 612962
11.30–2.30, 6.45–11 (12–2.30, 7–10.30 Sun)
Draught Bass Ⓗ
Smart, open-plan pub.
🏚 ⌂ 🍴 ◑ P

Lapford

Maltscoop
☎ (0363) 83330
11.30–2.30, 6–11
Adnams Broadside Ⓖ; **Draught Bass** Ⓗ; **Eldridge Pope Royal Oak** Ⓖ; **Marston's Pedigree** Ⓗ; **Wadworth 6X** Ⓖ; **Welsh Brewers Worthington BB** Ⓗ
Real village inn with wooden stillage behind the bar and an old inglenook. Wheelchair access to gents WC only.
🏚 Q ⌂ 🍴 ⥲ ◑ 🅰 P

Lower Ashton

Manor Inn
☎ (0647) 52304
11.30–2.30, 6 (7 Sat)–11 (12.30–2.30, 7–10.30 Sun; closed Mon, except bank hols)
Draught Bass; Cotleigh Tawny Ⓗ; **Wadworth 6X** Ⓗ
Unspoilt, small, two-bar, country pub in a lovely valley. Good food (nothing fried). Regular guest beers.
🏚 Q ⌂ 🍴 ◑ ◐ ♣ P

Lydford

Castle Inn
Off A386 ☎ (082 282) 242
11–3, 6–11
Courage Best Bitter, Directors Ⓗ
Slate-flagged, 16th-century free house by the castle, near the famous Lydford Gorge.
🏚 Q ⌂ 🍴 ⥲ ◑ ◐ 🅰 P

Meavy

Royal Oak
Off A386 ☎ (0822) 852944
11–3, 7–11
Draught Bass; Courage Best Bitter; Whitbread Boddingtons Bitter Ⓗ

15th-century, moorland pub on the village green near an ancient oak tree: a slate-floored bar with a granite fireplace. Inch's cider.
🏠 Q ⊛ ◖) 🖵 ♣ ⏚

Milton Abbot

Edgcumbe Arms
On A384 ☎ (082 287) 229
11-3, 6-11
Draught Bass; Wadworth 6X ℍ
19th-century pub with a large stone fireplace. Guest beers.
🏠 ⊛ ◖) 🖵 Å ⏚ P

Milton Combe

Who'd Have Thought It
Off A386, near Yelverton
☎ (0822) 853313
11-2.30, 6-11
Draught Bass; Blackawton Bitter; Eldridge Pope Royal Oak; Exmoor Ale; Wadworth 6X ℍ
16th-century pub in a wooded valley near Dartmoor.
🏠 Q ⊛ ◖) ⏚ P

Molland

Black Cock
SW of village, signed from A361 ☎ (076 97) 297
11-11
Cotleigh Tawny ℍ
Family pub with its own upmarket camping park and luxury cottages; heated swimming pool (Whitsun to end Sept). The house beer, Black Cock, is Cotleigh Harrier. Occasional guest ales.
🏠 ⊱ ⊛ 🛏 ◖) ♣ ⏚ P

Moreleigh

New Inn
Off B3207 ☎ (054 882) 326
12-2, 6.30-11
Palmers IPA ℊ
Excellent, traditional pub, off the beaten track. Not fancy or spoiled but has a reputation for good food. 🏠 Q ◖) ♣ P

Mortehoe

Ship Aground
The Square ☎ (0271) 870856
11-3, 5.30-11 (may vary summer)
Exmoor Ale; Marston's Pedigree ℍ
Attractive lounge bar with a nautical theme; close to good beaches and spectacular coastal walks. Guest beer often available; cider in summer.
🏠 ⊱ ⊛ ◖) Å ♣ ⏚

Newton Abbot

Wolborough Inn
Wolborough Street
☎ (0626) 61667
11-3, 6 (7 Sat)-11
Draught Bass ℍ

Very small, sports-oriented local. 🛏 ◖ ♣

Newton St Cyres

Beer Engine
Sweetham (by station, ½ mile off A377) ☎ (0392) 851282
11.30-3, 6-11 (11-11 Sat)
Beer Engine Rail Ale, Piston, Sleeper ℍ
Pub brewery with railway connections. Good value food; children welcome in the restaurant area. Live bands at weekends. 🏠 Q ⊛ ◖) Å ⊱ ♣ P

Okehampton

Plume of Feathers
Fore Street ☎ (0837) 52815
10.30-3, 6.30-11
Courage Best Bitter, Directors ℍ
Coaching inn of uncertain age: a popular town pub offering good value B&B. Q 🛏 ◖ ⏚ ♣ P

Ottery St Mary

London Inn
Gold Street ☎ (0404) 814763
11-3, 5.30-11 (11-11 Sat)
Draught Bass; Tetley Bitter ℍ
Modernised, 18th-century coaching house. The olde-worlde restaurant has genuine oak beams and horse brasses. Pool room, skittle alley and guest beers.
Q ⊱ ⊛ 🛏 ◖) ♣ ⏚ P

Parkham

Bell Inn
Off A39 ☎ (0237) 451201
11-3, 6-11 (may vary in winter)
Draught Bass ℊ; **Fuller's London Pride; Whitbread Flowers IPA** ℍ
Delightful, thatched inn at the edge of a thriving village. The low-beamed interior boasts a grandfather clock set into the wall. Beware of the hungry cat!
🏠 Q ◖) Å P

Parracombe

Hunters Inn
Heddons Mouth (signed off A39) ☎ (059 83) 230
11-2.30, 7-11 (may vary in summer)
Wadworth 6X; Whitbread Flowers Original ℍ
Edwardian, country house hotel in a spectacular, National Park valley, close to coastal walks. Beware of peacocks. Guest beers in summer. Family room in summer only. ⊱ ⊛ 🛏 ◖)

Peter Tavy

Peter Tavy Inn
Off A386 ☎ (0822) 810348
11-2.30 (3 Sat), 6.30-11
Butcombe Bitter ℊ

Ancient, moorland pub with low ceilings, flagstones and settles. Extensive and varied food menu; up to four guest ales. 🏠 ⊛ ◖) Å P

Plymouth

Archer Inn
11 Archer Terrace
11.30-3, 6-11 (11-11 Fri & Sat)
Draught Bass ℍ
Pleasantly furbished, small, locals' pub, over the footbridge from the station. ⇌

Boringdon Arms
13 Boringdon Terrace, Turnchapel
☎ (0752) 402053
11-3, 6-11 (11-11 Fri & Sat)
Draught Bass; Butcombe Bitter; Ind Coope Burton Ale; Summerskills Best Bitter ℍ
Homely, welcoming pub with good value beers. Situated across the River Plym from the city centre. 🏠 ⊱ ⊛ 🛏 ◖) ⏚ P

Dolphin Hotel
14 The Barbican
11-11
Draught Bass ℊ
Spartan, dockside hostelry, frequented by fishermen. Opposite the disused Western Railway station, now used to land fish. 🏠

Mechanic Arms
31 Stonehouse Street, Stonehouse (½ mile W of centre)
11-3, 6-11
Summerskills Best Bitter ℍ
Corner pub in a busy industrial area. No food Sun. ◖

Mountain Inn
Lutton, Cornwood (3 miles N of A38) ☎ (075 537) 247
11-3, 6 (7 Mon–Wed in winter)-11
Exmoor Ale; Fergusons Dartmoor Strong; Ind Coope Burton Ale ℍ
Cottage-style bar and furnishings with exposed cob walls and a large, granite fireplace. Set in a sleepy village. Burton Ale is sold as 'Mountain Ale'. 🏠 Q ⊱ ⊛ P

Pym Arms
Pym Street, Devonport
11-3, 6-11
Draught Bass; Eldridge Pope Royal Oak ℊ; **St Austell XXXX Mild** ℍ, **HSD; Summerskills Best Bitter; Wadworth 6X** ℍ
Side-street, drinkers' pub near the dockyard, frequented by students. Guest beers.
⇌ (Devonport)

Seven Stars
Seven Stars Lane, Tamerton Foliot (off B3373)
11-3, 6-11
Courage Best Bitter, Directors ℍ

Popular, suburban pub with low ceilings and a conservatory/restaurant at the rear. Small garden near a stream.
🏠 Q ⌘ ◑ ▶ ⊟ P

Stopford Arms
172 Devonport Road (near park) ☎ (0752) 562915
11–2.30 (3 Sat), 6–11
Courage Best Bitter, Directors Ⓗ
Small, corner, locals' pub with a loyal clientele.
⊟ ⇌ (Devonport)

Swan Inn
Cornwall Beach, Devonport ☎ (0752) 568761
12–3, 7–12
Gibbs Mew Bishop's Tipple; Ruddles Best Bitter, County; St Austell HSD; Ushers Best Bitter; Wadworth 6X Ⓗ
Stone-walled, split-level drinking house with an emphasis on music (late licence). Situated by the Tamar, with good sunset views. Guest beers.
🏠 ◑ ▶

Thistle Park Tavern
32 Commercial Road, Coxside (off A374) ☎ (0752) 667677
11–11
Adnams Broadside; Eldridge Pope Royal Oak; Greene King Abbot; Marston's Owd Rodger; St Austell HSD; Summerskills Best Bitter Ⓗ
Basic boozer with a wooden floor and a tendency towards stronger ales. Guest beers. 🏠

Three Crowns
The Parade, The Barbican
11–11 (11–2.30, 7–11 Mon)
Courage Best Bitter, Directors Ⓗ
Comfortable, one-bar pub; often busy, with outside tables on the cobbled quayside. ⛵ ⌘ ◑

Plympton

Lyneham Inn
On old A38, near Deep Lane
11–3, 6–11
Courage Best Bitter; John Smith's Bitter Ⓗ
Popular pub with a large garden; children also allowed in the rear lounge. ⌘ ◑ ▶ P

Plymtree

Blacksmiths Arms
OS053028 ☎ (088 47) 322
11–2.30 (4 Sat; not Mon), 6–11
Exmoor Ale; John Smith's Bitter Ⓗ
Traditional, village local with one large bar, a skittle alley, plus a sound-proofed music room. Varied menu of home cooking, incl. vegetarian and children's meals. Guest beers.
🏠 ⌘ ◑ ▶ ♣ ⊖ P

Poundsgate

Tavistock Inn
On A384, between Ashburton and the moor ☎ (036 43) 251
11–2.30 (3 summer), 6 (5 summer)–11
Courage Best Bitter; John Smith's Bitter Ⓗ
Traditional, granite pub in an isolated hamlet: a cosy, rugged front bar, a side room, and plenty of outside seating. All day breakfasts served. Good atmosphere. 🏠 ⛵ ⌘ ◑ ▶ ♣ ⊖ P

Princetown

Plume of Feathers
Plymouth Hill (B3212/B3357 jct) ☎ (082 289) 240
11–11
Draught Bass; St Austell HSD, Tinners Ⓗ
Traditional, Dartmoor pub, built in 1785, with two bars, log fires, exposed beams and granite walls. Popular with walkers and campers. Near the prison.
🏠 Q ⛵ ⌘ ⌷ ◑ ▶ Å ♣ ⊖ P

Rackenford

Stag Inn
Off A361 ☎ (088 488) 369
12–2.30, 6–11
Cotleigh Tawny; Exmoor Gold (summer) Ⓗ
Traditional, Devon thatched-tunnel inn, dating back to the 13th century. Skittles.
🏠 Q ⛵ ⌘ ⌷ ◑ ▶ ♣ P

Ringmore

Journeys End Inn
Off A379 ☎ (0548) 810205
11–3, 6.30 (7 winter)–11
Butcombe Bitter Ⓗ**; Exmoor Ale; Wadworth 6X** Ⓖ
Old, wood-panelled, thatched bar and a modern extension. Stancombe cider; guest beers. No Sun lunch in summer.
🏠 ⛵ ⌘ ⌷ ◑ ▶ Å ⊖ P

Roborough

Olde Inn
Off B3227/B3217
11–3, 5.30–11 (11–11 Sat in summer)
Adnams Mild Ⓗ
Thatched, 16th-century, village inn with two bars: CAMRA North Devon *Pub of the Year* 1991. Of its seven beers, six are guests that change at least twice a week. Only beers from independent breweries sold. Folk music Tue; trad. jazz Thu.
🏠 Q ⌘ ◑ ▶ ⊟ Å ♣ P

Seaton

Sleeper
Marine Place (by seafront)
11–11 (12 Fri & Sat; 11–2.30, 6.30–11 in winter)

Beer Engine Rail Ale, Piston, Sleeper Ⓗ
Spacious, three-bar, town pub. The high-ceilinged downstairs room displays paintings of the pub and the Beer Engine at Newton St Cyres. The upstairs family room is also a venue for live music on Fri and Sat nights.
⛵ ◑ ▶ ⊟ Å ♣

Shaldon

Shipwrights Arms
Ringmore Road
11–3, 5–11
Courage Best Bitter, Directors; John Smith's Bitter Ⓗ
Pub with a nautical flavour and an estuary view.
🏠 ⛵ ⌘ ◑ ▶ ⊟ ♣ P

Sidford

Blue Ball
On A3052 ☎ (0395) 514062
10.30–2.30, 5.30–11
Cornish JD, Steam Bitter, Royal Wessex Ⓗ
Friendly, three-bar, whitewashed, cob and thatch pub. The public bar has a large inglenook; comfy lounge and a pretty garden with a barbecue area. 🏠 Q ⛵ ⌘ ⌷ ◑ ▶ ⊟ ♣ ⊖ P

Sidmouth

Old Ship
Old Fore Street
10.30–3, 6–11 (12–2.30, 7–10.30 Sun)
Marston's Pedigree; Wadworth 6X; Whitbread Boddingtons Bitter Ⓗ
Panelled and beamed, old pub with smuggling associations; very busy in summer. The skeleton of a wattle and daub wall can be seen in the upstairs restaurant. 🏠 Q ◑ ▶

Silverton

New Inn
Fore Street ☎ (0392) 860196
12–3, 5.30–11 (11–11 Wed & Sat)
Draught Bass; Exe Valley Dob's Best Bitter, Devon Glory Ⓗ
Friendly, one-bar, village pub with excellent indoor barbecues. Occasional guest beer; Black Hand cider. 🏠 ⌘ ◑ ▶ ♣ ⊖

Slapton

Tower Inn
Near A379 ☎ (0548) 580216
11–2.30, 6–11
Eldridge Pope Royal Oak; Exmoor Ale; Gibbs Mew Bishop's Tipple; Hall & Woodhouse Tanglefoot; Palmers IPA; Wadworth 6X Ⓗ
Very interesting, 14th-century free house: one bar with several rooms. 🏠 Q ⛵ ⌘ ◑ ▶ Å ⊖ P

South Molton

Town Arms
East Street ☎ (076 95) 2531
11–11 (11–3, 6–11 Fri & Sat)
**Gibbs Mew Premium,
Salisbury** Ⓗ
Quiet, town-centre local with
above-average food at good
prices; try the curry. Cider in
summer. 🏰 🍴 ◖ ◗ ♣ ⌂ P

South Zeal

Oxenham Arms
☎ (0837) 840244
10.30–3, 6–11
**Draught Bass; St Austell
Tinners** Ⓖ
12th-century monastery, first
licensed in the 14th century.
Note the great granite stone in
the snug bar. A fascinating old
inn/restaurant. Gray's cider in
summer.
🏰 Q ⬤ 🍴 🚗 ◖ ◗ ▲ ⌂ P

Spreyton

Tom Cobley
On B3219 ☎ (064 723) 314
12–3 (not Mon), 6–11
**Cotleigh Tawny; Marston's
Pedigree** Ⓗ
Quiet, village local; its superb
function room has an indoor
barbecue. Home-made food (not
served Mon). Guest beers.
🏰 Q ⬤ 🍴 🚗 ◖ ◗ ♣ ✕

Talaton

Talaton Inn
On B3176 ☎ (0404) 822214
12–3, 7–11
**Draught Bass; Cornish Royal
Wessex** Ⓗ
Popular, family-run, village pub.
Good restaurant.
🏰 Q ⬤ 🍴 ◖ ◗ ◖ ♣ P

Tavistock

Bedford Hotel
1 Plymouth Road
☎ (0822) 613221
11.30–2.30, 6.30–11
**Draught Bass; Courage Best
Bitter** Ⓗ
Large hotel in the main square.
Real ale available in the Bedford
Bar. Families welcome in the
conservatory. 🏰 🍴 🚗 ♣ P

Thorverton

Exeter Inn
11–3, 6–11
**Courage Best Bitter,
Directors; Exe Valley Dob's
Best Bitter** Ⓗ
Old coaching inn with farm
implements and a well which
was uncovered during

---

alterations. Skittle alley and folk
club. 🏰 ⬤ 🍴 ◖ ◗ ♣ ⌂ P

Tiverton

Four in Hand
Fore Street ☎ (0884) 252765
11–3, 6 (5 Fri)–11 (11–11 Sat)
Draught Bass Ⓗ
Busy, central bar near the
cinema and bus station. Q ◖ ◗ ♣

Racehorse
Wellbrook Street (W of the
river) ☎ (0884) 252606
11–11
**Ruddles County; Ushers Best
Bitter; Webster's Yorkshire
Bitter** Ⓗ
Popular, friendly local; meals all
day. 🏰 ⬤ ◖ ◗ ♣

White Horse
Gold Street ☎ (0884) 252022
11–11
Draught Bass Ⓗ
Small but friendly, town-centre
local. Good value food (not
served Sun lunch). Guest beers.
⬤ 🚗 ◖ ◗ ◖

Topsham

Bridge Inn
Bridge Hill ☎ (0392) 873862
12–2.30, 6–10.30 (12–2, 7–10.30 Sun)
**Adnams Broadside; Exmoor
Gold; Gibbs Mew Bishop's
Tipple; Wadworth 6X,
Old Timer** Ⓖ
Unspoilt, old pub in the same
family for generations.
Q 🚗 ⬤ ◖ ◖ ≠ P

Torquay

Crown & Sceptre
2 Petitor Road, St Mary Church
11–3, 6–11 (11–11 Sat)
**Courage Best Bitter,
Directors; John Smith's
Bitter** Ⓗ
200 year-old, village pub, now
engulfed by Torquay. Regular
folk music; much local character.
Interesting guest beers.
🏰 🚗 ⬤ ◖ ◗ ♣ P

Totnes

Albert
32 Bridgetown Hill (Paignton
road) ☎ (0803) 863214
11–11
**Courage Best Bitter;
Wadworth 6X** Ⓗ
Lively, traditional pub with two
bars. ⬤ 🍴 ♣ ⌂

Trusham

Cridford Inn
☎ (0626) 853694
11–3, 6–11 (12–2.30, 7–10.30 Sun)

**Draught Bass; Cotleigh Old
Buzzard** Ⓖ; **Exmoor Ale** Ⓗ
Originally an old barn, a pub
since 1983. Stained-glass
windows and old church pews
give character. The ancient main
bar has a stone floor; the public
is more modern. Guest beers.
🏰 Q 🚗 🍴 🚗 ◖ ◗ ◖ ▲ ♣ ⌂ P

Welcombe

Old Smithy Inn
Off A39 ☎ (028 883) 305
11–3, 7–11 (11–11 summer; 12–2.30,
6–10.30 Sun)
**Butcombe Bitter; Marston's
Pedigree** Ⓗ
Thatched, 13th-century former
home of blacksmith Caleb
Wakely, at the head of a valley
in unspoilt countryside.
🏰 ⬤ 🚗 🍴 ◖ ◗ ▲ ⌂ P

Wembworthy

Lymington Arms
Lama Cross (Winkleigh road)
☎ (0837) 83572
11–3 (may extend), 6–11 (supper
licence)
**Eldridge Pope Hardy
Country, Royal Oak; Palmers
IPA** Ⓗ
Old coaching inn, rebuilt in the
1820s by Lord Portsmouth's
Eggesford Estate. Set in idyllic,
rural surroundings. Cider in
summer. 🏰 ⬤ 🚗 ◖ ◗ ♣ ⌂ P

Westcott

Merry Harriers
On B3181 ☎ (0392) 881254
12–2.30, 7–11 (12–2, 7–10.30 Sun)
Draught Bass Ⓗ
Friendly, roadside pub with a
restaurant and a reputation for
good food. 🏰 ⬤ ◖ ◖ ♣

Whimple

Paddock Inn
London Road (A30)
☎ (0404) 822356
11–3, 6–11 (11–11 Sat)
**Beer Engine Piston; Courage
Directors** Ⓗ
Comfortable roadhouse with a
bar/restaurant and a family
area/games room. Large range
of imported beers. Paddock
Pedigree is brewed by Courage.
Cider only sold to take away.
Q 🚗 ⬤ ◖ ◗ ▲ ♣ ⌂ P

Yelverton

Rock Inn
☎ (0822) 852022
11–2.30, 6–11
**Draught Bass; Charrington
IPA; St Austell HSD** Ⓗ
Multi-bar pub in a village set
off a major roundabout. Popular
with families. 🏰 🚗 ⬤ ◖ ◗ ▲ ♣ ⌂ P

Dorset

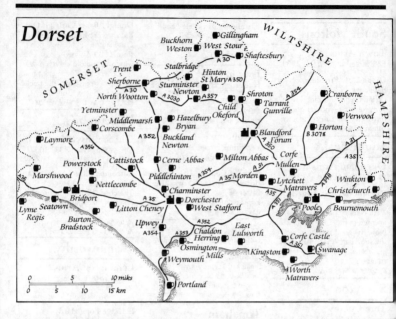

Dorset

 Eldridge Pope, **Goldfinch**, Dorchester; **Hall & Woodhouse**, Blandford Forum; **Palmers**, Bridport; **Poole**, Poole

Blandford Forum

Nelson's
77 Salisbury Street (A354)
☎ (0258) 451468
12–3 (not Mon–Wed), 7–11
Beer range varies Ⓗ
Cosy, friendly, candlelit bar with substantial, varied, home-cooked food. Three different beers a week. 🏠 🍴 🛏 🍺 ♣

Bournemouth

Brunswick Hotel
199 Malmesbury Park Road, Charminster (S of B3063)
10.30–11
Marston's Pedigree; Whitbread Boddingtons Bitter, Strong Country, Flowers Original, Wethered Winter Royal Ⓗ
Friendly, back-street local with a folk club on Fri eves. Function room. 🛏 🍺 🍴 🍴 ♣ ♣

Grange Hotel
57 Southbourne Overcliff Drive
10.30–3, 4.30–11
Draught Bass; Courage Directors; Marston's Pedigree Ⓗ
Clifftop bars catering for all. Live entertainment. Guest beer. 🍺 🛏 🍴 P

Old Thumper
113 Poole Road, Westbourne
11–3, 5–11

Ringwood Best Bitter, Fortyniner, XXXX Porter, Old Thumper Ⓗ
Busy, lively town pub, catering for all types. Friendly bar staff; reasonably priced beer. Guest beer. 🍴 ≋ (Branksome)

Bridport

Crown Inn
West Bay Road
☎ (0308) 22037
11–2.30, 6.30–11
Palmers BB, IPA Ⓗ
Popular, family-run, roadside Georgian inn, just off the bypass. Excellent food; friendly welcome. 🛏 🍴 🍺 🛏 ⚲ ♣ P

Oddfellows Arms
172 North Allington (B3162)
☎ (0308) 22665
11–2.30, 5.15–11 (11–11 Sat)
Palmers BB, IPA Ⓗ
Red-brick, terraced boozer with no pretensions. Friendly welcome. 🛏 🍴 ⚲ ♣ ♦

Buckhorn Weston

Stapleton Arms
2 miles N of A30
☎ (0963) 70396
12–3, 6–11
Brakspear Special; Exmoor Ale; Greene King Abbot Ⓗ
Spacious, village pub with two large bars and a dining area. The

keen landlord offers interesting guest beers and local cider. 🏠 Q 🍴 🛏 🛏 🍺 🍴 ⚲ ♦ ♦ P

Buckland Newton

Gaggle of Geese
Off village centre, from B3143
OS687050 ☎ (030 05) 249
12–2.30, 6.30–11
Draught Bass; Hall & Woodhouse Badger Best Bitter; Marston's Pedigree; Wadworth 6X Ⓗ
Welcoming, village local. Good food in both the bar and the separate restaurant. Skittle alley. Guest beers in summer. 🏠 🍴 🍺 🍴 ⚲ ♦ P

Burton Bradstock

Three Horseshoes
Mill Street ☎ (0308) 897259
11–2.30 (3 Sat), 6–11
Palmers BB, IPA, Tally Ho Ⓗ
A superb example of a Dorset thatched village inn. Renowned for its excellent beer, food and friendly welcome. Has been in every edition of this guide. 🏠 Q 🍴 🍺 🛏 🍴 ⚲ 🍴 ♦ P ✗

Cattistock

Fox & Hounds
Duck Street ☎ (0300) 20444
11–11 (11–2.30, 7–11 winter)
Cornish JD, Vallence's; Marston's Pedigree Ⓗ

17th-century village inn opposite the church. Flagstone floors, log fires and window seats help make this an outstanding example. Restaurant and skittle alley. Guest beers. Cider in summer.
🏨 Q 🅮 ⌂ ◑ ▶ ▲ ♣ ♨ P

Cerne Abbas

Red Lion

Long Street ☎ (0300) 341441
11.30–2.30, 6.30–11
Wadworth IPA, 6X; Young's Bitter H
Lively local in a tourist village, rebuilt after a fire in 1898. The large bar still has a Tudor fireplace and settles. Good variety of home-cooked food. Skittle alley. Guest beers
🏨 Q 🐾 🅮 ⌂ ◑ ▲ ♣ P

Chaldon Herring

Sailors Return

1 mile S of A352
OS791834 ☎ (0305) 853847
11–2.30, 7–11
Eldridge Pope Hardy Country; Wadworth 6X; Whitbread Strong Country H
Extended, thatched country pub with a stone floor, two bars and a restaurant. Good value bar food. Guest beer. Q 🅮 ⌂ ▶ ◑ P

Charminster

New Inn

North Street ☎ (0305) 264694
12 (11.30 Sat)–3, 7–11
Draught Bass; Charrington IPA H
Lively, village pub on the main road. Large public with an adjoining, Victorian-style conservatory; small lounge-cum-restaurant. The large garden runs down to a stream.
🏨 Q 🐾 🅮 ⌂ ◑ ♣ ◑ P

Child Okeford

Saxon Inn

Gold Hill (N end of village)
OS830133 ☎ (0258) 860310
11.30–2.30, 7–11
Draught Bass; Exmoor Ale H
Hidden up a narrow lane, this small, intimate pub takes its name from the Saxon fort on Hambledon Hill which overlooks the village. The garden has plenty of animal life.
🏨 🅮 ⌂ ♣ ♨ P

Christchurch

Castle Tavern

7 Church Street (bottom of High St) ☎ (0202) 485199
10.30–3, 11
Ringwood Best Bitter, Fortyniner, Old Thumper H
Popular, one-bar, high street pub. Upstairs meeting room

doubles as a family room in summer. Folk club Wed. Guest beers. 🍴 ◑ ▶ ≠

Corfe Castle

Fox Inn

West Street ☎ (0929) 480449
11–3, 6 (7 winter)–11
Gibbs Mew Bishop's Tipple; Ind Coope Burton Ale G**; Tetley Bitter** H**; Wadworth 6X; Wiltshire Stonehenge Bitter** G
Built in 1568, this stone pub has views of Corfe Castle. Meeting place of the 'Ancient Order of the Purbeck Marblers and Stonecutters'. Guest beer. A gem! 🏨 Q 🅮 ◑ ▲

Corfe Mullen

Holmebush

Wareham Road (1 mile E of A350 at Beacon Hill)
OS975953 ☎ (0202) 693637
11–2.30, 6–11
Whitbread Strong Country G
Totally unspoilt, wayside inn, run by the same family for 45 years. Piano in the lounge bar for the occasional sing-song.
🏨 Q 🅮 ▲ ♣ P

Lambs Green Inn

Lambs Green Lane (off A31)
11–2.30, 6–11
Draught Bass; Charrington IPA H
Country inn with good food and barbecues in summer. Restaurant seats 70. Children's play area. 🅮 ◑ ▲ P

Corscombe

Fox Inn

OS526053 ☎ (093 589) 330
12–3, 7–11
Cornish JD G**; Exmoor Ale** H
Traditional village inn with stone-flagged floors and slate bars. Food includes vegetarian option. Draught cider in summer only; beers vary.
🏨 Q 🐾 🅮 ◑ ⌂ ♣ ♨ P

Cranborne

Fleur de Lys

5 Wimborne Street (B3078)
11–2.30, 6–11
Hall & Woodhouse Badger Best Bitter, Tanglefoot H
Well-appointed, 16th-century coaching inn. Excellent food in the lounge bar, the main eating area. The separate, cosy village bar is enjoyed by locals and visitors alike. The subject of a Rupert Brooke poem.
🏨 Q 🅮 ⌂ ◑ ⌂ ⌂ ♣ ♨ P

Sheaf of Arrows

The Square ☎ (072 54) 456
11–2.30, 6–11
Ringwood Best Bitter; Wadworth 6X H

Friendly, Victorian, village-centre local. Two contrasting bars; a large, rather noisy, public, used by locals, and a small, quiet lounge. Function room. Q 🅮 ⌂ ◑ ▶ ♣

Dorchester

Bakers Arms

Monmouth Road
11–2.30, 6–11 (12–2, 7–10.30 Sun)
Eldridge Pope Dorchester, Hardy Country, Royal Oak H
Comfortable, cosy local which overlooks the railway. Formerly a bakehouse, its old ovens can still be seen in the bar. Good value food 🅮 ◑ ⌂ ≠ P

Old Ship

High West Street
10.30–2.30, 4.30–11 (10.30–11 summer)
Eldridge Pope Dorchester, Hardy Country, Royal Oak E
Single-bar, town pub with a nautical theme. Often crowded. Guest beer. 🅮 ◑ ⌂ ≠

White Hart

53 High East Street
☎ (0305) 263545
11–2.30, 6.30–11 (12–2.30, 7–10.30 Sun)
Adnams Bitter; Hall & Woodhouse Badger Best Bitter, Tanglefoot H
A glass-juggling, opera-singing, tri-gammon playing landlord presides over an active clientele which includes exponents of the arts of skittles, crib and pool. Often busy; always friendly; never a dull moment.
🏨 Q 🅮 ⌂ ◑ ⌂ ⌂ ♣ ♣ P

Try also: Tom Brown's, High East Street (Goldfinch)

Join CAMRA —
see page 480!

East Lulworth

Weld Arms

On B3070 ☎ (092 941) 211
11.30 (11 Sat)–2.30, 6.30–11
Cornish JD, Royal Wessex H
Picturesque pub, three miles from Lulworth Cove: two small snug bars and a large lounge, serving excellent food.
🏨 Q 🐾 🅮 ⌂ ◑ ⌂ ▲ ♣ P

Gillingham

Buffalo Inn

Wyke (off B3081)
11–2.30, 5.30–11
Hall & Woodhouse Badger Best Bitter, Tanglefoot (winter)**; Wells Eagle** H
Cosy, one-bar local on the outskirts of town. A collection of jugs and glasses adorns the beamed ceiling. Q 🅮 ◑ ▲ ♣ P

Dorset

Hazelbury Bryan

Antelope
Pidney (1 mile E of B3143)
OS745091 ☎ (0258) 817295
10.30–2.30, 6–11
Hall & Woodhouse Badger Best Bitter Ⓖ
A genuine locals' pub, unaltered since the 1950s. Probably the cheapest prices in Dorset.
Q ⚫ ♣ ⌀

Hinton St Mary

White Horse
200 yds E of B3092
OS786163 ☎ (0258) 72723
11–2.30, 6.30–11
Wadworth 6X Ⓗ
Easily-missed village pub with two contrasting bars. The excellent public bar features a tiled floor and a large, open fire. No eve meals Sun; book for Sun lunch. Guest beer.
⌂ Q ⚫ ◗ ➊ ⊟ ♣ P

Horton

Horton Inn
7 miles N of Wimborne on B3078 ☎ (0258) 840252
10–2.30, 6–11 (10.30 winter)
Courage Directors; Ringwood Best Bitter, Fortyniner Ⓗ
18th-century coaching inn, set in rural countryside. One well-appointed bar with a large, open fire and a relaxing atmosphere. High quality food and accommodation. Guest beer.
⌂ Q ⌕ ⚫ ⋈ ◗ ➊ ➤ P

Kingston

Scott Arms
West Street ☎ (0929) 480270
11–2.30, 6–10.30 (11 Fri/Sat)
Cornish Royal Wessex; Wadworth 6X; Whitbread Flowers Original Ⓗ
Scenic pub in an old village, well known for its TV and film-making roles. Splendid views of Corfe Castle. Popular for its food and garden.
⌂ ⌕ ⚫ ⋈ ◗ ➤ P

Laymore

Squirrel Inn
OS387048 ☎ (0460) 30298
11.30–2.30, 6–11 (12–2.30, 7–10.30 Sun)
Cotleigh Harrier; Courage Directors; Oakhill Yeoman; Wadworth 6X Ⓗ
Hilltop inn with superb views; a good starting base for exploring darkest Dorset and Somerset. Plain, unprepossessing bar with a friendly landlord and locals.
⌂ ⌕ ⚫ ⋈ ◗ ➊ ⊟ ♣ ⌀ P

Litton Cheney

White Horse Inn
OS549900 ☎ (030 83) 539
12–2.30 (3 Sat), 6.30–11
Palmers BB, IPA, Tally Ho Ⓗ
Attractive, streamside, village pub. A locals' pub in winter, but popular with tourists in summer. One of a declining number of all-year outlets for Tally Ho.
⌂ Q ⚫ ⋈ ◗ ⓵ ➤ ♣ ⌀ P

Lyme Regis

Angel Inn
Mill Green
☎ (029 74) 3267
11–2.30, 7–11
Palmers BB, IPA Ⓖ
Popular, friendly inn, with a strong local trade. Impressive collection of bottle beers (over 700). ⌕ ⚫ ⋈ ⓵ ⊟ ♣ P

Royal Standard
The Cobb ☎ (029 74) 2637
10–3, 7–11 (11–11 Sat)
Palmers BB, IPA, Tally Ho Ⓗ
Historic, 400 year-old inn, on the beach. Popular with young people and tourists.
⚫ ⓵ ➤ ♣ ⌀

Lytchett Matravers

Chequers Inn
High Street (off A350)
☎ (0202) 622215
11–11 (11–2.30, 6–11 winter)
Draught Bass; Cornish Original Ⓗ
Modernised, large pub, offering 18 country wines and Premier restaurant facilities. Polite and helpful staff. The children's play area has animals.
⌂ ⌕ ⚫ ◗ ➊ ♣ P

Marshwood

Bottle Inn
11–2 (may vary; 3 summer), 6–11
Exmoor Ale; Ruddles Best Bitter; Wadworth 6X Ⓗ
Genuine, olde-worlde, wayside inn with a skittle alley available for functions. The extensive menu caters for families. Wheelchair access to function room only. Cider in summer.
⚫ ⓵ ◗ ⓵ ➤ ♣ ⌀ P

Middlemarsh

White Horse
☎ (0963) 21219
11–3 (4.30 Fri), 6–11 (11–11 Sat & summer)
Wiltshire Stonehenge Bitter, Old Grumble Ⓗ**, Old Devil** Ⓖ
Large pub on the main road with a skittle alley, a games room and a restaurant. The one main bar has a massive fireplace. Regular guest beer. Cider in summer.
⌂ ⌕ ⚫ ⋈ ◗ ⓵ ➤ ♣ ⌀ P

Milton Abbas

Hambro Arms
3 miles N of A354, from Winterborne Whitchurch
OS810020 ☎ (0258) 880233
11–2.30, 6.30–11
Cornish JD, Royal Wessex Ⓗ
A fine, thatched, whitewashed inn, dating from 1760 and situated in one of Dorset's most picturesque villages. Noted for food. ⌂ Q ⚫ ⋈ ◗ ➊ ♣ P

Morden

Cock & Bottle
On B3075, ½ mile N of A35
11–2.30, 6 (7 winter)–11
Hall & Woodhouse Best Bitter, Tanglefoot; Wells Eagle Ⓗ
Unspoilt village pub in a rural setting. Friendly welcome; home-cooked food. Small function room. ⌂ ⌕ ⚫ ◗ ➊ ♣ P

Nettlecombe

Marquis of Lorne
Off A3066, 3 miles NE of Bridport OS517956
☎ (030 885) 236
11–2.30, 6–11 (12–2.30, 7–10.30 winter)
Palmers BB, IPA Ⓗ
16th-century inn with a panelled bar more like a living room. Separate dining room with a reputation for good food.
⌂ Q ⚫ ⋈ ◗ ➤ P

North Wootton

Three Elms
☎ (0935) 812881
11–2.30, 6.30 (6 Fri & Sat)–11
Ash Vine Bitter; Fuller's London Pride; Greene King Abbot; Smiles Best Bitter; Wadworth 6X Ⓖ
Super, large free house with a good food reputation (incl. vegetarian). The memorabilia includes Matchbox cars. Two guest beers. ⚫ ⋈ ◗ ➊ ♣ ⌀ P

Osmington Mills

Smugglers Inn
1½ miles off A353
☎ (0305) 833125
11–2.30, 6.30–11 (11–11 summer)
Courage Best Bitter, Directors; Ringwood XXXX Porter (Christmas)**, Old Thumper** Ⓗ
Popular family pub, near the sea, decorated with beams from Mudeford Quay (alongside plastic ones). Good food with wide choice, incl. Thai cuisine.
⌂ Q ⌕ ⚫ ◗ ➊ ➤ ♣ ⌀ P

Piddlehinton

Thimble
12–2.30, 7–11
Eldridge Pope Hardy Country; Hall & Woodhouse Badger Best Bitter, Tanglefoot Ⓗ
Pretty free house on the banks of the River Piddle. Cosy and welcoming. Beer fountain at the entrance to the car park.
🏠 Q 🍽 🌀 ▶ P

Poole

Beehive Hotel
234 Sandbanks Road, Lilliput (B3369) ☎ (0202) 748087
10.30–3 (2.30 winter), 5 (6 winter)–11
Eldridge Pope Dorchester, Hardy Country, Royal Oak Ⓗ
Large, busy, roadside pub, geared very much to the family: children's play area has supervision in the summer and school holidays. Spacious conservatory with barbecue. Guest beer.
👶 🍽 🍴 🌀 ▶ ♣ P 🍴

Bermuda Triangle
10 Parr Street, Lower Parkstone (off A35) ☎ (0202) 748087
11.30–3, 5.30 (5 Fri)–11 (11.30–11 Sat)
Exmoor Stag; Fuller's London Pride; Goldfinch Flashman's Clout Ⓗ
Pub with an interior based on the Bermuda Triangle mystery and war memorabilia. Local fish-special lunches. Beers may vary.
🍽 🌀 ⇌ (Parkstone) ⇦ P

Dorset Knob
164 Alder Road, Upper Parkstone (A3040)
11–3, 5.30–11 (11–11 Fri & Sat)
Hall & Woodhouse Badger Best Bitter Ⓗ
Comfortable pub with panelled walls. Caters for regulars and sportsmen. No food Sun.
🏠 👶 🍽 🌀 ▶ ⇌ (Branksome) ♣ P

Grasshopper
141 Bournemouth Road, Lower Parkstone (A35)
11–2.30, 6–11
Adnams Bitter; Hall & Woodhouse Badger Best Bitter, Tanglefoot Ⓗ
Large, plush, open-plan bar with a brick and beam decor and a curio collection. Separate restaurant and function room.
🍽 🌀 ▶ ⇌ (Branksome) P

Inn in the Park
26 Pinewood Road, Branksome Park (off The Avenue, off Westminster Road)
☎ (0202) 761318
11–2.30, 5.30–11
Adnams Bitter; Ringwood Best Bitter Ⓗ
Plush, residential inn near the sea. Cigarette cards collection. Meals in the dining area.
🏠 🍽 🍽 🌀 ▶ P

Lord Nelson
The Quay (opp. Poole Pottery)
11–11 (11–4, 6–11 Sat)
Hall & Woodhouse Badger Best Bitter, Tanglefoot; Wells Eagle Ⓗ
Busy, quayside pub with numerous nautical artefacts and flagstone floors. Regular live bands, and loud blues/rock music. Shower facilities for visiting yachtsmen. No food Sun. 👶 🍽 🌀 🍴 ⇌

Pure Drop Inn
7 East Street (off Lagland Street, near quay) ☎ (0202) 675312
11–3, 6 (7 winter)–11
Eldridge Pope Dorchester, Hardy Country, Royal Oak Ⓗ
Comfortable, locals' pub with recent redecoration. The large public bar at the front has a dartboard area and bar stools; small lounge at the rear. Guest beer. No food Sun.
🍽 🌀 🍴 ♣

Portland

Clifton Hotel
50 Grove Road, Easton
11–3, 7–11
Cornish JD, Vallence's Ⓗ
Large, characterful, one-bar pub, popular with locals and visitors. Good value food in the bar; separate Thai restaurant upstairs. Skittle alley.
🏠 🍽 🌀 ▶ ♣ P

Corner House
49 Straits, Easton
☎ (0305) 822526
11–3, 6–11
Eldridge Pope Dorchester, Hardy Country, Royal Oak Ⓗ
Unchanged, 19th-century, corner ale house: small, cosy bar and a separate games room. Beer yard outside. Winner of Eldridge Pope's *Cellar Supremo* award. 👶 🍽 🍽 ♣

Powerstock

Three Horseshoes
Off A3066, 3 miles NE of Bridport ☎ (030 885) 328
11–3, 6–11
Palmers BB, IPA, Tally Ho (summer) Ⓗ
Remote pub with fine views over the countryside. Deservedly popular for food (especially fish). Families always welcome. Boules in summer.
🏠 Q 👶 🍽 🌀 ▶ ▲ ♣ ⇦ P

Seatown

Anchor
Off A35 in Chideock
OS420918 ☎ (0297) 89215
11–2.30, 7–11 (11–11 summer)

Palmers BB, Tally Ho Ⓗ
Small, cosy pub on a stony beach. Popular with coastal path walkers, but no muddy shoes inside! 🏠 Q 👶 🍽 🌀 ▶ 🔔 ▲ ♣ P

Shaftesbury

Olde Two Brewers
St James Street (near centre)
11–3, 6–11
Courage Best Bitter; Wadworth 6X; Young's Special Ⓗ
Excellent free house near the bottom of famous Gold Hill, with superb views of Blackmore Vale. Many different drinking areas. Guest beers. 🏠 Q 🍽 ♣ P

Sherborne

Digby Tap
Cooks Lane ☎ (0935) 813148
11–3, 5.30–11
Beer range varies Ⓗ
Splendid, side-street, tap room with stone-flagged floors, between the station and the abbey. A real pub with a constantly-changing range of four beers. No food Sun.
▶ ⇌ ♣ ⇦

Skippers
Horsecastles (A352)
11.30–2.30, 5.30 (6.30 Sat)–11
Draught Bass; Butcombe Bitter Ⓗ
A drinkers' pub, serving good food. The bottle collection contains some quite rare specimens. At least three guest beers. 🍽 ▶ ⇦ P

Shroton

Cricketers
½ mile W of A350
OS859127 ☎ (0258) 860421
11–3, 6.30–11
Hall & Woodhouse Badger Best Bitter Ⓗ
Friendly local with a good restaurant. Popular with walkers and visitors to Hambledon Hill. Guest beers. 🏠 Q 🍽 ▶ ♣ P

Stalbridge

Stalbridge Arms
Lower Road
☎ (0963) 62447
12–2.30, 6–11
Eldridge Pope Dorchester; Oakhill Bitter; Wadworth 6X Ⓗ
Good drinking pub just off the main road. Skittle alley; boules in summer. Guest beers. No food Mon. 🏠 👶 🍽 ▶ ♣ P

Sturminster Newton

Bull
Bridge (A357) ☎ (0258) 72435
11–2.30, 6–11

Dorset

Hall & Woodhouse Badger Best Bitter; Wells Eagle ⓗ
Thatched, low-beamed, 16th-century inn, full of character. Warm welcome from the marathon-running landlord (pub is home of the Dorset Doddlers running – and beer club). Fish meals a speciality.
🏠 🛏 ✖ ⊛ ◖ ♣ P

Swanage

Black Swan
159 High Street (half way up hill to Herston)
☎ (0929) 422761
10.30–3, 6–11
Wiltshire Stonehenge Bitter ⓗ
Grade II-listed, built in 1600; a pleasant pub. Small restaurant; converted stables make an interesting children's room. Weekly folk music. Other Wiltshire beers sometimes available. Near Swanage railway. Q 🛏 ⊛ ◖ ▶ 𝚨 P

Durlston Castle
Lighthouse Road, Durlston Country Park OS035773
☎ (0929) 424693
11–11 (11–3, 7–11 winter; may vary)
Draught Bass; Charrington IPA ⓗ
An extraordinary building in a country park, overlooking the sea, with the famous 20-ton stone globe in the garden. Many rooms and restaurants give a medieval atmosphere, adding even more interest.
🏠 ⊛ ◖ 𝚨 P

Red Lion
High Street ☎ (0929) 423533
10.30–2.30, 5–11 (10.30–11 Sat in summer)
Whitbread Strong Country; Flowers Original ⓖ
Popular, down-to-earth pub, with a homely atmosphere. Collections of keys, tools, etc. Family room in summer.
🏠 ⛺ ⊛ ◖ ▶ 𝚨 ♣ ◠ P

Tarrant Gunville

Bugle Horn
2 miles N of Tarrant Hinton at A354 OS925128
☎ (025 889) 300
11.30–3, 6–11 (11.30–11 Sat)
Ringwood Best Bitter; Wadworth 6X ⓗ
Comfortably-furnished, village local in a peaceful setting on the edge of Cranborne Chase walking country.
🏠 Q ⊛ ◖ ♣ P

Trent

Rose & Crown
1½ miles N of A30 OS590184 ☎ (0935) 850776
12–2.30, 7 (6.30 summer)–11
Oakhill Bitter ⓗ

Converted from a farmhouse, with a licence to sell alcohol, to a very popular pub. Renowned for food (no meals Sun eve in winter). Guest beers.
🏠 Q ⛺ ✖ ⊛ ◖ 🚹 ⚑ 𝚨 ◠ P

Upwey

Old Ship
7 Ridgeway ☎ (0305) 812522
11–2.30, 6–11
Cornish Vallence's; Marston's Pedigree ⓗ
Very old, pleasant, beamed pub, mentioned by Hardy. Still has some semblance of the original cosy bar. Tiny car park.
🏠 Q ✖ ⊛ ◖ 𝚨 P

Verwood

Albion Inn
Station Road (B3081)
☎ (0202) 825267
11–2.30, 5 (6 Sat)–11
Gibbs Mew Salisbury, Bishop's Tipple ⓗ
CAMRA East Dorset *Pub of the Year* 1990. Real characters and a ghost called Wesley can be found here, as well as photos of the former railway station alongside. ⊛ ◖ ▶ ♣ P

West Stafford

Wise Man
☎ (0305) 263694
11–2.30, 6.30–11
Cornish JD; Royal Wessex ⓗ
Classical, 400 year-old, thatched, village pub with a public bar and a lounge bar serving food. Impressive collection of pipes and Toby jugs. 🏠 Q ⊛ ◖ ▶ ⚑ P

West Stour

Ship Inn
☎ (0747) 85640
11–3, 6–11 (may vary)
Draught Bass; Oakhill Bitter ⓗ
Coaching inn on A30, built in 1750. A stone-flagged public bar adjoins a red, plush lounge. Separate restaurant. A locals' pub which also attracts tourists.
🏠 Q ⛺ ⊛ ◖ ▶ ⚑ 🚹 ♣ P

Weymouth

Kings Arms
Trinity Road ☎ (0305) 770055
10–11
Archers Village; Cornish Royal Wessex; Marston's Pedigree ⓗ
Quayside pub with a traditional bar, decorated with nautical artefacts. Plusher lounge with comfy armchairs. Live folk music Sun. Guest beers.
Q ◖ ▶ 🚹 ⚑ ➤ ♣ ◠

Waterloo
Grange Road ☎ (0305) 784488
11–30–3, 6.30–11 (11–11 summer)

Gibbs Mew Local Line, Salisbury ⓗ
Corner pub just off the esplanade: a single bar with a dartboard. The small town garden is open in summer. Always popular with locals and can get smoky. Q ⊛ ◖ ➤ ♣ ♧

Weatherbury Hotel
7 Carlton Road North (off Dorchester Road)
☎ (0305) 786040
11–2.30, 5.30–11 (11–11 Fri & Sat)
Draught Bass ⓗ
Lively, out-of-town local with the largest selection of real ales in the area. Live music; home-cooked fare; guest beers.
Q ⊛ ⚑ ◖ ➤ ♣ P

Winkton

Fisherman's Haunt
On B3347 ☎ (0202) 484071
10.30–2.30, 6–11
Draught Bass; Courage Directors; Ringwood Fortyniner, XXXX Porter ⓗ
17th-century hotel with a relaxing atmosphere. Varied choice of reasonably-priced food. Children welcome in one lounge area. 🏠 ⊛ ⚑ ◖ ▶ P

Lamb Inn
Burley Road (off B3347)
☎ (0425) 72427
11–2.30, 5–11 (11–11 Sat)
Marston's Pedigree; Ringwood Best Bitter, XXXX Porter, Old Thumper; Wadworth 6X ⓗ
Deservedly popular free house in a green field setting. Real fire in the public bar; the restaurant bar offers a vegetarian option.
🏠 ⊛ ◖ ▶ ♣ P

Worth Matravers

Square & Compass
Off B3069 OS977777
11–3, 6–11
Hall & Woodhouse Tanglefoot; Marston's Pedigree; Whitbread Strong Country, Pompey Royal ⓖ
A bastion of the Purbecks. At 600 years old, it is like being in another age in this small, stone-built pub. It has been in the landlord's family for 85 years. Regional CAMRA *Pub of the Year* 1989. 🏠 Q ⊛ ♣ ◠ P

Yetminster

White Hart
High Street ☎ (0935) 872338
11.30 (11 Sat)–2.30, 7–11
Draught Bass; Oakhill Bitter ⓗ
Popular, 500 year-old, village-centre pub. The comfortable lounge bar has an impressive, large fireplace. Food at all times.
🏠 Q ⛺ ⊛ ◖ ▶ ➤ ♣ P

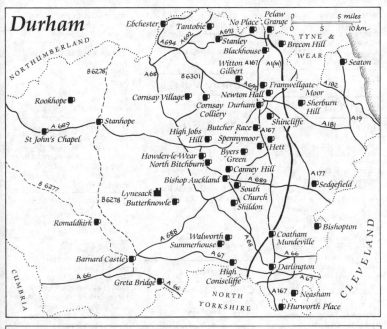

Durham

Butterknowle, *Lynesack*

Barnard Castle

Three Horse Shoes
Galgate (A67)
☎ (0833) 38774
11–4, 7–11 (11–11 Wed)
Draught Bass Ⓗ
Lively, 17th-century, town-
centre pub with a good,
traditional feel. Fine collection
of old local railway photos.
🏠 Q ⊗ ◖ 🌙 ⊕ Ⓛ ♣

Try also: King's Head (John
Smith's); **Old Well** (Free)

Bishop Auckland

Newton Cap
Newton Cap Bank Top (A689,
near bus station)
☎ (0388) 605445
11–3, 6.30–11
Camerons Strongarm Ⓗ
Real drinkers' haunt, and one of
the town's only unspoilt pubs: a
friendly, traditional bar and
separate pool room, with an
extra room used for events.
Excellent view over Wear
Valley from the rear. Try a
game of Ringo.
🏠 Q ⛲ ⊗ ◖ 🌙 ⊕ Ⓛ ♣ ♧

Sportsman Inn
Market Place
☎ (0388) 607376
11.30–4, 6–11
**Marston's Pedigree;
Whitbread Boddingtons
Bitter, Trophy** Ⓗ

One of the town's oldest public
houses. Quiet lunchtimes and
busy eves. A large and lively,
town-centre pub which retains
many of its original features,
incl. real fires and beautifully
carved oak beams. Keep an eye
open for the resident ghost.
🏠 ◖ ⛲ ♣ ♧

Try also: Post Chaise, Market
Place (John Smith's)

Bishopton

Talbot
The Green
☎ (0740) 30371
11–3, 6–11
**Camerons Bitter, Strongarm;
Everards Old Original** Ⓗ
Pleasant, village local with a
long lounge, a tiny snug and a
small, sheltered garden. The
centre of varied village activities
– from football to morris
dancing. 🏠 Q ⊗ ◖ 🌙 ♣ P

Blackhouse

Charlaw Inn
On B6532
☎ (0207) 232085
11–3, 6–11
**McEwan 80/–; Theakston
XB** Ⓗ
Large, five-roomed pub,
including a restaurant, an
outside children's play area and
a conservatory for families.
Very sociable owners. The bar

features regular pub games and
soccer memorabilia.
Q ⛲ ⊗ ◖ 🌙 ⊕ Ⓛ ♣ P

Brecon Hill

Smiths Arms
Castle Dene
☎ (091) 385 6915
12–3 (not Mon–Fri), 7–11
**Draught Bass; Stones Best
Bitter** Ⓗ
Traditional, three-roomed pub
under the A1(M). No food, just
good crack and good beer. Pews
in the family room. Closed
lunchtime, except weekends.
🏠 ⛲ ⊗ ⊕ ♣ P

Butcher Race

Coach & Horses
On A167, halfway between
Croxdale and Thinford
roundabouts ☎ (0388) 814484
12–11
**Vaux Samson; Wards
Sheffield Best Bitter** Ⓗ
Popular, roadside inn with one
long drinking area and a
separate restaurant.
🏠 ⊗ ◖ 🌙 Ⓛ P

Butterknowle

Royal Oak
1 Pinfold Lane
☎ (0388) 718178
6–11 (11–11 Sat)
**Camerons Bitter,
Strongarm** Ⓗ

Durham

Lively lounge with darts and pool; quieter bar with dominoes. A good, village local with a warm welcome (closed lunchtime, except weekends). 🏠 ♨ & ♣

Try also: **Malt Shovel**, Wham (Free)

Byers Green

Royal Oak
93 High Street
☎ (0388) 605918
12–3 (not Mon–Fri), 7–11 (may vary bank hols)
Camerons Bitter, Strongarm Ⓗ
Small, friendly, locals' pub whose plain exterior hides a bright, two-roomed interior with a central bar. The decor reflects the landlord's army connections. The small pool room can get crowded. A pub always guaranteeing a warm welcome. Lunches served weekends (closed weekday lunchtimes). ⊛ ◖ ▶ ♨ ♣

Canney Hill

Sportsman Inn
On A689
☎ (0388) 605160
11–2.30 (4 Fri & Sat), 7 (6 Fri & Sat)–11
Camerons Bitter, Strongarm; Everards Old Original Ⓗ
Bright and lively, roadside inn with a lounge, bar and a snug. The decor reflects horse racing connections. Children welcome during the day.
🏠 Q ⅏ ⊛ ♨ ♣ P

Try also: **Bay Horse**, Woodhouses (John Smith's)

Coatham Mundeville

Foresters Arms
On A167, near A1(M) jct
☎ (0325) 320565
11.30–3, 6–11 (11.30–11 Sat)
John Smith's Bitter, Magnet Ⓗ
Solid, old, stone-built local with two comfortable rooms and traditional character: bric-a-brac, old photos, jugs and plates a-plenty. No lunches Sun.
🏠 Q ⊛ ◖ ♣ P

Try also: **Stables** (Free)

Cornsay Colliery

Firtree (Monkey)
Hedley Hill Lane Ends (B6301, ½ mile S of Cornsay Colliery)
☎ (091) 373 3212
7–11
Vaux Lorimers Best Scotch Ⓗ
Built in 1868 and originally called the Monkeys Nest, this is a basic, one-room pub in a

family-owned house, with a local craft display in one front room. Open eves only. 🏠 Q ⊛ P

Try also: **Hamsteels Inn**, Quebec (Bass)

Cornsay Village

Black Horse
Old Cornsay
☎ (091) 373 4211
7 (6.30 Sat)–11 (12–3, 7–10.30 Sun)
Tetley Bitter Ⓗ
Friendly, neat, country village pub in rural West Durham, overlooking the beautiful Gladdow Valley. A large eating area leads off the main bar. Lunches served Sun only (closed weekday lunchtimes). No eve meals Mon. Well worth a visit. Guest beers in summer. Outside drinking on the village green.
Q ⊛ ◖ ▶ ♣ P

Darlington

Central Borough
Hopetown Lane
☎ (0325) 468490
11–11
Camerons Strongarm Ⓗ
Small, street-corner pub in an area of terraced housing. Very much a locals' pub with a loyal following, run by the same tenants for over 30 years. Near the impressive little Railway Museum on the original Stockton–Darlington line.
Q ⅏ ⇌ (North Rd) ♣

Falchion
Blackwellgate
☎ (0325) 462541
11–3.30, 6.30–11 (10.30 Tue & Wed)
Camerons Strongarm Ⓗ
Cosy, friendly, little bar in a central shopping street. Named after a legendary 'worm'-killing sword. A dominoes stronghold.
⅏ ♣

Golden Cock
13 Tubwell Row
☎ (0325) 468843
11–11 (may close afternoons)
Courage Directors; John Smith's Bitter, Magnet Ⓗ
18th-century, town-centre pub, modernised internally but retaining much character. Bar billiards played – the only table in town. Has a good turnover of interesting ales through a guest beer handpump. ♣

Tap & Spile
99 Bondgate
☎ (0325) 381679
11–3, 7–11
Camerons Bitter, Strongarm Ⓗ
Recreation of a Victorian ale house, with exposed brickwork, bare floorboards and stained-glass. Five or more regularly-

changed guest beers make a vital contribution to the pub's undoubted success. ◖

Three Crowns
Archer Street (near Archer Street Sports Centre – in Sun St!)
☎ (0325) 466040
11–3, 6–11
John Smith's Magnet Ⓗ
Hard-to-find, street-corner boozer with two bric-a-brac-crammed rooms. Specify handpulled beer – keg Magnet may otherwise be offered. Only five minutes' walk from the town centre – near Gladstone Street. ⅏ ♣

Traveller's Rest
West Auckland Road, Cockerton (A68, 1 mile W of centre)
☎ (0325) 463430
11–3 (4 Fri & Sat), 6–11
Courage Directors; John Smith's Bitter, Magnet Ⓗ
Attractive, 1920s, two-roomed local in a now-urbanised village. Large comfortable lounge and a small plain bar. The entrance passage is lined with old local photos. Built for the long-defunct Haughton Road Brewery Co. Q ⅏ ♣

Turk's Head
22 Bondgate
☎ (0325) 463191
11.30–11 (11–4, 6.30–11 Sat)
Everards Old Original; Hadrian Gladiator Ⓗ
Comfortable, 17th-century pub, much altered but with fine leaded brewery windows and nice wood panelling in what was once the separate smoke room. Real ale in the front lounge. Eve meals Mon–Thu.
◖ ⅏ ♣

Try also: **Cricketers** (John Smith's); **Pennyweight** (Vaux)

Durham City

Coldpitts Hotel
Hawthorn Terrace (A690, 200 yds from bus station)
☎ (091) 386 9913
11–3, 5.30–11 (11–11 Fri & Sat)
Samuel Smith OBB Ⓗ
Basic but friendly, city pub with a bar, small lounge and separate pool room. Good value beer.
🏠 Q ⅏ ⇌ ♣

Dun Cow
Old Elvet (near Shire Hall)
☎ (091) 386 9219
11–11
Whitbread Boddingtons Bitter, Castle Eden Ale Ⓗ
One of Durham's little gems: a two-roomed pub near the prison. The bar is as small as a snug, so can seem rather busy, but this just makes the pub seem

even more friendly. The larger lounge (with music) has a mixed clientele and is often full at weekends. Lunchtime snacks.
Q ⊕ ♿ ≋

Elm Tree
Crossgate (top of Neville Street)
☎ (091) 386 4621
12–3, 6–11 (12–11 Sat; 12–2, 7–10.30 Sun)
Vaux Samson Ⓗ
Friendly, regulars' pub; quiet midweek but busy and cosmopolitan at weekends, catering for grannies and bikers. Vaux guest beers. Q ⊕ ≋

Half Moon
New Elvet (Old Elvet jct)
☎ (091) 386 4528
11–11 (12–2, 7–10.30 Sun)
Draught Bass Ⓗ
A *Good Beer Guide* regular for many years; a pub which deserves its reputation as one of the premier outlets for Draught Bass in the county. Named after the crescent-shaped bar which dominates its split-level, open-plan design. ≋ ♣

Queens Head
Sherburn Road End, Gilesgate (A181 jct)
☎ (091) 386 5649
11–3, 7–11
Camerons Bitter; Marston's Pedigree Ⓗ
Popular pub at a busy road junction. Traditional decor; two rooms with a third area through an alcove. Live music usually Thu and Sun. Guest beers.
❀ ⛟ ◖ ⊕ ♣ P

Shakespeare
63 Saddler Street
☎ (091) 386 9709
11–11
McEwan 80/-; Theakston Best Bitter, XB; Younger No. 3 Ⓗ
Basic, old, city-centre pub, near the cathedral, with a small bar and a tiny snug. Friendly staff. Popular with all ages. Q ⊕ ≋

Victoria Hotel
86 Hallgarth Street (A177, near Dunelm House)
☎ (091) 386 5269
11–3, 6–11
McEwan 80/-; Theakston Best Bitter Ⓗ
A listed building; an old, three-room pub popular with locals and students. Collection of Toby jugs in bar and a large selection of whiskies.
⌂ Q ⛟ ⊕ ≋

Woodman Inn
23 Gilesgate (top of Claypath)
☎ (091) 386 7500
12–11
McEwan 80/-; Theakston XB Ⓗ
One-roomed local with a good mix of clientele. Pool, darts, dominoes and shove-ha'penny played. Hot and cold sandwiches. A pub known for its charity work and a former CAMRA branch *Best Pub* winner. ♣

Try also: Fighting Cocks (Bass); **New Inn** (Bass); **Rose Tree** (Vaux)

Ebchester

Chelmsford
Front Street
☎ (0207) 560213
11–3, 6–11
Vaux Samson Ⓗ
Friendly, popular, village local: two tastefully furnished rooms. Pleasant walks nearby.
⌂ Q ❀ ◖ ◗ ⊕ ♿ ♣ P

Framwellgate Moor

Marquis of Granby
Front Street (old Great North Road)
☎ (091) 386 9382
11–4, 6–11
Samuel Smith OBB Ⓗ
Friendly, two-roomed pub with an adjacent games room.
❀ ⊕ ♿ ♣ P

Tap & Spile
27 Front Street (old Great North Road)
☎ (091) 386 5451
11–3, 6–11
Camerons Bitter Ⓗ
Basically furnished, music-free pub with an ever-changing menu of up to nine guest beers. Excellent reference library.
Q ⚇ ◖ ⊕ ♿ ♣

Greta Bridge

Morritt Arms Hotel
Off A66
☎ (0833) 27232
11–3, 6–11
Butterknowle Conciliation Ale Ⓗ
Traditional country house hotel in a beautiful setting, yet just seconds from the A66. Strong local connections with literary giants; bars are dedicated to Dickens and Walter Scott. The murals in the cosy main bar are by the 'Guinness' artist, John Gilroy. ⌂ Q ❀ ⛟ ◖ ◗ ⊕ ♣ P

Hett

Hett Village Inn
Off A167, 1 mile N of Ferryhill
☎ (0388) 815036
7–11
Beer range varies Ⓗ
Tasteful, open-plan inn in a pleasant village. Quiz night Tue. Good value food; lunches served on Sun (closed lunchtime rest of the week). All beers are guest beers. ⌂ ❀ ◖ ◗ ▲ P

High Coniscliffe

Duke of Wellington
On A67
☎ (0325) 374283
11–3, 6–11
Camerons Strongarm Ⓗ
Traditional, one-roomed, village local, opposite a popular, riverside beauty spot. Quoits played. ⌂ ❀ ◖ ♣ P

High Jobs Hill

Colliery Inn
On A690
☎ (0388) 762511
11–3, 6–11
Vaux Samson Ⓗ
Quiet pub with a myriad of ornaments concerning mining and collieries. Wall lighting, red decor and plenty of brass give a warm, welcoming feel. Beware keg Samson; make sure to ask for cask. ⌂ Q ◖ ◗ P

Howden-le-Wear

Australian Hotel
Church Road (off A689, near Crook)
☎ (0388) 762666
11–11
Camerons Bitter, Strongarm Ⓗ
Lively, village local; a busy bar with separate games and pool rooms. A mynah bird keeps watch over bar room activities.
⌂ ⊕ ♣

Hurworth Place

Station
8 Hurworth Road (off A167)
☎ (0325) 720552
11–3, 6–11 (11–11 Sat)
John Smith's Bitter, Magnet Ⓗ
Locals' pub which welcomes visitors amidst its collection of aspidistras, ornate chimney pots and stuffed fish! A choice of bar, lounge or pool room. Guest beers. ⊕ ♣ P

Try also: Comet (John Smith's)

Neasham

Fox & Hounds
24 Teesway
☎ (0325) 720350
11–3 (4 Sat), 6.30–11
Vaux Samson, Double Maxim; Wards Sheffield Best Bitter Ⓗ
Good, village pub near a scenic stretch of the River Tees: a busy, friendly bar, a meals-based lounge and a smoke-free family conservatory. Children's play equipment outside.
Q ⚇ ❀ ◖ ◗ ⊕ ♿ ▲ ♣ P ⚔

Durham

Newton Hall

Newton Grange
Near Arnison Centre on way to
Frankland Prison
☎ (091) 386 0872
11–11
**Camerons Bitter; Tolly
Cobbold Original** Ⓗ
Well-appointed hotel with 13
en-suite bedrooms. Food a
speciality, but something for
everyone. ⊠⊛⊴◖▮⊟Ⴊ P

No Place

Beamish Mary Inn
Off A693, 500 yds from main
road OS215532
☎ (091) 370 0237
12–3, 6–11 (12–11 Fri & Sat)
**McEwan 80/-; Theakston
Best Bitter, XB** Ⓗ
Very lively, community pub of
Victorian character.
Memorabilia in the main bar; an
Aga range in the lounge-diner.
Music club – folk and blues – in
the converted stables. Limited
parking. Regular guest beers.
▦Q⊛⋈⊟ȺȺ♣P

Try also: **Sun Inn**, Beamish
Museum (S&N)

North Bitchburn

Red Lion
Off B6286
☎ (0388) 763561
12–3, 6–11
**John Smith's Bitter,
Magnet** Ⓗ
Pub with a warm, comfortable
atmosphere to be enjoyed in the
mainly locals' bar. The games
room offers competitive pool,
while the huge lounge serves
good, home-cooked food. The
real fire is surrounded by some
interesting, old furniture.
▦Q⊛◖▮⊟P

Pelaw Grange

Wheatsheaf
On main Chester-le-Street–
Birtley road
☎ (091) 388 3104
11–11
Stones Best Bitter Ⓗ
Lively bar with a good
atmosphere; comfortable lounge
with conservatory. Good value
food. Popular with families
(garden playground).
⊛◖⊟Ⴊ♣P

Romaldkirk

Kirk Inn
The Green
☎ (0833) 50260
12–3, 6–11
**Butterknowle Bitter,
Conciliation Ale; Whitbread
Castle Eden Ale** Ⓗ
Welcoming, single-bar pub on

the village green, next to the
'Cathedral of the Dale'. Acts as
the post office before morning
opening. Guest beers.
Adventurous menu (for both
food and ale). Thatcher's cider.
▦⊛◖▮ტ

Rookhope

Rookhope Inn
OS938428 ☎ (0388) 517215
12–3 (not Mon or winter), 7–11
Tetley Bitter Ⓗ
17th-century, village local with
two bars and a separate dining
room (meals served in summer
only). Guest beers.
▦Q⊛⋈◖▮⊟♣P

St John's Chapel

Golden Lion
Market Place (A689)
☎ (0388) 537231
11.30–3, 7–11
**Ruddles County; Webster's
Yorkshire Bitter** Ⓗ
Large, village pub with a genial
host. Holiday flatlets to let;
excellent menu. Get your fishing
licence here. ▦⊛⋈◖▮ȺP

Seaton

Seaton Lane Inn
Seaton Lane (B1404)
☎ (091) 581 2038
12–3, 7–11
Theakston Best Bitter Ⓗ
Basic but comfortable pub in a
former pit village; interesting
old photos depict local history.
Popular with locals; a regular in
this guide. Q⊠⊛⊟P

Sedgefield

Dun Cow Inn
Front Street
☎ (0740) 20894
11–3, 5.30–11
Theakston Best Bitter, XB Ⓗ
Busy pub in the middle of the
village, with friendly staff. Up
to four guest beers available
weekly. ⋈◖▮P

Golden Lion
1 East End
☎ (0740) 20371
11–11 (12–2, 7–10.30 Sun)
Theakston Old Peculier Ⓗ
Unspoilt, traditional pub,
offering lively local banter and
good beer. Very friendly service
in this, Sedgefield's 'bonniest'
boozer. ▦Q◖▮♣P

Nags Head
West End
☎ (0740) 20234
12–3, 7–11
**Draught Bass; John Smith's
Bitter; Tetley Bitter;
Whitbread Boddingtons
Bitter** Ⓗ
Cosy, pleasant pub with a

strong emphasis on football and
horse racing. A very warm
welcome assured. Q⊠◖▮P

Sherburn Hill

Moor Edge
Front Street
☎ (091) 372 1618
12–3 (4 Fri & Sat), 7–11
**Vaux Lorimers Best
Scotch** Ⓔ&Ⓗ**, Samson** Ⓔ**;
Wards Sheffield Best Bitter** Ⓗ
Typical village pub whose
character has gradually been
restored: the bar and lounge
have coal fires. Won Durham
CAMRA *Best Pub* award in Feb
1991. Quoits played.
▦Q⊟♣

Shildon

Timothy Hackworth
107 Main Street
☎ (0388) 772525
11–3, 8–11 (11–11 Sat)
**Camerons Bitter,
Strongarm** Ⓗ
Tidy, one-roomed town pub
with a thriving soccer team and
connections with the local
athletic club. No food Sun.
◖♣♣

Try also: **King William**
(Camerons)

Shincliffe

Rose Tree Inn
Low Road West (A177,
Stockton Rd)
☎ (091) 386 8512
11.30–11
**Vaux Samson, Double
Maxim; Wards Sheffield Best
Bitter** Ⓗ
Very popular, roadside inn with
outdoor play facilities for
children. Two rooms in
contemporary style with above
average beer prices.
Q⊛◖▮♣

Seven Stars
On A177
☎ (091) 384 8454
11.30–3.30, 6.30–11
**Vaux Samson; Wards
Sheffield Best Bitter** Ⓗ
1725 coaching inn; a smart,
upmarket, village pub, not
usually frequented by the hoi
polloi! Two well-furnished
rooms and a separate restaurant.
Beer prices very reasonable for
the area. Q⊛⋈◖▮⊟

Try also: **Avenue**, High
Shincliffe (Vaux)

South Church

Red Alligator
Next to St Andrew's Church
☎ (0388) 605644
11–3 (4 Sat), 7–11 (11–2.30, 7–10.30
Sun)

102

Vaux Samson; Wards Sheffield Best Bitter Ⓗ
Lively, roadside pub: a locals' bar but with a friendly welcome for all. Various knick-knacks all around, even hanging from oak beams. 🏚 Q ⓓ 🍺 ⇌ (Bishop Auckland) ♣ P

Spennymoor

Ash Tree
Carr Lane ($\frac{1}{2}$ mile from centre, on Greenways Estate)
☎ (0388) 814490
12–2 (4 Sat), 7–11
Vaux Samson; Wards Sheffield Best Bitter Ⓗ
Taken over by Vaux late 1990, a pub which maintains its reputation for serving fine quality beer. The hub of the estate community and worth the diversion from the town centre beer desert. Keen bar games players. 🍺 ⓓ ♣ P

Frog & Ferret
4 Coulson Street ($\frac{1}{4}$ mile from A167, on Thinford Road)
☎ (0388) 818312
11–11
Bateman XB; Theakston XB; Whitbread Boddingtons Bitter; Younger No. 3 Ⓗ
Newly refurbished pub in traditional style: a single room split by a bar, where the emphasis is on real ales – an oasis in a real ale desert; guest beers. Congenial atmosphere.

Stanhope

Bonny Moor Hen
25 Front Street
☎ (0388) 528214
11–4, 7–11
Whitbread Boddingtons Bitter, Castle Eden Ale, Flowers Original Ⓗ
Formerly the 'Phoenix', now refurbished, with a large friendly

bar and a separate lounge. Occasional guest beers. Excellent menu. 🏚 Q ✿ 🍺 ⋈ ⓓ 🍺 🚹 Ａ ⇌ (summer only) ♣ P

Try also: Grey Bull (S&N)

Stanley

Blue Boar Tavern
Front Street (100 yds from bus station)
☎ (0207) 231167
11–3, 7–11 (11–11 Fri)
Alloa Arrol's 80/-; Ind Coope Burton Ale; Stones Best Bitter Ⓗ
Olde-worlde former coaching house; a popular pub attracting a wide age range. Occasional live music in the large function room. Two regular guest beers from small independents.
Q ✿ 🍺 ⓓ 🚹 P

Summerhouse

Raby Hunt
☎ (032 574) 604
11.30–3, 6.30–11
Marston's Burton Best Bitter, Pedigree Ⓗ
Neat, welcoming, old stone free house in a pretty whitewashed hamlet. Homely lounge and a bustling locals' bar. Magnificent Raby Castle can be visited, five miles up the road. Good, home-cooked lunches (not served Sun). Occasional guest beers.
🏚 Q 🍺 ⓓ 🚹 ♣ P

Tantobie

Highlander Inn
White-le-Head (B6311)
☎ (0207) 232416
12–2.30 (summer only), 7–11
Belhaven 80/-; Marston's Merrie Monk, Pedigree Ⓗ
Popular, village pub. The bar appears very lively; the secluded lounge has a small

room used for dining. Guest beers. Note restricted hours (may open some lunchtimes, Mon–Fri, in winter).
Q ✿ 🍺 ⓓ 🚹 ♣ P 🍴

Walworth

Walworth Castle Hotel
☎ (0325) 485470
11–3, 6–11
Ruddles County Ⓗ
Grade I listed castle, dating from the 12th century, now a smart country hotel with two bars (open to non-residents). Guest beers. 🏚 ⋈ ⓓ ◗ P

Witton Gilbert

Glendenning Arms
Front Street (A691)
☎ (091) 371 0316
11–4, 7–11
Vaux Samson Ⓗ
Popular two-roomed local with a welcome as warm as the fire in winter. Mementoes and portraits on the walls show the horse racing and hunting connections. Sixteen years in this guide. 🏚 Q 🍺 ♣ 🍴

Travellers Rest
Durham Road (A691)
☎ (091) 371 0458
11–3.30, 6–11
McEwan 70/-, 80/-; Theakston Best Bitter, XB, Old Peculier; Younger No. 3 Ⓗ
Very well furnished example of a contemporary village pub, which draws visitors from a wide area. Split-level, no-smoking room off the main bar and an excellent conservatory, which is ideal for children. Boules played in summer.
🏚 Q ✿ 🍺 ⓓ ◗ P 🍴

Try also: Centurion, Langley Park (Vaux)

Opening Hours

The law regarding opening hours was relaxed, not before time, in 1988. Now pubs in England and Wales may open at any time during the permitted hours of 11am to 11pm (earlier opening is allowed by some local licensing districts). Sunday hours are standard: 12–3 and 7–10.30. The opening hours given for each pub description are correct at the time of going to press. However, publicans are at liberty to take advantage of the new flexibility and may stay open longer than the hours shown, or indeed close during the afternoons without prior notice. Where Sunday hours differ from those given above, this is noted. The Scottish licensing laws are more generous as far as opening is concerned and pubs may stay open longer.

Essex

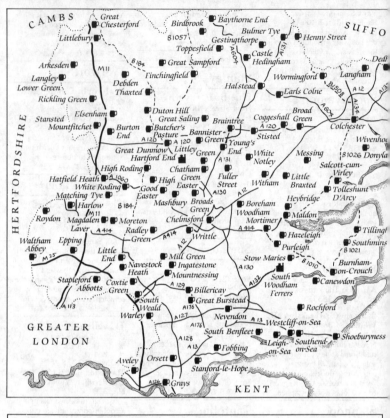

Aingers Green

Royal Fusilier
Weeley Road (S from Gt Bentley
village green then left; straight
on at crossroads)
☎ (0206) 250001
11–2.30, 6.30–11
**Adnams Bitter; Greene King
IPA** Ⓗ
Cosy, old, country pub,
refurbished and extended in a
tasteful manner. Guest beer.
🏠 Q ☞ ⊛ ⓓ ▲ ♣ P

Arkesden

Axe & Compasses
1⅓ miles N of B1038
OS483344 ☎ (0799) 550272
11–2.30, 6–11 (12–2.30, 7–10.30 Sun)
**Greene King IPA, Rayments
Special, Abbot** Ⓗ
Superb, welcoming, 17th-
century local in a picturesque
village. Interesting collection of
trade tools and implements.
Restaurant and bar meals (not
Mon eve). 🏠 Q ⊛ ⓓ ⊟ ♣ P

Aveley

Sir Henry Gurnett
Romford Road
OS563818 ☎ (0708) 864042
11–3, 6–11
**Courage Best Bitter,
Directors; Marston's
Pedigree; Whitbread
Boddingtons Bitter, Flowers
IPA, Castle Eden Ale** Ⓗ
Country pub in a converted
barn, which was once Sir
Henry's house. Playground for
children and a natural duck
pond in the garden. The upstairs
restaurant is open all day Sun
(book weekends). Four of the
above beers are available in
rotation. 🏠 ⊛ ⓓ ⓒ P

Bannister Green

Three Horseshoes
OS696206
☎ (0371) 820467
11–3, 6–11
Ridleys IPA Ⓗ
Pleasant, old pub at the corner

of the village green. No eve
meals Mon. 🏠 ⊛ ⓓ ⓒ ⊟ ♣ P

Baythorne End

Swan
On A604 at A1092 jct
☎ (044 085) 306
11–2.30, 6–11
Greene King IPA Ⓗ**, Abbot**
(winter) Ⓖ
Nicely restored, cosy pub with a
varied choice of food (no meals
Sun eve). Try not to miss the
entrance as it's hard to turn
back. 🏠 Q ⊛ ⓓ ⓒ ⊟ ♣ P

Beaumont-cum-Moze

Swan
Chapel Road (between B1035
and B1414)
☎ (0255) 861359
11–3 (2.30 winter), 6 (7 winter)–11
Adnams Bitter Ⓗ
Small, usually quiet, two-bar
pub in an out-of-the-way corner

104

Essex

of Essex. The saloon is decorated with views of an earlier Beaumont. Public bar and lounge prices are the same.
🏛 Q ⌂ ◖ ❶ ⊟ ♣ P

Billericay

Chequers
44 High Street (B1007)
☎ (0277) 651804
10–3, 5.30–11 (11–11 Sat)
Adnams Bitter; Ind Coope Benskins Best Bitter, Burton Ale; Tetley Bitter ⓗ
Charming, well-renovated, 16th-century pub in the town centre. Its previous three bars still form identifiably separate areas. Landlord has *Master Cellarman* awards. Limited parking. ◖ ⅋ ⇌ P

Coach & Horses
36 Chapel Street (off High Street by the church)
☎ (0277) 622873
10–3, 6–11 (varies Sat)
Greene King IPA, Abbot ⓗ
Pleasant, friendly, locals' pub; fine collection of jugs and elephants. Good range of home-cooked meals (no food Sun).
🏛 ⌂ ◖ ⇌ ♣ P

Railway
High Street (B1007)
☎ (0277) 652173
11–11
Greene King IPA, Abbot ⓗ
Busy Gray's house near the railway station. A true drinkers' pub, catering for all ages. Collection of railway and golfing prints. Small parking area. ⌂ ⇌ ♣ P

Birdbrook

Plough
The Street OS706411
☎ (044 085) 336
11–2.30, 5.30–11
Adnams Bitter; Greene King IPA, Abbot; Mauldons Special ⓖ
Traditional, village local with an interesting fireplace in the public bar and a cosy dining room (no eve meals Sun–Tue).
🏛 Q ⌂ ◖ ⊟ ♣ P

Boreham

Queens Head
Church Road
☎ (0245) 467298
10.30–2.30 (3 Fri & Sat), 6–11
Greene King IPA, Abbot ⓗ
Excellent, friendly and traditional, 17th-century village local behind the church. Has been in the same family for over 50 years. Good value in every way. No food Sun.
Q ⌂ ◖ ⊟ ♣ P

Bradfield

Strangers Home Inn
The Street
☎ (0255) 870304
11–3, 7–11 (11–11 summer)
Marston's Pedigree; Whitbread Castle Eden Ale ⓗ
Village pub with its own, large campsite. Separate restaurant and children's menu.
🏛 ⛺ ⌂ ◖ ▲ ♣ P

Braintree

Boar's Head
High Street (300 yds from ring road) ☎ (0376) 20119
11–11
Ridleys IPA ⓗ
Spacious, one-roomer with a central bar area. Olde-worlde structure but plushly renovated inside, with some original beams still intact. Loud jukebox and a mostly young clientele. Difficult access to car park. 🏛 ◖ ⇌ P

Try also: King William IV, London Rd (Ridleys)

Broad Green

Kings Arms
On A120
☎ (0376) 561581

11–3.30, 6–11
Greene King IPA, Rayments Special, Abbot ⓗ
Friendly, warm, roadside pub, popular with locals. Good selection of food at reasonable prices. Selection of books for sale for charity. 🏛 Q ⌂ ◖ ❶ ♣ P

Broads Green

Walnut Tree
Off A130
OS694125
☎ (0245) 360222
11–2.30, 6.30 (6 summer)–11
Ridleys IPA ⓗ&ⓖ
Clean, pleasant, three-bar, country pub. Includes a well-furnished lounge and a basic public with a real fire and a trophy cabinet. Entrance to both is through a cosy, middle snug.
🏛 Q ⌂ ⊟ ♣ P

Bulmer Tye

Fox
On A131, S of Sudbury
☎ (0787) 77505
11.30–3 (may vary), 6.30–11
Greene King IPA, Abbot ⓗ
Cosy, friendly, roadside inn with good value, home-cooked food. 🏛 Q ⌂ ◖ ❶ ⊟ ▲ ♣ P

Burnham-on-Crouch

New Welcome Sailor
74 Station Road (B1010)
☎ (0621) 784778
10.30–3, 6–11
Greene King IPA, Abbot ⓗ
Centre of the community for the workingmen of Burnham. Thriving teams for most pub games. No food Mon.
◖ ❶ ⇌ ♣ P

Olde White Harte
The Quay
☎ (0621) 782106
11–3, 6–11 (11–11 Sat)
Adnams Bitter; Tolly Cobbold Bitter ⓗ
Charming, old, riverside pub. Sit on the private jetty for superb views of the river.
🏛 Q ⌂ ⇌ ◖ ❶ P

Burton End

Ash
OS532237 ☎ (0279) 814841
11.30–3, 5.30–11
Greene King Rayments Special, Abbot ⓗ
17th-century, thatched cottage pub of character. Popular with Stansted Airport staff at lunchtime. Despite the proximity of the airport, noise is not a problem. Good, simple food at reasonable prices (no meals Tue eve). Wheelchair access to lounge only.
🏛 Q ⌂ ◖ ❶ ⊟ ⅋ ♣ P

Essex

Butcher's Pasture

Stag
Duck Street (1 mile W of B184)
OS608241 ☎ (037 184) 214
11–2.30, 6 (7 winter)–11 (12–2.30, 7.30–10.30 Sun)
Ridleys IPA Ⓖ
Basic, homely and unspoilt, village pub with plain wooden benches and tables in the public bar. Fine views over the Chelmer Valley from the garden. No food, but the landlord says to bring your own to eat with a pint.
🏠 Q 🏢 ♣ P

Canewdon

Chequers Inn
High Street ☎ (0702) 258251
11–3, 7–11
Bateman Mild; Greene King IPA, Raments Special, Abbot Ⓗ
Pub with an original main building from the 18th century, with exposed timber beams and brasses. The restaurant is housed in a former butcher's shop, later used as the pub cellar. A wide range of good, home-cooked food is always available. Saved from demolition by the locals with CAMRA support.
Q 🍃 🏢 ( ) ♣ P

Try also: Anchor, High St (Brent Walker)

Castle Hedingham

Bell Inn
10 St James Street (B1058)
☎ (0787) 60350
11.30–3, 6–11
Greene King IPA, Abbot Ⓖ
Excellent, genuine-timbered pub near the castle. Families welcome. No food Mon eve.
🏠 Q 🍃 🏢 ( ) 🍺 ♣ P

Chatham Green

Windmill
200 yds off A131
OS716151 ☎ (0245) 362415
10.30–3, 5.30 (6 winter)–11
Ridleys IPA Ⓖ
Small, one-bar, friendly local, close to the Essex Way footpath. 🏠 Q 🏢 ♣ P

Chelmsford

Endeavour
351 Springfield Road
☎ (0245) 257717
11–11 (12–2, 7–10.30 Sun)
Greene King IPA, Abbot Ⓗ
Comfortable, quiet and traditional, three-roomed pub. Good meals (no food Sun).
🏠 Q ( ) 🍺 ♣

Partners
30 Lower Anchor Street
☎ (0245) 265181
11–3, 5.30–11 (11–11 Sat)
Adnams Bitter; Greene King IPA, Abbot; Marston's Pedigree Ⓗ
Friendly, street-corner local with a games/family room and a small patio. No food weekends. Guest beers. 🍃 🏢 ( ) ♣ ♣ P

Red Lion
147 New London Road
☎ (0245) 354902
11–11
Adnams Extra; Ridleys IPA Ⓗ
Basic public bar with an unusual tiled canopy; comfortable saloon. Pool table. No food Sun.
( ) 🍺 ♣

Woolpack
23 Mildmay Road (off Odeon roundabout) ☎ (0245) 259295
11.30–3, 6–11 (11.30–11 Fri)
Adnams Extra; Ridleys IPA Ⓗ
Friendly, welcoming, cheery, back-street local. Quiz eves; live music Sun lunchtimes. Pool room. No food Sun; rolls only Sat. 🏢 ( ) ♣ P

Coggeshall

Fleece
West Street ☎ (0376) 561412
10–11
Greene King IPA, Abbot Ⓗ
Large pub with an ancient fireplace. Situated on the west side of town near the antique shops. 🏠 Q 🏢 ( ) 🄰

Try also: Porto-Bello Inn (Free)

Colchester

Artilleryman
54–56 Artillery Street (right off St Botolphs–Hythe road)
☎ (0206) 578026
10.30–2.30, 4.30–11 (10.30–11 Sat)
Greene King XX Mild, IPA, Raments Special, Abbot Ⓗ
Friendly, two-bar pub in the heart of new town. The jovial landlord balances a pint of beer on his belly!
Q 🏢 ( ) 🍺 ⟿ (Hythe & Town) ♣

British Grenadier
67 Military Road (opp. range church) ☎ (0206) 579654
11–2.30, 6–11 (11–11 Sat)
Adnams Bitter Ⓗ, **Old** Ⓖ
Workingman's pub in new town where traditional games are available on request. Pool table in the back bar; darts in the front. Happy hour 6–7. Snacks lunchtimes and eves.
Q 🍺 ⟿ (Town) ♣

Dragoon
Butt Road ☎ (0206) 573464
11–2.30, 5.15–11 (11–11 Fri & Sat)
Adnams Mild, Bitter, Old, Broadside Ⓗ

Friendly, two-bar pub close to the town centre. Basic public bar with pool table; comfortable, quiet saloon. Regular guest beers. The last good beer if walking to the football ground from town. Food Mon–Sat.
🏢 ( ) 🍺 ⟿ (Town)

Odd One Out
28 Mersea Road (100 yds from St Botolphs roundabout)
☎ (0206) 578140
11–2.30 (not Mon–Thu), 5.30 (6 Sat)–11
Archers Best Bitter; Mauldons Bitter; Thwaites Bitter Ⓗ
The no-frills, beer-drinkers' pub of Colchester! A gem! Guest beers. No-smoking area Fri and Sat only.
🏠 ♿ ⟿ (Town) ☺ 🕭

Tap & Spile
Crouch Street
☎ (0206) 573572
11–2.30, 5.30–11
Adnams Bitter; Crouch Vale SAS; Mauldons Special; Nethergate Bitter; Tolly Cobbold Original Ⓗ
Previously called the 'Hospital Arms', a pub with strong rugby connections. Recently refurbished as a Tap & Spile and offering very good value food (no meals Sun lunch). Guest beers (four change every week).
🏠 Q 🏢 ♣

Coxtie Green

White House
173 Coxtie Green Road
☎ (0277) 372410
11–3, 6–11
Adnams Bitter; Greene King IPA Ⓗ
Small, cosy and friendly, country inn, good for families in summer, with a playground in the large beer garden. No meals Sun. Regular guest ales.
🏢 ( ) 🍺 P

Debden

Plough
High Street
☎ (0799) 40396
12–3, 6–11 (12–11 some Sats)
Greene King IPA, Raments Special, Abbot Ⓗ
Cosy, 17th-century local with a superb garden for children. Summer barbecues.
🏠 Q 🏢 ( ) 🍺 ♣ P

Dedham

Lamb
131 Birchwood Road
☎ (0206) 322216
11–3, 5–11 (11–11 Sat)
Tolly Cobbold Bitter, Original Ⓖ
14th-century, listed building

with a thatched roof and two small bars. A lovely pub in a lovely village. No food Mon.
🍺 Q ⑧ ◐ 😋 ♣ P

Donyland

Walnut Tree
Fingringhoe Road, Rowhedge (off Hythe road, 3 miles along Military Road) OS021216
☎ (0206) 728149
11.45–2.30, 5.30 (7 winter)–11 (11.45–11 Sat)
Adnams Bitter; Felinfoel Double Dragon; Tolly Cobbold Bitter; Wadworth 6X Ⓗ
Comfortable, lively pub, a few miles from Colchester town centre. Good value food all week; interesting range of ales. Especially busy in summer. Guest beers. ⑧ ◐ 🍴 ♣ P

Duton Hill

Rising Sun
½ mile W of B184
OS603269 ☎ (037 184) 204
11–4, 6–11 (all day if busy)
Adnams Extra; Ridleys IPA Ⓗ
Timber-framed local in a rural setting, with a large garden and a children's play area. Good value food. 🍺 ⑧ ◐ 🍴 Å ♣ P

Earls Colne

Castle
High Street ☎ (0787) 222694
11–3, 5–11 (11–11 Thu–Sat)
Greene King XX Mild, IPA, Abbot Ⓗ
12th-century pub with a small, quiet public bar. Lunches Mon–Sat; eve meals Wed–Sat.
🍺 ⑧ 😋 ◐ 🍴 P

Try also: Drum (Free)

Elsenham

Crown
High Street (B1051)
☎ (0279) 812827
11–2.30, 6–11 (12–2.30, 7–10.30 Sun)
Ind Coope Benskins Best Bitter; Young's Special Ⓗ
Deservedly popular, village pub with a reputation for food (not served Mon eve or Sun). Friendly atmosphere; fine, pargetted exterior.
🍺 Q ⑧ ◐ 😋 ≈ ♣ P

Epping

Black Lion
293 High Road (B1393)
☎ (0378) 78670
11–2.30, 5.30–11 (11–11 Sat)
Adnams Bitter; Tetley Bitter; Young's Special Ⓗ
16th-century coaching inn; a traditional pub with a friendly atmosphere. Good food.
Q ⑧ ◐ 🍴 😋 ♣ P

Forest Gate Inn
Bell Common (just off B1393, on the Ivy Chimneys road)
☎ (0378) 72312
10–2.30 (3 Sat), 5.30–11
Adnams Bitter, Broadside; Greene King Abbot; Ridleys IPA Ⓗ
Traditional pub with no jukebox or gaming machines. Busy at weekends. Guest beers.
🍺 Q ⑧ ◐ P

Finchingfield

Red Lion
Church Hill (B1053)
☎ (0371) 810400
11–11
Adnams Extra Ⓖ**; Ridleys IPA** Ⓗ
500 year-old pub opposite the church in a picturesque village. Live music; good range of meals. 🍺 Q 😋 ⑧ 😋 ◐ 🍴 ♣ P

Fobbing

White Lion
Lion Hill OS716839
☎ (0375) 673281
11–3, 5.30–11
Ind Coope Burton Ale; Taylor Walker Best Bitter; Tetley Bitter Ⓗ
300 year-old pub with a plaque on the wall commemorating the Peasants' Revolt which started in the village. Eve meals only if booked; no lunches Sun.
🍺 Q ⑧ ◐ 😋 Å ♣ P

Fuller Street

Square & Compasses
E off A131 at Gt Leighs; left after 1 mile OS748161
☎ (0245) 361477
12–3, 6–11
Ridleys IPA Ⓖ
Cosy, olde-worlde, cottage-type pub. Jugs and teapots adorn the ceiling, with tasteful bric-a-brac around the walls. Small library of books by the hearth and a strange but friendly dog in residence. Altogether an isolated gem (close to the Essex Way). No eve meals Sun/Mon.
🍺 Q ⑧ ◐ 😋 Å ♣ P

Gestingthorpe

Pheasant
Audley End OS813376
☎ (0787) 61196
11–3.30, 6–11
Adnams Bitter; Greene King IPA, Abbot; Nethergate Bitter, Old Growler Ⓗ
Multi-roomed pub which is the focus of the village. Good food (book weekends); occasional live jazz and rock music. 🍺 😋 ⑧ ◐ ♣ P

Good Easter

Fountain
Main Road (A1060)
OS618110 ☎ (0245) 31230
11–3, 6–11
Ridleys Mild (winter)**, IPA** Ⓗ
Friendly, traditional, country pub. The small public bar is dominated by a pool table; darts and dominoes are played in the comfortable saloon bar. The garden has petanque.
🍺 ⑧ ◐ ♣ P

Grays

Bricklayers Arms
48 Bridge Road (near A126)
☎ (0375) 372265
11–2.30, 5.30–10.30 (11 Thu & Fri; 11–3, 7–11 Sat)
Charrington IPA; Fuller's ESB (winter) Ⓗ
Friendly, two-bar pub with a pool table in the public. Separate meeting room. Large garden. Lunches Mon–Fri.
⑧ ◐ 😋 P

Try also: Wharf (Taylor Walker)

Great Burstead

Duke of York
Southend Road (A129)
☎ (0277) 651403
10–2.30, 6–11
Greene King IPA, Abbot Ⓗ
An attractive Gray's house, formerly two cottages, with a restaurant built on the back. Still has a good pub atmosphere, along with a reputation for good food. No meals Sun.
⑧ ◐ P

Great Chesterford

Plough
High Street (near B1383 and M11 jct 9) ☎ (0799) 30283
11–3, 6–11
Greene King IPA, Abbot Ⓗ
Superb, 18th-century, village local. Recently modernised but retaining its inglenooks.
🍺 Q ⑧ ◐ ≈ ♣ P

Great Clacton

Robin Hood
211 London Road
☎ (0255) 421519
11–3 (4 summer), 6–11
Adnams Bitter; Draught Bass; Charrington IPA Ⓗ
Several medieval cottages, merged to form a large, multi-roomed pub with exposed beams. The emphasis is on food, incl. vegetarian dishes. Very friendly licensees.
🍺 😋 ⑧ ◐ 🍴 Å P

Try also: Apple Tree, Little Clacton (Free)

Essex

Great Dunmow

Cricketers
22 Beaumont Hill (B184)
11–3, 6–11
Ridleys IPA Ⓗ
Friendly local opposite the duck pond on the village green. Beer-only licence until 1976, when it was extended into the bakery next door. Good value food (no meals Wed eve).
Q ⧄ ◐ ▮ 🕿 ♣ P

Great Saling

White Hart
The Street (2 miles N of A120)
OS701254 ☎ (0371) 850341
11–3, 6–11
Adnams Extra; Ridleys IPA Ⓗ
Superb, Tudor pub with a timbered gallery in the saloon bar. The remains of the world's largest smooth-leaved elm (destroyed by Dutch elm disease in 1974) stand opposite the pub. The food speciality is the Essex Huffer (a very large filled bap), which they claim to have invented at the pub.
▦ Q ◐ ▮ 🕿 ♣ P

Great Sampford

Red Lion Inn
Finchingfield Road (B1053)
12–3, 5.30–11
Ridleys Mild, IPA Ⓗ
Pleasant and friendly local, offering a varied menu in the bar and separate restaurant.
▦ Q 🛏 ⧄ ◐ ▮ 🕿 ♣ P

Halstead

Dog Inn
37 Hedingham Road (A604)
☎ (0787) 477774
12–3, 6–11
Adnams Bitter; Nethergate Bitter, Old Growler Ⓗ
Old inn on the Colchester–Cambridge road with lounge and public bar areas. Original beams. Friendly landlord. Guest ciders from time to time.
▦ 🛏 ⧄ ◐ ▮ 🕿 ♣ P

Harlow

Willow Beauty
Hodings Road (off Fifth Avenue) ☎ (0279) 437328
11–3, 6–11
Greene King XX Mild, IPA, Rayments Special, Abbot Ⓗ
New town pub with an unattractive exterior which is due for improvement. The recently refurbished interior gives a pleasant outlook onto the cricket pitch. Busy at weekends.
⧄ ◐ ▮ 🕿 ♣ P

Try also: White Horse, Old Harlow

Harwich

Hanover Inn
65 Church Street
☎ (0255) 502927
10.30–3 (later Sat), 6.30–11
Tolly Cobbold Mild, Bitter, Old (winter)**; Whitbread Boddingtons Bitter** Ⓗ
Partly rebuilt in 1910 after a serious fire. This cosy, timbered pub is the current favourite of the local professional fishermen. Beer not cheap. ▦ 🛏 🕿 ♣

Try also: Alma, Kings Head St (Brent Walker)

Hatfield Heath

White Horse Inn
The Heath (A1060)
☎ (0279) 730351
11–3, 5–11
Greene King IPA, Abbot Ⓗ
Interesting pub, refurbished to retain three separate bars. Good restaurant facilities in the extended area of the large lounge bar (no food Sun eve). Friendly, with a pleasant outlook onto a large village green with a cricket pitch.
🛏 ◐ ▮ 🕿 ♣ P

Hazeleigh

Royal Oak
Fambridge Road (1 mile S of Maldon) OS849047
☎ (0621) 853249
11–3, 6–11
Greene King IPA Ⓖ
Friendly, welcoming local which has had the same licensees for 25 years. ▦ 🕿 ♣ P

Henny Street

Henny Swan
Off A131, on back road from Sudbury to Bures OS879384
☎ (0787) 269238
11–2.30, 6–11
Greene King IPA, Abbot Ⓗ
Plush inn with a riverside garden, a separate restaurant and a bright, new conservatory.
🛏 ◐ ▮ P

Heybridge

Maltsters Arms
Hall Road (100 yds off B1022)
☎ (0621) 853880
11–3, 6–11
Greene King IPA, Abbot, Winter Ale Ⓖ
Traditional, back-street, drinkers' pub. ♣

High Easter

Cock & Bell
Off A1060, 2 miles from Leaden Roding
☎ (024 531) 296

12–3, 7–11
Crouch Vale Best Bitter; Eldridge Pope Hardy Country; Shepherd Neame Master Brew Bitter, Bishops · Finger Ⓗ
Attractive, 14th-century building in a rather isolated village. A military collection features an armoured personnel carrier in the car park. Good reputation for food. Booking advisable for restaurant meals.
▦ 🛏 ◐ ▮ P

High Roding

Black Lion
High Street (B184 at edge of village)
☎ (0279) 872847
11–3, 6–11
Adnams Extra; Ridleys IPA Ⓗ
Classic, unspoilt, 15th-century inn offering a wide choice of home cooking. A friendly inn: the locals do a lot of charity work. ▦ Q ⧄ ◐ ▮ 🕿 ♣ P

Try also: Axe & Compasses, Aythorpe Roding (Free)

Ingatestone

Star
High Street
☎ (0277) 353618
11–3, 6–11
Greene King IPA, Abbot Ⓖ
Pub with a cosy, well-worn interior which offers a friendly welcome. Live folk and country music two or three times a week. Raging log fires a speciality in winter. The family room is small but pleasant and the converted bakehouse is also suitable for family use in summer. Courtyard at rear.
▦ Q 🛏 🛏 🕿 ♣ P

Langham

Shepherd & Dog
Moor Road (1½ miles W of A12) OS019318
☎ (0206) 272711
11–3, 5–11
Adnams Bitter; Greene King IPA, Abbot; Nethergate Bitter, Old Growler (winter) Ⓗ
Cosy, country free house with a small, separate dining room. Children welcome lunchtimes and early eves. Tasty sandwiches. ▦ 🛏 ◐ ▮ ♣ P

Langley Lower Green

Bull
OS437345 ☎ (0279) 777307
12–2.30, 6–11
Adnams Bitter; Greene King IPA, Rayments Special Ⓗ
Friendly and well worth finding. A pitch-penny game is concealed under a bench seat in

the saloon bar. Doubles as doctor's surgery on Wed afternoons! Occasional guest beer: usually Wells Bombardier.
🏠 🏢 🍴 ♿ ♣ P

Leigh-on-Sea

Crooked Billet
51 High Street, Old Town
11.30–3, 6–11 (11.30–11 summer, may vary)
Adnams Bitter; Greene King IPA; Ind Coope Burton Ale; Taylor Walker Best Bitter; Tetley Bitter; Young's Bitter Ⓗ
Excellent, small, two-bar, country-style pub, opposite the famous cockle sheds in Old Leigh conservation area, with panoramic views of the estuary. A 16th-century listed building boasting an open hearth in the public bar, and numerous local history pictures in the saloon.
🏠 Q 🍴 ◑ 🍺 ⇌

Try also: Smack Inn, Old Leigh (Grand Met)

Little Braxted

Green Man
Kelvedon Road OS849130
☎ (0621) 891659
11–3, 6–11
Ridleys IPA Ⓗ
Pleasant, country pub full of authentic brasses, curios and military memorabilia.
🏠 Q 🍴 ◑ 🍺 ♣ P

Little Bromley

Wheatsheaf
Shop Road (2 miles from A120) OS095286 ☎ (0206) 392891
10.30–3 (not Mon, Wed or Fri in winter), 7.30–11
Adnams Bitter; Ruddles Best Bitter Ⓗ
Small, Essex weatherboarded pub with a very warm, friendly atmosphere. 🏠 Q 🍴 ◑ P

Littlebury

Queens Head Inn
High Street (B1383)
☎ (0799) 22251
11.30–3, 6–11
Adnams Bitter; Marston's Pedigree Ⓗ
600 year-old, village local with many traditional features. English Tourist Board three crowns. Caters for shooting parties. Regular guest beers – up to five normally available. No eve meals Sun/Mon.
Q 🛏 🍴 ◑ P

Little End

White Bear
149 London Road (just off A113) ☎ (0277) 362185
11–3, 7–11 (may extend in summer)

Adnams Bitter; Ind Coope Benskins Best Bitter, Burton Ale Ⓗ
Fine, old, traditional pub with a superb, basic public bar which has been in this guide for many years. Lots of events in summer months, eg car and motorcycle meets. Restaurant is open weekends only; no bar meals Mon eve. May have guest beers from time to time. Book to camp. 🏠 Q 🍴 ◑ 🍺 ⛺ ♣ P

Littley Green

Compasses
OS699172 ☎ (0245) 362308
11–3, 6–11
Ridleys Mild, IPA Ⓖ
Ridleys' brewery tap (one mile from the brewery): a simple, friendly, country pub which has won several CAMRA awards, incl. East Anglian *Pub of the Year* 1990. The food speciality is the Essex Huffer. Traditional pub music nights on certain Mons. 🏠 Q 🍴 ♣ ♣ P

Magdalen Laver

Green Man
2 miles from A414/M11 jct OS508074 ☎ (0279) 411752
11–2.30 (3 Sat), 6–11
Greene King IPA, Abbot; Nethergate Bitter Ⓗ
Cosy, country pub with a log fire and a revolving pool table. Garden at the front. Difficult to find. 🏠 🍴 ◑ ♣ P

Maldon

Queens Head
The Hythe
☎ (0621) 854112
10.30–11 (10.30–3.30, 5–11 Tue & Thu)
Greene King IPA, Abbot Ⓗ
Excellent, three-bar pub with a nautical flavour. Overlooks the estuary. 🏠 Q 🍴 🍺 ♣ P

Manningtree

Crown
51 High Street (off A137)
☎ (0206) 392620
10.30–3.30, 6–11
Greene King XX Mild, IPA, Rayments Special, Abbot Ⓗ
Large, old coaching inn with many original features. Roomy, friendly public and saloon bars. Car park (with seating) overlooks the Stour Estuary.
🍴 🛏 ♣ P

Station Buffet
The Station (off A137)
☎ (0206) 391114
11–11 (12–3 only Sun)
Adnams Bitter, Old; Marston's Pedigree; Nethergate Old Growler; Wadworth 6X Ⓗ

Tiny, rough and ready pub where pleasant, local staff serve everyone from locals to commuters and visitors from the Continent. Very busy at commuter and lunchtimes (especially Sun). A rail buff's dream and an Essex institution. Guest beers.
🏠 Q 🍴 ◑ ⇌ P

Mashbury

Fox
Fox Road OS650127
☎ (0245) 31573
12–2.30 (not Tue), 6.30–11
Adnams Extra; Ridleys IPA Ⓖ
Delightful, remote pub with a growing reputation for good value and imaginative food (no meals Tue). Folk music first Sun of each month. Bar skittles.
🏠 Q 🍴 ◑ ♣ P

Matching Tye

Fox Inn
The Green (2 miles from Old Harlow, on the Matching Green road) OS516113
☎ (0279) 731203
12–3, 6–11
Ind Coope Friary Meux Best Bitter, Burton Ale Ⓗ
Quaint, village pub with three separate bar rooms. Many 'foxy' artefacts. No food Sun. Petanque in the garden.
🏠 🍴 ◑ 🍺 ♣ P

Try also: Hare & Hounds

Messing

Old Crown
Lodge Road (1 mile N off B1022) OS898190
☎ (0621) 815575
11–3.30, 6–11
Adnams Extra; Ridleys IPA Ⓗ
Charming, multi-beamed, typical rural Essex village local which also functions as a post office on Mon and Thu mornings. Locally reputed to be near where Boudicca's forces were slaughtered by the Romans. Children welcome.
🏠 Q ◑ ♣ P

Mill Green

Viper
Mill Green Road
OS641019 ☎ (0277) 352010
10–2.30, 6–11
Ruddles Best Bitter, County Ⓗ
Unspoilt, country pub in a quiet, woodland setting. Fine traditional public bar, with wooden wall seats and flooring; award-winning garden. Hub of local footpaths; a sylvan gem.
🏠 Q 🍴 ◑ ♣ P

Essex

Moreton

White Hart
Off A414 ☎ (0277) 890228
11–3, 6–11 (may vary)
**Adnams Bitter; Courage Best
Bitter; Greene King Abbot** Ⓗ
Old pub serving a farming
community; busy, friendly and
welcoming. Good food in the
bar or restaurant (fish a
speciality). Courage Best is sold
as 'Webster's Wonderful
Wallop'. ⚏ Q ⚙ ◖ ◗ ⊟ ⅙ ♣ P

Mountnessing

Prince of Wales
Roman Road (B1002)
☎ (0277) 353445
11–11
**Adnams Extra; Ridleys Mild,
IPA** Ⓗ
One bar pub opposite a fine
example of an Essex post mill.
Crib is popular. ⚏ ⚙ ◖ ◗ P

Navestock Heath

Plough
Sabines Road
OS538970 ☎ (0277) 372296
11–11
**Adnams Bitter; Bateman
Mild, XB, XXXB; Courage
Directors; Greene King
Abbot** Ⓗ
Excellent free house with a
changing beer range at good
prices; always at least one real
mild. Not easy to find, but well
worth the trouble. ⚏ ⚙ ◖ ◗ ♣ P

Nevendon

Jolly Cricketers
Nevendon Road (A127 slip
road – London bound – at
A132 jct)
☎ (0268) 726231
11.30–2.30, 5.30–11
**Ind Coope Burton Ale; Tetley
Bitter** Ⓗ
Large roadhouse (built in 1929)
on the outskirts of Basildon.
Relaxing atmosphere in the
lounge; the public bar offers
pool and darts. Wide range of
children's playground facilities.
⚙ ◖ ⊟ P

Orsett

Foxhound
18 High Road (near hospital)
☎ (0375) 891295
11–3.30 (4 Sat), 6–11
**Courage Best Bitter,
Directors** Ⓗ
Friendly, village inn with
historic photographs of the pub
displayed around the saloon bar,
where a tree trunk forms a pillar
in the centre. Popular with
farmers and pharmacists alike.
Good food (bookings only
eves). ⚏ ⚙ ◖ ⊟ ♣ P

Purleigh

Bell
The Street ☎ (0621) 828348
11–2.30, 6–11
**Adnams Bitter; Ind Coope
Benskins Best Bitter** Ⓗ
Attractive, 16th-century pub;
friendly and comfortable, with
superb views over the
Blackwater Estuary. Good value
food (no meals Sun). Wonderful
cat! ⚏ Q ⚙ ◖ ◗ P

Radley Green

Thatcher's Arms
Off A414, near Norton Heath
OS622054 ☎ (0245) 248356
12–2.30, 6–11
Adnams Extra; Ridleys IPA Ⓗ
Traditional, country pub with
log fires, a friendly atmosphere
and a large garden with
children's facilities.
⚏ Q ⚙ ◖ ◗ Å ♣ P

Rickling Green

Cricketers' Arms
½ mile W of B1383 OS511298
☎ (079 988) 322
11–3, 6–11
**Bateman XXXB; Tolly
Cobbold Mild, Original** Ⓖ
Enlarged pub in an idyllic
situation overlooking the village
cricket green. Excellent food.
Unusual gravity dispense
through barrel ends mounted in
the wall. ⚏ ⛺ ⚙ ⊨ ◖ ◗ ⊟ P

Rochford

Golden Lion
35 North Street (near post
office) ☎ (0702) 545487
12–11 (closed 3–5 when quiet)
**Crouch Vale Best Bitter;
Fuller's London Pride;
Greene King Abbot** Ⓗ
300 year-old, weatherboarded
pub with an emphasis on real
ale. Over 250 different beers
sold during 1990. Offers a wide
range of home-cooked food
lunchtimes. Mon folk nights
monthly. Dogs welcome. An ale
oasis, with four others on sale,
besides those listed, incl. a mild.
Q ◖ ⇌ ♣

Old Ship
12 North Street (opp. post
office) ☎ (0702) 544210
11–3, 5 (6 Sat)–11
**Ind Coope Burton Ale; Tetley
Bitter; Young's Bitter** Ⓗ
17th-century coaching inn with
a cobbled courtyard. Both the
inn and stable block are listed
buildings. Music Thu eves. Food
available, with specials daily,
but only till 8.30pm. A Burton
Ale cellarmanship award-holder.
⚙ ◖ ◗ ⇌ ♣ P

Roydon

White Horse
2 High Street (at B181 jct)
☎ (0279) 793131
11–2.30, 6–11
**Courage Best Bitter,
Directors** Ⓗ
Cosy pub with a welcoming
landlord. Two separate rooms
with bars, one featuring a large
fireplace in which people can sit.
Darts available Sun–Tue.
Q ◖ ◗ Å ⇌ ♣

St Osyth

White Hart
Mill Street ☎ (0255) 820318
11–3, 7–11
**Adnams Bitter; Wadworth
6X** Ⓗ
Village pub with a warm and
friendly atmosphere; close to
the 11th-century priory.
Occasional guest beers.
⚏ ⚙ ◖ ◗ ♣ P

Salcott-cum-Virley

Sun
The Street OS950137
☎ (0621) 860461
11–3, 6–11
Adnams Bitter Ⓗ; **Greene
King Abbot** Ⓖ; **Tolly
Cobbold Bitter** Ⓗ
Quiet, village local near the
Essex marshes and bird
sanctuary. Snacks. ⚏ Q ⊟ ♣ P

Shoeburyness

Parsons' Barn
Frobisher Way, North Shoebury
(behind ASDA)
☎ (0702) 297373
11–2.30 (3 Sat), 6–11 (11–11 Sat in
summer)
**Adnams Bitter, Broadside;
Greene King IPA, Abbot;
Ruddles Best Bitter;
Webster's Yorkshire Bitter** Ⓗ
Preserved (listed) barn built in
1763–64 on the site of a
former 15th-century barn
owned by a Mr Parsons, who is
buried in the nearby churchyard.
Display of farm implements.
Friendly hosts and service.
Good restaurant and bar food
(no meals Sun eve; phone for
restaurant). Barbecues in
summer. A spacious, family pub.
Winter ales sometimes available.
⚏ Q ⛺ ⚙ ◖ ◗ ⅙ ⇌ ♣ P

South Benfleet

Anchor
1 Essex Way (2 mins from
station) ☎ (0268) 756500
11–3, 5.30 (7 Sat)–11
**Ruddles Best Bitter,
County** Ⓗ
14th-century pub with exposed
beams and interesting historical

associations; popular for games. Live music every Wed and Sun; function room. Food includes steak and real ale pie; barbecues Fri/Sat in summer. Guest beers.
🏠 🕃 🅓 ⟁ ≠ (Benfleet) ♣ P

Southend-on-Sea

Liberty Belle
10 Marine Parade (B1016)
☎ (0702) 466936
10–11
Courage Best Bitter, Directors Ⓗ
Gimmick-free, seafront pub catering for serious drinkers, not disco-seekers. Decorated with a nautical theme; ramped throughout for wheelchairs. Regular guest beers. Snooker room. Accommodation in summer only.
🏠 🏢 🅓 ⚖ ≠ (Central)

Railway Hotel
Clifftown Road (opp. NCP car park, behind Central station)
☎ (0702) 343194
11–11
Draught Bass; Charrington IPA Ⓗ
Large, brick-built, Victorian public house (c. 1870), with large, stained-glass windows and in good decorative order throughout. Busy lunchtime trade with shoppers and office workers. Guest beer regularly available. Function room.
🅓 ⟐ ⚖ ≠ (Central) ♣

Try also: Dickens, rear of 119 High St (Charrington)

Southminster

Rose Inn
Burnham Road (B1021, between Southminster and Burnham-on-Crouch)
☎ (0621) 772915
11.30–2.30 (3 Sat), 5.30 (6 Sat)–11
Greene King IPA, Abbot, Winter Ale; Ridleys Mild (occasional) Ⓖ
Friendly, roadside inn, with two rooms: a real public bar and a room with more comfort. Improved menu and a larger garden this year (no food Wed eve or Sun). Guest ciders.
🏠 Q 🏢 🅓 ♣ ⇨ P

South Weald

Tower Arms
Weald Road
☎ (0277) 210266
11.30–2.30, 6–11
Adnams Bitter; Greene King IPA; Ruddles County; Webster's Yorkshire Bitter; Young's Special Ⓗ
16th-century, listed building and former shooting lodge. Set in an attractive village, opposite a delightful, 11th-century

church. A cosy, friendly local, if a bit on the expensive side. Ring the Bull played. Large garden with petanque pitches.
🏠 ⟐ 🏢 ♣ P

Stanford-le-Hope

Rising Sun
Church Hill ☎ (0375) 671911
11–3, 5.30–11
Courage Best Bitter; John Smith's Bitter; Ridleys IPA Ⓗ
Friendly local in the centre of town. Garden for summer use. No food Sun. 🏢 🅓 ⟐ ♣ P

Stansted Mountfitchet

Dog & Duck
Lower Street (off B1351)
OS516251 ☎ (0279) 812047
10–2.30, 6–11
Greene King Rayments Special, Abbot Ⓗ
Excellent, weatherboarded, village local with a lovely pub sign. Watch out for the low beam in the lounge. Good lunchtime snacks (not available Sun). 🏠 Q 🏢 🅓 ⚖ ♣ P

Try also: Queens Head, Lower St (Brent Walker)

Stapleford Abbotts

Rabbits
Stapleford Road (B175 near Passingford Bridge)
☎ (040 28) 203
11–2.30, 6–11
Ind Coope Benskins Best Bitter, Burton Ale Ⓗ
Cosy, comfortable pub with a children's play area in the large garden. Meals include vegetarian. 🏠 🏢 🅓 🅓 P

Stisted

Dolphin
Coggeshall Road (A120)
☎ (0376) 21143
10.30–3, 6–11
Adnams Extra; Ridleys Mild, IPA Ⓗ
Cosy, old pub with splendid beams and log fires in both bars. The garden is well suited to children. No eve meals Tue or Sun. 🏠 Q 🏢 🅓 🅓 ♣ P

Onley Arms
The Street (1 mile N of A120)
OS800048 ☎ (0376) 25204
11–3, 7–11
Ridleys IPA Ⓗ
Cosy, one-bar pub with a separate restaurant, built for Onley Estate workers and still the centre of village life. Reasonable prices for main course meals. Only traditional fish and chips available on Wed eves. No bar lunches Sun.
🏠 Q 🏢 🅓 🅓 ♣ P

Stow Maries

Prince of Wales
Woodham Road (old B1012)
☎ (0621) 828971
11–11
Crouch Vale Woodham IPA, SAS; Taylor Landlord Ⓗ
Recently completely refurbished; an excellent, traditional pub famed for its constantly-changing range of guest beers, incl. milds. Can get crowded. Very good food.
🏠 Q 🕃 🏢 🅓 🅓 ♣ ⇨ P

Thaxted

Star
Mill End (by B184)
☎ (0371) 830368
11–2.30, 5–11 (11–11 Fri & Sat)
Adnams Mild, Bitter, Broadside Ⓗ
Pub with exposed beams and vast brick fireplaces. Live music Fri and Sat. Wide range of guest beers. 🅓 P

Try also: Swan Hotel (Free)

Tillingham

Cap & Feathers
8 South Street (B1021)
☎ (0621) 779212
11–3, 6–11
Crouch Vale Woodham IPA, Woodham Mild, Best Bitter, SAS, Essex Porter (summer), **Santa's Revenge, Willie Warmer** Ⓗ
Unspoilt, 15th-century, village inn. Good value beer and food (home-smoked fish a speciality). 1989 CAMRA national *Pub of the Year*.
🏠 Q 🕃 🏢 🛏 🅓 ♣ ⇨ P

Tolleshunt D'Arcy

Queens Head
15 North Street
☎ (0621) 860262
11–2.30 (3 Fri, 3.30 Sat), 6 (7 Sat)–11
Greene King IPA, Abbot Ⓗ
Village pub with a beautiful (quiet) public bar and a comfortable saloon. Eve meals Fri/Sat.
🏠 Q 🏢 🅓 🅓 ⚖ ♣ P

Toppesfield

Green Man
3 Church Lane
OS739374
☎ (0787) 237418
11–2.30, 7–11
Greene King IPA, Abbot Ⓗ
Excellent, welcoming and roomy pub in a remote village. Well worth finding.
🏠 Q 🏢 🅓 🅓 ♣ P

Essex

Waltham Abbey

Old English Gentleman
85 Highbridge Street (between Waltham Abbey and Waltham Cross) ☎ (0992) 712715
11–11 (11–4, 7–11 Sat)
McMullen AK, Country Ⓗ
Old pub on the canalside, said to have a ghost. Mainly serves the local community and passing boats. Not far from the historic abbey. ♨ Q ✿ ⊟ ⌂ P

Walton-on-the-Naze

Royal Marine
3 Old Pier Street
☎ (0255) 674000
10.30–3, 6–11
Marston's Pedigree; Whitbread Boddingtons Bitter, Flowers IPA, Castle Eden Ale Ⓗ
Unusual, two-bar pub, popular with the local lifeboat crew. Parking difficult. ♨ Q ⊟ ⇌ ♣

Warley

Alexandra
114 Warley Hill (B186)
☎ (0277) 210456
11–2.30 (3 Fri & Sat), 6–11
Greene King XX Mild, IPA, Rayments Special, Abbot Ⓗ, **Winter Ale** Ⓖ
Classic, mid Victorian, two-bar pub, with an off-licence and operational gas mantles. Limited eve hours, not available Tue; no food Sun. Tiny car park.
(● ⊟ ⇌ (Brentwood) ♣ P

Westcliff-on-Sea

Cricketers Inn
228 London Road (A13)
☎ (0702) 343168
10.30–11 (10.30–2.30, 5.45–11 Sat)
Greene King IPA, Abbot Ⓗ
Tired-looking, large, town pub with three bars: the Tudor lounge, a public and the separate Sportsman, which has a TV and three match dartboards. Black vinyl seating. On a busy main road; small car park.
⊟ ⇌ P

Palace Theatre Centre
430 London Road (A13)
☎ (0702) 347816
12–2.30, 6–11
Crouch Vale SAS; Greene King IPA, Abbot Ⓗ
Popular, comfortable foyer bar with a courtyard patio and an adjoining restaurant area. Weekly, good quality guest beers; convivial atmosphere. Live music Sun lunch (piano) and Sun eve (rock, etc). Children admitted till 7pm. Parking difficult, but on a busy bus route. Recommended. Q ✿ ⌂ ⇌

Try also: **Melrose**, Hamlet Court Rd (Grand Met)

White Notley

Cross Keys
1 The Street ☎ (0376) 83297
11–3, 6.30–11
Ridleys Mild, IPA Ⓗ
Fine, village local built in the 14th century; formerly Chappells Brewery. Families welcome in the saloon bar. Eve meals Fri/Sat only.
♨ ✿ (● ⊟ ⇌ ♣ P

White Roding

Black Horse
On A1060 ☎ (0279) 76322
11–2, 6.30–11
Ridleys IPA Ⓗ
Village pub; refurbished, with one bar now a dining area, but still friendly. ♨ Q ✿ (● ♣ P

Witham

George
36 Newland Street
☎ (0376) 511098
10–2.30 (3 Fri), 5.30 (5 Fri)–11 (10–11 Sat)
Adnams Extra; Ridleys Mild, Bitter Ⓗ
Welcoming, town-centre pub: a basic, public bar and a quiet, 16th-century, timber-framed saloon. Separate children's/pool/meeting room. No food weekends. Limited parking.
Q ⌂ (⊟ ⌂ ⇌ ♣ P

Victoria
Faulkbourne Road, Powers Hall End (road to Terling)
OS807152 ☎ (0376) 511809
11–2.30 (3.30 Sat), 6 (7 Sat)–11
Ridleys IPA Ⓗ
Former country pub now on the edge of town: a large public bar and a comfortable lounge. Satellite TV. No lunches Sun; eve meals served Thu–Sat.
♨ ⌂ ✿ (● ⊟ ♣ P

Wivenhoe

Horse & Groom
55 The Cross
☎ (0206) 824928
10.30–3, 5.30–11
Adnams Bitter, Old, Broadside Ⓗ
Popular local with five darts teams. Interesting social mix in the public bar. No food Sun. Parking limited. ✿ (⊟ ♣ P

Rose & Crown
The Quay (just off B1028)
☎ (0206) 826371
11–11 (11–2.30, 6–11 winter)
Ind Coope Friary Meux Best Bitter, Burton Ale; Tetley Bitter Ⓗ
Quayside, timber-framed, one-bar pub, busy in summer. Wide range of customers. Difficult

parking for cars and boats. Outside drinking on quay tables; reasonably priced bar food. May flood during spring tides. ♨ (● ⇌ ♣

Try also: **Station Hotel** (Brent Walker)

Woodham Mortimer

Hurdlemakers Arms
Post Office Road OS813045
☎ (024 541) 5169
11–3, 6–11
Greene King IPA, Abbot Ⓗ, **Winter Ale** Ⓖ
Splendid, friendly, traditional pub with a stone-flagged saloon and a fine public bar. Good food. ♨ Q ⌂ ✿ (● ⊟ ⌂ ♣ P

Wormingford

Crown Inn
Colchester Road (B1508)
☎ (0787) 227405
11.30–3, 6–11
Greene King IPA, Abbot Ⓗ
17th-century pub with a large garden and barbecue. Pool table in the carpeted public bar. No meals Sun eve. ♨ ✿ (● ⊟ ♣ P

Writtle

Wheatsheaf
70 The Green (off A414, near Writtle Green)
☎ (0245) 420695
11–2.30, 5.30–11
Greene King IPA, Abbot Ⓗ
Small, friendly, two-bar local in a pleasant village with a green and duck pond. Snacks available both sessions. Q ✿ ♣ P

Young's End

Green Dragon
Upper London Road (A131, close to Essex Showground)
☎ (0245) 361030
11–3, 6–11 (11–11 Sat)
Greene King IPA, Abbot Ⓗ
Modernised lounge and an original public bar, which is a pleasure to see. Very good bar meals; restaurant with a deserved, good reputation. Spacious outdoor play area for children, with a large toy dragon. Q ✿ (● ⊟ ♣ ♠ P

ONLY A REAL COAL FIRE WILL DO.

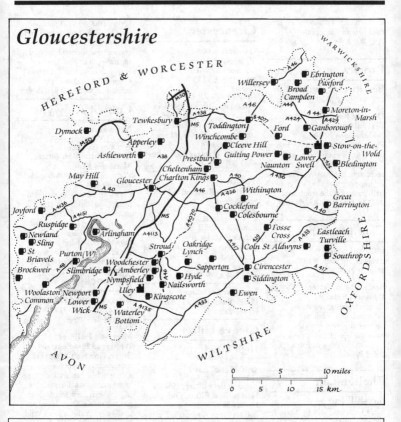

Gloucestershire

Donnington, *Stow-on-the-Wold*; **Uley**, *Uley*

Amberley

Black Horse
Off Minchinhampton Common
OS850016 ☎ (0453) 872556
11.30–2.30 (3.30 Sat), 6–11
**Greenalls Davenports Bitter;
Hook Norton Best Bitter; Ind
Coope Burton Ale; Tetley
Bitter** Ⓗ
Village pub, popular with both
locals and visitors. Extensive
blackboard menu and frequently
changing guest beers.
🏠 Q ☎ 🏵 ⛺ ◑ ◐

Apperley

Farmers Arms
On B4213
☎ (045 278) 307
11–2.30, 6–11
**Draught Bass; Hook Norton
Best Bitter; Wadworth 6X** Ⓗ
Comfortable, rustic farmhouse
atmosphere in a pub with
genuine beams, horse brasses
and a grandfather clock.
🏠 Q ☎ ◑ ◐ Å P

Try also: Coal House (Free)

Arlingham

Red Lion
The Cross
☎ (0452) 740269
11–2.30, 6.30–11
**Hook Norton Best Bitter;
Smiles Best Bitter; Wickwar
Brand Oak** Ⓗ
Simple, two-bar pub at the
village centre. Piano in the
lounge. Guest beers.
🏠 Q ☎ ◑ ◐ 🏵 ◑ ♣ P

Ashleworth

Boat Inn
The Quay (follow signs to Tithe
Barn, then keep going)
OS819251 ☎ (045 270) 272
11–2.30, 6–11
**Arkell's 3B; Smiles Best
Bitter, Exhibition** Ⓗ
Superb, old-fashioned pub on
the banks of the River Severn:
black leaded kitchen range,
scrubbed pine tables and quarry-
tiled floors. 🏠 Q ☎ 🏵 🏵 ♣ ⟲ P

Try also: Arkle (Donnington)

Bledington

Kings Head
The Green
☎ (0608) 658365
11–2.30, 6–11 (12–2, 7–10.30 Sun)
**Hook Norton Best Bitter;
Tetley Bitter; Wadworth
6X** Ⓗ
Comfortable, very popular,
village green pub which
specialises in food; booking
essential at weekends (no food
Sun eve). No-smoking
restaurant area. Children
admitted at lunchtime only.
🏠 ☎ 🏵 🏵 ◑ ◐ 🏵 Å
⇌ (Kingham) ♣ ⟲ P

Broad Campden

Bakers Arms
☎ (0386) 840515
11.30–3, 5.30–11
**Marston's Pedigree;
Wadworth 6X** (summer);
**Whitbread Flowers IPA,
Original** Ⓗ
Fine old Cotswold pub with a
genuine guest beer always
available (frequently from

Gloucestershire

Donnington). Folk music on the third Tue of the month.
🏚 Q 🍴 🍷 ♣ P

Brockweir

Brockweir Country Inn
Off A466 ☎ (0291) 689548
12–2.30, 7–11
Draught Bass; Hook Norton Best Bitter; Whitbread Boddingtons Bitter Ⓗ
Pub with oak beams from a ship locally-built many years ago. Tintern Abbey and Chepstow racecourse are nearby; salmon fishing possible; Offa's Dyke path runs past the front door.
🏚 Q 🌱 🍺 🍴 🍷 🐶 Å ♣ ⏎ P

Charlton Kings

Clock Tower
Cirencester Road (A435)
☎ (0242) 571794
11–3, 5–11
Banks's Mild, Bitter; Hanson's Bitter Ⓔ
Large, rambling, recently-extended, single-bar pub, decorated with memorabilia from the age of the horse and cart. On the edge of town.
🍺 🍴 🍷 P

Cheltenham

Bayshill Inn
85 St Georges Place (behind bus station)
☎ (0242) 524388
11–3, 5–11 (10.30–4, 6–11 Sat)
Hall & Woodhouse Tanglefoot; Wadworth IPA, 6X Ⓗ**, Old Timer** Ⓖ
Very popular, town-centre pub without frills. Good value lunches served, but hot snacks only in the eve, and cold food Sun. Cribbage is popular.
🍺 🚂 🍴 ♣ ⏎

Jolly Brewmaster
39 Painswick Road (near A46)
☎ (0242) 512176
11–2.30, 5.30 (6 Sat)–11
Marston's Pedigree; Whitbread WCPA, Flowers IPA, Original Ⓗ
Situated near the college of further education and popular with both students and staff. No food at weekends. 🏚 🍺 🍷 ♣

Kemble Brewery Inn
27 Fairview Street
☎ (0242) 243446
11.30–2.30 (3 Sat), 6–11
Archers Village, Best Bitter, Golden Ⓗ
Comfortable and friendly, back-street local, offering weekly-changing guest beers. Very popular for Sun lunch – come early. No eve meals at weekends. 🍺 🍷 🍴 ♣ ⏎

Cirencester

Golden Cross
20 Blackjack Street (near Corinium Museum)
☎ (0285) 652137
11–3, 6 (7 Sat)–11
Arkell's 2B, 3B Ⓗ
A real pub without gimmicks, relying on good beer, friendly and efficient service and good company. Appeals to all age groups. Arkell's 'guest' beers available, when brewed. Skittle alley 🍺 🍷 🍴 Å ♣

Talbot
14 Victoria Road (off A417 roundabout)
☎ (0285) 653760
11–2.30 (4 Sat), 6.30–11
Arkell's 2B, 3B Ⓗ
Friendly, comfortable local with good-value simple food. Try the home-made steak and kidney pie. No meals Sun. Skittle alley.
🍺 🚂 🍴 🍷 🐶 ♣ P

Try also: Corinium Court Hotel (Free); **Kings Head Hotel** (Free)

Cleeve Hill

High Roost
On B4632
☎ (0242) 672010
11.30–2.30 (3 Sat), 7–11
Archers Best Bitter; Hook Norton Best Bitter, Old Hooky Ⓗ
Pub set on the highest hill in the county, with expansive views through large bay windows across the Vale of Severn. Children allowed in for meals. Jukebox and bar skittles for entertainment. Reached by a flight of steps. 🍺 🚂 🍴 ♣ P

Cockleford

Green Dragon Inn
½ mile along Elkstone road, off A435 OS969142
☎ (024 287) 271
11–2.30, 6–11
Draught Bass; Butcombe Bitter Ⓖ**; Hook Norton Best Bitter** Ⓗ**; Theakston Old Peculier; Wadworth 6X; Whitbread Boddingtons Bitter** Ⓖ
Surprisingly large pub with a choice of two comfortable bars and many side rooms. Large car park in lane opposite. Jazz on Mon. Guest beers.
🍺 🍷 🍴 🐶 ⏎ P

Colesbourne

Colesbourne Inn
On A435 OS000133
☎ (024 287) 376
11–11
Wadworth IPA, 6X, Farmer's Glory (summer)**, Old Timer** Ⓗ

Large, 200 year-old pub, half-way between Cheltenham and Cirencester: a warm and comfortable lounge bar and a separate public bar. The emphasis is on food. A recent extension has added ten bedrooms. 🏚 🍺 🚂 🍴 🐶 ♿ ♣ P

Coln St Aldwyns

New Inn
OS146051 ☎ (0285) 75651
11–3, 6–11 (11–11 Sat)
Hook Norton Best Bitter; Marston's Pedigree; Wadworth 6X; Whitbread Flowers IPA Ⓗ
Excellent, 16th-century inn in a picturesque village. A two-year campaign by the villagers recently saved this pub from redevelopment and it has now been renovated and extended. Good quality food. Live music Sun night. 🏚 🌱 🍺 🚂 🍴 🍷 🐶 P

Dymock

Beauchamp Arms
On B4216 OS700312
☎ (053 185) 266
11–11
Marston's Pedigree; Whitbread Boddingtons Bitter, Flowers Original Ⓗ
Extended, 18th-century inn with a public bar, an uncluttered lounge and a small restaurant, offering excellent seasonal fare. No eve meals Thu or Sun. An ideal base for the famous Wild Daffodil Walk in spring. Cider in summer. 🏚 🍺 🍷 🐶 ♣ ⏎ P

Eastleach Turville

Victoria Inn
☎ (036 785) 277
11–2.30 (3 Sat), 6.30–11
Arkell's 3B, Kingsdown Ⓗ
18th-century pub overlooking a charming Cotswold village. Tasteful decor enhances the character. Good range of home-made food.
🏚 Q 🍺 🍷 🍴 🐶 ♣ ⏎ P

Ebrington

Ebrington Arms
Off B4035 ☎ (0386) 78223
11–2.30, 6–11
Donnington SBA; Hook Norton Best Bitter; Theakston XB Ⓗ
Friendly, old pub in the centre of the village, with a superbly preserved open fireplace in the dining area. No meals on Sun eves. 🏚 Q 🌱 🍺 🍷 🍴 🍷 ♣ ⏎ P

Ewen

Wild Duck
Drakes Island
☎ (0285) 770310
11–11

114

Draught Bass; Theakston XB (summer), Old Peculier (winter); Wadsworth 6X Ⓗ
Superb country house hotel, built in 1563 and retaining a slightly rustic feel with settles, old paintings and an imposing fireplace. An excellent family area is watched over by a parrot. Quality food, incl. fish. The house beer, Duck Pond Bitter, is Archers Village.
🏨 ⅀ ⊛ ◖◗ ⌖ P

Ford

Plough Inn
On B4077 OS088294
☎ (038 673) 215
11–11
Donnington BB, SBA Ⓗ
Splendid, unspoilt country pub which opens at 8am for truckers breakfasts. Note the rhyme on the front wall; the cellar used to be a gaol. No food Sun eve.
🏨 ⊛ ◖◗ ⚥ Å ♣ ⌖ P

Fosse Cross

Hare & Hounds
On A429 OS068095
☎ (0285) 720288
11–3, 6–11
Hook Norton Best Bitter; Wadsworth 6X Ⓗ
Comfortable, stone-built pub with an L-shaped bar. Snacks, children's and vegetarian meals are served in the bar and the separate restaurant. Adjacent caravan site. Guest beers.
🏨 ⅀ ⊛ ◖◗ ⚥ ♣ P

Ganborough

Coach & Horses
On A424, 3 miles N of Stow OS172292 ☎ (0451) 30208
11–2.30, 5.30–11
Donnington XXX, BB, SBA Ⓗ
Pleasant country pub on the main road, popular for its food and beer; it's the nearest pub to Donnington brewery. Occasional live entertainment. Pub games include bottle walking (not for the fainthearted). No food Sun eve.
🏨 ⅀ ⊛ ◖◗ ♣ ⌖ P

Gloucester

Dr Fosters
Kimberley Warehouse, The Docks ☎ (0452) 300990
10–11
Courage Best Bitter, Directors Ⓗ
Located in a renovated warehouse in the historic docks. Outdoor drinking on the quayside. Open all day Sun for food (11–10.30). ⅀ ⊛ ◖◗ ⚥ P

Fountain Inn
Westgate Street (110 yds from the Cross) ☎ (0452) 22562

11–11 (11–3, 6.30–11 Mon–Thu in winter)
Marston's Pedigree; Wadsworth 6X; Whitbread Boddingtons Bitter, Flowers Original Ⓗ
Reputedly one of the oldest ale houses in Gloucester, dating back to 1216, with a ghost in the cellar. Popular for lunchtime food. Guest beers.
🏨 ◖◗ ⚥ ⚥ ♣ ♧

Linden Tree
73 Bristol Road (A38, 1½ miles S of centre) ☎ (0452) 27869
11–2.30 (3 Sat), 5.30 (6 Sat)–11
Hook Norton Best Bitter; Wadsworth 6X Ⓗ
An excellent, well-kept pub in a Grade II listed building – quite different from the average town pub. Guest beers available and very good breakfasts. 🏨 ⚥ ◖◗

Old Crown
81 Westgate Street (near cathedral) ☎ (0452) 310517
11–11
Samuel Smith OBB, Museum Ⓗ
Reopened as pub in 1990, after 200 years of other use, most recently as an Army and Navy surplus store. Traditional public bar on the ground floor; plush lounge upstairs. One of the few Sam Smith's outlets in the county. 🏨 Q ◖◗ ⚥ ⅃

Whitesmiths Arms
81 Southgate Street
☎ (0452) 414770
11–2.30, 6 (7 Sat)–11
Marston's Pedigree; Whitbread Boddingtons Bitter, Flowers IPA, Original Ⓗ
Named after maritime metalworkers, this pub stands opposite the city docks and close to the National Waterways Museum. Recently refurbished; popular with office workers at lunchtime. 🏨 ◖◗ ♣

Great Barrington

Fox Inn
1 mile from the Barringtons turning off A40 OS204131
☎ (045 14) 385
11.30–2.30, 6.30–11 (12–2, 7–10.30 Sun)
Donnington XXX, BB, SBA Ⓗ
Excellent, stone-built pub in a beautiful position by the River Windrush; popular with walkers and locals. One of the only two pubs in the county that have been in every edition of this guide. No food Sun; cider in summer. 🏨 Q ⚥ ◖◗ ♣ ⌖ P

Guiting Power

Olde Inn
Winchcombe Road OS093249
☎ (0451) 850392

11–2.30, 6–11
Hook Norton Best Bitter; Theakston Best Bitter, XB Ⓗ
An excellent, Cotswold freehouse, popular with locals and tourists alike. A wide range of Danish food available.
🏨 Q ◖◗ ⚥ ♣

Try also: Farmers Arms (Donnington)

Hyde

Ragged Cot
On main Minchinhampton–Aston Down road OS887012
☎ (0453) 73116
11–2.30, 6–11
Marston's Pedigree; Theakston Best Bitter; Uley Old Spot Ⓗ
Popular free house, tastefully modernised and offering a good menu and selection of beers incl. guests. 🏨 Q ⊛ ⚥ ◖◗ ⚥ P

Joyford

Dog & Muffler
Between B4228 & B4432 OS579132 ☎ (0594) 832444
11–11 (12–3, 7–11 winter)
Ruddles County; Samuel Smith OBB Ⓗ
Lovely, olde-worlde pub with lots of character. Difficult to find but worth the trouble. The garden has a play area for children. No food Mon in winter. Q ⊛ ◖◗ ⚥ Å ♣ P

Kingscote

Hunters Hall
On A4135 ☎ (0453) 860393
11–2.30, 6.30–11
Hook Norton Best Bitter; Uley Old Spot; Wadsworth 6X Ⓗ
Old, creeper-covered, stone-built coaching inn. The various, high-beamed, connecting rooms have fine, flagged floors and the public bar is warmed by a big log fire. 🏨 Q ⅀ ⊛ ◖◗ ⚥ ♣ P

Lower Swell

Golden Ball
☎ (0451) 30247
11–2.30, 6.30–11
Donnington BB, SBA Ⓗ
Excellent but unspoilt village local with good food and cider. Limited parking.
🏨 ⊛ ⚥ ◖◗ ♣ ⌖ P

Lower Wick

Pickwick Inn
Off A38 OS712958
☎ (0453) 810259
11–2.30, 7–11
Draught Bass; Butcombe Bitter; Theakston Best Bitter Ⓗ
Recently renovated, country pub. 🏨 Q ⊛ ◖◗ ⚥ P

Gloucestershire

May Hill

Glasshouse Inn
Off A40 OS709213
☎ (0452) 830529
11–2.30, 6–11 (12–2, 7–10.30 Sun)
Butcombe Bitter; Whitbread WCPA 🄶
Friendly, old, country pub with an original, red-tiled floor. Food is limited to ploughman's on Sun. Guest beers are from small independents. Worth finding.
🏚 🍴 🄵 🅓 🚻 ♣ P

Moreton-in-Marsh

Black Bear
High Street ☎ (0608) 50705
11–3 (10.30–4 Tue), 6–11
Donnington XXX, BB, SBA 🄷
Busy pub at the very centre of town. Paved area for outside drinking. 🍴 🚪 🄵 🅓 🅐 ⚓ ♣ P

Nailsworth

Tipputs Inn
Bath Road (A46)
☎ (0453) 832466
11–3, 6–11
Hook Norton Old Hooky; Uley Old Spot; Whitbread Boddingtons Bitter 🄷
Comfortable free house at the top of a hill, south of town. L-shaped main bar and a second bar adjoining the restaurant. Guest beers. 🏚 🍴 🄵 🅓 🅖 ♣ P

Naunton

Black Horse
Off B4068 ☎ (0451) 850378
11–2.30, 6–11 (12–2, 7–10.30 Sun)
Donnington BB, SBA 🄷
Typical Donnington's local in a picturesque Cotswold village.
🏚 🍴 🚪 🄵 🅓 🅖 ♣ P

Newland

Ostrich
☎ (0594) 33260
12–3, 6–11
Hall & Woodhouse Tanglefoot; Marston's Pedigree; Whitbread Boddingtons Bitter, Pompey Royal 🄷
Small, unspoilt pub with a wealth of beams. Full of character, enhanced by a blazing log fire and a friendly atmosphere. Not many pubs like this remain. Above average pub food. 🏚 Q 🍴 🚪 🄵 🅐

Newport

Stagecoach Inn
On A38 ☎ (0453) 810385
11–2.30, 6–11
Draught Bass; Marston's Pedigree; Wadworth 6X; Whitbread Flowers Original; Wickwar Brand Oak 🄷
Nicely refurbished pub opposite

Newport Towers. It has been in the same family for 35 years. Good food is available until 10pm (vegetarian and children's menus). Booking strongly advised. Garden play area for children. 🏚 🌳 🍴 🄵 🅓 🅐 P

Nympsfield

Rose & Crown
Off B4066 ☎ (0453) 860240
11.30–2.30, 6.30–11
Theakston Best Bitter; Uley Bitter, Old Spot; Wadworth 6X; Whitbread Boddingtons Bitter 🄷
Large, village local with a good range of food. 🏚 🍴 🚪 🄵 🅓 ♣ P

Oakridge Lynch

Butchers Arms
Via Bisley, on N edge of village
OS915038 ☎ (028 576) 371
12–3, 6–11
Archers Best Bitter; Butcombe Bitter; Ind Coope Burton Ale; Ruddles Best Bitter, County; Tetley Bitter 🄷
A lively gem of a village pub, well worth seeking out. The fine, 18th-century building was formerly a slaughterhouse and butcher's shop; now there are three, sensitively modernised bars and a separate restaurant (eve meals Wed–Sat).
🏚 Q 🄵 🅓 🅐 ♣ P

Paxford

Churchill Inn
On B4479 OS184379
☎ (0386) 78203
11–2.30, 6–11
Hook Norton Best Bitter, Old Hooky 🄷
Pleasant, country local with a keen darts following and an Aunt Sally in the garden. Sun lunch served summer only; no meals Sun eve.
🏚 Q 🍴 🚪 🄵 🅓 🅐 ♣ ⌂

Prestbury

Plough
Mill Street ☎ (0242) 244175
11–2.30, 6–11
Whitbread WCPA, Flowers IPA, Original 🄶
Half-timbered, thatched pub with an attractive garden. Quoits played. Good range of lunchtime snacks. 🏚 Q 🍴 🄵 ♣

Purton (West)

Old Severn Bridge Hotel
1½ miles off A48, between Lydney and Blakeney
OS670046 ☎ (0594) 842454
12–2.30 (not Mon or Tue), 7–11
Greene King Abbot; Marston's Pedigree; Smiles

Best Bitter 🄷
Large, one-bar hotel with a cosy snug and beautiful views over the River Severn. Children's play equipment in the garden. Chinese meals available in eve if booked. 🏚 Q 🍴 🚪 🄵 🅓 🅐 P

Ruspidge

New Inn
On B4277
OS651119 ☎ (0594) 824508
7–11 (12–2.30, 7–11 Sat; 12–3, 7–10.30 Sun)
Archers Village, Golden 🄷
Fairly basic, village pub, open eves only during the week. The separate games room offers an interesting selection of games.
🏚 🍴 ♣ ⌂ P

St Briavels

George
High Street ☎ (0594) 530228
12–3, 7–11
Marston's Pedigree; Wadworth 6X 🄷
One-bar pub with beams and plenty of character, standing near the castle. Very popular with all ages. Guest beers. Eve meals in winter are only served Mon–Fri.
🏚 Q 🍴 🚪 🄵 🅓 🅖 🅓 ♣ P

Sapperton

Daneway Inn
N of A419, 4 miles W of Cirencester OS939034
☎ (028 576) 297
11–2.30 (3 Sat), 6.30–11
Archers Best Bitter 🄴&🄷;
Hall & Woodhouse Badger Best Bitter 🄷; **Wadworth 6X** 🄶
Superb, old canal-workers' inn, set in an idyllic position near the western end of Sapperton canal tunnel. Note the magnificent fireplace in the comfortable lounge. House beer, Daneway Bitter, is reputedly from Archers. One of the cheapest pubs in Gloucestershire. Guest beer.
🏚 Q 🌳 🍴 🄵 🅓 ♣ ⌂ P

Siddington

Greyhound
Ashton Road ☎ (0285) 653573
11.30–2.30, 6.30 (7 Mon & Sat)–11 (12–2.30, 7–10.30 Sun)
Hall & Woodhouse Tanglefoot; Wadworth IPA, 6X 🄷
First-rate, 17th-century inn, nestling between the canal and the railway line, both long disused. Two roaring fires and interesting furniture and artefacts add to its attraction. A small, quiet public bar and a lounge where tables can be booked for eve meals.
🏚 Q 🍴 🄵 🅓 🅖 🅓 ♣ P

Gloucestershire

Slimbridge

Tudor Arms
Shepherds Patch (follow signs
for Wildfowl Trust)
☎ (0453) 890306
11–2.30, 5 (7 winter)–11
**Draught Bass; Hook Norton
Best Bitter; Smiles Best
Bitter; Theakston Best Bitter;
Whitbread Flowers
Original** ⊞
Well-run, large, country pub.
Separate restaurant and no-
smoking family room.
⇔ ⊛ ⇔ ◖ ▌ ⊕ ♣ ▲ P ⅄

Sling

Orepool Inn
On B4228 ☎ (0594) 833277
11–11
**Draught Bass; Theakston
Best Bitter; Welsh Brewers
Worthington BB** ⊞
Tastefully-extended, 17th-
century, miners' inn with a quiet
snug, and family, function and
pool rooms. The beer garden
has a play area. Attached motel
and a campsite in the grounds.
Q ⇔ ⊛ ⇔ ◖ ▌ ⊕ ▲ ♣ ⊖ P

Southrop

Swan Inn
OS200035 ☎ (036 785) 205
12–3, 7–11
Morland Bitter ⊞
Attractive, creeper-covered,
village pub, dating back to the
17th century. The public has a
skittle alley attached, whilst
separate dining areas serve
imaginative, upmarket food.
Very small garden. Two guest
beers. ▲ ⇔ ⊛ ◖ ▌ ⊕ ♣

Stow-on-the-Wold

Queens Head
The Square ☎ (0451) 30563
11–2.30 (3 Sat), 5.30–11
Donnington BB, SBA ⊞
Fine, old Cotswold pub, popular
with tourists and locals alike.
Snacks lunchtime; meals eves,
except Sun. ⊛ ▌ ♣ ⊖

Stroud

Clothiers Arms
1 Bath Road (A46)
☎ (0453) 763801
11–2.30, 4.30–11
**Ind Coope Burton Ale;
Ruddles Best Bitter; Smiles
Best Bitter; Tetley Bitter;
Wadworth 6X** ⊞
Comfortable and welcoming
free house, displaying
memorabilia of the old Stroud
Brewery Company. Eve meals
finish at 9pm. Guest beers.
⊛ ◖ ▌ ⇌ ♣ P

Duke of York
22 Nelson Street
☎ (0453) 758715
12 (11.30 Fri)–2.30 (11.30–3 Sat),
7–11
**Butcombe Bitter; Smiles Best
Bitter** ⊞
Friendly, one-bar pub at the top
end of town. Guest beers.
◖ ▌ ⇌

Tewkesbury

Berkeley Arms
Church Street
☎ (0684) 293034
10.30–2.30 (3 Sat), 6.30–11
**Hall & Woodhouse
Tanglefoot** (summer);
**Wadworth 6X, Farmer's
Glory, Old Timer** ⊞
Ancient pub of character.
Access to the lounge is through
an unusual alleyway. Limited
range of meals, but a good
selection of lunchtime snacks.
Q ⇌ ◖ ▌ ⊕ ▲ ♣ ⊖

Try also: Albion (Ansells)

Toddington

Pheasant Inn
At B4632/B4077 jct
☎ (0242) 621271
12–2.30, 6–11
**Ansells Bitter; Banks's Bitter;
Ind Coope Burton Ale** ⊞
Two-bar pub next to the
Gloucestershire and
Warwickshire Railway HQ.
Occasional live entertainment.
Cider in summer.
⊛ ◖ ▌ ⊕ ♣ ⊖ P

Waterley Bottom

New Inn
E of N Nibley, along 1½ miles of
narrow lanes OS758964
☎ (0453) 543659
12–2.30, 7–11 (12–2, 7–10.30 Sun)
**Cotleigh Tawny; Greene
King Abbot; Smiles Best
Bitter** ⊞**, Exhibition;
Theakston Old Peculier** ⊜
Large, friendly free house in a
beautiful setting, surrounded by
steep hills. Two golf courses
nearby. A large-scale map
advisable for first-time visitors.
House beer, Cotleigh WB, is a
specially produced variant of
Harrier SPA.
▲ Q ⊛ ⇌ ◖ ▌ ⊕ ♣ ⊖ P

Willersey

New Inn
On B4632 (old A46)
☎ (0386) 853226
11–2.30, 6.30–11
Donnington BB, SBA ⊞
Lively, village pub serving the
local community. Overnight
accommodation includes a
family room. Skittle alley.
Q ⊛ ⇌ ◖ ▌ ⊕ ▲ ♣ ⊖ P

Winchcombe

Corner Cupboard
Gloucester Street (B4632)
☎ (0242) 602303
11.30–2.30, 5.30–11 (12–2.30, 7–10.30
Sun)
**Marston's Pedigree; Uley
Bitter; Whitbread
Boddingtons Bitter, Castle
Eden Ale, Flowers Original** ⊞
Two-bar pub allowing
customers to choose their own
style and company. Eve meals
only in the high-class restaurant
(open Tue–Sat; booking
advised). ▲ Q ⊛ ◖ ⊕ ♣ ⊖ P

Withington

Mill Inn
OS032154 ☎ (024 289) 204
11–2.30, 6–11
**Samuel Smith OBB,
Museum** ⊞
This is the place to bring your
American friends: an ancient,
stone-built inn of great
character, with many rooms and
magnificent fireplaces. The
lovely garden overlooks a
stream. ▲ ⊛ ⇌ ◖ ▌ ♣ P

Woodchester

Royal Oak
Church Road (off A46 by piano
works in N Woodchester)
OS839027 ☎ (0453) 872735
12–3, 7–11
**Adnams Bitter; Draught
Bass; Wadworth IPA, 6X** ⊞
Friendly free house with an
additional bar in the restaurant.
Occasional guest beer. Car park
is small. ▲ ⊛ ⇌ ◖ ▌ ♣ P

Try also: Ram (Free)

Woolaston Common

Rising Sun
1 mile off A48, near Netherend
OS590009 ☎ (059 452) 282
12–2.30 (not Wed), 6.30–11
**Hook Norton Best Bitter;
Theakston Best Bitter** ⊞
Lovely, country pub with
excellent views and a friendly
landlord. Beautiful floral display
in summer. The menu includes
genuine Indian curries. Guest
beers. Q ⊛ ◖ ▌ ▲ ♣ P

**ONLY A REAL COAL FIRE
WILL DO.**

117

Hampshire

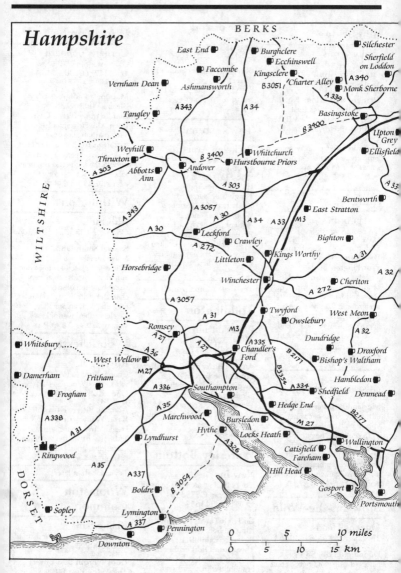

Hampshire

BERKS

East End • Faccombe • Burghclere • Ecchinswell • Silchester • Sherfield on Loddon

Vernham Dean • Ashmansworth • Kingsclere • Charter Alley • Monk Sherborne

A 343 • A 34 • A 339 • A 340

Tangley • Basingstoke

Weyhill • Thruxton • Abbotts Ann • Andover • Whitchurch • Hurstbourne Priors • Upton Grey • Ellisfield

B 3400

A 303 • A 343 • A 303 • A 33

WILTSHIRE

Bentworth • East Stratton

A 3057 • A 30 • A 34 • A 33 • M3

Leckford • Crawley • Kings Worthy • Bighton

Horsebridge • Littleton • A 31

A 3057 • Winchester • Cheriton • A 32

A 272 • A 272

Romsey • Twyford • West Meon

A 27 • M3 • Owslebury • A 32

Whitsbury • West Wellow • Chandler's Ford • Dundridge • Droxford

A 36 • A 27 • A 335 • B 2171 • Bishop's Waltham

Damerham • M27 • B 3354 • Hambledon • Denmead

Fritham • A 336 • Southampton • A 334 • Shedfield

Frogham • A 35 • Hedge End • B 2177

A 338 • Marchwood • Bursledon • M 27 • Wallington

A 31 • Lyndhurst • Hythe • Locks Heath

Ringwood • A 326 • Catisfield • Fareham

A 35 • A 337 • Hill Head • Gosport

DORSET • Boldre • B 3054 • Portsmouth

Sopley • Lymington • Pennington

Downton

0   5   10 miles
0   5   10   15 km

🏰 **Gale's**, Horndean; **Ringwood**, Ringwood

Abbotts Ann

Eagle
Off A343 ☎ (0264) 710339
11–2.30 (3 Fri & Sat), 6.30 (6
summer)–11
**Courage Best Bitter,
Directors; John Smith's
Bitter; Wadworth 6X** Ⓗ
Popular pub in an attractive,
thatched village. Its very
friendly landlord offers guest
beers according to local
demand. No food Mon.
🏰 Q ❧ 🏮 🌢 ▯ ◗ ▣ ♣ P

Aldershot

Albion
Waterloo Road
(off A323)
☎ (0252) 319286
12–3, 5.30–11 (11–11 Fri & Sat)
**Gale's XXXL, Best Bitter, 5X,
HSB** Ⓗ
Rumours of alteration have not
materialised; this remains a
good, basic, back-street local
with a cosy snug. A pleasant
atmosphere distinguishes it from
many other Aldershot

establishments. No food Sun
eve. 🏮 ◗ ▯ ▣ ⇌ ♣ ○

Garden Gate
4 Church Lane East
☎ (0252) 21051
11.30–2.30 (3 Sat), 6–11
**Greene King XX Mild, IPA,
Rayments Special, Abbot** Ⓗ
A superb addition to a poor
choice in the town: basic,
friendly and intimate, with a
highly popular mild. A pleasant
and quiet retreat from
Aldershot's more raucous
institutions. 🏰 ❧ ⇌ ♣ P

Draught Bass; Marston's
Burton Best Bitter; Ringwood
Fortyniner Ⓗ
Cosy, beamed pub with a
collection of chamber pots. Very
popular lunchtimes and can get
crowded. The atmosphere of a
village pub only five minutes
from the town centre. Q ◖ ≒

Royal Oak

Gosport Road, Lower
Farringdon (A32)
11–3, 6–11
**Courage Best Bitter,
Directors** Ⓗ
Cosy, beamed pub, complete
with antlers! Popular during the
day with business people; at
night a quiet locals' pub.
Children welcome. Guest beer.
▨ Q ⚭ ⊛ ◖ ◗ ♣ P

Andover

Lardicake

Adelaide Road (200 yds from
centre)
☎ (0264) 323447
11–11
**Archers Best Bitter, Golden;
Fuller's London Pride; John
Smith's Bitter** Ⓗ
Lively and unpretentious, back-
street pub near a small, modern
estate. Useful function room;
good value food (no meals Sun).
Guest beers. Car park eves only.
▨ ⊛ ◖ ◗ ♣ P

Merrie Monk

New Street
☎ (0264) 352675
11–2.30, 6–11 (Fri & Sat)
**Marston's Burton Best Bitter,
Pedigree** Ⓗ
Good, basic public bar with a
comfortable lounge and small
upstairs dining room. Eve meals
finish at 7.30pm. ⊛ ◖ ◗ ♣ P

Ashmansworth

Plough

Off A343
☎ (0635) 253047
12–2.30 (not Mon; not Tue, Jan–Mar),
6–11
**Archers Village, Best Bitter,
Golden** Ⓖ
In Hampshire's highest village,
one of its finest rural locals has
now been opened out into a
single bar but still retains its
atmosphere. Beer is served
direct from casks (cooled in
summer). Upmarket prices;
interesting guest beers.
▨ ⊛ ◖ ◗ ♧ P

Basingstoke

Chineham Arms

Hanmoor Road, Chineham (W
of A33)
☎ (0256) 56404
11.30–3, 5–11 (11.30–11 Fri & Sat)
**Fuller's Chiswick, London
Pride, ESB** Ⓗ

Well-designed pub with a much
better atmosphere than the
usual estate pub; situated on the
north-eastern outskirts of the
Basingstoke sprawl.
⚭ ⊛ ◖ ◗ ⅏ ♣ P

Bentworth

Sun

Sun Hill
☎ (0420) 62338
12–3, 6–11
**Draught Bass; Bunces Best
Bitter; Gale's HSB; Marston's
Pedigree** Ⓗ
Unspoilt, country pub with low
beams and bare floors, built in
1635. Old prints and farming
implements cram the walls.
Wood-burning stoves in two
splendid fireplaces. Guest beers.
▨ Q ⊛ ◖ ◗ P

Bighton

Three Horseshoes

Off A31/B3047
☎ (0962) 732859
11–2.30, 6–11 (12–2, 7–10.30 Sun)
Gale's XXXD, BBB, HSB Ⓗ
Delightful, rural local, well off
the beaten track. Country crafts
collection in the locals' bar;
relaxing atmosphere in the quiet
lounge. The Sea Angling Club
welcomes visitors. Handy for
Mid-Hants steam railway
(Ropley station two miles). No
food Mon.
▨ Q ⊛ ◖ ◗ ⅏ ♣ P

Bishop's Waltham

Bunch of Grapes

St Peters Street
☎ (0489) 892935
10–2 (2.30 Sat), 6 (5 Sat)–11 (12–2,
7–10.30 Sun)
**Courage Best Bitter,
Directors** Ⓖ
Pub in a narrow, medieval street
leading to the parish church. In
the same family for 80 years.
Unspoilt by time, with beer on
stillage behind the bar (incl. a
guest beer). Harvest Festival
held every autumn. Q ♣ ♧

Boldre

Red Lion Inn

Rope Hill
☎ (0590) 673177
10.30–3, 6–11
**Eldridge Pope Dorchester,
Royal Oak** Ⓗ
Built in the 1680s as three
houses and a stable which
always sold beer. Low beams
and large collections of chamber
pots (40), harnesses and gin and
man-traps. Superb hanging
baskets in summer. Good
quality food.
▨ Q ⊛ ◖ ◗ ⅏ P

Royal Staff

Staff Road
☎ (0252) 22932
12–3, 5–11
**Fuller's Chiswick, London
Pride** Ⓗ
One-bar, back-street local
offering more choice for the
beleaguered Aldershot drinker
with the recent addition of
Fuller's. A darts pub, liable to be
rowdy. ⊛ ◖ ≒ ♣ ♧

Alton

Eight Bells

Church Street
☎ (0420) 82417
11–3, 5–11 (11–11 Fri & Sat)

Hampshire

Burghclere

Queen
Harts Lane
☎ (0635) 27350
11–3, 6–11
**Adnams Bitter, Broadside;
Arkell's 3B** Ⓗ
Fine example of a country free
house with a strong local
following for games. The
conversation often centres on
racing (Newbury racecourse
nearby). No food Sun.
🏠 🍺 🌢 ♣ P

Buriton

Five Bells
High Street
☎ (0730) 63584
11–2.30, 6 (5 Fri)–11
**Ballard's Best Bitter; Ind
Coope Friary Meux Best
Bitter, Burton Ale; Tetley
Bitter** Ⓗ
400 year-old pub built from
local stone in a village at the
start of the South Downs Way.
A busy free house with a varied
menu of bar and restaurant
meals. Live music most Weds
(folk/jazz). 🏠 🍺 🌢 ⊞ ⚲ ♣ P

Bursledon

Linden Tree
School Road, Lowford (off
A27/A3025)
☎ (042 121) 2356
11–2.30, 6 (5 Fri)–11
**Draught Bass; Wadworth
IPA, 6X, Farmer's Glory** Ⓗ,
Old Timer Ⓖ
Excellent, comfortable, one-bar
pub with no obtrusive gaming
machines, just light piped music.
A pergola and children's play
area make it ideal in summer.
High quality, home-cooked food
(not served Sun). 🏠 🍺 🌢 ♣ P

Catisfield

Limes at Catisfield
Catisfield Lane
☎ (0329) 42926
11–2.30, 6 (7 Sat)–11
**Gale's HSB; Gibbs Mew
Salisbury; Bishop's Tipple** Ⓗ
A Victorian building converted
to a pub: a small, quiet lounge, a
busy public bar and a function
room. Petanque played.
🍺 🌢 ⊞ ♣ P

Chalton

Red Lion
Off A3 ☎ (0705) 592246
11–2.30, 6–11
Gale's XXXD (summer), **BBB,
5X, HSB** Ⓗ
Hampshire's oldest pub:
thatched and timber-framed, it
dates from the 13th-century
and has three bars; the public

---

has a large inglenook. A new
extension is of debatable
architectural merit, but adds
space. No eve meals Sun.
🏠 🍺 🌢 🍴 ♣ P

Chandler's Ford

Cleveland Bay
1 Pilgrims Close, Valley Park
(off Knightwood Road)
☎ (0703) 269814
11–11
**Hall & Woodhouse
Tanglefoot; Wadworth IPA,
6X, Farmer's Glory, Old
Timer** Ⓗ
Fairly typical new pub on the
edge of town, with lots of bare
brick and timber. One large, L-
shaped bar, with a variety of
seating areas, caters for all.
Monthly guest beer.
🏠 🍴 🍺 🌢 ⚲ P Ⓧ

Charter Alley

White Hart
White Hart Lane (off A339;
½ mile E of Ramsdell)
☎ (0256) 850048
12–2.30 (3 Sat), 7–11
**Bunces Best Bitter; Hook
Norton Best Bitter;
Ringwood Best Bitter** Ⓗ
Friendly pub with a small, old
front bar and a very large back
bar with a popular skittle alley;
also eating and games areas.
Excellent selection of guest ales;
welcoming hosts.
🏠 🍺 🌢 ♣ P

Cheriton

Flower Pots
Off A272
☎ (0962) 771318
11–2.30, 6–11
**Archers Village; Bunces Best
Bitter** Ⓖ
Fine, cottage-style, village inn
with recent extensions; this is
its 18th year in the *Guide*. A
family-run, genuine free house
welcoming all; an ideal stop for
visitors to the Watercress steam
railway at Alresford. Home-
cooked bar snacks. Regular
guest beers.
🏠 🍴 🍺 ⊞ ⚲ ♣ P

Cove

Plough & Horses
Fleet Road
☎ (0252) 545199
11–11
**Ind Coope Friary Meux Best
Bitter, Burton Ale; Tetley
Bitter; Young's Special** Ⓗ
Designated a 'Hampshire
Treasure' by Hants County
Council, this well-furnished pub
has a fascinating collection of
local victoriana. The landlord
came second in the 1991 *Burton
Grandmaster Cellarman*

---

competition. A very well run,
busy pub offering good value
pub fare (Mon–Sat). Young's is a
permanent 'guest'. 🍺 🌢 ♣ P

Crawley

Rack & Manger
Stockbridge Road (A272)
☎ (0962) 72281
11–2.30 (3 Sat), 6–11
**Marston's Mercian Mild,
Burton Best Bitter, Merrie
Monk, Pedigree, Owd
Rodger** Ⓗ
Cosmopolitan pub with a large,
quiet lounge and a lively public
bar. Weekend discos and 60s
nights. Circular pool table.
🏠 🍺 🌢 🍴 ⚲ ♣ P

Crondall

Hampshire Arms
Pankridge Street
☎ (0252) 850418
11–3, 5.30–11
**Courage Best Bitter,
Directors** Ⓗ
Deservedly popular, village
local with a strong food
emphasis (super steaks!), but a
real pub nonetheless. Its ancient
structure is pre-18th century.
Thriving petanque club; lovely
garden and comfortable
conservatory/restaurant (book
for meals). Q 🍺 🌢 🍴 ⚲ P

Horns
Bowling Alley (just off A287)
☎ (0252) 850560
11–3, 6–11
**Ruddles Best Bitter,
County; Webster's Yorkshire
Bitter** Ⓗ
Wonderful, unspoilt, traditional,
village local; partly 17th-
century with original oak beams
and cosy snugs. Warm and
welcoming. The landlord has
numerous awards. Can be very
busy at weekends but is
normally relaxed and quiet in
the week. Formerly the site of
the Duke of Winchester's
hunting lodge – hence its name.
No food Sun. 🏠 Q 🍺 🌢 ♣ P

Crookham Village

Black Horse
The Street
☎ (0252) 616434
11–2.30 (3 Fri & Sat), 5.30–11
**Courage Best Bitter,
Directors** Ⓗ
First-rate, welcoming, beamed,
village hostelry serving good
value food; very popular and
friendly, hosted by an ebullient
landlord. Near the Basingstoke
Canal and good for walks. The
garden, with an aviary, is
excellent for children. No food
Sun. Guest beer. Q 🍺 🌢 P

Hampshire

Damerham

Compasses
On B3078
☎ (072 53) 231
10.30–2.30, 6–11
Ind Coope Burton Ale;
Wadworth 6X Ⓗ
Village pub with a quiet lounge,
a lively public bar and a garden
with a children's play area.
Excellent food, incl. a vegetarian
option; large restaurant. Jazz
night Fri.
🏠 Q 🍽 ⛽ ◖ ▶ ⚘ ♣ P

Denmead

Fox & Hounds
School Lane (½ mile off B2150)
OS643125 ☎ (0705) 255421
12–2.30, 6–11
Morland Bitter, Old Speckled
Hen; Wadworth 6X Ⓗ
Secluded, locals' pub just
outside the village. Unknown to
many, which adds to its
character. Caters for all ages,
with a games room and guest
ales. Barbecue area in the
garden. 🍽 ◖ ▶ ⚘ ♣ P

Downton

Royal Oak
On A337 ☎ (0590) 642297
11–2.30, 6–11 (7–10.30 Mon–Thu in
winter)
Whitbread Pompey Royal,
Flowers Original; Wadworth
6X Ⓗ
Spotless and cosy pub, warmed
by three real fires; in the same
family for over 100 years and
mentioned in the *Domesday
Book*. A covered patio and a
children's garden are available,
but no dogs or children in the
bar. Inviting, home-cooked
food (cream teas summer
weekends). No jukebox or fruit
machines. 🏠 Q 🍽 ◖ ▶ ⚘ ▲ P ✗

Droxford

White Horse
On A32 ☎ (0489) 877490
11–2.30, 6–11
Courage Best Bitter; Gale's
HSB; Marston's Pedigree;
Morland Old Speckled Hen;
Wadworth 6X Ⓗ
16th-century coaching inn with
contrasting bars: a quiet lounge
and a noisier public. Low
ceilings and uneven floors, with
a well located in the gents! The
beer range may vary. No Sun
eve meals in winter.
🏠 Q ♿ 🍽 ◖ ▶ ⚘ ⛽ P ✗

Dundridge

Hampshire Bowman
Dundridge Lane (1 mile off
B3035)
OS579185 ☎ (0489) 892940

11–2.30 (may vary), 6–11
Gale's BBB, 5X, HSB Ⓖ
Pleasantly situated, off the
beaten track; one traditional,
brick-floored bar with a small
serving counter and casks lined
up behind. Once an abattoir,
now HQ of the Portuguese
Racing Sardine Club! No food
Sun eve or Mon. Guest beers.
🏠 Q 🍽 ◖ ▶ ▲ ♣ P

East End

Axe & Compasses
Off A343
☎ (0635) 253403
11–3, 6.30–11
Draught Bass; Charrington
IPA Ⓗ
Friendly, open-plan free house
in an historic village. Farming
implements on the walls and
sports photos in the eating area.
Guest beers. Eve meals Tue–Sat.
🏠 Q 🍽 ◖ ▶ ♣ P

East Stratton

Plough
Off A33 ☎ (0962) 89241
11–2.30 (not Mon), 6–11
Gale's BBB, HSB; Ringwood
Fortyniner Ⓗ
Basic, old pub in a village
mentioned in the *Domesday
Book*. Pleasant, friendly
atmosphere; popular with locals.
Skittle alley. No food Mon.
🏠 Q 🍽 🍽 ◖ ▶ ⚘ ♣ P

East Worldham

Three Horseshoes
Cakers Lane
☎ (0420) 83211
11–2.30, 6–11 (12–2.30, 7–10.30 Sun)
Gale's BBB, Best Bitter,
HSB Ⓗ
One-bar pub with unusual barrel
seats and a dining area. Can be
very quiet. Eve meals Tue–Sat.
Q 🍽 ◖ ▶ P

Ecchinswell

Royal Oak
Off A34/A339
☎ (0635) 298280
11–4, 6–11
Courage Best Bitter Ⓖ
Basic, classic, country local, with
three rooms off a corridor.
Interesting collection of bric-a-
brac in the public bar; dartboard
in the saloon. Sing-alongs Sat
nights. A true boozer's boozer.
Families welcome in the games
room. Q ♿ ⛽ P

Ellisfield

Fox
Green Lane (off A339)
☎ (0256) 83210

11.30–2.30, 6.30–11
Bunces Best Bitter; Gale's
HSB; Hall & Woodhouse
Badger Best Bitter,
Tanglefoot; Marston's
Pedigree; Theakston Old
Peculier Ⓗ
Country retreat with a good
selection of beers, just south of
modern Basingstoke. No eve
meals Mon.
🏠 Q 🍽 ◖ ▶ P

Emsworth

Coal Exchange
South Street
☎ (0243) 375866
10.30–3, 5.30–11 (10.30–11 Sat)
Gale's XXXD, BBB, 5X,
HSB Ⓗ
Small, old pub with a tiled
frontage, in an historic part of
town. One comfortable bar with
a good atmosphere. Special
sausage menu.
🏠 🍽 ◖ ▶ ⚘ ♣ P

Fairfield
125 New Brighton Road
☎ (0243) 373304
11–3, 6–11
Gale's BBB, HSB Ⓗ
Elegant, Regency-style,
detached building, to the north
of town, with two well-run,
contemporary bars, a pool area
and a restaurant. Live
entertainment at weekends.
♿ 🍽 ◖ ▶ ⛽ ♿ P

Eversley

White Hart
On A327
☎ (0734) 732817
11–2.30 (3 Fri & Sat), 5.30–11
Courage Best Bitter,
Directors Ⓗ
Genuine, village locals' pub with
very good value lunchtime
snacks (not served Sun). Plenty
of beams and character.
🏠 Q 🍽 ⛽ P

Ewshot

Windmill
Church Lane
☎ (0252) 850439
11–2.30, 5.30–11 (11–11 Sat)
Gale's HSB; Ind Coope
Benskins Best Bitter, Burton
Ale Ⓗ
Excellent rural pub on the
county border, set in four acres
of grounds that include an 18-
hole putting green. A
comfortable lounge and a
traditional public bar, fielding
one cricket and three hockey
teams. Barbecues summer Sun.
♿ 🍽 ◖ ▶ ♣ P

Hampshire

Faccombe

Jack Russell
Off A343
☎ (0264) 87315
12–2.30, 7 (6 summer)–11
Gale's Best Bitter, HSB Ⓗ
Friendly country inn with good
value beer and food (incl.
vegetarian option and children's
menu). Family garden with
playthings; children over five
allowed in conservatory.
Genuine wheelchair facilities.
Guest beers from independent
brewers.
🏠 Q 🏃 ⑧ 🛏 ⑴ ▮ ㋴ ♣ P

Fareham

Buccaneer
On A27
☎ (0329) 230800
11–3, 5–11 (11–11 Sat)
**Draught Bass; Courage Best
Bitter** Ⓗ
A pleasant Courage 'Harvester'
which caters for all; comfortable
and welcoming. ⑴ ▮ ㋴ ⇌ P

Farnborough

Prince of Wales
184 Rectory Road (off A325)
☎ (0252) 545578
11.30–2.30, 6–11
**Brakspear Bitter; Eldridge
Pope Royal Oak; Fuller's
London Pride; Hall &
Woodhouse Badger Best
Bitter, Tanglefoot; Wadworth
6X** Ⓗ
The best free house for miles,
offering an enterprising range of
guest beers; a convivial,
traditional hostelry which is
crowded most of the time.
Excellent lunches, Mon–Sat.
The licensee also owns the Six
Bells in Farnham. Q ⑴ ㋴ ♣ P

Fritham

Royal Oak
2 miles off B3078
☎ (0703) 812606
11–3 (may extend in summer), 6–11
**Whitbread Strong Country,
Flowers Original** Ⓖ
Unspoilt, rustic, thatched pub
deep in the New Forest. The
large, open hearth is still used
for smoking hams. Guest beer.
🏠 Q ⑧ ㋴ ♣

Frogham

Foresters Arms
Abbotswell Road (signed off
A338 at Fordingbridge)
OS173129 ☎ (0425) 652294
11–3, 6–11 (11–11 Sat in summer)
**Hook Norton Best Bitter;
Taylor Landlord** Ⓗ
In the heart of the New Forest,
this friendly, busy pub provides
a range of beers rarely seen in
this area, from two constantly-

changing guest beer pumps.
Mini-beer festival Aug Bank
Holiday weekend.
🏠 🏃 ⑧ ⑴ ▮ Å ♣ P

Froyle

Hen & Chicken
Upper Froyle (A31)
☎ (0420) 22115
11–2.30, 6–11
**Adnams Broadside;
Brakspear Special; Courage
Best Bitter; King & Barnes
Festive; Wadworth 6X** Ⓗ
Handsome, old coaching inn,
where beams and brass abound.
A food-oriented pub with good
value bar food and an upmarket
restaurant; separate family
room; locals congregate in the
bar. 🏠 Q 🏃 ⑧ ⑴ ▮ P

Try also: Prince of Wales,
Lower Froyle (Free)

Gosport

Queens Hotel
143 Queens Road (off Stoke
Road/St Andrews Road)
☎ (0705) 525518
11.30–2.30 Fri), 7 (6 Fri)–11
(11–11 Sat)
**Archers Village; Fuller's
London Pride; Greene King
Abbot** Ⓗ
Genuine free house; a friendly,
back-street, locals' pub with a
large, segmented bar. Two
regularly changing guest beers.
🏠 ♣

White Swan
Forton Road (A32, ¾ mile from
ferry) ☎ (0705) 584138
11–3 (4 Sat), 5.30 (6.30 Sat)–11
**Courage Best Bitter,
Directors; John Smith's
Bitter** Ⓗ
Basic, locals' pub boasting six
darts teams and an eye-catching
pool table. Guest beers. No
food Sun. ⑴ ♣

Hambledon

New Inn
West Street (off B2150)
☎ (0705) 632466
12–2.30, 7–11
**Gale's BBB; Eldridge Pope
Hardy Country; Ringwood
Fortyniner, Old Thumper** Ⓗ
Pleasant, old, village local with
two bars and a friendly
atmosphere. Uncomplicated,
with no food – just good, old-
fashioned drinking and
socialising. Occasional guest
beers. 🏠 ⑧ ⑧ ⊟ ♣ P

Hammer Vale

Prince of Wales
Hammer Lane (off A3 signed
Bulmer Hill)
OS867326
☎ (0428) 52600

11–3, 6–11 (11–11 Sat)
Gale's XXXD, BBB, HSB Ⓖ
Red-brick, country pub with
attractive stained-glass
windows, in a picturesque
setting. Live music Sun eve,
when no eve meals are served.
🏠 ⑧ ⑴ ㋴ Å ♣ P

Hartley Wintney

Waggon & Horses
High Street
☎ (025 126) 2119
11–11
**Courage Best Bitter,
Directors** Ⓗ
Small, locals' pub where a very
pleasant atmosphere prevails.
Wadworth 6X is a regular
'guest'. No food Sun.
🏠 Q ⑧ ⑴ ⊟

Havant

Robin Hood
Homewell
☎ (0705) 482779
11–11
**Gale's XXXD, BBB, 5X,
HSB** Ⓖ
Town-centre, single-bar pub
which has retained its character;
open fires and a small games
area. Busy lunch trade.
🏠 ⑧ ⑴ ⇌ ♣ P

Hawkley

Hawkley Inn
Pococks Lane (2 miles off A325
at West Liss)
OS747291
☎ (0730) 84205
12–2.30 (3 Sat), 6–11
**Ballard's Trotton, Best Bitter;
Fuller's London Pride** Ⓗ
The only pub in a small village;
a comfortable and sometimes
very busy free house in a quiet
location. Home-cooked food in
the bar or restaurant. The no-
smoking area has bar billiards.
Parking can be difficult. Walkers
welcome.
🏠 ⑧ ⑴ ♣ ㋴ ✗

Hayling Island

Maypole
9 Havant Road (A3023)
☎ (0705) 463670
11–11
Gale's XXXD Ⓗ**/**Ⓖ**, BBB, Best
Bitter** (summer)Ⓗ**, 5X** Ⓖ**,
HSB** Ⓗ
Large, two-bar, main road pub.
It features a circular pool table,
but of most interest is a
magnificent bank of six handpumps c. 1945. Not all of them
are used – some beer is served
straight from the cellar. No
meals Mon eve.
🏠 ⑧ 🛏 ⑴ ⊟ Å ♣ P

Hedge End

Barleycorn
Lower Northam Road
☎ (0489) 784171
11–2.30 (3 Sat), 5.30 (5 Fri)–11 (12–2, 7–10.30 Sun)
Marston's Mercian Mild, Burton Best Bitter, Pedigree Ⓗ
Village pub with one bar divided into two distinct drinking areas. Popular with all ages and a good, community local. No food Sun. ⊛ ◖ ♣ P

Hill Head

Osborne View
67 Hill Head Road
☎ (0329) 664623
11–2.30 (4 Fri), 6–11 (11–11 Sat)
Hall & Woodhouse Badger Best Bitter, Tanglefoot; Wadworth 6X Ⓗ
Popular, village local with the emphasis on food. Good views of the Solent and the Isle of Wight. Ask the landlord to put up the dartboard. Live jazz Sun eve. ◖ ♣ P

Horsebridge

John O'Gaunt
Off A3057
☎ (0794) 388394
11.30–2.30 (11–3 Sat), 6–11
Palmers IPA Ⓗ
Friendly, village free house with a shove-ha'penny board on the bar. Two guest beers always available. Car park nearby. No meals Tue eve. ⚑ ⊛ ◖ ♣

Hurstbourne Priors

Hurstbourne
On B3400
☎ (0256) 892000
11–11
Gale's HSB; Wadworth 6X Ⓗ
Pub at the heart of the Bourne Valley with an idyllic outlook across the cricket ground to the ivy-clad church. Formerly owned by Whitbread and called the 'Portsmouth Arms'. Regular guest beers. Q ⍽ ◖ ♣ P

Hythe

Lord Nelson
High Street
☎ (0703) 842169
11–3, 6–11 (11–11 Sat)
Whitbread Strong Country, Flowers Original Ⓗ
Small, waterfront pub with quaint bars. Its gardens overlook Southampton Water and yacht marina. Good value lunches. Convenient for the Southampton ferry. Guest beers. Q ⊛ ◖ ◖ ♣ ⌣

Kingsclere

Swan
Swan Street
☎ (0635) 298314
11–2.30, 5.30–11
Eldridge Pope Best Bitter; Tetley Bitter; Wadworth 6X Ⓗ
Spacious, atmospheric pub with a gallery. Notable for the absence of keg bitter! Regular guest beers. No food Sun.
⚑ Q ⊛ ⍽ ◖ ▶ P

Kings Worthy

Cart & Horses
London Road (A33/A333 jct)
☎ (0962) 882360
11–3, 6–11 (11–11 bank hols)
Marston's Burton Best Bitter, Pedigree, Owd Rodger Ⓗ
Large, smart, upmarket, busy roadhouse with a good selection of food at all times. It has a restaurant, children's playground and a large garden; a converted, 300 year-old barn acts as a skittle alley/family room. The bar is a quiet, drinker's retreat.
⚑ ⍿ ⊛ ◖ ▶ ⍾ & ♣ ⌣ P ⊬ ✗

Leckford

Leckford Hutt
On A30 ☎ (0264) 810738
11–2.30, 7–11
Marston's Burton Best Bitter, Pedigree, Owd Rodger Ⓗ
Friendly, traditional local with an open fire and a 200ft well. Blow billiards table (bring your own equipment). Occasional musical eves; barbecues twice yearly; whippet racing.
⚑ Q ⊛ ◖ ▶ ⍾ ♣ P

Liss

Temple
Forest Road
☎ (0730) 892134
11–3, 6–11
Gale's BBB, HSB Ⓗ
Friendly, locals' pub in Liss Forest, a mile north of the main village. Built c. 1870 by Solomon Hounsome, hence its name. ⊛ ◖ ▶ ♣ P

Littleton

Running Horse
88 Main Road (1 mile off A272) ☎ (0962) 880218
11–2.30 (3 Sat), 6–11
Gibbs Mew Wiltshire, Salisbury, Bishop's Tipple Ⓗ
Small pub knocked through into one bar but still retaining 'public' and 'lounge' ends. The large garden for families has animals, birds and play equipment. No meals Wed eve.
⚑ ⊛ ◖ ▶ ♣ P

Locks Heath

Lock Stock & Barrel
Locks Heath Centre (off A27)
☎ (0489) 589316
11–2.30 (3 Sat), 6–11
Adnams Bitter, Broadside; Hall & Woodhouse Badger Best Bitter, Tanglefoot Ⓗ
Although in a shopping precinct, this pub has a fascinating collection of locks, stocks and barrels. A rare chance to drink an East Anglian brew, too. Live music often Thu nights. Eve meals Thu/Fri only.
⊛ ◖ ▶ & ♣ ♣

Long Sutton

Four Horseshoes
The Street (Well Road)
☎ (0256) 862488
11–2.30, 6–11
Gale's XXXL (summer), BBB, Best Bitter, 5X, HSB Ⓗ
Compact, isolated local, superbly situated a mile from the village. A good blend of locals and foodies who travel miles for the pub fare and friendly, relaxed atmosphere; wonderfully exuberant landlord. Good value Sun roasts (no meals Sun eve).
⚑ Q ⊛ ◖ ▶ ▲ ♣ P

Lymington

Tollhouse Inn
167 Southampton Road, Buckland (A337)
☎ (0590) 672142
11–3, 6–11
Ringwood Best Bitter; Wadworth 6X Ⓗ
Busy, prominent, roadside pub with contrasting bars and a large menu. Over 300 year old and full of historical and antique items. Book Sun lunch. Guest beers. ⚑ Q ⍾ ⊛ ◖ ▶ ⍽ P

Lyndhurst

Mailmans Arms
High Street
☎ (0703) 284196
11–2.30, 6–11
Marston's Burton Best Bitter, Pedigree Ⓗ
Friendly and comfortable pub in a popular New Forest town. Occasional live entertainment; barbecues in summer. Family room at lunchtime only. Good value lunches. ⚑ Q ⍾ ⊛ ◖ ♣

Marchwood

Pilgrim
Hythe Road (off A326; S end of village)
☎ (0703) 867752
11–2.30 (3 Sat), 6–11
Draught Bass; Courage Best Bitter, Directors; Welsh Brewers Worthington BB Ⓗ

Hampshire

Beautiful, thatched inn with immaculate gardens; hanging baskets are a speciality. Home-cooking, with a vegetarian option and children's menu. Eve meals in the adjacent restaurant. 🏠 Q ◖ ◗ & P

Monk Sherborne

Mole
Ramsdell Road
☎ (0256) 850033
11–2.30, 6–11
Morland Bitter, Old Masters Ⓗ
Small, country pub offering a homely welcome, good food and a warm atmosphere. No meals Mon eve. 🏠 🏱 ◖ ◗ ◖ ♣ P

North Warnborough

Anchor
The Street
☎ (0256) 702740
10.30–2.30, 6–11 (12–2.30, 7–10.30 Sun)
Courage Best Bitter, Directors Ⓗ
Friendly, cheerful and homely, two-bar pub tucked away in a side-street; famous for its charity contributions. Originally an old brewery serving a single pub. 🏠 ◖ ♣ P

Oakhanger

Red Lion
The Street
☎ (0420) 472232
11–3, 6–11
Courage Best Bitter, Directors Ⓗ
Cosy, village pub frequented by singing card players! Wood fires and a brisk food trade in the lounge. The landlord is fond of prints, photos and big fish. Guest beer. 🏠 Q 🏱 ◖ ◗ ◖ P

Owslebury

Ship
Off B2177
☎ (0962) 777358
11–2.30, 6–11
Marston's Mercian Mild, Burton Best Bitter, Pedigree Ⓗ
Cosy, one-bar, country inn with low beams (reputed to be old ships' timbers), in a sleepy hamlet near Marwell Zoo. Locals meet here for banter; visitors for a quiet drink. No food Sun. 🏠 🚲 🏱 ◖ ◗ ♣ P

Pennington

Musketeer
North Street
☎ (0590) 676527
11.30–3, 6–11
Brakspear Bitter; Felinfoel Cambrian, Double Dragon;

Ringwood Best Bitter Ⓗ
Attractive, one-bar pub in the village centre; originally a coaching inn. A real free house with an interesting choice of beers, incl. occasional guests. No food Sun. 🏠 Q 🏱 ◖ ◗ P

Petersfield

Good Intent
40 College Street (A3 northbound)
☎ (0730) 63838
11.30–2.30, 6–11 (12–2.30, 7–10.30 Sun; closed Mon)
Adnams Bitter, Broadside; Ballard's Best Bitter; Draught Bass; Hall & Woodhouse Tanglefoot Ⓖ
16th-century free house with real beams in its rambling single bar; opposite the old Churchers College. Beer is served straight from the cellar; the handpumps are for display only.
🏠 🏱 ◖ ◗ ◖ P

Old Drum
16 Chapel Street
☎ (0730) 64159
11–2.30, 5.30–11 (10.30–4, 7–11 Sat)
Ind Coope Friary Meux Best Bitter, Burton Ale Ⓗ
A low building, dating from the 17th century, near the town square. Busy at lunchtime for good food (not served Sun), quieter eves. Large, prize-winning garden and decorative sprays on the ceiling.
🏱 🚲 ◖ ◗ ◖ ≠ ♣ P

Portsmouth

Alexandra
Wingfield Street, Landport
☎ (0705) 823876
11–2.30, 6–11
Draught Bass Ⓗ
One of the city's few Bass houses. A friendly, comfortable, single-lounge, estate pub. Convenient for the shops and continental ferries. 🏱 P

Compass Rose
Sywell Crescent, Anchorage Park (off A2030)
☎ (0705) 673037
11–3 (Fri & Sat), 6 (5 Wed–Fri)–11
Gibbs Mew Wiltshire, Salisbury, Bishop's Tipple Ⓗ
Plush, five year-old pub in a new estate. Busy with food trade at lunchtime, but more like a locals' pub in the eve. No eve meals Sun in winter.
🏱 ◖ ◗ & ≠ (Hilsea) P

Connaught Arms
119 Guildford Road, Fratton
☎ (0705) 825873
11–2.30 (3 Fri & Sat), 6–11
Gale's HSB; Wadworth 6X; Whitbread Fremlins Bitter Ⓗ
Comfortable and friendly, one-

---

bar local nestling in the back-streets. Home-cooked lunches, Mon–Sat. Guest beers.
🏱 ◖ ≠ (Fratton)

Eldon Arms
15 Eldon Street, Southsea
☎ (0705) 851778
11–2.30 (3.30 Sat), 6–11
Eldridge Pope Hardy Country, Royal Oak Ⓗ
An interesting, glazed exterior on a large, single-bar pub which has been extended into a neighbouring cottage. Separate restaurant area. Guest beers.
🏱 ◖ ◗ ≠ ♣

Electric Arms
190–192 Fratton Road, Fratton
☎ (0705) 823293
10.30–3, 6–11 (11–11 Sat)
Ind Coope Burton Ale Ⓗ
Comfortable local with a pleasant ambience and, reputedly, the friendly ghost of a former landlady! No lunches Sun. ◖ ◖ ≠ (Fratton) ♣

Landmark
249 Fratton Road, Fratton
☎ (0705) 821949
12–3, 6–11 (11–11 Sat)
Gale's HSB; Marston's Pedigree; Wadworth 6X; Whitbread Boddingtons Bitter, Best Bitter Ⓗ
Large, single public bar with a wood floor and bare brick walls; seating is mostly on old church pews. Guest beer served from the cask on the bar. The best value lunches in Portsmouth.
🏱 ◖ ◗ ≠ (Fratton) ♣ ○ P

Mermaid
222 New Road, Copnor
☎ (0705) 824397
11–3, 6–11
Fuller's London Pride; Wadworth 6X; Whitbread Boddingtons Bitter, Strong Country Ⓗ
Superlative local with a rare Victorian wrought-iron canopy outside, and figures above the bar. An unusual heated footrail runs through the bars. Guest beers. 🏱 ◖ ◖ & ♣

Olde Oyster House
291 Locksway Road, Milton (off A288) ☎ (0705) 827546
11–2.30, 6–11 (11–11 Sat & summer)
Gale's HSB; Marston's Pedigree Ⓗ
Large, 1930s-style pub, a former Portsmouth United Breweries house. Near the old Milton Locks, once part of the Portsmouth–London canal. A lively public bar with a quieter lounge. Guest beer. 🏱 ◖ & ♣ P

Red White & Blue
Fawcett Road
☎ (0705) 814470
11–11
Gale's BBB, HSB, 5X Ⓗ

Recently enlarged, but still a compact, corner local, with a spare set of handpumps on the customer's side of the bar. Crowded on darts/doms nights. Try a Red White and Blue cocktail.
◖ ⇌ (Fratton) ♣

Ship & Castle
90 Rudmore Road, Rudmore
☎ (0705) 660391
11–3, 6–11
Gale's BBB, HSB Ⓗ
Well-hidden, friendly, locals' pub, by the continental ferry port but originally on the waterfront, overlooking Whale Island. Small garden.
❀ ♿ ♣ P

Swan
100 Copnor Road, Copnor (A288) ☎ (0705) 662445
11–2.30, 6–11
Draught Bass; Charrington IPA Ⓗ
Large, established, main road local: two bars with a congenial and relaxed atmosphere. A traditional community pub. No food Sun. ❀ ◖ ⊟ ♣ P

Tap
17 London Road, North End
☎ (0705) 699943
11–11
Banks & Taylor Shefford Mild; Banks's Bitter; Fuller's London Pride, Mr Harry; Gibbs Mew Bishop's Tipple; Hall & Woodhouse Tanglefoot Ⓗ
Enterprising and successful free house offering a good range of beers, in the North End shopping area. A rare outlet for real mild in the city. Excellent range of good value food.
◖ ◗ ♿ ◯

Wig & Pen
1 Landport Terrace, Southsea
☎ (0705) 820696
11–3, 6.30–11
Gale's HSB; Whitbread Boddingtons Bitter Ⓗ
Once the 'Balmoral', this Brewer's Tudor pub serves good value weekday lunches. A single bar, but two distinct areas. Two quiz teams. Always a guest beer from an independent brewery.
◖ ⇌ ♣

Wine Vaults
43 Albert Road, Southsea
☎ (0705) 864712
11–3, 5.30–11 (11–11 Sat)
Draught Bass; Ringwood Old Thumper; Wadworth 6X; Whitbread Boddingtons Bitter Ⓗ
Thriving, ever-popular free house with 12–15 real ales on offer: a must. Good value food. Occasional beer festival. Guest beers. ◖ ◗ ♿

Ringwood

Inn on the Furlong
12 Meeting House Lane
☎ (0425) 475139
11 (10.30 Wed)–11
Ringwood Best Bitter, Fortyniner, XXXX Porter, Old Thumper Ⓗ
Excellent, thriving local in the centre of a market town. A central bar serves a multi-roomed pub with flagstones and traditional wooden furnishings. Pleasant conservatory/restaurant (with a no-smoking zone) and a patio. Guest beers.
♔ ⛀ ❀ ◖ ◗ ◯

Romsey

Tudor Rose
Cornmarket
☎ (0794) 512126
10–11
Courage Best Bitter, Directors Ⓗ
Small, friendly, 15th-century ale house in the town centre. Live folk music Sun eve; tables in the cobbled courtyard in summer. Its 19th year in the *Guide*!
♔ Q ❀ ◖ ♿ ♣

Rotherwick

Coach & Horses
The Street
☎ (0256) 762542
11–2.30, 5.30–11
Adnams Broadside; Eldridge Pope Best Bitter; Fuller's London Pride; Hall & Woodhouse Badger Best Bitter, Tanglefoot; Ringwood Old Thumper Ⓗ
18th-century inn with normally ten or more beers, incl. monthly guests, some on gravity dispense. ♔ Q ❀ ◖ ◗ P

Shedfield

Sams Hotel
Upper Church Road (off B2177) ☎ (0329) 832213
4.30–11 (12–11 Fri & Sat)
Marston's Mercian Mild, Burton Best Bitter, Pedigree Ⓗ
Traditional, roadside, country inn with three bars. Impromptu folk music Sat night. HQ of Shedfield Cricket Club (pitch opposite) and reputedly the birthplace of British petanque (boules). ♔ ❀ ⊟ ♣ P

Wheatsheaf
Botley Road
☎ (0329) 833024
11–3, 6–11
Marston's Burton Best Bitter, Pedigree, Owd Rodger Ⓗ
Cosy, two-bar, country pub. The large garden has children's playthings and a DIY barbecue. Home-cooked, chip-free food (not served Sun). ♔ ◖ ⊟ ♣ P

Sherfield on Loddon

White Hart
Reading Road
☎ (0256) 882280
11–2.30, 6–11
Courage Best Bitter, Directors; Fuller's London Pride Ⓗ
Old coaching inn, dating from 1642, now a one-bar pub with a separate eating area. Large lawn with children's space.
❀ ◖ ◗ P

Silchester

Calleva Arms
Silchester Common
☎ (0734) 700305
10.30–2.30, 4.30–11 (10.30–11 Sat)
Gale's BBB, Best Bitter, 5X, HSB Ⓗ
A pub with something for everyone: a basic public bar, a spacious, quiet lounge, pleasant garden and a family conservatory. ♔ Q ⛀ ❀ ⊟ ⛺ ♣ P

Sleaford

New Inn
Farnham Road (A325, 3 miles N of Bordon)
☎ (0420) 472227
11–2.30, 5.30–11 (11–11 Sat)
Courage Best Bitter Ⓗ
Large pub with contrasting bars on a busy main road: bustling public and a tranquil saloon. Good choice of meals. The car park is tricky. ♔ Q ❀ ◖ ◗ ⊟ ♣ P

Sopley

Woolpack
Ringwood Road (B3347, W side of one-way system)
☎ (0425) 72252
11–11
Marston's Pedigree; Wadworth 6X; Whitbread Best Bitter Ⓗ
Unspoilt, 17th-century pub near the River Avon and a Saxon church. Picturesque garden; varied menu in the good restaurant. Piano every night. Guest beers.
♔ Q ❀ ◖ ◗ ⊟ ♿ ⛺ P

Southampton

Bald Faced Stag
36 Edward Road, Freemantle (off Foundry Lane)
☎ (0703) 778571
11–3, 7–11
Marston's Mercian Mild, Burton Best Bitter, Pedigree Ⓗ
Back-street, community pub, the only one locally with a snug. Hard to find. ⛀ ❀ ⊟ ♣ P

Hampshire

Crown & Sceptre

30 Bevois Valley Road, Bevois
Valley (A335, 1¼ miles NE of
centre) ☎ (0703) 227081
12–3 (not Mon–Thu), 7 (5
Mon–Thu)–11
**Gibbs Mew Local Line,
Salisbury, Bishop's Tipple** Ⓗ
Very much a pub for young
people: lively and sometimes
noisy. A quieter atmosphere
may be enjoyed early eve, or
during college holidays. Floodlit
patio. ⑧ ◖ ▶ ⊞ ♣

Freemantle Arms

33 Albany Road, Freemantle
(off Firgrove Rd, near A3057)
☎ (0703) 772092
10.30–3, 6 (7 Sat)–11
**Marston's Mercian Mild,
Burton Best Bitter,
Pedigree** Ⓗ
Friendly local in a quiet cul-de-
sac: a lively public bar and a
quieter lounge with plenty of
plant life. Popular, colourful
garden with a large patio.
⬥ ⑧ ⊞ ♣

Guide Dog

38 Earls Road, Bevois Town (1½
miles NE of centre)
☎ (0703) 220188
11.30–2.30, 6–11
**Wadworth IPA, 6X, Old
Timer** Ⓗ
Southampton's smallest pub in
the city's prime drinking area,
named after its charity work but
non-guide dogs are not
admitted. Bar snacks available.
Guest beers in summer. ♣

Marsh

42 Canute Road (under A3025
Itchen Bridge)
☎ (0703) 635540
11–11 (11–5, 8–11 Sat)
**Marston's Mercian Mild,
Burton Best Bitter,
Pedigree** Ⓗ
No-frills, friendly local near
Ocean Village. Probably the last
remaining docklands pub with
its original character. Formerly a
lighthouse (which explains the
semi-circular bars). Pool room.
⑧ ◖ ♣

New Inn

16 Bevois Valley Road, Bevois
Valley (A335, 1½ miles NE of
centre) ☎ (0703) 228437
11.30–3, 6.45–11
**Gale's XXXD, BBB, Best
Bitter, 5X, HSB, Prize Old
Ale** Ⓗ
Cosy, ale-drinkers' local offering
a warm welcome to all. Caters
for devotees of Belgian beer and
malt whiskies. Good value
lunches. ◖ ♣

Park Inn

37 Carlisle Road, Shirley (off
A3057, Romsey Road)
☎ (0703) 787835
11–3 (3.30 Sat), 5 (6 Sat)–11

Hall & Woodhouse

**Tanglefoot; Wadworth IPA,
6X, Old Timer** Ⓗ
Popular, friendly, side-street
local close to the shopping
centre. Unobtrusive background
music played. Slightly more
upmarket than most local pubs.
⑧ ♣

Platform Tavern

Town Quay
☎ (0703) 212036
11–8 (may extend)
**Marston's Border Mild,
Burton Best Bitter, Pedigree,
Merrie Monk** Ⓗ**, Owd
Rodger** (winter) Ⓖ
Small, docklands pub close to
God's House Museum, Ocean
Village and ferries: the old city
walls form part of the pub's
structure. Recently taken over
by an award-winning
Southampton landlord, formerly
of the Junction. No food Sun.
Q ◖ ♣

Richmond Inn

108 Portswood Road,
Portswood (A335)
☎ (0703) 554523
11–11
**Marston's Mercian Mild,
Burton Best Bitter,
Pedigree** Ⓗ
Genuine local with an
uncomplicated public bar and a
plusher lounge. Ocean liner
prints proliferate. Good whisky
selection. ⑧ ⊞ ⇌ (St Denys) ♣

Salisbury Arms

126 Shirley High Street, Shirley
(A3057)
☎ (0703) 774624
10–3 (4 Sat), 6 (7 Sat)–11
**Marston's Mercian Mild,
Burton Best Bitter,
Pedigree** Ⓗ
Genuine, working-class local; a
single-bar but with well-
separated areas. Lively at
weekends. Lunchtime snacks.
⬥ ♣

Wellington Arms

56 Park Road, Freemantle
☎ (0703) 227356
11.30–2.30, 6 (7 Sat)–11 (12–2.30,
8–10.30 Sun)
**Courage Directors; Palmers
IPA; Ringwood Best Bitter,
Fortyniner, XXXX Porter, Old
Thumper; Wadworth 6X** Ⓗ
Busy, comfortable, back-street
free house with two lounges. A
veritable shrine to the Iron
Duke – get there early for a
good look round!
⑧ ◖ ▶ ⇌ (Central)

Steep

Cricketers

1 Church Road
☎ (0730) 61035
11.45–2.30, 5.45–11
**Gale's XXXD, BBB, Best

Bitter, HSB Ⓗ
One-bar pub, popular with
locals and walkers alike. In a
rural setting, it enjoys a good
local trade and caters for all
ages. Games room and dining
area. ⌂ ⑧ ⋈ ◖ ▶ ✕ ♣ P

Tangley

Cricketers Arms

Off A343
☎ (0264) 70283
11–2.30 (not Thu), 7–11
**Whitbread Boddingtons
Bitter, Strong Country** Ⓗ
Remote, welcoming, country
pub, part 17th-century. A
cricketing theme prevails in the
extension; a large inglenook
graces the public bar. Genuine
wheelchair facilities. Guest beers
and Bunces Bodyline, a brewery
blend, only for this pub.
⌂ ⑧ ◖ ▶ ⊞ ⅙ ♣ P

Thruxton

White Horse

Wire Mead Lane (right beside
A303) ☎ (0264) 772401
11–2.30 (3 Sat), 6–11
**Bunces Best Bitter; Ringwood
Best Bitter** Ⓗ
Low-beamed, village pub with a
small dining room for bar snacks
(Tue–Sat), where children are
also welcome. Occasional guest
beers. ⌂ Q ◖ ▶ P

Twyford

Phoenix

High Street
☎ (0962) 713322
11.30–2.30, 6–11 (12–2.30, 7–10.30
Sun)
**Marston's Burton Best Bitter,
Pedigree** Ⓗ
Friendly, popular, village inn
with good value food
(vegetarians catered for), a log
fire and a skittle alley/function
room. Spitfire theme in the bar.
⌂ ⑧ ◖ ▶ ⇌ (Shawford) ♣ P

Upton Grey

Hoddington Arms

Bidden Road
☎ (0256) 862371
11–2.30, 6–11
**Morland Bitter, Old Masters,
Old Speckled Hen** Ⓗ
Very pleasant, listed, village pub
and restaurant in a lovely
setting, close to the Basingstoke
Canal. ⌂ Q ⬥ ⑧ ◖ ▶ ♣ P

Vernham Dean

George

Off A343
☎ (0264) 87279
11–2.30 (3 Sat), 6–11
**Marston's Burton Best Bitter,
Pedigree** Ⓗ

Beautiful, brick and timber building with low beams. Good home-cooked food (Mon–Sat) but no chips! A dominoes stronghold at weekends. Deservedly popular.
🏠 Q 🛏 🍽 🍺 🕰 ♣ P

Wallington

White Horse
44 North Wallington (off A27/A32/M27 jct 11)
☎ (0329) 235197
11–2.30, 5–11
Draught Bass G
Pleasantly situated by the river and accessible by footbridge from Fareham High Street. Beer is brought from the cellar behind the bar. Bar lunches Mon–Fri; eve meals in the restaurant only. Guest beers.
🏠 Q 🛏 🍽 🍺

West Meon

Red Lion
Warnford Road (A32)
☎ (0730) 829264
12–11
Ind Coope Friary Meux Best Bitter, Burton Ale H
Pub over 300 years old, on the main road. The small lounge is warmed by log fires in the inglenook; the Village Bar has another open fire, with an old, carved-wood screen. Extensive menu. Snooker room upstairs. Good village local with a congenial atmosphere.
🏠 🍽 🍺 🕰 🚲 Å ♣ P

West Wellow

Rockingham Arms
Canada Road (A36, 1 mile from centre)
☎ (0794) 22473
11.30–2.30, 6–11
Wadworth 6X H
Smartly furnished pub with a games bar and a restaurant. Up to five guest beers. Q 🍽 🍺

Weyhill

Weyhill Fair
On A342, just N of A303
☎ (026 477) 3631
11.30–2.30, 6 (7 Sat)–11 (12–2.30, 7–10.30 Sun)

Gale's HSB; Marston's Pedigree; Morrells Bitter, Varsity H
Free house with a constantly-changing selection of guest beers (normally incl. a mild by gravity). A 'coming soon' board ensures a return visit. No meals Sun eve.
🏠 Q 🛏 🍽 🍺 ♣ 🕰 P 🍴

Whitchurch

Prince Regent
London Street
☎ (0256) 892179
11–11
Archers Best Bitter; Hop Back GFB H, **Summer Lightning** G
The hard-working, unconventional landlord has carved himself a niche here in a small town with much competition. The beer and food are exceptional value. Music club Wed eve. Occasional guest beers. 🍽 🍺 ♣ P

Whitsbury

Cartwheel
3 miles NNW of Fordingbridge
☎ (072 53) 362
11–2.30, 6–11
Adnams Broadside; Bunces Best Bitter; Greene King Abbot; Ind Coope Burton Ale; Wiltshire Old Grumble H
Comfortable free house in a remote village just outside the New Forest, previously a barn, a bakery and a wheelwright's – hence the name. Constantly-changing beer range; imaginative menu. 🏠 🍽 🍺 ♣ P

Winchester

Bell
St Cross Road, St Cross (A333 at S edge of city)
☎ (0962) 865284
11–2.30, 5–11 (11–11 Sat)
Marston's Mercian Mild, Burton Best Bitter, Pedigree H
Splendid, old inn adjoining the 12th-century Hospital of St Cross (England's oldest charity).

The quiet, friendly lounge is good for conversation, while the down-to-earth, bustling public bar is used by games players. No food Sun.
🏠 🛏 🍽 🍺 🚲 ♣ P

County Arms
Romsey Road (A3090, by hospital)
☎ (0962) 851950
10.30–11 (10.30–3, 5.30–11 Sat)
Marston's Mercian Mild or **Border Mild, Burton Best Bitter, Pedigree** H
Very busy, friendly local catering for all, incl. local prison officers, hospital staff and students. Good value, wide-ranging food (roasts on Sun). Active sports teams. Limited parking. 🏠 🏠 🍽 🍺 🚲 ♣ P

Exchange
9 Southgate Street
☎ (0962) 854718
10–11
Courage Best Bitter, Directors; John Smith's Bitter H
A thriving pub, despite its uninspiring design. Good value food all day. Patio at the rear (the nearest thing to a beer garden in the city centre).
🍽 🍺 🕰 ♣

Fulflood Arms
28 Cheriton Road (300 yds off A272) ☎ (0962) 865356
12–2.30, 6–11 (12–2.30, 7–10.30 Sun)
Marston's Burton Best Bitter, Pedigree H
Traditional, quiet, two-bar local tucked away behind the station. Its tiled sign still proclaims 'Winchester Brewery'. 🛏 🚲 ♣

King Alfred
Saxon Road (off Hyde Street)
☎ (0962) 854370
11–3.30, 5.30–11
Marston's Burton Best Bitter, Pedigree, Owd Rodger (winter) H
A once legendary pub, slowly returning to its former glory under new management. Large public bar, with a pool table, and a small, cosy lounge. The large beer garden offers barbecues in the summer, and petanque. 🍽 🍺 🕰 ♣ 🍴

⚱

Public Bars

The Public Bar is fast disappearing from our pubs. This unpretentious haven of cheaper beer, traditional games and no-frills decor must be saved. Not everyone wants to sit in plush armchairs, amongst pot plants and wall-to-wall carpeting. In recognition of the threat to the Public Bar, we award the tankard symbol to entries where such retreats can be found. Let's continue to have a choice.

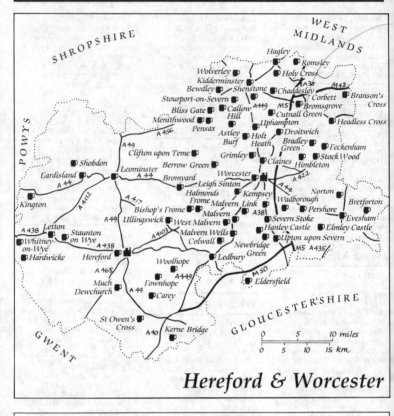

Hereford & Worcester

🏭 *Jolly Roger*, Worcester; **Wye Valley**, Hereford

Astley Burf

Hampstall Inn
Off B4196
☎ (029 93) 2600
11.30–2.30, 6–11
**Greenalls Davenports Mild,
Bitter** Ⓗ
Attractive, riverside inn with
mooring and fishing, a nice
family room, a children's menu
and a play area. Enjoys a quiet,
rural location but is popular in
summer. Good value food.
🛏 ⊛ ◖ ▶ ⊞ P

Berrow Green

Admiral Rodney
On B4197
☎ (0886) 21375
11–11 (12–2.30, 7–11 winter)
**Banks's Mild; Ruddles
County; Webster's Yorkshire
Bitter** Ⓗ
Welcoming and easy-going,
large, country free house with a
strong nautical feel; separate
restaurant. Convenient for
walkers on the Worcestershire
Way. 🏠 ⊛ ◖ ▶ ⊞ ▲ ♣ P

Bewdley

Black Boy
Wyre Hill (off A456 at
Welchgate)
11–3, 7–11
Banks's Mild, Bitter Ⓔ
Friendly, locals' pub with
several small rooms, popular for
games. Worth the half-mile
uphill walk from the river.
Q ⊛ ◖ ⊞ ♣

Cock & Magpie
Severnside North
☎ (0299) 403748
11–11 (11–3, 6–11 Mon–Fri in winter)
Banks's Mild, Bitter Ⓔ
Traditional local on a former
quayside by the Severn (wellies
useful when the river floods!).
Q ⊞ ⇌ (SVR) ♣

Hop Pole
Cleobury Road (A456)
☎ (0299) 402127
11–2.30, 6–11 (may vary in summer)
**Marston's Burton Best Bitter,
Pedigree** Ⓗ
An ever-present *Good Beer
Guide* entry: a pleasant, two-

roomed hostelry a mile's drive
from the river. Boules in
summer. 🏠 Q ◖ ▶ ⊞ ♣ P

Little Pack Horse
High Street (by Severnside
South) ☎ (0299) 403762
11–2.30, 6–11 (may vary in summer)
**Ansells Bitter; Ind Coope
Burton Ale; Lumphammer** Ⓗ
The original outlet and flagship
of the Little Pub Co. chain: a
classic, traditional pub with
stone floors, low black beams
and small rooms covered in old
photos and artefacts. Renowned
for its 'sizzlers' and Desperate
Dan pies. Lumphammer is
brewed for the chain by Ind
Coope. 🏠 Q ◖ ▶ ♣

Try also: George Hotel
(M&B)

Bishop's Frome

Chase Inn
☎ (0885) 490234
12 (11.30 Sat)–3.30, 5–11
**Hook Norton Best Bitter;
Wye Valley Hereford
Supreme** Ⓗ

Well-run pub in a village that has a reputation for good pubs. The landlord will read your Tarot cards. Food perhaps a little pricey (restaurant closed Sun eve). ⚓ ⊛ ♨ ◖ ▮ ⊟ ♣ P

Try also: Green Dragon (Free)

Bliss Gate

Bliss Gate
Left off A456; 2½ miles W of Bewdley OS746725
12–2.30 (3.30 Sat), 6–11
Marston's Burton Best Bitter, Pedigree Ⓗ
Quiet, friendly local with a good selection of whiskies. Beer bottles adorn the bar.
⚓ Q ⊛ ⊟ ♣ P

Bradley Green

Mad O'Rourkes Kipper House
Feckenham Road OS987618
☎ (052 784) 376
11–3, 6–11
Ansells Mild; Ind Coope Burton Ale; Lumphammer Ⓗ
A fine example of the Mad O'Rourke style: trawler in the car park; diesel engine in the bar! Good food, in large portions. ⚓ ⊛ ◖ ▮ ⊟ ▲ P

Branson's Cross

Cross & Bowling Green
Alcester Road
☎ (056 44) 2472
11–11 (11–3, 6–11 Sat)
Ansells Mild, Bitter; Marston's Pedigree; Tetley Bitter Ⓗ
The site of a pub for 500 years and a gibbet before that, now a small lounge and a larger restaurant/lounge. Playground in the large garden. No food Sun. ⚓ ⊛ ◖ ▮ ⊟ ▲ P

Bretforton

Fleece
The Cross (50 yds S of B4035)
☎ (0386) 831173
11 (10 Sat)–3, 6–11
Hook Norton Best Bitter; M&B Brew XI; Uley Hogshead, Pig's Ear Ⓗ
Famous old inn, owned by the National Trust. The interior has remained untouched for many years: inglenook, antiques, and a world-famous pewter collection. A beer festival is held early in July; ciders in summer.
⚓ Q ❧ ⊛ ◖ ▮ ⊟ ♣ ⊕ ⚡

Bromsgrove

Red Lion Hotel
High Street ☎ (0527) 35387
10.30–11
Banks's Mild, Bitter Ⓔ

Busy, one-roomed pub: a mild drinker's retreat. No food Sun.
⊛ ◖ ⇌ ♣ P

Bromyard

Crown & Sceptre
7 Sherford Street
☎ (0885) 482441
11.30–2.30 (3.30 Sat), 6.30–11
Banks's Bitter; Hook Norton Best Bitter; Wood Parish Ⓗ
Deservedly popular; the only free house in Bromyard: a plain but comfortable bar area, large inglenook, old maps and adverts. Friendly service and good pub grub (no meals Wed or Sun eve). Occasional guest beer. ⚓ ⊛ ⋈ ◖ ▮ P

Callow Hill

Royal Forresters
On A456, 2 miles from Bewdley ☎ (0299) 266286
11–3, 5.30–11 (11–11 Sat)
Greene King Abbot; John Smith's Bitter Ⓗ
Pleasant, popular inn on the main Bewdley–Ludlow road. Guest beers, incl. a mild.
⚓ Q ⊛ ♣ P

Carey

Cottage of Content
☎ (0432) 840242
12–2.30 (3 Sat in summer), 7 (6 Sat in summer)–11
Draught Bass; Hook Norton Best Bitter, Old Hooky Ⓗ
Aptly named pub in an idyllic setting. 500 years old, it has a warren of oak-beamed rooms and simple, but comfortable furnishings. The tremendous character is not spoilt by the excellent range of food. May be closed Tue/Thu lunch (phone ahead). ⚓ ⊛ ⋈ ◖ ▮ ⊟ ♣

Chaddesley Corbett

Swan
High Street ☎ (056 283) 302
11–3.30, 7–11
Batham Mild, Best Bitter Ⓗ
Spacious, country pub with a bowling green and garden. Lively bar, unusual lounge, children's room and restaurant. Jazz Thu.
⚓ Q ❧ ⊛ ◖ ▮ ⊟ ▲ ⊕ P

Claines

Mug House
Claines Lane ☎ (0905) 56649
11–11 (11–3, 5.30–11 winter)
Banks's Mild, Bitter Ⓔ
Ancient, unspoilt, village pub situated in the churchyard. Tug-of-War team. Parking limited. No food Sun. Family room in summer. ⚓ Q ❧ ⊛ ◖ ▮ ▲ ♣

Clifton upon Teme

Lion Inn
The Village ☎ (088 65) 617
12–3, 7 (6 Fri & Sat)–11
Banks's Mild Ⓗ&Ⓔ
Homely, traditional, half-timbered, village inn with a comfortable lounge and a separate restaurant (no food Mon). ⚓ Q ⊛ ⋈ ◖ ▮ ⊟ ♣ P

Colwall

Chase Inn
Chase Road, Upper Colwall (200 yds off B4218, Wyche road, signed 'British Camp')
☎ (0684) 40276
12–2.30 (not Tue), 6–11 (12–2, 7–10.30 Sun)
Donnington BB, SBA; Wye Valley HPA, Hereford Supreme Ⓗ
Straightforward free house, tucked away in a backwater of the Malvern Hills. Strict no kids/fruit machine policy. Limited, but wholesome menu till 8.30pm (no food Sun eve). Bar billiards. Q ⊛ ◖ ▮ ⊟ ♣ P

Cutnall Green

New Inn
On A442 ☎ (029 923) 202
11.30–3, 5.30–11
Marston's Burton Best Bitter, Pedigree Ⓗ
Small, welcoming, country pub. Good food always available in the bar and dining room.
⚓ ⊛ ◖ ▮ ⊟ ♿ ▲ P

Droitwich

Railway Inn
Kidderminster Road
☎ (0905) 770056
11.30–3, 5.30–11 (11.30–11 Fri & Sat)
Marston's Burton Best Bitter, Merrie Monk, Pedigree Ⓗ
200 year-old coach house, now a canalside pub, close to the restored basin. Lively atmosphere; railway memorabilia. ⊛ ⋈ ◖ ▮ ⇌ ♣ ⊕ P

Riflemans Arms
Station Street (off Ombersley Way) ☎ (0905) 770327
11–2.30, 5–11 (11–11 Sat)
Banks's Mild, Bitter Ⓔ
Banks's premier 'Pint & Platter' pub; a friendly local which attracts customers of all ages. Excellent, home-cooked food.
⊛ ⋈ ◖ ▮ ⊟ ⇌ P

Eardisland

White Swan
Main Road ☎ (054 47) 565
12–2.30, 6–11
Marston's Burton Best Bitter, Pedigree Ⓗ

Old, country pub in a famous, picturesque village. Low beams add character to a pleasant lounge and a traditional public bar. The lounge tends to be very food-oriented at weekends (food stops at 9pm).
🏚 🌢 🖱 ♣ P

Eldersfield

Greyhound
Lime Street (off B4211)
OS814305 ☎ (0452) 840381
11–3, 6–11
Butcombe Bitter G
A real village pub complete with stone flags, wood panels and settles. Seats outside in summer (mind the free-ranging chickens). Off the beaten track; worth finding. 🏚 Q 🏚 ⚐ ▲ ♣ P

Elmley Castle

Queen Elizabeth
Main Street ☎ (038 674) 209
11–3, 7–11
Marston's Burton Best Bitter H
16th-century, black and white inn in a picturesque village. A traditional bar, with games and an inglenook, gives access to a homely lounge with old tables and settles. Visited by its namesake in 1575 and unchanged under the current landlord for the last 30 years.
🏚 Q 🏚 ⚐

Evesham

Trumpet Inn
Merstow Green (near Almonry Museum at S end of centre)
☎ (0386) 446227
11–2.30, 5–11 (may extend in summer)
Draught Bass; M&B Brew XI H
Pleasant, town pub just off the main street; a single bar, though not cavernous. The Bass sell-off is expected to make this a new free house in a town with little customer choice. No meals winter Sun. Guest beer.
🏚 🌢 ⇥ ♣ P ✗

Feckenham

Rose & Crown
High Street ☎ (052 789) 2188
11–2.30, 6–11
Adnams Bitter H; **Banks's Mild, Bitter** E; **Welsh Brewers Worthington BB** H
Welcoming, village pub; the lounge features unusual, high-backed settles. Large, enclosed garden where children are welcome. 🏚 Q 🏚 🖱 ⚐ ⚑ ♿

Fownhope

Green Man Inn
On B4224 ☎ (0432) 860243
11–2.30, 6–11 (12–2.30, 7–10.30 Sun)

Hook Norton Best Bitter; Marston's Pedigree; Samuel Smith OBB H
Attractive 500 year-old coaching inn of character, with links to the Civil War and fishing rights on the Wye. Good value food and beer; a regular entry in this guide. Separate restaurant.
🏚 Q ⇥ 🏚 ⊭ 🖱 ⚐ ♿ P

Grimley

Camp House Inn
Camp Lane (1½ miles off A443)
OS836607 ☎ (0905) 640288
11–3, 6–11
Whitbread Flowers IPA, Original H
Pleasant, family-run pub in a lovely, scenic spot on the riverbank, offering an unspoilt, relaxed atmosphere. Original quarry-tiled floors; peacocks, geese, ducks, etc. outside. Guest beers from Whitbread.
🏚 Q ⇥ 🏚 🖱 ⚐ ♿ ▲ ♣ P

Hagley

Station
Worcester Road (200 yds from A456 jct) ☎ (0562) 882549
11–11 (may vary)
Banks's Mild, Bitter H
Very smart hostelry at the centre of a busy, but tidy village. A railway theme pervades and there is a display of old prints of the area; note the leaded glass above the bar. Hosts many charity events, such as quizzes. 🏚 🖱 ⇥ P

Halmonds Frome

Majors Arms
1 mile off A4103 at Fromes Hill ☎ (053 186) 371
12–2.30 (summer only), 5 (6 Sat)–11
Marston's Burton Best Bitter, Pedigree G
Quiet and friendly, hillside pub with panoramic views. Occasional live music soirées are the only disturbance to the rural tranquillity. Guest beer and cider in summer. Note: closed winter lunchtimes.
🏚 Q 🏚 🖱 ▲ ♣ ♿ P

Hanley Castle

Three Kings
Off B4211 ☎ (0684) 592686
11–3, 7–11
Butcombe Bitter; Jolly Roger Shipwrecked; Theakston Best Bitter H
Traditional, multi-roomed pub next to the church in a sleepy village; a real gem. Live music Sun eve; folk music Thu eve. CAMRA *Regional Pub of the Year* 1990. No food Sun eve.
🏚 Q ⊭ 🖱 ⚐ ♣ ♿

Hardwicke

Royal Oak
On B4348 ☎ (049 73) 248
11–3 (not Tue & Wed in winter), 6–11
Fuller's ESB; Marston's Burton Best Bitter, Pedigree H
Isolated, 16th-century pub with two separate drinking areas. Boasts a successful outside catering trade, as well as a reputation for good pub food.
🏚 Q 🖱 ⚐ 🖱 ▲ ♣ ♿ P

Headless Cross

Gate Hangs Well
Evesham Road
☎ (0527) 401293
12–3, 5.30–11 (12–11 Sat)
Ansells Mild, Bitter H
One-roomed but traditional local with a good atmosphere. Can get crowded at weekends.
🏚 🖱

Seven Stars
75 Birchfield Road
☎ (0527) 402138
12–11
Ruddles Best Bitter, County; Webster's Yorkshire Bitter H
Locals' pub with a public bar, a lounge and an adjoining games room. Excellent value lunches; Bulmers cider. 🖱 ⚐ ♿

Hereford

Barrels
69 St Owen Street
11–2.30 (4 Wed & Thu), 5–11 (11–11 Fri & Sat)
Wye Valley Hereford Bitter, HPA, Hereford Supreme, Brew 69 H
Lively home of Wye Valley brewery, often loud with music Sat eve. Guest beer. Beer festival August. 🏚 🖱 ⇥ ♣ ♿

Hop Pole
Commercial Road
☎ (0432) 265019
11–3, 5–11
Draught Bass; M&B Mild H
Bustling, town pub, popular with all ages: spacious lounge with a public bar and restaurant/function room to the rear. Eve meals till 9.30.
⊭ 🖱 ⚐ ▲ ♣ P

Jolly Roger
88 St Owen Street
☎ (0432) 274998
11–11
Jolly Roger Quaff Ale, Blackbeard, Old Hereford Bull H
The latest addition to the Jolly Roger chain and Hereford's second brew pub. Pirate mural on the outside wall; professionally fitted out on a galleon theme; guest beer and separate restaurant.
🏚 🖱 🖱 ⇥ ♿ P

Saracens Head

1 St Martins Street
☎ (0432) 275480
11–3, 6.30–11
**Draught Bass; Felinfoel
Double Dragon; Marston's
Pedigree** Ⓗ
Popular free house on the banks
of the River Wye. The lounge
has a 'locals' feel to it; separate
dining area. Occasional guest
beers. Q ⊛ ◖ ▶ ♣

Vaga Tavern

26 Vaga Street, Hunderton
Estate ☎ (0432) 273601
11.30–3, 5.30–11 (11–11 Sat)
Banks's Mild, Bitter Ⓔ
Popular pub which predates the
surrounding estate by a few
decades: a club-type, 'plush'
lounge and a basic, locals' bar.
One of the four Banks's pubs
that give respite to Whitbread-
dominated Hereford. ⊕ ♣ P

Himbleton

Galton Arms

OS943586
☎ (090 569) 672
12–2.30, 6.30–11
Banks's Mild, Bitter Ⓔ
Very friendly local with an
attractive garden area for a
relaxing summertime drink in
the heart of the countryside.
🏚 Q ⊛ ◖ ▶ ⊕ Å ♣ ♨ P

Holt Heath

Red Lion

At A443/ B4196 jct
☎ (0905) 620236
11–2.30, 5.30–11
**Ansells Mild, Bitter; Ind
Coope Burton Ale** Ⓗ
Traditional village, two-roomed
inn. The comfortable lounge has
a blazing log fire; the bar has a
separate games area. Excellent
menu of good food. Guest beer.
🏚 ⊛ ◖ ▶ Å ♣ ♨ P

Holy Cross

Bell & Cross

Belbroughton Road
OS923788 ☎ (0562) 730319
11–2.30, 6–11
**Draught Bass; M&B Mild,
Brew XI** Ⓗ
Unspoilt, welcoming country
pub: three small, cosy rooms.
Large garden. 🏚 Q ⊛ ⊕

Kempsey

Huntsman

Green Street Village (1¼ miles
off A38) ☎ (0905) 820336
12–3, 6 (7 winter)–11
Banks's Mild, Bitter Ⓔ
Welcoming, village pub offering
a wide range of good value
food. Traditional bar; cosy
lounge with country furniture in
its alcoves and a regular guest

beer on handpump. Children's
play area, skittle alley and Sam
the Great Dane for company.
🏚 Q ⊛ ⟟ ◖ ▶ ⊕ Å P

Kerne Bridge

Kerne Bridge Inn

On B4228 ☎ (0600) 890495
12–3, 7–11 (11–11 Sat & bank hols)
**Adnams Bitter; Whitbread
Pompey Royal** Ⓗ
Value-for-money free house on
the banks of the Wye. A stone
facade conceals a friendly,
straightforward, family-oriented
pub. Guest beers in summer.
⊛ ⟟ ◖ ▶ ⊕ ♣ ♨ P

Kidderminster

Grand Turk

207 Sutton Road (opp. general
hospital) ☎ (0562) 66254
11–3 (4 Fri), 6–11 (11–11 Sat)
Banks's Mild, Bitter Ⓔ
Three-roomed local with a
friendly landlord; children
welcome. Food available all day
Sat. Q ⊛ ◖ ▶ ⊕ ♣ ♨ P

Station

Fairfield (off A448)
☎ (0562) 822764
11–3, 6–11 (11–11 Fri & Sat)
**Greenalls Davenports Bitter;
Tetley Bitter** Ⓗ
Excellent local near the station
and start (or end) of the Severn
Valley steam railway. The small
bar caters for the games-
oriented local populace.
Q ◖ ⊕ ⟟ ♣ P

Yew Tree

Chester Road North (A449,
opp. Rose Theatre)
☎ (0562) 751786
11–2.30, 6–11
Banks's Mild, Bitter Ⓔ
Popular, two-roomed local: a
lively bar and small, cosy
lounge. The garden is popular in
summer for barbecues and the
landlord organises charity fund-
raising events throughout the
year. Q ⊛ ⊕ ♣ P

Kington

Royal Oak Hotel

Church Street
☎ (0544) 230484
10.30–3, 5.30–11
**Marston's Burton Best Bitter,
Pedigree** Ⓗ
The first and last pub in
England, popular with pub game
enthusiasts. Good, plain
cooking. 🏚 ⊛ ⟟ ◖ ▶ ⊕ ♣ P

Swan Hotel

Church Street
☎ (0544) 230510
12–2.30, 6.30–11
**Ansells Bitter; Whitbread
Boddingtons Bitter** Ⓗ
A large, single lounge bar,
featuring an original stone
fireplace. Reasonably-priced

food with a good vegetarian
selection; the splendid 17th-
century restaurant predates the
pub (no eve meals Sun in
winter). 🏚 ⟟ ◖ ▶

Ledbury

Brewery Inn

Bye Street ☎ (0531) 4272
11–2.30, 7–11 (12–2.30, 7–10.30 Sun)
**Marston's Burton Best Bitter,
Pedigree** Ⓗ
Recently renovated pub, whose
splendid small snug bar has kept
much of its character.
Frequented by locals keen on
games. 🏚 Q ⊛ ◖ ▶ ⟟ ⇌ ♣ ♨

Feathers Hotel

The Homend ☎ (0531) 5266
11–2.30, 5.30–11 (12–2.30, 7–10.30
Sun)
**Draught Bass; Felinfoel
Double Dragon; M&B Brew
XI; Welsh Brewers
Worthington BB** Ⓗ
Lounge bar in a 15th-century,
three-star hotel, once a principal
port of call for stagecoaches en
route to South Wales. Guest
beers. No lunches weekends.
🏚 Q ⊛ ◖ ▶ ⇌ P

Leigh Sinton

Royal Oak

Malvern Road ☎ (0886) 32664
11–3, 6–11
**Marston's Burton Best Bitter,
Pedigree** Ⓗ
Very friendly and attractive,
two-roomed, village local, run
by a congenial Irish landlord. A
wealth of unusual artefacts.
🏚 Q ⊛ ◖ ⊕ ♣ P

Leominster

Black Horse

South Street ☎ (0568) 611946
11–2.30, 6–11 (11–11 Sat)
Wadworth 6X Ⓗ
Traditional, two-bar local with a
dining area at the rear (no food
Sun eve). Occasional live music.
Always two guest beers.
🏚 ◖ ▶ ⊕ ⇌ ♣ P

Grape Vaults

Broad Street ☎ (0568) 611404
11–2.30, 6–11
**Marston's Burton Best Bitter,
Pedigree; Wood Special** Ⓗ
Well-run, superbly restored, free
house with real character. On-
street parking. Beers may vary.
🏚 Q ◖ ▶ ⇌

Greyhound

6 Rainbow Street
☎ (0568) 612901
12–3, 7–11
**Theakston Best Bitter;
Younger Scotch** Ⓗ
Busy, town-centre free house
with a comfortable lounge
downstairs and basic public bar
on the first floor. Separate
restaurant. 🏚 ◖ ⊕ ⇌ ♣ P

Hereford & Worcester

Letton

Swan Inn
On A438 ☎ (054 46) 304
11–11 (11–3, 6–11 Mon & Tue)
Draught Bass; Hook Norton Best Bitter Ⓗ
Rejuvenated, roadside pub with a basic but cosy public bar and a lounge recovering well from a corporately bland refit. Separate restaurant. Occasional guest beers. 🏠 🏢 🍴 ⚓ Å ♣ P

Malvern

Star
59 Cowleigh Road
12–3, 6–11
Banks's Mild, Bitter Ⓔ; **Draught Bass; M&B Brew XI** Ⓗ
Friendly, homely, three-roomed pub: a dull exterior hides a magnificent Victorian interior. The bar has a separate games area with skittle alley. Live folk music. Limited parking.
🏠 🏢 🍴 ♣ P

Malvern Link

Bakery Inn
Worcester Road
☎ (0684) 572201
11–2.30, 5.30–11
Marston's Burton Best Bitter, Pedigree Ⓗ
Large, busy, two-bar, town pub with darts and pool in the bar, and a more sophisticated lounge. Younger customers appreciate the landlord's collection of blues music.
🍴 ⚓ 🚲 ♣ P

Malvern Wells

Malvern Hills Hotel
Wynds Point (A449)
☎ (0684) 40237
11–2.30, 6–11
Draught Bass; Hook Norton Best Bitter; Wood Parish Ⓗ
Comfortable lounge bar in an upmarket weekend retreat, on the ridge of the Malvern Hills, close to the 'British Camp' hill fort. Hill walkers are welcome but are requested to remove muddy boots. Extensive lunchtime cold table. 🏠 🏢 🚪 ☐ P

Menithwood

Cross Keys
Between A443 and B4202
OS709690 ☎ (058 470) 425
11–3, 6–11
Courage Directors Ⓗ; **Marston's Burton Best Bitter** Ⓔ, **Pedigree** Ⓗ
Roadside pub in quiet countryside; very popular with the local community. The piano in the lounge provides ample opportunities for impromptu sing-alongs. 🏠 Q 🏢 ♣ P

Much Dewchurch

Black Swan
On B4348 ☎ (0981) 540295
11–2.30, 6.30–11
Crown Buckley Dark, Best Bitter Ⓗ
14th-century inn, one of the oldest in the county: a comfortable lounge and a recently renovated public bar where shove-ha'penny is played. Guest beers.
🏠 🏢 🍴 ⚓ ♣ P

Newbridge Green

Drum & Monkey
On B4211 ☎ (068 46) 2238
11.30–2.30, 5–11
Banks's Mild, Bitter; Donnington BB; Theakston Best Bitter; Wadworth 6X Ⓗ
Busy, black and white, country pub with lots of character. One large bar area is divided into cosy sections while the restaurant is housed in a barn.
Guest beers. 🏢 🍴 Å ♣ P

Norton

Norton Grange Hotel
At A435/A439 jct
☎ (0386) 870215
11–3, 6 (7 winter)–11
Marston's Burton Best Bitter, Pedigree Ⓗ
Family-run, main-road hotel. The restaurant caters for children. Garden set back from the road.
🏠 🏢 🛏 🍴 Å ♣ P

Pensax

Bell
On B4202 ☎ (0299) 896677
11–2.30, 7–11 (may vary in summer)
Hook Norton Best Bitter; Taylor Landlord; Wood Special Ⓗ
Traditional snug and a coal-stove heated bar. The comfortable dining room serves *Cordon Bleu* meals: Sun lunch a speciality; vegetarians and children's menus available. Beer range may vary; guest beers.
🏠 Q 🏢 🍴 ⚓ ♣ P

Pershore

Millers Arms
8 Bridge Street
☎ (0386) 553864
11.30–2.30 (3 Sat), 7–11
Adnams Mild, Broadside; Hall & Woodhouse Badger Best Bitter, Tanglefoot; Wadworth 6X, Old Timer Ⓗ
Comfortable, olde-worlde, market town pub with a traditional appearance. The landlord has a passion for fine ales. Eve meals and children's menu in summer only. Guest beers. 🏢 🍴 ♣

Romsley

Manchester Inn
Bromsgrove Road
OS964779 ☎ (0562) 710242
11–3, 5.30–11
M&B Highgate Mild, Brew XI Ⓔ
Roadside pub next to the North Worcestershire Path. A homely public bar is complemented by a larger, comfortable lounge. A good summertime pub, having a sizeable garden. No eve meals Sun. 🏠 🏢 🍴 ⚓ ♿ Å ♣ P

St Owen's Cross

New Inn
At A4137/B4521 jct
☎ (098 987) 274
12–3, 6–11
Draught Bass; Courage Directors; Smiles Brewery Bitter Ⓗ
Isolated, 16th-century free house, with settles, benches and grand fireplaces. The unusual pewter beer engines originally came from a bar in Ross-on-Wye. Caravan site. Occasional guest beers. 🏠 🏢 ⚓ 🍴 Å P

Severn Stoke

Rose & Crown
On A38 ☎ (0905) 371249
11.30–2.30, 6–11
Ansells Mild, Bitter; Ruddles Best Bitter Ⓗ
Attractive, black and white, village pub near the river (note the flood levels). A huge log fire adds to a cosy atmosphere in winter and a large garden makes for pleasant summertime drinking. Cricket team. Good, simple, but slightly pricey food (no meals Sun).
🏠 🏢 🍴 ♣ P ✗

Shenstone

Plough Inn
Off A450/A448
OS863735 ☎ (056 283) 340
11–3, 7–11
Batham Best Bitter Ⓗ
Large, basic public bar and a lounge converted from two small rooms. A classic country pub, hard to find but worth the effort. 🏠 Q 🏢 🚪 ♣ ☐ P

Shobdon

Bateman Arms
☎ (056 881) 374
12–2.30, 7–11
Wood Parish Ⓗ
Pleasant, country pub near Shobdon Aerodrome. Original features include high-backed settles. Eve meals in the restaurant. Guest beer in summer. 🏠 🏢 🍴 🚪 Å P

Staunton on Wye

New Inn
Off A438 ☎ (098 17) 346
12–2.30 (not Mon in winter), 7–11
Theakston Best Bitter Ⓗ
Friendly free house with a
comfortable lounge and a public
bar; separate dining room.
Guest beers. ⌂ ⬢ Ⓒ Ⓓ Ⓔ ♣ P

Stock Wood

Bird in Hand
Stock Green ☎ (0386) 793158
11–2.30, 6.30–11 (11–11 Sat)
Banks's Mild, Bitter Ⓔ;
Draught Bass Ⓗ
Bustling, country pub; the
lounge is smart and
comfortable, while the bar is
traditional and welcoming.
Good range of lunchtime food
(not served Sun or Mon).
⌂ Q ⬢ Ⓒ Ⓓ P

Stourport-on-Severn

Rising Sun
50 Lombard Street (opp. fire
station) ☎ (029 93) 2530
10.30–11
Banks's Mild, Bitter Ⓔ
Small, friendly, town pub: an
alcoved lounge and small bar,
plus a pleasant, outside drinking
area overlooking the canal.
Meals Tue–Sat lunchtime and
early eve. ⬢ Ⓒ Ⓓ

Rock Tavern
80 Wilden Lane (1 mile from
town, left off Hartlebury Road)
☎ (029 93) 2962
11–11
**Batham Best Bitter; HP&D
Mild, Entire** Ⓗ
Recently refurbished to a high
standard: one main room split
into drinking and food areas. *A
la carte* restaurant. Ⓒ Ⓓ ⚲ P

Ullingswick

Three Crowns
1½ miles from A417 (½ mile E of
village) OS605497
☎ (0432) 820279
12–3 (4 Sat; not Tue). 7–11
**Ansells Bitter; Ind Coope
Burton Ale; Tetley Bitter** Ⓗ
Relaxing and friendly free house
where a central, hop-garlanded
bar divides the pub into two
fine, traditional drinking areas.
Good beer and good food exist
side by side. ⌂ Q ⬢ Ⓒ Ⓓ ⚲ P

Uphampton

Fruiterers Arms
Off A449 OS839649
☎ (0905) 820462
12–2.30, 7–11
**Donnington BB; John Smith's
Bitter** Ⓗ

Rural pub to the north of
Ombersley. ⌂ ⬢ Ⓒ Ⓔ P

Upton upon Severn

Little Upton Muggery
Old Street ☎ (068 46) 3620
11–3, 6–11
**Ind Coope Burton Ale;
Lumphammer** Ⓗ
A Little Pub Co. theme pub, its
decor based on pottery mugs.
There is a working pottery at
the rear. Noted for its Desperate
Dan pies. ⌂ Ⓒ Ⓓ ⚲

Wadborough

Masons Arms
OS899475 ☎ (0905) 840524
11.30–2.30, 6.30–11 (12–2.30, 7–10.30
Sun)
Banks's Mild, Bitter Ⓗ
Cosy and welcoming, village
pub with a reputation for good
food (no meals Sun eve). Smart
lounge and a characterful bar.
⬢ Ⓒ Ⓓ Ⓔ ♣ P

West Malvern

Brewers Arms
Lower Dingle (B4232, then
footpath) ☎ (0684) 568147
11–2.30 (3 Sat), 6–11
**Marston's Burton Best Bitter,
Merrie Monk, Pedigree** Ⓗ
Cosy, village pub with a small
public bar and an even smaller
lounge. Ideally positioned for
walkers on the Malvern Hills.
Views over Herefordshire from
the neat garden. Folk sessions
every Tue night. Q ⬢ Ⓒ Ⓓ ♣

Whitney-on-Wye

Rhydspence Inn
On A438, 1½ miles W of
village ☎ (049 73) 262
11–2.30, 7–11
**Marston's Pedigree;
Robinson's Best Bitter** Ⓗ
The Welsh border cuts through
this 14th-century drovers' inn
which maintains many original
features. *A la carte* restaurant;
quoits played; children welcome
at lunchtime.
⌂ Q ⛲ ⬢ ⋈ Ⓒ Ⓓ Å ♣ ⌂ P

Wolverley

Queens Head
Off B4189 ☎ (0562) 850433
11–2.30, 5.30–11 (11–11 Sat)
Banks's Mild, Bitter Ⓔ
Two-room, village local in a
picturesque setting; popular all
year but particularly with
summer visitors. Q ⬢ Ⓒ Ⓔ ♣ P

Woolhope

Butchers Arms
½ mile E of village on Putley
road ☎ (0432) 820281

11–2.30, 7 (6 summer)–11
**Hook Norton Best Bitter, Old
Hooky; Marston's
Pedigree** Ⓗ
Ancient and isolated free house
that successfully marries beer
and good value food to
maintain a good atmosphere –
the original interior includes real
fires, latch doors and very low
beams. ⌂ Q ⬢ ⋈ Ⓒ Ⓓ Å P

Worcester

Cardinals Hat
Friar Street ☎ (0905) 21890
12–3, 5.30–11 (11.45–11 Sat)
**Jolly Roger Ale,
Shipwrecked** Ⓗ
A comfortable Jolly Roger Co.,
multi-roomed pub – the oldest
in Worcester (1518): exposed
beams and lots of oak panelling.
A jug and bottle shop stands
next door and there are plans to
install an antique working
brewery. Regular guest beers.
⛐ Ⓒ Ⓔ ⇌ (Foregate St) ♣ ⌂ P

Crown & Anchor
Hylton Road ☎ (0905) 421481
12–2.30 (3 Sat), 6–11
**Marston's Burton Best Bitter,
Merrie Monk, Pedigree** Ⓗ
Unpretentious, friendly,
roadside pub on the west bank
of the Severn. The lounge is
popular with students; locals
enjoy the bar. Function room
with skittle alley. ⬢ Ⓒ Ⓔ ♣ ⌂

Dragon Inn
The Tything ☎ (0905) 25845
11–11
**Marston's Burton Best Bitter;
Theakston XB** Ⓗ
Lively, one-roomed pub with a
varied clientele, close to the city
centre. Regular guest beers.
⬢ Ⓒ ⇌ (Foregate St)

Little Sauce Factory
London Road
☎ (0905) 350159
11–2.30, 6–11
**Ind Coope Burton Ale;
Lumphammer** Ⓗ
A Little Pub Co. theme pub,
decorated with Worcester Sauce
bottles and impressive tiling
(note the ceiling). It has a
relaxed atmosphere and is a
popular eating place (excellent
food). Live folk music Mon.
Limited parking. Q Ⓒ Ⓓ P

Virgin Tavern
Tolladine Road
☎ (0905) 23988
11–3, 5.30–11
**Marston's Burton Best Bitter,
Merrie Monk, Pedigree, Owd
Rodger** (winter) Ⓗ
Friendly estate pub a mile from
the city centre, offering a good
selection of moderately priced
food. Garden to the rear; ample
parking at the front.
⬢ Ⓓ ⚲ ⇌ (Shrub Hill) P

Hertfordshire

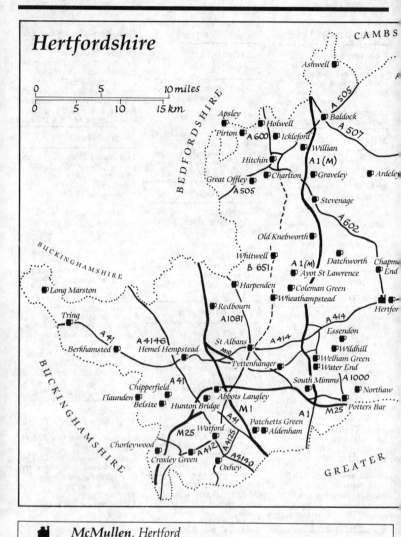

McMullen, *Hertford*

Abbots Langley

Swan
College Road (near Leavesden Hospital) ☎ (0923) 672539
11–11
Greene King XX Mild, IPA, Rayments Special, Abbot Ⓗ
Two-bar pub, rare in this area: a comfortable saloon and a basic public, popular with locals and the staff of the nearby hospital.
🏠 🕮 🍺 ♣ P

Aldenham

Roundbush
Just off B462 OS145985
☎ (0923) 857165
11–3 (4 Sat), 5.30–11

Ind Coope Benskins Best Bitter, Burton Ale Ⓗ
Genuine country pub (c. 1800), with two distinctly different bar areas catering for all. Shove-ha'penny played.
🏠 🕮 🍺 ♣ P

Apsley

Albion
Durrants Hill Road, Hemel Hempstead
☎ (0442) 235116
11.30–3.30 (2.30 Tue–Thu), 5–11
Ind Coope Benskins Best Bitter; Tetley Bitter Ⓗ
Split-level pub with roadside lounge and public bars. Downstairs, at canal level, is another bar where beer is

served direct from the cask (open May–Sept). Seems to have avoided many years of brewery 'improvements'. No food winter weekends.
🏠 🕮 🍺 ♣ ♠

Ardeley

Jolly Waggoner
Off B1037, ½ mile from village
OS310272 ☎ (043 886) 350
11.30–3, 6–11
Greene King IPA, Abbot Ⓖ
Picturesque, 16th-century, pinkwashed former cottages in a charming village setting; two small, intimate bars. Impressive row of barrels behind the bar; recommended food.
🏠 Q 🕮 🕮 🍺 ♣ P

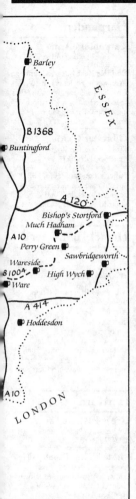

inglenook. Convenient for GB Shaw's house. Excellent restaurant and enormous garden. No eve meals Sun/Mon. Can be busy in summer and on bank hols – best visited off-peak. Piped classical music. Guest beer.
🏠 Q 🍴 ⌂ ◑ 🍺 & ♣ ⌂ P

Baldock

White Hart
21 Hitchin Street
☎ (0462) 893247
11–2.30 (3.30 Fri, 4 Sat), 5.30 (7 Sat)–11
Greene King XX Mild, IPA, Rayments Special, Abbot Ⓗ
Pleasant, one-bar pub with photographs of old Baldock around the walls. Limited parking. ⇌ ♣ P

Barley

Chequers
London Road (B1368, S end of village)
☎ (0763) 848378
12–2.30, 6–11
Greene King IPA, Abbot Ⓗ
Comfortable, one-bar, country pub with wood panelling, good food, a large garden and a petanque court. 🏠 🍴 ◑ ♣ P

Belsize

Plough
Plough Lane
OS035009 ☎ (0923) 262800
11–3, 5.30–11
Greene King IPA; Ind Coope Benskins Bitter Ⓗ
Isolated pub in a small hamlet near Sarratt. Pleasant and friendly; popular with horse-riders and walkers. The large car park makes it very busy in fine weather. 🏠 🍴 ◑ & ♣ P

Berkhamsted

Boat
Gravel Path, Ravens Lane (off A41 at Baptist church, next to canal bridge)
☎ (0442) 877152
11–3, 5.30–11
Fuller's Chiswick, London Pride, Mr Harry, ESB Ⓗ
Winner of Fuller's Brewery *Pub of the Year* for 1990; a modern, canalside pub offering a warm welcome to a wide-ranging clientele. A large patio faces the canal. Summer barbecues weekend eves and Sun lunch.
🍴 ◑ 🍺 ⇌ P

Rising Sun
George Street (by Grand Union Canal)
☎ (0442) 864913
11–3, 6–11

Ind Coope Benskins Best Bitter Ⓗ
Friendly, quiet, canalside local which is hard to find because it has no road frontage. Function/darts room at the rear. The steep steps and the canal lock could be perilous to the over-indulgent! Gated garden to safeguard children.
🍴 ◑ 🍺 ⇌ ♣

Bishop's Stortford

Fox
74 Rye Street
☎ (0279) 651623
11–4.30, 5.30–11
Courage Best Bitter, Directors; Greene King IPA, Rayments Special, Abbot Ⓗ; **Mauldons Bitter** Ⓖ
Early 18th-century, cottage pub comprising a small lounge bar and two public bars. No carpets. Lousy but noisy darts team. The garden leads down to the river.
🏠 Q 🍴 ◑ 🍺 ♣ P

Buntingford

Crown
17 High Street (off A10 bypass)
☎ (0763) 71422
12–3, 5.30–11 (12–11 Sat)
Banks & Taylor Shefford Bitter; Mauldons Squires; Ruddles Best Bitter, County Ⓗ
Excellent, small town pub. Popular with the locals and business community. Weekly guest beers. 🏠 🍴 ◑ 🍺

Chapmore End

Woodman
30 Chapmore End (off B158)
OS328163
☎ (0920) 463143
12–3, 6–11
Greene King IPA, Abbot Ⓗ
Tiny, rural pub which somehow still manages to have something for everyone. Keep the children amused in the large, rear garden, relax in the small, front garden or simply enjoy the conversation in the small bars. XX Mild is often available.
🏠 Q 🍴 🍺 ♣

Charlton

Windmill
Charlton Road (1 mile from Hitchin centre)
☎ (0462) 432096
10.30–2.30, 5.30–11
Adnams Broadside Ⓗ; **Mansfield Riding Mild** Ⓖ; **Wells Eagle** Ⓗ
Refurbished, village pub with a pleasant atmosphere. Good home-cooked food served daily. Peacock and ducks in the garden. Q 🍴 ◑ & ♣ P

Ashwell

Rose & Crown
69 High Street OS268396
☎ (046 274) 2420
10.30–2.30, 6–11 (12–2, 7–10.30 Sun)
Greene King IPA, Abbot Ⓗ
Unspoilt, late 15th-century, timber-framed, village pub. Its excellent variety of good wholesome food includes children's dishes.
🏠 Q 🍴 ◑ ♣ P

Ayot St Lawrence

Brocket Arms
Shaws Corner OS196168
☎ (0438) 820250
11–2.30, 7–11
Adnams Extra; Greene King IPA, Abbot; Marston's Pedigree; Wadworth 6X Ⓗ
14th-century building housing a charming pub with a huge

135

Chipperfield

Royal Oak
1 The Street
12–2.30, 6 (6.30 Sat)–11 (12–2.30, 7–10.30 Sun)
Adnams Bitter; Hook Norton Best Bitter; Ind Coope Benskins Best Bitter Ⓗ, **Burton Ale** Ⓖ
Smart pub with a wide-ranging clientele in an attractive village. Function room available for hire. No food Sun. Shut the Box played. ▣ Q ▩ ◖ ♣ P

Chorleywood

Black Horse
Dog Kennel Lane (off A404)
☎ (0923) 287252
11–11
Adnams Bitter; Ansells Mild; Ind Coope Benskins Best Bitter, Burton Ale Ⓗ
Enjoying a fine setting on the common; one bar divided into several small areas. Two log fires and a stone floor. Good lunchtime specials; children are allowed in the eating area (no food Sun). ▣ ▩ ◖ ▶

Old Shepherd
Chorleywood Bottom
OS029958 ☎ (0923) 282740
11–3, 5.30–11
Ind Coope Benskins Best Bitter; Tetley Bitter; Wadworth 6X Ⓗ
Hard to find but worth the effort. Good lunchtime specials served. Thomas the Tank Engine is still in residence.
🛏 ◖ ⊖ ♣

Try also: White Horse (Greene King)

Coleman Green

John Bunyan
1 mile off B6129 and B651 near Wheathampstead
OS189128 ☎ (058 283) 2037
11–2.30 (3 Sat), 6–11
McMullen AK, Country Ⓗ
Isolated pub, well worth seeking out: a single bar with a separate darts area. Large collection of plates and jugs, so leave your bull tethered outside. Good, reasonably priced fast food. Large garden with plenty of room for children. No food Sun eve. ▣ Q ▩ ◖ ▶ ♣ P

Croxley Green

Sportsman
2 Scots Hill (A412)
☎ (0923) 773021
11–3, 5.30–11
Ind Coope Benskins Best Bitter, Burton Ale; Tetley Bitter Ⓗ
Friendly pub with a local atmosphere. Definitely for the sportsman: darts, dominoes and bar billiards. Good lunchtime food (not served weekends).
▩ ◖ ⊖ (Croxley) ♣ P

Datchworth

Plough
5 Datchworth Green (off A602, 2 miles from Watton)
OS269182 ☎ (0438) 813000
11.30–2.30 (3 Sat), 6–11
Greene King XX Mild, IPA, Abbot Ⓗ
Small, village local with one cosy bar. ▣ Q ◖ P

Essendon

Candlestick
West End (off B158)
OS262083 ☎ (0707) 261322
11.30–2.30, 5.30–11 (12–2.30, 7–10.30 Sun)
McMullen AK, Country Ⓗ
Welcoming pub, off the beaten track: a real public bar and a comfortable lounge with a dining area (book eve meals, served Tue–Fri). Try counting the 200-plus candlesticks. Snacks only Sun. ▣ Q ▩ ◖ ▶ ♣ P

Flaunden

Bricklayers Arms
Hogpits Bottom OS017013
☎ (0442) 833322
11–2.30 (3 summer), 6 (5.30 summer)–11
Adnams Bitter; Brakspear Bitter, Special; Fuller's London Pride Ⓗ
Sympathetically extended, old village pub which can get very busy. Diners are catered for in a restaurant area where children are permitted. Two guest beers always available. No food Sun eve. ▣ Q ▩ ◖ ▶ P

Try also: Green Dragon (Free)

Graveley

George & Dragon
19 High Street (B197)
OS232278 ☎ (0438) 351362
11–3, 5–11 (11–11 Fri & Sat)
Greene King IPA, Rayments Special, Abbot Ⓗ
Georgian facade on a one-bar pub, known locally as 'Mad Mick's'. Cockney nights Sat and live music Thu. Active golf and clay pigeon clubs (own shooting field). No food Sun eve. Ask for shove-ha'penny. Q ▩ ◖ ▶ ♣ P

Great Offley

Bull
High Street (off A505)
☎ (046 276) 319
11.30–2.30, 6–11 (11–3, 7–11 Sat)
Fuller's Chiswick, London Pride Ⓗ, **ESB** Ⓖ
Straightforward, village local.
Q ▣ ♣ P

Harpenden

Carpenters Arms
14 Cravells Road (off A1081)
11–3, 5.30–11
Ruddles Best Bitter, County; Webster's Yorkshire Bitter Ⓗ
Cosy and welcoming pub with a fine collection of celebration ales. Popular menu (no meals Sun or Mon eves). ▣ Q ▩ ◖ ▶ P

Gibraltar Castle
70 Lower Luton Road
☎ (0582) 460005
11–3, 5.30–11 (11–11 Sat)
Fuller's London Pride, ESB Ⓗ
An old roadside inn, recently acquired by Fuller's and refurbished. Meals available at most times. ⇝ ◖ ⅙ ♣ P

Hemel Hempstead

Old Bell
51 High Street
☎ (0442) 252867
10.30–2.30, 6 (7 Sat)–11
Adnams Bitter; Ind Coope Benskins Best Bitter, Burton Ale Ⓗ
Immaculate, multi-roomed, old inn of great character. Many local societies meet in the upstairs function rooms. The small car park is accessed via a narrow driveway. No food Sun.
Q 🛏 P

Hertford

Great Eastern Tavern
29 Railway Place
☎ (0992) 583570
11–2.30, 6 (7 Sat)–11
McMullen AK, Country Ⓗ
Cosy, old-fashioned, street-corner local with strong railway connections. Fine views of Hertford East signalbox! Eleventh consecutive year in the *Good Beer Guide*.
▩ ◖ ⇝ (East) ♣

Three Tuns
34 St Andrew Street
☎ (0992) 587706
11.30–2.30 (3 Sat), 5 (6.30 Sat)–11
Ansells Mild; Ind Coope Burton Ale; Tetley Bitter; Wadworth 6X Ⓗ
Vastly improved pub in the 'Antique' quarter of town: a well-appointed main bar and a cosy, sunken area to the rear. The adventurous selection of guest beers is soon to include a house beer. No food Sun.
▩ ◖ ⇝ (North) ♣

High Wych

Rising Sun
1 mile W of A1184, near Sawbridgeworth
☎ (0279) 724099
12–3, 5.30 (5 Fri & Sat)–11

Hertfordshire

Courage Best Bitter, Directors Ⓖ
Unspoilt, traditional pub, run by the same family for decades and known to locals as Sid's. Beer is drawn straight from the cask. Occasional guest beers.
🏠 Q 🍺 ♣ P

Hitchin

Cock Hotel
High Street ☎ (0462) 434673
10.30–2.45, 5–11 (12–2, 7–10.30 Sun)
Greene King IPA, Rayments Special, Abbot Ⓗ
Small, town-centre hotel which started life as a 16th-century inn. A pleasant pub with a divided drinking area; a quiet oasis. Good home-cooked food (Mon–Sat). 🏠 ◖ & ♣ P

Cricketers
53 Bedford Road (A600)
11–2.30 (3.30 Sat), 7–11 (12–2, 7–10.30 Sun)
Ind Coope Benskins Best Bitter; Tetley Bitter; Young's Special Ⓗ
Pleasant, two bar local; the public bar has a pool table. A garden and play area can be found at the rear of the car park behind the pub. Quiet lunchtimes. No food Sun.
🍺 ◖ ♣ P

Hoddesdon

Golden Lion
23 High Street
☎ (0992) 463146
11–3, 5.30–11
Adnams Bitter; Ind Coope Benskins Best Bitter; Tetley Bitter Ⓗ
Pleasant, town-centre pub with an interesting upper bar. No food Sun; snacks only Sat.
Q 🍺 ◖ & P

Holwell

New Inn
Bedford Road (A600, ¾ mile N of Ickleford) OS175329
☎ (0462) 712345
12–3, 6 (5 summer)–11 (12–2, 7–10.30 Sun)
Greene King IPA, Abbot Ⓗ
Small, one-roomer with beams and brasses. Sun lunchtime barbecue (May–Aug). For camping/caravanning, contact the landlord. No food Sun.
🏠 Q 🍺 ◖ ♣ P

Hunton Bridge

Kings Head
Bridge Road (off A41, S of M25 jct 20) ☎ (0923) 262307
11–3, 5.30–11
Ind Coope Benskins Best Bitter, Burton Ale; Tetley Bitter Ⓗ
Popular, old pub whose large garden backs on to the canal.

The old canal stables are now a skittle-alley-cum-darts room-cum-children's area. Guest beers. No food Sun eve. 🍺 ◖ ♣ P

Ickleford

Cricketers
Arlesley Road (off A600, beyond church) OS185320
☎ (0462) 432629
11–3 (4 Thu & Fri), 6–11 (11–11 Sat)
Adnams Bitter; Banks & Taylor Shefford Bitter; Tetley Bitter; Wadworth 6X Ⓗ
Lively, village alehouse drawing custom from near and far. Specialises in guest beers from all over Britain; often at least eight available, some on handpump, some with gravity dispense. No food Sun.
🍺 🏠 ♣ ◔ P

Old George
Arlesley Road (off A600, by church) ☎ (0462) 432269
11–3, 5.30–11 (11–11 Sat)
Greene King XX Mild, IPA, Rayments Special, Abbot Ⓗ
Old, country pub with a warm and friendly lounge and an extremely basic bar. Very good food. 🏠 Q 🍺 ◖ ♣ P

Long Marston

Boot
34 Station Road
☎ (0296) 662587
11–2.30, 5–11 (11–11 Sat)
Adnams Broadside; Hook Norton Best Bitter Ⓗ
Pub destroyed by bombing in WW II and rebuilt in the late 40s. The result is a pub which is out of style with its surroundings but which is nevertheless a centre of local life. Two guest beers. The restaurant has a no-smoking area. 🏠 🍺 ◖ 🅰 ♣

Queens Head
38 Tring Road
☎ (0296) 668368
12–3, 5.30–11 (11–11 Sat)
Fuller's Chiswick, London Pride, ESB Ⓗ
Thriving, village local which publishes a monthly newsletter, full of pub events and local news. A lovely, old building with low, beamed ceilings and many nooks and crannies. Speciality curries served Thu eves; no food Sun.
🏠 ⛄ 🍺 ◖ 🅰 ♣ P

Much Hadham

Bull Inn
High Street (2 miles S of A120)
☎ (027 984) 2668
11–2.30, 5.30–11
Greene King IPA; Ind Coope Burton Ale; Tetley Bitter Ⓗ
Large, friendly, old village pub

with a garden. Good food always available.
🏠 🍺 ◖ 🍴 & 🅰 ♣ P

Try also: Nags Head (Hadham Ford)

Northaw

Two Brewers
Northaw Road West (B156)
☎ (0707) 52420
11–3, 6–11
Ind Coope Benskins Best Bitter, Burton Ale; Tetley Bitter Ⓗ
One-bar pub divided into small areas to maintain an intimate atmosphere. Occasional guest beers. Dining area. 🍺 ◖ P

Try also: Sun (Allied)

Old Knebworth

Lytton Arms
Park Lane (off B197, 1½ miles past station) OS229202
☎ (0438) 812312
11–3, 5–11 (11–11 Fri & Sat)
Adnams Bitter; Banks & Taylor SOS; Draught Bass; Charrington IPA Ⓗ
Very popular, large, country pub near Knebworth Park. The varying range of four guest beers always includes one mild. House beer, Knebworth Ale, is from Banks & Taylor. Guest ciders in summer.
🏠 🍺 ◖ ◔ P

Oxhey

Haydon Arms
76 Upper Paddock Road (off A4008)
☎ (0923) 34834
11–3, 5.30–11 (11–11 Wed, Fri & Sat)
Ind Coope Benskins Best Bitter Ⓗ
Traditional, back-street, community pub: two bars and an outdoor drinking area. Collection of Watford FC mugs behind the bar. Regular guest beers. No food Sun.
🍺 ◖ 🍴 (Bushey) ♣

Try also: Victoria (Allied); **Villiers Arms** (Allied)

Patchetts Green

Three Compasses
½ mile off B462
☎ (0923) 856197
11–3, 5.30–11 (11–11 Fri & Sat)
Greene King IPA; Ind Coope Benskins Best Bitter, Burton Ale; Tetley Bitter Ⓗ
Deceptively large pub in rural surroundings, where the conservatory doubles as an eating area (no food Sun eve). Excellent children's facilities; display of carpenter's tools. Guest beers. ⛄ 🍺 ◖ P

137

Hertfordshire

Perry Green

Hoops Inn

4 miles S of A120, from Little
Hadham OS439173
☎ (027 984) 3568
11.30–3, 6–11
**Adnams Bitter; Greene King
IPA** Ⓗ
Oak-beamed, country pub in a
pleasant location with
comfortable bars and attractive
gardens. Good value meals (not
served Sun eve). Guest beers.
🏚 Q 🍴 🌙 ♿ P

Pirton

Cat & Fiddle

7 Great Green OS146316
☎ (0462) 712245
11.30–2.30, 5.30 (6 Sat)–11
**Adnams Broadside; Wells
Eagle** Ⓗ
Beamed, village pub on the
green, with interior wrought
ironwork. Always a friendly
welcome. 🏚 🍴 🌙

Potters Bar

Artful Dodger

High Street (40 yds from
A111/A1000 jct)
☎ (0707) 57198
11–11
**Charrington IPA; Courage
Directors or Younger IPA;
Greene King IPA, Abbot;
Theakston Best Bitter** Ⓗ
Wine bar/café-style pub serving
good quality food. Always at
least five beers available, incl. a
regular guest.
🏚 🍴 ♿ ♣

Redbourn

Cricketers

East Common
☎ (0582) 792410
11–2.30, 5.30–11
**Ind Coope Benskins Best
Bitter; Tetley Bitter** Ⓗ
Friendly, village pub with two
contrasting bars. An African
Grey parrot resides in the
lounge bar. Food (incl. a
vegetarian choice) is available
all week, except Sun lunchtime.
Q 🍴 🌙 ♿ ♣ P

St Albans

Blue Anchor

145 Fishpool Street
☎ (0727) 55038
11–3, 5.30 (6 Sat)–11
McMullen AK, Country Ⓗ
Unspoilt public bar where darts
and dominoes dominate; large
lounge bar opening onto a
riverside garden. The cheapest
pub in St Albans. No food Sun
eve.
🏚 Q 🍴 🌙 🍽 ♣ P

Farriers Arms

Lower Dagnall Street (off
A5183) ☎ (0727) 51025
11–2.30, 5.30 (7 Sat)–11
McMullen AK, Country Ⓗ
A proper, no-frills drinking
establishment with many
sporting activities, incl. golf,
sailing and football. Parking can
be difficult. Q 🍴 ♣

Garibaldi

61 Albert Street (off Holywell
Hill)
☎ (0727) 55046
11–3, 5–11 (11–11 Fri & Sat)
**Fuller's Chiswick, London
Pride, ESB** Ⓗ
Busy, side-street pub with a
central bar. Good value, home-
cooked food, incl. vegetarian
dishes (not served Sat or Sun
eves). 🍴 🌙 🍽 (Abbey) 🍽

Goat

Sopwell Lane (off Holywell Hill)
☎ (0727) 833934
11–3, 5.30–11
**Greene King IPA, Abbot;
Hook Norton Best Bitter, Old
Hooky; Marston's Pedigree;
Wadworth 6X** Ⓗ
Five hundred year-old pub with
a central bar and various seating
areas. The range of beers can
change. Children welcome in
the dining area. Very busy at
weekends; jazz band Sun lunch.
Two real fires.
🏚 🍴 🌙 🍽 (Abbey)

Verulam Arms

41 Lower Dagnall Street
☎ (0727) 833323
12–3, 6–11
**Ind Coope Benskins Best
Bitter, Burton Ale; Tetley
Bitter** Ⓗ
Plush, well-kept, street-corner
local, converted to one bar in
neo-Victorian style. The
landlord is a *Master Cellarman*.
Petanque played in summer.
🍴 🌙 ♣

White Lion

Sopwell Lane (off Holywell Hill)
☎ (0727) 50540
11–3, 6 (5.30 Fri)–11 (11–11 Sat)
**Adnams Bitter; Ind Coope
Burton Ale; Tetley Bitter** Ⓗ
Historic, friendly, two-bar pub.
Boules, backgammon and good
food on offer. No food Sun or
Mon eves.
Q 🍴 🌙 🍽 (Abbey) ♣

Sawbridgeworth

King William IV

7 Vantorts Road
☎ (0279) 722322
11–11
**Courage Best Bitter,
Directors** Ⓗ
17th-century inn set back from
the main street near the centre
of town. Can be very busy at
weekends. 🏚 Q 🍴 🌙 🍽 🍽

Market House Hotel

42 Knight Street (300 yds off
A1184) ☎ (0279) 722807
11–3, 5.30–11
**Adnams Mild, Old, Extra,
Broadside; Banks & Taylor
SOD** Ⓗ
Ancient building serving good
food (incl. vegetarian and
children's). Separate restaurant
area. 🏚 🍴 🌙 🍽 P

South Mimms

Black Horse

65 Blackhorse Lane (just off
B556) ☎ (0707) 42174
11–3, 5.30–11
Greene King IPA, Abbot Ⓗ
Classic public bar with a
thriving darts team; cosy saloon
with horsey theme. No food
weekends. 🏚 🍴 🌙 ♣ P

Stevenage

Two Diamonds

19 High Street, Old Town
☎ (0438) 354527
11–2.30 (3 Fri & Sat), 6 (7 Sat)–11
**McMullen AK, Country,
Stronghart** Ⓗ
Pub taking its name from the
original owners. Recently
modernised to a very high
standard, but not distracting
from the original building which
still upholds all the traditional
requirements of a good boozer.
Q 🍴 🌙 ♣

Tring

Kings Arms

King Street (near Natural
History Museum)
☎ (044 282) 3318
11.30–2.30, 7–11
Wadworth 6X; Wells Eagle Ⓗ
Hard to find, but difficult to
miss, this excellent, back-street
local offers an ever-changing
range of beers, incl. three
guests. Home-made snacks and
meals always available.
🏚 Q 🍴 🌙 ♣ 🍽

Tyttenhanger

Plough

Tyttenhanger Green (off A414,
via Highfield Lane)
OS182059 ☎ (0727) 57777
11.30–2.30 (3 Sat), 6–11 (12–2.30,
7–10.30 Sun)
**Brakspear Bitter; Fuller's
London Pride; Greene King
Abbot; Hook Norton Best
Bitter; Marston's Pedigree;
Theakston Best Bitter** Ⓗ
Popular free house overlooking
open farmland: a single L-shaped
bar with an open fireplace as a
central feature. Good lunchtime
food (no meals Sun). Huge
collection of bottled beers on
display – definitely not for sale!
The range of draught beers may
vary. 🏚 🍴 🌙 P

Ware

New Rose & Crown
35 Watton Road
☎ (0920) 462572
11.30–2.30, 5–11 (11–11 Fri & Sat)
Greene King XX Mild, IPA, Rayments Special, Abbot Ⓗ
Small, open-plan pub with pine cladding. Opening hours may be extended. Ⓓ ♣

Station Hotel
Station Road
☎ (0920) 463604
11–2.30, 5.30 (7 Sat)–11
McMullen AK Ⓗ
Friendly local, far more attractive than the station opposite: a cosy lounge and an unspoilt public bar. Let the pub take the strain! Ⓓ ⊟ ♣

Try also: Victoria (McMullen)

Wareside

Chequers
On B1004, Much Hadham–Ware road
☎ (0920) 467010
12–2.30, 6–11
Adnams Bitter; Hall & Woodhouse Badger Best Bitter; Theakston Best Bitter; Younger IPA; Young's Special Ⓗ
Friendly, village pub enjoying an excellent atmosphere. Good value, home-cooked food (Sun lunch in restaurant; no Sun eve food). Guest beers.
🏠 ⇥ Ⓓ ⊟ ♣ P

White Horse
On B1004, 2 miles from Ware
☎ (0920) 462582
11–3, 6–11
Greene King Rayments Special, Abbot Ⓗ
Olde-worlde, village pub with many exposed beams and two roaring fires in winter. Functional public bar. Wheelchair access to the public bar only.
🏠 Q ⇥ ⊛ Ⓓ ⊟ 👶 Å P

Water End

Old Maypole
Warrengate Road (off B197)
☎ (0707) 42119
11–2.30 (3 Sat), 5.30–11
Greene King IPA, Abbot Ⓗ
16th-century country pub with a separate family room. Near North Mymms Park.
🏠 Q ⇥ ⊛ Ⓓ P

Woodman
Warrengate Road (off B197)
☎ (0707) 50502
11–3, 5.30–11
Courage Directors; Marston's Pedigree Ⓗ
Old free house, popular with veterinary students. Guest beer;

house beer, Woodman's Best, is thought to be a Courage brew.
Q ⊛ Ⓓ P

Watford

Nascot Arms
11 Stamford Road (off Langley Road) ☎ (0923) 31336
11–3, 5.30–11
Greene King XX Mild, IPA, Rayments Special, Abbot Ⓗ**, Winter Ale** Ⓖ
Two-bar, street-corner, town pub which can get very crowded. A covered area for children is usually available (a bit chilly in winter). No food Sun. ⊛ ⇥ (Junction)

Welham Green

Hope & Anchor
Station Road
☎ (0707) 262935
11–2.30 (3 Sat), 5.30 (6 Sat)–11
Courage Best Bitter, Directors; John Smith's Bitter Ⓗ
19th-century pub with a sporty public bar. Watch out for the scissors in the saloon bar, otherwise you could be adding to the tie collection. Large, prize-winning garden. Food served Mon–Fri.
⊛ Ⓓ ⊟ ⅙ ⇥ ♣ P

Wheathampstead

Nelson
Marford Road
☎ (058 283) 2196
11–3, 5–11
Fuller's Chiswick, London Pride, ESB; Theakston Best Bitter; Wadworth 6X; Young's Special Ⓗ
Tastefully renovated, ex-Benskins pub featuring a 50ft,

illuminated well behind the bar. Ten handpumps offer a range of guest beers. Reasonably-priced, home-cooked meals (Mon–Sat). 🏠 Q ⊛ Ⓓ ♣ P

Whitwell

Maidens Head
67 High Street
☎ (0438) 871392
11.30–3, 6–11 (11.30–11 Wed & Sat)
McMullen AK, Country Ⓗ
Timbered, village pub of character with friendly locals and staff. Bar snacks also available Sun lunch.
🏠 Q ⊛ Ⓓ ▶ ♣ P

Wildhill

Woodman
47 Wildhill (between B158 and A1000, near Essendon)
OS263068 ☎ (0707) 42643
11.30–2.30, 5.30–11
Greene King IPA, Abbot; McMullen AK Ⓗ
A truly locals' local where visitors are welcomed and where the darts area does not impose on the bar area. TV in a separate room. No food Sun.
Q ⊛ Ⓓ ♣ P

Willian

Three Horseshoes
Baldock Lane (opp. church, up tiny side lane) OS224307
☎ (0462) 685713
11–11
Greene King IPA, Rayments Special, Abbot Ⓗ
Cosy, one-room, country pub drawing a wide cross-section of clientele. Keen contract bridge players always wanted. Park carefully in the lane. Home cooked bar snacks (Mon–Sat).
🏠 Q Ⓓ ♣

Home Brewing: The CAMRA Guide

If you are a keen brewer yourself – an expert or a beginner – you shouldn't ignore the words of wisdom in Graham Wheeler's **Home Brewing**, priced £4.99 and available from all good book stores or direct from CAMRA, 34 Alma Road, St Albans, Herts, AL1 3BW (post free).

Humberside

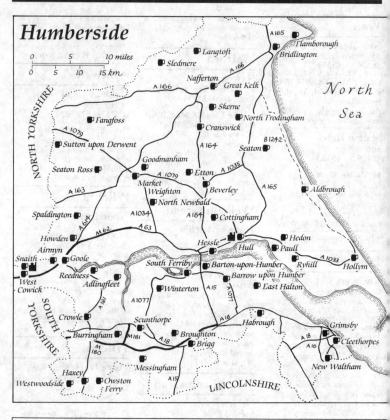

Humberside

```
0        5        10 miles
0    5    10    15 km
```

NORTH YORKSHIRE

Langtoft
Sledmere

Flamborough
Bridlington

A 165

Nafferton

A 166

Great Kelk

North Sea

Fangfoss

Skerne

North Frodingham

Cranswick

Sutton upon Derwent

Seaton

B 1242

Seaton Ross

Goodmanham

Etton

A 1035

Aldbrough

Market Weighton

A 1079

Beverley

A 165

North Newbald

A 1034

A 164

Cottingham

Spaldington

A 63

Hessle

Hedon

Howden

M 62

Hull

Paull

Ryhill

A 1033

Hollym

Airmyn

Snaith

Goole

Reedness

South Ferriby

Barton-upon-Humber

East Halton

West Cowick

Adlingfleet

Barrow upon Humber

SOUTH YORKSHIRE

Winterton

A 15

A 1077

Crowle

A 1077

Scunthorpe

A 18

Habrough

Grimsby

Burringham

M 181

Broughton

A 18

Cleethorpes

M 180

Brigg

A 16

Haxey

Messingham

New Waltham

Westwoodside

Owston Ferry

A 15

LINCOLNSHIRE

🏭 **Hull**, Hull; **Old Mill**, Snaith

Adlingfleet

Cross Keys Inn
Grange Road ☎ (072 475) 547
12–3, 7.30 (7 summer)–11 (supper licence)
Old Mill Bitter; Theakston XB; Younger Scotch Ⓗ
Modernised village-centre pub near the RSPB Blacktoft Sands reserve. A comfortable bar with an adjacent eating area. A warm welcome assured. 🏠 🛏 🖧 ( ) P

Airmyn

Percy Arms
High Street ☎ (0405) 764408
11.30–3, 5.30 (6.30 winter)–11
Courage Best Bitter, Directors; John Smith's Bitter, Magnet Ⓗ
17th-century village inn, named after a local landowner, overlooking the banks of the River Aire. One long room with an old-fashioned kitchen range at the 'tap room' end. The conservatory displays an Oakwell Ales sign. No meals Sun eve. 🏠 🛌 🖧 ( ) 🅰 ♣ P

Aldbrough

George & Dragon
1 High Street (B1242)
☎ (0964) 527230
12–3, 7–11 (12–11 Sat)
Theakston XB; Younger Scotch, No. 3 Ⓗ
Renovated, historic inn which is almost 500 years old. Welcoming atmosphere; popular for its good quality food in both bar and restaurant. Accommodation available in adjoining cottages.
🏠 🛏 🖧 ( ) 🖧 🅰 P

Barrow upon Humber

Royal Oak
High Street (off A1077)
☎ (0469) 30318
11–11 (11–4, 6–11 Sat)
Bass Mild XXXX, Draught Bass; Stones Best Bitter Ⓗ
Smart, busy village pub. No food on Sun. 🖧 ( ) ♣ ♠ P

Try also: Barrow Squash Club (Free)

Barton-upon-Humber

Volunteer Arms
13 Whitecross Street (off A1077) ☎ (0652) 32309
11–3, 6.45–11
Burtonwood Mild, Best Bitter Ⓗ
Small, two-roomed pub with a rather plain exterior, but very pleasant inside. Street parking opposite. 🖧 ( ) 🅰 ⇌

Wheatsheaf
Holydyke (A1077/B1218 jct)
☎ (0652) 33175
11–3, 6.45–11
Wards Mild, Sheffield Best Bitter Ⓗ
Fine old pub with a lounge bar and a separate snug. No food at weekends. 🖧 (🅰 ⇌ P

Try also: Blue Bell (Free)

Beverley

Monks Walk
Highgate ☎ (0482) 862710
12–3, 7–11

Humberside

Marston's Pedigree;
**Whitbread Boddingtons
Bitter, Trophy, Castle Eden
Ale** H
Tastefully-renovated, historic
inn with small narrow bar area
and a restaurant area. 100 yards
from the magnificent Beverley
Minster. 🏚 🕮 ⓛ 🌓 ➤ P

Oddfellows Arms
15 Eastgate ☎ (0482) 868139
12–3, 7–11 (11–11 Fri & Sat)
**Hull Mild; John Smith's
Bitter** H
Very small, classic, street-corner
local near the station and
Wednesday Market. Local
celebrity 'Beverley Bob', the
oldest regular, has been
awarded a free pint every night
for the rest of his life. ➤

Rose & Crown
North Bar Without (at York
Road jct) ☎ (0482) 862532
11–3, 6–11
**Wards Mild, Thorne Best
Bitter, Sheffield Best Bitter,
Kirby** H
Prominently-situated, next to
the North Bar and the nearest
pub to Beverley racecourse.
Also handy for Beverley
Westwood, a large area of
common land. Comfortable,
friendly atmosphere and good
food. Regular guest beers.
🕮 ⓛ 🌓 ♣ P

Royal Standard
30 North Bar Within
☎ (0482) 882434
11–3 (4.30 Fri, 5 Sat), 7–11
**Wards Mild, Thorne Best
Bitter** H
Small, historic pub with a gem
of a front bar. Maintains a
traditional atmosphere and is
very sports oriented, being near
the racecourse. Popular with
the rugby club members, too.
Q 🕮 🕮 ♣

White Horse Inn (Nellies)
Hengate (next to bus station)
☎ (0482) 861973
11–3, 7–11 (11–11 Sat)
**Samuel Smith OBB,
Museum** H
Traditional pub with many gas-
lit rooms, stone-flagged floors,
Victorian pictures, huge mirrors,
iron ranges and an ancient and
venerable gas cooker. Regular
music nights upstairs. A must
for visitors and usually very
busy. 🕮 ⓛ 🔄 P

Woolpack Inn
37 Westwood Road (near
Westwood Hospital)
☎ (0482) 867095
11.30–2.30, 7–11
**Burtonwood Mild, Best
Bitter** H
Small, traditional local, tucked
away in a residential area close

to Beverley Westwood.
Interesting photographs. Hull
CAMRA *Pub of the Year* 1989.
🕮 ⓛ

Bridlington

Cricketers Arms
28 Quay Road
☎ (0262) 675504
11–3, 6–11
**John Smith's Bitter,
Magnet** H
Fairly basic local, stretching
back from the small snug at the
front, past the bar to the pool
room at the rear. ➤ ♣

Hilderthorpe Hotel
Hilderthorpe Road
☎ (0262) 672205
11–11
**Bass Mild XXXX, Draught
Bass; Stones Best Bitter** H
Basic local, popular with
fishermen; a dominoes pub.
Straightforward but good meals
in summer. 🕮 🔁 ⓛ 🌓 ➤ ♣

Old Ship Inn
90 St Johns Street (old town)
☎ (0262) 670466
11–4, 7–11
**Hull Mild; Wards Thorne
Best Bitter** H
Thriving local by the old town,
with a good, traditional
atmosphere. Facilities for
children include a covered
outdoor play area. Dominoes
played. 🕮 🔁 🕮 ⓛ ♣

Ridings
Hilderthorpe Road
☎ (0262) 672900
11–3, 6–11
**Bass Mild XXXX, Draught
Bass; Theakston Best Bitter;
Younger Scotch** H
Bright local by the railway
station with a fine room for
functions. Good basic lunches.
ⓛ ♣

Brigg

Brocklesby Ox Inn
Bridge Street (A15/A18)
☎ (0652) 650292
11.30–3, 6.30–11 (7 Mon & Tue in
winter)–11 (11–11 Sat, & Thu & Fri in
summer)
**Burtonwood Best Bitter,
Forshaw's** H
Homely, traditional local,
displaying plenty of copper and
brass ornaments. The jukebox is
full of golden oldies; live music
Fri nights. No food Mon–Wed
in winter. 🕮 🕮 ⓛ ♣ P

Queens Arms
Wrawby Street (A15/A18)
☎ (0652) 53174
11–3, 6.30–11 (11–11 Sat)
**Bass Mild XXXX, Draught
Bass; Theakston XB** H
Pleasant, open-plan lounge bar
where quizzes alternate with
jazz on Tue. Good value meals;

children welcome in the dining
room (no food Sun or Mon
eves). 🛏 ⓛ 🌓 ➤

Broughton

Red Lion
High Street ☎ (0652) 52560
11–3, 6–11 (11–11 Fri & Sat)
**Mansfield Riding Mild,
Riding Bitter** H
Smart, unaltered pub with a
small bar, a medium-sized
lounge/dining room and a large
games room. Specialises in good
value, home-cooked meals; it is
advisable to book Sun lunch. No
food Sun eve or Mon. Has its
own bowling green.
Q 🕮 ⓛ 🔄 🏕 ♣ P

Burringham

Ferry Boat Inn
High Street ☎ (0724) 782468
12–3, 6.30 (5 Fri)–11
**Theakston XB, Old Peculier;
Younger No. 3** H
Popular Trentside village local:
a small public bar and lounge,
plus a larger room with a
jukebox. The excellent outdoor
drinking area features caged
birds and farm animals. The beer
is pricey for the area.
🕮 🕮 ⓛ 🔄 ➤ (Althorpe) ♣ P

Cleethorpes

Crows Nest
Balmoral Road
☎ (0472) 698867
11–3, 6.30–11 (11–11 Sat)
Samuel Smith OBB H
Big, three-roomed, 1950s estate
pub. Recent refurbishments have
made a real improvement to the
atmosphere. Good value bed
and breakfast available.
Q 🔁 🕮 🛏 🔄 P

Smugglers
12 High Cliff Road
☎ (0472) 696200
11–11
**McEwan 80/-; S&N Matthew
Brown Mild; Theakston Old
Peculier; Younger Scotch
Bitter, No. 3** H
Unusual basement pub and
restaurant, facing the beach.
🕮 🛏 ⓛ 🏕 ➤ ♣

Willys
17 High Cliff Road
☎ (0472) 602145
11–11
**Bateman Mild, XB; Willys
Original, Coxwains, Old
Groyne** H
Deservedly popular brew pub,
attracting a cosmopolitan
clientele; very busy at
weekends. Two or more guest
beers are always available
(suggestions welcomed).
Brewery may be viewed. ⓛ ➤

Humberside

Cottingham

Cross Keys
Northgate ☎ (0482) 840118
11–3.30, 5–11 (11–11 Sat)
Tetley Mild, Bitter Ⓗ
Popular pub with several
drinking areas around the
central bar, resulting from
'knock-throughs'. The bar is
basic; the lounge has a video
jukebox. Separate pool room
and darts area. Regular quiz
nights. Popular with students.
🏚 ◖ ≈ ♣ P

Cranswick

Pack Horse
Main Street ☎ (0377) 70298
12–3 (not Mon–Fri), 7–11
**Tetley Bitter; Younger
Scotch, IPA** Ⓗ
Small, village local with a long,
pleasantly decorated, single
room which is both cosy and
comfortable.
🏚 🏛 ≈ (Hutton Cranswick) ♣ P

Crowle

White Hart
High Street ☎ (0724) 710333
11.30–3, 7–11
**Courage Directors; John
Smith's Bitter** Ⓗ
400 year-old, beamed hostelry,
with a friendly atmosphere, at
the village centre. The plaque
over the door states it to be the
oldest pub in the Isle of
Axholme. 🏛 ◖ ▶ P

East Halton

Black Bull
Townside ☎ (0469) 540207
11.30–3, 5–11 (11–11 Fri & Sat)
**Bass Mild XXXX, Draught
Bass; Stones Best Bitter** Ⓗ
Well-kept village local: a
friendly bar and a comfortable
lounge. Weekly quiz night and
usual pub games.
Q ◖ ◗ ⌂ ♣ P

Etton

Light Dragoon
½ mile off B1248
☎ (0430) 810282
12–3, 6.30–11 (12.30–3, 7–11 winter)
Younger IPA, No. 3 Ⓗ
18th-century pub in a fine
estate village. Food and passing
trade is important but it retains
a local pub feel, particularly in
the bar. Folk club, first Tue of
each month, features top acts.
🏚 🏛 ◖ ⌂ ♣ P

Fangfoss

Carpenters Arms
On main Pocklington-Full
Sutton road OS767532
☎ (075 96) 222
11–3, 6–11

John Smith's Bitter Ⓗ
A country pub which is busy,
comfortable and welcoming.
Eve meals served Tue–Sat; half
portions available for children.
🏚 Q ◖ ◗ Å ♣ P

Flamborough

Royal Dog & Duck
☎ (0262) 850206
11–4, 6.30–11
**Draught Bass; Stones Best
Bitter** Ⓗ
Old, village-centre pub with
beams, bric-a-brac and a
comfortable atmosphere. Good
meals (incl. local specialities) are
served. Separate dining room.
🏚 🏛 🏛 ◖ ◗ ⌂ Å ♣ P

Goodmanham

Goodmanham Arms
Main Street ☎ (0430) 872379
12–3 (not Mon–Thu), 7–11
**Old Mill Bitter; Theakston
Best Bitter** Ⓗ
Quaint village local opposite a
Norman church on the Wolds
Way long distance footpath.
The front room bar is used by
the local rural community.
Families welcome. Fresh
sandwiches made to order.
🏚 Q 🏛 ◖ ♣ P

Goole

Old George
Market Place ☎ (0405) 763147
11–3, 7–11
**Bass Light, Draught Bass;
Stones Best Bitter** Ⓗ
Lively, town-centre pub with an
emphasis on food at lunchtimes
(except Sun). Local history
memorabilia adorns the walls.
Guest beers. 🏛 ◖ ≈ ♣ P

Try also: Woodlands (John
Smith's)

Great Kelk

Chestnut Horse
Main Street (between
A165/B1249/A166)
OS105583 ☎ (026 288) 263
11–11 (11–3, 7–11 winter)
**Draught Bass; Stones Best
Bitter; John Smith's Bitter** Ⓗ
Attractive, cottage-style inn
serving a small, rural
community. Excellent, good
value meals; children can be
catered for by agreement with
the landlord. 🏚 Q 🏛 ◖ ◗ ⌂ Å ♣ P

Grimsby

Corporation
88 Freeman Street
☎ (0472) 356651
11–11
**Bass Mild XXXX, Draught
Bass** Ⓗ
A busy, long-established pub on
a main shopping street, recently

refurbished in a traditional
manner. The small back room is
ideal for a quiet conversation.
Ask to see the wood panel
about a murder!
◖ ⌂ ≈ (Docks) ♣

Hope & Anchor
148 Victoria Street
☎ (0472) 342565
11–11
**Tetley Mild, Bitter; Ind
Coope Burton Ale** Ⓗ
Mid 19th-century pub, close to
the town centre. Due for
refurbishment, after which four
guest beers will be available.
🏛 ◖ ⌂ ≈ (Town)

Palace Buffet
Victoria Street
☎ (0472) 342837
11–11
**Bass Mild XXXX, Draught
Bass; Stones Best Bitter** Ⓗ
A Victorian house which was
once the bar of the now
demolished Palace Theatre. A
Grade II listed building, it has
been internally altered over the
years. Convenient for the
National Heritage Fishing
Museum. Guest beers.
🏛 ◖ ⌂ ♣ P

Rutland Arms
26–30 Rutland Street (behind
Ramsdens store, off Cleethorpe
Road) ☎ (0472) 241345
11–11
**Old Mill Mild, Bitter,
Bullion** Ⓗ
A long, single bar with a games
area at one end. The feel of a
locals' pub is very much in
evidence: don't expect a quiet
drink, somebody will soon be
chatting to you! Popular with
all age groups. Good value ale
and food (no meals Sun). Live
entertainment Sun and Wed.
🏛 ◖ ≈ (New Clee) ♣ P

Spiders Web
Carr Lane (off Clee Road)
☎ (0472) 692065
11–11
**Courage Best Bitter,
Directors; John Smith's
Bitter** Ⓗ
Excellent local comprising a
basic bar, a comfortable lounge
and a function room, which
regularly offers live entertainment. Beer garden has some
children's play equipment.
🏛 ◖ ♣ P

Swigs
21 Osborne Street
☎ (0472) 354773
11–11
**Bateman XB; Willys
Original** Ⓗ
Narrow, town-centre bar in the
style of a continental café.
Emphasis on food at lunchtime
and a tendency towards a
younger clientele eves. Can be

extremely busy at weekends.
The second permanent outlet
for Willys' Cleethorpes-brewed
ales. Guest beers. ◖ ⪫ (Town)○

Try also: Yarborough Vaults,
Old Market Place (John Smith's)

Habrough

Horse & Hounds
Station Road (Immingham side
of station) ☎ (0469) 576940
11–11 (may close 3–7)
**S&N Matthew Brown Mild;
Theakston XB, Old Peculier;
Younger IPA, No. 3** ⊞
Part of the Habrough Hotel, but
has a good local trade. A
tastefully converted former
farmhouse and rectory, it
probably offers the best pub
food in Humberside. Also has a
firm commitment to keeping
beer as cheap as many, more
basic, town pubs.
⌂ Q ⊛ ⇔ ◖ ▯ ⊟ ⪦ ⪫ P

Haxey

King's Arms
Low Street (A161 jct)
☎ (0427) 752328
11–3, 6.30–11
**John Smith's Bitter;
Theakston Old Peculier** ⊞
Pleasant and popular local in a
village famous for the Haxey
Hood game. No food Sun; eve
meals Thu and Fri only.
⊛ ◖ ▮ ▲ ♣ P

Hedon

Shakespeare Inn
9 Baxtergate (near
B1239/B1362 jct)
☎ (0482) 898371
11–11
**Vaux Samson; Wards Mild,
Thorne Best Bitter, Sheffield
Best Bitter, Kirby** ⊞
A cosy and friendly one-
roomer. Over 3000 beer mats
adorn the ceiling; other
interesting artefacts include
breweriana and Hedon
memorabilia. Real, freshly-
squeezed orange juice from a
Dutch fruit press is also
available. Meals served
12–2.45 (6.45 Fri). ⌂ ⊛ ♣ P

Hessle

George Inn (Top House)
40 Prestongate (pedestrianised
street off the square)
☎ (0482) 648698
11–11
**Bass Mild XXXX; Stones Best
Bitter** ⊞
Welcoming, traditionally-run
pub that is well thought of
locally. Three contrasting rooms
offer something for most tastes.
⊛ ◖ ⊟ ⪫ ♣ P

Hollym

Plough Inn
Northside Road (off A1033)
☎ (0964) 612049
12–3, 7–11 (11–11 Sat)
Tetley Mild, Bitter ⊞
200 year-old village pub of
wattle and daub construction,
retaining some old features, incl.
three rooms, one of which is a
games room. A very cosy pub,
especially on a winter's eve. The
garden has a children's play
area. ⌂ ⅓ ⊛ ⇔ ◖ ⊟ ▲ ♣ P

Howden

Barnes Wallis
Station Road (B1228, 1 mile N
of town) ☎ (0430) 430639
7–11 (12–3, 7–11 Sat)
Old Mill Bitter ⊞
At least three guest beers and a
large range of foreign bottled
beers are available in this
comfortable and friendly inn.
One L-shaped room, plus a
separate pool room. Lunchtime
opening Sat/Sun only.
⌂ Q ⊛ ▲ ⪫ P

Hull

Bay Horse
113 Wincolmlee (400 yds N of
North Bridge on W side of
river) ☎ (0482) 29227
11–11
**Bateman Mild, XB, XXXB,
Victory** ⊞
Bateman's only tied house north
of the Humber. An extension
has added a splendid lounge and
widened the pub's appeal,
although it still caters for local
factory workers at lunchtime
and the amateur RL club. The
bar is small and friendly, with a
good mix of customers; quiet
lounge. No food Sun. Special
WC for wheelchairs.
⌂ Q ◖ ⊟ ⅙ ♣ P

Duke of Edinburgh
1 De La Pole Street (first left
after crossing River Hull on
A63 to ferry terminal)
☎ (0482) 225382
12–3, 7–11
Camerons Bitter ⊞
Small, boisterous dockland pub
supported by dedicated locals
and lorry drivers. Can be noisy
with regular discos, but has a
friendly and generous
atmosphere. ♣

Duke of Wellington
104 Peel Street, Spring Bank
(between Spring Bank and
Beverley Road)
☎ (0482) 29603
11–3, 6–11
**Hull Mild; Taylor Landlord;
Tetley Bitter** ⊞
Back-street, re-styled, Victorian
local which is popular with

students and often crowded.
Still the nearest thing to a free
house in Hull, it features two
regular guest beers. ⊛ ♣ P

East Riding
37 Cannon Street ($\frac{1}{2}$ mile N of
centre, between Beverley Road
and river) ☎ (0482) 29134
11.30–3.30 (4 Fri; 12–3 Sat), 6.30–11
Tetley Mild, Bitter ⊞
Small, street-corner, two-
roomed, industrial pub. The no-
nonsense bar features rugby
league memorabilia, whilst the
cosy lounge is wood-panelled.
Hull CAMRA *Pub of the Year*
1990. ⊟ ♣

Gardeners Arms
Cottingham Road (B1233, 100
yds from A1079 jct)
☎ (0482) 42396
11–11
Tetley Mild, Bitter ⊞
Close to the university, with a
bar popular with locals and
students. A large lounge
features a video jukebox and
discos. Forecourt tables for
summer drinking. ⊛ ◖ ▮ ♣ P

George Hotel
Land of Green Ginger (between
Guildhall and Whitefriargate,
Old Town) ☎ (0482) 226373
11–11 (10.30 Wed; 12–2, 7–10.30 Sun)
**Bass Mild XXXX, Draught
Bass** ⊞
Historic former coaching inn,
although only a single room
with bare floorboards remains of
the original. Look for the
smallest window in Hull,
situated at the side of the
archway once used by ostlers.
Upstairs restaurant (no meals
Sun). ◖

Grapes Inn
Sykes Street (N of Freetown
Way, near centre)
☎ (0482) 24424
12–4, 7–11
**Camerons Bitter; Tolly
Cobbold Mild, Bitter,
Original** ⊞
Friendly local which is a major
attraction for its unusual range
of beer in an area of limited
choice. Regular discos and live
music at weekends. ⌂

Green Bricks
9a Humber Dock Street (E side
of marina) ☎ (0482) 29502
11.30–4.30 (5 Sat), 7–11
**Bass Mild XXXX, Draught
Bass; Stones Best Bitter** ⊞
There is a comfortable and
traditional feel to this single-
roomer which, nevertheless,
features distinct bar, darts and
lounge areas, around a central
servery. Very busy at weekends
due to the proximity of the
marina. No food Sun. ◖ ♣

Humberside

Old Blue Bell
Market Place ☎ (0482) 24382
11–3 (4 Sat), 6.30 (7 Sat)–11
**Samuel Smith OBB,
Museum** Ⓗ
Famous pub in the old town
with an original layout retaining
a snug, a corridor and a long,
narrow bar. Pool room upstairs.
The far end of the bar features a
collection of multi-sized bells.
Count them if you can. Back
yard for summer drinking.
🏠 🍴 🍺 ♣

Olde White Harte
25 Silver Street (down alley off
North Side) ☎ (0482) 26363
11–11 (11–4.30, 6.30–11 Sat)
**Theakston XB; Younger IPA,
No. 3** Ⓗ
A superb courtyard pub with
lots of dark timber, stained-glass
and two large sit-in fireplaces. A
central staircase leads to the
restaurant, scene of the Plotters
Parlour, scene of the Civil War
meeting which refused King
Charles entry to the city. Good
food (no bar meals Sun). 🏠 ♣

Station Inn
202 Beverley Road (A1079, ¾
mile from centre)
☎ (0482) 41482
11–11
Tetley Mild, Bitter Ⓗ
Traditional, refurbished, street-
corner local in Tetley's mock-
Tudor style. Next to the site of
the former Hull-Hornsea and
Withernsea railway. Warm cosy
back room and tiled floor in the
bar. Reputation for quiz nights
and good value food.
🏠 🍴 🍺 ♣ P

Wellington Inn
55 Russell Street (near A1079,
Beverley Road/Freetown Way
jct) ☎ (0482) 29486
11.30–11
**Mansfield Riding Mild,
Riding Bitter, Old Baily** Ⓗ
Friendly local at the edge of the
city centre; several areas linked
around a central bar. Landlord
has a very impressive mobile
real ale bar for hire. 🏠 🍺 ♣ P

Whalebone Inn
165 Wincolmlee (between Scott
Street and Sculcoates bridges)
☎ (0482) 27980
11.30–3.30, 5–11 (11–11 Fri & Sat)
Tetley Mild, Bitter Ⓗ
Popular old pub in the heart of
an industrial area. The name is
derived from the city's former
whaling trade.

Langtoft

Ship Inn
Front Street ☎ (0377) 87243
12–3, 7–11
**Camerons Bitter,
Strongarm** Ⓗ
Cosy, friendly, village local with

a reputation for good food
(supper licence till midnight).
Children welcome in the pool
room and restaurant.
🏠 🍴 🚲 🍴 🍺 ♣ P

Market Weighton

Half Moon
39 High Street
☎ (0430) 872247
11–4, 7–11 (11–11 Fri & Sat)
**Burtonwood Mild, Best
Bitter** Ⓗ
Friendly local in the centre of a
market town. One very long
drinking area: a public bar at
one end and a comfortable,
well-appointed lounge at the
other. No food Wed. 🏠 🍴 ♣ P

Messingham

Bird in the Barley
Northfield Road
☎ (0724) 762994
11–3 (not Mon), 5–11
**Ruddles Best Bitter, County;
Webster's Yorkshire Bitter,
Choice** Ⓗ
Smart, roadside pub, situated
between Messingham and
Scunthorpe: a single room with
a large bar, offering excellent
lunchtime meals and an
enterprising choice of guest
beer. No food Mon. 🏠 🍴 P

Try also: Green Tree (Bass)

Nafferton

Cross Keys
North Street (200 yds off
A166) ☎ (0377) 44261
12–2.30 (4 Sat), 7–11
**Old Mill Bitter; John Smith's
Bitter; Younger Scotch** Ⓗ
A friendly, spacious and yet
cosy local at the northern end
of the village. Several rooms
cater for all tastes. 🍴 🍴 🚲 🍺 ♣

New Waltham

Harvest Moon
Station Road (400 yds from
A16) ☎ (0472) 822025
11–3, 6–11 (11–11 summer)
**Ind Coope Burton Ale; Tetley
Mild, Bitter** Ⓗ
Large, village pub, aimed more
at the young and affluent, as
opposed to the traditional beer
drinker. 🚲 🍴 🍴 ♿ P

North Frodingham

Star
Main Street (B1242)
☎ (0262) 488365
7–11 (12–3, 7–10.30 Sun)
**Camerons Bitter,
Strongarm** Ⓗ
Relaxed and friendly, with good
food from an imaginative menu
(not served Thu). Separate
games area in a new extension.

Old BP sign instructs customers
to 'Buy from the pumP'. Note:
closed lunchtime, except Sun.
🏠 ♿ 🍴 🍴 ♣ P

North Newbald

Gnu
The Green (400 yds from
A1034)
7 (8 winter)–11 (12–11 Sat)
**Camerons Bitter; Tolly
Cobbold Mild** Ⓗ
Impressive-looking, square-set
pub with working stables. The
cosy snug and the bigger
lounge are both comfortable
and have a good, mainly local
trade. Country and western
concerts Sun eves. On the
Wolds Way walking route.
Please do not park on the
village green. Note closed
lunchtime, except weekends.
🏠 🏠 🚲 🍴 ♣ P

Owston Ferry

Crooked Billet
Silver Street ☎ (042 772) 264
11–3, 7–11
**Wards Mild, Thorne Best
Bitter** Ⓗ
Trent-side village pub with
pool, darts and boxing, plus
occasional live music. Meals
available lunchtime, Tue–Sun,
and Wed–Fri eves.
🏠 Q ♿ 🏠 🍴 🍴 ♿ ♣ P

Paull

Humber Tavern
Main Street ☎ (0482) 899347
12–3, 7–11 (11–11 Fri, Sat & summer)
**Tetley Bitter; Webster's
Yorkshire Bitter, Choice,
Wilson's Mild** Ⓗ
Victorian building backing on to
the Humber Estuary, with fine
views from the rear patio.
Excellent for outside drinking
on warm summer nights; three
large, well-decorated rooms
within. 🏠 ♿ 🏠 🍴

Try also: Crown Inn (Bass)

Reedness

Half Moon Inn
Main Street ☎ (0405) 704484
12–3, 7–11 (supper licence)
**Marston's Pedigree;
Whitbread Trophy, Castle
Eden Ale, Flowers Original** Ⓗ
200 year-old village pub near
the Blacktoft Sands RSPB
reserve. Family-owned, with
good food always available.
🏠 🍴 🍴 🚲 ♿ ♣ P

Ryhill

Crooked Billet
Pitt Lane (400 yds off A1033)
☎ (0964) 622303
11–3 (not Tue or Thu), 7.30–11
Tetley Mild, Bitter Ⓗ

Traditional, old pub with a 17th-century frontage and an olde-worlde, wood-panelled bar. Half of the split-level lounge is stone paved. Formerly a smugglers' haunt, now the main 'sport' is arm wrestling. Good home-cooked food.
🏠 🍸 🚪 ♣ P

Scunthorpe

Honest Lawyer
70 Oswald Road (opp. the museum) ☎ (0724) 849906
11–11
Bateman XXXB; Hull Mild; Ind Coope Burton Ale; Tetley Bitter; Theakston Old Peculier; Whitbread Boddingtons Bitter 🅷
A modern development of a restaurant into a thriving town-centre pub, popular with the younger generation. Its two levels are furnished in dark wood, with authentic photos and legal items. Guest beers are changed regularly but prices are inflated. Eve meals 5–7pm.
🍸 ≥ ♣ P

Riveter
50 Henderson Avenue ☎ (0724) 862701
11.30–3 (4 Sat), 5.30 (7 Sat)–11
Old Mill Mild, Bitter, Bullion 🅷
Modern split-level pub with two lounge areas and a games room. Very busy in eves. Small car park at side. No meals at weekend. 🍸 🚪 ♣ P

Seaton

Swan Inn
On B1244 ☎ (0964) 533582
11–3.30 (4 Sat), 7–11
John Smith's Bitter 🅷
Friendly, village local with an enthusiastic landlord and a cosy atmosphere. Good outdoor area at the rear for children. Not far from Hornsea Mere. 🏠 🎱 🚪 P

Seaton Ross

Black Horse
South Side OS777417 ☎ (0759) 318481
7–11 (12–3, 7–10.30 Sun)
John Smith's Bitter; Taylor Landlord; Tetley Bitter 🅷
Welcoming, comfortable pub on the south side of the village; separate conservatory and function room. Good value food (no meals Tue). Lunchtime opening only Sun and bank holidays. 🏠 Q 👶 🎱 🍸 🚪 🅰 ♣ P

Skerne

Eagle Inn
Wandsford Road ☎ (0377) 42178
11–3, 7–11

Camerons Bitter; Tolly Cobbold Original 🅷
Unspoilt and extremely welcoming beer house without a bar. The beer is served from the cellar, using a Victorian cash register beer engine, and brought to your table. A rare find. 🏠 Q 🎱 ♣ P

Sledmere

Triton Inn
On B1252/B1253 ☎ (0377) 86644
12–3 (not Mon or Thu), 7–11
Tetley Bitter; Younger Scotch 🅷
Splendid pub next to Sledmere House and surrounded by typical Wolds countryside. Children welcome in the restaurant and front hall. 🏠 👶 🎱 🛏 🍸 🚪 ♣ P

Snaith

Brewers Arms
10 Pontefract Road (A645) ☎ (0405) 862404
11–2.30, 6–11
Old Mill Bitter, Bullion 🅷
Excellent conversion of an impressive country lodge, dating from 1720. Note the original well in the centre of the lounge. A secret tunnel reputedly runs to the local stately home. Separate restaurant. 🎱 🛏 🍸 🚪 P

South Ferriby

Hope & Anchor
Sluice Road (A1077) ☎ (0652) 635242
11–3, 6–11 (11–11 Sat)
Mansfield Riding Mild, Riding Bitter, Old Baily 🅷
Situated at the confluence of the Rivers Ancholme and Humber, with superb views from the rear. Family room and children's play equipment in the garden. A small snug leads off the large front bar. No eve meals in winter. 👶 🎱 🍸 🚪 ♣ P

Spaldington

Plough
Main Street (2 miles E of B1228, N of Howden) OS765337 ☎ (0430) 431591
7–11
John Smith's Bitter; Tetley Bitter; Younger Scotch 🅷
Comfortable, open-plan pub, frequented by beer drinkers during the week and diners at weekends. 'He Man' steaks available, up to 72oz – the landlord is a butcher! Note: lunchtime opening Sun and bank holidays only.
Q 🎱 🍸 🚪 ♣ P

Sutton upon Derwent

St Vincent Arms
Main Street ☎ (0904) 608349
11–3, 6–11
Courage Directors; John Smith's Bitter; Taylor Landlord; Theakston XB, Old Peculier; Younger IPA 🅷
Excellent village inn; the cosy bars have roaring fires in winter. Popular with local and passing trades for its friendly atmosphere and good value home-cooking (separate restaurant; half-portions available for children). 🏠 Q 👶 🎱 🍸 🚪 🅶 P

West Cowick

Ship
73 High Street (off A1014) ☎ (0405) 860326
12–4 (not Mon–Fri), 7–11
Camerons Bitter 🅷
Popular, village local with an accent on pub games and community activities. Note: closed weekday lunchtime.
🏠 ♣ P

Westwoodside, Isle of Axholme

Park Drain Hotel
Park Drain (400 yds off B1396) OS726988 ☎ (0427) 752255
11.30–3.30, 5.30–11 (11–11 Wed–Sat)
John Smith's Bitter 🅷
Unusual, remote, Victorian pub, built for the proposed mining community. The large bar, comfortable lounge and excellent restaurant are warmed by straw-fired central heating. Note the waterwells in the car park. No meals Mon eve. No-smoking area in restaurant. Guest beers. 🏠 🎱 🍸 🚪 🅰 ♣ P

Winterton

Cross Keys
5 King Street (near market place) ☎ (0724) 732215
11–3 (4 Sat), 5 (7 Sat)–11
Bass Special, Draught Bass 🅷
Basic, three-roomed, locals' pub. Family room in the former dining area. 🏠 👶 🎱 🚪 ♣ P

Try also: Butchers Arms (Courage)

Join CAMRA —
see page 480!

Isle of Wight

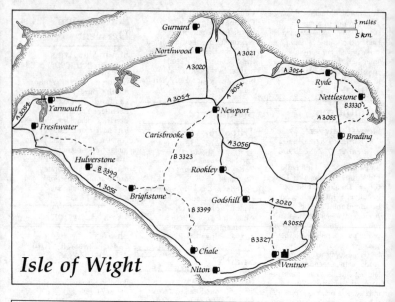

Isle of Wight

🏰 **Burts**, *Ventnor*

Brading

Anglers
Yarbridge (off A3055, E at traffic lights)
☎ (0983) 406212
10.30–3 (2 winter), 6–11
Gale's XXXL, Best Bitter, HSB Ⓗ
Unusual, basic, one-bar pub in rural setting. One of 20 Whitbread pubs to be leased to Gale's. 🍴 ◖ ◗ ⛵ P

Brighstone

Countryman
Limerstone Road
☎ (0983) 740616
11–3, 6.30–11.30
Gibbs Mew Wiltshire; Ind Coope Burton Ale Ⓗ
Modern pub with splendid views over the sea. Uninspiring exterior, but pleasant bar, presided over by enthusiastic landlord. 🍴 🍽 ◖ ◗ ▲ ♣ P

Carisbrooke

Shute Inn
Clatterford Shute, Clatterford Road (left at top of village crossroads)
☎ (0983) 523393
10.30–3, 6–11
Draught Bass; Charrington IPA Ⓗ
Popular locals' pub set in a Georgian hotel, nestling underneath Carisbrooke Castle. Pleasant and welcoming atmosphere. 🍽 ◖ ◗ ♣ P

Chale

Wight Mouse
Clarendon Hotel (on B3399, 100 yds from A3055)
☎ (0983) 730431
11–11
Burts VPA; Marston's Pedigree; Wadworth 6X; Whitbread Boddingtons Bitter, Strong Country Ⓗ
Very busy, extensively-altered, old stone pub next to its hotel. Accent on food and families. Massive garden with pets and play area. Nearby is Blackgang Chine theme park.
🍴 🐕 🍽 ⌂ ◖ ◗ ▲ P

Freshwater

Royal Standard
School Green Road
☎ (0983) 753227
11–11
Burts Mild, VPA; John Smith's Bitter Ⓗ
Homely town pub in a village hotel. Excellent public bar and good value food in pleasant restaurant area. ⌂ ◖ ◗ ♣ P

Try also: Vine Inn (Gale's)

Godshill

Taverners Inn
Eden Dale (corner of main village street, opp. model village)
☎ (0983) 840707
11–11
Draught Bass; Fuller's ESB;

Ruddles County; Whitbread Boddingtons Bitter, Strong Country Ⓗ
Refurbished and extended pub/restaurant with much character. Excellent garden for children. Enterprising menu. Beer range varies (guest beers) and is considerably limited in winter. 🐕 🍽 ◖ ◗ ♣

Try also: Griffin (Whitbread)

Gurnard

Portland Arms
2 Worsley Road
☎ (0983) 292948
11–3, 6–11
Courage Directors; John Smith's Bitter Ⓗ
Comfortable village pub, recently opened. 🐕 🍽 ▲

Hulverstone

Sun
On B3399 ☎ (0983) 740403
10.30 (11 winter)–3, 7–11
Gale's Best Bitter, HSB Ⓖ
Excellent country pub in quiet, isolated village. Lovely views from the large garden attached to this very old, thatched pub. Eve meals Fri/Sat only in winter. 🍴 Q 🍽 ◖ ◗ P

Nettlestone

Roadside Inn
Nettlestone Green, Seaview
☎ (0983) 612381
11–11
Gale's XXXL (summer), **BBB,**

Best Bitter, 5X, HSB Ⓗ
Friendly village local with two
large bars. Popular with
discerning drinkers. Eve meals in
summer only.
🏠 ⛺ 🅱 ⊘ ◗ ▶ ⊟ Å ♣ P

Newport

Railway Medina
1 Sea Street (left at law courts in
High Street) ☎ (0983) 528303
10.30–3, 6–11 (11–11 summer)
Gale's BBB, HSB Ⓗ
Superb, ex-Whitbread, street-
corner pub, now much used by
local CAMRA members.
Adjacent to old railway station
and opposite site of old Mew
Langton brewery. Railway
photographs and memorabilia in
the comfortable lounge; good,
basic public bar. Q 🅱 ⊟ ♣

Try also: Princess Royal
(Whitbread); Castle
(Whitbread)

Niton

Buddle Inn
St Catherine's Road (follow
signs to St Catherine's Point)
☎ (0983) 730243
11–3, 6–11 (11–11 Fri, Sat & summer)
Whitbread Boddingtons
Bitter, Strong Country;
Marston's Pedigree Ⓗ
Very ancient, stone-built pub
with strong smuggling
connections. Recent extensive
refurbishment has still left
considerable character. Range of
beers varies. Run by CAMRA-
member landlord. Guest beers.
🏠 ⛺ 🅱 ◗ ▶ ♣ P

Northwood

Travellers Joy
85 Pallance Road (off B3325)
☎ (0983) 298024

11–2.30, 5–11 (11–11 Fri, Sat &
summer)
Courage Directors; Gibbs
Mew Bishop's Tipple;
Ringwood Old Thumper;
Ruddles County; Theakston
Old Peculier; Younger IPA Ⓗ
Excellent beer exhibition pub,
unique to the island and well
worth seeking out. Guest beers;
good value food. Petanque
played. ⛺ 🅱 ◗ ▶ Å ♣ P

Try also: Horseshoe (Gale's)

Rookley

Chequers Inn
(Off A3020, turn right at start
of village) ☎ (0983) 840314
11–3, 6–11
Courage Best Bitter,
Directors; Webster's
Yorkshire Bitter Ⓗ
Ex-Whitbread pub, sold into the
free trade and extensively
refurbished at some expense to
character. An extremely popular
pub/restaurant which,
nevertheless, still retains its
flagstone-floored public.
Excellent food.
🏠 Q 🅱 ◗ ▶ ⊟ Å ♣ P

Ryde

Castle
164 High Street (steep climb
from ferry) ☎ (0983) 811138
10.30–11
Gale's XXXL (summer), BBB,
5X, HSB Ⓗ
Split-level, one-bar town pub
with notable etched windows.
Keen games following, incl.
shove-ha'penny. Bulmers cider.
🏠 ≈ ♣ ⌂

Hotel Ryde Castle
The Esplanade (¼ mile from pier)
☎ (0983) 63755
11–11 (12–2.50, 7–11 Sun)
Draught Bass; Ind Coope

Burton Ale; Welsh Brewers
Worthington Dark, BB Ⓗ
Pleasant and comfortable hotel
bar in a magnificent Gothic
mansion. Reasonable bar prices
for area; good value restaurant
attached. Convenient for
seafront and ferries. No-
smoking area at lunchtime.
🏠 Q ⛺ 🅱 ◗ ▶ ≈ P ⁑

Try also: Railway Tavern,
Lake Huron (Gale's)

Ventnor

Spyglass Inn
Esplanade (W end of Esplanade)
☎ (0983) 855338
11–5 (3 winter), 7–11
Ind Coope Burton Ale Ⓗ
Superb rambling pub which
welcomes 'kids, dogs and
muddy boots' and hosts
occasional real ale events. Well
worth a visit. Also sells
Spyglass Kingrock Ale (Gibbs
Mew Wiltshire). Regular live
music. 🏠 Q ⛺ 🅱 ◗ ▶ ⊟ Å P ⁑

Try also: Mill Bay (Burts)

Yarmouth

Kings Head
Quay Street
☎ (0983) 760351
11–11 (11–3, 6.30–11 winter)
Gale's HSB; Marston's
Pedigree; Whitbread
Boddingtons Bitter, Strong
Country, Flowers Original Ⓗ
Old town pub with much
character, adjacent to car ferry.
Not all the beers are always on.
The Wheatsheaf down the alley
is known locally as the 'Kings
Legs'. 🏠 🅱 ⋈ ♣ ⌂

Try also: Bugle (Whitbread);
Wheatsheaf (Whitbread)

BLANKET PRESSURE

A term often heard in CAMRA circles is Blanket Pressure.
Essentially, this is the cellarman's application of a light covering of
carbon dioxide to beer in the cask to prevent air from making
contact with the beer.

The intention is to improve the 'shelf-life' of the beer, by not
allowing air to react with the beer, but it also prevents the beer
from maturing properly. Even worse, careless use can result in the
beer becoming gassy, like keg beer.

Kent

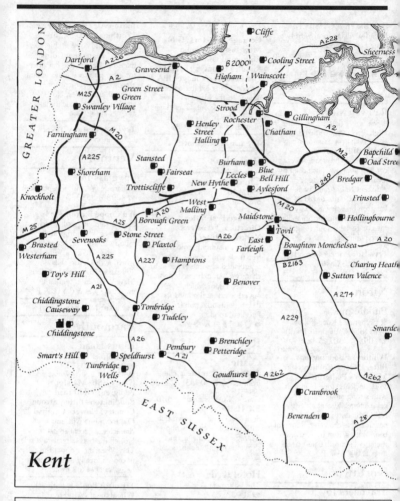

Kent

Goacher's, Tovil; **Larkins**, Chiddingstone; **Shepherd Neame**, Faversham

Ashford

Beaver Road Off-Licence
36 Beaver Road (A2070, 400
yds S of station)
☎ (0233) 622904
11 (3 Wed)–10.15 (12–3, 7–10.15 Sun)
Beer range varies G
Off-licence with a choice of at
least two beers during the week,
and four at weekends. Fine ales,
beers and porters from all
around the country, on average
20% cheaper than pub prices.
Tastings possible. ≠

Hare & Hounds
Maidstone Road, Potters
Corner (A20, 2½ miles from
centre)
☎ (0233) 621760
11–2.30, 6–11
**Courage Best Bitter,
Directors; John Smith's
Bitter** H
Friendly, busy and well-run pub,
just out of town. Popular for its
steaks, fresh fish and home-
cooked specials. Function room
available. John Smith's is served
through a sparkler. No eve
meals Tue or Sun. ✿ ◖ ▶ P

Aylesford

Bush
17 Rochester Road
☎ (0622) 717446
11–2.30, 6 (7 Sat)–11
**Courage Best Bitter,
Directors; Shepherd Neame
Master Brew Bitter; John
Smith's Bitter** H
Friendly village local with an
interesting tie collection.

Occasional piano sing-alongs.
No crisps; no food Sun, or Mon
eve. ✿ ◖ ▶ ≠ P

Bapchild

Fox & Goose
The Street (off A2)
☎ (0795) 472095
12–3, 7–11
Courage Best Bitter H
Comfortable, one-bar pub, the
HQ of Sittingbourne Amateur
Boxing Club. The large garden
has an aviary. ✿ ◖ P

Benenden

King William IV
The Street (B2086)
☎ (0580) 240636
11–3, 6–11 (11–11 Sat)
Shepherd Neame Master

Kent

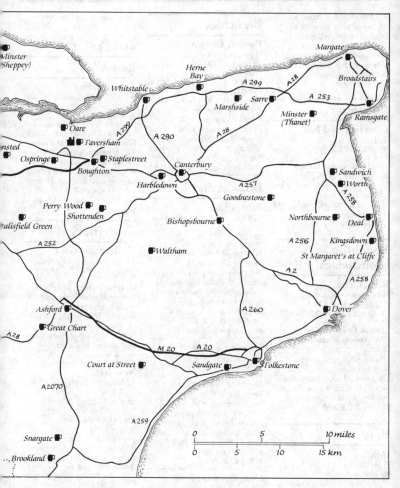

Brew Bitter, Spitfire ℍ
Excellent, village local. The
basic public bar has a one-armed
bandit, jukebox, etc.; the saloon
bar is relaxed, quieter and a bit
more 'OK-Ya'. Lunches served
Mon–Sat; eve meals Wed–Sat.
🏠 Q ✻ ◗ ◖ ⬦ ♣ P

Benover

Woolpack Inn
Benover Road (B2162, 1 mile S
of Yalding) OS483704
☎ (089 273) 356
11–2.30 (3.30 Sat), 6–11
**Shepherd Neame Master
Brew Bitter** ℍ
Attractive, 17th-century,
country pub with beams and
stone floors, comfortable bars
and a good family room. Have a
look at the skeleton in the
cupboard! Excellent food with
generous portions, but
ploughman's only Sun lunch (no
food Sun eve). 🏠 ➴ ✻ ◗ ◖ P

Bishopsbourne

Mermaid
400 yds off A2
☎ (0227) 830581
11–2.30, 6–11
**Shepherd Neame Master
Brew Bitter** ℍ
Attractive, little pub in a
typically Kentish village; well
worth a detour from the A2.
Unusual electronic heads and
tails tosser by the dartboard.
Lunchtime snacks available.
🏠 Q ✻ ◖ ♣ ◗

Blue Bell Hill

Robin Hood
364 Common Road, Chatham
(1 mile W of village and A229)
OS734628 ☎ (0634) 861500
11–2.30, 6–11
**Courage Best Bitter,
Directors** ℍ
Pub in a rural setting, with three
bars and an inglenook. Live

music (summer) and barbecues
in the garden. A 17th-century
pub catering for all tastes and
always offering a friendly
welcome. No food Sun.
🏠 ➴ ✻ ◗ ◖ ⬦ ▲ ♣ P

Borough Green

Fox & Hounds
Maidstone Road (A25)
☎ (0732) 882334
11–2.30, 6–11
Everards Tiger; Harveys BB ℍ
Cosy, friendly, village pub; a
deceptively old building,
decorated with many pictures of
foxes. An ideal pull-in for the
passing traveller with a thirst.
Large garden. No food Sun.
✻ ◖ ⬦ ⚓ P

Railway Hotel
4 Wrotham Road (A227)
☎ (0732) 882016
11–3, 6–11 (11–11 Sat)
**Greene King XX Mild, IPA,
Abbot** ℍ

149

Kent

Solid, Victorian building, a myriad of small bars, with a large, open fire in the saloon. The 'Northern' head on the beers causes raised eyebrows! One of the few outlets for mild in Kent. Guest beers.
🏠 ◖ 🕮 🛏 ♣ P

Boughton

Queens Head Inn
111 The Street
☎ (0227) 751369
11–4, 6–11
Shepherd Neame Master Brew Bitter, Spitfire 🅗
Unpretentious, 16th-century inn offering good value accommodation and food. Good for games, too.
Q 🏠 🛏 ◖ 🌓 🕮 🍴 ♣ P

Boughton Monchelsea

Red House
Hermitage Lane (2 miles S of B2163 and E of A229)
OS783489 ☎ (0622) 743986
12–3, 7–11 (11–11 Sat)
Exmoor Gold; Greene King IPA, Abbot; Wadworth 6X 🅗
Isolated pub, worth finding – if you can! Always a good selection of five or six beers, plus over 20 imported bottled beers. One dark beer is always available (mild, old or porter).
🏠 Q 🛏 🏭 🌓 Å ♣ 🍴 P

Brasted

Bull
High Street (A25)
☎ (0959) 562551
10.30–2.30, 6–11 (10.30–11 Sat & bank hols)
Shepherd Neame Master Brew Bitter, Master Brew Best Bitter, Spitfire, Bishops Finger 🅗
Pub where the bar is comprised of linked rooms, one mainly for food and passing trade, the other mainly for locals. Neo-Tudor style decor; friendly service. Bat and Trap played.
🏭 ◖ 🌓 🍴 ♣ P

Bredgar

Sun
The Street (B2163)
☎ (062 784) 221
11–2.30, 7 (6 Fri & Sat)–11 (12–2.30, 7–10.30 Sun)
Courage Best Bitter, Directors; John Smith's Bitter 🅗
Comfortable, single-bar, country pub in a modern style, catering for all ages. The large garden features an adventure playground. 🏠 🏭 ◖ 🌓 P

Brenchley

Rose & Crown
High Street (off A21)
☎ (0892) 722107
10.30–3, 6–11
Harveys Pale Ale; Marston's Pedigree; Tetley Bitter; Wadworth 6X; Whitbread Fremlins Bitter 🅗
Friendly local on the Blossom Route with beamed and plastered old stables and a separate dining area; coppered bar. An open, log fire in winter is the main feature. 🏭 🏭 🏭 ◖ 🌓 P

Broadstairs

Brown Jug
204 Ramsgate Road, Dumpton Park (A255)
☎ (0843) 62788
11–3 (4 Sat), 6–11
Whitbread Fremlins Bitter, Flowers Original 🅗
In an area lacking decent real ale; a flint-walled pub of quiet character run by two sisters. Special sports nights: crib, dominoes, darts, chess *et al.* Excellent! 🏭 Q 🏭 🌓
🚃 (Dumpton Park) ♣ P

Neptune's Hall
1–5 Harbour Street
☎ (0843) 61400
10–4, 6–11
Shepherd Neame Master Brew Bitter 🅗
Busy, two-bar, Victorian pub, a short puff from the picturesque harbour below. A regular entry in this guide, it is always worth a visit. Often packed with locals and visitors alike.
🏭 🏭 ◖ 🌓 🚃 ♣

Olde Crown Inn
23 High Street
☎ (0843) 61747
10.30–3 (4 Fri), 6–11 (10.30–11 Sat & summer)
Ruddles Best Bitter, County 🅗
Two-bar, High Street pub with a lively public, hosting an energetically-run, charitable Winkle Club. The sun lounge serves as a children's area and the extensive menu caters for children and vegetarians. Don't forget to bring your winkle!
◖ 🌓 🕮 🚃 ♣

Brookland

Woolpack
On A259, 1 mile S of Brookland, by sharp bends OS798245
☎ (0679) 344321
11–2.30, 6–11
Shepherd Neame Master Brew Bitter, Spitfire 🅗
Remote, beacon-keeper's cottage, c. 1410, with smuggling connections; a two-bar pub with very low beams

and a large inglenook. A collection of water jugs adorns the bar. Spinning Jenny played.
🏭 Q 🏭 ◖ 🌓 ♣ P

Burham

Toastmasters
65–67 Church Street (100 yds from Rochester Rd)
☎ (0634) 861299
12–4, 5.30–11 (12–11 Fri & Sat)
Fuller's ESB; Goacher's Dark; Greene King IPA; Harveys BB; Young's Special 🅗
Family-run free house with seven real ales, and real cider in summer. Restaurant and bar meals (not served Sun/Mon eves). Large collection of pewter tankards. 🏭 ◖ 🌓 ⌂ P

Canterbury

Canterbury Tales
12 The Friars (opp. Marlowe Theatre) ☎ (0227) 768594
11.30–2.30, 5.30–11
Goacher's Light; Shepherd Neame Master Brew Bitter 🅗
Attractive, old pub, decorated in elegant 1920s pastels and full of theatrical memorabilia. Beware of practical jokes. Guest beers always available.
🛏 ◖ 🌓 🚃 (East/West) ♣

New Inn
19 Havelock Street (just off ring road, E side of town)
☎ (0227) 464584
11–3 (3.30 Sat), 6–11
Beer range varies 🅗
Tiny, friendly free house, popular with students and staff from nearby colleges. Beers change frequently; usually a choice of six real ales. 🏭 ◖

Olive Branch
39 Burgate, The Buttermarket
☎ (0227) 462170
11–11
Ind Coope Friary Meux Best Bitter, Burton Ale; Young's Special 🅗
Opposite the mediaeval Christ Church gate of the cathedral: an ideal location for visitors. Seating outside in The Buttermarket. Good, home-made food. 🏭 ◖ 🚃 (East/West)

Charing Heath

Red Lion
Tile Lodge Road (off A20)
OS928493
☎ (023 371) 2418
11–2.30, 6.30–11
Shepherd Neame Master Brew Bitter 🅗
Two-bar pub enjoying friendly, local trade. The outside drinking area is the village green; the saloon has a real fire. Meals in the bar or restaurant (no food Tue or Sun). 🏭 Q ◖ 🌓 P

Chatham

Alexandra Hotel
43 Railway Street
☎ (0634) 843959
11–3 (4 Sat), 5 (7 Sat)–11
Shepherd Neame Master Brew Bitter, Spitfire Ⓗ
Recently refurbished pub near the station, with a relaxed and friendly atmosphere.
◐ ▶ ᵫ ⇌ ♣

Ropemakers Arms
70 New Road (near station)
☎ (0634) 402121
12–3, 5 (7 Sat)–11
Adnams Bitter; Goacher's Light; Greene King Abbot; Younger Scotch Ⓗ
Free house where a good, friendly, homely atmosphere pervades. No food at weekends.
◐ ♣ ᛫

Shipwrights Arms
69 Richard Street (behind Allders) ☎ (0634) 813684
11–2.30, 6 (7 Sat)–11 (12–3 Sun, closed Sun eve)
Greene King IPA, Abbot Ⓖ
Much-threatened free house with a Truman-tiled facade. Guest beers. No food Sun; closed Sun eve. ᛫ ◐ ⇌

Chiddingstone

Castle Inn
Off B2027, Leigh–Penshurst road ☎ (0892) 870247
11–3, 6–11
Harveys BB; Larkins Bitter; Shepherd Neame Master Brew Bitter Ⓗ
Historic, tile-hung inn (1420) in an unspoilt NT village. Small, traditional public bar; larger, olde-worlde saloon; separate restaurant. Garden and patio with a grapevine at the rear.
᛫ Q ⊛ ◐ ▶ ᛃ Å

Chiddingstone Causeway

Little Brown Jug
On B2027, opp. Penshurst station ☎ (0892) 870318
11.30–2.30, 6–11
Bateman Mild; Harveys BB Ⓗ
Good, country pub, to suit all tastes: a basic public bar with a comfortable saloon and an adjacent restaurant, serving a good range, incl. vegetarian dishes. Live pianist Wed eves; live music also some Tue eves. Usually three guest beers.
᛫ Q ⇌ ⊛ ᛃ ◐ ▶ ᛃ Å ⇌ (Penshurst) ♣ P

Cliffe

Black Bull
Church Street
☎ (0634) 220893

12–2.30, 7–11
Adnams Bitter; Bateman XXXB; Goacher's Dark; Whitbread Fremlins Bitter Ⓗ
Traditional free house offering regular guest beers. Try the SE Asian food in the cellar restaurant (national Guinness award for pub food). ᛫ ◐ ♣ P

Try also: All four pubs in Cliffe sell real ale

Cooling Street

Staff of Life
Cooling Street (turn into Merryboys Road from B2000)
☎ (0634) 221023
12–3, 7–11
Courage Best Bitter; Ind Coope Burton Ale; Morland Old Speckled Hen Ⓗ
Large pub in a lovely setting: one main bar, plus a garden bar which is often open (children's play area with an 'enchanted' tree). Beers are frequently changed and are taken from a large list. No food Sun eve.
⊛ ◐ ▶ P

Court at Street

Welcome Stranger
On B2067, halfway between Lympne and Aldington
OS090354 ☎ (0233) 720400
12–2.30 (3 Sat), 6–11
Shepherd Neame Master Brew Bitter Ⓗ
Quiet, one-bar pub where beer (not lager) drinkers can enjoy ribald conversation. Recently redecorated. A good range of bottled beers is available, alongside regularly-changed guest beers and occasional cider.
Q ↻ P

Cranbrook

Prince of Wales
High Street ☎ (0580) 713058
11.30–2.30, 6.30–11
Harveys BB Ⓗ
Renowned and lively, town-centre free house. Both bars can get very busy, especially at weekends. Guest beers and occasional mini beer festivals.
᛫ ᛃ ⊛ ◐ ▶ ᛃ ♣

Dartford

Foresters
15 Great Queen Street (off A226 at East Hill)
☎ (0322) 223087
11–11
Courage Best Bitter, Directors Ⓗ
A focal point for surrounding streets: a pub with a bustling public bar. ⊛ ⇌ ♣ P

Fulwich

150 St Vincents Road (off A226, E of centre)

☎ (0322) 223683
11–2.30, 6.30–11 (11–11 Fri & Sat; 12–2.30, 7–10.30 Sun)
Ind Coope Burton Ale; Tetley Bitter Ⓗ
Thriving, locals' pub with a large public bar where the licensee displays a number of awards for good cellar-keeping.
◐ ᛫ ᛃ ♣

Try also: Royal Oak, Spital St (Shepherd Neame)

Deal

Royal Hotel
Beach Street (next to pier)
☎ (0304) 375555
10.30–3, 6–11
Draught Bass Ⓗ
Small, cosy bar – don't be put off by its imposing hotel surroundings.
᛫ Q ᛃ ᛃ ⇌

Ship Inn
141 Middle Street (parallel to seafront)
☎ (0304) 372222
11–11
Draught Bass; Charrington IPA; Fuller's ESB; Greene King Abbot; Shepherd Neame Master Brew Bitter Ⓗ
Cosy pub with a nautical theme. Live music (Mabel on the piano). Vegetarian menu available. ᛫ ⊛ ◐ ᛃ ⇌

Star & Garter Hotel
101 Beach Street
☎ (0304) 375131
11–11
Shepherd Neame Master Brew Bitter, Bishops Finger Ⓗ
Seafront hotel: a smart saloon bar and a shabby, but welcoming, public bar. Occasional 'guest' Shepherd Neame polypin on the bar.
ᛃ ᛃ ♣ ♣

Dover

Boars Head
46–48 Eaton Road
☎ (0304) 204490
11–11
Greene King Rayments Special; Whitbread Boddingtons Bitter Ⓗ
Refurbished corner local, friendly and welcoming. Guest beers are regularly supplied (the menu is on the wall!). The range of beers above may change.
᛫ ⊛ ◐ ⇌ (Priory) ♣

Eagle Hotel
London Road (opp. Sainsburys)
☎ (0304) 201543
11–11
Courage Best Bitter, Directors; John Smith's Bitter Ⓗ
Large, noisy, two-bar pub with a separate games room.
ᛃ ⇌ (Priory) ♣

Kent

Royal Oak
Lower Road, River (off A256, by the river)
☎ (0304) 822073
11–11
Shepherd Neame Master Brew Bitter, Spitfire 🄷
Large, open-plan pub in a popular, residential part of town. ◖ ≹ (Kearsney) ♣ P

East Farleigh

Walnut Tree
Forge Lane OS743530
☎ (0622) 726368
12–3, 6–11
Shepherd Neame Master Brew Bitter, Spitfire 🄷
Low-beamed, country pub with interesting memorabilia. The large beer garden can get quite busy. Home-cooked food.
⌂ Q ❀ ◖ ◗ ≹ ♣ P

Eccles

Walnut Tree
230 Bull Lane (2 miles W of A229, between M2 and M20)
☎ (0622) 717419
11–11
Courage Best Bitter, Directors; Goacher's Dark, Old; John Smith's Bitter 🄷
Enterprising, village pub near the Friars at Aylesford. Meat dishes a speciality (the landlord is an ex-butcher). Guest beers. Wheelchair ramp to the main entrance.
⌂ ☗ ❀ ◖ ◗ ♿ ♣ P

Fairseat

Vigo Inn
Wrotham Road (A227, 1 mile N of Wrotham)
☎ (0732) 822547
12–2.30 (3 Sat; not Mon), 6–11
Harveys XX Mild, BB; Goacher's Dark; Young's Bitter, Special 🄷
Ancient, drovers' inn, named in honour of a local resident who fought in the Battle of Vigo. Two quiet bars; a real haunt of ale drinkers. The only noise is that of gentle conversation, except when the daddlums table is in use (Kentish form of skittles). Goacher's house bitter on sale. ⌂ Q ♣ ⚲ P

Farningham

Chequers
High Street ☎ (0322) 865222
11–11
Fuller's London Pride, ESB; Morland Old Speckled Hen 🄷
Enterprising free house in a pleasant village, just off the A20. Always serves a range of guest beers. ❀

Faversham

Mechanics Arms
44 West Street
☎ (0795) 532693
10.30–3, 6.30–11
Shepherd Neame Master Brew Bitter 🄷
Nine years in the *Guide*; an unspoilt, friendly and welcoming local of a kind that is increasingly hard to find. ❀ ⊟

Shipwrights Arms
Hollowshore (signed off Oare Rd; mind the pot holes!) OS017636 ☎ (0795) 533163
11–3, 7–11
Adnams Broadside; Bateman XXXB; Shepherd Neame Master Brew Bitter; Younger IPA, No. 3; Young's Special 🄶
Isolated, historic, weather-boarded pub. Difficult to find but worth the effort. No mains electricity or water! Bateman's Mild available May–Sept. Limited menu, but good quality home cooking. ⌂ ☗ ❀ ◖ ◗ ⚲ P

Folkestone

Clifton Hotel
The Leas (near Leas Cliff Hall)
☎ (0303) 851231
11–3, 6–11
Draught Bass 🄷
Relaxing and comfortable bar in a three-star hotel overlooking the sea. Q ☗ ❀ ⛟ ◖ ◗ ≹ (Central)

Frinsted

Kingsdown Arms
The Street ($1\frac{1}{2}$ miles E of B2163, between M2 and M20)
☎ (062 784) 420
12–3, 7–11
Bateman XXXB; Ind Coope Burton Ale; Marston's Pedigree 🄷
Enterprising, village pub which caters for all tastes: two, contrasting bars and a separate restaurant (book for Sun lunch). Guest beers; cider in summer.
❀ ◖ ◗ ⊟ P

Gillingham

King George V
1 Prospect Row, Old Brompton (back-streets, between Chatham and the old dockyard)
☎ (0634) 842418
11–3, 6 (7 Sat)–11
Draught Bass 🄷
A warm, cosy atmosphere in a pub with naval and military connections. Regular guest ales and a varied collection of malt whiskies. No food Sun. ◖ ♣

Roseneath
79 Arden Street (200 yds off High Street) ☎ (0634) 52553
11.30–5, 7–11 (11.30–11 Sat)
Goacher's Light; Greene King Abbot 🄷
Enterprising, back-street local offering a selection of good value, home-made meals. Regular guest ales. Watch out for Golly the snakehound! Occasional beer festivals held in a marquee in the garden.
❀ ◖ ◗ ≹ ♣

White House
147 Pier Road (B2004)
☎ (0634) 51152
12–3, 7–11 (11–11 summer)
John Smith's Bitter 🄷
Excellent pub on the edge of town. Live jazz Thu; guest ales; unusual menu. Worth finding.
☗ ❀ ◖ ◗ ♣ P

Try also: United Services, Arden St (Shepherd Neame)

Goodnestone

Fitzwalter Arms
The Street (follow the walls of the Fitzwalter Estate)
OS255546 ☎ (0304) 840303
12–3, 7–11
Shepherd Neame Master Brew Bitter, Master Brew Best Bitter, Spitfire, Bishops Finger 🄷
Old gate lodge of the Fitzwalter Estate, now a friendly, three-bar pub. Bar billiards; occasional theme nights. ⌂ Q ⊟ ♣

Goudhurst

Green Cross Inn
Station Road (A262, 1 mile W of village) ☎ (0580) 211200
11–2.30, 6–11
Exmoor Ale; Harveys BB; Shepherd Neame Master Brew Bitter 🄷
Authentic, country pub with a large, uncluttered front bar and a restaurant at the rear. Warmed by a wood-burning stove and once known as the 'Railway Hotel'. Good quality food; no Sun lunches, except on special occasions. ⌂ Q ❀ ⛟ ◖ ◗ ♣ P

Gravesend

Darnley Arms
9 Trafalgar Road (off A227, just beyond centre)
☎ (0474) 334051
11–3, 5.30–11
Mansfield Old Baily; Morland Bitter 🄷
Friendly, street-corner local serving a range of beers – a welcome change from the run-of-the-mill pubs in the area. ≹

Jolly Drayman
1 Love Lane (Wellington Street, off A226 at the BP garage, E of centre) ☎ (0474) 352355
11–2.30, 5–11 (11–11 Sat)
Draught Bass; Charrington IPA 🄷

Old, low-ceilinged pub, known locally as the 'Coke Oven'. Guest beers and occasional ciders. No food at weekends. ⚲ ◖ ⅋ ≉ ○ P

New Inn
1 Milton Road (A226, central one-way system)
☎ (0474) 566651
10–11
**Marston's Pedigree;
Whitbread Fremlins Bitter** Ⓗ
Unspoilt locals' pub in the town centre, with Rigden's windows. Almost the last of its type and worth preserving. ⚞ ⚲ ⅋ ≉ ♣

Prince Albert
26 Wrotham Road (A227, just off centre)
☎ (0474) 352432
10–2.30, 6–11 (10–11 Sat)
Shepherd Neame Master Brew Bitter Ⓗ
Town pub with a lively public bar and a quiet saloon. No food Sun lunchtime.
◖◗ ⅋ ⚬ ⅋ ♣ P

Windmill Tavern
45 Shrubbery Road
☎ (0474) 352242
11–11
**Ruddles Best Bitter, County;
Webster's Yorkshire Bitter** Ⓗ
Hard-to-find, but lively pub on Windmill Hill, the highest part of town. Three bars and a notable garden. Guest beers.
⚬ ⚲ ◖◗ ⅋ ⚬ ♣ P

Great Chart

Hooden Horse
The Street (A28, 2 miles from Ashford)
☎ (0233) 625583
11–2.30, 6.30–11
Bateman Mild; Goacher's Light; Hook Norton Old Hooky Ⓗ
Tastefully refurbished in early 1991 with tiled and timber floors, and scattered chairs and tables, some with crib scorers. A very welcoming village pub. Regular selection of guest ales.
Q ◖◗

Green Street Green (Dartford)

Ship
On B260, towards Longfield from Dartford Tunnel
☎ (047 47) 2279
11–2.30 (12–3.30 Sat), 6–11
**Courage Best Bitter,
Directors; Young's Bitter** Ⓗ
Deservedly popular, two-bar pub, part of which dates from the 17th century. Excellent value lunches – the pizzas are especially recommended. Children's room in summer only. ⚞ Q ⚬ ⚲ ◖◗ ⅄ ♣ P

Halling

Plough
High Street (A228)
☎ (0634) 240200
11.30–3, 6–11
**Courage Best Bitter,
Directors** Ⓗ
Friendly, village local offering good value food. Bar billiards played. ⅋ ⚲ ◖◗ ⅋ ⅋ ♣ P

Try also: Homeward Bound, High St (Shepherd Neame)

Hamptons

Artichoke Inn
Park Road (signed off Hadlow–Plaxtol roads)
☎ (0732) 810763
11.30–2.30, 7–11
**Fuller's London Pride;
Marston's Pedigree; Young's Special, Winter Warmer** Ⓗ
Remote, two-bar, country pub with an emphasis on food. Low beams, lots of copper and a magnificent inglenook. Garden and courtyard drinking area for summer eves. ⚞ Q ⚲ ◖◗

Harbledown

Old Coach & Horses
Church Hill (just off A2)
☎ (0227) 761330
11.30–2.30 (3 Sat), 6 (7 Sat)–11
Adnams Bitter; Greene King IPA Ⓗ
Pub near Black Prince's Well and opposite Canterbury's old leper hospital. Guest beers; good range of food. Built on a hillside, the beer garden is precipitous. ⚞ ⚲ ◖◗ ⅄ P

Henley Street

Cock Inn
B2009 from A2, through Cobham; turn left for Henley St, 1 mile out of village
OS663672 ☎ (0474) 814208
12–2, 5–11 (12–11 Fri & Sat)
Adnams Bitter; Ind Coope Burton Ale; Taylor Walker Best Bitter Ⓗ
Popular, village pub featuring interesting wartime posters in the saloon bar. Bar snacks available. ⚞ ⚲ ⅋ ⅋ P

Herne Bay

Heron
Station Road
☎ (0227) 372990
11–2.30 (4 Fri), 5.30–11 (11–11 Sat)
Shepherd Neame Master Brew Bitter Ⓗ
Pub with a modern exterior and a comfortable, lively interior. The basic family room has electronic games.
⚲ ⚲ ◖◗ ⅋ ⅄ ≉ ♣ P

Prince of Wales
173 Mortimer Street
☎ (0227) 374205
10–3, 6–11
Shepherd Neame Master Brew Bitter Ⓗ
Pub close to the seafront, featuring a high-ceilinged, Victorian interior, with good glass and woodwork. Pool and bar billiards played.
⚬ ⅋ ⚬ ⅄ ≉ ♣

Rose Inn
111 Mortimer Street
☎ (0227) 375081
10–11
Everards Tiger; Shepherd Neame Master Brew Bitter Ⓗ
Smart, comfortable pub in a pedestrianised area, close to the seafront. Guest beers and good value snacks. ◖◗ ⅋ ≉

Higham

Chequers Inn
Church Street (over bridge at station) ☎ (047 482) 2794
11–3, 6–11
Courage Best Bitter Ⓗ
Friendly, two-bar, village local which hosts occasional theme nights. Bottle-conditioned Russian Stout available. No food Sun lunch. ⚲ ◖◗ ⅋ ≉ ♣ P

Hollingbourne

Pilgrims Rest
Upper Street (B2163, top of high street, Pilgrims Way)
☎ (0622) 880210
11–2.30 (3 Sat), 7–11
Adnams Bitter; Shepherd Neame Master Brew Bitter; Wadworth 6X Ⓗ
One-bar pub with wood-panelled walls and a beamed ceiling, still retaining separate areas, including a restaurant. The games/function room can be used for families. Guest beer when turnover allows. Live music every Wed.
⚲ ◖◗ ⅋ ⚬ ⅄ ≉ ♣ P

Kingsdown

Kings Head
Upper Street (B2057)
10.30–3, 6–11
Draught Bass; Charrington IPA Ⓗ
Friendly, village pub with a separate restaurant. ⅋ ♣

Knockholt

Harrow
Harrow Road, Knockholt Pound (300 yds from Pound towards Sevenoaks) ☎ (0959) 32168
11–2.30 (3 Sat), 6–11
Shepherd Neame Master Brew Bitter, Master Brew Best Bitter, Spitfire, Bishops Finger Ⓗ

153

Kent

Pub dating in part from the 14th century. Sympathetically extended to include an old stable, giving a split-level drinking and food area (eve meals Thu–Sat). All the elements of the village local; set on its outskirts, in wonderful walking country. 🏠 🏨 ◖ ▶ ♣ P

Lynsted

Black Lion
☎ (0795) 521229
11–3, 6–11
Courage Best Bitter, Directors Ⓗ
Lively and energetic, community-spirited local. Live music alternate Fris. Q 🏨 ◖ ▶ P

Maidstone

Admiral Gordon
1 Milton Street (A26, 1 mile from centre)
☎ (0622) 726803
11–2.30, 6–11 (11–11 Sat)
Courage Best Bitter Ⓗ
Small and friendly, two-bar street-corner local. The saloon bar decor is in keeping with the pub name. Guest beers. Good value food; no meals Tue eve, or Sun. ఈ 🏨 ◖ ▶ ⊞ ≠ (West)

Dragoon
40 Sandling Road (A229, N of centre) ☎ (0622) 752620
10–3, 6–11 (11–11 Sat)
Shepherd Neame Master Brew Bitter Ⓗ
Friendly, split-level, corner local with an emphasis on pub games: two bar billiards tables, darts, euchre and two quiz teams. No food at weekends. Limited parking. ◖ ≠ (East) ♣ P

Fishers Arms
22 Scott Street
☎ (0622) 753632
11–3, 6–11 (11–11 Sat)
Courage Best Bitter Ⓗ
Large, single-bar pub on a street corner; upstairs function room. Guest beers include Goacher's, and others from a Courage-approved list. No food at weekends. 🏨 ◖ ≠ (East) ♣

Greyhound
77 Wheeler Street
☎ (0622) 754032
11–3, 5–11 (11–11 Sat)
Shepherd Neame Master Brew Bitter, Spitfire Ⓗ
The centre of Kent's film industry: an amateur film club meets here and thespians abound! Home-cooked food and occasional barbecues.
🏨 ◖ ▶ ⊞ ≠ (East/Barracks) ♣ P

Pilot
25 Upper Stone Street (A229, one way system southbound)
☎ (0622) 691162
11–3, 6 (7 Sat)–11

Harveys XX Mild (summer), BB, Old Ⓗ
Much improved of late and offering the only Harvey's in town, giving more choice to discerning drinkers. Petanque played. No meals Sun lunch.
🏠 🏨 ◖ ▶ ♣

Margate

Orb
243 Ramsgate Road (A254)
☎ (0843) 220663
11–11
Shepherd Neame Master Brew Bitter, Spitfire Ⓗ
Pub which has appeared in this guide every year since 1976: a popular, two-bar local with a long-standing following. Look out for the special garden events such as barbecues and Greek nights. Live music on occasions, played by the landlord. 🏠 🏨 ◖ ▶ ♣ P

Spread Eagle
25 Victoria Road
☎ (0843) 293396
11.30–3, 5.30–11 (11.30–11 Sat)
Fuller's London Pride; Greene King IPA; Hesket Newmarket Blencathra Bitter; Hook Norton Old Hooky; Morland Old Masters; Young's Special Ⓗ
Excellent, Victorian, corner pub with a changing range of independent ales. Worth the walk to the top of the high street (past the parish church). Basketball played. No food Sun.
ఈ 🏨 ◖ ▶

Marshside

Gate Inn
Chislet turn off A28 in Upstreet
☎ (022 786) 498
11–2.30 (3 Sat), 6–11
Shepherd Neame Master Brew Bitter, Master Brew Best Bitter, Stock Ale, Bishops Finger (summer) Ⓖ
Lively, country pub with something for everyone, even a duck-infested garden. No lager in Lent. Voted *Best Pub in the South East* by CAMRA in 1989, and puts on its own beer festival in August. Shove-ha'penny and bagatelle played. No-smoking area lunchtimes only.
🏠 Q ఈ 🏨 ◖ ▶ ⟐ ⚤ ♣ P ⚒

Minster (Sheppey)

Prince of Waterloo
428 Minster Road
☎ (0795) 872458
11–11
Greene King XX Mild, IPA, Abbot Ⓗ
Popular, village local, close to the ancient abbey. ఈ 🏨 ◖ P

Minster (Thanet)

Saddlers
7 Monkton Road (B2047)
☎ (0843) 821331
11–2.30, 6–11 (11–11 Sat)
Shepherd Neame Master Brew Bitter Ⓗ
Excellent, friendly, two-bar local at the village centre. Good value meals lunch and eve (not served Sun). Bat and Trap played. 🏨 ◖ ▶ ⊞ ≠ ♣

New Hythe

Bricklayers Arms
440 New Hythe Lane (1 mile N of A20 and E of A228)
☎ (0622) 718151
11–2.30, 6–11 (12–2, 7–10.30 Sun)
Courage Best Bitter, Directors; Young's Special Ⓗ
Friendly pub where nobody would feel out of place. Fishing and windsurfing in nearby lakes. Guest beers. No food Sun.
🏠 🏨 ◖ ▶ ⊞ ⚿ ≠ ♣ P

Northbourne

Hare & Hound
The Street OS334521
☎ (0304) 365429
10.30–3, 6–11
Draught Bass; Shepherd Neame Master Brew Bitter; Webster's Yorkshire Bitter; Whitbread Flowers Original Ⓗ
Busy, country pub in a rural village – popular for food. Beers vary. Playground in the garden.
🏨 ◖ ▶ P

Oad Street

Plough & Harrow
☎ (0795) 843351
11–11
Greene King XX Mild, IPA; Rayments Special, Abbot; Shepherd Neame Master Brew Bitter Ⓗ
Thriving, popular local with an energetic landlord. A rare outlet for mild in the area. Guest beers.
🏠 ఈ 🏨 ◖ ⊞

Oare

Three Mariners
2 Church Road
☎ (0795) 533633
10–3 (4 Sat), 7–11
Shepherd Neame Master Brew Bitter, Spitfire Ⓗ
Rambling pub with a nautical theme at the village centre. Book for meals at lunchtime. Bat and Trap played. 🏠 ఈ 🏨 ◖ ▶ P

Ospringe

Anchor
33 The Street (A2)
☎ (0795) 532085

11–3, 7–11
**Shepherd Neame Master
Brew Bitter** H
Pleasant local; shove-ha'penny
played. 🏠 🍴 ⚓ 🚌 ♣

Pembury

Black Horse
12 High Street (old A21)
☎ (089 282) 2012
11–11
**Adnams Bitter; Harveys BB,
Old; Young's Special** H
Refurbished and extended pub,
retaining its olde-worlde
flavour. A real community pub
at the village centre. Seating is
provided mainly by ex-church
pews, which add to its character.
Varied menu in the bar and Le
Bistro restaurant. Summer
barbecues. 🏠 Q 🍴 🍺 🍷

Perry Wood

Rose & Crown
OS042552 ☎ (0227) 752214
12–2.30 (3 Sat), 7–11 (closed Mon)
**Shepherd Neame Master
Brew Bitter; Wadworth 6X;
Whitbread Boddingtons
Bitter, Fremlins Bitter** H
15th-century inn set in pleasant
woodland. Live music most
Tues; barbecues at weekends.
Bat and Trap pitch; guest beers.
Booking advisable for
restaurant. 🏠 Q 🍴 🍷 P

Petteridge

Hopbine Inn
Petteridge Lane (off A21, ½ mile
S of Brenchley) OS667413
☎ (0892) 722561
12–2.30, 6–11
**King & Barnes Mild, Sussex,
Broadwood, Old, Festive** H
Attractive, part-weatherboard
and tile-hung, country pub in an
idyllic setting. The friendly
welcome, good food and full
range of beers make it well
worth seeking out. Live folk
music every fourth Sun eve. No
food Wed. 🏠 🍴 🍺 ♣ P

Plaxtol

Golding Hop
Sheet Hill (E of A227, ½ mile N
of village centre)
OS600547
11–3, 6–11
**Adnams Bitter, Broadside;
Young's Special, Winter
Warmer** G
Cottage-like pub, both inside
and out, perched on a hillside,
surrounded by orchards. The
bar comprises four areas on
three levels. Always two guest
beers; Weston's cider. Basement
no-smoking area.
🏠 🍴 ♣ 🍷 P 🍴

Ramsgate

Churchill Tavern
The Paragon (overlooking
Royal Harbour)
☎ (0843) 587862
11–11 (11–3, 6–11 Sat)
**Felinfoel Double Dragon;
Fuller's London Pride, ESB;
Greene King Abbot;
Ringwood Old Thumper;
Taylor Landlord** H
Lately known as Van Gogh or
Steptoe's, Churchill's has been
totally rebuilt, using much old
wood and materials. Popular
with the young, and a beer
drinker's treat. Printed handouts
and calling cards on the bar
extol and promote real ale to all.
Guest beers. 🏠 🚌 🍺 ♣ 🍷

Rochester

Britannia
376 High Street
☎ (0634) 401514
11–3.30, 6.30–11 (11–11 Sat)
**Goacher's Light; Greene
King IPA, Abbot** H
A free house offering two guest
beers; a pleasant, town lounge
between Chatham and
Rochester railway stations. No
food Sun. 🍺 🚉

Coopers Arms
10 St Margarets Street (near
castle, cathedral and river – 200
yds S of A2)
☎ (0634) 404298
11–2.30 (3.30 Sat), 5.30 (6.30 Sat)–11
(may open all day Sat in summer)
**Courage Best Bitter,
Directors; John Smith's
Bitter** H
Ancient and appealing hostelry
with two cosy and inviting bars,
both well and suitably furnished.
The possibly haunted building
and site are of much historic
interest. Attractive, secluded,
prize-winning garden. No food
Sun. 🏠 Q 🍴 🍺 🚉 P

George Vaults
35 High Street
11–11
**Courage Best Bitter; John
Smith's Bitter** H
Basic, town-centre pub with
piped 60s music. 🚌 🚉

Granville Arms
83 Maidstone Road (B2097)
☎ (0634) 45243
11–3, 7–11
Greene King IPA, Abbot H
Comfortable pub with a
pleasant, cosy atmosphere. No
meals Thu eve or Sun. 🍺 🍷 🚉 ♣

Greyhound
68 Rochester Avenue
☎ (0634) 844120
10–3, 6–11 (10–11 Sat)
**Shepherd Neame Master
Brew Bitter** H

Victorian, terraced local with
suitable period furnishings in
the saloon, including four *chaises
longues* and an original range.
The public is plainer and more
down to earth. No food Sun.
🏠 🍺 🍷 🚉

Who'd Ha' Tho't It
9 Baker Street (50 yds off
B2097, Maidstone Road)
☎ (0634) 841131
11–11
Beer range varies H
Bustling, basic, back-street
boozer with a good mix of
clientele. A real drinking pub
offering a constantly-changing
choice of eight beers, mostly
from small independent
breweries. Cider in summer. No
food at weekends.
🏠 🍺 🍷 🍴

St Margaret's at
Cliffe

Hope
High Street
10.30–11
**Shepherd Neame Master
Brew Bitter** H
Tastefully refurbished, long, thin
bar; friendly, and not devoted
to the holiday trade at the
locals' expense.
🍺 🍷 ♣ P

Sandgate

Clarendon Inn
Brewers Hill (off A259)
☎ (0303) 48684
11–3 (11.30–2.30 winter), 6–11
**Shepherd Neame Master Brew
Bitter, Master Brew Best
Bitter** *or* **Spitfire** H
Small, old pub on a hill with
Channel views. Winner of
CAMRA *Best Pub* (Folkestone
area) 1990. It was once a
brewery, hence Brewers Hill.
Note the old Hythe Mackeson
brewery sign (partly obscured)
on a wall at the bottom of the
hill. Meals good: try the
seafood (no meals Thu eve).
🏠 Q 🍺 🍷 🍴 🍴

Ship Inn
65 High Street (A259)
☎ (0303) 48525
11–2.45, 6–11
Gale's HSB G; **Ind Coope
Friary Meux Best Bitter** H,
Burton Ale G
The energetic landlord of this
busy, two-bar pub claims to sell
more Burton Ale per square inch
of bar space than any other pub
in the world! Excellent
blackboard menu. HQ of
Sandgate Clog Morris.
Caricatures of locals adorn the
public bar walls.
🍺 🍷 🍴 🍴 ♣

Kent

Sandwich

Crispin
2 High Street (near old toll bridge) ☎ (0304) 617365
11–11
Draught Bass ; Charrington IPA Ⓗ
Large, corner pub: a single drinking area divided into cosy sections. 🏠 ◖ ◗ ♣ ♣

Market Inn
7 Cattle Market (opp. Guildhall) ☎ (0304) 612033
11–11
Shepherd Neame Master Brew Bitter, Bishops Finger Ⓗ
One-bar, terraced pub: small, cosy and popular. Generous portions of home-cooked food. ◖ ◗ ≉

Sarre

Crown Inn
Ramsgate Road (A28/A253 jct) ☎ (0843) 47808
11–11
Shepherd Neame Master Brew Bitter, Spitfire Ⓗ
Old staging post known locally as the 'Cherry Brandy House', recently refurbished with a sympathetically built hotel annexe. Low beams, cosy rooms, a restaurant, and its own famous cherry brandy, by ancient charter. Part of the Abbey Inns chain.
🛏 🅫 ◖ ◗ 🅐 P

Sevenoaks

Royal Oak Tap
2 High Street (A225) ☎ (0732) 458783
11–3, 6–11
Ruddles County ; Webster's Yorkshire Bitter ; Whitbread Boddingtons Bitter Ⓗ
Old pub situated in the oldest part of town, close to the entrance to Knole Park. The left-hand bar has a pleasant, time-worn look and the guest beer is changed at least twice weekly. 🏠 🅫 ◖ ♣ P

Try also: Anchor, London Rd (Bass), **Vine**, Pound Lane (Ind Coope)

Sheerness

Red Lion
High Street, Bluetown (between dockyard and steel works) ☎ (0795) 663165
12–3, 6 (8 Sat)–11 (12–3, 8–11 Sun)
Greene King Rayments Special, Abbot Ⓗ
A haven with a congenial landlord who has a firm commitment to real ale. Guest beers; the Red Lion IPA house beer is supplied by Greene King. Q ◖ 🅐 ≉

Shoreham

Royal Oak
2 The High Street ☎ (095 92) 2319
10.30–2.30 (3 Sat), 6–11
Adnams Bitter ; Marston's Pedigree Ⓗ
Pub with walls covered with paintings by local artists (for sale), and large cartoons of locals. Try the games, incl. Toad in the Hole, table skittles and bar billiards. Ask about the games of Tripletell and Connect Four. Guest beers.
🏠 🅫 ◖ ◗ 🅐 ≉ ♣ ☺

Try also: Crown, High St (Greene King)

Shottenden

Plough
Soleshill Road (off A252, near Chilham) ☎ (0227) 730244
12–3.30, 7–11
Greene King IPA, Abbot ; Shepherd Neame Master Brew Bitter Ⓗ
Popular and busy pub, with something to offer everyone. Live jazz and barbecues Sat eves in summer. The house beer, Plough Bitter, is brewed by Goacher's. Guest beers. Book for Sun lunch; no eve meals Tue or Sun. 🏠 🅫 ◖ ◗ P

Smarden

Bell
Bell Lane (1 mile from village) OS870430 ☎ (0233) 77283
11.30–2.30, 6–11
Fuller's London Pride ; Goacher's Light ; Harveys Pale Ale ; Ringwood Old Thumper ; Shepherd Neame Master Brew Bitter Ⓗ
Four-bar pub (one bar for non-smokers), featuring stone floors and low beams. Always busy but service is prompt. Occasional changes to the beer range. The family room tends to be overrun by other customers when busy. 🏠 Q 🛏 🅫 ⋈ ◖ ◗ 🅐 ▲ ♣ ☺ P ⅋ ✕

Smart's Hill

Bottle House
Coldharbour Road (off B2188, 1 mile S of Penshurst ; follow signs) OS516421 ☎ (0892) 870306
11–2.30, 6–11
Ind Coope Burton Ale ; King & Barnes Sussex ; Young's Bitter Ⓗ
Attractive, country pub in a remote setting. Dates back to the late 15th century, although has been much altered since then. Separate restaurant with good, fresh food (closed Sun eve and Mon). Guest beers.
🏠 🅫 ◖ P

Snargate

Red Lion
On B2080, Brenzett–Appledore road OS990286 ☎ (0679) 344648
11–3, 7–11
Adnams Bitter ; Bateman XB Ⓖ
Wonderfully unspoilt, unpretentious, small, rural pub: real fires; stone and timber floors; marble counter top. Piano and Toad in the Hole played. Large garden. Guest milds and Biddenden cider. A must if you are in the area. 🏠 Q 🅫 🅐 ♣ ☺ P

Speldhurst

George & Dragon
Speldhurst Hill (2 miles W of A264) ☎ (0892) 863125
11–3, 6–11
Greene King Abbot ; Harveys Pale Ale, BB, Old ; King & Barnes Broadwood Ⓗ
Classic, country pub which dates back to 1212. A large, stone-flagged public bar and a cosy saloon, plus an upstairs restaurant, combine to make it one of the least spoilt pubs in the county. Well worth a visit. No eve meals Sun.
🏠 Q 🅫 ◖ ◗ P

Stalisfield Green

Plough
Stalisfield Road (2 miles N of Charing) OS954529 ☎ (0795) 89256
11 (12 winter)–3, 6 (7 winter)–11 (closed Mon)
Adnams Extra ; Harveys BB ; Ind Coope Burton Ale ; Shepherd Neame Master Brew Bitter Ⓗ
Old and welcoming pub of character, set in impressive countryside. Shut the Box and shove-ha'penny played. Comfortable family room; booking advised for the restaurant.
🏠 Q 🛏 🅫 ◖ ◗ 🅐 ▲ ♣ P

Stansted

Black Horse
Tumblefield Road (1 mile from A20, at top of Wrotham Hill) ☎ (0732) 822355
11–2.30, 6 (7 winter)–11
Whitbread Fremlins Bitter Ⓗ
A real local – the centre of village life and a deserved, long-standing entry in this guide. The landlord was the first in the area to obtain guest beers (changed every two months). Bat and Trap played.
🏠 🛏 🅫 ◖ ◗ ▲ ♣ P

Staplestreet

Three Horseshoes

Follow Staplestreet sign out of Boughton ☎ (0227) 750842
11–11 (11–3, 6–11 Thu & Fri)
Shepherd Neame Master Brew Bitter 🄶
A typically Kentish building, with a list of landlords going back to 1690, a collection of stone bottles, many table-top games and bar billiards. Cheap meals.
🛏 Q ⊛ ◖ ▌ 🅰 (Hernhill) ♣ P

Stone Street

Padwell Arms

On Ivy Hatch–Seal road
☎ (0732) 61532
12–2.30, 6–11
Hall & Woodhouse Badger Best Bitter; Harveys BB; Hook Norton Old Hooky; Young's Bitter 🄷
Old pub set in the heart of the Garden of England, enjoying pleasant views across the orchards. Ideal for summer eves. Guest beers. Eve meals finish at 8.30pm. 🛏 ◖ ▌ ♣ P

Strood

Horseshoe

51 Cuxton Road (A228, one-way system)
☎ (0634) 718414
11–3, 6–11 (11–11 Fri & Sat)
Shepherd Neame Spitfire 🄷
Friendly and vibrant local offering good value bar meals (not served Sun). ⊛ ◖ ▌ ⇌ ♣ P

Sutton Valence

Kings Head

North Street
☎ (0622) 843264
11–2.30 (3 Sat), 5–11
Adnams Tally Ho; Courage Best Bitter, Directors; John Smith's Bitter 🄷
A cosy, quiet, beamed saloon and a traditional public bar. The bottle and jug is now used as a family room. Adnams is replaced with a guest ale in summer. Garden access is via the restaurant.
🛏 Q ⛵ ⊛ ◖ ▌ 🅀 🅰 ♣ P

Swanley Village

Red Lion

Swanley Village Road
☎ (0322) 662676
11–2.30, 6–11 (12–2, 7–10.30 Sun)
Courage Best Bitter 🄷
Pleasant, village pub serving Young's Special as a guest beer. À la carte restaurant open Fri and Sat eves (used as a family room at other times). No food Sun. ⛵ ⊛ ◖ ▌ 🅀 ♣ P

Tonbridge

Rose & Crown

125 High Street (A26)
☎ (0732) 357966
11–3, 6–11 (11–11 Sat)
Draught Bass; Whitbread Fremlins Bitter 🄷
Small, comfortable bar in an imposing and historic hotel. A good place for meeting friends, conducting business or reading the paper. An adjacent lounge is comfortably furnished and suitable for children. Q ⊛ 🛏 ◖ ▌

Royal Oak

Lower Haysden Lane (follow signs to Haysden, S of town, 2 miles) ☎ (0732) 350208
11–3, 5.30–11
Adnams Bitter; Fuller's London Pride 🄷
Friendly, enterprising ale house in a pleasant, rural setting, close to Haysden Country Park. Tasting notes describing beers sold are chalked up on a board in the bar. No keg beer; two guest ales. Eve meals Fri and Sat only. 🛏 ⊛ ◖ ▌ ♣ P

Uncle Tom's Cabin

54 Lavender Hill (off Pembury Road, A2014)
☎ (0732) 365044
11–2.30 (3.30 Fri & Sat), 6–11 (may vary)
Greene King XX Mild, IPA 🄷
Friendly free house in a residential street, always with two guest beers available, usually from small independent breweries; the best selection of beers in Tonbridge. No keg bitter. ⊛ ⇌ ♣

Toy's Hill

Fox & Hounds

OS471520 ☎ (0732) 750328
11–3, 6–11
Greene King IPA, Abbot 🄷
Pub which has survived the 1986 closure threat by its previous owners (Allied) and the 1987 hurricane, though the surrounding woods have not. A single-bar, rural pub with domestic furniture and magazines to browse. Enjoys a hill-top location, near Chartwell. Lunchtime snacks.
🛏 Q ⛵ ⊛ ⊛ P

Trottiscliffe

Plough

Taylors Lane (1 mile N off A227, near M20 jct 2)
☎ (0732) 822233
11.30–3, 6–11
Whitbread Boddingtons Bitter, Fremlins Bitter; Flowers Original 🄷
Popular, 15th-century, village pub at the foot of the North Downs. The lounge has many beams with horse brasses and is popular with diners, but the public bar is also very comfortable. The landlord actively utilises the freedom to stock guest beers. No food Sun eve. 🛏 ⊛ ◖ ▌ 🅀 ♣ P

Tudeley

George & Dragon

Five Oak Green Road (B2017, Tonbridge–Paddock Wood road)
☎ (0892) 832521
11–3, 6–11
Courage Best Bitter, Directors 🄷
Picturesque, 16th-century pub: a cosy, beamed saloon and a games-oriented public bar. Overlooks hop gardens and sells the best pint of Courage in the area. Shove-ha'penny and Bat and Trap played.
🛏 ⊛ ◖ ▌ 🅀 ♣ P

Tunbridge Wells

Beau Nash Tavern

61 Mount Ephraim (A264, by common) ☎ (0892) 39350
11.30–2.30, 5.30–11 (11–3, 6–11 Sat)
Gale's HSB; King & Barnes Sussex; Ruddles Best Bitter, County; Webster's Yorkshire Bitter 🄷
Small, friendly, secluded pub, attracting customers from all walks of life. The cuisine is excellent and fairly priced. A great place to take a partner.
Q ⊛ ◖ ▌ 🅵 ⇌

Brokers Arms

5–11 Langton Road (A264, opp. golf club)
☎ (0892) 541000
11–3 (4 Sat), 6–11
Greene King Abbot; Harveys Pale Ale, BB; Larkins Porter (winter); **Marston's Pedigree** 🄷
Free house on the edge of the common, with split-level, bare-brick floors, a homely inglenook and a bare-beamed ceiling. Friendly atmosphere generated by hosts and staff; very efficient service in the bar and upstairs restaurant. Guest beers.
🛏 Q ◖ ▌

Crystal Palace

69 Camden Road (near Calverly shopping precinct)
☎ (0892) 548412
11–2.30, 7–11
Harveys XX Mild, Pale Ale, BB, Old 🄷
The only Harveys tied house in Tunbridge Wells. The saloon bar is excellent. A place of refuge from the nearby shopping centre; a lively social club meets in the public bar. Patio has a barbecue for summer use. ⊛ ◖ ▌ ♣

Kent

Wainscott

Stag
65 Wainscott Road (just off A228, Grain Road)
☎ (0634) 718359
11–2.30, 6–11
Charrington IPA Ⓗ
Pleasant, village local offering guest beers. ⊞ P

Waltham

Lord Nelson
Kake Street ☎ (0227) 70628
12–2.30, 7–11 (closed Tue)
Adnams Bitter; Hall & Woodhouse Tanglefoot; Shepherd Neame Master Brew Bitter; Wells Bombardier Ⓗ
Attractive, elegant, Georgian pub with a collection of blacksmith's implements. Huge steaks and fresh fish feature on the menu.
🏠 Q ❀ 🛈 ▶ ⊞ ⅋ ♿ ♣ ⏁ P

Try also: Compasses, Crundale (Free)

Westerham

General Wolfe
High Street (A25, W end of town) ☎ (0959) 562104
11–3, 6–11
Greene King IPA, Rayments Special, Abbot Ⓗ
Low-ceilinged, weatherboarded house of much character; the safest bet in this popular tourist town. Greene King XX Mild may replace the new Rayments brew. No food at weekends. Very small car park. 🏠 🛈 ♣ P

West Malling

Bull
1 High Street (next to railway line) ☎ (0732) 842753
11–2.30, 6–11
Draught Bass; Everards Old Original; Goacher's Dark Ⓗ
Pub with a low, beamed ceiling and plastered and wood-panelled walls. The horseshoe-shaped bar was formerly a separate snug and public, the dividing wall now removed. Guest beer always available.
❀ ⇌ ♣

Lobster Pot
47 Swan Street (400 yds from station) ☎ (0732) 843265
12–2.30, 6–11
Adnams Bitter; Goacher's Dark; Marston's Pedigree; Theakston Best Bitter; Wadworth 6X Ⓗ
Compact, multi-bar pub with a wine bar atmosphere. Two guest beers available. Pool and darts room upstairs, and a restaurant off the main bar, to complement the good range of bar meals. 🛈 ▶ ⇌

Try also: Swan, Swan St (Charrington)

Whitstable

Coach & Horses
37 Oxford Street (A290)
☎ (0227) 264732
11–3 (3.30 Sat), 6.30–11
Shepherd Neame Master Brew Bitter Ⓗ
Popular, high street local offering seasonal barbecues and sing-alongs. ❀ 🛈 ⊞ ♿ ⇌ ♣

Noah's Ark
83 Canterbury Road (A290)
☎ (0227) 272332
11–3, 6–11
Shepherd Neame Master Brew Bitter, Spitfire Ⓗ
Basic, friendly local which has had a recent change of ownership, but the same landlord for 28 years. Euchre sessions Fri eve and Sun lunchtime. Bar snacks available.
❀ ⊞ ⇌ ♣ P

Smack
Middle Wall (near the beach)
☎ (0227) 273056
10.30–3 (4.30 Fri & Sat), 6.30–11
Shepherd Neame Master Brew Bitter Ⓗ
Wood-panelled pub named after the oyster smacks whose crews used to drink here. A running club meets here on Tue. Bar snacks served.
❀ ♿ ♣ P

Worth

St Crispin
The Street (off A258)
☎ (0304) 612081
10.30–3, 6–11
Adnams Broadside Ⓖ**; Gale's HSB; Marston's Merrie Monk** Ⓗ**, Pedigree** Ⓖ**; Shepherd Neame Master Brew Bitter** Ⓗ
Old, village pub, near the pond and church. Tastefully refurbished and extended; popular locally for meals. Read the old sign just inside the door! Guest beers are often available and the beer range is liable to change.
🏠 Q ❀ 🛏 🛈 ▶ Å ♣ ⏁ P

Long leases: new security for tenants? (see page 5)

BEER FESTIVAL CALENDAR 1992

Excellent opportunities for sampling a wide variety of real ales are provided by CAMRA's many beer festivals, staffed by CAMRA members. The venues below have all held festivals in the months indicated in the last few years, though precise details of 1992 arrangements are not available as we go to press. For more information, consult CAMRA's newspaper, *What's Brewing*, or contact CAMRA on (0727) 867201 closer to the time.

JANUARY
Atherton
Bradford
Exeter
York

FEBRUARY
Basingstoke
Battersea
Durham
Eastleigh
Hove
Johnstone
Luton
Tyneside
Wrekin

MARCH
Acton
Bristol
Darlington
Fleetwood
Furness
London Drinker
Oldham
Rugby
Wigan

APRIL
Darlaston
Ealing
Farnham
Greenmount Fair
 (N Ireland)
Newcastle
Swansea

MAY
Alloa
Barnsley
Camden (Cider and
 Perry Exhibition)
Cleethorpes
Dudley
Grays
Great North Western

Halifax
Lincoln
Maidstone
Merseyside
Wolverhampton
Yapton

JUNE
Chester
Dorking
Greenwich
Kirklees
Oxford
Salisbury
Surrey

JULY
Ashton Canals
Canterbury
Chelmsford
Colchester
Cotswolds
Derby
Exeter
Furness
Fleetwood
Stirling
Sussex
Tyneside
Wirral
Woodcote (Reading)

AUGUST
Great British Beer
 Festival
Cambridge
Cornwall
Durham
Dengie Hundred
Hereford
Peterborough
Portsmouth

SEPTEMBER
Burton upon Trent
Chappel & Wakes Colne

Heart of England
Ipswich
Maidstone
Sheffield
Shrewsbury
Strathspey

OCTOBER
Bath
Bedford
Blackburn
Cardiff
Darlington
Edinburgh
Furness
Hull
Holmfirth
Keighley
Lancaster
Leeds
Llandudno
Loughborough
Middlesbrough
Northampton
Norwich
Nottingham
Peckham
Potteries
Rochford
Stoke-on-Trent
Wrekin

NOVEMBER
Aberdeen
Dorchester
Dudley
Eastleigh
Jersey
Mid Wales
Pig's Ear (London)
Taunton

DECEMBER
Bury
Holmfirth
Kirklees

Lancashire

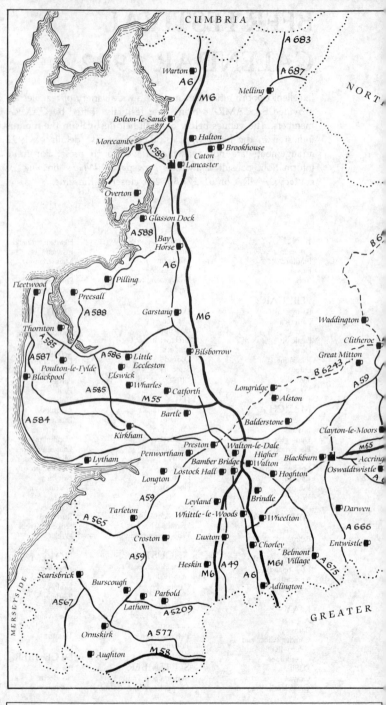

CUMBRIA

Warton — A6 — M6
Melling
Bolton-le-Sands
Morecambe — Halton — Brookhouse
A589 — Caton — Lancaster
Overton
Glasson Dock
A588 — Bay Horse
A6
Fleetwood — Pilling
Preesall
A588 — Garstang — M6
Thornton — Waddington
A595 — Clitheroe
A587 — A586 — Little Eccleston — Bilsborrow — Great Mitton
Poulton-le-Fylde — Elswick — B6243 — A59
Blackpool — Wharles — Catforth — Longridge
A585 — Bartle — Alston
M55 — Balderstone
A584 — Kirkham — Clayton-le-Moors
Preston — Walton-le-Dale — M65 — Accring
Lytham — Penwortham — Higher Walton — Blackburn — Oswaldtwistle
Bamber Bridge — Hoghton — A
Longton — Lostock Hall
A59 — Leyland — Brindle
Tarleton — Whittle-le-Woods — Wheelton — Darwen
A565 — A59 — Euxton — A666
Croston — Chorley — A675 — Entwistle
Heskin — A49 — Belmont Village
Scarisbrick — M6 — A6 — M61
Burscough — Adlington
A567 — Parbold — GREATER
Lathom — A5209
Ornskirk — A577
Aughton — M58

MERSEYSIDE

NORTH

B6...

Lancashire

Accrington

Great Eastern
Arnold Street (off A679, 300
yds from centre)
☎ (0254) 234483
12–5, 7–11 (12–11 Sat)
Thwaites Mild, Bitter Ⓗ
Recently renovated but
retaining character; very much a
friendly local. 🏠 ⇌ ♣

Nags Head
78 Blackburn Road
☎ (0254) 233965
11–11
Thwaites Best Mild, Bitter Ⓗ
Three-roomed, street-corner
local, close to the town centre
and bus and rail stations. ⇌ ♣

Try also: Abbey (John
Smith's); **New Brewery**,
Maudsley St (John Smith's)

Adlington

Cardwell Arms
Chorley Road (A673)
☎ (0257) 480319
12–3, 6 (7 winter)–11 (11–11 Sat;
11–5, 7–11 winter Sat)
**Vaux Samson; Wards
Sheffield Best Bitter** Ⓗ
Modernised, main road pub
with a separate vault at the rear.
No food Tue. 🏠 🍺 ♣ P

White Bear
5a Market Street
☎ (0257) 482357
11–11
**Theakston Best Bitter, XB,
Old Peculier; Younger
Scotch** Ⓗ
Excellent, three-roomed, stone-
built, town-centre pub on the
main road. Good atmosphere
and good value food, incl. local,
prize-winning black pudding.
Meals served 12–2 and
5.30–8.30 (not Mon eve).
Open all day Sun for food.
🏠 ❧ 🍺 🍴 🏠 ⇌ ♣

Alston

White Bull
Preston Road (B6243,
Grimsargh–Longridge road)
☎ (0772) 784151
11–3, 6–11 (11–11 Sat)
Thwaites Best Mild, Bitter Ⓗ
Spacious pub with two real fires,
popular with the young crowd.
Eve meals Tue–Sat only, until
8.30. 🏠 🍺 🍴 ♣ P

Aughton

Dog & Gun
223 Long Lane (¾ mile E of
A59)
☎ (0695) 423303
12–3, 5.30–11 (12–2, 7–10.30 Sun)
**Burtonwood Mild, Best
Bitter, Forshaw's** Ⓗ
Typical, village-style local,
unusually situated on the edge
of town. Excellent bowling
green in an attractive garden
setting at the rear.
🏠 Q 🍺 🏠 ⇌ (Aughton Park) ♣ P

Stanley Arms
St Michaels Road (off A59)
11–11
**Cains Bitter; Walker Mild,
Bitter, Best Bitter** Ⓗ
Comfortable, old, village pub,
opposite the church in a quiet
road, but near the main
Liverpool–Preston road. Good
value food. Crown green
bowling.
🏠 🍺 🍴 ⇌ (Town Green) ♣ P

Town Green Inn
17 Town Green Lane
11–11
Tetley Walker Mild, Bitter Ⓗ
Stone built-pub, unusual for the
area, with much character.
🏠 ⇌ (Town Green) ♣ P

Bacup

New Inn
11 Rochdale Road
☎ (0706) 873130
11–11
Thwaites Best Mild, Bitter Ⓗ
Comfortable, four-roomed local
with a central bar, traditional,
wood-panelled ceilings and
interesting, 19th-century
murals. 🏠 ❧ 🍺

Try also: British Queen,
Union St (Banks's)

Balderstone

Myerscough
Whalley Road (A59)
☎ (0254) 812222
11.30–3, 5.30–11 (11–11 Sat)
**Robinson's Mild, Best Bitter,
Old Tom** Ⓗ
Pleasant, country pub with a
large, wood-panelled lounge
and a separate, quiet front room,
warmed by a real fire. A
genuine welcome for locals and
strangers alike. Quiz nights
most Weds. 🏠 Q ❧ 🍺 🍺 🍴 P

Bamber Bridge

Old Hob Inn
8–9 Church Road (off A6/A49)
☎ (0772) 36863
11.30–3, 5.30–11
**Theakston Best Bitter, Old
Peculier** Ⓗ
17th-century, thatched pub
with a wood-panelled bar and a
small restaurant. Children can
use the side room at mealtimes.
Situated on the southern edge
of the town: an unusual, rural
setting in an industrial area.
Pavement tables for summer.
Q 🍺 🍴 ⇌ P

Try also: Black Bull (John
Smith's)

Bartle

Sitting Goose
Sidgreaves Lane (A5085)
OS486329 ☎ (0772) 690344

Lancashire

11–3, 6–11 (11–11 Fri & Sat)
Thwaites Best Mild, Bitter Ⓔ
Comfortable pub in Fylde countryside. Enjoy its cosy atmosphere. Good restaurant and large garden for children.
🛏 ⊛ ⓒ ▶ ⑂ P

Bay Horse

Bay Horse
Bay Horse Lane (400 yds E of A6) OS493529
☎ (0524) 791204
11–3, 5.30–11
Mitchell's Mild, Best Bitter Ⓗ
Old building where small rooms have been knocked into one main room, but some character remains. An open fire and padded window benches add comfort. The family room has a pool table. Converted barn for functions. 🏠 🛏 ⊛ 🛏 ⓒ ▶ 𝔸 ♣ P

Try also: **Fleece** (Mitchell's)

Belmont Village

Black Dog
2 Church Street
OS674163 ☎ (020 481) 218
12–4, 6.30–11
Holt Mild, Bitter Ⓗ
Popular, moorland village pub on the old Bolton–Preston road. The landlord whistles the classics and puts on occasional live orchestras. No jukebox. No food Mon.
🏠 Q 🛏 🛏 ⓒ ▶ ⑂ ♣ P

Try also: **Wrights Arms** (Allied)

Bilsborrow

Owd Nell's
St Michaels Road (just off the A6, by Lancaster Canal)
☎ (0995) 40010
11–11
Marston's Pedigree;
Whitbread Boddingtons
Bitter, Castle Eden Ale Ⓗ
Canalside pub with a thatched roof and many attractions. Good outside facilities for children. Bar food is served and there is an informal restaurant next to the pub. Craft shops are also attached. Popular with canal users. Owd Nell's house bitter is brewed by Whitbread.
🏠 🛏 ⊛ 🛏 ⓒ ▶ ⑂ 🛏 P

White Bull
Garstang Road
(A6, Preston–Lancaster road)
☎ (0995) 40324
12–3, 7–11 (may vary in summer)
S&N Matthew Brown Mild;
Theakston Best Bitter;
Younger No. 3 Ⓗ
Canalside pub on the main A6; friendly and unspoilt.
🏠 Q ⊛ ♣ P

Blackburn

Imperial
25 Davenport Road
☎ (0254) 54460
11–3, 6–11
Thwaites Mild, Bitter Ⓗ
Classic, small-roomed, terraced local, spared the open-plan treatment. ⊿

Moorgate Arms
Livesey Branch Road (A6062, ¼ mile from football ground)
☎ (0254) 51408
12–3, 6–11 (11–11 Fri & Sat)
Thwaites Mild, Bitter Ⓗ
Old, corner pub with etched windows, situated near the Leeds–Liverpool Canal. Children allowed in the small beer garden. Unusual snacks.
⊛ ⑂ ≠ (Mill Hill)

Quarrymans
Dukes Brow ☎ (0254) 51691
12–3 (4 Sat), 7–11
Thwaites Mild, Bitter;
Whitbread Boddingtons
Bitter Ⓗ
Open-plan local, hung with assorted plates.

Uncle Toms Cabin
42 Larkhill Street
☎ (0254) 54345
11–4.30 (3 Tue), 7–11 (11–11 Fri & Sat)
Thwaites Mild, Bitter Ⓗ
Lively local lurking behind Thwaites brewhouse. Handy for the markets. ⓒ ⊿ ≠

Woodlands Hotel (Pecker's Bar)
(A677, Preston New Road, 1 mile W of centre)
☎ (0254) 691122
11–11
Courage Directors; John
Smith's Bitter Ⓗ
Bar on the ground floor of a main road hotel. Nightly disco after 8.30. Close to Billinge Hill Country Park. ⊛ 🛏 P

Try also: **Railway Hotel**, Pleasington (Grand Met); **Thwaites Arms** (Thwaites)

Black Lane Ends

Hare & Hounds
Skipton Old Road (3 miles from Colne centre on old Colne–Skipton road) OS928433
☎ (0282) 863070
12–3 (not Tue or Thu), 6.30–11
Taylor Dark Mild, Bitter
Ale Ⓗ
Friendly pub, set high in a remote Pennine landscape. Good value, home-cooked food available until 9pm. Live music (country and jazz) on Wed and at weekends. 🏠 ⓒ ▶ ⑂ ♣ P

Blackpool

Bispham Hotel
70 Red Bank Road, Bispham (A584, 200 yds from Queens Promenade)
☎ (0253) 51752
11–3 (4 Sat), 6 (7 Sat)–11
Samuel Smith OBB Ⓗ
Traditional, 1930s pub, popular with locals and holiday-makers. Thriving tap room; home-cooked meals (not Sun).
ⓒ ⊿ ♣ P

Empress Hotel
59 Exchange Street, North Shore (400 yds from rail and bus stations)
☎ (0253) 20413
11–11 (1am Fri & Sat, Easter–Nov)
Thwaites Best Mild, Bitter Ⓗ
Large, friendly, Victorian hotel close to seafront entertainment. Good value food (served only in the holiday season). Well-appointed family room.
🛏 🛏 ⓒ ▶ ⊿ ≠ (North) ♣

Highlands Hotel
206 Queens Promenade, Bispham (opp. Bispham tram stop) ☎ (0253) 54877
11–11
Thwaites Mild, Bitter Ⓗ
Delightfully situated, large, modern, residential hotel on the seafront. Regular theme nights, also sport and general knowledge quizzes; piano at weekends. Children allowed in the restaurant area.
Q ⊛ ⓒ ▶ ⑂ ⑂ ♣ P

Mount Pleasant
103 High Street, North Shore
☎ (0253) 293335
11–11
S&N Matthew Brown Mild;
Theakston Best Bitter, XB,
Old Peculier Ⓗ
Small, friendly, corner local, close to rail and bus stations and the promenade. Pool and darts played. ⊿ ≠ (North) ♣

New Mariners
8 Norbreck Road, Bispham (just off promenade)
☎ (0253) 51154
11–11
John Smith's Bitter;
Whitbread Boddingtons
Bitter Ⓗ
Seaside pub in the shadow of the giant Norbreck Castle hotel. Children permitted in the games room.
ⓒ ▶ ⑂ ♣ P

Raikes Hotel
Liverpool Road (off Church Street) ☎ (0253) 294372
11–11
Draught Bass; Stones Best
Bitter Ⓗ
Large, suburban pub with a bowling green and barbecues in

Lancashire

summer. No food Sun. Children welcome.
Q 🍴 🍺 🕮 & ⇌ (North) ♣ P

Ramsden Arms Hotel
204 Talbot Road (near bus and rail stations)
☎ (0253) 23215
10.30–11
Ind Coope Burton Ale; Jennings Bitter; Tetley Walker Mild, Bitter; Whitbread Boddingtons Bitter Ⓗ
Excellent, award-winning, country-style pub on the fringe of the town centre, offering good, economical accommodation. Well worth a visit. 🏠 🍴 🕮 ⇌ (North) ♣ P

Saddle
286 Whitegate Drive, Marton (A583/Preston Old Road jct)
☎ (0253) 63065
11.30–3, 5.30–11 (11.30–11 Fri & Sat)
Bass Mild XXXX, Special, Draught Bass Ⓗ
Small, locally renowned pub with a friendly atmosphere. Recent alterations. Q 🍴 P

Welcome Inn
Vicarage Lane, Marton (off A583, near Normid hypermarket) ☎ (0253) 65372
11–11
Burtonwood Mild, Best Bitter, Forshaw's Ⓗ
Large, modern pub on the outskirts of town with a warm and friendly atmosphere. Cosy, intimate lounge and large vaults with a snooker table; good value food. Children's play area in the beer garden. Blackpool CAMRA *Pub of the Year* 1990.
🏠 Q ⇌ 🍴 🕮 🍺 🕮 & ♣ Å P

Wheatsheaf
192–194 Talbot Road (near bus and railway stations)
☎ (0253) 25062
10.30–11
S&N Matthew Brown Mild; Theakston Best Bitter, XB, Old Peculier Ⓗ
Recently modernised, down-to-earth, locals' pub close to the town centre; full of character. Pool table. Q ⇌ (North) ♣

Try also: **No. 4**, Newton Drive (Thwaites)

Bolton-le-Sands

Blue Anchor
Main Road (off A6)
☎ (0524) 823241
11–11
Mitchell's Mild, Best Bitter, ESB Ⓗ
Robust, friendly local at the heart of a large village. Separate games room and snug. Parking difficult.
🍺 🍴 🍷 ♣

Brierfield

Waggon & Horses
Colne Road (100 yds from roundabout interchange of A56/M65 jct 12)
☎ (0282) 63962
11.30–3, 5–11 (11.30–11 Fri & Sat)
Thwaites Best Mild, Bitter Ⓗ
A former CAMRA *Best Refurbished Pub* award-winner; a popular, roadside house which hosts various meetings. One room is still gas-lit.
🏠 🍺 🍴 ⇌ ♣ P

Brindle

Cavendish Arms
Sandy Lane (B5256, Leyland–Blackburn road)
☎ (025 485) 2912
11–3, 5.30–11 (11–11 Sat)
Burtonwood Mild, Best Bitter Ⓗ
Traditional, village pub with lots of stained-glasswork and wood carvings. Public bar and dining room. Originally named the 'Gerrard Arms', after the family who lived at nearby Hoghton Towers. Within easy reach of M6 and M61 motorways. Children welcome at mealtimes.
🏠 Q 🍺 🍴 🕮 ♣ P

Brookhouse

Black Bull
Brookhouse Road
☎ (0524) 770329
11.30–3, 6–11
Thwaites Best Mild, Bitter Ⓔ
Extensive, well-furnished lounge and a lively vault. A paved area by the beck provides outside drinking space. 🍺 🛏 🍴 🕮 ♣ P

Burnley

Cattle Market
10 Elizabeth Street
☎ (0282) 21151
11–3, 5.30–11
Burtonwood Best Bitter, Forshaw's Ⓗ
Town-centre pub, opposite the police station. A spartan and friendly public bar; piano sing-alongs at weekends. No food weekends.
🍴 🕮 ⇌ (Central) ♣

Garden Bar
133 St James Street
☎ (0282) 414895
11–3, 7–11
Lees GB Mild, Bitter, Moonraker Ⓗ&Ⓔ
Town-centre pub, popular with young people at weekends; live music Thu. Striking decor; the unusual layout reflects a conversion from an original bar and a car showroom. No food Sun. 🍴 ⇌ (Central)

General Scarlett
243–245 Accrington Road (A679, 400 yds from M65 jct 10) ☎ (0282) 831054
12–4, 7–11
Moorhouse's Black Cat Mild, Premier, Pendle Witches Brew Ⓗ
Lively, two-roomed, locals' pub opposite the brewery.
⇌ (Rose Grove) ♣ P

Lanehead
Hillingdon Road
☎ (0282) 59491
11–3, 7–11 (11–11 Fri & Sat)
Thwaites Bitter Ⓗ
Cosy, estate pub with friendly hosts. Busy tap room; excellent, cheap lunches. 🍺 🍴 🕮 P

Manor Barn
Padiham Road (A671; entrance first right off Lakeland Way)
☎ (0282) 56744
11–3, 5.30–11
Burtonwood Best Bitter Ⓗ
Deservedly popular, split-level pub with a separate restaurant in converted farm buildings (open all day Sun for meals).
🍺 🍴 🍷 P

Try also: **Mechanics, Shuttle Bar** (Free)

Burscough

Martin Inn
Martin Lane (off A570/B5242)
OS414127 ☎ (0704) 892302
11.30–3, 5.30–11
Courage Directors; John Smith's Bitter; Tetley Walker Mild Ⓗ
Remote, but welcoming, inn near Martin Mere Wildfowl Trust; stone-floored in part. Separate cottage grill restaurant.
🏠 🍺 🛏 🍴 🍷 ♣ P

Catforth

Running Pump
Catforth Road (off B5269, 400 yds before village centre)
☎ (0772) 690265
11–3, 6–11
Robinson's Mild, Best Bitter Ⓗ, **Old Tom** (winter) Ⓖ
Cosy, rural Fylde pub; warm and friendly. The family dining room offers a children's menu. Look out for the original village pump at the front of the pub.
🏠 Q ⇌ 🍴 Å ♣ P

Caton

Ship
23 Lancaster Road (A683)
☎ (0524) 770265
11.30–3, 6.30–11
Thwaites Best Mild, Bitter Ⓔ
Small, 1680s coaching inn with a split-level lounge, very much in the country pub mould.
🍺 🛏 🍴 ♣ P

Lancashire

Station

Hornby Road (A683)
☎ (0524) 770323
11–3, 6–11 (11–11 Sat)
Mitchell's Mild, Best Bitter Ⓗ
Dated 1830 (pre-railway!).
Several comfortable rooms set
around a small bar. Bowling
green. ♨ ⊛ ◖ ▶ ♣ P

Chorley

Malt n' Hops

Friday Street (behind station)
☎ (025 72) 60967
12–2.30, 5–11 (12–11 Fri & Sat)
**Moorhouse's Pendle Witches
Brew; Taylor Landlord;
Webster's Yorkshire Bitter,
Wilson's Mild; Whitbread
Boddingtons Bitter** Ⓗ
Small, comfortable free house
just north of the town centre;
ideal for train-spotters. Public
car park opposite. A local
CAMRA award-winner. Four
regular guest beers weekly. ⇌

Market Tavern

21 Cleveland Street
☎ (025 72) 77991
11–4, 7–11
**Ind Coope Burton Ale;
Walker Mild, Best Bitter,
Winter Warmer** Ⓗ
Small, busy, town-centre pub
next to the popular market. Four
small rooms full of atmosphere
and character. Local black
puddings are a speciality.
Lancashire CAMRA *Pub of the
Year* 1989. ♨ Q ◖ ◖ ⇌

Queens Tavern

6 Preston Road (A6)
☎ (025 72) 75902
11.30–3, 6.30–11 (11.30–11 Fri & Sat)
**Whitbread Chester's Mild,
Boddingtons Bitter, Trophy,
Castle Eden Ale** Ⓗ
Large local with an imposing
frontage on a main road.
Parking is not easy. ◖ ▶ ⇌ ♣

Shepherds Arms

38 Eaves Lane (opp. bus garage,
near Leeds–Liverpool Canal
bridge 66) ☎ (025 72) 75659
11–11
Theakston Best Bitter Ⓗ
Friendly local on the north side
of town: an opened-out lounge
bar, a front room, a cosy, part-
enclosed snug and a vault at the
rear. A plaque on the wall lists
only eleven licensees since
1902. ⊕ ⇌ ♣

Spinners Arms

Cowling Road
☎ (025 72) 65144
11–11 (11–3.30, 5–11 Mon–Thu in
winter)
**Theakston XB; Younger
No. 3** Ⓗ
Next door to William Younger's
depot, a pub with an L-shaped
bar and side rooms for food and
games. Close to the

Leeds–Liverpool Canal. Children
welcome at mealtimes.
⊛ ◖ ▶ P

Clayton-le-Moors

Old England For Ever

13 Church Street (off A680,
near canal)
☎ (0254) 233435
11–4.30, 7–11
**Burtonwood Mild, Best
Bitter** Ⓗ
Small, friendly, unspoilt local
with an original tiled hallway.
Handy for the Leeds–Liverpool
Canal. ◖ ♣

Try also: Wellington
(Thwaites)

Clitheroe

Cross Keys

49 Lowergate
☎ (0200) 28877
4–11 (11–11 Thu–Sat)
**Vaux Lorimers Best Scotch;
Wards Thorne Best Bitter,
Sheffield Best Bitter** Ⓗ
Popular pub with young people
and close to the town centre.
Guest beer in summer, plus
occasional ciders. ⊛ Å ↻
(summer weekends only) ♣ ↺

Station

King Street
☎ (0200) 23604
11–11
Thwaites Mild, Bitter Ⓗ
Large, multi-roomed pub near
the town centre. A friendly,
busy local with three pool
tables, and darts. The
comfortable lounge is used as a
family room during the day. Eve
meals in summer only.
♨ Q ⊛ ⋈ ◖ ▶ ⊕ Å
⇌ (summer weekends only) ♣ P

Try also: Waggon & Horses
(Thwaites)

Colne

Spinners Arms

12 Primet Hill (A56, 50 yds
from station) ☎ (0282) 863495
12–11½ (may vary)
Tetley Walker Mild, Bitter Ⓗ
Small, locals' pub with a
separate darts room. Lunchtime
bar snacks. ⇌ ♣ P

Try also: Red Lion (Taylor);
Shepherds (Tetley)

Cowpe

Buck

Cowpe Road (½ mile off A681
at Waterfoot)
☎ (0706) 213612
12–2 (not Mon–Thu, 4 Sat), 7–11
**John Smith's Bitter; Thwaites
Best Mild, Bitter; Whitbread
Boddingtons Bitter** Ⓗ
Comfortable, two-roomed local

in a quiet village. Good value
lunches (Fri–Sun only).
♨ ⊛ ◖ ♣ P

Croston

Black Horse

Westhead Road
☎ (0772) 600338
11–11 (supper licence)
**Banks's Mild, Bitter; Draught
Bass; Burton Bridge Bridge
Bitter, Porter; Moorhouse's
Premier, Pendle Witches
Brew** Ⓗ
Excellent, large, village pub with
a restaurant and family room;
an example to all free houses,
with 240 different beers
available each year. Bowling
green and local
CAMRA award-winner and
West Pennine Pub of the Year
1990. Four guest beers always
available, plus house beers.
♨ ⇥ ⊛ ◖ ▶ ⊕ ⎣ ⇌ ♣ ↻ P

Darwen

Crown Hotel

24 Redearth Road
☎ (0254) 703192
11–11
**Courage Directors; John
Smith's Bitter; Thwaites Mild,
Bitter** Ⓗ
Large, refurbished, open-lounge
pub; a separate snooker room
has a jukebox. Just off the town
centre. ♨ ⊕ ⇌ ♣

Entwistle Arms

15 Entwistle Street
☎ (0254) 703575
12.30–3, 6.15–11 (12–11 Sat)
Thwaites Best Mild, Bitter Ⓗ
Comfortable, locals' pub in
the town centre, behind St
Peter's Church. Emphasis on
pub games. ⇌ ♣

George Inn

9 Bolton Road
☎ (0254) 701709
11–11
Thwaites Mild, Bitter Ⓗ
Revamped, town-centre pub
with a number of rooms. Handy
for breakfast (served
9am–midday). ♨ ◖ ♣

Golden Cup Inn

610 Blackburn Road (A666)
☎ (0254) 702337
12–3, 5.30 (5 Fri, 7 Sat)–11
Thwaites Mild, Bitter Ⓗ
One of the oldest pubs in
Darwen: three small rooms.
Low ceilings add to its cosy
feel. Attractive cobbled
forecourt for summer drinking.
⊛ ◖ P

Greenfield Inn

Lower Barn Street (25 yds off
Cranberry Lane)
☎ (0254) 703945
12–3, 5.30–11 (12–11 Fri & Sat)

Marston's Pedigree; Taylor Landlord Ⓗ
Small, one-roomed pub, off the beaten track, next to the Blackburn–Bolton railway line. Nice and friendly, with good value food. Guest beers. Ⓓ Ⓓ

Sunnyhurst Hotel
Tockholes Road
OS680225 ☎ (0254) 873035
11–3, 7–11 (12–11 Sat)
Thwaites Mild, Bitter Ⓗ
Small, tidy, two-roomed pub with a games room at the back and a homely atmosphere. Situated close to Darwen Moors and Tower; ideal for walkers and ramblers. ⊛ ♣

Try also: **Cemetery** (Thwaites); **Craven Heifer** (S&N); **Red Lion Hotel** (Burtonwood)

Elswick

Boot & Shoe
Beech Road (off B5269)
☎ (0995) 70206
12–3, 6–11 (11–11 Sat)
Thwaites Best Mild, Bitter Ⓗ
Large, attractive, modern, village local offering a friendly welcome and a good selection of food. A large family room is complemented by a spacious outdoor play area. Barbecues every Fri eve in summer.
⊛ Q ⤢ ⊛ ⋈ Ⓓ Ⓓ ♿ ⚑ ♣ P

Entwistle

Strawbury Duck Hotel
Overshaws Road (signed from the Edgworth–Darwen Roman road) OS727178
☎ (0204) 852013
12–3 (not Mon), 7–11 (12–11 Sat)
Hartleys XB; Marston's Pedigree; Taylor Best Bitter, Landlord Ⓗ
Old, isolated but busy country pub, next to the station: a good base for walks in hill country, woods and around reservoirs. Authentic Indian cuisine available. Up to three guest beers a week. Children welcome until 8.30pm. Open all day Sun for food.
⚑ ⤢ ⊛ ⋈ Ⓓ Ⓓ ⊟ ⥱ P

Euxton

Euxton Mills Hotel
Wigan Road (A49/A581 jct)
☎ (025 72) 64002
11.30–3, 5.30–11
Burtonwood Mild, Best Bitter Ⓔ**, Forshaw's** Ⓗ
Very cosy, comfortable pub with excellent meals. Children allowed in the rear room for food. Q Ⓓ Ⓓ ⊟ ♣ P

Fence-in-Pendle

Harpers Inn
Harpers Lane (300 yds from A6068/B6248 jct)
☎ (0282) 66249
11.30–3, 8–11
Theakston Best Bitter; Thwaites Mild, Bitter Ⓗ
Attractive, open-plan pub with a split-level layout. The upper level restaurant area caters for families (opens 11.30 Sun).
Q Ⓓ Ⓓ P

Try also: **White Swan** Wheatley Lane Rd (Free)

Fleetwood

North Euston Hotel
The Esplanade (just off promenade) ☎ (0253) 876525
11–3.30, 6–11 (11–11 Sat in summer)
Draught Bass; Ruddles Best Bitter, County; Webster's Yorkshire Bitter, Wilson's Mild, Bitter Ⓗ
Large, Victorian edifice close to the sea, pier and tram terminus. Large elegantly-appointed public rooms and a family room.
⤢ ⋈ Ⓓ Ⓓ ♿ P

Queens
Poulton Road (at Beach Road jct) ☎ (0253) 876740
11–11
Thwaites Best Mild, Bitter Ⓗ
Busy pub in a residential area at the junction of two major roads. A central bar serves several alcoves; different areas for snooker and pool. ⊛ Ⓓ P

Wyre Lounge Bar
Marine Hall, The Esplanade (200 yds from pier)
☎ (039 17) 71141
11–3.30, 7–11
Moorhouse's Premier, Pendle Witches Brew; Taylor Landlord Ⓗ
Popular amenity at the Marine Hall complex. A comfortable lounge bar offering an excellent choice of regularly changed guest beers.

Garstang

Royal Oak
Market Place
☎ (099 52) 3318
11–3.30, 7–11 (11–11 Thu–Sat)
Hartleys XB; Robinson's Mild, Best Bitter, Old Tom Ⓗ
Old coaching inn: modern furniture in the three lounges detracts little from its old-fashioned feel. Drinking area outside on the old market square. ⊛ ⋈ Ⓓ ♣ P

Glasson Dock

Caribou
Victoria Terrace

☎ (0524) 751356
11.30–3, 7–11
Thwaites Best Mild, Bitter Ⓗ
Old pub, named after a ship skippered by a former owner. Public car park by the basin. Family room in summer.
⚑ ⤢ ⋈ Ⓓ ♣

Try also: **Dalton Arms** (Thwaites)

Great Mitton

Owd Ned's River View Tavern
Mitton Hall (B6246, 2 miles from Whalley)
OS718385 ☎ (025 486) 544
11–11
Marston's Pedigree Ⓗ
Overlooking the River Ribble, in picturesque country, a pub placing an emphasis on food and providing good facilities for children (high-chairs supplied). Opens 7.30am for breakfast. Guest beers. ⤢ ⊛ ⋈ Ⓓ ♣ P

Halton

White Lion
Church Brow
☎ (0524) 81120
11–3, 6–11
Mitchell's Mild, Best Bitter Ⓗ
17th-century local with a restful, country ambience; a single bar and games room off.
⚑ ⊛ Ⓓ ♣ P

Haslingden

Foresters Arms
Pleasant Street
☎ (0706) 216079
12–3, 7–11 (11–11 Sat)
Theakston XB; Webster's Yorkshire Bitter, Wilson's Bitter Ⓗ
Unspoilt, compact, locals' pub, convenient for the town centre. ♣

Try also: **Valley Weaver Hotel** (Banks's)

Heskin

Farmers Arms
Wood Lane (B5250)
OS532154 ☎ (0257) 451276
12–3, 5–11
Hartleys XB; Whitbread Chester's Mild, Bitter, Boddingtons Bitter, Castle Eden Ale Ⓗ
Country pub with an attractive exterior and a cosy interior. Large, safe garden for children. Home-cooked meals served 12–2 and 6–8pm.
⤢ ⊛ Ⓓ ⊟ ♣ P

Higher Walton

Mill Tavern
15 Cann Bridge Street (A675)
☎ (0772) 38462

Lancashire

11.30–3, 5.30–11
**Burtonwood Best Bitter,
Forshaw's** Ⓗ
Large, tastefully modernised
local: a pleasant, open-plan
lounge with a small games area.
The landlord sponsors a motor
cycle race team and still has a
Jensen waiting for repair in the
yard. Bus stop outside. No food
weekends. ◖ ♣ P

Hoghton

Black Horse
Gregson Lane (off
Preston–Blackburn old road)
☎ (025 485) 2541
11.30–11
**Theakston Best Bitter;
Younger IPA** Ⓗ
Large, friendly, open-plan pub
with plush seating and a
separate games area. The
traditional English, home-
cooked fare is good value
(vegetarian option), and is
served 12–2pm. ⊛ ◖ ♣ P

Kirkham

Queens Arms
7 Poulton Street (A585)
☎ (0772) 686705
11–11
**S&N Matthew Brown Mild;
Theakston Best Bitter, XB,
Old Peculier** Ⓗ
Fine, well-run, lively, town-
centre local, always busy and
full of character. The friendly
landlord serves an excellent
range of pizzas. Barbecues in
summer. ⊛ ◖ 🄰 ♣ ♣

Lancaster

Golden Lion
Moor Lane ☎ (0524) 39447
12–3, 7–11
**Theakston Best Bitter, XB,
Old Peculier** Ⓗ
A pub since at least 1612. An
L-shaped bar leads into a games
room (bar billiards and skittles).
No-smoking 'Heritage' room off
the bar displays Lancaster
memorabilia. Caters for all.
⇌ ♣ ✗

John O'Gaunt
55 Market Street
☎ (0524) 32011
11.30–3 (11–5 Sat), 7–11 (11.30–11
Fri)
**Ind Coope Burton Ale;
Jennings Bitter; Tetley
Walker Bitter** Ⓗ
Pub with a handsome, original
frontage. Usually busy, it is
popular with both students and
older customers. Frequent live
music. Newspapers provided.
Varied menu of home-cooked
food; eve meals (not available
Sat eve) finish early. ◖ ◗ ⇌

Moorlands
Quarry Road
12–3 (not Mon), 7–11

Mitchell's Mild, Best Bitter Ⓗ
Lively, turn-of-the-century local.
The decor of its many rooms
makes some concession to the
1990s but includes original
stained-glass. ⊞ ♣

Priory
36 Cable Street
☎ (0524) 32606
11–3, 6–11 (11–11 Fri & Sat)
**Mitchell's Mild, Best Bitter,
ESB** Ⓗ
A creditable effort by Mitchell's
– one of its own pubs with a
regular guest beer. Currently a
cavernous single bar with
vaguely Tudor furnishings, but
alterations are mooted. Adjacent
to bus station. ⇌ ♣ ♡

Ring O'Bells
52 King Street
☎ (0524) 64747
11.15–3, 6.30–11
**Mitchell's Mild, Best Bitter,
ESB** Ⓗ
Noteworthy Georgian exterior
on a town-centre lounge bar,
popular with students. Quiet at
lunchtimes when light snacks
are available. ⇌ ♣

Try also: Brown Cow
(Thwaites)

Lathom

Railway Tavern
Station Road, Hoscar Moss
(¾ mile N of A5209)
OS469116
11–3, 5.30–11 (11–11 Thu)
**Jennings Bitter; Tetley
Walker Mild, Bitter** Ⓗ
Comfortable, unpretentious and
unspoilt pub by a rural railway
station. Try the home-made
individual hotpots.
🄰 Q ⊛ ◖ ◗ ⊞ ⇌ (Hoscar) ♣ P

Ship Inn
Wheat Lane (300 yds from
A5209, over canal swing
bridge) OS452115
☎ (0704) 893117
12–3, 6–11
**Taylor Landlord; Tetley
Walker Bitter; Theakston
Best Bitter** Ⓗ
Known locally as the 'Blood
Tub', this authentic free house
has expanded to take over the
cottage next door. Guest beers.
No food Mon eve or Sun.
Q ⊛ ◖ ◗ ♣

Leyland

Crofters Arms
373 Leyland Lane
☎ (0772) 422420
11–3, 6–11
Theakston Best Bitter Ⓗ
A real locals' pub with darts and
pool teams using the games
room. ⊛ ◖ ⊞ ♣ P

Dunkirk Hall
Dunkirk Lane (B5248/B5253
jct) ☎ (0772) 422102

11.30–3, 5–11 (11–11 Fri)
**Courage Directors; John
Smith's Bitter** Ⓗ
Converted, 17th-century
farmhouse, now a listed building
and featuring flag floors, oak
beams and panelling. Children
allowed in for meals. ⊛ ◖ ◗ ♣ P

Original Ship
95 Towngate
☎ (0772) 456674
11–11
Theakston Best Bitter, XB Ⓗ
Pine-panelled, comfortable,
town-centre pub with a spacious
games area and one large bar.
No food Sun. ⊛ ◖ ⇌ ♣ P

Little Eccleston

Cartford Country Inn &
Hotel
Cartford Lane (½ mile off A586,
through village, next to toll
bridge) ☎ (0995) 70166
11.30–3, 6.30–11
**Marston's Pedigree;
Moorhouse's Pendle Witches
Brew; Taylor Landlord;
Whitbread Boddingtons
Bitter** Ⓗ
Delightfully situated,
comfortable free house by the
River Wyre, offering 1½ miles of
fishing rights. Extensive bar
menu with daily specials.
Outdoor play area. Look out for
George, the resident friendly
ghost, a 170 year-old sheep
rustler. Excellent range of
regular guest beers.
🄰 Q ⇌ ⊛ ◖ ◗ ♣ ♣ P

Longridge

Alston Arms
Inglewhite Road
☎ (0772) 783331
11–11
Theakston Best Bitter Ⓗ
Small, friendly pub on the
outskirts of town, on the road
to Chipping. Large beer garden
and children's play area with
animals, a double-decker bus
and a tractor. ◖ ◗

Old Oak
111 Preston Road (B6243)
☎ (0772) 783648
12–2 (5 Sat), 5 (7 Sat)–11
**Theakston Best Bitter, XB,
Old Peculier** Ⓗ
Stone-built pub on the road
from Preston, with oak settles
around the fire. 🄰 ◖ ◗ ♣ P

Towneley Arms
41 Berry Lane
☎ (0772) 782219
11.30–3.30, 6–11
Tetley Walker Mild, Bitter Ⓗ
Town-centre pub next to a
closed railway station. Wood-
panelled rooms. The large
roaring fire is especially
welcome in winter. 🄰 Q ⊞ P

Longton

Dolphin (Flying Fish)
Marsh Lane OS459254
☎ (0772) 612032
12–3 (not Mon–Fri), 7–11
Thwaites Best Mild, Bitter Ⓗ
Remote farmhouse on the edge
of Longton Marsh; a haunt of
wildfowlers and clay pigeon
shooters. A small, old-fashioned
tap room, and a lounge in a new
extension. Visitors arriving by
boat on the River Douglas,
please sign the visitors' book.
Closed weekday lunchtimes.
🅰 Q 🏠 🚻 ♣ P

Lostock Hall

Victoria
Watkin Lane (A582)
☎ (0772) 35338
11–3, 6–11
**John Smith's Bitter,
Magnet** Ⓗ
Popular pub with a large vault
where a friendly welcome is
assured. Home of the local
pigeon club. Occasional
performances by a brass band.
Bus stop outside.
🏠 🚻 ⬅ ♣ P

Lytham

Hole in One
Forest Drive (off B5261, by
Fairhaven golf course)
☎ (0253) 739968
11–3, 6–11 (11–11 Fri & Sat)
Thwaites Bitter Ⓗ
Busy local, a pleasant, modern
pub on a new housing estate.
Good, home-cooked lunches.
🏠 🚻 ⬅ (Ansdell) ♣ P

Queens
Central Beach
☎ (0253) 737316
11–3, 5–11 (11–11 summer)
**Theakston Best Bitter, XB,
Old Peculier; Younger
Scotch** Ⓗ
Busy pub overlooking the green
and estuary.
🚻 🏠 🚻 ♣

Melling

Melling Hall
☎ (052 42) 21298
12–2.30 (not Wed in winter), 6–11
**Hartleys XB; Taylor
Landlord; Whitbread
Boddingtons Bitter** Ⓗ
17th-century manor house,
converted in the 1940s to a
well-appointed hotel. The
friendly locals' bar is entered via
the left-hand door. Garden play
area. 🅰 🏠 🚻 🏠 ♣ P

Mereclough

Kettledrum Inn
302 Red Lees Road
☎ (0282) 24591

11–3, 5.30–11
**Courage Directors; John
Smith's Bitter; Theakston
Best Bitter, XB, Old Peculier** Ⓗ
Attractive, roadside pub on the
outskirts of Burnley, with a
gaslit restaurant upstairs serving
a wide variety of meals
(booking advisable). Regular
guest beers. 🅰 Q 🏠 🚻 ♣ P

Morecambe

Joiner's Arms
39 Queen Street
☎ (0524) 418105
11–11
Thwaites Best Mild, Bitter Ⓗ
Lively and unpretentious local,
attracting a varied clientele.
Children admitted to the back
(games) room. Sandwiches
available at all times. ♣

Victoria
14 Victoria Street
☎ (0524) 418176
11–3, 7–11
Thwaites Bitter Ⓗ
Single bar, extending back a
long way from the road. Dark
decor and curious ceiling
ornaments. Live bands Thu.
🚻 ⬅ ♣

Newchurch in Pendle

Lamb Inn
☎ (0282) 698812
12–3, 7–11
**Moorhouse's Premier;
Theakston Best Bitter** Ⓗ
Quiet, country pub, popular
with tourists in summer. The
decor reflects its proximity to
Pendle Hill (ie witches) and the
pub has a lot of old relics. Guest
beer in summer (usually
Moorhouse's Pendle Witches
Brew). 🅰 🏠 🚻 🚻 🅿 🏠 P

Ormskirk

Golden Lion
41 Moor Street
☎ (0695) 572354
11–11
Tetley Walker Mild, Bitter Ⓗ
A Tudorish exterior houses a
pleasantly refurbished, town-
centre pub: a handsome bar and
a comfortable, split-level lounge.
Courtyard for summer drinking.
No food Sun. 🏠 🚻 ♣

Greyhound
100 Aughton Street
☎ (0695) 576701
11–11
Walker Mild, Bitter Ⓗ
Characteristic, market town
local, slightly opened out but
retaining separate rooms, incl. a
well patronised public bar
without TV or piped music.
Close to a public car park.
🅰 Q 🏠 🚻 ⬅ ♣

Horse Shoe
24 Southport Road
☎ (0695) 572956
11–11
Tetley Walker Mild, Bitter Ⓗ
Friendly alehouse in a terrace
opposite the civic hall and the
famous tower-and-steeple parish
church. 🅰 🚻 ⬅ ♣

Queen Inn
81 Aughton Street
☎ (0695) 572114
11–11
Vaux Samson Ⓗ
Handsome, town pub opposite a
public car park. Recent
refurbishment has retained the
pleasant, hall bar and several
small rooms. 🚻 🚻 ♣

Oswaldtwistle

Golden Cross
Union Road (B6234, ½ mile
from A977 jct)
☎ (0254) 397513
11–3, 6–11
**Ind Coope Burton Ale; Tetley
Walker Bitter** Ⓗ
Modernised and extended, a
lively pub in the centre of the
village. Wheelchair access from
the rear car park. 🏠 🚻 ⬅ ♣ P

Try also: **Bridge**, Henry St,
Church (Bass)

Overton

Globe
40 Main Street (on road to
Sunderland Point)
☎ (0524) 858228
11–4, 7–11
Mitchell's Mild, Best Bitter Ⓗ
Renovated in 1990, with a
large conservatory at the front
(reinstating an original feature),
leading to a single bar with a
games area round the corner.
Good play area in the garden.
No eve meals Mon–Thu in
winter. 🚻 🏠 🚻 🚻 ♣ P

Try also: **Ship** (Thwaites)

Padiham

Hand & Shuttle
1 Eccleshill Street
☎ (0282) 71795
11.30–3, 6–11
Thwaites Bitter Ⓗ
Small, town-centre pub with a
games room and a quiet lounge.
Lunchtime snacks available.
Q ♣ P

Railway
27 Station Road
☎ (0282) 72175
12–11
**Burtonwood Mild,
Forshaw's** Ⓗ
Lively, town-centre pub with a
good atmosphere.
Entertainment several nights a
week. Open-plan layout. A

former Matthew Brown house, purchased by the Paramount chain in August 1990. ❀ ♿ ♣

Parbold

Railway Hotel
2 Station Road
☎ (0257) 462917
11–4, 6–11 (11–11 Sat)
Burtonwood Mild, Best Bitter, Forshaw's Ⓗ
Popular, village pub, full of railway 'numerasignia' – a must for railway enthusiasts. Daily newspapers provided. Children welcome until 8pm.
Q ♞ ⇌ ♣ P

Stocks Tavern
16 Alder Lane
☎ (0257) 462902
11.30–3, 5.30–11 (11.30–11 Sat in summer)
Tetley Walker Mild, Bitter Ⓗ
Busy local at the edge of the village. Return of a *Good Beer Guide* regular. Q ◐ ◑ ⊟ ⇌ ♣ P

Penwortham

St Teresa's Parish Centre
Queensway (off A59, Liverpool road) ☎ (0772) 743523
12–5 (not Mon–Fri), 7–11
Burtonwood Mild, Best Bitter, Forshaw's; Ind Coope Burton Ale; Tetley Walker Mild, Bitter Ⓗ
Large, popular, three-bar, Catholic club: a comfortable lounge, games room and a concert room, offering regular live entertainment. A thriving club with 18 handpumps and two regular guest beers monthly. CAMRA *Club of the Year* 1990. Children welcome lunchtimes at weekends. Restricted entry: members' guests and affiliated Catholic club members. ♞ ⊟ ♿ ♣ P

Pilling

Golden Ball
School Lane (off A588)
OS403488 ☎ (0253) 790212
11 (11.30 Fri)–3.30 (not Mon–Thu in winter), 7–11 (11–11 Sat)
Thwaites Best Mild (summer), **Bitter** Ⓗ
A 'hardy-perennial' in this guide: a mainly locals' pub in winter; popular in summer with coach parties, caravanners and bowlers (two crown greens at the back). Good facilities for families. The pub dates from 1904 and has photos of old Pilling along the lounge walls.
♨ ♞ ❀ ◐ ◑ ⊟ ⛺ ♣ P

Poulton-le-Fylde

Old Town Hall Tavern
Church Street
☎ (0253) 892257
11–11
Ruddles County; Webster's Yorkshire Bitter, Choice Ⓗ
Town-centre pub, previously council offices and before that the 'Bay Horse' pub. Accessible from all parts of the Fylde and next to a shopping centre and large car park. Regular quiz and karaoke nights. ◐ ♿ ⇌ ♣

Queens
Higher Green
☎ (0253) 883471
11–11
Bass Special, Draught Bass Ⓗ
Large, Victorian pub opposite the local park and near the village square. Q ⊟ ⇌ ♣ P

Preesall

Saracens Head
Park Lane (B5377, $\frac{3}{4}$ mile off A588) ☎ (0253) 810346
12–3, 5–11
Thwaites Best Mild, Bitter Ⓗ
Very popular, village pub. The introduction by the new landlord of a full meals service has seen trade take off, especially eves. Look for the 'head' guarding the car park. Real fire in the tap room.
♨ ❀ ◐ ◑ ⊟ ⛺ ♣ P

Preston

Black Horse
166 Friargate
☎ (0772) 52093
10.30–11 (10.30–3.30, 7.30–11 Sat; 7.30–10.30 Sun, closed Sun lunch)
Hartleys Fellrunners, XB; Robinson's Mild, Bitter, Best Bitter, Old Tom Ⓗ
Superb, town-centre pub in a busy shopping area. This Grade II listed building has side rooms and an upstairs bar and boasts an unusual, tiled, curved bar, wood-panelled walls, stained-glass screens and a mosaic floor. A thriving meeting place, full of character. Q ⇌

Fox & Grapes
Fox Street
☎ (0772) 52448
10.30–11
Theakston Best Bitter, Old Peculier; Younger IPA, No. 3 Ⓗ
Small, one-bar, town-centre pub, recently refurbished in 1920s style. Popular and often crowded. ◐ ⇌

George Hotel
89 Church Street (near bus station)
☎ (0772) 51529
11–3, 7–11
Thwaites Mild, Best Mild, Bitter, Daniel's Hammer Ⓔ
Old-fashioned, town-centre boozer with several drinking areas off a small bar. Unusually, both the Thwaites Milds are on offer. ⊟ ♣

Lamb & Packet
91a Friargate
11.30–11 (11.30–3, 6.30–11 Sat; closed Sun lunch)
Thwaites Best Mild, Bitter Ⓗ
Small, comfortable, one-bar, town pub near the polytechnic; often crowded during term-time. Eve meals 4.30–6.30 Mon–Fri. ◐ ◑ ⇌

Mitre Tavern
90 Moor Lane
☎ (0772) 51918
11.30–3, 6.30–11 (11–11 Sat)
Vaux Lorimers Best Scotch, Samson; Wards Sheffield Best Bitter Ⓗ
Popular, two-bar, 1960s local on the main road. ◐ ⊟ ♿ ♣ P

Moor Park
15 Garstang Road
11–3, 6.30–11
Theakston Best Bitter Ⓗ
Large, brick pub with a columned frontage and a flag-pole. Comfortably furnished, it was the last pub to brew its own beer in Preston (ceased 1968). Entertainment three nights a week. No-smoking area at lunchtime only. No food weekends. ◐ ♣ P ✗

New Britannia
6 Heatley Street
☎ (0772) 53424
11–3 (4 Fri & Sat), 6–11 (closed Sun lunch)
Hartleys XB; Marston's Pedigree; Whitbread Trophy, Castle Eden Ale Ⓗ
Small, one-bar pub near Lancashire Polytechnic. Popular with the heavy metal creed but all are made welcome. Often crowded at weekends. No food Sat. ◐ ⇌ ○

New Inn
27 Queen Street
☎ (0772) 51602
12–11
Thwaites Best Mild, Bitter Ⓗ
Comfortable, two-bar, urban pub. ⊟ ♣ P

Old Blue Bell
114 Church Street
☎ (0772) 51280
11–2.30 (4 Sat), 5.30 (7 Sat)–11
Samuel Smith OBB Ⓗ
Very old, comfortable, town-centre pub with one large room and two small snugs. No food Sun. ◐ ♿ ⇌ P

Real Ale Shop
47 Lovat Road (off Georges Road, A6)
☎ (0772) 201591
11–2 (Sat only), 5–10 (12–2, 7–10 Sun)
Moorhouse's Pendle Witches Brew; Taylor Landlord Ⓗ
Back-street off-licence with a constantly-changing range; 200 different beers each year. Exotic imported beers and fruit wines also available. ○

Royal Oak
36 Plungington Road
☎ (0772) 52496
10.45–4.15, 6 (7 Sat)–11
Whitbread Boddingtons Mild, Bitter Ⓔ
Popular, basic Boddingtons local – a type fast becoming extinct. Small bars; beer served from unmarked spouts. 🍽 ♿ ♣

Sun
112 Friargate
☎ (0772) 52335
11–4, 7–11
Thwaites Mild, Bitter Ⓗ
Comfortable, two-roomed, town-centre pub comprising a small vault and a large lounge. No food Sun. ◑ ⇌ ♣

Try also: New Welcome, Cambridge St (Thwaites); **Wheatsheaf**, Watery Lane, Ashton (Tetley)

Rawtenstall

Rams Head
2 Newchurch Road
☎ (0706) 213687
11–11
Bass Mild XXXX, Special, Draught Bass Ⓗ
Comfortable local by the market, with a spacious outdoor drinking area at the rear. Large lounge and a separate pool room. 🍺 ⇌ ◑ ♣

Try also: Sun Inn (Thwaites)

Scarisbrick

Heatons Bridge Inn
2 Heatons Bridge (B5242)
☎ (0704) 840549
11.30–11
Tetley Walker Mild, Bitter Ⓗ
Cosy canalside inn; well furnished with an abundance of bric-a-brac. 🍺 Q 🍺 ◑ ♣ P

Tarleton

Cock & Bottle
Church Road (off A59)
☎ (0772) 812258
11–3, 6–11 (11–11 Fri & Sat)
Thwaites Best Mild, Bitter Ⓗ
Modernised, village pub with a basic vault and a plush lounge. Dining facilities (home cooking); children's garden at the rear. 🍺 ◑ ▶ 🍽 ♣ P

Thornton

Burn Naze
1 Gamble Road (off B5268)
☎ (0253) 852954
11–11 (11–3.30, 7–11 Wed)
Tetley Walker Dark Mild, Mild, Bitter; Whitbread Boddingtons Bitter Ⓗ
Late Victorian pub of much character, popular with locals and standing next to the ICI complex. Has one of the few remaining public bars in the area. 🍺 🍽 ◑ ♣ P

Waddington

Lower Buck Inn
Church Road
☎ (0200) 28705
11–3, 6–11 (11–11 Thu–Sat)
Robinson's Bitter; Taylor Best Bitter; Tetley Walker Bitter Ⓗ
Unaltered, Dickensian pub in a Grade I listed building. A good, village local with facilities for families. Guest beer. 🍺 Q 👶 🍺 🍽 ◑ ▶ ⚲ ♣ P

Try also: Higher Buck (Thwaites)

Walton-le-Dale

White Bull
109 Victoria Road (A675/B6230)
☎ (0772) 54138
12 (2 Tue & Thu)–11
Whitbread Boddingtons Bitter Ⓗ
Friendly, locals' pub: a split-level interior with a separate games room. ♣ ♣ P

Try also: Victoria (Boddingtons)

Warton

Black Bull
Main Street
☎ (0524) 732865
11–3, 6–11
Mitchell's Best Bitter Ⓗ
Small, village local in a 15th-century building, offering a genuine country atmosphere. 🍺 🍽 ◑ ♣ P

Waterfoot

Jolly Sailor
Booth Road, Booth Place
☎ (0706) 214863
11–3, 7–11
S&N Matthew Brown Mild; Theakston Best Bitter, Old Peculier; Younger Scotch Ⓗ
Open-plan lounge and a small pool room. ♣

Try also: Olde Boot & Shoe (Thwaites)

Wharles

Eagle & Child
Church Road (2 miles off B5269, Kirkham road, near radar station)
OS448356 ☎ (0772) 690312
12–3 (not Mon–Fri in winter), 7–11
Wadworth 6X; Whitbread Boddingtons Bitter Ⓗ
Rural free house with a thatched roof and low-beamed ceilings; warm and cosy. A very popular pub close to HMS Inskip radar station and between Kirkham and Inskip village. Guest beers. 🍺 Q ◑ ⚲ P

Wheelton

Dressers
Briers Brow (off A674)
☎ (0254) 830041
11–3, 5.30–11
Hartleys XB; Marston's Pedigree; Whitbread Boddingtons Bitter Ⓗ
Popular, low-beamed free house in a row of cottages, half a mile from the Leeds–Liverpool Canal. 'Slaters' restaurant above. Children welcome at lunchtime. 🍺 👶 🍺 ◑ ▶ ♣ P

Whittle-le-Woods

Royal Oak
216 Chorley Old Road
☎ (0254) 76485
2.30–11
Theakston Best Bitter Ⓗ
Small, terraced pub full of atmosphere and offering a friendly welcome. Home-made pickles available. A meeting place for mature motorcycle enthusiasts. 🍺 🍺 ♣

⇌ Rail and Underground Stations ⊖

If a pub stands within half a mile of a rail or tube station, we include the appropriate symbol. The name of the station is only given when it differs from the name of the town itself, or when there is more than one station in the town. Where there are several convenient stations, we mention the nearest.

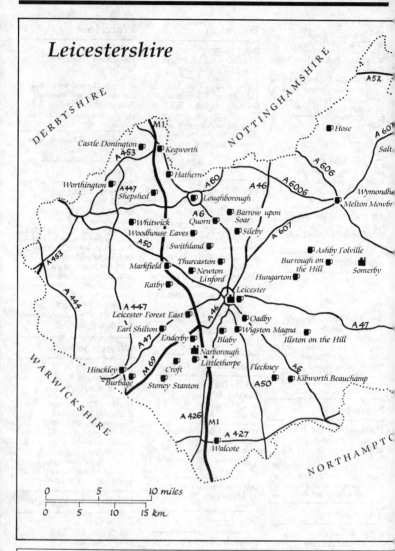

Leicestershire

(Map of Leicestershire showing M1, A52, A453, Castle Donington, Kegworth, Hathern, Worthington, Shepshed, A447, Loughborough, A60, A46, A6006, A606, Hose, Salt, Wymondham, Melton Mowbray, Whitwick, Quorn, Barrow upon Soar, Woodhouse Eaves, Sileby, Swithland, A50, Markfield, Thurcaston, Newton Linford, A607, Ashby Folville, Burrough on the Hill, Somerby, Ratby, Hungarton, Leicester, Leicester Forest East, A447, A46, Oadby, A47, Earl Shilton, Enderby, Wigston Magna, Illston on the Hill, A47, Hinckley, M69, Blaby, Narborough, Littlethorpe, Fleckney, A6, Kibworth Beauchamp, Burbage, Croft, Stoney Stanton, A50, A426, M1, A427, Walcote, Warwickshire, Derbyshire, Nottinghamshire, Northampton)

```
0        5        10 miles
0    5       10      15 km
```

🏭 **Everards**, Narborough; **Hoskins, Hoskins &
Oldfield**, Leicester; **Parish**, Somerby

Ashby Folville

Carington Arms
Folville Street
☎ (0664) 840228
11–2, 6 (7 winter)–11 (11–11 Sat;
12–2.30, 7–10.30 Sun)
**Adnams Bitter; Everards Mild
(summer), Tiger, Old
Original** Ⓗ
This former Ruddles, village
pub, has an open bar and a
separate dining area. Skittle
alley/function room available.
Food every day (roast Sun). The
pleasant garden has a petanque
court. Guest beer. 🏠 ⊛ ◖ ▶ ♣ P

Barrow upon Soar

Navigation
Mill Lane ☎ (0509) 412842
11–2.30, 6–11
**Courage Directors; Marston's
Pedigree** Ⓗ
Very welcoming, canalside pub,
particularly popular in summer
for its patio garden with
moorings. Large, L-shaped
lounge and snug which doubles
as a family room. Skittle alley.
No food weekends. 🚂 ⊛ ◖ Å ♣

Riverside
Bridge Street ☎ (0509) 412260

11–2.30 (3 Sat), 7–11
**Courage Best Bitter,
Directors; John Smith's
Bitter** Ⓗ
Fronting onto the River Soar,
this pub has two large lounge
bars: one decorated in an Art
Deco style; the other more
traditional, with a separate
restaurant area (no eve meals
Sun/Mon). Extensive drinking
area outside, with moorings.
Popular with the younger
set.
⊛ ◖ ▶ Å P

Try also: Hammer & Pincers
(Ind Coope)

11.30–2.30, 5.30 (6.30 Sat)–11
(12–2.30, 7–10.30 Sun)
**Marston's Mercian Mild,
Burton Best Bitter,
Pedigree** Ⓗ
Named after the two trees
which stood in the grounds
before the pub was built in
1925. Still a real pub: no meals;
sandwiches only. Large garden
with children's play area.
🏚 Q ✸ ⊟ ♣ P

Burrough on the Hill

Stag & Hounds
Main Street ☎ (066 477) 375
12–2 (3 Sat; not Mon & Tue or winter
Mon–Fri), 7–11
**Marston's Mercian Mild,
Pedigree; Parish Special,
Baz's Bonce Blower** Ⓗ
Pub next door to the Parish
brewery until 1991 when the
latter moved. Two beers,
home-cooked food, and live
music on Thu.
🏚 ✸ ◑ ▲ ♣ ➹ P

Castle Donington

Cross Keys
Bondgate ☎ (0332) 812214
11–2.30, 5.30 (6 Sat)–11
**Draught Bass; Wards
Sheffield Best Bitter; Vaux
Samson** Ⓗ
Popular free house with one
spacious, characterful bar. A
large log fire provides
atmosphere in winter. Handy
for East Midlands Airport and
events at the nearby motor
racing circuit. Guest beers. No
food Sun. 🏚 ✸ ◑ ▲ ♣ P

Lamb
Station Road ☎ (0332) 810591
11–3, 6–11
**Marston's Burton Best Bitter,
Pedigree** Ⓗ
Small and comfortable, two-
roomed, Victorian local.
Friendly welcome for regulars
and visitors alike. ⊟ ♣ P

Croft

Heathcote Arms
Hill Street ☎ (0455) 282439
11–2.30, 5.30–11 (11–11 Sat)
**Adnams Bitter; Everards
Mild, Beacon, Tiger, Old
Original** Ⓗ
Unspoilt, old pub on top of a
hill overlooking the river.
Relaxed and friendly
atmosphere; good, traditional,
home-cooked food. Alley and
table skittles. Guest beer.
🏚 Q ✸ ◑ ▶ ⊟ ♣ P

Earl Shilton

Red Lion
High Street ☎ (0455) 843356
11–2.30, 5.30 (6 Sat)–11

Blaby

Egyptian Queen
Cedar Road ☎ (0533) 771044
11–2.30 (3 Sat), 6–11 (12–2, 7–10.30
Sun)
**Courage Directors; John
Smith's Bitter** Ⓗ
Spacious estate pub with a
relaxed atmosphere. It opened
in the 1960s as a theme pub,
and traces of the original
Egyptian-style decor can still be
seen. No food Sun lunch or
Wed, Fri and Sat eves.
✸ ◑ ⊟ ♣ P

Burbage

Sycamores Inn
Windsor Street
☎ (0455) 239268

Draught Bass; M&B Mild Ⓗ
Basic, beer drinker's pub on the
main road. Still has three
separate rooms and one central
bar. ✸ ⊟ ▲ ♣ P

Enderby

Plough Inn
Mill Hill ☎ (0533) 863307
11–2.30, 5–11
**Marston's Burton Best Bitter,
Pedigree** Ⓗ
Recently refurbished pub in a
prominent position at the top of
a hill on the B582. Now a
Marston's managed house, but
formerly a quarrymen's free
house. The main dining area is
largely separated from the rest
of the pub. ✸ ◑ ▶ P

Exton

Fox & Hounds
The Green ☎ (0572) 812403
11–2.30, 6.30–11 (12–2.30, 7–10.30
Sun)
**Marston's Pedigree; Samuel
Smith OBB** Ⓗ
Ivy-covered, 17th-century,
former coaching inn,
overlooking the village green. A
traditional bar and a separate
lounge with dining area.
🏚 ✸ ⋈ ◑ ⊟ ▲ ♣ P

Fleckney

Old Crown Inn
High Street ☎ (0533) 402223
12–2.30 (11.30–3.30 Sat), 5–11
(12–2.30, 7–10.30 Sun)
**Adnams Bitter; Everards
Mild, Beacon, Tiger, Old
Original** Ⓗ
One long, L-shaped room with
a quiet snug in the top corner.
Recently refurbished but not
over-done and still retains its
local character. Guest beers.
◑ ▶ ▲ ♣ P

Hathern

Dewdrop Inn
Loughborough Road
☎ (0509) 842438
12–2.30, 7–11
**Hardys & Hansons Best Mild,
Best Bitter** Ⓗ
Small, traditional pub with a
tiny lounge. Offers a large
selection of malt whiskies, many
of which are not on display due
to lack of space behind the bar.
Popular with locals. Limited
parking. Q ⊟ ♣ P

Three Crowns
Wide Lane ☎ (0509) 842233
12–2.30, 5.30–11 (12–11 Sat)
Draught Bass; M&B Mild Ⓔ
Quiet local with three drinking
areas. Ownership and beers may
change, as pub may be sold as
part of Bass's exercise to meet
pub limits set by MMC report.
🏚 ✸ ⊟ ♣ P

Leicestershire

Hinckley

Greyhound Inn
New Buildings
☎ (0455) 615235
11–2.30, 5 (5.30 Sat)–11 (12–2, 7–10.30 Sun)
Marston's Mercian Mild, Burton Best Bitter, Pedigree Ⓗ
Lively, traditional, four-room pub with live jazz on Wed and Thu. Room set aside for families Sat lunchtime. Q ⑧ ◖ 🖫 ⇌ ♣

Hose

Black Horse
Bolton Lane ☎ (0949) 60336
11–2.30, 7–11 (12–2, 7–10.30 Sun)
Home Mild, Bitter Ⓗ
Authentic, unaltered, village ale house with a busy bar, a cosy lounge and a skittle alley.
🏛 Q ⑧ 🖫 ♣ P

Hungarton

Black Boy
Main Street ☎ (053 750) 601
11–2.30, 6–11
M&B Mild, Brew XI Ⓗ
Friendly, village pub with a small, comfortable lounge and a larger, more basic bar. Excellent, filling, home-cooked food and snacks (no meals Sun lunchtime). Also sells local and home-made produce. Large car park; rural aspect. 🏛 Q ⑧ ◖ 🖫 ▲ ♣ P

Illston on the Hill

Fox & Goose
Main Street ☎ (053 755) 340
11–2.30 (not Mon–Fri), 7–11 (12–2, 7–10.30 Sun)
Adnams Bitter; Everards Beacon, Tiger, Old Original Ⓗ
Unspoilt village pub, with local memorabilia in the bar.
🏛 Q ⑧ 🖫 ♣

Kegworth

Cap & Stocking
Borough Street
☎ (0509) 674814
11.30–3, 6–11
Draught Bass; M&B Highgate Mild Ⓖ; **Welsh Brewers Worthington BB** Ⓗ
Old-fashioned, back-street pub with beer served in jugs straight from the cellar. Stuffed animals and an antique Wurlitzer add to the atmosphere. Guest beers in rotation (from jug).
🏛 ⑧ ◖ 🖫 ♣ ☺

Oddfellows Arms
Packington Hill
☎ (0509) 672552
11–11
Marston's Pedigree Ⓗ
Popular, two-roomed local, offering a variety of pub games.

Barbecue Sat eve in summer. Meeting place of the local Hat Club. ⑧ ⇌ ◖ 🖫 ♣ P

Kibworth Beauchamp

Coach & Horses
2 Leicester Road
☎ (0533) 792247
11.30–3, 5–11 (11–11 Sat)
Ansells Bitter; Draught Bass; Ind Coope Burton Ale; Tetley Bitter Ⓗ
Friendly, old coaching inn, popular with locals and passing trade. Excellent, home-made bar snacks and restaurant meals available. Look for original coin-filled beams. 🏛 ⑧ ◖ 🖫 ♣ P

Leicester

Black Boy
35 Albion Street (behind Grand Hotel) ☎ (0533) 540422
11–11 (11–2.30, 7–11 Sat; 12–2, 7–10.30 Sun)
Draught Bass Ⓗ; **M&B Mild** Ⓔ
Excellent town pub; very popular with business people weekday lunchtimes. Wood-panelled lounge with a restored Victorian ceiling. Eve meals on request. Q ⇌ ⑧ ◖ 🖫 🖫 ♣

Black Horse
65 Narrow Lane, Aylestone (off B5418, near canal)
☎ (0533) 832811
11–2.30, 6–11 (11–11 Sat)
Everards Mild, Beacon, Tiger, Old Original Ⓗ
A pub for some 200 years; in its original form it also functioned as a farm. Today it has a bar, lounge and snug downstairs, and a function room with a pool table upstairs. Guest beers. 🏛 Q ⑧ ◖ 🖫 ♣

Pump & Tap
Dunns Lane ☎ (0533) 540324
12–3 (not Mon–Fri), 6–11
Ind Coope ABC Best Bitter, Burton Ale; Tetley Bitter Ⓗ
Two basic bars with sawdust on the floors and old church furniture. Handpump sets and taps are displayed on the walls. Popular with students. Occasional live music. ⑧ ◖

Rainbow & Dove
185 Charles Street (opp. main police station)
☎ (0533) 555916
11.30–3, 5.30 (7 Sat)–11 (12–2, 7–10.30 Sun)
Bateman Mild; Hoskins Beaumanor, Penn's Ale, Churchill's Pride, Old Nigel Ⓗ
One-roomed, town-centre, beer drinker's pub, a regular CAMRA meeting place. A map made of old shive holders adorns the end wall. Live music Sun nights. Guest beers.
◖ 🖫 ⇌ ♣

Salmon Inn
19 Butts Close Lane (200 yds behind St Margarets bus station)
☎ (0533) 532301
10.30–11 (10.30–3, 5.30–11 Tue & Wed)
Banks's Mild, Bitter Ⓔ
Friendly, locals' pub with a cosy lounge and a basic bar. Close to the new Shires shopping centre. Due for refurbishment. 🖫

Sir Charles Napier
Glenfield Road
☎ (0533) 621022
11–11 (11–3, 6–11 Sat)
Courage Directors; John Smith's Magnet Ⓗ
Deceptively spacious 1930s pub, at the end of a row of terraced houses. Still retains the original, three-room layout (incl. a smoke room). Q ◖ 🖫 ♣

Tudor
Tudor Road ☎ (0533) 620087
11–2.30 (3 Sat), 6–11 (12–2.30, 7–10.30 Sun)
Everards Mild, Beacon, Tiger, Old Original Ⓗ
Popular, Victorian, corner pub in a terraced, residential area. Cosy lounge; lively bar; games room. Guest beers. ⇌ ⑧ ◖ 🖫

Victoria Jubilee Inn
112 Leire Street (just off A46, Melton Road, out of city)
☎ (0533) 663599
11–2.30 (3.30 Sat), 6–11
Marston's Burton Best Bitter, Pedigree Ⓗ
Friendly, locals' pub in a terraced, residential area. ⑧ ◖ ♣

Leicester Forest East

Red Cow
Hinckley Road
☎ (0533) 387878
11–11 (11–3, 6–11 Sat)
Everards Mild, Beacon, Tiger, Old Original Ⓗ
Old, thatched, ivy-clad pub, an Everards Original Inn. Recently refurbished and extended rearwards to provide additional facilities. Accommodation is in the adjacent annex. Two guest beers usually available.
⇌ ⑧ ⇌ ◖ 🖫 P

Littlethorpe

Plough Inn
Station Road ☎ (0533) 862383
11–2.30 (3 Sat), 6–11
Adnams Bitter; Everards Beacon, Tiger, Old Original Ⓗ
Comfortable, well-maintained and friendly, thatched local, dating back to the 16th century. Excellent, home-cooked food available in the bar and lounge or in the separate dining area. Long alley skittles. Guest beer.
Q ⑧ ◖ 🖫 🖫 ⇌ (Narborough) ♣ P

Loughborough

Blacksmiths Arms
Wards End ☎ (0509) 237540
11.30–2.30 (3 Sat), 7–11 (12–2.30, 7–10.30 Sun)
Home Mild, Bitter; Theakston XB, Old Peculier; Younger No. 3 Ⓗ
Popular, 1930s, town-centre pub, recently modernised. Occasional live music. Q ◖ ◖ ♣

Duke of York
126 Nottingham Road
☎ (0509) 216234
11.30–3, 6 (7 Sat)–11 (12–2.30, 7–10.30 Sun)
Draught Bass; M&B Mild Ⓔ
Down-to-earth, locals' pub with no frills. Under threat of being sold as Bass comply with the MMC report. ⊟ ⇌ ♣ P

Greyhound
69 Nottingham Road
☎ (0509) 216080
11.30–2.30, 5.30–11 (11–11 Fri & Sat)
Marston's Border Mild, Pedigree Ⓗ
Lively pub, popular with the motorcycle fraternity. A welcome for all. ⊛ ◖ ⊟ ⇌ ♣ P

Old Pack Horse
Woodgate (100 yds from A6, near Court) ☎ (0509) 214590
11–11 (11–4, 7–11 Sat)
Hardys & Hansons Best Mild, Best Bitter, Kimberley Classic Ⓗ
Old coaching inn, tastefully redecorated to retain many original items, incl. the stables. Popular at lunchtimes with professionals, especially lawyers. Very small car park.
⌂ ◖ ⇌ ♣ P

Peacock Inn
26 Factory Street (off Leicester Road) ☎ (0509) 214215
11.30–2.30, 7–11
Draught Bass; M&B Mild Ⓗ
Popular cosy, traditional, three-roomed local near the steam railway. ⌂ ⊛ ⊟ ◖ ♣ P

Swan in the Rushes
The Rushes ☎ (0509) 217014
11–2.30 (3.30 Sat), 5 (6.30 Sat)–11
Bateman XXXB; Marston's Border Exhibition, Merrie Monk, Pedigree; Tetley Bitter Ⓗ
Thriving, cosmopolitan ale house with a large range of continental bottled beers. Live music at weekends in the separate function room. Good value, home-cooked food (eve meals finish at 8pm). Rotating guest mild policy, plus regular guest beers. ⌂ Q ⊛ ◖ ⊟ ⊟ ♣ P

Windmill
Sparrow Hill
☎ (0509) 216314
11–2.30, 5.30–11

Marston's Mercian Mild, Burton Best Bitter, Pedigree Ⓗ
Loughborough's oldest pub, sympathetically extended and refurbished by the brewery. A traditional public bar and a small lounge, with a comfortable drinking area linking both. All meals are home-cooked with Spanish specialities (eve meals by arrangement).
⌂ ⊟ ◖ ⇌ ♣ P

Try also: Albion, Canal Bank (Free); **Old English Gentleman**, Ashby Rd (Bass); **Priory**, Nanpantan (Home)

Markfield

Queens Head
Ashby Road
☎ (0509) 242496
12–2.30, 6–11 (12–2, 7–10.30 Sun)
Marston's Pedigree Ⓗ
A traditional, basic English pub with no frills. ⌂ ⊟ ♣ P

Melton Mowbray

Mash Tub Inn
58 Nottingham Street
☎ (0664) 510041
11–2.30, 7–11 (12–2, 7–10.30 Sun)
Bateman Mild; Hoskins Beaumanor, Penn's Ale, Old Nigel Ⓗ
Comfortable, split-level, town-centre pub with a number of distinct seating areas. Regular guest beer. No food Sun. ◖ ⇌ ♣

Newton Linford

Bradgate
Main Street ☎ (0530) 242239
11–11 (11–2.30, 5.30–11 winter)
Everards Mild, Beacon, Tiger, Old Original Ⓗ
Recently-modernised, large and spacious pub-restaurant, close to Bradgate Park. Guest beers in summer. Not to be mistaken for the Bradgate Arms in nearby Cropston. ⇌ ⊛ ◖ ◗ P

North Luffenham

Horse & Panniers
Church Street
☎ (0780) 720091
11–2, 6–11
Adnams Bitter; Everards Beacon, Tiger, Old Original Ⓗ
Excellent, two-roomed village pub, known locally as the 'Nag & Bag'. A Grade II listed building, dating from 1640, and previous winner of Everards *Best Kept Cellar* competition. Guest beer. ⌂ ⊟ ♣ P

Oadby

Cow & Plough
Stoughton Farm Park, Gartree Road (signed from A6)
☎ (0533) 710355

12–7 (12–3 Sun)
Hoskins & Oldfield Mild, Bitter Ⓗ
An old, converted barn, with a genuine, elegant, Victorian bar decorated with breweriana and old advertising signs. A genuine atmosphere. One guest beer. Note restricted opening; no Sun eve session. Q ⇍ ⊛ ⊟ ♣ ⊃ P

Oakham

Wheatsheaf
Northgate ☎ (0572) 723458
11–2.30 (3 Fri & Sat), 6–11
Adnams Bitter; Everards Beacon, Tiger Ⓗ
17th-century, two-roomed pub, popular with locals. Friendly atmosphere. ⌂ Q ⋈ ⇌

Try also: White Lion (Free)

Quorn

Royal Oak
High Street ☎ (0509) 413502
11.30–2.30, 6.30–11
Draught Bass; M&B Mild Ⓗ
Basic, three-roomed pub on the main road. A very small lounge with a serving area linking to the bar. Q ⊛ ⊟ ♣

Ratby

Plough
Burroughs Road
☎ (0533) 392103
11–3, 5.30–11
Marston's Burton Best Bitter, Pedigree Ⓗ
Friendly, village local with a restaurant. ⌂ ⇍ ⊛ ◖ ◗ ♣ P

Saltby

Nags Head
Back Street ☎ (0476) 860491
12–2.30, 7–11
Greene King Abbot; Ruddles Best Bitter Ⓗ
A friendly landlord hosts this 200 year-old, stone-built pub, with beams and a panelled bar. Interesting bar billiard room with a newly-acquired bar skittles game. Good, home cooking and four-poster accommodation.
⌂ Q ⊛ ⋈ ◖ ◗ ⊟ ♣ P

Sewstern

Blue Dog Inn
Main Street ☎ (0476) 860097
12–2.30, 6–11 (11–11 Sat)
Courage Directors; John Smith's Bitter; Whitbread Boddingtons Bitter Ⓗ
Built in the 1640s, a friendly pub near the 'Viking Way' and Woolsthorpe Manor. It was used as a hospital in Cromwell's time and has a ghost called Albert. No eve meals Sun.
⌂ ◖ ◗ ♣ P

Leicestershire

Shepshed

Crown
Brook Street
☎ (0509) 502665
12–3, 5–11 (11–11 Sat)
**Everards Tiger, Old
Original** H
Formerly an 18th-century
coaching inn, this lively local
has four, interconnecting rooms,
each with its own distinctive
character. Easy parking on
market place. Regular guest
beers. ♨ ☗ ◖ ♣ P

Railway
160 Charnwood Road
☎ (0509) 503283
11–11 (12–2.30, 7–10.30 Sun)
**Marston's Mercian Mild,
Pedigree** H
Busy, locals' pub with a good
basic bar. Known locally as the
'Bottom Railway'. Much
railway memorabilia. ☗ ☗ ♣ P

Richmond Arms
Forest Street
☎ (0509) 503309
11.30–2.30, 7–11
Draught Bass; M&B Mild H
Friendly, village local with two,
not dissimilar rooms. There's
always someone to play
dominoes with; dartboard in the
lounge. ☗ ◖ ☗ P

Sileby

Free Trade Inn
27 Cossington Road
☎ (050 981) 4494
11.30–2 (2.30 Fri, 3 Sat); 5.30 (6.30
Sat)–11
**Everards Mild, Beacon, Tiger,
Old Original** H
Pleasant, thatched pub in a Soar
Valley village, between
Leicester and Loughborough.
Beware of low oak beams.
Popular with locals. Regular
guest beers. ☗ ◖ ♣ P

Railway Inn
King Street
☎ (050 981) 2447
11–2.30 (3.30 Sat), 5.30–11 (12–2,
7–10.30 Sun)
Draught Bass; M&B Mild E
A real no-frills pub, with a basic
lounge and an even more basic
bar. Under threat of being sold
in the great Bass pub sale.
☗ ☗ ♣ P

Stoney Stanton

Francis Arms
Huncote Road
☎ (045 527) 2034
11–2.30, 5.30–11
**Marston's Burton Best Bitter,
Merrie Monk, Pedigree** H
Basic, beer drinker's pub with a
collection of rifles on the ceiling.
Two separate rooms. No meals,
just cobs. ☗ ❄ ☗ ☗ Å ♣ P

Swithland

Griffin Inn
Main Street ☎ (0509) 890535
11–2.30, 6–11
**Adnams Bitter; Everards
Mild, Beacon, Tiger, Old
Original** H
Large, friendly, well-run inn
with distinctive drinking areas.
Situated in Charnwood Forest,
near Bradgate Park. Skittle alley.
Guest beers. ❄ ☗ ◖ ◗ P

Thurcaston

Wheatsheaf Inn
203 Leicester Road
☎ (0533) 362972
11–2.30, 5.30 (6.30 Sat)–11 (11–2.30,
7–10.30 Sun in winter)
**Everards Beacon, Tiger, Old
Original; Hook Norton Old
Hooky** H
Cosy, old, village pub, popular
with locals and visitors. No
separate public bar; the skittle
alley has been refurbished.
Close to Bradgate Park. Guest
beers from the Everards
portfolio. ♨ Q ☗ ◖ P

Upper Hambleton

Finch's Arms
Oakham Road
☎ (0572) 756575
11–11 (11–3.30, 6–11 winter)
**Greene King Rayments
Special; Ruddles Best Bitter,
County** H
Upmarket pub on a peninsula in
Rutland Water, very popular
with tourists. A lounge bar and
a restaurant only, with food
available at all times (vegetarian
options). Guest beers.
♨ Q ◖ ◗ P

Walcote

Black Horse
Main Street ☎ (0455) 552684
12–2.30 (not Tue), 5.30 (6 Sat)–11
(12–2.30, 7–10.30 Sun)
**Hook Norton Best Bitter, Old
Hooky; Taylor Landlord** H
Busy and comfortable, roadside
pub, renowned for its authentic
oriental bar meals (no food Tue).
Separate dining area. Guest
beers. ♨ ◖ ◗ ☙ P

Whitwick

Three Horseshoes
11 Leicester Road
☎ (0530) 37311
11–3, 6.30–11 (12–2, 7–10.30 Sun)
Draught Bass; M&B Mild H
Traditional village local, popular
and unspoilt. ♨ ♣ P

Wigston Magna

Meadowbank
Kelmarsh Avenue
☎ (0533) 811926

11–2.30, 6–11 (11–11 Sat)
Banks's Mild, Bitter E
Newish estate pub in the
Banks's style: friendly,
comfortable and functional, with
good use of wood and brick.
The food and beer are both
excellent value (no food Sun).
TV in bar; table skittles.
☗ ◖ ☗ ♣ P

Woodhouse Eaves

Curzon Arms
44 Maplewell Road
☎ (0509) 890377
11–11 (11–2.30, 6–11 winter)
**Courage Directors; John
Smith's Bitter** H
Lively, village local with a
comfortable lounge and a
welcoming public bar. Food is
standard pub fare, plus a
vegetarian dish. ☗ ◗ ☗ ♣ P

Worthington

Maltshovel
Main Street ☎ (0530) 222343
12–2 (not Mon, 2.30 Sat), 7–11
Marston's Pedigree H
Lovely, village pub with a
welcoming atmosphere. Garden
has a variety of animals and
playground equipment for
children. Excellent, home-
cooked food (no meals Mon).
♨ Q ☗ ◖ ☗ Å ♣ P

Wymondham

Hunters Arms
Edmondthorpe Road
☎ (057 284) 633
11.30–2.30, 6.30–11
**Draught Bass; Greene King
IPA, Rayments Special,
Abbot** H
Cosy and comfortable, village
inn offering excellent food.
Separate restaurant with
inventive menu (open Fri/Sat
eves and Sun lunch; no bar
meals Sun eve, or Mon).
♨ ☗ ◖ ◗ ☗ ♣ P

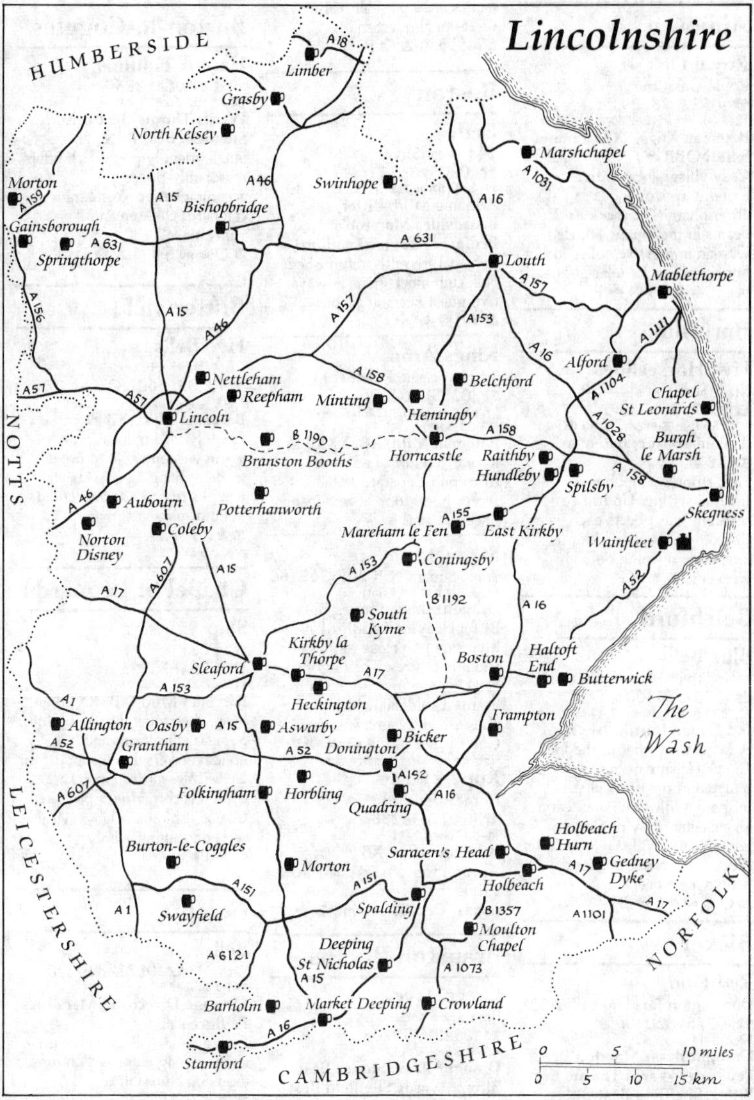
Lincolnshire
HUMBERSIDE
NOTTS
LEICESTERSHIRE
CAMBRIDGESHIRE
NORFOLK
The Wash
Limber
A 18
Grasby
North Kelsey
Marshchapel
A 1031
Morton
A 159
Swinhope
A 46
A 15
A 16
Bishopbridge
Gainsborough
A 631
Springthorpe
A 631
Louth
A 157
Mablethorpe
A 156
A 15
A 46
A 157
A 153
A 1111
A 16
Alford
Nettleham
Reepham
A 158
Belchford
A 1104
Chapel St Leonards
A 57
A 57
Lincoln
Minting
Hemingby
A 1028
Burgh le Marsh
B 1190
A 158
Branston Booths
Horncastle
Raithby
Hundleby
Spilsby
A 158
Skegness
A 46
Aubourn
Potterhanworth
A 155
Norton Disney
Coleby
Mareham le Fen
East Kirkby
Wainfleet
Coningsby
A 153
A 607
A 15
B 1192
A 52
A 17
South Kyme
A 16
Kirkby la Thorpe
Boston
Haltoft End
Sleaford
A 17
Butterwick
A 153
Heckington
A 1
Frampton
Allington
Oasby
A 15
Aswarby
Bicker
A 52
Grantham
A 52
Donington
A 152
A 607
Folkingham
Horbling
Quadring
A 16
Holbeach Hurn
Burton-le-Coggles
Saracen's Head
A 17
Gedney Dyke
Morton
A 151
A 151
Holbeach
A 17
A 1
Swayfield
Spalding
B 1357
A 1101
Moulton Chapel
A 6121
Deeping St Nicholas
A 15
A 1073
Barholm
Market Deeping
Crowland
A 16
Stamford
0
5
10 miles
0
5
10
15 km

Bateman, *Wainfleet*

Alford

Half Moon

West Street ☎ (0507) 463477
10.30–3.30, 6–11
Draught Bass; Bateman XB; Vaux Samson Ⓗ
Popular and welcoming market town pub with a cosmopolitan clientele. Supper licence to 1am Fri and Sat. Guest beers usually include a mild. Host to many clubs and societies.
❀ ◖ ◗ ⊟ ♣ P

Allington

Welby Arms

The Green
☎ (0400) 81361
12–2.30, 5.30 (6.30 Sat)–11
Courage Directors; John Smith's Bitter, Magnet Ⓗ
Comfortable village pub well worth seeking out. Real ale dominates but there is also excellent food, incl. local specialities. Petanque played in summer. ♨ Q ❀ ◖ ◗ ⊟ ▲ ♣ P

Aswarby

Tally Ho

Main Road
☎ (052 95) 205
12–2.30, 6–11
Bateman XB; Greene King IPA Ⓗ
Roadside inn with good food and accommodation: a long-standing entry in this guide. Regular guest beer.
♨ ❀ ⊨ ◖ ◗ P

Lincolnshire

Auburn

Royal Oak
Royal Oak Lane
☎ (0522) 788291
12–2.30, 7–11 (12–2.30, 7–10.30 Sun)
Bateman XB, XXXB; Samuel Smith OBB Ⓗ
Cosy village local with a friendly, welcoming atmosphere. The mock Tudor beams in the lounge are clad with an impressive collection of horse brasses. Regular guest beers. ▓ ▧ ◖ ▮ ♣ ♣ P

Barholm

Five Horseshoes
Main Street
☎ (077 836) 238
12–2.30 (Sat/Sun only), 7 (5 Fri)–11
Adnams Bitter; Bateman XXXB Ⓗ
Fine, stone-built pub in a tranquil setting. Up to five different guest beers each week. Relaxed atmosphere. Note: lunchtime opening only at weekend. ▓ ▚ ▧ P

Belchford

Blue Bell
Main Street
☎ (0507) 533602
11–2.30 (may extend), 7–11
Ind Coope Burton Ale Ⓗ
A worthy member of the Ind Coope Cellarmanship Guild. Situated in the heart of the unspoilt Wolds, the pub features an amazing array of old farm implements. Will stay open after 2.30 if requested. No food Mon. Guest beers.
▓ Q ▧ ▨ ◖ ♣ ♣ P

Bicker

Red Lion
Donnington Road (just off A52)
☎ (0775) 820300
12–3, 6–11
Draught Bass; Marston's Pedigree; Wards Thorne Best Bitter, Sheffield Best Bitter; Whitbread Boddingtons Bitter Ⓗ
A many-roomed pub with old-fashioned decor; pool played in bar. A local outpost for rock bands (in the function room most Fri eves). Meals in dining room or bar snacks.
▓ ▧ ◖ ♣ ♣ P

Bishopbridge

Bell Inn
On A631 ☎ (067 37) 272
11–3, 6–11
Ind Coope Burton Ale; Tetley Mild, Bitter Ⓗ
Remote free house with a basic bar, a comfortable lounge and a pleasant dining room. Pub games are a popular feature. Occasional guest milds.
▨ ▧ ◖ ▮ ▤ Å ♣ P

Boston

Eagle
144 West Street
☎ (0205) 361116
11–3, 6 (5 Thu & Fri)–11 (11–11 Sat)
Adnams Mild, Bitter, Broadside; Marston's Pedigree; Taylor Landlord Ⓗ
Busy bar, recently refurbished. Folk club meets here. Always two guest beers available.
▓ ▧ ◖ ▮ ⇌ ♣ ↺

Kings Arms
13 Horncastle Road
☎ (0205) 364296
11.30–3, 6.30 (5.30 Mon & Fri)–11 (11–11 Sat)
Bateman Mild, XB, XXXB Ⓗ
Recently refurbished, smart town pub. Separate restaurant serves good food at reasonable prices. ▓ ▨ ◖ ▮

Magnet
South Square ☎ (0205) 369186
11–3, 6–11 (11–11 Sat)
Draught Bass; Stones Best Bitter; Taylor Landlord Ⓗ
Riverside pub close to music and arts centres. The Pilgrim Fathers were imprisoned in the nearby Guildhall, which now houses a Heritage Museum. Guest beers. ▓ ◖ ▮ ⇌ ♣ ↺

Ropers Arms
Horncastle Road
☎ (0205) 362881
11–3 (4 Sat), 7–11
Bateman Mild, XB Ⓗ
A warm welcome is guaranteed at this street-corner local. A regular CAMRA haunt. ▨ ♣ ↺

Branston Booths

Green Tree
Bardney Road
☎ (0522) 791208
11–4 (5 Sat), 7–11
Draught Bass; Stones Best Bitter; Wards Sheffield Best Bitter Ⓗ
Cosy and welcoming village local. Drive carefully along the straight or you will miss it. Restaurant at the rear caters for children and vegetarians. Guest beers. ▓ Q ▧ ◖ ▮ Å ♣ P

Burgh le Marsh

Inn on the Marsh
Storeys Lane
☎ (0754) 810582
11–4 (3 Tue & Thu), 6–11
Bateman XB, XXXB; Wards Sheffield Best Bitter Ⓗ
Olde-worlde country pub whose peaceful atmosphere makes it popular with all ages.
▓ Q ▧ ♣

Burton-le-Coggles

Hare & Hounds
☎ (047 684) 295
12–2 (not Mon), 7–11
Wards Thorne Best Bitter, Sheffield Best Bitter Ⓗ
Small, friendly pub which offers reasonably-priced accommodation. Restaurant caters for children and vegetarians.
▓ Q ▧ ▨ ◖ ▮ ▤ Å ♣ P

Butterwick

Five Bells
Church Street
☎ (0205) 760282
11–3, 7–11
Bateman Mild, XB Ⓗ
Friendly village local, with a warm welcome. Good use is made of hanging baskets and troughs to provide a splendid floral display in summer.
▓ ▧ ◖ ▮ ♣ P

Chapel St Leonards

Ship
Sea Road
☎ (0754) 72975
11–3, 7–11
Bateman Mild, XB, XXXB Ⓗ
Busy, cheerful and friendly pub, popular with locals and holidaymakers. Keen support for *Guide Dogs for the Blind*. Large garden and children's play area. Coarse fishing available. Meals served in summer only.
▓ ▧ ◖ ▮ Å ♣ P

Coleby

Bell
Far Lane ☎ (0522) 810240
11.30–3, 7–11
Courage Directors; Marston's Pedigree Ⓗ
Ever-popular village pub with an increasing emphasis on food (booking advisable).
▓ ▚ ▧ ◖ ▮ P

Coningsby

Leagate Inn
Leagate Road
☎ (0526) 42370
11.30–2.30, 7–11
Marston's Pedigree; Taylor Landlord; Whitbread Castle Eden Ale Ⓗ
Fine 16th-century coaching inn, with a large garden and fish ponds. Original beams and flagstones; priest's hole above the fireplace. Jaguar Car Club and Koi (tropical fish) Keeper's Society meet here. Popular for food. Regular guest beers.
▓ ▧ ◖ ▮ ↺ P

Crowland

George & Angel
2 North Street
☎ (0733) 210550
10.30–3, 6–11 (10.30–11 Sat)
Ansells Mild; Ruddles Best Bitter, County; Webster's Yorkshire Bitter Ⓗ
Popular, small, town pub with a basic bar and a comfortable lounge. A Grade II listed building near Trinity Bridge and Crowland Abbey.
🏠 Q 🅴 ⬧ ♣ P

Deeping St Nicholas

Blue Bell
Main Road
☎ (0775) 88202
11–2.30, 6.30–11
Wells Eagle, Bombardier Ⓗ
Two rooms of character: oak beams, wood-panelling and real fires. Meals are home cooked by the landlord, at any reasonable time. Large play area at rear; tables at front. Caravans may stay overnight in grounds by arrangement. 🏠 Q 🏵 🅴 🍴 🅴 🅰 P

Donington

Queen Inn
49 Station Street (off A52 bypass)
☎ (0775) 820281
11–3, 6.30–11
Courage Directors; John Smith's Magnet Ⓗ
Basic, roadside local offering a friendly welcome. Snacks available. 🏠 🏵 ♣ P

East Kirkby

Red Lion
Main Road
☎ (079 03) 406
11–3, 7–11
Bateman XB; Vaux Samson Ⓗ
Situated near the Lincolnshire Air Museum (housing its Lancaster Bomber), this friendly village local has a landlord with a passion for all things past, incl. clocks and steam engines. Guest beers. 🏠 ⭍ 🏵 🅰 P

Folkingham

New Inn
West Street
☎ (0529) 7371
11–2 (not Mon–Wed), 5.30–11 (11–11 Sat)
Marston's Pedigree; Taylor Landlord; Whitbread Boddingtons Bitter Ⓗ
Friendly pub with a separate pool room. Originally built to house the warden of a workhouse next door.
🏠 Q 🚪 🍴 ♣

Frampton

Moores Arms
Church End
OS328392 ☎ (0205) 722408
10.30–3, 6.30–11
Draught Bass; Stones Best Bitter Ⓗ
Smart and busy, with a good garden and an excellent restaurant. 🏵 🍴 🍴 P

Gainsborough

Elm Cottage
138 Church Street
☎ (0427) 615474
11–2.30, 6.30–11
Bass Mild XXXX, Special Ⓗ
Pleasant pub at the northern edge of the town centre, hidden behind a supermarket. Excellent food. Fine collection of porcelain plates and local paintings. Handy for the football ground. 🍴 ➤ 🚆 P

Horse & Groom
1 Beaumont Street
☎ (0427) 613388
11–11
Tetley Mild, Bitter Ⓗ
Large, one-bar, street-corner pub on the road between Central station and town centre. Live music some eves; bar skittles. Beer range may vary.
🚪 🍴 ➤ ♣ P

Gedney Dyke

Chequers
☎ (0406) 362666
11–3, 7–11
Adnams Mild, Bitter; Draught Bass; Bateman XB; Greene King Abbot Ⓗ
Comfortable country pub, well worth seeking out, especially if hungry as well as thirsty. Bridge played — beginners welcomed.
🏠 🏵 🍴 ♣ P

Grantham

Angel & Royal
High Street ☎ (0476) 65816
11–2.30 (4 Sat), 6 (7 Sat)–11
Adnams Bitter; Draught Bass; Bateman XXXB; Courage Directors Ⓗ
Historic coaching inn, associated with Richard III; fine masonry, timbered ceilings and tapestries. Large real fire (spit roasts in winter) in Angel Bar. Three star hotel accommodation. No-smoking area. Guest beers.
🏠 Q 🏵 🚪 🍴 🅴 P 🍴

Beehive
10–11 Castlegate
☎ (0476) 67794
11–3, 7–11 (11–11 Fri)
Adnams Bitter, Broadside Ⓗ
Friendly town pub with a unique living pub sign.
⭍ 🏵 🍴 ➤

Chequers
25 Market Place
☎ (0476) 76383
12–3 (4 Sat), 7 (5 Thu)–11 (12–11 Fri)
Home Bitter; Theakston Best Bitter, XB, Old Peculier; Younger IPA, No. 3 Ⓗ
Lively, town-centre alehouse which attracts a good cross-section of people. Lunchtime food is all home-made. Note the pump clip collection, also the pictures for sale, painted by local artists, in the back room. 🍴

Joiners Arms
9 North Street
☎ (0476) 65288
11–2.30, 4.30 (5.30 winter)–11 (11–11 Sat); 11–5, 7–11 Sat in winter)
John Smith's Bitter, Magnet Ⓗ
Friendly, corner local: a comfortable, L-shaped room with pool and darts at one end. Popular with all ages. 🍴 ♣

Royal Queen
Belton Lane
☎ (0476) 64410
11.30–3, 6.30–11 (11–11 Sat in summer)
Courage Directors; John Smith's Bitter Ⓗ
Large and busy, modern pub: two bars and a conservatory at the rear with smart, tasteful decor. ⭍ 🏵 🍴 🅴 P

White Lion
53 Bridge End Road
☎ (0476) 62084
11–11
Courage Directors; John Smith's Bitter Ⓗ
Lively town local. Darts, pool and football enthusiasts in the bar; lounge is chatty and friendly. 🏵 🍴 🅴 ➤ ♣

Try also: **Five Bells**, Brook St (Free); **Shirley Croft Hotel**, Harrowby Rd, (Bateman)

Grasby

Cross Keys
Brigg Road (A1084)
☎ (065 262) 247
12–3 (may extend), 7–11 (12–11 Sat)
Camerons Bitter, Strongarm Ⓗ
Pleasant, two-roomed pub on a hillside. The garden contains a children's play area. Convenient for Viking Way walkers. No food Mon eve. 🏠 🏵 🍴 🅴 ♣ ♣ P

Haltoft End

Castle
On A52
☎ (0205) 760393
11–3, 7–11
Bateman Mild, XB, XXXB Ⓗ
Friendly local on main tourist route. Good adventure playground.
🏠 Q 🏵 🚪 🍴 ♣ 🌙 P

Lincolnshire

Heckington

Nags Head
34 High Street
☎ (0529) 60218
11–3, 7–11
**Ruddles Best Bitter, County;
Webster's Yorkshire Bitter** Ⓗ
300 year-old, oak-beamed pub
with a friendly welcome.
Emphasis on catering, with
many home-made dishes.
⌂ ◖ ⌷ Å ⇌ P

Hemingby

Coach & Horses
☎ (065 887) 280
12–2.30 (Sat only), 7–11 (12–2,
7–10.30 Sun)
Bateman Mild, XB Ⓗ
Pleasant village pub which is
the true centre of the local
community. Oak panels and low
beams throughout. Note
lunchtime opening weekends
only. ⌂ ⌖ ♣ P

Holbeach

Bell Hotel
21 High Street (B1105)
☎ (0406) 23223
10.30–3, 6–11
Elgood's Bitter Ⓗ
Friendly pub with good
conversation. Extensive
collection of malt whiskies.
⇌ ◖ ⌷ ♣ ♠

Holbeach Hurn

Rose & Crown
Marsh Road
☎ (0406) 26085
11–11
Elgood's Bitter Ⓗ
Happy, rural pub with a mixed
clientele. Serves a touring
caravan park, set in 600 acres.
Boules on Sun. ⌂ ⌖ ◖ Å ♣ P

Horbling

Plough
4 Spring Lane
☎ (0529) 240263
11–2, 7–11
**Greene King IPA, Abbot;
Wards Sheffield Best Bitter** Ⓗ
Small, village local: a tiny snug,
pool in the back bar, quiet
lounge. Good value food and
accommodation. One of the few
pubs owned by a parish
council. Guest beers.
⌂ Q ⇌ ⇌ ◖ ⌷ ♣ P

Horncastle

Red Lion
Bullring
☎ (0507) 523338
11–3, 7–11
Tetley Bitter Ⓗ
Friendly market town pub
which supports a flourishing

theatre in the converted stables.
Meals should be booked in
advance. ⌂ ⇌ ◖ ⌷ P

Try also: **Black Swan**
(Bateman); **Ship** (Courage)

Hundleby

Hundleby Inn
Main Road ☎ (0790) 52577
11–3, 6.30–11
Draught Bass; Bateman XB Ⓗ
Popular, two-bar, wood-
panelled pub. Strong links with
Guide Dogs for the Blind.
⌂ ⌖ ◖ ⌷ Å ♣ P

Kirkby la Thorpe

Queens Head
Church Street
☎ (0529) 305743
11.30–2.30, 6–11
Draught Bass Ⓗ
Comfortable, well-converted,
village pub offering a friendly
welcome and good food.
⌖ ◖ ⌷ P

Limber

New Inn
High Street
☎ (0469) 60257
11–2.30, 6–11 (11–11 Sat)
**Bateman XXXB; McEwan
80/-; Tetley Bitter** Ⓗ
Pub owned by the Earl of
Yarborough – whose name is
used to describe a poor bridge
hand and also adorns many
pubs in the area not owned by
him. A magnificent mausoleum
is close by. At least two guest
beers, incl. a mild. Food not
always available at weekend.
⌂ Q ⌖ ⇌ ◖ ⌷ ♣ P

Lincoln

Harvest Moon
Wolsey Way, Glebe Park (new
estate off A158)
☎ (0522) 526309
12–2.30, 6–11 (11–11 Sat)
**Theakston Best Bitter, XB;
Younger Scotch** Ⓗ
Converted farmhouse on a large
housing estate in the east of the
city. Can be noisy and smoky.
Large restaurant at rear. ♣ P

Jolly Brewer
27 Broadgate
☎ (0522) 528583
11–11
**Draught Bass; Everards
Tiger; Theakston XB;
Younger Scotch, No. 3** Ⓗ
Popular, one-bar, town-centre
pub, serving a wide range of
real ales to a varied range of
clients. Interesting Art Deco
interior and multi-coloured
exterior. Excellent guest beers
and Bulmers Traditional cider.
⌂ ⌖ ◖ ⌷ ⇌ ♣ ○ P

Millers Arms
88 High Street
☎ (0522) 520939
11–11
**Courage Best Bitter,
Directors; John Smith's
Bitter, Magnet** Ⓗ
Friendly town pub with three
distinct drinking areas, plus a
courtyard. Good collection of
horse brasses in the lounge.
Guest milds are available in
rotation. ⌂ ◖ ⇌ ♣ P

Prince of Wales
77a Bailgate
☎ (0522) 528894
11–3 (2.30 winter), 7–11
**John Smith's Bitter,
Magnet** Ⓗ
Pleasant and popular, two-
roomed pub in the heart of the
Uphill tourist area. Wide range
of excellent meals at lunchtime
(eves summer only). Good
collection of plates on walls.
Landlord very keen on Welsh
rugby. ⌂ ◖ ⌷ ♣

Queen in the West
Moor Street, Carholme Road
(20 yds from A57)
☎ (0522) 526169
11–3, 5.30–11
**Adnams Bitter; Bateman XB;
Taylor Landlord; Theakston
XB; Wards Sheffield Best
Bitter; Younger No. 3** Ⓗ
Pleasant pub in the west end of
the city. Popular with local
workers at lunchtime. Fine
collection of old bottles and
bric-a-brac. Beer range may
vary. Q ◖ ♣

Sippers
26 Melville Street
☎ (0522) 527612
11–3, 6–11
**Bateman Mild, XXXB;
Courage Directors; John
Smith's Bitter, Magnet** Ⓗ
Street-corner pub in the city
centre – previously known as
the 'Crown & Cushion'. Full of
seafaring memorabilia. Very
popular with workers from local
factories at lunchtime; quieter
eves. Q ◖ ⇌ ♣

Small Beer Off-Licence
91 Newland Street West (off
A57) ☎ (0522) 528628
10.30–10.30
**Bateman XXXB; Taylor
Landlord; Wards Sheffield
Best Bitter** Ⓗ
Popular, well-established off-
licence with an ever-varying
range of guest beers. Wide
range of British and foreign
bottled beers.

Strugglers
83 Westgate
☎ (0522) 524702
11–3, 5–11 (11–11 Fri & Sat)
**Bass Mild XXXX, Draught
Bass** Ⓗ

Lincolnshire

Busy, basic and bursting with
people; a veritable little gem,
reflecting all aspects of Lincoln
life. Reputed to have a secret
passage to the adjacent castle.
Home of a successful Sunday
football team. Q ✿ 🍴 ♣

Victoria
6 Union Road
☎ (0522) 536048
11–11
**Bateman XB; Everards Old
Original; Taylor Landlord;
Theakston Old Peculier** 🅗
Flagship pub of the Small Beer
wholesale chain. Two or three
guest beers always available,
incl. a mild. Superb food;
occasional live music; even a
guest crisp policy and the odd
character behind the bar –
simply the best. Q 🍴 🔄

Louth

Old Whyte Swanne
45 Eastgate
☎ (0507) 601312
11–3 (2 Wed & Fri), 7–11 (11–11 Sat)
**Bass Mild XXXX, Draught
Bass; Stones Best Bitter** 🅗
Built in 1612 – the oldest pub
in Louth, with a magnificent
public bar at the front and a
modern lounge at the rear,
reputedly haunted by a
subterranean ghost. Next to
public car park (free eves).
🏚 ✿ 🍴 ♣

Wheatsheaf
62 Westgate
☎ (0507) 606262
11–3, 5–11
**Draught Bass; Stones Best
Bitter; Tetley Bitter** 🅗
Situated in a quiet Georgian
terrace, this inn, dating from
1625, is equally attractive
inside and out. Meals Mon–Fri.
🏚 Q ✿ 🍴 🔄 P

Woodman Inn
134 Eastgate
☎ (0507) 602100
11–3 (4 Wed, Fri & Sat), 5–11
**Courage Directors; John
Smith's Bitter** 🅗
Comfortable, friendly, two-
roomed pub. ✿ 🍴 🔄 ♣ P

Woolpack
Riverhead Road
☎ (0507) 606568
11–3, 7–11
Bateman Mild, XB, XXXB 🅗
A former 19th-century wool
merchant's house, now a
traditional, friendly inn with
three rooms to suit all tastes.
The short walk from the town
centre is well rewarded.
🏚 Q ✿ 🔄 ♣ P

Try also: Boars Head,
Newmarket (Bateman)

Mablethorpe

Montalt Arms
8 George Street (off High
Street)
☎ (0507) 472794
11–3, 7–11
**Draught Bass; Bateman
XXXB; Stones Best Bitter;
Tetley Bitter** 🅗
A comfortable, L-shaped wood-
panelled lounge bar with a well-
appointed restaurant. The pub is
named after a local medieval
knight who was killed in a duel.
Photographs of old
Mablethorpe adorn the walls.
Not a typical seaside trippers'
pub. Limited parking. 🏚 ✿ 🍴 ▶ P

Mareham le Fen

Royal Oak
Main Street ☎ (065 886) 357
11–3, 7–11
Bateman XB, XXXB
(winter) 🅗
Sir Richard Mint once lived in
this 500 year-old thatched pub,
which is popular with both
locals and visitors.
Misbehaviour may result in a
visit to the stocks in the
attractive garden. 🏚 ✿ 🍴 ▶ P

Market Deeping

Vine
19 Church Street
☎ (0778) 342387
11–2.30, 5.30–11
**Adnams Broadside; Wells
Eagle, Bombardier** 🅗
Former 1870s prep school, now
a very friendly local: a large,
busy bar with a smaller lounge.
Hosts many social events, incl.
quiz nights and charity
functions. Organises bus trips.
🏚 Q ✿ 🍴 🔄 ♣ P

Marshchapel

Greyhound
Seadyke Way
☎ (047 286) 267
11–3, 7–11
Bateman Mild, XB, XXXB 🅗
Two-bar, village pub with
unusual and attractive settles in
the public bar. 🏚 Q 🍴 ▶ ♣ P

Minting

Sebastopol
Church Lane (1½ miles from
A158)
☎ (065 887) 688/364
12–2, 7–11
**Adnams Bitter, Broadside;
Bateman XB; Wards Kirby** 🅗
Comfortable, 16th-century,
village local, offering excellent
food in pleasant surroundings.
No meals Tue eves.
🏚 🐾 ✿ 🍴 ▶ 🔄 👟 ♣ P

Morton (Bourne)

Five Bells
Haconby Lane (400 yds E of
A15, next to church)
☎ (0778) 570332
12–2 (2.30 Sat), 7–11
**Greene King Abbot; Tetley
Bitter; Wards Mild, Thorne
Best Bitter, Sheffield Best
Bitter** 🅗
Comfortable and welcoming
village pub, popular with young
people. Separate restaurant
(closed Sun and Mon eves).
🏚 ✿ 🍴 P

Morton (Gainsborough)

Crooked Billet
Crooked Billet Street
☎ (0427) 612584
11–3, 6.30–11
Bass Mild XXXX, Special 🅗
Traditional, three-bar pub
sporting a collection of naval
hats. Q 🔄 ♣

Moulton Chapel

Wheatsheaf
4 Fengate ☎ (0406) 380525
12–3 (not Wed; 11.30–4 Sat), 7–11
**Elgood's Bitter; Greene King
IPA** 🅗
Friendly, two-room pub in an
out-of-the-way Fenland village.
Collection of pottery pigs and
other 'pigeriana'. One or two
guest beers. Camping and eve
meals, both by arrangement.
🏚 ✿ 🍴 👟 P

Nettleham

Plough
The Green ☎ (0522) 750275
11–3, 7–11
Bateman Mild, XB 🅗
A friendly, stone-built, village
pub. Landlord is well known for
his rabbit pies and geniality –
no food Sun. Excellent facilities
for meetings or special
occasions. Outdoor drinking in
the small courtyard. 🐾 ✿ 🍴 ♣

White Hart
14 High Street
☎ (0522) 751976
11.30–3, 7–11
**Bateman Mild, XB, XXXB,
Victory** 🅗
Once a courthouse, now a
village local with a busy public
bar and a quieter lounge.
🐾 🍴 ▶ 🔄 ♣ P

North Kelsey

Royal Oak
High Street ☎ (0652) 678544
12–3, 7–11
**Bateman XXXB; Stones Best
Bitter; Vaux Samson; Wards
Sheffield Best Bitter** 🅗

179

Lincolnshire

Friendly and popular; an excellent village pub with an open-plan bar, a separate games room and a small snug. General knowledge quiz nights Tue; music quiz alternate Sat.
🏠 🍴 🍺 🍷 ♣ P

Try also: Queens Head, North Kelsey Moor (Free)

Norton Disney

St Vincent Arms
Main Street
☎ (0522) 788478
12–2.30, 7–11
Adnams Bitter; Bateman Mild, XXXB; Marston's Pedigree Ⓗ
Friendly village pub with a lively public bar. The village has connections with Walt Disney and his family origins. Three regular guest beers on handpumps. 🏠 🍴 🍺 🍷 ♣ P

Oasby

Houblon Arms
Main Street (off B6403)
☎ (052 95) 215
12–3, 7–11
Ansells Bitter; Ind Coope Burton Ale; Taylor Landlord Ⓗ
Fine village inn, built using local stone. Beams and brass abound; open fires give off a pleasant aroma of woodsmoke. Popular with locals and nearby town dwellers for the ale and the good value food.
🏠 Q 🍴 🏠 🍷 P

Potterhanworth

Chequers
Cross Street (off B1178)
☎ (0522) 790189
12–3 (Fri-Sun only), 7–11
Mansfield Riding Mild, Riding Bitter, Old Baily Ⓗ
Friendly, village local with a popular host; a single room with the emphasis on food. Doubles dartboard. Beer garden at the rear. Restricted lunchtime opening. Q 🍴 🍷 ♣ P

Quadring

White Hart
7 Town Drove
☎ (0775) 821135
11–3, 6.30–11
Bateman Mild, XB, XXXB Ⓗ
Busy village local which offers a welcoming atmosphere and caters for all ages. 🏠 🍴 P

Raithby

Red Lion
Main Road ☎ (0790) 53727
11–3 (Sat/Sun only), 7–11
Home Bitter; Theakston XB, Old Peculier Ⓗ

Attractive pub, with an intimate restaurant, in a picturesque Wolds village. Enterprising landlord with culinary skills has built a reputation for excellent home-made food; fresh pizzas available at the bar. Lunchtime opening at weekends only.
🏠 🍴 🏠 🍷 ♣ P

Reepham

Fox & Hounds
Station Road ☎ (0522) 750427
11–3, 7–11
Ruddles Best Bitter Ⓗ
Friendly, village pub with a lively bar and a quiet, comfortable lounge. Regular quiz night. Guest beers.
Q 🏠 ♣ P

Saracen's Head

Saracen's Head
Washway Road
☎ (0406) 22708
10.30–3, 6–11
Greene King Abbot Ⓖ; **Wards Sheffield Best Bitter** Ⓗ
An unspoilt, hospitable pub, situated on a sharp bend. Regular weekend sing-alongs.
🏠 Q 🍺 🏠 ♣ P

Skegness

Vine Hotel
Vine Road (off Drummond Road, 1 mile S of centre)
☎ (0754) 610611
11–3, 6–11
Bateman Mild, XB, XXXB Ⓗ
Attractive building in a secluded setting; reputedly the haunt of smugglers in former times, and visited by Alfred, Lord Tennyson. A sanctuary from the hurly-burly of the resort in summer and a biting east wind in winter. 🏠 🍴 🏠 🍷 ♣ P

Sleaford

Marquis of Granby
65 Westgate ☎ (0529) 303223
11–2.30, 5.30–11
Ind Coope Burton Ale; Tetley Bitter Ⓗ
Cosy, popular local with a small, covered courtyard at the back.
🏠 🍴 🍷 ♣

Nags Head
64 Southgate
☎ (0529) 413916
11–3, 6.30–11 (11–11 Sat)
Bateman XB, XXXB Ⓗ
Friendly, no-frills town pub. Excellent range of filled rolls. Occasional live music.
🏠 🍴 🍷 ♣ P

Waggon & Horses
3 Eastgate ☎ (0529) 303388
11–3, 6.30–11 (11–11 Sat)
Bass Mild XXXX, Draught Bass; Stones Best Bitter Ⓗ
Large, open-plan pub which can

get very crowded in the evening. Good value lunches.
🏠 🍴 🍷 P

South Kyme

Hume Arms
High Street ☎ (0526) 861004
11.30–2.30, 7–11
Bateman XB; Tetley Bitter; Wards Sheffield Best Bitter Ⓗ
Quiet village pub opposite the river; separate bar, lounge and restaurant. 🏠 🍴 🍷 🏠 ♠ P

Spalding

Lincolnshire Poacher
11 Double Street
☎ (0775) 766490
11–3, 6–11
Home Bitter; Marston's Pedigree; Theakston XB, Old Peculier Ⓗ
A recently refurbished, ancient riverside pub in the town centre. Guest beers. 🏠 🍴 🍷 ⬧ ⭗

Red Lion
Market Place ☎ (0775) 722869
10.30–3.30, 5–11
Adnams Bitter; Draught Bass Ⓗ
A popular, well-appointed bar in a town-centre hotel. Guest beers. 🏠 🍴 P

Try also: Ship Albion, Albion St (Bateman); **White Horse**, Churchgate (Samuel Smith)

Spilsby

White Hart
Cornhill, Market Square
☎ (0790) 52244
11–3, 7–11 (11–11 Fri & Sat)
Hardys & Hansons Best Bitter, Kimberley Classic Ⓗ
Large, comfortable, town-centre coaching inn with its own 150 year-old posting box – reputedly the oldest in the country. 🏠 🍴 🍷 🏠 ♣ P

Springthorpe

New Inn
Hill Road ☎ (0427) 83254
11–3, 7–11
Bateman XXXB; Ruddles Best Bitter Ⓗ
Small, country pub on a village green – very picturesque. Fine food served in the small restaurant. 🏠 Q 🍴 🏠 ♣ P

Stamford

Daniel Lambert
20 St Leonards Street
☎ (0780) 55991
12–3, 6–11
Taylor Best Bitter, Landlord Ⓗ
Excellent, one-roomed, free house with a homely atmosphere. Guest beer.
🏠 🏠 ⭗ ♣

Dolphin

60 East Street
☎ (0780) 55494
11–2.30, 6–11
**Mansfield Riding Bitter;
Wells Eagle** Ⓗ
An 18th-century building,
divided into several small
rooms. Stamford's unique game,
Push Penny, is played here.
🍴 ◑ ➹ ♣

White Swan

21 Scotgate
☎ (0780) 52834
11–3, 6–11
**Bateman Mild, XB, XXXB,
Victory** Ⓗ
A former Manns pub,
refurbished by Bateman and
reopened in 1988. Winner of
local CAMRA *Pub of the Month*
award.
🍴 ♣

Swayfield

Royal Oak

27 High Street
☎ (047 684) 247
11–2.30, 6–11
**Adnams Broadside; Draught
Bass** Ⓗ
Real stone walls, real exposed
beams and a real fire all combine
to create a delightful, cosy
atmosphere. Villagers, local
townsfolk and ramblers all
enjoy their favourite tipple here.
Excellent home-cooking.
🍴 Q 🍴 ◑ P

Swinhope

Clickem Inn

On B1203, 3 miles from
Binbrook
☎ (047 283) 253
11–2.30 (not Mon, 3 Sat), 7–11

**Bateman XXXB; Theakston
XB** Ⓗ
This isolated but popular Wolds
pub is a genuine free house. Its
name derives from the click of
the gate to the field opposite,
into which farmers drove flocks
whilst drinking at the pub.
Children welcome in games
area. Always two guest beers.
🚲 ➹ 🍴 ◑ ♣ P

Wainfleet

Red Lion

33 High Street
☎ (0754) 880301
11–3, 7–11 (11–11 Sat)
Bateman Mild, XB, XXXB Ⓗ
Large pub, just off the market
place and the nearest Bateman
outlet to the brewery. Spacious
bar and a cosy lounge with an
imposing fireplace.
🍴 🍴 🛏 ◑ ⛽ Å ➹ ♣ P

LAGER: THE GREAT BRITISH CON

Firstly, let's dispel one myth: CAMRA is not anti-lager. We have
even been prominent in our support of genuine lager brewers, such
as Budvar of Czechoslovakia. What CAMRA has always opposed
is the great British lager con.

Lager is a classic beer style, indigenous to Bohemia and Bavaria and
copied with skill in many parts of the world. It differs from ale not
merely in colour (indeed, not all lagers are amber), but in the use
of different types of malts, hops, and, in particular, yeasts. The
lager yeasts sink to the bottom of the wort during fermentation
(hence lagers are 'bottom-fermented'; with 'top-fermented' ales
the yeast sits on the top). Lager fermentation is also at a colder
temperature and the beer is allowed a much longer conditioning
('lagering') period at the brewery, often up to three months.

Sadly, in the last 30 years, British brewers have appropriated
continental names for poor quality lager-type beers brewed in this
country. They tend to brew them at much lower gravities than the
European originals, and seldom allow them a good lagering period.
They treat them like keg beers, filtering them, pasteurising them
and forcing them to the bar with carbon dioxide, whereas true
lagers are usually not filtered but drawn off their low-lying yeast,
the pressure of their own natural lively carbonation carrying them
to the bar.

Glossy advertising campaigns have now taken lager to over 50%
of British beer sales and, thus, fake continental beers have been
elbowing out our own native beer styles. Thankfully, the tide has
begun to turn. Imports of genuinely flavoursome European beers
have shown British lagers to be pale imitations, and interest in cask
ale has begun to surge. The heyday of British lager may already be
over.

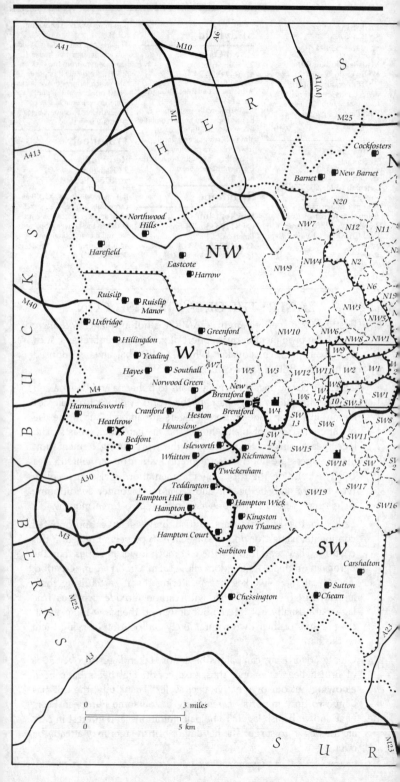

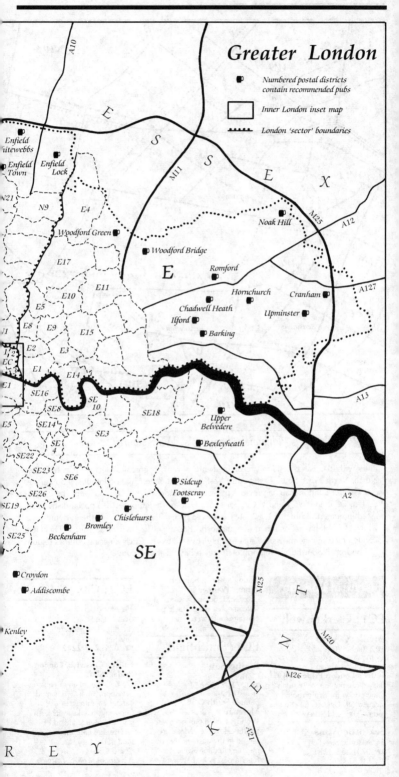

Greater London

- Numbered postal districts contain recommended pubs
- Inner London inset map
- London 'sector' boundaries

A10

E S S E X

M11

M25   A12

Enfield Whitewebbs

Enfield Town   Enfield Lock

N21   N9   E4   Noak Hill   M25   A12

Woodford Green

Woodford Bridge   A127

E17   E   Romford

E10   E11   Hornchurch   Cranham

E5   Chadwell Heath   Upminster

E8   E9   E15   Ilford   A127

E1, 2   E2   E3   Barking

EC   E1   E14

E1   SE16   A13

SE8   SE10   SE18   Upper Belvedere

SE14   SE3   Bexleyheath

E5   SE4

SE22   Sidcup

SE23   SE6   Footscray   A2

SE26   Chislehurst

SE19   Bromley

SE25   Beckenham

Croydon   SE

Addiscombe

Kenley   M25   K E N T   M20

M26

S U R R E Y   K   A21

Greater London

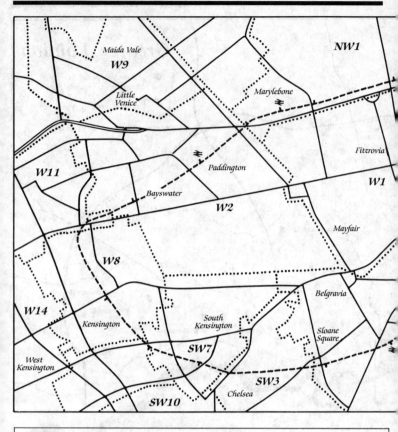

W9 · Maida Vale · NW1 · Little Venice · Marylebone · Fitzrovia · W11 · Paddington · W1 · Bayswater · W2 · Mayfair · W8 · Belgravia · W14 · Kensington · South Kensington · Sloane Square · West Kensington · SW7 · SW3 · SW10 · Chelsea

Fuller's, *Chiswick*; **Young's**, *Wandsworth*

Pubs within Greater London are divided into seven geographical sectors: Central, East, North, North West, South East, South West and West, reflecting London postal boundaries (see Greater London map on previous pages). Look under Central London for postal districts EC1 to EC4, and WC1 and WC2. For each of the surrounding sectors, postal districts are listed in numerical order (E1, E2, etc.), followed in alphabetical order by the outlying areas which do not have London postal numbers (Barking, Chadwell Heath, etc.). The Inner London map, above, shows the area roughly covered by the Circle Line and outlines regions of London (Bloomsbury, Holborn, etc.) which have featured pubs.

Central London

EC1: Clerkenwell

Artillery Arms
102 Bunhill Row
☎ (071) 253 4683
11–11 (11–3, 7–11 Sat)
Fuller's London Pride, ESB Ⓗ
Busy, little pub opposite Bunhill cemetery, with hardly room to swing a cat. Upstairs function room. ◖ ⇌ (Old St) ⊖ ♣

Sekforde Arms
34 Sekforde Street
☎ (071) 253 3251
11–11 (8–11 Sat)

Young's Bitter, Special, Winter Warmer Ⓗ
Excellent food and a warm welcome in a comfortable pub. Upstairs function room.
Q ◖ ◗ ⇌ (Farringdon) ♣ ♣

EC1: Smithfield

Rising Sun
Cloth Fair
☎ (071) 726 6671
11.30–11 (12–3, 5–11 Sat)
Samuel Smith OBB, Museum Ⓗ
Wood-panelled pub near Smithfield market. Meals are served in the upstairs bar which may be hired for private functions. ◖ ◗ ⇌ (Barbican) ⊖

EC2: City

Fleetwood
36 Wilson Street
(W side of Broadgate development)
☎ (071) 247 2242
11–9.30 (11–3 Sat)
Fuller's Chiswick, London Pride, ESB Ⓗ
On the edge of an interesting development area, this modern bar has an enthusiastic following, thanks to its keen staff and high standard of service. Possibly the best pub food in the City.
Q ⑧ ◖ ◗ ⇌
(Liverpool St/Moorgate) ⊖

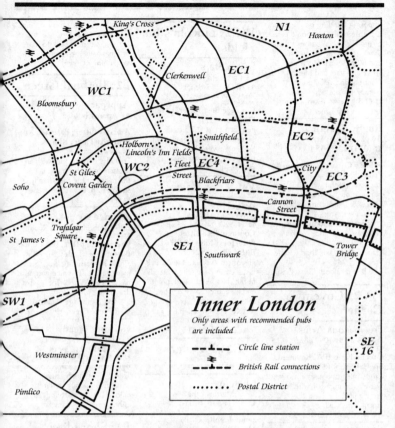

Inner London

Only areas with recommended pubs
are included

— **—⊥—** — Circle line station

⊥ British Rail connections

········· Postal District

EC3 : City

East India Arms
67 Fenchurch Street
☎ (071) 480 6562
11–9 (11–3 Sat; closed Sun)
**Young's Bitter, Special,
Winter Warmer** Ⓗ
Perennially popular pub – not
London's cheapest, but one of
the best. No jeans.
Q ⇌ (Fenchurch St) ⊖

Lamb Tavern
10–12 Leadenhall Market
☎ (071) 626 2454
11–9 (closed weekends)
Young's Bitter, Special Ⓗ
Multi-level pub in the heart of
the Victorian covered market.
Crowded at lunchtime and early
eve. Ⓓ ⇌ (Fenchurch St)
⊖ (Monument) ♣

Three Lords
27 Minories
11–9 (closed weekends)
Young's Bitter, Special Ⓗ,
Winter Warmer Ⓖ
Light and airy, ground-floor bar
– less hectic than some City
pubs. No smoking in the
basement bar.
Ⓓ ⇌ (Fenchurch St) ⊖
(Tower Hill/Tower Gateway) ✗

EC4 : Blackfriars

Black Friar
174 Queen Victoria Street
☎ (071) 236 5650
11.30–9.30 (closed weekends, except
in summer)
**Adnams Bitter; Draught
Bass; Marston's Pedigree;
Tetley Bitter** Ⓗ
Worth the price of a pint to
view the listed, Art Nouveau
interior which features scenes of
monastic life. ⊛ Ⓓ ⇌ ⊖

EC4 : Cannon Street

Banker
Cousin Lane
☎ (071) 283 5206
11–3, 5–9 (11–9 Fri; closed weekends)
**Fuller's Chiswick, London
Pride, ESB** Ⓗ
Split-level pub beneath Cannon
Street station, with views of the
Thames. Riverside patio.
⊛ Ⓓ ⇌ ⊖

EC4 : Fleet Street

Punch Tavern
99 Fleet Street
☎ (071) 353 8338

11–11 (10 Thu & Fri)
**Adnams Bitter; Greene King
IPA; Marston's Pedigree;
Tetley Bitter; Wadworth
6X** Ⓗ
Pub where the ornately
decorated interior almost makes
up for the high prices charged.
Ⓓ ⊖ (St Paul's)

WC1 : Bloomsbury

Lamb
94 Lamb's Conduit Street
☎ (071) 405 0715
11–11
**Young's Bitter, Special,
Winter Warmer** Ⓗ
Splendid, welcoming hostelry
with loyal regulars from all
walks of life. Rare original
Victorian snob screens and a
pleasant no-smoking snug bar.
Substantial snacks and salads
early eves. Monthly quiz nights.
Q ⊛ Ⓓ ⇌ (King's Cross)
⊖ (Russell Sq) ♣ ✗

WC1 : Holborn

Cittie of Yorke
22 High Holborn
☎ (071) 242 7670
11.30–11 (11.30–3, 5.30–11 Sat;
closed Sun)
Samuel Smith OBB, Museum Ⓗ

Greater London

Imposing building on the site of a 15th-century inn. Some parts of the Victorian 'baronial' hall date back to the original inn, and fittings such as a triangular stove and vats add interest. The front bar and cellar are less memorable but add space.
🏛 Q ◖ ▮ ⅃ ≋ (Farringdon)
⊖ (Chancery Lane) ♣

Rugby Tavern
19 Great James Street
☎ (071) 405 1384
11–11 (closed Sat)
Fuller's Chiswick, London Pride, ESB Ⓗ
Popular, tastefully furnished pub, just off Lamb's Conduit Street. A 19th-century theme pervades: mirrors and photographs of local history. Patronised by office workers and local residents alike. Darts team. Good value food for the area.
Q ◖ ▮ ⊖ (Holborn/Russell Sq)

WC2 : Covent Garden

Freemasons Arms
Long Acre ☎ (071) 836 3115
11–11
Greene King IPA, Rayments Special, Abbot Ⓗ
Large, busy pub just off Covent Garden. Lounge bar with food service upstairs. Near the Freemasons Hall.
◖ ▮ ≋ (Charing Cross) ⊖

Marquess of Anglesey
Bow Street ☎ (071) 240 3216
11–11
Young's Bitter, Special Winter Warmer Ⓗ
Busy, corner pub near the market hall and Theatre and London Transport museums. Upstairs bar and restaurant.
◖ ▮ ≋ (Charing Cross) ⊖

Marquis of Granby
51 Chandos Place
11–11
Adnams Bitter; Ind Coope Burton Ale; Taylor Walker Best Bitter Ⓗ
Narrow, wedge-shaped pub with multitudinous prints on the walls. Selection of malt whiskies; the guest beer may vary. Eve meals finish early.
◖ ▮ ≋ (Charing Cross) ⊖

WC2 : Holborn

Newton Arms
31 Newton Street
11–11 (11–3, 5.30–11 Sat; closed Sun)
Adnams Bitter; Ind Coope Burton Ale; Taylor Walker Best Bitter; Tetley Bitter Ⓗ
Modern pub at the base of an office block, attracting a largely local clientele. ◖ ▮ ⊖

WC2 : Lincoln's Inn Fields

Seven Stars
53 Carey Street (off Strand)
☎ (071) 242 8521
11–11 (may be earlier; closed weekends)
Courage Best Bitter, Directors Ⓗ
Founded in 1602, a traditional olde-worlde pub, popular with the legal profession (law courts nearby). Q ◖ ▮ ≋ (Blackfriars)
⊖ (Temple)

WC2 : St Giles

Angel
61 St Giles High Street
12–11 (12–3, 7–11 Sat; closed Sun)
Courage Best Bitter, Directors; John Smith's Bitter Ⓗ
Historic pub where the cellar is believed to be haunted. Stands in the shadow of Centrepoint and is reputed to be on the site of the inn where felons on the way to Tyburn called for a last drink. No food Sat.
◖ ⊖ (Tottenham Ct Rd) ♣

WC2 : Trafalgar Square

Chandos
29 St Martins Lane
☎ (071) 836 1401
11–11
Samuel Smith OBB, Museum Ⓗ
Large, popular, wood-panelled pub with an upstairs bar and restaurant. It features a floodlit figure of a cooper on the roof.
◖ ▮ ≋ (Charing Cross) ⊖

East London

E1 : Spitalfields

Pride of Spitalfields
3 Heneage Street
☎ (071) 247 8933
11–11
Fuller's London Pride, ESB; Theakston Old Peculier Ⓗ
Single-bar pub appealing to visitors and locals alike; good value for this part of London. Handy for Brick Lane's famous curry houses. Guest beers.
🏛 🛏 ◖ ⊖ (Aldgate E)

E1 : Stepney

Ship on the Green
60 Stepney Green
☎ (071) 791 2073
12–3.30, 6–11
Tolly Cobbold Bitter, Original Ⓗ
Comfortable, East End local with pictures, motor horns and

other bric-a-brac on the ceiling. Once known as the 'Ace of Hearts', but now back to its original name. ≋ (Limehouse)
⊖ (Stepney Green)

E2 : Bethnal Green

Approach Tavern
47 Approach Road
11–11
Adnams Bitter; Bateman XB; Everards Tiger; King & Barnes Sussex Ⓗ
Friendly, two-bar pub with an upstairs room for meetings. In the hands of the King family since 1928. Beer range varies.
▥ ⊖

Dundee Arms
339 Cambridge Heath Road
11–11
Greene King IPA; Ind Coope Burton Ale; Tetley Bitter Ⓗ
Single bar featuring boxing memorabilia. The tiled entrance has a recessed hook for use by draymen.
◖ ▮ ≋ (Cambridge Heath)
⊖ (Bethnal Green) ♣

Nelson's Head
32 Horatio Street (off Hackney Road) ☎ (071) 739 6054
11.30–3, 5–11 (12–4, 7–11 Sat)
Bateman Mild, XB, XXXB Ⓗ
The only Bateman's pub in London and a rare outlet for mild in the capital. Subdued lighting and piped music.

E2 : Shoreditch

Ship & Blue Ball
13 Boundary Street
☎ (071) 729 1192
12–3, 5.30–11 (8–11 Sat)
Premier Pitfield Bitter, Hoxton, Dark Star Ⓗ
The brewery's only London tied house. Two other Premier Pitfield ales are also available.
◖ ≋ (Liverpool St/Old St) ⊖ ♣

E3 : Bow

Bromley Arms
51 Fairfield Road
☎ (081) 980 4266
11–11
Shepherd Neame Master Brew Bitter, Spitfire Ⓗ
Small, one-bar pub, opposite Bow bus garage.
🏛 🍴 ⊖ (Bow Rd) ♣

E3 : Bromley by Bow

Beehive
104–106 Empson Street
11.30–3, 5–11
Brains SA Ⓗ
Back-street local offering an imaginative choice of guest beers (at least three); welcome

variety for the area.
🏠 ◖ ⊟ ⇌ (Devons Rd)
⊖ (Bromley by Bow) ♣

E4 : Chingford

Royal Oak
219 Kings Head Hill
☎ (081) 529 1492
11–3, 5.30–11 (11–11 Sat, public bar only)
McMullen AK, Country, Stronghart Ⓗ
Two, distinctive bars: the public is clean and comfortable; the lounge is quiet. 🏠 ◖ ◗ ⊟ ♣ P

E5 : Clapton

Anchor & Hope
15 High Hill Ferry (foot of Harrington Hill)
☎ (081) 806 1730
11–3, 5.30 (6 Sat)–11
Fuller's London Pride, ESB Ⓗ
Tiny, no-frills pub beside the River Lea. Often very busy due to its reputation for superb beer at excellent prices. 🏠 ⇌ ♣

E8 : Hackney

Lady Diana
95 Forest Road
11–3, 5.30–11
Adnams Bitter; Fuller's Chiswick, London Pride; Greene King Abbot; Marston's Pedigree; Premier Pitfield Dark Star Ⓗ
Friendly local, offering good value. Pizzas feature on the menu. Beer range may vary.
🏠 ◖ ◗

E9 : Homerton

Royal Standard
84 Victoria Park Road
☎ (081) 985 3224
12–3 (5 Sat), 5.30 (7 Sat)–11
Courage Best Bitter, Directors; Marston's Merrie Monk, Pedigree Ⓗ
Friendly, two-bar local near Victoria Park. The landlord takes pride in his beer. 🏠 ⊟

E10 : Leyton

Drum
559 Lea Bridge Road
11–11
Eldridge Pope Royal Oak; Greene King IPA, Abbot; Theakston XB; Younger Scotch Ⓗ
A good place for a quiet pint – no piped music! Q

Holly Bush
Grange Road
11.30–3, 7–11
Greene King IPA, Abbot Ⓗ
Recently renovated, back-street free house, in an area dominated by keg. Undoubtedly the best bet for visitors to nearby Orient FC. 🏠 ⇌ (Midland Rd) ♣

Tap & Spile
886 Lea Bridge Road
11–3.30, 5.30–11 (11–11 Fri & Sat)
Tolly Cobbold Mild, Original Ⓗ
Chain pub where six other beers from a wide range are usually available. Skittles played. ♣ ♢

E11 : Leytonstone

Red Lion
640 High Street
☎ (081) 558 6846
11–11
Ind Coope Burton Ale; Tetley Bitter Ⓗ
Corner pub with an impressive facade, despite the scars of an earlier incarnation. Its large, single bar is brightened by friendly staff. No food Sun.
🏠 ◖ ⇌ (High Rd) ⊖

E14 : Stepney

Queens Head
8 Flamborough Street
11–2.30, 5.30 (7.30 Sat)–11
Young's Bitter, Special, Winter Warmer Ⓗ
Traditional, East End local, with a warm welcome for all. No food weekends.
◖ ⊟ ⇌ (Limehouse) ⊖ ♣

E15 : Stratford

Princess of Wales
25 West Ham Lane
11–11 (11–3, 7–11 Sat)
Ind Coope Burton Ale; Tetley Bitter; Young's Special Ⓗ
Friendly pub, deservedly popular, where the landlord takes great pride in his beer (occasional guests). ◖ ⇌ ⊖

E17 : Walthamstow

College Arms
807–809 Forest Road
☎ (081) 531 8001
11–11
Eldridge Pope Royal Oak; Greene King IPA, Abbot; Nethergate Old Growler; Younger Scotch Ⓗ
A typical Wetherspoon conversion from a shop – well done. Beers may vary.
Q ◖ ⇌ (Wood St)

Coppermill
205 Coppermill Lane
11–11
Fuller's London Pride, ESB; Ind Coope Burton Ale; Marston's Pedigree; Morland Bitter; Tetley Bitter Ⓗ
Small, back-street free house on the western edge of Walthamstow, near a vast expanse of waterworks, reservoirs and marshes.
Q ⇌ (St James St) ⊖ (Black Horse Rd)

Flowerpot
128 Wood Street
11–3, 5.30–11 (11–11 Sat)
Draught Bass Ⓗ
Good, old-style drinkers' pub; no frills, just some of the best Bass in London. Q ⇌ (Wood St)

Pig & Whistle
185 Wood Street
☎ (081) 509 3766
11–11
Courage Directors; Marston's Border Exhibition, Pedigree Ⓗ
Very busy, one-bar, modern conversion from a shop. Food all day; quiz Mon.
🏠 ◖ ◗ ⇌ (Wood St)

Village
31 Orford Road
☎ (081) 521 9982
11–11
Fuller's London Pride, ESB; Marston's Pedigree; Morland Old Masters; Whitbread Boddingtons Bitter Ⓗ
Quiet, modern pub with a display of over 50 cameras.
⛱ 🏠 ◖ ◗ ⧫ ⇌ (Central) ⊖

Barking

Britannia
1 Church Road (near A123)
☎ (081) 594 1305
11–3, 5–11 (11–11 Sat)
Young's Bitter, Special, Winter Warmer Ⓗ
The only Young's tied house in Essex, with a large, comfortable saloon and a basic public bar. Warm, friendly atmosphere.
🏠 ◖ ⊟ ⇌ ⊖ ♣ P

Chadwell Heath

White Horse
118 High Road (A118)
☎ (081) 597 0229
11–11
Ind Coope Benskins Best Bitter, Burton Ale; Tetley Bitter Ⓗ
A 'White Horse' has been on this site, on the Roman road to Colchester, since Elizabethan days. The present pub, about 100 years old, has a comfortable interior and a large garden with an outside bar in summer. 🏠 ◖ ⇌ ♣ P

Cranham

Thatched House
348 St Marys Lane (B187)
☎ (040 22) 28080
12–3 (later in summer), 5.30–11
Adnams Bitter; Draught Bass; Charrington IPA; Greene King IPA Ⓗ
Friendly, locals' pub on the edge of the countryside, with a garden, family room, restaurant area and a large car park.
⛱ 🏠 ◖ ◗ P

187

Greater London

Hornchurch

Bull Inn
High Street ☎ (040 24) 42125
11–11 (11–3.30, 6–11 Fri & Sat)
Ind Coope Friary Meux Best Bitter, Burton Ale; Tetley Bitter Ⓗ
Traditional, neat, town-centre pub with a dining area off the main bar (no food Sun). Music at background level.
🅶 🄲 ≠ (Emerson Pk) P

Chequers
North Street
☎ (040 24) 42094
11–3 (4 Sat), 5.30 (6 Sat)–11
Ind Coope Friary Meux Best Bitter; Tetley Bitter Ⓗ
Friendly town pub offering excellent value ales. Separate games room; music is kept at background level. Meals Wed–Fri.
🄲 ≠ (Emerson Pk) ♣ P

Try also: Cricketers, High St (Grand Met)

Ilford

Rose & Crown
Ilford Hill ☎ (081) 478 7104
11–11
Adnams Bitter; Greene King Abbot; Ind Coope Benskins Best Bitter, Burton Ale; Tetley Bitter; Wadworth 6X Ⓗ
Large, one-bar local offering an excellent beer range. Comfortable and friendly; regular quiz nights. 🄶 🄲 ♣ ♣

Noak Hill

Bear
Noak Hill Road
11–3.30 (4 Fri & Sat), 5.30 (6 Sat)–11
Draught Bass; Charrington IPA Ⓗ
Much improved and extended local, with a large garden.
🄴 🄶 🄲 🄳 🄶 P

Romford

Durham Arms
101 Brentwood Road
11–3.30, 5 (6 Sat)–11
Ind Coope Burton Ale; Tetley Bitter Ⓗ
Pleasantly decorated pub outside the town centre. The safe garden for children has swings and a slide. Regular quiz nights; occasional live music and barbecues in the summer. No food Sun. 🄶 🄲 P

Upminster

Huntsman & Hounds
2 Ockendon Road, Corbets Tey
☎ (040 22) 20429
11–11
Taylor Walker Best Bitter;

Tetley Bitter Ⓗ
Friendly, family pub near the countryside, with a family room and a well-equipped playground for children. Meals all day Mon–Sat. 🄴 🄴 🄶 🄲 🄳 🄴 🄰 P

Woodford Bridge

Crown & Crooked Billet
13 Cross Road
11–3.30, 5.30–11 (11–11 Fri)
Draught Bass; Charrington IPA Ⓗ
Pleasant pub with a recent extension in keeping with its existing decor. No food Sun.
🄶 🄲 P

Woodford Green

Cricketers
299–301 High Road
11–3 (4 Sat), 5.30–11
McMullen AK, Country, Stronghart Ⓗ
Comfortable and friendly, traditional local offering excellent value; the beer is cheaper in the basic public bar. Pub golf society. 🄶 🄲 🄶 ♣ P

Travellers Friend
496–498 High Road
☎ (081) 504 2435
11–11
Courage Best Bitter, Directors; Greene King Abbot; Marston's Pedigree; Ridleys IPA Ⓗ
A gem: a traditional, wood-panelled local retaining its original snob screens. Good atmosphere; friendly staff. Courage Best is sold as 'Webster's Wonderful Wallop'. A pub which has never sold keg bitter. Q 🄶 🄲 🄴 (Woodford) P

North London

N1: Barnsbury

Crown
116 Cloudesley Road
☎ (071) 837 7107
11–11
Fuller's Chiswick, London Pride, ESB Ⓗ
19th-century pub retaining original features; the long, U-shaped bar has snob screens and etched-glass partitions divide separate drinking areas. Patio at the front; dining area at the rear (à la carte). 🄴 Q 🄲 🄳 🄴 (Angel) ♣

N1: Canonbury

Marquess Tavern
32 Canonbury Street (off A104) ☎ (071) 354 2975
11–11
Young's Bitter, Special, Winter Warmer Ⓗ

Elegant, Georgian building on the New River. A large, single, smart lounge with a food bar and a plainer public area with darts and shove-ha'penny. No food Sun.
🄴 Q 🄶 🄲 🄳 ≠ (Essex Rd)
🄴 (Highbury & Islington) ♣

N1: Hoxton

George & Vulture
63 Pitfield Street
11–3 (4 Sat), 5 (7 Sat)–11
Fuller's Chiswick, London Pride, ESB Ⓗ
Friendly, two-bar pub in a back-street area of Hoxton. Popular, with a strong local following. Lunches and eve snacks served.
🄶 🄶 ≠ (Old St) 🄴

N1: Islington

Compton Arms
4 Compton Avenue
☎ (071) 359 6883
11–11
Greene King IPA, Rayments Special, Abbot Ⓗ
A hidden oasis – immediately behind the busy Highbury Corner. Can be busy early eves.
Guest beers. Q 🄶 🄲
≠ (Highbury & Islington) 🄴

Earl of Radnor
106 Mildmay Grove (off Balls Pond Road)
☎ (071) 241 0318
11–11
Fuller's Chiswick, London Pride, ESB Ⓗ
Small, friendly, corner house, with Victorian decor; snob screens feature prominently in the centre of the pub. Meals available 12–9.30pm.
Q 🄶 🄲 🄳 🄶 ≠ (Dalston Kingsland) ♣

N1: King's Cross

Malt & Hops
33 Caledonian Road
11 (12 Sat)–11
Felinfoel Double Dragon; Gibbs Mew Local Line, Premium, Salisbury, Bishop's Tipple; Tetley Bitter Ⓗ
Conveniently situated for the public transport interchange; a lively pub with up to eleven beers at times. Good value food.
🄲 ≠ 🄴 🄴

N2: East Finchley

Old White Lion
121 Great North Road
(A1000) ☎ (081) 444 0554
11–11
Draught Bass; Charrington IPA; Fuller's London Pride; Young's Special Ⓗ
Fine, 1930s Wenlock brewery house with a good public bar. The huge saloon/lounge makes

clever use of different areas. Convivial atmosphere; all tastes catered for. ✿ ❨ 🖢 🖢 ⊖ ♣ P

Welch's Ale House
130 High Road (A1000)
11–3, 5.30–11 (11–11 Sat)
Fuller's London Pride; Greene King Abbot; Marston's Pedigree; Ruddles County; Wadworth 6X; Webster's Yorkshire Bitter H
Popular, busy former shop, often crowded. Regular guest beers and a good range of country wines. No food at weekends. ❨ ♣ ◌

Windsor Castle
The Walks, Church Lane (off A1000) ☎ (081) 883 5763
11–11
Greene King Abbot; McMullen Country; Marston's Pedigree H
Homely, well-run, welcoming and friendly McMullen free house, occasionally offering additional beers. No food Sun.
✿ ❨ 🖢 🖢 ♣

N6 : Highgate

Red Lion & Sun
25 North Road
12–4, 6–11 (12–11 Thu & Fri; 11.30–11 Sat)
Draught Bass; Charrington IPA; Young's Special H
Pub known for its panelled bar and loyal and knowledgeable local customers. Recommended lunches. One of many good pubs in this village.
Q ✿ ❨ 🖢 ⊖ ♣

N7 : Holloway

Admiral Mann
9 Hargrave Place
☎ (071) 485 4793
11–3 (4 Sat), 5.30 (7 Sat)–11
McMullen AK, Country H
Long-standing Mac's house. Well hidden, but worth finding for its beers. Separate, down-to-earth public bar.
Q ✿ ❨ 🖢 ⇌ (KentishTown) ⊖ ♣

N9 : Lower Edmonton

Beehive
Little Bury Street
11–3, 5.30–11 (11–11 Sat)
Ind Coope Burton Ale; Tetley Bitter; Young's Bitter H
One-bar, estate pub, popular with all sections of the local community. Quiz night Tue. Parking can be difficult. ✿ ❨ ♣ P

N11 : New Southgate

Northern Star
130 High Road
11–11

Courage Best Bitter; Ind Coope Friary Meux Best Bitter; Tetley Bitter H
A fine Victorian facade belies the modern interior, with its single, island servery and MTV screens. Loyal locals continue to frequent this oasis despite recent changes. No food Sun.
❨ ⇌ (New Southgate)
⊖ (Arnos Grove)

N12 : North Finchley

Tilted Glass
359 Ballards Lane
☎ (081) 445 2556
11–11
Adnams Broadside; Morland Bitter; Thwaites Bitter; Webster's Yorkshire Bitter H
Cosmopolitan lounge near the bus station. Its enterprising owner offers a changing variety of guest beers, often giving excellent value for money. Q ❨

N19 : Holloway

JJ Moon's
37 Landseer Road
☎ (071) 263 4658
11–11
Eldridge Pope Royal Oak; Greene King IPA, Abbot; Theakston XB; Younger Scotch H
Pleasant, corner local with a central bar. Boasted Britain's cheapest pint at the time of the survey. Food available at all times with roast lunches on Sun. Guest beers (possibly a mild).
✿ ❨ 🖢 ⇌ (Upper Holloway) ◌

N20 : Whetstone

Cavalier
67 Russell Lane (off A109)
11–3, 5.30–11 (11–11 Fri & Sat)
Courage Best Bitter, Directors; John Smith's Bitter H
1930s, estate pub in classic mock-Tudor style. The public bar is well patronised; the spacious, comfortable lounge features a station clock. Children's play area next to the large patio/garden. ✿ ❨ ♣ P

N21 : Winchmore Hill

Green Dragon
889 Green Lanes (A105)
11–11
Courage Best Bitter, Directors H
London CAMRA's *Pub of the Year* 1989 continues to keep up its high standards. The large rear patio is very popular on summer eves, with barbecues Fri and Sat. Note the over-21 rule in the saloon bar. No food Sun.
✿ ❨ 🖢 ⇌ ♣ P

N22 : Wood Green

Phoenix
Alexandra Palace
11–11
Ansells Mild; Courage Best Bitter, Directors; Ind Coope Burton Ale; John Smith's Bitter; Tetley Bitter H
Superb, 1920s, Gatsby-style free house bar at the south-western end of the Alexandra Palace complex. The manager has a passion for real ale (guest beers). An internal beer garden offers skittles and summer barbecues. The best beer for miles. ➷ ✿ ❨ ⇌ (Alexandra Palace) ⊖ (Wood Green) ♣ P

Try also: **Starting Gate**, Station Road (Taylor Walker)

Barnet

Albion
74 Union Street (off A1000)
11–3, 5.30 (7 Sat)–11 (12–2.30, 7–10.30 Sun)
Adnams Bitter; Ind Coope Benskins Best Bitter, Burton Ale H
Tucked away off the busy High Street, this friendly, one-bar pub is very much a focal point of the local community. Meals Mon–Fri. ✿ ❨ 🖢 P

Olde Mitre Inn
58 High Street (A1000)
11–11 (11–3, 7–11 Sat)
Ind Coope Benskins Best Bitter, Burton Ale; Tetley Bitter H
The last surviving original coaching inn in the town, recently renovated with the care due to such a historic landmark. No food Sun.
Q ❨ ⊖ (High Barnet) P

Olde Monken Holt
193 High Street (A1000)
11–11
Courage Best Bitter, Directors H
Standing on the fringe of Hadley Common; a well patronised, wood-panelled pub affording a warm welcome to locals and travellers alike. Good food. Q ✿ ❨ 🖢

Try also: **Moon Under Water** (Free)

Cockfosters

Trent Tavern
Cockfosters Road (A111)
11–3, 5–11 (11–11 Fri & Sat)
Courage Best Bitter, Directors; John Smith's Bitter H
Spacious, 1950s, two-bar pub on a busy main road. Handy for Trent Park. ✿ ❨ 🖢 ⊖ ♣ ✿

189

Enfield Lock

Greyhound
425 Ordnance Road
11–2.30 (3.30 Sat), 6.30 (7 Sat)–11
McMullen AK, Country Ⓗ
Fine, unspoilt, two-bar pub on
the River Lea. Well worth a
visit for those exploring the
river on foot or by boat. No
food at weekends.
Q ⚫ ◖ ⊟ ♣ ♣ P

Enfield Town

Cricketers
18 Chase Side Place
☎ (081) 363 5218
11–3, 5.30–11 (11–11 Sat)
McMullen AK, Country Ⓗ
Tucked away in a quiet
backwater, off the town centre;
a good public bar and a
comfortable lounge. Bar
billiards. Q ◖ ⊟ ≈ (Enfield
Chase) ♣ P ⋉

Old Wheatsheaf
3 Windmill Hill (on A110)
11–3, 5.30, (7 Sat)–11
**Greene King IPA; Taylor
Walker Best Bitter; Tetley
Bitter** Ⓗ
London CAMRA's *Pub of the
Year* 1990. Two bars, both to
saloon standard. Cribbage and
dominoes are popular with
locals in the former public bar.
Noted for its excellent, home-
cooked lunches (not served Sun).
Good range of malt whiskies.
Q ◖ ≈ (Enfield Chase) ♣ P

Wonder
1 Batley Road
11–3.30 (4.30 Sat), 5.30 (7 Sat)–11
McMullen AK, Country Ⓗ
An archetypal back-street,
locals' pub: a traditional public
bar with sing-alongs at the
piano on Sat eves; small, cosy
saloon. ⚫ Q ⚫ ◖
≈ (Gordon Hill) ♣ P

Enfield Whitewebbs

King & Tinker
Whitewebbs Lane
11–3, 5.30–11
**Adnams Bitter; Ind Coope
Burton Ale; Taylor Walker
Best Bitter; Tetley Bitter** Ⓗ
Historic, 17th-century inn of
great character, set in fine, rural
surroundings. Winner of awards
for its splendid ale, excellent
food and well-tended floral
displays. No food Sun.
⚫ ⚫ ◖ ⋏ ♣ P

New Barnet

Railway Bell
13 East Barnet Road
☎ (081) 449 1369
11–11

**Eldridge Pope Royal Oak;
Greene King IPA, Abbot;
Theakston XB; Younger
Scotch** Ⓗ
Apart from conversation and
the sound of handpumps, the
most noise comes from passing
125s. Railway memorabilia
abounds in this JD Wetherspoon
house Q ⚫ ◖ ▶ ≈ P

NW1: Camden Town

Spread Eagle
41 Albert Street
☎ (071) 267 1410
11–3, 5–11 (11–11 Fri & Sat)
**Young's Bitter, Special,
Winter Warmer** Ⓗ
Comfortable, large, refurbished
pub, attracting cosmopolitan
patrons. Wood-panelled
throughout and handy for
Camden market.
Q ◖ ⊟ ⊖ (Camden Rd) ⊖

NW1: Marylebone

Perseverance
11 Shroton Street
☎ (071) 723 7469
11–11
**Draught Bass; Charrington
IPA** Ⓗ
Pleasant pub near Church Street
market. One-roomer with a
horseshoe-shaped bar and
extensive wood panelling. No
meals Sat eve or Sun.
Q ◖ ≈ ⊖ (Edgware Rd)

NW3: Belsize Park

Sir Richard Steele
91 Haverstock Hill
☎ (071) 722 1003
11–11
**Draught Bass; Charrington
IPA** Ⓗ
Lively pub with regular live jazz
upstairs. Customers of all ages;
unusual collection of bric-a-brac
and interesting glassware. Try
the food (12–9.30pm). ⚫ ◖ ⊖

NW3: Hampstead

Flask
Flask Walk ☎ (071) 435 3240
11–11
**Young's Bitter, Special,
Winter Warmer** Ⓗ
Characterful pub, recently
modified, gaining a family
conservatory, but retaining its
saloon and public bars.
Q ⊱ ◖ ⊟ ⚫ ⊖ ♣

Holly Bush
22 Holly Mount
11–11
Ind Coope Benskins Best

**Bitter, Burton Ale; Tetley
Bitter** Ⓗ
Traditional local with gas
lighting in the front bar; an
unspoilt pub converted from
stables in the 18th century. Live
music/cabaret in the rear bar
Tue–Thu eves. Children
welcome. Pavement drinking
area. ⚫ ⚫ ⊱ ⚫ ◖ ⊟ ⊖ ♣

Horse & Groom
68 Heath Street
11–11
**Young's Bitter, Special,
Winter Warmer** Ⓗ
Imposing, Edwardian building
with a separate cocktail bar. The
main bar is little changed with a
comfortable interior. Can get
crowded at night. No food Sun.
Q ◖ ⊖

Spaniards Inn
Spaniards Road
11–11
**Draught Bass; Charrington
IPA** Ⓗ
Attractive, old pub with low
ceilings and small rooms for
intimate drinking. Pleasant
garden. Guest beers. Q ⚫ ◖ P

NW4: Hendon

Chequers
20 Church End
☎ (081) 203 5658
12–3, 5.30–11 (11–11 Fri & Sat)
**Courage Best Bitter,
Directors** Ⓗ
Open-plan pub which retains
two distinct serveries and
drinking areas; busy and
cosmopolitan. A natural spring
rises in the disused cellar. No
food Sun. ⚫ ◖ ▶ P

NW5: Dartmouth Park

Lord Palmerston
33 Dartmouth Park Hill
11–11
**Courage Best Bitter,
Directors** Ⓗ
Comfortable establishment, well
run by the local tenant family. A
new conservatory permits
children. Try the home-cooked
pies at lunchtime.
Q ⚫ ◖ ⅃ ⊖ (Tufnell Pk)

NW5: Kentish Town

Pineapple
51 Leverton Street
☎ (071) 485 6422
12–11
**Ind Coope Friary Meux Best
Bitter, Burton Ale; Marston's
Pedigree** Ⓗ
Genuine free house in a quiet,
Victorian back-street, drawing a
regular local trade. Cosy and
traditional, it boasts fine Bass
mirrors. ⅃ ♣ ♣

Greater London

NW6: Kilburn

Queens Arms
High Road ☎ (071) 624 5735
11–11 (11–4, 6.30–11 Sat)
**Young's Bitter, Special,
Winter Warmer** Ⓗ
1950s, corner pub, wood-
panelled and friendly, displaying
a variety of prints on its walls.
Roof garden. No food Sun.
🏠 🍴 ◖ ♿ ⇌ (Kilburn High
Rd) ⊖ (Kilburn Pk) ♣ P

NW7: Mill Hill

Rising Sun
137 Marsh Lane
☎ (081) 959 3755
12–3, 5.30–11 (11–11 Fri & Sat in
summer)
**Ind Coope Burton Ale;
Taylor Walker Best Bitter** Ⓗ
This well-appointed pub, set in
almost rural surroundings, is
believed to be the oldest in
Middlesex, and retains a great
deal of charm. Note the outdoor
loos! Can get very crowded in
summer. No food Sun/Mon.
Q 🍴 ◖ ▶ ♣ P

NW8: St John's Wood

Blenheim
Loudoun Road
11–3, 5.30 (6.30 Sat)–11
Greene King IPA, Abbot Ⓗ
Popular, L-shaped, locals' bar.
Regrettably no longer sells mild.
Q ◖ ⇌ (S Hampstead)
⊖ (St John's Wood) P

Knights of St John
7 Queens Terrace
11–3, 5.30–11
**Mansfield Riding Mild; Wells
Eagle, Bombardier** Ⓗ
Three-storey building with a
listed frontage. The landlord
won the Wells *Best Kept Cellar*
award in 1989 and 1990.
⇌ (S Hampstead)
⊖ (St John's Wood) ♣

Rossetti
23 Queens Grove
☎ (071) 722 7141
11–3, 5.30–11 (11–11 Sat)
Fuller's London Pride, ESB Ⓗ
Back-street pub with a
difference: a split-level lounge
bar with marble-topped tables
and a tiled floor. Both bar meals
and the upstairs restaurant
feature Italian cuisine.
Q 🍴 ◖ ⊖ P

NW9: Kingsbury

JJ Moon's
553 Kingsbury Road
11–11
**Greene King Abbot;
Theakston XB; Younger
Scotch** Ⓗ
One of the smaller pubs in the
Wetherspoon chain. Good
lunchtime food, incl. roast meat
dishes and a vegetarian option.
Can get crowded weekend eves.
Guest beers. Q ◖ ▶ ⊖

NW9: West Hendon

White Lion of Mortimer
3 York Parade (A5)
☎ (081) 202 8887
11–11
**Eldridge Pope Royal Oak;
Greene King IPA, Abbot;
Theakston XB; Younger
Scotch** Ⓗ
Probably London's largest free
house, with a vast ground-floor
drinking area, plus a bar and
dining area on the first floor.
Q 🍴 ◖ ♿ ⇌ (Hendon) ♻

NW10: Harlesden

Fishermans Arms
50 Old Oak Lane
11–11 (11–4, 7–11 Sat)
**Ind Coope Benskins Best
Bitter, Burton Ale; Tetley
Bitter** Ⓗ
Two-bar pub with a busy
lunchtime trade and a strong
following for darts and bar
billiards. In a railway
community, close to the canal.
No food Sun.
🍴 ◖ ⊟ ⇌ (Willesden Jct) ⊖ ♣

Grand Junction Arms
Acton Lane
☎ (081) 965 5670
11–11
**Young's Bitter, Special,
Winter Warmer** Ⓗ
Large, comfortable, canalside
pub with three bars. The
extensive garden at the rear
may soon have an outside bar
and regular barbecues in
summer. Good value food all
day (except Sun), incl.
vegetarian dishes.
Q 🍴 ◖ ▶ ⊟ ⇌ ⊖ P

NW10: Neasden

Outside Inn
312–314 Neasden Lane
☎ (081) 452 3140
11–11
**Eldridge Pope Royal Oak;
Greene King IPA, Abbot;
Theakston XB; Younger
Scotch** Ⓗ
Two-level pub with a large
island bar and an eating area at
the rear. A JD Wetherspoon
house, converted from a
Woolworth's store, in a
pedestrian precinct. Guest beers.
Handy for the Grange Museum.
No food Sun eve.
Q ◖ ▶ ⊖

Eastcote

Case is Altered
High Road
☎ (081) 866 0476
11–3, 5–11 (11–11 Fri & Sat)
**Ind Coope Benskins Best
Bitter, Burton Ale; Tetley
Bitter** Ⓗ
Grade II listed ex-farmhouse
with a stone-flagged floor. The
original stables are now part of
the bar. Very popular pub.
🏠 Q 🍴 ◖ ▶ P

Harefield

Plough
Hill End Road
**Brakspear Bitter; Fuller's
London Pride; Greene King
Abbot; Marston's Pedigree;
Samuel Smith OBB;
Theakston XB** Ⓗ
Off the beaten track; a one-bar
free house, near the hospital and
very busy in the summer. Good
value food (not served Sun) and
barbecues. Usually three more
beers available, though the
range varies. 🏠 🍴 ◖ P

White Horse
Church Hill ☎ (0895) 822144
11–3, 6–11
**Ansells Mild; Ind Coope
Benskins Best Bitter, Burton
Ale; Tetley Bitter** Ⓗ
Excellent, friendly local on the
outskirts of this sprawling
village. Cask mild is extremely
rare for this part of the world.
Mole's Bitter is a resident guest
beer.
🏠 Q 🍴 ◖ ▶ ♣ ♻ P

Harrow

Castle
West Street ☎ (081) 422 3155
11.30–11 (11–11 Fri & Sat)
Fuller's London Pride, ESB Ⓗ
Little-changed, two-bar pub in a
conservation area; popular and
friendly. Parking is not easy.
Q 🍴 ◖ ⇌ (Harrow-on-the-
Hill) ⊖ ♣

Northwood Hills

Northwood Hills Hotel
66 Joel Street (opp. station)
☎ (092 74) 25355
11–3, 5–11
**Ind Coope Benskins Best
Bitter, Burton Ale; Tetley
Bitter** Ⓗ
Large 1930s pub, a former
hotel where local boy Elton
John began his professional
career. Lunches served Mon–Fri.
Large bottled beer collection.
The landlord holds the Burton
Master Cellarman Award. Guest
beers. 🍴 ◖ ⊖ P

Greater London

South East London

SE1 : Southwark

Founders Arms
52 Hopton Street
☎ (071) 928 1899
11–4, 5
Young's Bitter, Special,
Winter Warmer Ⓗ
Very spacious public house with
very good views of the Thames,
just yards from the riverbank;
reached by steps from
Blackfriars Bridge.
⑧ ⓓ ⓓ ⓰ ⇌ (Blackfriars) ⊖

Gladstone Arms
Lant Street ☎ (071) 407 3692
11–4, 5 (7.30 Sat)–11
Draught Bass; Charrington
IPA Ⓗ
Busy, friendly, back-street local.
ⓓ ⇌ (London Bridge) ⊖
(Borough) ♣

Prince William Henry
217 Blackfriars Road
☎ (071) 928 2474
11–11 (11–3, 7–11 Sat)
Young's Bitter, Special,
Winter Warmer Ⓗ
Comfortable, modern pub,
handy for the South Bank. Busy
lunchtime and early eves.
Q ⓓ ⓓ ⓰ ⇌ (Waterloo) ⊖

Ship
68 Borough Road
11–11
Fuller's Chiswick, London
Pride, ESB Ⓗ
One large, comfortable bar,
very busy weekday lunchtimes
and early eves. Quiet at the
weekend.
⑧ ⓓ ⓓ ⇌ (London Bridge) ♣

Ship Aground
33 Wolseley Street
☎ (071) 237 3314
11–11 (11–4, 7–11 Sat)
Courage Best Bitter,
Directors Ⓗ
Well-run, family pub offering
good value meals. ⑧ ⓓ ⓰

Wheatsheaf
6 Stoney Street
☎ (071) 407 1514
11–11 (11–3, 7–11 Sat)
Courage Best Bitter,
Directors; Young's Special Ⓗ
Small Victorian gem near
Southwark Cathedral. Regular
guest ale from small
independent breweries.
ⓓ ⓔ ⇌ (London Bridge) ⊖

SE1 : Tower Bridge

Anchor Tap
28 Horsleydown Lane,
Bermondsey
☎ (071) 403 4637
12–3, 5.30–11 (12–11 Wed–Sat)

Samuel Smith OBB,
Museum Ⓗ
John Courage's first pub, owned
by Samuel Smith since the
closure of the Horsleydown
brewery. A gem of a pub with
lots of little rooms on the
ground floor. Two minutes'
from Tower Bridge.
Q ⓓ ⓓ ⓔ ⇌ (London Bridge)
⊖ (Tower Hill) ♣ ✕

SE3 : Blackheath

Bitter Experience
129 Lee Road (off A20)
☎ (081) 852 8819
11–9.30 (10–2, 3–9.30 Sat; 12–2, 7–9
Sun)
Beer range varies Ⓖ
Off-licence with a vast range of
real ales (usually six available)
and ciders, sold from a
temperature-controlled room at
the back of the shop. A
selection of English and foreign
bottled beers is also on offer.
⊖

SE4 : Brockley

Wickham Arms
64 Upper Brockley Road
☎ (081) 692 3023
11–11
Courage Bitter Ale, Best
Bitter, Directors Ⓗ
Well-established, cosmopolitan
neighbourhood pub; open-plan
but with distinct areas, incl. a
large, wood-panelled saloon.
Q ⑧ ⓓ ⇌

SE5 : Camberwell

Cambria Arms
40 Kemerton Road
☎ (071) 733 9001
11–11
Draught Bass Ⓗ
Friendly, back-street local
sporting an imposing, Victorian
exterior. Excellent wood-
panelled walls and red
upholstered furniture make the
saloon bright and comfortable.
Note the old Toby mirror.
Snooker upstairs at the
landlord's discretion. No food at
weekends. Q ⑧ ⓓ ⓰
⇌ (Loughborough Jct) ♣

Station Tavern
18 John Ruskin Street
☎ (071) 703 3256
11–4, 5.30 (7 Sat)–11
Charrington IPA Ⓗ
An oasis of tranquillity; a 50s
time-warp just off the hectic
Camberwell Road. This
otherwise plain local retains
superb coving in the public bar
and leaded lights in the
windows and the partition
which forms the jug and bottle,
sadly now unused.
🍺 Q ⓔ ♣

SE6 : Catford

Catford Ram
9 Winslade Way
☎ (081) 690 6206
11–11
Young's Bitter, Special,
Winter Warmer Ⓗ
Split-level pub in the shopping
precinct. Photos of turn-of-the-
century Catford decorate the
walls. Q ⓰ ♣ ♣

SE8 : Deptford

Birds Nest
32 Deptford Church Street
☎ (081) 692 1928
11–11
Bateman XXXB; Theakston
Best Bitter, XB, Old Peculier;
Webster's Yorkshire Bitter Ⓗ
Lively pub offering a wide
range of guest beers which are
changed regularly. 72-seat
theatre upstairs with regular
performances; good decor.
Rather expensive to say the
least. ⓓ ⇌

Dog & Bell
116 Prince Street (off A200)
☎ (081) 692 5664
11–11
Fuller's London Pride, ESB Ⓗ
Small, friendly, back-street free
house with an even smaller
snug, if you can find it. At least
two guest beers from
independent breweries. Q ⓓ ⇌

Royal George
85a Tanners Hill
☎ (081) 692 2594
11–3, 5.30–11 (11–11 Fri & Sat)
Samuel Smith OBB,
Museum Ⓗ
Attractive, busy, locals' pub
with a pool room upstairs.
Popular quiz nights Wed.
⑧ ⓓ ⇌ (New Cross) ⊖ ♣

SE10 : Greenwich

Ashburnham Arms
23 Ashburnham Grove
☎ (081) 692 2007
12–11
Shepherd Neame Master
Brew Bitter, Bishops Finger Ⓗ
Friendly, back-street local,
specialising in vegetarian meals.
Bar billiards. ⑧ ⓓ ⓓ ♣ ♣

Cricketers
22 King William Walk
☎ (081) 858 3630
11–11 (11–4, 7–11 Sat)
Charrington IPA Ⓗ
Excellent, little, two-bar pub in
the heart of Greenwich, near the
Cutty Sark, Maritime Museum
and Seamen's Hospital. Friendly
and very popular with a quiet,
sedate atmosphere at times. A
regular in this guide.
ⓓ ⓔ ⓐ ⇌ ♣

Frog & Radiator
1–3 Woolwich Road
☎ (081) 858 7317
11–3, 5–11
Ruddles Best Bitter, County; Webster's Yorkshire Bitter [H]
Basic and noisy, locals' pub with a friendly atmosphere. No food weekends. ⚒ ◐ ♣

Mitre
291 Greenwich High Road
☎ (081) 858 0367
12–3, 6–11 (12–11 Fri; 11–11 Sat)
Draught Bass; Charrington IPA; Fuller's London Pride; Young's Special [H]
An oasis in an area dominated by yuppy restaurants and bars. Sumptuous Chesterfield seating. A rarity in that it still retains a small, private bar. Q ◐ ⊟ ≠

Richard I (Tolly's)
Royal Hill ☎ (081) 692 2996
11–3 (4 Fri & Sat), 5.30 (6 Fri & Sat)–11
Young's Bitter, Special, Winter Warmer [H]
Classic, back-street local: two lively bars with a collection of old Greenwich prints. O'Hagan's famous sausages are served here. Q ✿ ◐ ⊟ ≠ ♣

SE14: New Cross

Rose
272 New Cross Road
☎ (081) 692 3193
11–4.30, 5.30 (7 Sat)–11
Courage Best Bitter, Directors; Young's Special [H]
Busy, but comfortable pub opposite New Cross Gate station. The interior is divided by glass screens. Limited parking. ✿ ◐ ≠ (New Cross Gate) ⊖ P

SE16: Bermondsey

Manor Tavern
78 Galleywall Road
☎ (071) 237 3396
11–3, 5–11 (11–11 Thu–Sat)
Charrington IPA [H]
Isolated, unspoilt, locals' pub with a strong darts following. Q ✿ ◐ ⊟ ≠ (S Bermondsey)

SE18: Shooters Hill

Bull
151 Shooters Hill
☎ (081) 856 0691
11–3, 5.30 (7 Sat)–11
Courage Best Bitter, Directors [H]
Two-bar local, almost at the top of Shooters Hill, complete with its original outdoor gents' loo. Meals served Mon–Fri. Q ✿ ◐ ⊟ ♣

Red Lion
6 Red Lion Place
☎ (081) 856 0333
11–11
Courage Best Bitter, Directors [H]
Originally a Beasley's house; a pub has been on this site for centuries. Highwayman connections. Q ✿ ♣ P

SE18: Woolwich

Army House
45 Artillery Place (near B210/A205 jct)
☎ (081) 854 6300
11–11
Courage Best Bitter [H]
Friendly but basic, one-bar local. Guest beers.
✿ ♿ ≠ (Woolwich Arsenal) ♣

SE19: Upper Norwood

Royal Albert
42 Westow Hill (A214)
☎ (081) 670 1208
11–11
Draught Bass; Charrington IPA; Fuller's London Pride [H]
Pub with a front public bar and a side entrance to the lounge at the rear where a 150-jug collection hangs from the beams. Close to Crystal Palace Park and the National Sports Centre. No food weekends. Q ✿ ◐ ⊟ ▲ ≠ (Gipsy Hill/Crystal Palace) ♣

SE22: East Dulwich

Clockhouse
196a Peckham Rye
☎ (081) 693 2901
11–11
Young's Bitter, Special [H]
Multi-roomed pub with an upper level in the front bar and a decor reminiscent of a gentlemen's club: green, padded seating and wood panelling. Note the collections of timepieces, jugs and bottle labels from defunct breweries. Meals Mon–Fri.
Q ✿ ◐ ◗ ≠ (Peckham)

Crystal Palace Tavern
193 Crystal Palace Road
☎ (081) 693 4968
12–11
Ind Coope Burton Ale; Taylor Walker Best Bitter [H]
Traditional and friendly, back-street, corner local; very popular, attracting a varied clientele. Quiz nights and special events are regular features. Note the etched-glass screen between the bars which is subject to a preservation order. Q ✿ ⊟ ♣

Uplands Tavern
90 Crystal Palace Road
☎ (081) 693 2662
11.30–3 (4 Sat), 7.30–11 (11.30–11 Fri; 12–3, 7.30–10.30 Sun)
Courage Best Bitter, Directors; John Smith's Bitter [H]
Large, barn-style pub featuring live music: jazz Thu; disco Fri; family music Sat and Sun. Possible guest ale. Hot snacks at lunchtime. ⚒ ✿ ≠

SE23: Forest Hill

Dartmouth Arms
7 Dartmouth Road
☎ (081) 699 1693
11–3 (4 Fri & Sat), 5.30 (7 Sat)–11
Courage Best Bitter, Directors [H]
Typical high street local with a thriving public bar at the front. Very close to Forest Hill station (originally Dartmouth Arms station). ✿ ⊟ ≠ ♣ P

Prince of Wales
52 Perry Rise
☎ (081) 699 7591
11–11
Draught Bass; Charrington IPA; Fuller's London Pride [H]
Quiet and friendly, one-bar local, mainly serving the surrounding residents. Very busy at weekends but conversation always remains a key feature. No food Sat/Sun.
Q ✿ ◐ ≠ ♣

Railway Telegraph
112 Stanstead Road
☎ (081) 699 6644
11–3, 5.30–11 (11–11 Fri & Sat)
Shepherd Neame Master Brew Bitter, Master Brew Best Bitter, Stock Ale, Spitfire, Bishops Finger [H]
Pub where the saloon is pleasantly divided into several drinking areas and is tastefully decorated with railway memorabilia. The public bar retains many original features. The Motor Cycle Action Group regularly meets here and raises large sums for charity. No food Sun. ♨ ✿ ◐ ⊟ ≠ ♣

SE24: Herne Hill

Commercial
212 Railton Road
11–11
Draught Bass; Charrington IPA; Greene King IPA [H]
Excellent, Victorian, family pub with a rugby theme, opposite the station. Q ⊟ ≠ ♣

SE25: South Norwood

Albion
26 High Street (A213/A215 jct) ☎ (081) 653 0558
11–11
Courage Bitter Ale, Best Bitter, Directors; Young's Special [H]
Busy, friendly, crossroads pub offering good value beer. Live music Thu and Fri. No food weekends. ✿ ◐ ≠ (Norwood Jct)

Greater London

SE26 : Sydenham

Bricklayers Arms
189 Dartmouth Road
☎ (081) 699 1260
11–11
Young's Bitter, Special Ⓗ
Recently refurbished, popular house. A quiet area at the rear leads to a delightful children's room and garden. A gem.
🏨 Q ⚒ 🕭 🍺 ⇌ ♣ ♠

Dulwich Wood House
39 Sydenham Hill
☎ (081) 693 5666
11–3, 5.30–11 (11–11 Fri & Sat)
Young's Bitter, Special, Winter Warmer Ⓗ
Deservedly busy, two-bar pub with a country atmosphere. The large garden boasts a petanque piste for adults, a climbing frame for children, and a barbecue in summer (the garden bar uses electric pumps). No meals Sun. 🏨 Q ⚒ 🕭 🍺 ⇌ (Sydenham Hill) ♣ P

SE27 : West Norwood

Hope
49 Norwood High Street
11–11
Young's Bitter, Special, Winter Warmer Ⓗ
Excellent local behind the station. Friendly, with a warm welcome assured. Typical Young's decor. Often very busy at weekends. Q ⚒ ⇌ ♣

Addiscombe

Claret Wine Bar
5a Bingham Corner, Lower Addiscombe Road (A222)
☎ (081) 656 7452
11.30–11
Eldridge Pope Royal Oak; Palmers IPA Ⓗ
Always four real ales available in this dark but welcoming bar in a parade of shops. Frequently-changed guest beers. ⚒ 🕭 ⇌

Cricketers
47 Shirley Road (A212)
☎ (081) 654 3833
11.30–2.30 (3 Fri), 5 (6 Sat)–11
Courage Best Bitter, Directors; John Smith's Bitter, Magnet Ⓗ
Brewer's Tudor pub, with dark wood-panelled interiors, providing a welcome to customers of all ages. No food Sun. ⚒ 🕭 ⇌ (Woodside) ♣ P

Beckenham

Coach & Horses
Burnhill Road (off A222)
☎ (081) 650 9142
11–3, 5.30–11

Courage Best Bitter, Directors; John Smith's Magnet Ⓗ
A family local with a garden. Meals served Mon–Sat.
⚒ 🕭 ⇌ (Beckenham Jct)

Jolly Woodman
9 Chancery Lane (off A222)
☎ (081) 650 3664
11–3, 5–11.30 (11–11 Fri & Sat)
Draught Bass; Charrington IPA Ⓗ
Popular, back-street local. No food weekends.
Q ⚒ 🕭 ⇌ (Beckenham Jct) ♣

Bexleyheath

Bitter Experience
Broadway ☎ (081) 304 2039
11–2, 6–9 (10.30–9.30 Thu–Sat; 7–9 Sun)
Adnams Bitter; Greene King Abbot; King & Barnes Sussex; Moorhouse's Premier; Shepherd Neame Master Brew Bitter Ⓖ
Off-licence which is now the only reliable outlet for independent real ale in Bexley Borough. Guest beers and ciders. ⇌

Robin Hood & Little John
Lion Road ☎ (081) 303 1128
11–2.30, 6–11 (12–2.30, 7–10.30 Sun)
Courage Bitter Ale, Best Bitter, Directors; John Smith's Bitter Ⓗ
Small, cosy local with a friendly atmosphere. One guest beer every month. No food Sun; eve meals on request. Q ⚒ 🕭 ♣

Royal Oak (Polly Clean Stairs)
Mount Road
☎ (081) 303 4454
11.30–3, 7–11
Courage Best Bitter, Directors Ⓗ
The former Upton village stores, now a village-style local in a residential area: a gem. Cold food only served (not Sun). ⚒ 🕭 P

Bromley

Bitter End
139 Masons Hill (A21)
☎ (081) 466 6083
12–3, 5–10 (9 Mon; 11–10 Sat; 12–2, 7–9 Sun)
Camerons Bitter; Fuller's London Pride; Greene King IPA, Abbot; King & Barnes Festive Ⓖ
Enterprising off-licence where the range is always liable to change; almost a beer festival in a shop. A connoisseur's delight with special brews from Premier also available. Various ciders, too. ⇌ (Bromley S) ☉

Bricklayers Arms
143 Masons Hill (A21)
11–3, 5.30–11
Shepherd Neame Master Brew Bitter, Spitfire Ⓗ
Superb, main road local whose landlord celebrates 21 years this year. A quiet, happy pub, comfortable and very friendly. Good wholesome food at very reasonable prices. A lovely boozer. Q 🕭 ⚒ ⇌ (Bromley S) ♣

Freelands Tavern
31 Freelands Road (off A222)
11–11
Courage Best Bitter, Directors Ⓗ
Excellent, back-street, suburban local, lively when there is a darts match and at weekends. Warm, friendly welcome.
⚒ 🕭 ⚒ ⇌ (Bromley N) ♣

Star & Garter
High Street (opp. cinema)
11–3, 5–11
Taylor Walker Best Bitter; Tetley Bitter; Young's Special Ⓗ
Classic, ornate, Victorian exterior: one of Bromley's few listed buildings. A lively, friendly, comfortable pub. TV available for major sporting events only. Its good central position ensures a thriving trade. 🕭 ⇌ ⚒ (Bromley N/S)

Chislehurst

Bulls Head
Royal Parade
11–4, 5–11
Young's Bitter, Special, Winter Warmer Ⓗ
Large, terraced, ivy-clad, listed building with a sumptuous interior and an unusual upstairs lounge. The ballroom is especially noteworthy. Highly recommended.
🏨 Q ⚒ 🛏 🕭 ⚒ ⇌ P

Crown
School Road
11–3, 5.30–11
Shepherd Neame Master Brew Bitter, Spitfire Ⓗ
One of London and the South East's best jazz venues on Sun and Thu nights. Top name players, plus a resident trio; no charge on the door – excellent value. A pub overlooking the historic common. ⚒ 🕭 ⚒ P

Queens Head
High Street ☎ (081) 467 3490
11–3, 5.30–11
Ind Coope Burton Ale; Taylor Walker Best Bitter; Tetley Bitter; Young's Special Ⓗ
Two-bar, Elizabethan pub, tastefully refurbished with lots of bric-a-brac and comfy sofas. Note the moulded wood bar.
⚒ 🕭 ▶ P

Greater London

Croydon

Builders Arms
65 Leslie Park Road (off A222)
☎ (081) 654 1803
11.30–3, 5 (6.30 Sat)–11 (11–11 Fri)
Fuller's Chiswick, London Pride, ESB Ⓗ
Small, two-bar, country-style pub, refurbished in the 'polished wood and bookcase' style. No eve meals Sat/Sun. ⑧ ⓒ ▶ ⇌
(E Croydon/Addiscombe)

Crown
90 Stanley Road (off A235)
☎ (081) 684 4952
11–11
Ruddles County; Webster's Yorkshire Bitter Ⓗ
Excellent, street-corner local. Its large bar has a collection of plates on the walls and a full range of games (ask). Live music Sat and Sun nights; modern jazz Tue nights. Eve meals until 8pm Mon–Fri. ⓒ ▶ ♧

Dog & Bull
24 Surrey Street (off High Street)
☎ (081) 688 3664
11–11
Young's Bitter, Special, Winter Warmer Ⓗ
Plain, one-bar pub in Croydon's street market; a local 'institution'. Excellent value food weekday lunchtimes.
Q ⑧ ⓒ ⇌ (E/W Croydon) ♧

George
132 Canterbury Road (off A23)
☎ (081) 689 7911
11–3, 5.15–11
Charrington IPA; Fuller's London Pride Ⓗ
Street-corner local, its split level providing a reminder of the former, separate, lower public bar. No food Sun. ⓒ ♧

Golden Lion
144 Stanley Road (off A235)
11–11
Courage Best Bitter, Directors; John Smith's Bitter Ⓗ
Warm, friendly, street-corner local with keen darts teams and regular fund-raising activities.
⑧ ⓔ ♧

Nowhere Inn Particular
78 Sumner Road (off A235)
☎ (081) 681 7469
11–11
Adnams Bitter; Fuller's London Pride, ESB; Samuel Smith OBB Ⓗ
Former Allied pub, sold in 1990 and refurbished to provide a smart, comfortable free house. The open-plan bar has seating around the walls and old, framed advertising posters. A different guest beer each month. No food Sun eve. ⓒ ▶ ⅄ ♧

Porter & Sorter
Station Road (unmarked)
☎ (081) 688 4296
11–11 (11–3, 7–11 Sat; closed Sun eve)
Courage Best Bitter, Directors Ⓗ
Back-street pub decorated with a railway theme, serving commuters and post office workers. The last original building in the area, since the station was rebuilt; long may it survive. No food at weekends.
⑧ ⓒ ⇌ (E Croydon) ♣ P

Footscray

Seven Stars
High Street ☎ (081) 300 2059
11–11
Draught Bass; Charrington IPA; Fuller's ESB (winter) Ⓗ
16th-century pub retaining many nooks and crannies. Good value for the area and popular. No food Sun. ⑧ ⓒ P

Kenley

Wattenden Arms
Old Lodge Lane (off A22 at Kenley station)
☎ (081) 660 8638
11–11
Draught Bass; Charrington IPA Ⓗ
Justifiably-acclaimed, upmarket local, run by the current licensee for over 25 years. The wood panelled bar has a patriotic theme. Excellent pub lunches (Mon–Sat). Q ⑧ ⓒ P

Sidcup

Charcoal Burner
Main Road ☎ (081) 300 0313
10.30–4, 5–11
Courage Best Bitter, Directors Ⓗ
Comfortable, modern pub. Guest beer. ⑧ ⓒ ⓔ P

Upper Belvedere

Royal Standard
Nuxley Road
☎ (032 24) 32774
11–3, 5.30–11 (11–11 Mon, Fri & Sat)
Draught Bass; Charrington IPA Ⓗ
Popular local with a maritime flavour. Guest beers (Greene King IPA on a regular basis). No food Sun. ⅃ ⑧ ⓒ ▶ P

South West London

SW1: Belgravia

Grouse & Claret
14–15 Little Chester Street
☎ (071) 235 3438
11–11 (11.30–3, 6–11 Sat)

Brakspear Bitter; Courage Directors; Mansfield Old Baily; Marston's Pedigree; Whitbread Boddingtons Bitter Ⓗ
Split-level, two-bar pub with a separate wine bar and restaurant. Beer range may vary.
ⓒ ▶ ⇌ (Victoria) ⊖

Star Tavern
6 Belgrave Mews West
☎ (071) 234 2806
11.30–3, 5.30 (6.30 Sat)–11 (11.30–11 Fri)
Fuller's Chiswick, London Pride, ESB Ⓗ
Unspoilt, mews pub with two real fires; 18 years in the *Guide*. No food Sun.
⛫ ⓒ ⊖ (Hyde Pk Corner)

Turks Head
10 Motcomb Street
11–11
Draught Bass; Charrington IPA Ⓗ
Comfortable, Georgian pub with raised seating at the rear, surrounded by bookshelves. No food Sun.
ⓒ ▶ ⊖ (Hyde Pk Corner)

SW1: Pimlico

Rising Sun
44 Ebury Bridge Road
11–11 (11–3, 7–11 Sat)
Young's Bitter, Special Ⓗ
Popular locals' pub near the coach station. Opens at 7.30am for breakfasts (weekdays only).
Q ⑧ ⓒ ▶ ⇌ (Victoria) ⊖

SW1: St James's

Red Lion
23 Crown Passage
11–11 (11–3, 7–11 Sat)
Ruddles Best Bitter, County; Webster's Yorkshire Bitter Ⓗ
Small, unspoilt pub in an alley-way, reputedly the second oldest licence in the West End.
ⓒ ⊖ (Piccadilly Circus)

SW1: Sloane Square

Fox & Hounds
29 Passmore Street
11–3, 5.30–11 (12–2, 7–10.30 Sun)
Draught Bass; Charrington IPA Ⓗ
Small, cosy pub just off Sloane Square, holding probably the only remaining beer and wine licence. Q ⊖

SW1: Trafalgar Square

Old Shades
37 Whitehall
11–11 (11–3, 7–11 Sat; closed Sun eve)
Draught Bass; Charrington IPA; Young's Bitter Ⓗ

195

Greater London

Long, wood-panelled bar with a lounge at the rear. Obtains its licence from Buckingham Palace. 🏠 🍺 🥂 ⇌ (Charing Cross) ⊖

SW1: Westminster

Barley Mow
104 Horseferry Road
☎ (071) 222 2330
11–11 (11–4, 7–11 Sat)
**Ruddles Best Bitter, County;
Webster's Yorkshire Bitter** 🅷
Large, comfortable pub with a fine collection of Hogarth prints. Grand piano in the bar; occasional live music. 🍺 🥂
⇌ (Victoria)⊖ (St James's Pk)

Buckingham Arms
62 Petty France
☎ (071) 222 3386
11–11 (11–3, 7–11 Sat; 12–2.30, 7–10.30 Sun)
**Young's Bitter, Special,
Winter Warmer** 🅷
Excellent pub near the Passport Office. 🍺 🥂 ⇌ (Victoria)
⊖ (St James's Pk)

Morpeth Arms
Millbank ☎ (071) 834 6442
11–11
**Young's Bitter, Special,
Winter Warmer** 🅷
Comfortable pub overlooking the Thames near Vauxhall Bridge and the Tate Gallery. Remains open on Sun afternoon for food only.
🍺 🥂 ⇌ (Vauxhall) ⊖ (Pimlico) ♣

Paviours Arms
Page Street ☎ (071) 834 2150
11–11
**Fuller's Chiswick, London
Pride, ESB** 🅷
Large, three-bar pub in Art-Deco style. 🍺 🍽 🥂 ⊖ (Pimlico) ♣

Westminster Arms
Storeys Gate
☎ (071) 222 8520
12–11 (8 Sat: closed Sun eve)
**Adnams Bitter; Brakspear
Bitter; Fuller's London Pride;
Marston's Pedigree;
Nethergate Bitter; Whitbread
Boddingtons Bitter** 🅷
Small pub and downstairs wine bar near Parliament Square, Westminster Abbey and Central Hall. Recently redecorated to appear more spacious. Beer range may vary.
🍺 🥂 ⊖ (St James's Pk)

SW2: Brixton

Hope & Anchor
Acre Lane ☎ (071) 274 1787
11–11
**Young's Bitter, Special,
Winter Warmer** 🅷
Award-winning, large, single-bar pub, attracting a mixed local clientele. Friendly welcome.
🏠 Q 🍺 🥂 🍽 ⇌ ⊖ ♣

SW2: Streatham

JJ Moon's
2 Streatham Hill
11–11
**Eldridge Pope Royal Oak;
Greene King IPA, Abbot;
Theakston XB; Younger
Scotch** 🅷
Recently refurbished, large, Victorian house on a major road intersection. No pool, darts or music – in true Wetherspoon style. Guest beer every Fri.
Q 🍽 🍺 🥂 ⇌ (Streatham Hill) P

SW3: Chelsea

Princess of Wales
145 Dovehouse Street
☎ (071) 351 5502
11–11 (11–4, 8–11 Sat)
**Courage Best Bitter,
Directors** 🅷
Small pub behind the Royal Marsden Hospital.
Q 🍺 ⊖ (S Kensington)

Rose
86 Fulham Road
☎ (071) 589 6672
11–3, 5 (7 Sat)–11 (11–11 Fri)
**Fuller's Chiswick, London
Pride, ESB** 🅷
Ornate pub with much wood and tile work and a theatre upstairs. 🍺 🍽 ⊖ (S Kensington)

SW6: Fulham

Jolly Brewer
308–310 North End Road
11–11
**Ruddles County; Webster's
Yorkshire Bitter; Young's
Bitter** 🅷
Popular, busy, street-market local. ⊖ (Broadway) ♣

SW6: Parsons Green

White Horse
1 Parsons Green
☎ (071) 736 2115
11.30 (11 Sat)–3, 5 (7 Sat)–11
**Adnams Bitter; Draught
Bass; Charrington IPA; M&B
Highgate Mild; Traquair
House Ale** (winter) 🅷
Large, popular and busy, upmarket pub facing the green, with a terrace for outside drinking. Hearty breakfasts served at weekends. Hosts beer festivals once or twice a year.
🍺 🍽 ⊖

SW6: West Brompton

Atlas
16 Seagrave Road
11–11
**Ruddles Best Bitter;
Webster's Yorkshire Bitter** 🅷

Popular, side-street local, handy for Earls Court Exhibition Centre. 🍽 ⊖ ♣

SW7: South Kensington

Anglesea Arms
15 Selwood Terrace
☎ (071) 373 7960
11–3, 5.30 (7 Sat)–11
**Adnams Bitter; Brakspear
Special; Eldridge Pope Hardy
Country; Greene King
Abbot; Whitbread
Boddingtons Bitter; Young's
Special** 🅷
Consistently popular, beer-drinkers' free house, often very busy. Guest beer. No music machines. Q 🍽 🍺 🥂 ⊖

SW8: Battersea

Old Red House
133 Battersea Park Road
(A3205) ☎ (071) 622 1664
11–11
**Courage Best Bitter,
Directors; Wadworth 6X** 🅷
Family pub; darts and quizzes Mon–Thu; discos and live music weekends. Warm and friendly. 🍽 🍺 🥂 ⇌ (Battersea Pk/Queenstown Rd) ♣ P

Plough Inn
518 Wandsworth Road (B224 jct) ☎ (071) 622 2777
11–11
**Young's Bitter, Special,
Winter Warmer** 🅷
One-bar pub, comfortably furnished, which retains a public bar end. Formerly the tap of the Plough Brewery whose premises remain next door. No food Sun.
🍽 🍺 🥂 ⇌ (Wandsworth Rd) ♣

SW8: Kennington

Roebuck
84 Ashmole Street (off A3)
☎ (071) 820 9793
11–11
**Draught Bass; Charrington
IPA** 🅷
Pub where the decor matches the tasteful exterior – very swish. Greene King IPA occasionally replaces the Charrington.
🍽 🍺 ♿ ⇌ (Vauxhall) ⊖ (Oval)

SW8: South Lambeth

Priory Arms
83 Lansdowne Way
☎ (071) 622 1884
11–11
**Hop Back Summer Lightning;
Webster's Yorkshire Bitter;
Young's Bitter, Special** 🅷
Small, friendly pub and restaurant on the main road,

refurbished by its new owner. Raised darts area; wooden seating outside. Special afternoon prices for senior citizens. A guest beer changes monthly. ☎ ◖ ❶ ❿ (Stockwell) ♣

Surprise
Southville ☎ (071) 622 4623
11–3 (4 Sat), 5 (7 Sat)–11 (11–11 summer)
Young's Bitter, Special, Winter Warmer ⊞
Small, very friendly pub by Larkhall Park, recently redecorated. A small room at the back has a pinball machine and walls covered with caricatures of the locals. Boules team in summer.
🚲 Q ☎ ◖ ❶ ⇌ (Wandsworth Rd) ❿ (Stockwell) ♣

SW10 : West Brompton

Fox & Pheasant
1 Billing Road
11–3, 5.30–11
Draught Bass; Charrington IPA; Wadworth 6X ⊞
Tiny, two-bar pub, much used by locals. Near Chelsea football ground.
☎ ◖ ⊟ ❿ (Fulham Broadway)

SW10 : West Chelsea

Chelsea Ram
22 Burnaby Street
11–3, 5.30–11 (11–11 Fri & Sat)
Young's Bitter, Special, Winter Warmer ⊞
Comfortable pub, built in the 1880s but not licensed until 1984. No jukebox or piped music. Q ◖

SW11 : Clapham Junction

Beehive
197 St John's Hill
11–3, 5.30–11
Fuller's Chiswick, London Pride, ESB ⊞
Small, welcoming local, full of characters. Good value lunches Mon–Fri. ◖ ⇌

Plough
89 St John's Hill
☎ (071) 228 9136
11–11
Young's Bitter, Special, Winter Warmer ⊞
Recently refurbished pub, offering jazz on Wed and Sat. Home-cooked lunches Mon–Fri.
🚲 ☎ ◖ ⇌ ♣

SW12 : Balham

Nightingale
97 Nightingale Lane
☎ (081) 673 1637
11–3, 5.30–11 (11–11 Fri & Sat)

Young's Bitter, Special, Winter Warmer ⊞
Between Clapham and Wandsworth commons, almost a country local in the town, run by staff who care. Good beer, good company; often busy – especially at weekends. Sun lunchtime is something very special. Crib played; golf society. Q ⇌ ☎ ◖ ❶ ⇌ (Wandsworth Common) ❿ (Clapham S) ♣

Prince of Wales
270 Cavendish Road
☎ (081) 673 5864
11–11
Courage Best Bitter, Directors; Hop Back GFB; John Smith's Bitter ⊞
Typical, two-bar pub, popular at lunchtimes. Beer prices are well displayed. No music in the saloon bar; strong Irish flavour in the public bar. Its service to the local community is legendary.
Q ☎ ◖ ⇌ ❿ (Clapham S)

SW13 : Barnes

Bulls Head
373 Lonsdale Road
☎ (081) 876 5241
11–11
Young's Bitter, Special, Winter Warmer ⊞
Renowned, seven day-a-week jazz venue, overlooking the Thames. The art of good conversation lives on here. Restaurant at the rear.
☎ ◖ ❶ ⇌ (Barnes Bridge) ♣

Coach & Horses
27 Barnes High Street (A3003)
☎ (081) 876 2695
11–11 (11–3, 5.30–11 Mon–Wed)
Young's Bitter, Special, Winter Warmer ⊞
A village pub in town; a small 18th-century gem with a good atmosphere. The Paddock Room at the rear of the courtyard is available for hire.
🚲 Q ☎ ◖ ⇌ (Barnes Bridge)

Red Lion
2 Castelnau (A306)
☎ (081) 748 2984
11–11
Fuller's Chiswick, London Pride, ESB ⊞
Imposing, main road pub near Barn Elms playing fields and reservoir. Ornate rear dining room, plus comfortable lounge and bar areas. Children allowed in the dining room until 9pm.
☎ ◖ ❶ ⅃ ⇌

Sun Inn
7 Church Road (A3003)
☎ (081) 876 5893
11–11
Ind Coope Burton Ale; Taylor Walker Best Bitter; Tetley Bitter; Young's Special ⊞

Rambling, wooden-floored pub opposite Barnes Pond. 1700s original features include a listed staircase. Eve meals served Tue–Thu. 🚲 Q ☎ ◖ ❶ ⇌ P

SW14 : Mortlake

Railway Tavern
11 Sheen Lane
☎ (081) 878 7361
11–11
Hall & Woodhouse Badger Best Bitter, Tanglefoot; Wadworth 6X; Wells Eagle ⊞
Pub where a small, traditional front room leads into a larger modern area where the bar is situated. Guest beer. ☎ ◖ ❶ ⇌ ♣

SW15 : Putney

Jolly Gardeners
Lacy Road ☎ (081) 788 7508
11–11
Fuller's Chiswick, London Pride, ESB ⊞
Comfortable, two-bar pub, with occasional live music. Friendly welcome. No food Sun.
Q ☎ ◖ ⇌ ♣

SW16 : Streatham

Pied Bull
498 Streatham High Road
☎ (081) 764 4003
11–3, 5.30–11 (11–11 Sat)
Young's Bitter, Special, Winter Warmer ⊞
Two, contrasting bars in a well-managed, roadside pub. Very handy for harassed shoppers; a regular in this guide.
🚲 Q ◖ ❶ ⅃ ⇌ (Common) ♣ P

SW17 : Tooting

Castle
High Street ☎ (081) 672 7018
11–11
Young's Bitter, Special, Winter Warmer ⊞
Large, three-roomed pub near the shops and market. ◖ ⅃ ❿ (Broadway) P ⅄ (lunchtime)

Gorringe Park Hotel
29 London Road
☎ (081) 648 4478
11–11
Young's Bitter, Special, Winter Warmer ⊞
Busy, popular pub. Still an oasis in a beer desert. ☎ ◖ ❶ ♣ ♣

SW18 : Earlsfield

Country House
2 Groton Road
☎ (081) 874 2715
11–3, 5.30–11 (11–11 Sat)
Courage Bitter Ale, Best Bitter, Directors; John Smith's Bitter ⊞
Quiet, two-bar, back-street local, excellently run. Copper-topped tables in the lounge. A rare find in London. Q ⅃ ⇌ ♣ ♣

Greater London

SW18: Wandsworth

Alma
499 Old York Road (opp. station) ☎ (081) 870 2537
11–3, 5–11 (11–11 Sat)
Young's Bitter, Special, Winter Warmer Ⓗ
Large, Victorian, corner pub: one large room with an island bar, featuring period mirrors and interesting murals. Derives its name from a Crimean battle.
🏛 ◖ ◗ ⇌ (Town)

Old Sergeant
104 Garratt Lane
11–3, 5–11 (11–11 Mon, Fri & Sat)
Young's Bitter, Special, Winter Warmer Ⓗ
Very friendly, two-bar pub, near the brewery. No food Sun. ◗ ♣

Spread Eagle
71 Wandsworth High Street
☎ (081) 874 1326
11–11
Young's Bitter, Special, Winter Warmer Ⓗ
Pub with magnificent glass screens in its large, comfortable saloon; smaller back room, mainly for diners at lunchtime, and a popular public bar. Eve meals Mon–Fri.
Q ◖ ◗ ⇌ (Town) P

SW19: Merton

Princess Royal
25 Abbey Road
☎ (081) 542 3273
11–3, 5 (6.30 Sat in winter)–11
Courage Best Bitter, Directors; John Smith's Bitter; Wadworth 6X Ⓗ
Locals' corner pub with a friendly atmosphere: a small public bar and a larger, comfortable saloon. John Smith's is served by swan necks into lined glasses. No food Sun.
☢ ◖ ⇌ (S Wimbledon) ♣

SW19: Wimbledon

Alexandra
33 Wimbledon Hill Road
☎ (081) 947 7691
11–11 (public bar only 3–5.30 Mon–Thu)
Young's Bitter, Special, Winter Warmer Ⓗ
Popular, four-bar pub close to the station. The small, red room is a no-smoking area; the large public bar regularly has live piano music. Separate wine bar and restaurant. Q ☢ ⇌ ⊕ ♣ 🍴

Hand in Hand
6 Crooked Billet (off Woodhayes Road, B281)
11–11
Young's Bitter, Special, Winter Warmer Ⓗ

Large pub where the one room forms a horseshoe round the bar. Two alcoves provide more intimate areas and a small room off the bar doubles as a games and children's area. Can be very busy in summer.
🏛 Q ☢ ◖ ◗ ♣

Rose & Crown
55 High Street (A219)
☎ (081) 947 4713
11–11
Young's Bitter, Special, Winter Warmer Ⓗ
Very popular, old, village pub near the common, with a small no-smoking area at the rear of the main bar. Over-21s only.
Q ☒ ☢ ◖ ◗ P 🍴

Carshalton

Railway Tavern
47 North Street (off A232)
12–3, 5.30–11
Fuller's Chiswick, London Pride, ESB Ⓗ
Small, street-corner pub, recently refurbished, with much ornate glasswork and mirrors.
◖ ♣ ♣

Cheam

Red Lion
17 Park Road
11–3, 5.30–11 (11–11 Thu–Sat)
Draught Bass; Charrington IPA; Greene King IPA Ⓗ
Reputedly built in the 16th century and now consisting of a number of separate drinking areas around a central bar; some low ceilings and wood panelling. No food Sun.
🏛 Q ☢ ◖ ♣ ♣

Chessington

North Star
271 Hook Road, Hook (A243)
☎ (081) 397 4227
12–11 (11–3, 5.30–11 Sat)
Draught Bass; Charrington IPA; M&B Highgate Mild Ⓗ
Popular with locals and passing trade. The beer range is liable to change and there may be a guest. Lunches Mon–Fri.
Q ☒ ☢ ◖ ♣

Kingston upon Thames

Bricklayers Arms
53 Hawks Road (off A2043)
☎ (081) 546 0393
11–3 (4 Fri & Sat), 5.30 (6 Sat)–11
Courage Best Bitter, Directors; John Smith's Bitter Ⓗ
Busy pub on the edge of the Fairfield area. Most of the wide-ranging meals are prepared by the landlord himself (eve meals till 8pm, Mon–Fri). Weekly raffles. ☒ ☢ ◖ ◗ ♣

Cocoanut
11 Mill Street (off Fairfield South) ☎ (081) 546 3978
11–3, 5.30–11 (11–11 Sat)
Fuller's Chiswick, London Pride, ESB Ⓗ
Originally a two-room pub which has been tastefully converted to a single bar. The community atmosphere has been maintained. Q ☢ ♣

Druids Head
3 Market Place
☎ (081) 546 0723
11–11 (12–2, 7–10.30 Sun)
Whitbread Wethered Bitter, Flowers Original Ⓗ
The oldest pub in Kingston, dating from 1723 or earlier. Much of the building is listed, including the staircase and the function room ceiling. The only pub left in the Market Place, where once all buildings around the market hall were pubs.
Q ☢ ⇌ ♣

Lamb
16 Acre Road (off A307)
☎ (081) 549 5544
11–2.30, 5–11 (11–11 Fri & Sat)
Courage Best Bitter, Directors; Hall & Woodhouse Badger Best Bitter Ⓗ
Side-street local which has raised money for seven guide dogs. The Hall & Woodhouse Best is occasionally replaced with Tanglefoot. No food Sun.
☢ ⇌ ♣

Park Tavern
New Road (off Park Road)
11–11
Marston's Pedigree (summer); **Young's Bitter, Special, Winter Warmer** Ⓗ
A former Charrington tied house, the nearest pub to the Kingston gate of Richmond Park. Parking difficult. Guest beer. Food service planned.
🏛 Q ☢ ♣

Wych Elm
Elm Road ☎ (081) 546 3271
11–3, 5–11 (11–11 Sat)
Fuller's Chiswick, London Pride, ESB Ⓗ
Welcoming pub with an ornate but comfortable lounge and a basic, tidy public bar. Impressive floral displays. Off the beaten track but worth finding. No food Sun. ☢ ◖ ⇌

Richmond

Orange Tree
Kew Road ☎ (081) 940 0944
11–11
Young's Bitter, Special, Winter Warmer Ⓗ
Extremely popular pub in a large, Victorian building, supporting a fringe theatre upstairs. Excellent bar and

restaurant meals cater for children and vegetarians (pre-theatre menu for eve theatre-goers). No meals Sun eve.
🍴 Q 🏠 🕪 ≢ ⊖

Princes Head

The Green ☎ (081) 940 1572
11–11
Fuller's Chiswick, London Pride, ESB Ⓗ
Attractive pub, established c. 1740 on a site facing a picturesque green. The lounge bar is in traditional style, enhanced with old prints and photographs of Richmond's bygone days. Good, home-cooked bar food. 🏠 🕪 ≢ ⊖

Red Cow

Sheen Road
☎ (081) 940 2511
11–11
Young's Bitter, Special, Winter Warmer Ⓗ
Fine local with many original Victorian features. The simply furnished, compact, but comfortable lounge is friendly and welcoming with its real fire. Occasional live music. Good food (not served Sun eve).
🍴 🍺 🕪 🍽 ⊖ ♣

White Cross Hotel

Water Lane ☎ (081) 940 6844
11–11
Young's Bitter, Special, Winter Warmer Ⓗ
A fine, Thames-side pub, recently renovated but retaining its many special qualities. A well furnished function room, adjoining the bar, now provides added space. Wide range of good, home-cooked food. Outdoor riverside terrace bar for summer drinking.
🍴 Q 🏠 🕪 ≢ ⊖

Surbiton

Bun Shop

22–26 Berrylands Road (off A240) ☎ (081) 399 3124
11–11
Adnams Bitter; Greene King IPA, Abbot; Young's Bitter, Special Ⓗ
Long-established free house with live music and skittles in the function room. Q ↻ ≢ ♣

Waggon & Horses

1 Surbiton Hill Road (A240)
11–3, 5–11
Young's Bitter, Special, Winter Warmer Ⓗ
Pub on a crossroads opposite the assembly rooms, run by the present landlord since 1967. The only Young's pub in the Royal Borough to retain its public bar. Frequent charity collections. Children welcome Sun lunchtimes. No food at weekends. Q ↻ 🏠 🕪 🔌 ♣

Sutton

Jenny Lind

53 Carshalton Road (A232)
12–11
Ind Coope Friary Meux Best Bitter, Burton Ale; Tetley Bitter Ⓗ
Well decorated, one-bar pub with a games area. Named after the opera-singing 'Swedish Nightingale' who once visited the area. Note the galleried exterior. No food Sun.
🏠 ↻ ≢ ♣

Lord Nelson

32 Lower Road (off A232)
☎ (081) 642 4120
11–11
Young's Bitter, Special, Winter Warmer Ⓗ
Long, one-bar pub with former saloon and public ends still evident. Distinctive, brown and green, tiled exterior. 🏠 ♣

West London

W1: Fitzrovia

Bricklayers Arms

31 Gresse Street
11–11
Samuel Smith OBB, Museum Ⓗ
Small, wood-panelled pub with an upstairs bar for food.
↻ ⊖ (Tottenham Ct Rd) ♣

George

55 Great Portland Street
11–11 (11–8 Sat)
Greene King XX Mild, IPA, Rayments Special, Abbot Ⓗ
Ornate pub also known as the 'Gluepot'. Conducted cellar tours available.
Q ↻ 🕪 ⊖ (Oxford Circus)

George & Dragon

151 Cleveland Street
12–11 (12–3, 7–11 Sat)
Draught Bass; Charrington IPA; Fuller's London Pride; Young's Special Ⓗ
Small, corner local drawing a mainly local clientele. Lunches Mon–Fri. ↻ 🔌 ⊖ (Gt Portland St)

King & Queen

1 Foley Street
☎ (071) 636 5619
11–11 (11–3, 7–11 Sat)
Ruddles Best Bitter, County; Webster's Yorkshire Bitter Ⓗ
Impressive, red-brick, Gothic building, with friendly service.
↻ ⊖ (Goodge St)

W1: Marylebone

Beehive

7 Homer Street
11–3, 5.30–11
Whitbread Boddingtons

Bitter, Wethered Bitter, Flowers Original Ⓗ
Small, cosy, locals' pub. ↻ ≢ ⊖

Dover Castle

43 Weymouth Mews
11–11 (11–3, 7–11 Sat)
Adnams Bitter; Marston's Pedigree; Morland Old Masters; Ruddles County; Whitbread Boddingtons Bitter Ⓗ
Cosy, panelled, mews pub; an old coaching inn dating from 1777. Note the mirrors under the beam to enable coachmen in the public bar to see when passengers in the saloon were ready to leave.
Q ↻ ⊖ (Regents Pk)

Turners Arms

26 Crawford Street
11–3, 5.30–11
Shepherd Neame Master Brew Bitter Ⓗ
A welcome oasis in a sea of the big brewers. ↻ ≢ ⊖ ♣

Windsor Castle

29 Crawford Place
11–11
Draught Bass; Charrington IPA Ⓗ
Comfortable pub, decorated with a British Royalty theme in the landlord's inimitable style.
Q ↻ ⊖ (Edgware Rd)

Worcester Arms

89 George Street
11–11 (11–3, 5.30–11 Sat)
Brakspear Bitter; Marston's Pedigree; Nethergate Casks IPA, Bitter; Thwaites Bitter Ⓗ
Busy free house with some attractive woodwork and a nice Courage Alton mirror.
↻ ⊖ (Baker St) ♣

W1: Mayfair

Guinea

30 Bruton Place
11–11 (11–3, 6.30–11 Sat; closed Sun)
Young's Bitter, Special Ⓗ
Small, intimate, mews pub; there has been a pub on this site since 1423. High class restaurant at the rear. Originally known as the 'Old One Pound One'. Winner of 1991 *Steak and Kidney Pie* competition. No lunch Sat.
Q ↻ 🕪 ⊖ (Green Pk)

Windmill

6–8 Mill Street
11–11 (closed Sun eve)
Young's Bitter, Special, Winter Warmer Ⓗ
Split-level pub with a first-floor restaurant, recently acquired by Young's. Choose your new Bentley (from the showrooms opposite) while enjoying a pint.
↻ 🕪 ⊖ (Oxford Circus)

Greater London

W1: Soho

Ship
116 Wardour Street
11–11 (closed Sun)
Fuller's Chiswick, London Pride, ESB Ⓗ
Corner local with nice windows and woodwork, frequented by film industry workers.
◖ ⊖ (Oxford Circus)

W2: Bayswater

Archery Tavern
4 Bathurst Street
11–11
Adnams Bitter; Fuller's London Pride; Tetley Bitter; Wadworth 6X; Whitbread Boddingtons Bitter Ⓗ
Wood-fronted pub next to a mews with working stables. Prints cover the walls.
◖ ⇌ (Lancaster Gate) ♣

Victoria Tavern
10a Strathearn Place
☎ (071) 262 5696
11–3, 5–11 (11–11 Thu & Fri)
Draught Bass; Charrington IPA; Fuller's London Pride; Wadworth 6X Ⓗ
Victorian, 'dumbbell-shaped' pub. Its walls are partly panelled and the remainder covered with pictures and Victorian bric-a-brac. Queen Victoria is reputed to have visited here when opening Paddington Station. Wine bar downstairs where Sun lunch is served.
Q ◖ ⇌ (Paddington) ⊖
✗ (lunchtime only)

W2: Paddington

Marquis of Clanricarde
36 Southwick Street
11–11
Courage Best Bitter, Directors Ⓗ
Large, comfortable pub with live music at weekends. ◖ ⇌ ⊖

White Hart
31 Brook Mews North
☎ (071) 402 4417
12–11
Courage Best Bitter, Directors Ⓗ
Wood-panelled pub, well hidden at the end of the mews. An ex-Reffel's of Bexley house, with a separate room for food.
◖ ⇌ ⊖

W3: Acton

Kings Head
High Street ☎ (081) 992 0282
11–11
Fuller's Chiswick, London Pride, ESB Ⓗ
Horseshoe-shaped bar displaying many prints of 19th-century Acton. Jasper the parrot

is still sharp on the draw. Daily newspaper rack. Meals until 8pm (not Sun). Q ◖ ⊖ (Town)

W4: Chiswick

Bell & Crown
72 Strand-on-the-Green
☎ (081) 994 4164
11–11
Fuller's Chiswick, London Pride, ESB Ⓗ
Busy, riverside pub with a conservatory overlooking the Thames and Kew Bridge. Handy for the Engine Museum. No weekend lunches.
Q ◖ ⇌ (Kew Bridge)

Duke of York
107 Devonshire Road
11–3, 5.30–11 (11–11 Sat)
Fuller's London Pride, ESB Ⓗ
Corner pub with a tiled facade and much interior woodwork; very much a local.
◖ ⊖ (Turnham Green) ♣

Windmill
214 Chiswick High Road
11–11
Fuller's Chiswick, London Pride, ESB Ⓗ
Excellent pub decorated in Swiss chalet style. Very busy at times, serving excellent food (no meals Sun eve).
🅱 ◖ ▮ ⊖ (Turnham Green) ♣

W5: Ealing

Fox & Goose
Hanger Lane ☎ (081) 997 2441
11–11
Fuller's Chiswick, London Pride, ESB Ⓗ
A tiny public bar and large saloon in a welcome refuge from the Hanger Lane gyratory system. Very busy weekday lunchtimes.
🅱 ◖ ▮ ▯ ⊖ (Hanger Lane) P

Plough
297 Northfield Avenue
☎ (081) 577 1416
11.30–11
Fuller's Chiswick, London Pride, ESB Ⓗ
There has been a pub on this site in Little Ealing for more than 200 years. The current one boasts two bars; the saloon features alcoves, and a conservatory leads to a small garden. Deservedly popular.
▦ 🅱 ◖ ▮ ⊖ (Northfields) P

Red Lion
13 St Mary's Road
☎ (081) 567 2541
11–3, 5.30–11 (11–11 Fri & Sat)
Fuller's Chiswick, London Pride, ESB Ⓗ
Near what used to be the Ealing film studios (now BBC); a gem of a pub with walls lined with film and TV photos.
Q 🅱 ◖ ⇌ (Broadway) ⊖

Rose & Crown
Church Place, St Mary's Road
11–3, 5.30–11
Fuller's Chiswick, London Pride, ESB Ⓗ
Very popular, family local, tucked away at the side of St Mary's church. You may have to spill-over into the excellent garden in nice weather, as the bars get extremely crowded.
Q 🅱 ◖ ▯ ⊖ (S Ealing) ♣

Wheatsheaf
41 Haven Lane
11–11
Fuller's Chiswick, London Pride, ESB Ⓗ
Small, one-bar, back-street pub that has waited long for entry into the *Guide* and now has found the right landlord. A local full of character and characters.
Q 🅱 ◖ ⇌ (Broadway) ⊖

W6: Hammersmith

Black Lion
2 South Black Lion Lane
☎ (081) 748 2639
11–3, 5.30–11
Ruddles Best Bitter, County; Webster's Yorkshire Bitter Ⓗ
17th-century inn with a 300 year-old chestnut tree in the beer garden.
🅱 ◖ ⊖ (Stamford Bridge) ♣

Blue Anchor
13 Lower Mall
☎ (071) 748 5774
11.30–3.30, 5.30–11 (11–11 Fri, Sat & summer)
Courage Best Bitter, Directors Ⓗ
Busy, Thames-side pub, almost under Hammersmith Bridge. A pewter bar-top and eight pewter-mounted handpulls feature. Eve meals in summer only. ◖ ▮ ⊖

Builders
81 King Street
11–11 (11–11 Sat)
Young's Bitter, Special, Winter Warmer Ⓗ
Two-bar pub in a busy shopping area. 🅱 ◖ ⊖

Cross Keys
57 Black Lion Lane
11–11
Fuller's Chiswick, London Pride, ESB Ⓗ
Popular pub, midway between King Street and the Thames.
🅱 ◖ ⊖ (Stamford Bridge) ♣

Dove
19 Upper Mall
11–11
Fuller's London Pride, ESB Ⓗ
Historic, 17th-century pub, overlooking the Thames. *Rule Britannia* was composed in an upstairs room. Listed in the *Guinness Book of Records* as having the smallest public bar 4'2" × 7'10". ◖ ▮ ▯ ⊖

Thatched House

115 Dalling Road
☎ (081) 748 6147
11–11
Young's Bitter, Special, Winter Warmer Ⓗ
Popular local with a great atmosphere. Barbecues in summer.
⊛ ◖ ⊖ (Ravenscourt Pk)

W7: Hanwell

Fox

Green Lane (off A3002)
☎ (081) 567 3912
11–3, 5.30–11
Courage Best Bitter, Directors Ⓗ
Quiet, one-bar pub, just off the Grand Union Canal and popular with boat people. Fine food – lunches are exceptionally good value with huge portions, but beer is not cheap. Note the ferocious-looking fish in the aquarium! Q ⊛ ◖ ♣

Viaduct

221 Uxbridge Road (A4020)
11–11
Fuller's Chiswick, London Pride, ESB Ⓗ
Attractive two-bar pub in the shadow of Brunel's Wharncliffe viaduct. The public bar is lively on quiz night (Mon), with beer as the prize. ⊛ ◖ ⊟ ≈ ♣ P

White Hart

324 Greenford Avenue (off B455) ☎ (081) 578 1708
11–11
Fuller's London Pride, ESB Ⓗ
Large, three-bar pub, recently refurbished to a high standard; one of the few pubs left in the area that still boasts an off-licence. Antique handpumps adorn one wall of the saloon bar. Q ◖ ⊟ ≈ (Castle Bar Pk) ♣

W8: Kensington

Britannia

1 Allen Street
☎ (071) 957 1864
11–11 (11–3, 5.30–11 Sat)
Young's Bitter, Special, Winter Warmer Ⓗ
Busy, wood-panelled pub with a small public bar; the split-level lounge has two bars and a conservatory which is a no-smoking area at lunchtime. Meals served Mon–Sat.
Q ⊛ ◖ ⊖ (High St Kensington) ⅋

Windsor Castle

114 Campden Hill Road
☎ (071) 927 8491
11–11
Draught Bass; Charrington IPA Ⓗ
Three-bar pub built in 1835; unspoilt, with much wood panelling and a cosy atmosphere. No music or machines. Note the vine in the

garden. No eve meals Sun.
Q ⊛ ◖ ◗ ⊖ (Notting Hill Gate)

W9: Little Venice

Warwick Castle

6 Warwick Place
11–11
Draught Bass; Charrington IPA; Fuller's London Pride; Morrells Varsity Ⓗ
Excellent, traditional pub, near the Regents Canal basin. Guest beers. ⌨ ◖ ◗ ⊖ (Warwick Ave)

W9: Maida Vale

Warrington

93 Warrington Crescent
11–11
Brakspear Special; Fuller's London Pride, ESB; Ruddles County; Young's Special Ⓗ
Large, Victorian gin palace with florid decoration and a semi-circular marble bar.
◖ ◗ ⊖ (Warwick Ave)

W11: Holland Park

Prince of Wales

14 Princedale Road
11–3, 5–11 (11–11 Sat)
Draught Bass; Charrington IPA Ⓗ
Victorian pub with nice etched windows. A right of way used to run through one bar. ⊛ ◖ ◗ ⊖

W12: Shepherd's Bush

Crown & Sceptre

57 Melina Road
11–11 (7–11 Sat if QPR are at home)
Fuller's Chiswick, London Pride, ESB Ⓗ
Popular, back-street local. Lunches served Mon–Fri.
◖ ⊖ (Goldhawk Rd) ♣

W14: West Kensington

Britannia Tap

150 Warwick Road
☎ (071) 602 1649
11–11 (11–3, 6–11 Sat)
Young's Bitter, Special, Winter Warmer Ⓗ
Small, friendly pub with a lot of character. Can get busy at lunchtimes; meals served Mon–Fri. Q ◖ ≈ (Kensington Olympia) ⊖ (Earl's Ct)

Seven Stars

253 North End Road
☎ (071) 385 6273
11–11
Fuller's Chiswick, London Pride, ESB Ⓗ
Two-bar pub built in 1930 in Art-Deco style. ⊛ ⊖

Warwick Arms

160 Warwick Road
☎ (071) 603 3560
11–3, 5–11 (11–11 Fri & Sat)

Fuller's Chiswick, London Pride, ESB Ⓗ

One-bar pub dating from 1828. The rear section has exposed brickwork and attractive Wedgwood pump handles. Regular barbecues in summer. No eve meals Sun. Q ◖ ◗ ≈ (Kensington Olympia) ⊖ (Earl's Ct) ♣

Bedfont

Beehive

333 Staines Road, Feltham
☎ (081) 890 8086
12–4, 5.30–11 (may vary)
Fuller's London Pride, ESB Ⓗ
Excellent pub with a friendly, lively atmosphere: an attractive lounge and a well-kept garden with a children's play area. Good value, home-cooked food (not served Sun); barbecues in summer. ⊛ ◖ P

Brentford

Brewery Tap

17 Catherine Wheel Road (canal bank) ☎ (081) 560 5200
11–11
Fuller's London Pride, ESB Ⓗ
Cosy pub in the heart of the old Brentford dockland: modernised, but retaining many original features. Trad. jazz Thu eves; piano Sun eves; quiz every other week. No food weekends. Q ⊛ ◖ ≈ ♣

O'Riordans Tavern

High Street ☎ (081) 560 5543
11–11
Adnams Bitter; Draught Bass; Bateman XB; Felinfoel Double Dragon; Wadworth 6X Ⓗ
Noted London stout house with frequently-changed real ales. The interior and wall furnishings are of much interest. Direct access to the riverside walk and convenient for Kew Bridge Steam Museum. No meals weekends. ⌨ Q ◖ ≈ (Kew Bridge) ⊖ (Gunnersbury) P

White Horse

24 Market Place
☎ (081) 560 0188
11–3, 5.30–11 (11–11 Thu–Sat)
Draught Bass; Charrington IPA Ⓗ
Historic inn, off the High Street; tastefully modernised and roomy, with a conservatory and an attractive, Brent riverbank garden. Carvery roast Mon–Fri and Sun lunchtimes (no meals Sun eve or Sat). Guest beer. ⌨ Q ⊛ ◖ ◗ ≈ ♣

Cranford

Queens Head

123 High Street (off A312)
☎ (081) 897 0722
11–11

Fuller's Chiswick, London Pride, Mr Harry, ESB Ⓗ
Lovely, Tudor-style pub comprising one bar, but two distinct drinking areas. A lounge to the side is used for dining (home-cooked food) but does not have a bar of its own. Families are welcome. One of the biggest sellers of Fuller's occasional brew Mr Harry. No eve meals at weekends.
🏠 🍴 ◖ ▶ ♣ P

Greenford

Black Horse
425 Oldfield Lane North
☎ (081) 578 1384
11–11
Fuller's London Pride, ESB Ⓗ
On the Paddington arm of the Grand Union Canal; a busy and friendly pub which is a perennial entry in this guide. The large garden has a children's play area. Moorings available. Watch out for the parrot! Q 🍴 ◖ 🖴 ➼ ⊖ ♣ P

Hampton

White Hart
70 High Street (A304)
☎ (081) 979 5352
11–3, 5.30–11 (11–11 Fri & Sat)
Brakspear Special; Greene King Abbot; King & Barnes Mild, Festive Ⓗ
Comfortable, tasteful, mock Tudor pub with a relaxed atmosphere. Eight handpumps serve regularly-changed beers; a true free house. Good value home-cooked lunches (no food weekends). 🏠 Q 🍴 ◖ 🖴

Hampton Court

Kings Arms
Lion Gate, Hampton Court Road ☎ (081) 977 1729
11–11
Adnams Broadside; Hall & Woodhouse Badger Best Bitter, Tanglefoot; Wadworth 6X; Old Timer; Wells Eagle Ⓗ
Imposing, historic pub with a friendly atmosphere, beside the palace's Lion Gate and world famous maze. Sawdust on the floor in the public bar; mosaic flooring in the saloon. Pub billiards. Guest beers. Opens at 9am for refreshments.
Q 🍴 ◖ 🖴 ♣ ♣

Hampton Hill

Windmill
80 Windmill Road (off A312)
☎ (081) 979 6398
11–3 (3.30 Sat), 5.30–11
Draught Bass; Charrington IPA Ⓗ
Small, comfortable pub offering friendly, efficient service. Note

the glazed terracotta frontage, with Charrington's green and white stained-glass. Presentation cheques to the local MENCAP branch are on display in the darts area. No food Sun.
🍴 ◖ ♣ P

Hampton Wick

White Hart
High Street ☎ (081) 977 1786
11–11
Fuller's Chiswick, London Pride, ESB Ⓗ
Large pub with a tasteful oak-panelled lounge and an award-winning garden with a barbecue. Wide range of good, home-cooked food available, incl. breakfasts 8–10am. Karaoke night Wed in a separate hall. 🍴 ◖ ▶ 🖴 ➼ P 🍴

Harmondsworth

Crown
High Street ☎ (081) 759 1007
11–3, 5–11 (11–11 Fri & Sat)
Courage Best Bitter, Directors Ⓗ
Cosy, one-bar pub, not far from Heathrow Airport: two real fires and lots of little nooks and crannies. Food is good and available at most times. Various guest beers. 🏠 Q 🍴 ◖ ▶ ♣

Hayes

Blue Anchor
Printing House Lane (off A312)
☎ (081) 573 0714
11–11
Ruddles Best Bitter, County; Webster's Yorkshire Bitter Ⓗ
Smart, one-bar pub with several drinking areas, situated on the towpath of the Grand Union Canal and within easy reach of the town centre. Fuller's London Pride is the regular guest beer.
🍴 ◖ ▶ ➼ ♣

Heathrow

Crown
49 Bath Road (A4)
☎ (081) 759 9581
11–3, 5.30–11
Courage Best Bitter, Directors Ⓗ
Small, two-bar house on the northern edge of the airport, with a Concorde Museum in the saloon bar. Hardly room to swing a cat in the public. Good value food. Q ◖ ▶ 🖴 ♣ P

Heston

Master Robert Hotel (Robert Inn)
366 Great West Road (A4)
☎ (081) 570 6261
11–3, 5–11 (11–11 Fri & Sat)
Fuller's Chiswick, London Pride, ESB Ⓗ

Recently extended, large establishment situated at a junction on the A4. The pub entrance is in Sutton Lane. No real ale in the cocktail bar.
🛏 🍴 🖂 ◖ ▶ P

Hillingdon

Star
Blenheim Parade, Uxbridge Road ☎ (081) 573 1096
11–11
Draught Bass; Charrington IPA; Fuller's London Pride Ⓗ
Friendly and comfortable local with a basic bar. No food Sun.
🍴 ◖ ♣

Hounslow

Earl Russell
274 Hanworth Road (A314)
☎ (081) 570 1560
11–11
Fuller's London Pride, ESB Ⓗ
Traditional, Victorian local with a friendly atmosphere. Good value lunches (Mon–Fri).
🍴 ◖ 🖴 ➼ ⊖ (Central) ♣ P

Jolly Farmer
177 Lampton Road (off A4)
☎ (081) 570 1276
11–11
Courage Best Bitter, Directors Ⓗ
Popular, cosy local near the junction with the Great West Road. Friendly licensees offer very good, home-cooked lunches and bar snacks (Mon–Fri). Guest beers.
🍴 ◖ 🖴 ⊖ (Central) P

Isleworth

Castle
18 Upper Square, Old Isleworth
☎ (081) 560 3615
11–3, 5.30–11 (11–11 Fri & Sat)
Young's Bitter, Special Ⓗ, **Winter Warmer** Ⓖ
Large, one-roomed bar with a separate restaurant. The spacious conservatory away from the bar is suitable for families. Close to the River Thames. Sun lunch and eve meals only in restaurant.
🏠 🍴 ◖ ▶

Town Wharf
Swan Street ☎ (081) 847 2287
11.30–3, 5.30–11 (may vary; 11–11 summer)
Samuel Smith OBB, Museum Ⓗ
Splendid, two-bar pub, on the site of a disused wharf. Well-planned, the comfortable upstairs lounge has a balcony and the riverside terrace provides a pleasant outdoor drinking area. Family room in downstairs bar. Quizzes Mon eve. 🛏 🍴 ◖ ▶ ♣ P

New Brentford

Lord Nelson
9 Enfield Road
11–11
Fuller's London Pride, ESB Ⓗ
London Pride outsells every
other beer and lager put
together in this pub, which must
say something for its quality.
An astonishing variety of
unusual and exotic food is
always available and the wine
list makes a good read. A pub
where the old world meets the
new. 🏚 ◖ ▶ 🖼 ≉ ♣

Norwood Green

Plough
Tentelow Lane (off A3005)
11–11
**Fuller's Chiswick, London
Pride, ESB** Ⓗ
The oldest pub in the area and
certainly the most attractive.
Recently refurbished to the
highest standards, it now offers
a much larger drinking area. A
country pub in an urban setting.
Q 🛥 🏚 ◖ ♣

Ruislip

Six Bells
Duck's Hill Road (A4180)
☎ (0895) 639466
11–11 (11–3, 5.30–11 Jan–Mar)
**Ind Coope Benskins Best
Bitter, Burton Ale; Tetley
Bitter** Ⓗ
Comfy local on the outskirts of
Ruislip; a stone-flagged floor
and low ceilings. Skittle alley;
barbecues in summer. Guest
beers (Greene King IPA or
Theakston XB). 🏚 Q 🏚 ◖ ♣ ▶ P

White Bear
Ickenham Road (B466)
11–11
**Courage Best Bitter,
Directors** Ⓗ
Grade II listed (ex-Harmen's
brewery) pub with a lively
public bar. Fuller's London Pride
is a regular guest.
🏚 ◖ ▶ 🖼 ⊖ ♣ P

Ruislip Manor

JJ Moon's
12 Victoria Road
☎ (0895) 622373
11–11
**Eldridge Pope Royal Oak;
Greene King IPA, Abbot;
Theakston XB; Younger
Scotch** Ⓗ
A traditional style, mock
Victorian ale house, converted
from an old Woolworth store.
The landlord previously spent
eight years at a Fuller's pub
listed in this guide. Always very
busy; highly recommended.
Guest beers. Q 🏚 ◖ ▶ 🖼 ⊖ ▭

Southall

Old Oak Tree
The Common
11–11
**Courage Best Bitter,
Directors** Ⓗ
Off-the-beaten-track, canalside
pub, with moorings. Easier to
find by boat than by road. Bar
billiards. 🏚 ◖ 🖼 ♣ P

Scotsman
96 Scotts Road
11–3, 5.15–11
Fuller's London Pride, ESB Ⓗ
Street-corner local with a very
lively, games-oriented public
and a much more quiet, sedate
and comfy saloon. 🏚 Q ◖ 🖼 ♣

Teddington

Builders Arms
38 Field Lane (just off A313)
11–3, 5.30–11
**Courage Best Bitter,
Directors** Ⓗ
Small, very friendly pub
somewhat hidden away but well
worth finding. A buffalo head
hangs over the fireplace in the
saloon bar. Regular cribbage
school. Guest beer. No food
weekends. Q 🏚 ◖ 🖼 ≉ ♣

Queen Dowager
49 North Lane (just off A313)
11–3 (4 Sat), 5.30 (7 Sat)–11 (11–11
Fri)
**Young's Bitter, Special,
Winter Warmer** Ⓗ
Small pub, off the main street,
convenient for shops and car
parks. A surprisingly large,
pleasant garden lies to the side
and rear. Named after Queen
Adelaide, widow of William IV,
who returned to Teddington
after his death. Q 🏚 ◖ 🖼 ≉ ♣

Twickenham

Eel Pie
11 Church Street (off A305)
11–11
**Adnams Mild; Everards
Tiger; Hall & Woodhouse
Badger Best Bitter,
Tanglefoot; Wadworth 6X,
Old Timer** Ⓗ
Ex-wine bar near the riverside in
Twickenham's oldest shopping
street, offering traditional and
continental lunches (not Sun). A
popular venue for rugby fans (a
mile from the stadium). ◖ ≉ ♣

Pope's Grotto
Gross Deep (A310)
11–3, 5.30–11 (11–11 Sat)
**Young's Bitter, Special,
Winter Warmer** Ⓗ
Large, comfortable pub with a
relaxed and friendly
atmosphere, overlooking
Radnor Gardens and the
Thames and popular with all

ages. Excellent, good value food
served. Within walking distance
of the town centre. 🏚 Q 🏚
◖ ▶ 🖼 ≉ (Strawberry Hill) P

Prince Albert
30 Hampton Road (A311)
11–11
**Fuller's Chiswick, London
Pride, ESB** Ⓗ
Small, Victorian pub, popular
with all sectors of society and
often crowded. Extensions to
bar areas in recent years have
been in keeping with the rest of
the pub. Car park is filled with
tables in summer. 🏚 Q 🏚 ◖
≉ (Strawberry Hill) ♣ P

Uxbridge

Crown & Sceptre
High Street ☎ (0895) 36308
11–11
**Courage Best Bitter,
Directors** Ⓗ
Good, traditional pub, offering
an extensive range of home-
cooked specials, incl. fish dishes,
at reasonable prices. Try the
award-winning steak and kidney
pies (no food Sun). Guest beer.
🏚 🏚 ◖ ⊖ ♣

General Elliott
St Johns Road
12–3, 5–11 (11–4, 7–11 Sat)
**Ind Coope Benskins Best
Bitter, Burton Ale; Tetley
Bitter** Ⓗ
Comfortable, canalside pub with
a range of guest beers. 🏚 ◖ ▶ P

Three Tuns
High Street ☎ (0895) 33960
11–3, 5.30–11 (11–11 Thu–Sat)
**Ind Coope Burton Ale; Tetley
Bitter** Ⓗ
350 year-old, Grade II listed
building, catering well for an
office lunchtime trade. Two
guest beers. Eve meals in
summer only. 🏚 🛥 🏚 ◖ ⅄ ⊖

Whitton

Admiral Nelson
123 Nelson Road
11.30–11
**Fuller's Chiswick, London
Pride, ESB** Ⓗ
Busy, high street pub, popular
with Harlequins RFC (near
Twickenham). Supports a very
successful tug-of-war team.
Varied menu with food available
at all times, Mon–Sat. Trad. jazz
Tue eves. 🏚 🏚 ◖ ▶ ≉ ♣

Yeading

Walnut Tree
115 Willow Tree Lane (off
A312) ☎ (081) 845 0849
11.30–3, 5.30–11
Fuller's London Pride, ESB Ⓗ
Lively locals' pub with a soccer
team and golfing society. Pub
games predominate. 🏚 ◖ ▶ 🖼 ♣

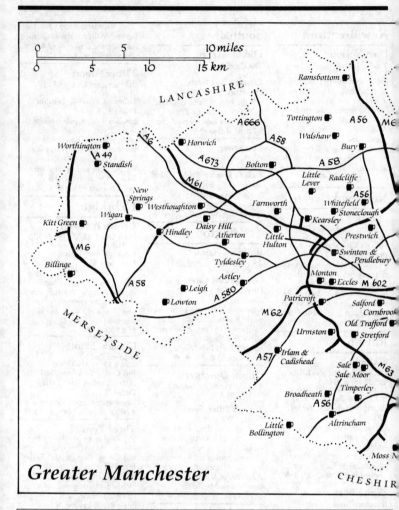

Greater Manchester

Greater Manchester

Hydes' Anvil, *Manchester*; **Holt**, *Cheetham*; **Lees**, *Middleton Junction*; **Oak**, *Heywood*; **Robinson's**, *Stockport*; **West Coast**, *Chorlton-on-Medlock*

Altrincham

Bakers Arms
Pownall Road
11.30–3, 5–11 (11.30–11 Mon, Fri & Sat)
Hydes' Anvil Mild, Bitter Ⓔ
Modern pub with a lively vault, next to Sainsbury's. The only Hydes' pub in Altrincham. Live music and discos in the lounge.
⊞ ≠ ♣ P

Orange Tree
Old Market Place (A56)
☎ (061) 928 2600
11–11
Ruddles Best Bitter;
Webster's Yorkshire Bitter,
Wilson's Mild, Bitter Ⓗ

Once the smallest pub in Altrincham, where, in 1823, a man sold his wife for 1/6d. Regular guest beer, with an emphasis on independent brewers. Note the old prints of the Market Place, showing other pubs now gone. No eve meals Sun. ⌣ ◖ ◗ ≠ ♣

Ancoats

Jolly Angler
47 Ducie Street
☎ (061) 236 5307
11.30–4, 5.30–11 (11.30–11 Fri & Sat)
Hydes' Anvil Mild, Bitter Ⓗ
Basic, one-roomed pub with occasional folk music and sing-alongs. ⌣ ≠ (Piccadilly) ♣

Smiths Arms
37 Sherratt Street (off A62)
☎ (061) 236 0861
11–11 (11–4, 7–11 Sat)
Tetley Walker Mild, Bitter Ⓗ
Four-roomed community pub on the fringe of the city centre; unchanged since the 1920s.
⌂ ⌣ ⊞ ≠ (Piccadilly) ♣ P

Ashton-under-Lyne

Dog & Pheasant
528 Oldham Road
☎ (061) 330 4894
12–4, 7.30–11 (12–11 Sat)
Marston's Mercian Mild,
Burton Best Bitter,
Pedigree Ⓗ

separate tap room and raised no-smoking lounge. No meals Sat. ◖ ♣ P ⅄

Ross's Arms
130 Higher Green Lane
☎ (0942) 874405
12–11
Holt Mild, Bitter; Tetley Walker Dark Mild, Bitter; Walker Bitter; Whitbread Boddingtons Bitter Ⓗ
A large, comfortable lounge, a smaller tap room with a pool table and a two-storey restaurant at the rear. Outside there is a beer garden, patio and children's play area. Astley bridge on the Bridgewater Canal is 100 yards away. Guest beers. ⊛ ⋈ ◖ ⊟ Å ♣ P

Atherton

Atherton Arms
6 Tyldesley Road
☎ (0942) 882885
11.30–11
Holt Mild, Bitter Ⓗ
Ex-Labour Club: a huge, L-shaped lounge, with several seating areas, and a large tap room with snooker and pool tables. There is another bar in the main entrance corridor.
⊟ ◖ ≋ ♣ P

Letters Inn
Wigan Road ☎ (0942) 883289
12–11
Tetley Walker Dark Mild, Bitter Ⓗ
Comfortable, town-centre local with separate tap room and L-shaped lounge, where the bar is at one side, leaving the other side clear. Meals Mon–Sat.
⊛ ◖ ⊟ ♣ P

Beswick

Britannia
2 Rowsley Street (off A662)
☎ (061) 223 1604
12–11
Lees GB Mild, Bitter Ⓗ
Heartwarming, side-street gem in the shadow of gasholders. Continues to thrive despite the lack of nearby homes or jobs. The vault has darts (incl. a Manchester board), TV and panelled seating; the lounge has a pool table and etched-glass. Warm atmosphere in both rooms. Food Mon–Fri. ⊛ ◖ ⊟ ♣

Billinge

Hare & Hounds
142 Upholland Road
☎ (0744) 892843
12.30–3.30, 7–11
Tetley Walker Mild, Bitter Ⓗ
Popular, large, red-brick pub. Two rooms, free from distractions, where conversation and good beer are foremost. Guest beers. Q ⊟ ♣ P

Near the Daisy Nook Country Park, this opened-up pub has retained four separate and comfortable areas. ⊱ ⊛ ◖ P

Heros of Waterloo
3 Mossley Road
John Smith's Bitter Ⓗ
Large, one-roomed pub opposite the former Ladysmith Barracks. Guest beers. ⊛ ◖ ♣ P

Oddfellows Arms
Kings Road, Hurst
☎ (061) 330 6356
12–11
Robinson's Mild, Best Bitter Ⓗ & Ⓔ
Many-roomed pub with a village atmosphere. Retains original features, such as the stained-glass bar, to give a cosy and welcoming feel. Reputed to be where the NUM was started. Known locally as the Vestry.
⊛ ◖

Witchwood
152 Old Street
11.30–3 (4 Sat), 5 (7 Sat)–11 (11.30–11 Fri)
Banks's Bitter; Holt Bitter; Marston's Pedigree; Old Mill Bullion; Theakston Best Bitter Ⓗ
Highly regarded free house with sufficient turnover to allow up to nine beers to be available. Well-known regionally for the quality live music most nights. Due to be extended to provide a bar separate from the music room. Regular guest beers. ◖ ≋

Astley

Cart & Horses
221 Manchester Road
☎ (0942) 870751
12–11
Holt Mild, Bitter Ⓗ
Large, open-plan lounge, formerly two rooms with a standing area in front of the bar;

Holts Arms
(Foot o' Causeway)
Crank Road ☎ (0744) 622705
2 (12 summer)–11
**Burtonwood Mild, Best
Bitter** Ⓗ
Unspoilt *Guide* regular with a
unique interior, although a
major refurbishment is
imminent. Crown green
bowling; bowling parties held.
🏚 Q ▦ ◖ ♣ P

Try also: Foresters Arms,
Main St (Burtonwood)

Blackley

Golden Lion
47 Old Market Street (just off
A664) ☎ (061) 740 1944
11–11 (11–4, 7–11 Sat)
Holt Mild, Bitter Ⓗ
Large, turn-of-the-century pub
with vault, lounge, snug and
lobby area. One of three Holt
houses in a village where
traditional beers from seven
other brewers can also be
sampled. Q ▦ 🚆 ♣

Pleasant
390 Chapel Lane (off A6104)
1 (12 Sat)–11
**Robinson's Mild, Best
Bitter** Ⓗ**, Old Tom** (winter) Ⓖ
Small, community pub with
vault, lounge and Golf Society
club room, on the fringe of
18th-century Crab Village.
Q ▦ 🚆 ♣

Bolton

Ainsworth Arms
606 Halliwell Road
(A6099/A58 jct)
☎ (0204) 40671
11.30–3, 5.30–11 (11–11 Sat)
**Ind Coope Burton Ale;
Walker Mild, Best Bitter** Ⓗ
Well-run and extremely popular
pub, attracting custom from a
wide section of the local
community. 🏚 ◖ ♣

Clifton
94 Newport Street (opp.
station) ☎ (0204) 392738
11–11 (11–3, 7–11 Sat)
**Jennings Bitter; Tetley
Walker Mild, Bitter** Ⓗ
Comfortable, homely, town-
centre local, which has kept its
character despite refurbishment.
No food Sun. Regular guest
beers. ◖ 🚆 ♣

Dog & Partridge
Manor Street
☎ (0204) 388596
12–2.30 (11.30–4 Sat), 7–11 (closed
Sun lunch)
Thwaites Best Mild, Bitter Ⓗ
Well-run, town-centre local.
One of only a few in the
vicinity not to have dress
restrictions. 🚆 🚆 ♣

Howcroft Inn
36 Pool Street (via Vernon
Street, off St Georges Road)
☎ (0204) 26814
12–4 (5 Sat), 5.30 (7 Sat & winter)–11
Walker Mild, Best Bitter Ⓗ
Excellent, old-fashioned, back-
street local just outside the
town centre, with a vault, snug
and two other rooms. A former
CAMRA award-winner for the
best refurbishment of an urban
pub. The bowling green gets
crowded in summer. 🏚 ▦ ◖ ♣ P

Little John
Lever Street ☎ (0204) 72096
11.30–11
Tetley Walker Mild, Bitter Ⓗ
Traditional local in a mainly
industrial area. Regular guest
beers. Q ▦ 🚆

Maxim's
Bradshawgate
☎ (0204) 23486
11.30–4, 7.30–11 (closed Sun)
Vaux Samson Ⓗ
Large, modernised, town-centre
pub which doubles as a disco.
Crowded and noisy at
weekends. Children welcome at
lunchtimes. Cellar visits possible
when quiet. Weekly-changed
guest beers from small
breweries. ◖ 🍺 🚆

Sweet Green Tavern
Crook Street
☎ (0204) 392258
11.30–3, 6–11
**Hydes' Anvil Bitter; Tetley
Walker Mild, Bitter** Ⓗ
Excellent, town-centre local near
the railway station. ▦ 🚆 🚆

York Hotel
112–114 Newport Street
11–11 (11–4, 7–11 Sat)
**Burtonwood Best Mild, Best
Bitter, Forshaw's** Ⓗ
Comfortable, open-plan pub,
deservedly popular. Bolton's
only regular *Good Beer Guide*
entry. ◖ 🚆 ♣

Bredbury

Arden Arms
Ashton Old Road (A6017)
11–3, 5.30–11
**Robinson's Mild, Best
Bitter** Ⓔ
Pleasant, comfortable, multi-
roomed pub which seems to
have escaped Robinson's
modernisation schemes. Situated
in a semi-rural location on the
border of Stockport and
Tameside, it has a large, fairly
well-equipped play area for
children. ▦ ♣ P

Rising Sun
57 Stockport Road East
☎ (061) 430 4326
11–3, 5.30–11
Holt Bitter; Webster's

Yorkshire Bitter, Wilson's
Mild, Bitter Ⓗ
Thriving, lively local within
staggering distance of the
railway station. Tends to get
rather crowded at weekends.
Enclosed garden is good for
families. ▦ ◖ 🚆 ♣

Broadbottom

Cheshire Cheese
65 Lower Market Street
☎ (0457) 762339
7–11 (12–11 Sat)
Thwaites Mild, Bitter Ⓗ
Small, one-roomed, end-of-
terrace pub with three, separate
drinking areas – bar, lounge and
games area. One, occasional
guest beer. 🏚 🅰 🚆 ♣

Broadheath

Railway Inn
153 Manchester Road (A56)
☎ (061) 941 3383
11–11 (11–3, 7–11 Sat)
**Whitbread Boddingtons
Bitter** Ⓗ
Unspoilt, small, terraced pub
next to the railway bridge. The
two rooms are named after
Manchester's two mainline
stations (Victoria and Piccadilly).
The pub was the last ale-only
house in the area. ◖ 🚆 ♣

Bury

Help Me Thro'
141 Crostons Road
12–3, 5.30 (7 Sat)–11
Thwaites Best Mild, Bitter Ⓗ
Locals' pub in a cottage setting,
with other good pubs close by.
🏚 Q ▦ 🚆 ♣ P

Napier Inn
102 Bolton Street
☎ (061) 764 3649
12–3 (4.30 Fri; not Tue in winter), 7–11
(11.30–11 Sat)
Thwaites Best Mild, Bitter Ⓗ
Bury Brewery Company etched-
windows grace this pub, the
nearest to the southern
terminus of the East Lancs
Steam Railway. A new emphasis
on food is illustrated by hygiene
diplomas on the bar (no meals
Mon eve). ◖ 🍺 🚆 ♣

Rose & Crown
36 Manchester Old Road
☎ (061) 764 6461
12–3, 7 (5 Fri)–11 (12–11 Sat)
**Moorhouse's Pendle Witches
Brew; Taylor Landlord;
Thwaites Best Mild, Bitter;
Whitbread Boddingtons
Bitter** Ⓗ
A short walk from the town
centre: a compact pub featuring
a range of guest beers
unequalled in variety in Bury.
The name may change to Tap &
Spile. No food Sat or Sun.
◖ 🚆 🚆 ♣ ⏺

Castleton

Blue Pitts Inn
842 Manchester Road
☎ (0706) 32151
12–5, 7.30–11 (12–11 Fri)
Lees GB Mild, Bitter Ⓗ
Welcoming, village local in an
old railway building. The cellar
was once used as a mortuary for
the Blue Pitts village. Function
room available. Definitely
haunted (ask the landlady).
Q Å ≉ ♣ P

Chadderton

Rifle Range Inn
372 Burnley Lane (⅛ mile from
A627(M) ☎ (061) 624 0874
11.30–3 (4 Sat), 5.30 (7 Sat)–11
Lees GB Mild, Bitter Ⓗ
Busy, three-roomed local near
the football ground. The large
vault has strong sporting and
musical connections. Eve meals
finish at 8pm; no food Sun.
Ⓙ ♣ P

Cheadle

Printers Arms
220 Stockport Road (A560)
☎ (061) 491 1448
11.30–11
**Robinson's Mild, Best
Bitter** Ⓔ
Traditional, family-run local,
comprising a main bar with a
snug and tap room off. Thriving
darts teams. Good value beer
for the area. Meals served
Mon–Fri. ⊛ Ⓙ ♣ P

Queen's Arms
177 Stockport Road (A560)
☎ (061) 428 3081
11.45–11 (11.45–4, 7–11 Sat)
Robinson's Mild, Bitter Ⓗ
Multi-roomed, traditional pub; a
rare outlet for Robinson's
ordinary bitter. Garden has a
children's play area and the
family room is available until
7.30pm. No meals at the
weekend. ⊞ ⌣ ⊛ Ⓙ ♣ P

Cheadle Hulme

Church
90 Ravenoak Road (A5149)
☎ (061) 485 1987
11–3, 5–11 (11–11 Fri & Sat)
Robinson's Mild, Best Bitter Ⓗ
Thriving, exceptionally well-
run, friendly pub, popular with
all age groups. The unspoilt,
multi-roomed arrangement
contributes to a lively
atmosphere. Although trade is
always brisk, the service is
excellent. ⊞ Q ⊛ Ⓙ ⊟ ≉ ♣ P

Cheetham

Queens Arms
6 Honey Street (300 yds off
Cheetham Hill Road)

☎ (061) 834 4239
11.30–4, 7 (6 Wed & Thu)–11
(11.30–11 Fri)
**Bateman XB, XXXB, Victory;
Taylor Landlord** Ⓗ
Recently enlarged but retains a
rare example of an Empress
Brewery façade. Splendid view
of the Irk Valley and the city
from the large beer garden.
Belgian bottled beers and British
guest beers. ⊞ ⊛ Ⓙ ≉ (Victoria)
♣

Chorlton-on-Medlock

King's Arms
4a Helmshore Walk (off A6)
☎ (061) 273 1053
12–11
**West Coast Mild, Best Bitter,
Porter, Yakima Grande PA,
Extra Special** Ⓗ
A run-down estate hides this
1908-vintage showcase for the
superb West Coast beers
brewed here. Beside the listed
ales, try Guiltless Stout and look
for one-off brews. Frequent live
music eves (styles vary). Not to
be missed when in Manchester.
It's only hard to find the first
time! Book for Sun lunch; no
meals Sun eve or 5–8 Sat.
Ⓙ ≉ (Piccadilly) ♣ P

Clayton

Strawberry Duck
74 Crabtree Lane (off A662)
☎ (061) 223 4415
11.30–11 (11.30–4.30, 7–11 Sat)
**Holt Mild, Bitter; Whitbread
Boddingtons Bitter** Ⓗ
Welcoming, well-run free house
standing by Lock 13 of the
Ashton Canal. Recently
refurbished and extended in a
manner to put most brewery
schemes to shame, with a
Lancashire range as the centre-
piece. No meals weekends.
⊞ Ⓙ ⊟ ♣ P

Compstall

Andrew Arms
George Street
☎ (061) 427 2281
11–3, 5.30–11
**Robinson's Mild, Best
Bitter** Ⓗ
Stone-built pub set in an
attractive industrial village
where the former mill pond now
forms the basin of Etherow
Country Park. Always popular
and deservedly so. ⊛ Ⓙ ⊟ ♣ P

Cornbrook

Cornbrook Inn
256 Chester Road (A56)
☎ (061) 872 2857
12–3, 7–11
**Vaux Samson; Wards
Sheffield Best Bitter** Ⓗ

Former Tetley Walker pub with
a half-tiled exterior, now due for
refurbishment. Adjacent to the
former Cornbrook Brewery.
⊟ ♣

Hope Inn
297 Chester Road (A56)
☎ (061) 848 0038
11–4, 7–11
Hydes' Anvil Light, Bitter Ⓔ
Small, basic, street-corner house
in an area which once boasted a
multitude of pubs and
breweries. ⊟ ♣

Daisy Hill

Rose Hill Tavern ('Bug')
Leigh Road ☎ (0942) 815529
12–11
Holt Mild, Bitter Ⓗ
A former Tetley pub; large,
spacious and comfortable. Next
to the station. ⊟ ≉ ♣ P

Delph

Horse & Jockey
Huddersfield Road (A62)
☎ (0457) 874283
1–2.30 (Sat only), 8–11 (12–2, 8–10.30
Sun)
**Marston's Mercian Mild,
Owd Rodger; Moorhouse's
Pendle Witches Brew** Ⓗ
Isolated old pub on the road
into the high Pennines; can be
very windy. Good atmosphere,
enhanced by real fires in both
rooms. Guest beers. ⊞ Q Å P

Denshaw

Rams Head
(Owd Tupps)
Ripponden Road (A672, 1 mile
N of village) ☎ (0457) 874802
7–11 (12–2.30, 7–10.30 Sun)
Taylor Golden Best Ⓖ,
Landlord; Theakston XB Ⓗ,
Old Peculier Ⓖ
An isolated, windswept haven
offering beers straight from the
barrel. In the wilds of winter
you'll be loath to leave the
roaring fires and cosy interior.
Guest ales. A classic, not to be
missed. Closed lunchtime,
except Sun. Children not
admitted. ⊞ Q

Denton

Dog & Partridge
148 Ashton Road
☎ (061) 336 3954
12.30–11
Robinson's Mild (occasional),
Bitter, Old Tom (occasional) Ⓗ
Surprisingly large, multi-
roomed, town pub.
Unashamedly a locals' house
with few signs of alteration, and
some unusual features. One of
the few Robinson's houses to
serve ordinary (but arguably
better) Bitter. Q ⊟ ≉ ♣

Red Lion Hotel

1 Stockport Road
☎ (061) 336 2066
11–11 (12–4, 7–11 Sat)
Hydes' Anvil Mild, Light, Bitter Ⓔ
Imposing, red-brick, town-centre local. The interior has been opened-up but still retains four separate rooms to cater for all tastes. A warm welcome is assured, but it can be busy on Fri and Sat nights. ◖ ⇌

Didsbury

Royal Oak

729 Wilmslow Road (A5145)
☎ (061) 445 3152
11–3, 5–11 (11–11 Sat)
Marston's Border Mild, Burton Best Bitter, Pedigree Ⓗ
Busy, unspoilt, multi-roomed pub, famous for its good-value ploughman's lunches (served Mon–Fri). Decor includes spirit vats and Victorian posters. Waitress service in some rooms after 8pm. So popular that many people stand outside in warmer weather.
Q ⊛ ◖ ⇌ (E Didsbury)

Station

682 Wilmslow Road (B5093)
☎ (061) 445 3152
11–11
Marston's Mercian Mild, Burton Best Bitter, Pedigree Ⓗ
The last remaining locals' pub in the increasingly trendy village of Didsbury. A warm and friendly welcome is always guaranteed. Although tiny, it is very popular and can be busy at weekends. Lots of railway memorabilia; plentiful flowers in summer. Q ⊛ ⊟ ♣

Diggle

Diggle Hotel

Station Houses (off A670, via Huddersfield Rd)
☎ (0457) 872741
12–3, 7–11 (12–11 Sat)
Taylor Golden Best, Landlord; Whitbread OB Mild, Boddingtons Bitter, OB Bitter Ⓗ
Well-kept village pub, comprising a bar and two rooms. Often visited by morrismen in summer. Accent on food. ⊛ ⇔ ◖ ▶ P

Dukinfield

Lamb Inn

103 Crescent Road
☎ (061) 330 4944
11–11
Whitbread Boddingtons Bitter Ⓗ
Well cared-for and popular pub with a good vault and a comfortable lounge. Handsome red-brick exterior with Dutch gables. ⊛ ◖ ⊟ ♣ P

Eccles

Crown & Volunteer

171 Church Street (A57)
11–5, 7–11
Holt Mild, Bitter Ⓗ
Popular, community pub with a busy social scene. Boasts an attractive 1930s-style interior with most of its original features intact. Occasional live music.
Q ⊟ ⇌ ♣

Failsworth

Bridge Inn

464 Oldham Road (A62)
12–3, 7 (7.30 Sat)–11
Marston's Burton Best Bitter, Pedigree Ⓗ
Lively, open-plan pub with cosy alcoves; popular at weekends. The Pedigree is unusual for the area. Stands by a bridge over the Rochdale Canal. ⊟

Farnworth

Victoria

42–44 Market Street (old A666) ☎ (0204) 794581
12–11
Vaux Lorimers Best Scotch, Samson; Wards Sheffield Best Bitter Ⓗ
No-frills, three-roomed, town-centre hostelry. Windows proclaim 'Walkers Falstaff Ales'. Note the collection of water jugs on the tap room ceiling.
⊟ ⇌ ♣ P

Gatley

Horse & Farrier

144 Gatley Road (A560)
☎ (061) 428 2080
11.30–3.30, 5.30–11 (11.30–11 Sat)
Hydes' Anvil Light, Bitter Ⓔ, **Strong** Ⓖ
A multi-roomed, old coaching house with attractive stained-glass windows, wood panelling and tiled fireplaces. Call in after a visit to the nearby cinema.
Meals Mon–Fri. ◖ Q ⊛ ◖ ⇌ ♣ P

Gorton

Waggon & Horses

736 Hyde Road (A57)
☎ (061) 223 3019
11–11
Holt Mild, Bitter Ⓗ
Large, thriving pub with a strong local flavour and the cheapest beer for miles.
⊠ ⇌ (Ryder Brow) ♣ P

Heald Green

Griffin

124 Wilmslow Road (A34)
☎ (061) 437 1596
11–11

Holt Mild, Bitter Ⓔ
Deceptively-large, three-roomed pub with a strong local following. The snug has no music or fruit machines. Keen prices for the area. Unpromising modern exterior, but the interior is traditional and comfortable. Meals Mon–Fri. Q ◖ ⊟ ♣ P

Heaton Mersey

Griffin

552 Didsbury Road (A5145)
☎ (061) 432 2824
12–11
Holt Mild, Bitter Ⓗ
Multi-roomed local with a classic, mahogany bar. Sells the cheapest beer in the area, so not surprisingly is often very busy.
⊛ ⇌ (E Didsbury) P

Heaton Norris

Nursery

Green Lane (off A6)
☎ (061) 432 2044
11.30–3, 5.30–11 (11.30–11 Sat & bank hols)
Hydes' Anvil Mild, Bitter Ⓔ
Large, comfortable, 1930s pub well hidden away in a pleasant suburban area. Traditional layout: vault, smoke room, lobby and lounge, with fine wood panelling. Immaculate bowling green. Children admitted Mon–Fri lunch, if dining. Limited menu Sat and no food Sun. Q ⊛ ◖ ⊟ ♣ P

Heywood

Wishing Well

89 York Street (A58, just out of centre) ☎ (0706) 65673
11–11
Taylor Golden Best, Landlord; Younger Scotch Ⓗ
Many-roomed, welcoming free house with an interesting, tiled entrance hall. Heavy rock and blues night every Thu and Sun. Guest beers. Cheap bed and breakfast. ⇔ ◖ ♣ P

Hindley

Eddington Arms

186 Ladies Lane (½ mile N of A58, from centre)
☎ (0942) 59229
12–11
Holt Mild, Bitter; Tetley Walker Mild, Bitter Ⓗ
The best thing to happen to Hindley drinkers for a long time: the arrival of a young licensee with a fresh, progressive outlook. The house beer is a closely-guarded secret. Guest beers. ⊛ ⇌ ♣

Ellesmere Inn

32 Lancaster Road (100 yds S of A58, Bolton Road)
☎ (0942) 56922
11.30–4.30, 7–11

Burtonwood Dark Mild, Best Bitter H
Friendly, two-roomed pub, with a very good atmosphere. Live music Sat and Sun; sing-alongs and other regular entertainments. Q ⊞ ≉ ♣

Horwich

Toll Bar
2 Chorley New Road (A673/B5238 jct)
☎ (0204) 696320
12–2 (3 Fri, 4 Sat), 7–11
Thwaites Mild, Bitter H
Home of the Horwich Morrismen; also hosts a folk club Mon. Handy for walks to Rivington and Winter Hill.
🏠 Q ⛵ ⊞ ♣ P

Try also: Bowling Green (Tetley Walker)

Hyde

Bush
278 Market Street
☎ (061) 368 2495
11.30–3 (4 Sat), 5.30 (7.30 Sat)–11 (11.30–11 Fri)
Robinson's Mild, Best Bitter, Old Tom (winter) H
Sociable, two-roomed local frequented by all age groups: a large, comfortable lounge (which gets busy at weekends), plus a pool room. Pool and darts teams and fishing and bowling clubs all contribute to a busy social calendar. ◖ ♣ P

White Lion
Clarendon Place
☎ (061) 368 2948
11–4, 6–11 (11–11 Sat)
Robinson's Mild, Best Bitter E, Old Tom H
Superb, Victorian, town pub with an attractive, red-glazed tiled exterior (Kays' Atlas Brewery). Opened-out lounge but retaining its original tap room and impressively long bar.
◖ ◗ P

Try also: Red Lion (Robinson's)

Irlam & Cadishead

Coach & Horses
Liverpool Road (A57)
Tetley Walker Bitter; Whitbread Boddingtons Mild, Bitter H
Comfortable, open-plan, L-shaped lounge and a long, authentic vault, geared to drinking, darts and dominoes. No meals weekends.
🍴 ◖ ⊞ ⛄ ♣ P

Kearsley

Clockface
65 Old Hall Street (off A5082)
☎ (0204) 71912

11–3.30, 5 (7 Sat)–11
Tetley Walker Mild, Bitter H
Friendly, old-fashioned ale house with a neon sign. The very epitome of what a pub should be; run by the present landlord for 30 years. ⊞ ♣

Kitt Green

Old Springs
Spring Road (5 mins from M6 jct 26)
☎ (0942) 211209
12–3.30 (3 winter), 6.30 (7 winter)–11
Burtonwood Mild, Best Bitter, Forshaw's H
Small, early 19th-century stone pub, with an old well (from which the pub gets its name). Busy bowling green; bowling parties in summer. Good value food. 🏠 Q ⛄ ◖ ◗ ⊞ ♣ P

Leigh

Brewery Inn
Brewery Lane (off A572)
12–5.30 (4.30 Fri & Sat), 8 (7 Fri & Sat, 7.30 Mon)–11
Tetley Walker Mild, Bitter H
Street-corner local with a small, central bar serving a tap room and a large lounge with a pool table and darts. Another small lounge is away from the bar. The pub has changed with the times but still retains a good, local atmosphere. ⊞ ♣ P

Railway Hotel
Twist Lane ☎ (0942) 673916
11–11
Ind Coope Burton Ale; Tetley Walker Dark Mild, Mild; Walker Best Bitter H
Large lounge with an alcove seating area and plenty of standing room. The long bar has a mirror finish. Separate games room. ◖ ◗ ♣

Victoria
68–70 Kirkhall Lane
☎ (0942) 606114
12–4, 7–11 (12–11 Sat)
Tetley Walker Dark Mild, Bitter H
Excellent, end-of-terrace, town pub. The entrance is through a short, panelled corridor, which has lounges and a tap room off. The tap room is served via a large hatch. ⊞ ♣ P

Levenshulme

Sidings
Broom Lane (B6178, off A6)
☎ (061) 257 2084
12–11
Holt Mild, Bitter H
Recent, award-winning building, with a large lounge and a games-oriented vault. Comfortable, friendly and busy, with regular charity events. Vegetarian option available on menu. ⛄ ◖ ⊞ ⛄ ≉ ♣ P

Little Bollington

Old No. 3
Lymm Road (A56, Altrincham road) ☎ (0925) 756115
11.30–3, 5.30–11
Courage Directors; John Smith's Bitter H
Much-extended, former coaching house, reputedly haunted. A popular mooring point on the canal. Good quality and value, home-made food.
🏠 ⛄ ◖ ◗ P

Swan with Two Nicks
Park Lane (off A56)
11.30–3, 5.30–11
Whitbread Chester's Mild, Boddingtons Bitter, Castle Eden Ale H
A typical, Cheshire country pub, beside the canal at the back of Dunham Hall and deer park.
🏠 ⛄ ◖ ⛄ P

Littleborough

Queens
Church Street ☎ (0706) 79394
12–3.30, 6 (7 Sat)–11 (12–11 Fri)
Thwaites Best Mild, Bitter H
Refurbished pub in the centre of town, popular with the locals. Eve meals finish early. ◖ ≉ ♣

Little Hulton

Dun Mare
277 Manchester Road West (A6)
12–4, 6–11 (12–11 Fri)
Walker Mild, Bitter H
Sensitive, Walker 'house-style' treatment has revealed an old mosaic-tiled facade; the former brewery name is just discernible. Framed 1964 price list shows bitter at 1/7d. Q ⛄ ⊞ ♣ P

Try also: Duke's Gate (Holt)

Little Lever

Horse Shoe
Lever Street ☎ (0204) 72081
11–3, 6–11
Hydes' Anvil Mild, Bitter E
Traditional, two-room pub with lounge and vault. ⊞

Lowton

Hare & Hounds
1 Golborne Road
☎ (0942) 728387
12–11
Ind Coope Burton Ale; Tetley Walker Dark Mild, Bitter H
Large, open-plan pub; low beams, two lounge areas, one sunken tap room area and a large beer garden with children's playground. Eve meals until 8pm.
🏠 ⛄ ◖ ◗ ⛄ ♣ P

Greater Manchester

Manchester City Centre

Castle Hotel
66 Oldham Street (A62)
11.30–5.30, 7.30–11 (11.30–5, 8–11 Sat)
Robinson's Mild, Bitter, Best Bitter, Old Tom [H]
Robinson's only outlet in the city centre. A listed, multi-roomed pub; well run, unpretentious and friendly.
♉ ◖ ⊞ ♿ ⇌ (Victoria/Piccadilly) ♣

Circus
86 Portland Street
☎ (061) 236 5818
12–11 (may close weekend eves)
Tetley Walker Bitter [H]
Tiny, basic, totally unspoilt, two-roomer with wood panelling and a quadrant bar – a unique survivor in the city centre. Opening hours can vary.
Q ⇌ (Piccadilly/Oxford Rd)

Dutton
37 Park Street (off A665)
11.30–3, 4.30–11 (11.30–11 Fri & Sat)
Hydes' Anvil Mild, Bitter [E]
100 year-old, wedge-shaped, street-corner local within sight of Strangeways Prison. It was packed with newsmen during the riot! Good value snacks.
Q ⊞ ♿ ⇌ (Victoria) ♣

Peveril of the Peak
127 Great Bridgewater Street
12–3, 5.30 (7 Sat)–11 (closed Sun)
Webster's Choice, Wilson's Mild, Bitter [H]
Pub with Manchester's favourite landlady (20 years here). A classic, triangular in shape. Look for the exterior tiling and the wood and stained-glass interior. Named after a famous stage coach.
⌂ ⊞ ♣

Unicorn Hotel
26 Church Street
11.30–11 (11.30–3, 7–11 Sat)
Bass Light, Draught Bass; Stones Best Bitter [H]
Large, well-restored, oak-panelled pub, popular with market traders and mature customers. ♿ ⇌ (Victoria/Piccadilly)

Vine
38 Kennedy Street
☎ (061) 236 3943
11–11 (11.30–4.30 Sat; closed Sun)
Courage Directors; John Smith's Bitter [H]
Busy, city-centre pub with a listed original exterior. A one-roomed pub until 15 years ago when it was extended into the upstairs and downstairs rooms of the building next door. The basement makes a cosy eatery.
◖ ⇌ (Oxford Rd)

Marple

Bowling Green
161 Stockport Road
☎ (061) 427 7918
11.30–11
Holt Bitter; Webster's Yorkshire Bitter, Wilson's Mild, Bitter [H]
The bowling green itself vanished years ago and is now a car park. The pub, however, thrives, with its large vault, pool table and interlinking lounge. Robust atmosphere to say the least! Holt Bitter is a permanent guest in this Wilson's house.
❀ ⊨ ◖ ⊞ ⇌ (Rose Hill) ♣ P

Crown Inn
Hawk Green Road
☎ (061) 427 2678
11–3, 5.30–11 (11–11 Sat & Sun)
Robinson's Mild, Best Bitter [H]
Originally a farmers' pub now mostly a haunt of the young. Strong accent on food. ❀ ◖ ◗ P

Hatters Arms
Church Lane
☎ (061) 427 1529
11–3, 5.30–11
Robinson's Mild, Best Bitter [H]
Stone-built, end-of-terrace local with small, cosy rooms and a good vault. ♣

Marple Bridge

Travellers Call
134 Glossop Road
☎ (061) 427 4169
11–2.30, 4.30–11 (11–11 Sat)
Robinson's Mild, Best Bitter [H]
Extensively-altered, stone pub. The bar is in the L-shaped lounge and is very much the focal point of this sociable pub. Separate games room with TV.
❀ ◖ ◗ ♣ P

Middleton

Brunswick
122 Oldham Road
☎ (061) 643 2125
12–3, 7–11 (12–11 Fri & Sat)
Belhaven 80/-; Ind Coope Burton Ale; Taylor Landlord; Tetley Walker Bitter [H]
Basic, no-frills boozer with loud rock music in the back room. Very popular with bikers, but all are welcome.

Old Boar's Head
Long Street ☎ (061) 643 3520
11.30 (12 Sat)–3, 5.30 (7 Sat)–11
Lees GB Mild, Bitter [H]
Multi-roomed, ancient inn with stone-flagged floors, timber beams and wattle and daub walls. Original features include the court sessions room, retained in a recent renovation, confirming Lees commitment to its home town. Wheelchair WC.
❀ ◖ ♿ P

Tandle Hill Tavern
14 Thornham Lane, Slattocks, OS898091 ☎ (0706) 345297
12–3 (not Mon–Fri in winter), 7 (7.30 winter)–11
Lees Bitter [H], Moonraker [E]
Isolated hostelry near Tandle Hill Country Park, approached on foot through the park or along a bumpy, unmetalled road. Regular charity quiz nights. Moonraker is available most of the year, which is uncommon. Families welcome in the games room. ⌂ ◖ ◗ ♣

Milnrow

Waggon Inn
Butterworth Hall (off B6225)
11–11
Burtonwood Mild, Best Bitter [H]
Busy, village local built in the 18th century; a warm welcome is guaranteed. Separate family room. ♉ ❀ ⇌ ♣ P

Monton

Drop Inn
204–206 Monton Road (B5229) ☎ (061) 789 5068
11.30–4.30, 5.30 (7 Sat)–11 (11–11 Fri)
Courage Directors; John Smith's Bitter, Magnet [H]
Unusual, H-shaped pub, originally two shops. Comfortable interior with two bars. Live jazz Wed eve. Lunches Mon–Fri. ◖ ⊞ ♣

Park Hotel
142 Monton Road (B5229)
☎ (061) 787 8608
11–11 (11–4, 7–11 Sat)
Holt Mild, Bitter [E]
Popular 50s pub in the posher part of Eccles. Large vault and lounge, and a pleasant snug (unusual for pubs of this era). Strong community spirit.
Q ⊞ ♣ P

Mossley

Tollemache Arms
415 Manchester Road
☎ (045 783) 2354
11–3, 5–11
Robinson's Mild, Best Bitter [H]
Popular, cosy local alongside the Huddersfield Narrow Canal. Oak panelling and a tidy, original bar. ⌂ Q ❀ P

Moss Nook

Tatton Arms
Trenchard Drive (off B5166)
☎ (061) 437 2505
11.30–3, 5 (5.30 Sat)–11
Robinson's Mild, Best Bitter [E]

17th-century coaching house, tastefully extended over the years. Note the original fire surround and wood panelling. The garden is great for plane spotting. No food Sun.
🏠 🍴 ◖ ♣ P

Moston

Blue Bell

493 Moston Lane
11–11 (11–4, 7–11 Sat)
Holt Mild, Bitter Ⓗ
Large, Edwardian pub with a modified, semi-open-plan layout. Caters for all ages. The busiest pub in an area dominated by Bass and Wilson's. Q ➤ 🍴 ♣ P

Dean Brook Inn

St Mary's Road (100 yds from station) ☎ (061) 682 4730
11–11 (11–4, 7–11 Sat)
Marston's Mercian Mild, Burton Best Bitter, Pedigree Ⓗ
Pub converted from half a dozen terraced houses, with three distinct drinking areas around a central bar. A regulars' pub with a strong community spirit. ◖ ⊞ ➤ (Dean Lane) ♣ P

Newhey

Bird in the Hand (Top Bird)

113 Huddersfield Road (A640)
11.30–3, 5–11 (11.30–11 Sat)
Samuel Smith OBB Ⓗ
Small, popular locals' pub. ➤ ♣

New Springs

Colliers Arms

Wigan Road (B5238, 1½ miles E of town) ☎ (0942) 831171
1.30–5, 7.30–11
Burtonwood Mild, Best Bitter Ⓗ
Superb and untouched, 18th-century, canalside pub. A journey into the past, not to be missed. Look out for the robins. Limited parking. 🏠 Q 🍴 ⊞ ♣ P

Newton Heath

Robin Hood

237 Droylsden Road (off A62) ☎ (061) 681 5167
12–4 (4.30 Sat), 7 (7.30 Sat)–11
Marston's Mercian Mild, Burton Best Bitter Ⓗ, **Merrie Monk** (winter), **Owd Rodger** (winter) Ⓖ
Comfortable, two-roomed pub, appealing to an older clientele. No jukebox or pool table.
🏠 ◖ ▮ ⊞ ♣ P

Oldham

Dog & Duck

25 St Domingo Street
11.30–3, 5–11 (11–11 Sat)
Banks's Mild, Bitter Ⓔ

Red-brick, three-storey, detached, town-centre pub, tastefully refurbished, despite having a mainly open-plan layout. Timber fireplace (gas fire) with mirror; black and white photographs on the walls. Good selection of Irish music on the jukebox. Separate pool room. ➤ (Werneth) ♣

Gardeners Arms

Dunham Street, Waterhead
11.30–11 (11.30–5, 7–11 Sat)
Robinson's Mild, Best Bitter Ⓗ
Popular, four-roomed local with a fine combination of brasses and tiles in the bar area. Entertainment on Sat nights.
🏠 ◖ ♣ P

Wheatsheaf Inn

14 Derker Street, Derker (off B6194) ☎ (061) 633 0597
5–11 (12–11 Fri; 12–4, 7–11 Sat)
Webster's Green Label; Whitbread OB Mild, OB Bitter, Bentley's Yorkshire Bitter Ⓗ
Red-brick, terraced local, recently refurbished in traditional style. A former Wilson's tied house which had been closed for several years. Two separate bars, each with a fireplace; pool room. Regular guest beers. 🏠 ➤ (Derker) ♣

Old Trafford

Tollgate

Seymour Grove, Old Trafford ☎ (061) 872 2941
11–11 (11–3, 7–11 Sat, when United are at home)
Banks's Mild, Bitter Ⓔ
Built in 1986 on the site of the original Trafford toll bar. A comfortable pub with much incongruous victoriana, including a stagecoach and passenger in a bell tower! Convenient for Man. United FC and Lancashire CC. No food weekends. ◖ ⊞ 👤 ➤ ♣ P

Patricroft

Stanley Arms

295 Liverpool Road (A57) ☎ (061) 788 8801
11–11
Holt Mild, Bitter Ⓗ
Beautiful example of a street-corner pub: a small front vault, a best room with a piano and a games room at the rear. Sing-alongs at weekends. ⊞ 👤 ➤ ♣

White Lion

133 Liverpool Road (A57) ☎ (061) 707 5184
11–11
Holt Mild, Bitter Ⓗ
Classic, street-corner local with separate darts, vault and music rooms. Popular sing-alongs around the piano at weekends.
⊞ 👤 ➤ ♣

Prestwich

Commercial Inn

271 Bury Old Road, Heaton Park ☎ (061) 773 3661
12–11
Tetley Walker Mild, Bitter Ⓗ
Well-run, friendly local with a good social mix. Popular with sportsmen; the pub has its own football and cricket teams. Comfortable lounge and snug, plus a well-used vault. Home-cooked food (children's menu).
🍴 ◖ ▮ ➤ (Heaton Park) ♣ P

Royal Oak

23 Whittaker Lane (100 yds off A665) ☎ (061) 773 8663
11–11
Hydes' Anvil Light, Bitter Ⓔ
Although tucked away, this friendly local attracts a good mix of clientele. Pleasant decor in the comfortable lounge and 'newsroom', basic vault.
Q ⊞ ➤ (Heaton Park) ♣ P

Radcliffe

Masons Arms

Sion Street ☎ (061) 725 9322
12–11 (12–3.30, 7–11 Mon–Fri in winter)
Thwaites Mild, Bitter Ⓗ
In a semi-rural location, yet close to the town centre, a pub with a cosy atmosphere and welcoming hosts. Ancient game of 'Bullring'. 🏠 🍴 ◖ ▮ ⊞ ♣ P

Old Cross Hotel

Eton Hill Road ☎ (061) 723 2063
12–3, 5 (7 Sat)–11
Holt Mild, Bitter Ⓗ
Basic and friendly local, untouched since the 1930s. Jukebox, pool table, fruit machine, etc. available but the music is not obtrusive. Bare floors, original wood and glasswork; three, cosy rooms around the bar. 🏠 ➤ (not Sun)

Ramsbottom

Royal Oak

Bridge Street ☎ (0706) 822786
12–5, 7–11 (12–11 Fri & Sat)
Thwaites Best Mild, Bitter Ⓗ
Friendly, village-centre pub near the East Lancs Light Railway. The lounge features brassware, paintings and plates; games room; cosy snug. ➤ ◖ ♣

Rochdale

Albert

62 Spotland Road ☎ (0706) 45666
11–11
Burtonwood Mild, Best Bitter Ⓗ

211

Busy, multi-roomed pub in the traditional style, with a friendly, welcoming atmosphere. An active games room offers all the traditional pursuits. Free 'golden oldie' jukebox. ♣

Entwistle Arms
111 Halifax Road, Hamer
☎ (0706) 32890
11.30–11 (11.30–4, 7–11 Sat & bank hols)
Thwaites Best Mild, Bitter Ⓗ
Traditional local with a warm welcome. ⌂ ☎ ⌂ ⌂ ♣ P

Merry Monk
234 College Road (30 yds from A6060/B6222 jct)
11.30–11
Marston's Border Mild, Burton Best Bitter, Pedigree Ⓗ
Friendly and unpretentious, back-street local with an unusual Ring the Bull game in the lounge. Two guest beers. ♣ P

Navigation
116 Drake Street (A640, near station) ☎ (0706) 523566
11–11 (11–4, 7–11 Sat)
Holt Mild, Bitter Ⓗ
Two-roomed local on a main street: an attractive lounge and an active games room. The good lunchtime menu includes a vegetarian option. ☎ ⌂ ⌂ ≠ ♣

Tap & Spile
Hope Street (off Whitworth Road, A671, ½ mile from centre)
12–3, 7–11 (11–11 Sat; may vary)
Thwaites Mild, Bitter Ⓗ
Huge, four-roomed hostelry hidden away down a side-street. Formerly the 'Two Ships'. Often very busy. Note the splendid wooden war memorial plaque in the front room. Home of the Toad Preservation Society. Live music at times. Ever-changing guest beers (eight–ten available). ⌂ ⌂ ⌂

Royton

Dog & Partridge
148 Middleton Road (B6195)
☎ (061) 620 6403
11–11
Lees GB Mild, Bitter Ⓗ
Three-roomed pub with a spacious lounge: a good locals' local. Over 50 different malt whiskies. No food Sun. ⌂ ⌂

Greyhound
1 Elly Clough, Holden Fold (off A663) ☎ (061) 624 4504
11.30–3, 7–11
Lees GB Mild, Bitter Ⓔ
Popular, friendly local in what used to be part of rural Royton. Worth finding. Q ☎ ⌂ ♣ P

Puckersley Inn
22 Narrowgate Brow (via Dogford Road, off A671)

12.30–11 (12–4.30, 7.30–11 Sat; 12–3, 7.30–10.30 Sun)
Lees GB Mild, Bitter Ⓗ
Popular, detached, stone-fronted pub, on the edge of a built-up area. Pleasantly and comfortably furnished, the interior has beams, horse brasses and mirrors; separate lively vault. Panoramic views from the car park. Q ☎ ⌂ ♣ P

Sale

Railway Inn
35 Chapel Road
11.30–3 (4 Sat), 5.30–11 (11.30–11 Fri)
Robinson's Mild, Best Bitter, Old Tom (winter) Ⓔ
Rendered unimaginatively open-plan in the mid 70s, this pub still retained its regulars, and has recently been comfortably refurbished. Access to the Bridgewater Canal across the road. ☎ ⌂ ⌂ ≠ ♣ P

Sale Moor

Legh Arms
178 Northenden Road (A6144/B5166 jct)
11.30–11 (11.30–4, 7–11 Sat)
Holt Mild, Bitter Ⓔ
Large, multi-roomed local, acquired from Taylor's Eagle Brewery in 1924. Retains many original features. The island bar serves a large vault, lounge, snug, lobby and smoke room. Bowling green. Live music in the lounge Tue, Fri, Sat and Sun nights. Q ☎ ⌂ ♣ P

Salford

Ashley Brook
517 Liverpool Street, Seedley (just off A5186)
11–11
Holt Mild, Bitter Ⓗ
New pub, cleverly blended into adjacent, terraced properties. Licence was first sought in the 1920s, but a local campaign, led by a methodist minister, helped permission to be granted in the 90s! Good wheelchair facilities. Q ⌂ ⌂ ⌂ ♣ P

Braziers Arms
54 Hodson Street (off Blackfriars Road)
11–11
Whitbread Boddingtons Mild, Bitter Ⓗ
Superb, unspoilt, cottage pub in a terraced street. The back door leads to the main road. Quiet snug. Q ⌂ ≠ (Victoria) ♣

Crescent
20 The Crescent (A6, by River Irwell) ☎ (061) 736 5600
12–2.30 (not Sat), 5.30 (7.30 Sat)–11 (12–11 Fri)
Beer range varies Ⓗ
Enterprising, multi-roomed free

house with two bungalow range fires, an old mangle and other paraphernalia. The extensive and constantly-changing beer menu is displayed on a large blackboard. Thriving cat population. Tiny garden. ⌂ ☎ ⌂ ≠ (Salford Crescent) ♣ ⌂ P

Eagle Inn
19 Collier Street (off Trinity Way, near A6041)
☎ (061) 834 8957
12–5, 7–11 (12–11 Fri & Sat)
Holt Mild, Bitter Ⓗ
Well-known, much-loved back-street local; the last beer house in Salford to convert to a full licence. Cheap sandwiches at lunchtime. ⌂ ⌂ ≠ (Victoria) ♣

Peel Park Inn
270 Chapel Street (A6, next to Salford Royal Hospital)
☎ (061) 832 2654
11–11
Courage Directors; John Smith's Bitter, Magnet Ⓗ
Smart, single-room pub with a tiny frontage. ☎ ⌂ ⌂ ♣

Union Tavern
105 Liverpool Street
11–4.30, 7–11
Holt Mild, Bitter Ⓗ
Honest, basic boozer in a desolate area on the fringe of the enterprise zone.
⌂ ≠ (Salford Crescent) ♣ P

Welcome
Robert Hall Street (off A5066)
11–4, 6.15–11
Lees GB Mild, Bitter Ⓔ
Smart, comfortable, modern local close to the Salford Quays development. The 'handpumps' activate electric motors. Old Salford photos decorate the walls. ⌂ ♣ P

Stalybridge

Station Buffet
Stalybridge Station, Rassbottom Street (end of Platform 1)
12–3 (not Sun, Mon or Tue), 5 (7 Sat)–11
Moorhouse's Premier Ⓗ
Outstanding, Victorian station buffet packed with original features and radiating character. Three guest beers that change daily and a large range of bottled foreign beers are available. Sadly under threat from BR. CAMRA *Regional Pub of the Year*. ⌂ Q ☎ ≠ ⌂

White House
1 Water Street
11–11
S&N Matthew Brown Mild; Theakston Best Bitter, XB, Old Peculier Ⓗ
Dating from the 1820s but much altered, this pub is now a good free house, offering a

range of bottled beers from all over the world. Full and noisy most eves. ◖ ≢

Standish

Horseshoe

Wigan Road
☎ (0257) 421240
2 (12 Sat)–11
Burtonwood Mild, Best Bitter Ⓗ
Comfortable, village local; its lounge resembles a mini-Labour club. Sing-along at weekends. Small car park. ◖ ◗ ⌐ P

Stockport

Arden Arms

23 Millgate (behind Asda)
11.30–3, 5.30–11 (11.30–11 Fri & Sat)
Robinson's Mild, Best Bitter, Old Tom Ⓗ
Timeless gem with many traditional features, including an unusual snug, only accessed by walking through the bar. Live folk music at weekends. Local CAMRA *Pub of the Year 1990*. No food Sun. Q ⊛ ◖ ♣ P

Blossoms

2 Buxton Road, Heaviley (A6)
☎ (061) 480 2246
11.30–3.30, 5.30–11
Robinson's Mild, Best Bitter, Old Tom Ⓗ
Classic, multi-roomed, street-corner local, oozing character. The Bells brewery poster in the cosy lounge, and the doorstep mosaic denote its former owners. Good value lunchtime snacks. Live folk music Sat eves. ⌐ ≢ ♣ P

Boars Head

Market Place ☎ (061) 480 3978
11.30–4 (3 Wed, 3.30 Mon & Thu), 7 (6 Fri)–11 (closed Sun)
Samuel Smith OBB, Museum Ⓗ
Vibrant, market local appealing to all tastes. Live music three nights, with a late licence in the music room. ◖ ≢ ♣

Grapes

1c Castle Street, Edgeley
☎ (061) 480 3027
11–11 (11–4, 7–11 Sat)
Robinson's Mild, Best Bitter, Old Tom (winter) Ⓗ
Popular, lively pub in a shopping precinct, near Stockport County FC. Free public car park at rear. ⌐ ≢ ♣

Midway

263 Newbridge Lane (400 yds from ring road, A626)
☎ (061) 480 2068
11.30–3, 5 (7 Sat)–11
Courage Directors; John Smith's Bitter, Magnet Ⓗ
Comfortable, welcoming, one-bar pub, decorated in country style with beams and brasses. A terrace at the rear overlooks the

River Goyt; families welcome here and in restaurant (open Sat eve and Sun lunch). Good bar lunches all week. ⊛ ◖ P

Olde Vic

Chatham Street, Edgeley
12–3, 5.30–11 (11–11 Fri & Sat)
Marston's Pedigree; Taylor Landlord Ⓗ
Small, popular free house just three minutes' walk from the station. Often crowded and, despite the air purifier, smoky. Three guest beers of consistently high quality always available, but pricey. Occasional guest ciders. ⊛ ≢ ⌂

Pack Horse

Market Place ☎ (061) 480 5686
11–11
Ind Coope Burton Ale; Tetley Walker Mild, Bitter Ⓗ
Recently-renovated: two separate rooms and a large standing area around the bar. Busy at lunchtimes, especially market days (Fri and Sat). No food Sun. ◖ ≢

Red Bull

14 Middle Hillgate
11–3, 5–11 (11–11 Fri; 11.30–3, 7–11 Sat)
Robinson's Mild, Best Bitter Ⓗ
Old pub with a rambling, characterful interior which includes wood panelling and stone-flagged floors. Friendly and busy atmosphere. Short but imaginative lunchtime menu (Mon–Fri). ⌂ Q ◖ ≢ P

Woolpack

70 Brinksway (A560)
11.30–3, 5.30 (7.45 Sat)–11 (11.30–11 Fri)
Marston's Pedigree; S&N Matthew Brown Mild; Tetley Walker Bitter; Theakston Best Bitter Ⓗ
Rescued from closure by the current owners and now a thriving free house. Comfortable and traditional, with a lively vault where the accent is on darts. One guest beer always available. Weekly guest mild may replace the Matthew Brown. ◖ ◗ ≢ ♣ P

Stoneclough

Lord Nelson

Kearsley Hall Road (off A667)
11–3, 7–11
Thwaites Mild, Bitter Ⓗ
Basic, multi-roomed pub facing the 'Horseshoe' pub across the river. ⌐ ≢ (Kearsley)

Stretford

Melville

Barton Road
11–11 (11–3.45, 7–11 Sat)
Holt Mild, Bitter Ⓔ
Large roadhouse (1930s

Brewer's Tudor): an oasis in a minor beer desert and claiming Holt's highest barrelage.
Q ⊛ ⌐ ≢ (Humphrey Park) ♣ P

Swinton & Pendlebury

Cricketer's Arms

227 Manchester Road, Swinton (A6, near A572 jct)
11.45–3.30 (4 Sat), 7–11
Holt Mild, Bitter Ⓔ
Small, friendly, old local with a thriving public bar. ⌐ ♣

Lord Nelson Hotel

653 Bolton Road, Pendlebury (A666 at B5231 jct)
12–11
Holt Mild, Bitter Ⓔ
Large, late 60s-style pub; a big, basic vault and an enormous lounge with a stage. Always busy and can have a club-like atmosphere. ⊛ ⌐ ♣ P

Timperley

Quarry Bank Inn

151 Bloomsbury Lane
11.30–3, 5.30–11 (11.30–11 Fri & Sat)
Hydes' Anvil Mild, Bitter Ⓔ**, Strong** (winter) Ⓖ
Thriving, village local with a lively vault. Recently refurbished and now has an eating area and a family room. The menu caters for vegetarians and children. Eve meals 6–8pm; no food Sun eve. Bowling green. ⛄ ⊛ ◖ ◗ ♣ P

Tottington

Hark to Towler

Market Street
☎ (0204) 883856
12–3, 5.30–11 (12–11 Fri & Sat)
Thwaites Mild, Bitter Ⓗ
Sympathetic renovation has enhanced the pub's fine tile, marble and woodwork features. A local for all ages whose unusual name derives from an old lead dog of the Holcombe Hunt. ⌂ ⊛ ⌐ ♣ P

Tyldesley

Colliers Arms

105 Sale Lane (A577, 1 mile E of centre) ☎ (061) 790 2065
12–11
Holt Bitter; Wilson's Mild, Bitter Ⓗ
Pleasant, roadside local with cobbled front, separate tap room and long, comfortable lounge. ⌐ ♣ P

Half Moon

Elliot Street ☎ (0942) 873206
11–4 (5 Sat), 7–11
Holt Mild, Bitter; Whitbread Boddingtons Bitter Ⓗ
Large lounge with a bar and a separate pool room, busy at weekends. Premises have been

Greater Manchester

licensed since 1781 but have only been a pub since 1984. Guest beers. 🏠 ♣

Uppermill

Cross Keys
Running Hill Gate (1 mile up Church Road, off A670)
11–3, 6.30–11 (11–11 summer)
Lees GB Mild, Bitter Ⓗ
Attractive, 18th-century, stone building, overlooking Saddleworth church. The public bar has a stone-flagged floor and a Yorkshire range. The focus of many activities, incl. mountain rescue! Jazz and folk nights. 🏠 Q 🏠 ◖ ♣ P

Urmston

Manor Hey
130 Stretford Road
11.30–3, 7–11
Theakston Best Bitter; Younger Scotch, No. 3 Ⓗ
Good, home cooking, with a roast on Sun (vegetarian options), in the lounge of a hotel. ⋈ ◖ ≥ P

Walshaw

White Horse
Hall Street ☎ (020 488) 3243
12–3, 7–11
Thwaites Mild, Bitter Ⓗ
Typical, friendly local on the edge of the countryside. Lunches Mon–Fri. Q 🏠 ♣ P

Westhoughton

White Lion
2 Market Street (A58)
11–11
Holt Mild, Bitter Ⓗ
Typical Holt's boozer: multi-roomed and hardly altered over the years. Note the geyser and fine etched-windows above the bar. Q 🏠 🏠 ≥ (Daisy Hill & Westhoughton) ♣ P

Whitefield

Coach & Horses
71 Bury Old Road (A665)
11.30–11 (11.30–5, 7–11 Sat)
Holt Mild, Bitter Ⓗ
Built in 1830 and virtually unchanged. Once a staging post for the Burnley to Manchester mail coach and still used by today's postmen. 14 years in this guide. Q 🏠 🏠 ≥ (Besses O'th' Barn) ♣ P

Eagle & Child
Higher Lane (A667, near M62 jct 17) ☎ (061) 766 3024
12–11
Holt Mild, Bitter Ⓗ
Large, 1930s pub with an imposing, mock-Tudor exterior and a genuine, Holt interior. Comfortable and friendly, it boasts one of the few remaining bowling greens in the area. Cheap food. Q 🏠 ◖ ◗ 🏠 ≥ (Besses O'th' Barn) ♣ P

Wigan

Beer Engine (ex-Poolstock Leisure Club)
69 Poolstock Lane (B5238/Swan Meadow) ☎ (0942) 42497
11–11
Taylor Landlord; Tetley Walker Dark Mild, Bitter; Walker Best Bitter Ⓗ
Multi-roomed, converted snooker club, with a comfortable lounge and a separate vault. Day membership available (free to CAMRA members). Bowling green. Guest beers. 🏠 ◖ ◗ 🏠 ≥ (NW) ♣ P

Bird I' Th' Hand (Th' En 'Ole)
100–102 Gidlow Lane (off B5375) ☎ (0942) 41004
11.30–11
Ind Coope Burton Ale; Tetley Walker Dark Mild, Mild, Bitter Ⓗ
Popular locals' pub which has recently been renovated. Walker's mosaic above the doorways. 🏠 ◖ ◗ 🏠 ♣ P

Bold Hotel
161 Poolstock Lane (B5238)
12–6.30, 7–11 (11–11 Fri & Sat)
Burtonwood Mild, Best Bitter Ⓗ
Archetypal, cosy local.
Q 🏠 🏠 ♣

Millstone
67 Wigan Lane (old A49, N of centre, near rugby ground)
☎ (0942) 45999
12–4.30, 7.30–11
Thwaites Best Mild, Bitter Ⓗ
Pleasant, town pub with a friendly atmosphere. Possibly the best value beer in Wigan.
Q 🏠 ◖ ♣

Raven Hotel
5 Wallgate ☎ (0942) 43865
11–11 (12–3 not winter), 7–10.30 Sun)
Ind Coope Burton Ale; Walker Mild, Bitter, Winter Warmer Ⓗ
Ornate, Victorian, town-centre pub with many original features. Eve meals till 8pm.
🏠 🏠 ◖ ◗ ≥ (NW & Wallgate)

Seven Stars
262 Wallgate ☎ (0942) 43126
12–4 (5 Sat), 7.30 (7 Sat)–11
Thwaites Best Mild, Bitter Ⓗ
Splendid, ex-Magee's pub; handy for the canal and Wigan Pier. Very comfortable and friendly. 🏠 ≥ ♣ P

Silverwell
Darlington Street (Hindley road)
☎ (0942) 41217
12–4, 7–11

Ind Coope Burton Ale; Walker Mild, Best Bitter Ⓗ
Large, multi-roomed, town pub. Popular with locals but also offers a welcome to visitors. Basic vault, but magnificent wood panelling and glass throughout. 🏠 ◖ ◗ 🏠 ♣ ♣

Springfield
47 Springfield Road (off B5375)
11.30–3.30, 5.30–11
Walker Mild, Best Bitter, Winter Warmer Ⓗ
Imposing, ex-Oldfield Brewery house. Popular with locals and football fans alike. Sadly the once-famous bowling green is no more. 🏠 ⋈ ♣ ♣ P

Swan & Railway
80 Wallgate (opp. NW station)
11–3.30, 5.30 (6 Sat)–11 (12–2.30, 7–10.30 Sun)
Banks's Mild, Bitter; Bass Mild XXXX, Draught Bass; Courage Directors; John Smith's Bitter; Stones Best Bitter Ⓗ
Victorian pub offering the town centre's widest range of excellent value beers. Fine collection of clocks and railway memorabilia. No food Sun.
⋈ ◖ 🏠 ≥ (NW & Wallgate)

Tudor House Hotel
New Market Street
11–11
Bass Mild XXXX, Draught Bass; Stones Best Bitter Ⓗ
Splendid, family-run hotel with a friendly atmosphere. Breakfast and meals from 7am. Guest beers. 🏠 🏠 ⋈ ◖ ◗ ≥ (NW & Wallgate) ♂

Woodford

Davenport Arms (Thief's Neck)
550 Chester Road (A5102)
11–3.30, 5.15 (5.30 Sat)–11
Robinson's Mild, Best Bitter Ⓗ, Old Tom (winter) Ⓔ
Classic, country pub: multi-roomed and unspoilt, on the edge of the prosperous suburbs. In the same family for 60 years – its current licensee is fourth generation. Mild outsells all the lagers put together. Flying memorabilia. 🏠 Q 🏠 ◖ 🏠 ♣ ♣ P

Worthington

Crown
Platt Lane (between A5106 and A49, Bradley Lane, at Standish)
11–11
McEwan 80/-; S&N Matthew Brown Mild; Taylor Landlord; Theakston Best Bitter, XB Ⓗ
Not to be missed: a country pub with antique furniture, guest beers and a wide range of good value meals. 🏠 Q ◖ P

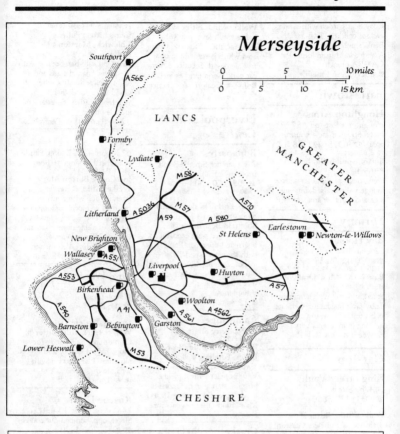

Merseyside

0 5 10 miles
0 5 10 15 km

LANCS

GREATER
MANCHESTER

Southport
A565
Formby
Lydiate
M58
Litherland A5036 M57 A59 A580 A570
St Helens Earlestown
New Brighton
Wallasey A551
Liverpool
Birkenhead
A553
A540 A41 Woolton
Barnston Bebington A4562
Lower Heswall A561 Garston
M53
Huyton
A57
Newton-le-Willows

CHESHIRE

🏭 *Cains, Liverpool*

Barnston

Fox & Hounds

Barnston Road (near Storeton
Lane jct)
☎ (051) 648 7685
11.30–3, 5.30–11 (12–3, 7–11 Sun)
**Ruddles Best Bitter, County;
Webster's Yorkshire Bitter,
Choice, Wilson's Mild** Ⓗ
Cosy village pub: three rooms,
each with a real fire. Good food
Mon–Sat (no chips).
🛏 Q 🕸 🍴 🖚 ♣ P

Bebington

Cleveland Arms

31 Bebington Road, New Ferry
(near New Chester Road)
☎ (051) 645 3282
11–11 (12–3, 7–11 Sun)
Thwaites Best Mild, Bitter Ⓗ
A regular entry for many years.
Good beer, good service and
good company assured. Open-
plan, with a darts and pool
room. A previous local
CAMRA *Pub of the Year* winner
which has maintained its
standards. 🖚 ♣

Great Eastern

New Ferry Road (towards River
Mersey from New Ferry)
☎ (051) 645 3282
11–11 (may close afternoons)
Banks's Mild, Bitter Ⓔ
Spacious, two-room pub with
award-winning beer garden.
Lounge quiet during week;
country music on Fri. Some
doors, windows and timbers
came from Brunel's original
Great Eastern ship which was
broken up on a nearby bank of
the Mersey. No food Sun.
🕸 🍴 🖚 🚻 🖚 P

Rose & Crown

57 The Village (main road, opp.
Civic Centre) ☎ (051) 645 5024
11.30–3, 5.30–11
Thwaites Best Mild, Bitter Ⓗ
Excellent, bustling, friendly old
local, popular with office
workers at lunchtime and local
residents at night. No food Sun.
Q 🍴 🖚 🖚 ♣ P

Birkenhead

Copperfield

Market Street (near town hall)

☎ (051) 647 9837
11–11 (11–3, 7.30–11 Sat; 7.30–10.30
Sun)
John Smith's Bitter Ⓗ
Rarely a dull moment in this
bustling town-centre pub.
Popular with office workers
lunchtime and clubgoers in the
eve. Simple, open-plan layout,
with video jukebox. No lunches
weekends. 🍴 🖚 (Hamilton Sq)

Fireman's Arms

36 Oliver Street (rear of bingo
hall)
☎ (051) 647 8226
11–11
Wilson's Bitter Ⓗ
Hectic shoppers' pub by day
and equally hectic pre-club pub
by night. A comfortable, one-
roomer, served by a single bar.
🖚 (Central)

Old House at Home

30 Queen Street, Tranmere (up
hill from Green Lane station)
☎ (051) 666 1578
11–11
Banks's Mild, Bitter Ⓔ
Excellent local with an
enthusiastic landlord. Public and
lounge are served by one bar.

215

Merseyside

Cosy beer garden with swings, etc. for children. The first Banks's pub to receive *Pub of Month* award from local CAMRA branch.
🏮 🍺 ⇌ (Green Lane) ♣

Earlestown

Houghton Arms
Houghton Close (off A572, Hotel Street, in new housing area) ☎ (0925) 222338
12–5, 6.30–11
Burtonwood Mild, Best Bitter 🅗
Long, open-plan pub: a narrow lounge with a raised drinking area and a games area. ⇌ ♣ P

Formby

Bay Horse
13 Church Road
☎ (0704) 874229
11.30–3, 5.30–11 (11.30–11 Fri & Sat)
Bass XXXX Mild, Draught Bass 🅗
Smart, old pub with adjoining Toby Grill restaurant. Genuine pub vaults. The warm and inviting lounge gets very crowded. 🏠 Q 🏮 🍺 ⇌ P

Garston

King Street Vaults
74 King Street
☎ (051) 427 5850
11–11
Walker Mild, Bitter 🅗
Basic, locals' pub near Garston Docks. Very keen on pub games, especially darts. 🍺 ♣

Huyton

Crofters
Twickenham Drive (A5080, Archway Road jct)
12–11
Draught Bass 🅗
Built in 1990, this modern pub uses re-cycled brick and has an 'old' feel to it. The 'rooms' inside are to a human scale. Pity there's only one real ale!
🏮 🍺 🅹 ♿ ⇌ P

Rose & Crown
2 Archway Road (by church)
☎ (051) 489 1735
11–11
Walker Mild, Bitter 🅗
Large, three-roomed, between-the-wars pub, built on the site of old Barker's brewery.
🏠 🏮 🍺 🍺 ⇌ ♣ P

Litherland

Priory
64 Sefton Road (off A5036, corner of School Lane)
☎ (051) 928 1110
11.30–11
Ind Coope Burton Ale;

Walker Mild, Bitter 🅗
Large, multi-level pub with most facilities. Situated in an area which is something of a real ale desert. Security camera car park. Good lunches incl. Sun.
🏮 🍺 🍺 ⇌ (Seaforth & Litherland) ♣ P

Liverpool: *City Centre*

Bonapartes
21a Clarence Street, L3 (off Brownlow Hill)
☎ (051) 709 5089
11.30–midnight (7–midnight Sat; 7–10.30 Sun)
Vaux Lorimers Best Scotch, Samson; Wards Mild, Sheffield Best Bitter 🅗
Two-roomed pub; candlelit bistro and open bar. Popular with students especially after 11pm (2am licence applied for). No real ale in upstairs bar. Occasional guest beers; good value lunches.
🏮 🍺 ⇌ (Lime St) ⊖ (Central)

Cambridge
51 Mulberry Street, L7
12–11 (12–3, 7–11 Sat)
Burtonwood Mild, Best Bitter, Forshaw's 🅗
Two-roomed, split-level pub. Very popular with students, hospital staff and, occasionally, locals. Splendid Sun breakfasts. Many fund-raising events for charity. 🍺

Cracke
13 Rice Street, L1 (off Hope Street, towards Anglican cathedral) ☎ (051) 709 4171
12–11
Marston's Pedigree; Oak Best Bitter 🅗
A must, both for the Oak beer and the pub itself. The many separate drinking areas have been retained in Liverpool's traditional pub. Excellent value food. Occasional non-Whitbread guest beers.
🏮 🍺 🍺 ⇌ (Lime St) ⊖ (Central) ♣

Cross Keys
13 Earle Street, L3 (off Tithebarn Street)
☎ (051) 236 4819
11–11 (closed Sat & Sun)
Robinson's Best Bitter; Tetley Walker Mild, Bitter 🅗
Somewhat hard-to-find, in the business quarter. A split-level, L-shaped drinking area caters for city workers and all-comers. Busier early in the day as a result, and closed at weekends. Upstairs function room.
🍺 ⊖ (Moorfields) ♣

Everyman Bistro
Hope Street, L1 (beneath Everyman Theatre)
☎ (051) 708 9545

11.45–midnight (closed Sun)
Cains Bitter; Fuller's Chiswick; Marston's Pedigree 🅗
Basement café-bar, popular with thespians. Enamel signs and a café-style create atmosphere. Good value food, incl. vegetarian dishes. Entertainers include poets.
🍺 ▶ ⇌ (Lime St) ⊖ (Central) ○

Lion
67 Moorfields, L2 (opp. facade of former Exchange station)
11–11 (11–5, 7–11 Sat)
Ind Coope Burton Ale; Walker Mild, Bitter 🅗
Friendly pub with a mixture of business and local customers. A feast of good wood, glass and tiles, plus a fine dome. Bargain lunches. Winter Warmer replaces Burton Ale when in season. 🍺 🍺 ⊖ (Moorfields)

Lord Warden
21 London Road, L3 (opp. Odeon Cinema)
☎ (051) 207 1719
11.30–11
Jennings Bitter; Tetley Walker Dark Mild, Bitter 🅗
Comfortable pub, handy for shopping, art gallery and museums. L-shaped bar with separate three 'rooms'.
⇌ ⊖ (Lime St)

Roscoe Head
24 Roscoe Street, L1 (off Leece Street, opp. bombed-out church)
☎ (051) 709 4490
11 (12 Sat)–11
Ind Coope Burton Ale; Jennings Bitter; Tetley Walker Mild, Bitter 🅗
Customers come first in this small, unspoilt, traditional local. Has a front snug as well as two lounges off the bar area. Winner of many awards; current local CAMRA *Pub of the Year* – an excellent pub. Extensive tie collection in lounge. No lunches Sun.
Q 🍺 🍺 ⇌ (Lime St) ⊖ (Central)

Royal
St James Street, L1
11–11
John Smith's Bitter 🅗
Small pub with two rooms and corridor space. Close to the Albert Dock, Chinatown and Anglican Cathedral. 🍺 ♣

White House
185 Duke Street, L1 (corner of Berry Street)
☎ (051) 709 9094
11–11
Walker Mild, Bitter 🅗
Chinatown pub with two distinctly separate rooms, served from one bar. Public bar with TV and pool table.
♿ 🍺 ⇌ (Lime St) ⊖ (Central) ♣

Liverpool: *East*

Claremont
70 Lower Breck Road, L6
11–11
Tetley Walker Dark Mild, Mild, Bitter Ⓗ
Basic, two-roomed, street-corner local. Guest bitter normally available. ⌐ ♣

Edinburgh
4 Sandown Lane, L15 (off Wavertree High Street)
12–11
Walker Mild, Bitter Ⓗ
Small, street-corner pub, just off a busy shopping area. Very much a community pub. ⌐

Farnworth Arms
1 Farnworth Street, L6 (corner of Kensington)
☎ (051) 260 4190
12–11
Tetley Walker Dark Mild, Mild, Bitter Ⓗ
Friendly Irish house with two rooms served by a central bar. A warm, lively, community pub in a good shopping area. ⌐ ♣

Royal Hotel
213 Smithdown Road, L15 (A562, near Toxteth Cemetery)
☎ (051) 733 6408
12–11
Tetley Walker Mild, Bitter Ⓗ
Wonderfully ornate exterior (mosaics); gaslit lounge with wood panelling and stuffed animals. ⌐ ♣

Waldeck
113 Lawrence Road, L15 (near Wellington Road/Gainsborough Road jct) ☎ (051) 733 7703
12–3.30, 5–11 (12–11 Thu–Sat)
Walker Mild, Bitter, Winter Warmer Ⓗ
Small bar with a Liverpool waterfront mural along its length and a pool table in an alcove. Much larger lounge. Some fine old Walker stained-glass survives. Occasional live music. ⌐ ♣

Willowbank
329 Smithdown Road, L15 (A562 opp. Sefton General)
☎ (051) 733 5782
12–11
Ind Coope Burton Ale; Walker Mild, Bitter, Winter Warmer Ⓗ
Imposing pub set back from the main road. The lounge at the rear is adorned with old tramway pictures. Table service often available. No food Sun. ⓼ ◖ ⌐ ♿ ♣

Liverpool: *North*

Abbey
153 Walton Lane, L4
☎ (051) 207 0036
11–11
Walker Mild, Bitter Ⓗ
A three-storey building with a pleasing blend of timber and maroon tilework. Compact interior with bar and snug areas. Close to Everton FC. ⌐ ♣

Breckside (Flat Iron)
377 Walton Breck Road, L4 (Anfield Road jct)
☎ (051) 263 4694
12–11
Tetley Walker Dark Mild, Mild, Bitter Ⓗ
Impressive, three-roomed local close to Liverpool FC. Nickname comes from the shape of the bulding. ⓼ ⌐ ♣

Bull
2 Dublin Street, L3 (within 1 mile of Pier Head, along Gt Howard Street)
☎ (051) 207 1422
11.30–11
Tetley Walker Mild, Bitter Ⓗ
Unpretentious and deservedly popular small pub with a big Irish welcome, an easy mix of blue and white collars, and hearty lunchtime snacks. A true, classic Liverpool pub in every way. ⌐

Clock
167 Walton Road, L4 (A59 between Everton Valley and Spellow Lane) ☎ (051) 207 3594
11–11
Walker Mild, Bitter Ⓗ
Small, two-roomed local with a bustling bar and a cosy lounge. Close to Everton FC. ⌐ ⇌ (Kirkdale) ♣

Crown Vaults
25 Kirkdale Road, L5 (end of 'Scottie' Road, near Rotunda)
12–11
Tetley Walker Dark Mild, Mild, Bitter Ⓗ
Pub with a tiled exterior which looks small but is quite large inside, with well-defined 'areas'. Live music, disco, and quiz nights. ⇌ (Sandhills)

Melrose Abbey
331 Westminster Road, L4
☎ (051) 922 3637
11.30–11
Tetley Walker Dark Mild, Mild, Bitter Ⓗ
Three-roomed local: busy bar and two lounges – one with a real fire. A popular venue for male and female darters, off-duty railmen and well-behaved football supporters of both local persuasions. ♿ ⌐ ⇌ (Kirkdale) ♣

Prince Arthur
93 Rice Lane, L9 (A59, midway between flyover and hospital)
12–11
Walker Mild, Bitter Ⓗ
Former CAMRA preservation award-winning pub. A veritable feast of original woodwork, etched glass, tiling and mosaic, sensitively restored outside and in. A narrow, L-shaped bar, lots of standing space in the corridor and a cosy lounge: a fully-appreciated pub, not merely a showpiece.
⌐ ⇌ (Rice Lane/Walton)

Selwyn
106 Selwyn Street, L4 (Delamore Street jct)
☎ (051) 525 0747
11–11
Tetley Walker Mild, Bitter Ⓗ
Three-roomed pub: bar with darts, lounge with pool and music, and a quiet snug.
◖ ◗ ⌐ ⇌ (Kirkdale)

Liverpool: *South*

Anglesea Arms
36 Beresford Road, L8 (opp. High Park street market)
☎ (051) 727 4784
11.30–11 (11–11 Sat)
Tetley Walker Mild, Bitter Ⓗ
Splendid hostelry close to a good shopping area. Lunchtime meals on request. A worthy pub to visit. ⓼ ⌐

Croxteth
145 Lodge Lane, L8
☎ (051) 733 7610
11–11
Tetley Walker Mild, Bitter Ⓗ
Imposing, large building with a coat of arms over the door. Interior has been 'opened-out', with an island bar. Live music and bingo featured.
⓼ ♿ ⇌ (Edge Hill) ♣

Mosley Arms
156 Mill Street, L8 (town end)
☎ (051) 709 2721
11–11 (11–5, 7–11 Sat)
Tetley Walker Mild, Bitter Ⓗ
Ornate corner local. Popular with an older clientele. Walker's old livery on the facade.
♨ ⓼ ⌐ ♿

Poet's Corner
27 Park Hill Road, L8 (off Dingle end of Park Road)
☎ (051) 727 3240
11–11
Tetley Walker Mild, Bitter Ⓗ
Two-roomed, side-street local. Sign shows Merseyside poets Henri, Patten and McGough.
⓼ ⌐

Storrsdale
43–47 Storrsdale Road, L18
☎ (051) 724 3464
5–11 (11–11 Wed–Sat)
Tetley Walker Dark Mild, Mild, Bitter Ⓗ
A comfortable neighbourhood pub. A real ale oasis in a pub desert. Guest beers may be added.
Q ♨ ⌐ ⇌ (Mossley Hill) ♣

Merseyside

Lower Heswall

Black Horse
Village Road
☎ (051) 342 2254
11.30–11 (12–3, 7–11 Sun)
Bass Mild XXXX, Special, Draught Bass H
Popular village pub; refurbished with a sunken conservatory whilst retaining a bar and snug.
Q ◖ ⊟ ♣

Lydiate

Running Horses
25 Bells Lane (off A567, alongside canal)
☎ (051) 526 3989
12–11
Ind Coope Burton Ale; Walker Mild, Best Bitter, Winter Warmer H
Pub of character on the bank of Leeds–Liverpool Canal, popular with the fishing fraternity. Underwent a tasteful re-vamp and extension in spring 1991. Family room, mini-farmyard and play area. No meals Sun.
▩ ⛬ ⋈ ◖ ⊟ ⅄ ♣ P

New Brighton

Albion Hotel
104 Albion Street
☎ (051) 639 1832
11.30–3, 5–11 (11.30–11 Thu–Sat)
Courage Directors; John Smith's Bitter H
A lively hotel on its regular function nights, incl. 1950–1960s rock and folk. Families welcome lunchtimes and before 7pm in the function room. ▩ ⛬ ◖ ◗ ⅄ ⇌ P

Commercial
19 Hope Street
☎ (051) 639 2105
11.30–11
Ind Coope Burton Ale; Walker Mild, Bitter, Best Bitter H
Traditional, two-roomed, street-corner local with a basic bar and

cosy lounge (table service). A peaceful haven for day trippers and popular with the older age group. Black and white pictures of Victorian New Brighton.
Q ⊟ ⅄ ♣

Newton-le-Willows

Old Crow
248 Crow Lane East
☎ (0925) 225337
12–3.30 (11–5 Fri & Sat), 7–11
Jennings Bitter; Tetley Walker Mild, Bitter H
Large, two-roomed local: a well-lit lounge and a games room. Landlord runs his own beer festival. Outdoor drinking area. ▩ ◖ ♣ P

St Helens

Duke of Cambridge
27 Duke Street (A570)
☎ (0744) 613281
12–11
Vaux Lorimers Best Scotch, Samson, Double Maxim H
Busy pub, close to town centre. The change of beer from Tetley to Vaux has doubled trade. Guest beers from within the group. ▩ ⊟ ⇌ (Central) ♣

Hope & Anchor
174 City Road
☎ (0744) 24199
11.30–3.30 (5 Fri), 6.30–11 (11.30–11 Sat)
Tetley Walker Mild, Bitter H
Large pub opposite Victoria Park. Disco some nights (loud!).
⊟ ♣

Wheatsheaf
36 Westfield Street (A58)
☎ (0744) 37453
12–11
Tetley Walker Dark Mild, Bitter H
Busy, one-bar, town-centre local. ◖ ⇌ (Central)

Southport

Blowick Hotel
147 Norwood Road (near A570) ☎ (0704) 530229

11.30–3, 5.30–11 (11–11 Thu–Sat)
Tetley Walker Mild, Bitter H
Recently-refurbished, friendly local on the outskirts of town.
▩ ◖ ⊟ ⇌ (Meols Cop) ♣ P

Blundell Arms
34 Upper Aughton Road, Birkdale (off A5267)
☎ (0704) 69912
11.30–3, 5–11 (11.30–11 Sat)
Walker Dark Mild, Bitter H
Tastefully refurbished village local. Large vault/games room and medium-sized lounge. Home of Southport Bothy Folk Club. ◖ ⊟ ⇌ ♣ P

Bold Arms
59–61 Botanic Road, Churchtown (B5244)
☎ (0704) 28192
11.30–11
Hydes' Anvil Bitter; Ind Coope Burton Ale; Jennings Bitter; Tetley Walker Dark Mild, Mild, Bitter H
Old coaching inn in a picturesque part of town. Very popular: quizzes and weekend discos. Winner of several local CAMRA awards.
▩ ⛬ ◖ ⊟ ♣ P

Wallasey

Stanley's Cask (McCullochs)
212 Rake Lane, New Brighton (B5143)
11.30–11 (12–3, 7–11 Sun)
McEwan 70/-, Younger IPA, No. 3 H
Popular free house catering for all ages. Regular guest beers.
▩ ◖

Woolton

Cobden Vaults
85 Quarry Street
☎ (051) 428 2978
11.30–11
John Smith's Bitter H
Friendly, olde-worlde-style pub in a conservation conscious village. Beer served in oversized glasses. Much bric-a-brac. ⊟

🏇

Family Rooms

Where a pub welcomes children in a separate family room, we provide the rocking horse symbol.

But for more detailed information on real ale pubs which offer excellent family facilities, consult Jill Adam's **Pubs For Families**, now in its second edition and priced £4.95. Copies are available at all good book shops or direct from CAMRA, 34 Alma Road, St Albans, Herts, AL1 3BW (post free).

CAINS – LIVERPOOL'S NEW BREWERY

Liverpool has its own brewery again. The Robert Cain Brewery commenced the brewing of traditional beers in spring 1991. Cains Traditional Bitter was launched in March and was so popular that it was difficult to keep up with demand.

Merseysiders found that Cains Traditional Bitter was to their taste. It is a bitter with a distinctive character – a welcome change from the bland tastes of many of today's beers. Wherever it has gone on sale it has sold well. Yet you will not find many pubs in this guide listed as selling Liverpool's new beer. Why?

In 1990 Whitbread closed the Higsons brewery following their take-over of both this Liverpool brewery and Boddingtons of Manchester. 209 years of brewing in Liverpool came to an end. To add insult to injury, Whitbread continued to use the Higsons name for beers produced in Sheffield. Higsons beers had taste and character, those from Sheffield had neither. As a result, you will find no Higsons pubs in this guide.

Cains bought the Higsons brewery from Whitbread and, after a period brewing only beer for the supermarket trade, they launched the traditional cask beer. Cains owns no pubs of its own, so the first priority has been to secure some outlets. The Mersey branches of CAMRA and Cains itself have been working to increase the number of outlets that serve Cains beers. But with details not yet finalised, it has not been possible to include many such pubs in this year's *Guide* (order next year's now!).

However, on visiting the Merseyside area we hope you will try ales from Liverpool's new brewery. To help you find Cains beers, the local branches have produced distinctive window stickers – look out for them. Also, the local pub newspaper, *Mersey Drinker*, carries a complete list of outlets, updated each edition.

Cains is the result of a determined campaign which refused to accept that Merseyside could no longer have its own brewery. Many people played their part; now we can all celebrate by having a pint of Merseyside beer again.

Norfolk

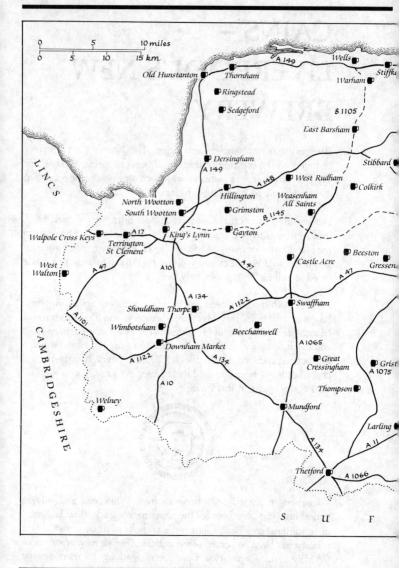

Scale:
0 — 5 — 10 miles
0 — 5 — 10 — 15 km

Wells
A 149
Old Hunstanton
Thornham
Stiffkey
Warham
Ringstead
B 1105
Sedgeford
East Barsham
Dersingham
A 149
Stibbard
A 148
West Rudham
Hillington
Weasenham All Saints
Colkirk
North Wootton
Grimston
South Wootton
B 1145
King's Lynn
Gayton
Walpole Cross Keys
A 17
Terrington St Clement
Castle Acre
Beeston
Gressen...
West Walton
A 47
A 10
A 47
LINCS
CAMBRIDGESHIRE
Shouldham Thorpe
A 134
A 1122
Swaffham
Wimbotsham
Beechamwell
Downham Market
A 1122
A 134
A 10
A 1065
Great Cressingham
Grist...
A 1075
Thompson
Welney
Mundford
Larling
A 134
A 11
Thetford
A 1066
S   U   F

🏠 **Reepham**, *Reepham*; **Woodforde's**, *Woodbastwick*

Acle

Rebas Riverside Inn
Old Road (A1064, off new
Acle bypass)
☎ (0493) 750310
11–3, 6.30–11
**John Smith's Bitter;
Woodforde's Wherry** Ⓗ
Small pub with a friendly
atmosphere, handy for the River
Bure with moorings 300 yards
away. ♨ Q ⛵ ◖ ▶ ᕦ P

Attleborough

Griffin Hotel
Church Street
☎ (0953) 452149
10.30–2.30, 5.30–11 (12–2, 7–10.30
Sun)
**Greene King Abbot;
Marston's Pedigree;
Whitbread Wethered
Bitter** Ⓗ
A comfortable atmosphere in a
16th-century coaching inn at
the centre of this market town.
Fresh local produce is served in
the bar and restaurant (incl.
vegetarian dishes). Guest beer.
♨ Q ⛵ ᕦ ◖ ▶ ᕦ ᕦ ᗡ ♣ ⛺ P

Beechamwell

Great Danes Head
The Green
☎ (036 621) 443
11–2.30, 7–11 (11–11 Sat)
**Adnams Bitter; Wells
Bombardier** Ⓗ

220

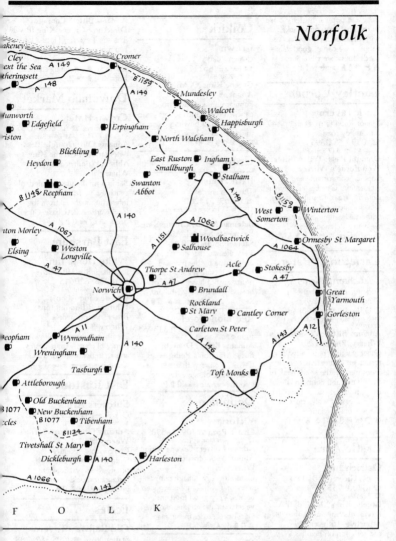

Norfolk

Village pub which caters for all
ages and tastes. Cosy and
relaxed with a good trade in
food. Guest beer.
🏚 Q 🍴 ◑ ▶ 🅰 ♣ P

Try also: White Hart, Foulden
(Free)

Beeston

Ploughshare
The Street (2 miles off A47 W
of Dereham)
☎ (0328) 701845
11–2.30, 6–11
**Adnams Bitter, Old; Greene
King Abbot** Ⓗ
16th-century village pub with a
large garden and a separate
restaurant. Guest beers and
'Beeston Gem' house beer.
🏚 🛏 🍴 ◑ ▶ ♣ P

Blakeney

Manor Hotel
The Quay ☎ (0263) 740376
11–2.30, 6–11
**Adnams Bitter; Bateman
XXXB** Ⓗ
Comfortable hotel bar
overlooking salt marshes. Very
good, reasonably priced food
served in the bar, lounge and
dining room. Q 🛏 🍴 🛌 ◑ ▶ P

Blickling

Buckinghamshire Arms
11–3, 6–11 (11–11 summer)
**Adnams Bitter, Broadside;
Woodforde's Wherry** Ⓗ
Old, unspoilt pub with a snug.
By Blickling Hall. Guest beer.
🏚 🛏 🍴 🛌 ◑ ▶ P

Try also: Walpole Arms,
Itteringham (Free)

Briston

Green Man
Hall Street ☎ (0263) 860993
11–3, 5.30–11
**Greene King IPA, Abbot;
Woodforde's Wherry** Ⓗ
Popular, village pub extended to
include a pool room. Superb log
fire and original beams.
🏚 🛏 🍴 ◑ ▶ 🛆 ♣ ♨ P

Brundall

Yare
Station Road ☎ (0603) 713786
10.30–2.30 (3 Sat), 5.30–11
**Courage Directors; John
Smith's Bitter; Woodforde's
Wherry, Phoenix** Ⓗ

Norfolk

Busy and popular hostelry close to the boatyards and stacked with Broadland photos/curios. Families welcome; good value food. Guest beers Fri–Sun. 🏠 ⛱ 🍴 ( ) ❂ ⇌ ♣ P

Cantley Corner

Cock Tavern
Manor Road (3 miles from A47 on Cantley road)
☎ (0493) 700895
11–3 (4 Sat), 6 (7 Sat)–11
Draught Bass; Tetley Bitter; Woodforde's Wherry ⒣
Popular, comfortable and welcoming. One bar but several drinking areas, to suit all tastes. Good value food, incl. a barbecue in summer. Families welcome. Petanque played. Guest beers. 🏠 ⛱ 🍴 ( ) ▲ ♣ P

Carleton St Peter

Beauchamp Arms
Buckenham Ferry (between Claxton and Langley)
OS350044 ☎ (0508) 480247
11–3 (not Mon–Fri), 6–11 (11–11 summer)
Adnams Bitter; Woodforde's Wherry, Phoenix ⒣
Quiet, country pub with a bar, restaurant and extensive boat moorings, on the south bank of the River Yare. Formerly a hotel, near the site of the old ferry. Pleasant walks close by. Good family facilities.
🏠 Q ⛱ 🍴 ( ) ⊟ ⅄ ▲ ♣ P

Castle Acre

Ostrich Inn
Stocks Green (off B1065)
☎ (0760) 755398
12–3, 7 (6 summer)–11
Greene King XX Mild, IPA, Rayments Special, Abbot ⒣
Attractive, 16th-century coaching inn on Peddars Way, in an historic village with a ruined priory and castle. Caters for locals and tourists with good meals. Q ⛱ 🍴 ( ) ⅄ ▲ P

Cley next the Sea

George & Dragon Hotel
High Street
☎ (0263) 740652
11–2.30, 6.30–11
Greene King IPA, Rayments Special, Abbot ⒣
The Norfolk Naturalists Trust was founded here and a bible on the lectern records bird sightings. A pub with a fine stained-glass window of George and the Dragon. Accommodation includes a four-poster. 🏠 🍴 ⊟ ( ) ⅄ ♣ P

Colkirk

Crown
Crown Road
☎ (0328) 862172
10.30–2.30, 6–11
Greene King XX Mild, IPA, Abbot ⒣
Popular pub with two wood-panelled bars which serves good food and has a bowling green at the rear. Guest beer.
🏠 Q 🍴 ( ) ⅄ ♣ P

Cromer

Bath House
The Promenade
☎ (0263) 514260
11–3, 5–11 (closed mid Jan to mid March)
Bateman XXXB; Greene King Rayments Special, Abbot; Samuel Smith OBB ⒣
Very pleasant bar on the lower promenade by the pier and beach. Outside seating on the prom. A split-level single bar hosted by a friendly landlord. Regular guest beers. 🍴 ⊟ ( )

Red Lion Hotel
Brook Street ☎ (0263) 514964
10.30–2.30, 5.30–11
Adnams Bitter; Draught Bass; Marston's Pedigree ⒣
Classic, old bar with a refurbished lounge extending into the bar area. ⊟ ( ) P

Deopham

Victoria
Church Road ☎ (0953) 850783
12–2.30 (not Mon or Tue), 7–11
Adnams Bitter; Greene King Abbot; Woodforde's Wherry ⒣
Quiet, friendly, village pub: a single bar with original wooden beams. Very good food, incl. vegetarian and children's dishes. Guest beer; cider in summer.
🏠 ( ) ⅄ ♣ ⌂ P

Dersingham

Feathers Hotel
Manor Road ☎ (0485) 540207
11–2.30, 5.30–11
Adnams Bitter; Charrington IPA ⒣
Fine, carrstone building with wood-panelled bars. Good meals in the bar and restaurant, with children and vegetarians catered for. Barbecues in summer in the extensive garden; games bar in an old stable block. Close to Sandringham House.
🏠 🍴 ⊟ ( ) ⅄ ▲ ♣ P

Dickleburgh

Crown
The Street ☎ (0379) 741475
11–3, 5.30–11

Adnams Bitter; Courage Directors; Greene King IPA ⒣
The small exterior hides a long room divided into three areas. Splendid real fire and quite charming surroundings. Guest beer. 🏠 ( ) ♣ P

Downham Market

Crown Hotel
Bridge Street ☎ (0366) 382322
11–2.30, 6–11 (11–11 Fri & Sat)
Adnams Old; Draught Bass; Bateman XB; Greene King Abbot; Woodforde's Wherry ⒣
Bar in a totally unrenovated, old coaching inn featuring interesting material from the local wartime RAF base. Guest beers. Q ⊟ ( ) P

East Barsham

White Horse Inn
Fakenham Road (B1105)
☎ (0328) 820645
11–2.30, 6 (7 winter)–11
Greene King Abbot; Whitbread Boddingtons Bitter; Woodforde's Wherry ⒣
Traditional, country pub with plenty of steps within, beams and an inglenook. Good food. Guest beer. 🏠 ⛱ 🍴 ⊟ ( ) ♣ P

East Ruston

Butchers Arms
Oak Street ☎ (0692) 650237
12–3, 7–11
Adnams Bitter; Woodforde's Wherry ⒣
Comfortable, recently refurbished, rural pub with ornate windows. Separate restaurant (booking advised); guest beers. ⛱ 🍴 ( ) P

Eccles

Old Railway Tavern
Station Road ☎ (095 387) 788
12–2.30, 5.30–11
Adnams Bitter; Greene King IPA, Abbot ⒣
Known locally as the 'Tap'. Mind your head on entering. The landlord is rightly proud of his beer and his food (no meals Sun lunch).
🏠 Q 🍴 ( ) ⇌ (Eccles Rd) ♣ ⌂ P

Edgefield

Three Pigs
On B1149, 3 miles S of Holt
OS098344 ☎ (0263) 87634
11–2.30, 6 (7 winter)–11
Adnams Bitter; Woodforde's Wherry ⒣
Unspoilt pub, over 200 years old, with a single brick-fronted bar which is thought to have had smuggling connections. Small site for five caravans (CC

approved). Guest beer in summer. Home-cooked food (not served Mon eve).
🍴 Q 🕯 🌀 🚪 🕭 ♣ P

Elsing

Mermaid
Church Street
☎ (0306) 637640
11–3, 7–11
Adnams Bitter; Draught Bass; Woodforde's Wherry Ⓗ
Olde-worlde pub and restaurant; hot and cold food available seven days a week. Pool and darts played. Occasional guest beers.
🍴 Q 🕯 🌀 🌀 ♣ P

Erpingham

Spread Eagle
2 miles W of A140, Norwich–Cromer road
☎ (0263) 761591
11–2.30, 6.30–11
Woodforde's Wherry, Phoenix, Norfolk Nog, Baldric, Headcracker Ⓗ
Famous country pub by the site of the old brewery, on the Weavers Way. Separate dining room and 'club' room with pool, darts, football and electronic games.
🍴 🕯 🌀 🌀 🕭 ♣ ⌖ P

Gayton

Crown
Lynn Road ☎ (055 386) 252
11–3, 6–11
Greene King XX Mild, IPA, Rayments Special, Abbot Ⓗ
Comfortable, welcoming pub with a roaring fire on a winter's day. Popular with visitors, and the centre of village life. Noted for its food. 🍴 🕯 🌀 🌀 ♣ P

Gorleston

New Entertainer
Pier Plain ☎ (0493) 653218
11.30–3, 7–11 (11–11 Sat)
Adnams Mild, Bitter, Broadside; Greene King IPA, Abbot Ⓗ
A friendly landlord and a good range of ales make this former Lacon's pub well worth seeking out. Good local trade in sandwiches Mon–Fri lunchtimes. Q ♣ P

Short Blue
High Street ☎ (0493) 602192
11–11
Courage Directors; Scotties Golden Best Bitter; John Smith's Bitter Ⓗ
Friendly local in the main street, sporting a strong nautical theme with much stained-glass and memorabilia. Heavy wood panelling in the single bar. Good selection of food (especially fish) served 12–2

and 6.30–8.30. Guest beers.
🍴 Q 🕯 🌀 P

Great Cressingham

Windmill Inn
Water End (off A1065)
☎ (076 06) 232
11–2.30, 6.30–11
Adnams Bitter, Broadside; Draught Bass; Greene King IPA; Samuel Smith OBB Ⓗ
Original, oak-beamed pub with three bars and four other drinking areas, incl. a conservatory. Large garden and full camping/caravanning facilities. Lesser known guest beers often available.
🍴 Q 🌀 🕯 🌀 🕭 ♣ P

Great Yarmouth

Albert Tavern
20–21 Southgates Road
☎ (0493) 855016
11.30–3, 6–11
Charrington IPA Ⓗ
Recently modernised, quayside pub; its large bar has a games room to one side. Good range of guest ales. 🌀 🍴 🌀 🌀 ♣ 🌀

Clipper Schooner
Friars Way (off South Quay, next to fire station)
☎ (0493) 854926
11–11
Adnams Mild, Bitter, Broadside Ⓗ
Built in 1938 by Lacon's; a large single bar with comfortable seating. Guest beer.
🕯 🌀 🌀 ♣

Red Herring
24–25 Havelock Road
☎ (0493) 853384
11–3, 6–11
Adnams Mild, Bitter Ⓗ
One-bar pub with pool played in a separate room. Popular with both locals and holiday-makers. Two regular ales and up to five guests from smaller breweries, plus cider in summer. Twice-yearly beer festivals; books and records sold in aid of local charities. 🌀 ⌀

Ship Inn
4 Greyfriars Way (behind town hall) ☎ (0493) 855533
11.30–3.30, 7.30–11 (closed Sun)
Marston's Pedigree; Whitbread Flowers IPA, Original Ⓗ
17th-century, two-bar inn with a 13th-century cellar, part of Greyfriars Abbey. Close to the harbour and museums. A warm atmosphere prevails. Guest beer.
🍴 Q 🌀 🕯 🌀 🌀 🚋 (Vauxhall) ♣

Gressenhall

Swan
The Green (off B1146)
☎ (0362) 860340

11.30–3, 7–11
Greene King IPA, Abbot Ⓗ
Friendly, locals' pub handy for Norfolk Rural Life Museum. Special pensioners' lunches on Thu. Guest beer.
🍴 Q 🕯 🌀 🌀 ♣ P

Try also: Bull, East Dereham (Greene King)

Grimston

Bell
Gayton Road (B1153)
☎ (0485) 600312
11–3, 7 (6 summer weekends)–11
Whitbread Boddingtons Bitter, Flowers IPA Ⓗ
Small, village pub transformed by an enterprising landlord. Guest beers, plus a highly regarded, good value restaurant.
🍴 Q 🕯 🌀 🌀 ♣ P

Griston

Waggon & Horses
Church Road OS944944
☎ (0953) 883847
11–3, 6.30–11
Greene King IPA, Rayments Special, Abbot Ⓗ
Large, comfortable pub with a high standard of decor. Good food always available.
Q 🌀 🕯 🌀 🌀 ♣ P

Happisburgh

Hill House
The Hill (100 yds from B1159)
☎ (0692) 650004
11–3, 7–11
Adnams Bitter; Woodforde's Wherry Ⓗ
Imposing building but a fairly small single-bar interior with an inglenook. Proper family facilities in an adjoining building. Guest beers.
🍴 Q 🌀 🕯 🚋 🌀 🕭 P

Harleston

Cherry Tree
74 London Road (B1143, ½ mile from centre) ☎ (0379) 852345
11–2.30, 6–11
Adnams Mild, Bitter, Old, Broadside Ⓗ
Unspoilt, village pub where the lounge is heated by a cooking range and the public bar by a wood-burner. Snacks served.
🍴 Q 🕯 🕭 ♣ P

Heydon

Earle Arms
Off B1149 ☎ (026 387) 376
11–3, 6.30–11
Adnams Bitter, Broadside; Greene King Abbot Ⓗ
Unspoilt pub in a picturesque village. 🍴 🌀 🕯 🌀 🌀 🕀 ♣ P

Norfolk

Hillington

Ffolkes Arms
Lynn Road ☎ (0485) 600210
11–2.30, 5.30–11
Adnams Bitter; Charrington IPA; Greene King Abbot Ⓗ
Large, open-plan pub with brick arches and alcoves. A new restaurant and motel block has recently been built. Good quality food.
🏠 Q 🏉 🛏 🕪 🕭 Å ♣ P

Hunworth

Hunny Bell
The Green (2 miles from Holt)
☎ (0263) 712300
11–3, 6–11
Adnams Bitter; Greene King Abbot; Woodforde's Wherry Ⓗ
Long-established, welcoming free house on the green of a picturesque village. Real log fire and good food. Occasional guest beer. 🏠 Q 🍴 🏉 🕪 🕭 P

Ingham

Swan
Swan Corner (B1151, Stalham–Sea Palling road)
☎ (0692) 81099
11–11 (11–3, 7–11 winter)
Adnams Bitter; Woodforde's Wherry Ⓗ
Lovingly-restored, thatched pub, parts of which date back to the 14th century. Friendly and welcoming with an emphasis on food. Guest beers.
🏠 🍴 🏉 🛏 🕪 🕭 P

King's Lynn

London Porterhouse
78 London Road
☎ (0553) 766842
11.30–2.30 (3 Fri, 4 Sat), 5.30 (7 Sat)–11
Greene King IPA, Rayments Special, Abbot Ⓖ
Tiny, welcoming pub with a varied clientele, where regular events range from conkers to quizzes. The only gravity dispense in the area.
Q 🏉 🕪 🍴 ♣

Tudor Rose
St Nicholas Street
☎ (0553) 762824
11–3, 5 (5.30 Sat)–11
Adnams Bitter, Broadside; Draught Bass Ⓗ
15th-century, timbered pub with oak-beamed bars and a restaurant. Excellent, home-cooked food, prepared on fresh ingredients. One bar is quiet, the other noisy. Guest beers. Q 🏉 🛏 🕪 🍴 ≥

White Horse
9 Wootton Road
☎ (0553) 763258

11–3, 6–11
Webster's Yorkshire Bitter Ⓗ
Busy, two-roomed, town pub near the Gaywood Clock. Always full of activity with many pub teams. Guest beers.
♣ P

Wildfowler
Gayton Road (B1145)
☎ (0553) 775786
11–2.30, 6–11 (12–2.30, 7–10.30 Sun)
Ind Coope Burton Ale; Tetley Bitter Ⓗ
Lively pub on the edge of town, close to the hospital. Popular with youngsters but large enough for quiet tables to be found. 🏉 🕪 🕭 P

Larling

Angel
On A11 ☎ (0953) 717963
11–11
Courage Best Bitter; Everards Tiger; John Smith's Bitter Ⓗ
Popular with both the local farming community and visitors. The beer range is subject to change but is always excellent. Eve meals Fri and Sat only.
🏠 🏉 🕪 🕪 ≠ (Harling Rd) ♣ P

Letheringsett

Kings Head
Holt Road (A148, 1 mile from Holt) ☎ (0263) 712691
11–3, 6–11
Adnams Bitter; Draught Bass; Greene King IPA, Abbot Ⓗ
Comfortable, old, beamed pub in a delightful garden setting, adjoining old brewery buildings. A quiet walk from the water mill nearby, along the River Glaven. Families welcome. Guest beers. 🏠 Q 🏉 🕪 🍴 🕭 ♣ P

Mundesley

Royal Hotel
Paston Road (B1159)
☎ (0263) 720096
11–2.30, 5.30–11
Adnams Bitter; Greene King IPA, Abbot Ⓗ
Old, beamed bar in a hotel with Nelson connections. Good food at reasonable prices in a comfortable dining room (incl. vegetarian option). Lots of charm and character. Guest ale. 🏠 Q 🚲 🛏 🕪 🍴 P

Mundford

Crown Hotel
Off A1065 ☎ (0842) 878233
11.30–3, 6.30–11 (11–11 Sat)
Ruddles County; Webster's Yorkshire Bitter Ⓗ
Multi-roomed, 17th-century coaching inn. Very much the centre of the community as a village pub should be. Guest beer. 🏉 🛏 🕪 Å ♣ P

New Buckenham

Kings Head
Market Place (B1113)
☎ (0953) 860487
11.30–2.30, 7–11
Marston's Pedigree; Whitbread Boddingtons Bitter, Flowers Original Ⓗ
Traditional, friendly local on the village green, with a regular guest ale during the summer. No eve meals Mon. 🏠 🏉 🕪 ♣

Try also: George (Brent Walker)

North Walsham

Scarborough Hill House Hotel
Old Yarmouth Road (1 mile from centre) ☎ (0692) 402151
11–3, 7–11
Bateman XB Ⓖ
Hotel with a bar and dining area; set in large grounds in rural surroundings on the outskirts of town. Occasional guest beer.
🏠 Q 🚲 🍴 🛏 🕪 Å P

North Wootton

Red Cat
Station Road
☎ (0553) 631244
11–2.30, 6–11
Adnams Bitter; Woodforde's Phoenix Ⓗ
Warm and welcoming hotel with a well-stocked bar. Its name derives from a mummified cat in the bar. The house beer, Red Cat, is specially brewed for the pub by Woodforde's.
🏠 🚲 🛏 🕪 ♣ P

Norwich

Black Horse
50 Earlham Road (B1108, ½ mile W of City Hall)
☎ (0603) 624682
10.30–3.30, 5.30–11 (10.30–11 Sat)
Adnams Extra; Marston's Pedigree; Theakston Best Bitter; Whitbread Flowers Original; Woodforde's Wherry Ⓗ
Busy yet comfortable pub with a friendly atmosphere and an excellent carvery restaurant. Covered outdoor area. Guest beer. Q 🏉 🕪 ♣ 🍽 P

Bread & Cheese
111 Adelaide Street (500 yds from A47) ☎ (0603) 615303
11–3, 5.30 (7 Sat)–11
Adnams Bitter; Draught Bass Ⓗ
Friendly, corner local. Note the original Bullards stained-glass windows. Guest beer. 🏉 🕪 🕭 P

Catherine Wheel

61 St Augustines (A140)
☎ (0603) 627852
11–3, 5–11 (11–11 Fri & Sat)
**Adnams Bitter; Draught
Bass; Ind Coope Burton Ale;
Tetley Bitter** Ⓗ
Recently refurbished to a bare
beams and brick decor. The bar,
unusually, has a well. The
sizeable upstairs bar/food area
offers vegetarian dishes. Guest
beers. ♨ ☎ ◖ ♣ P

Freemasons

Hall Road ☎ (0603) 623768
11–5.30, 7.30–11
**Courage Best Bitter,
Directors** Ⓗ
A busy single bar, very popular
at lunchtimes, plus a well-used
function room. Guest beer. ◖ ♣

Gardeners Arms

Timber Hill ☎ (0603) 621447
11–11
**Adnams Bitter; Draught
Bass; Greene King IPA; Ind
Coope Burton Ale; Tetley
Bitter** Ⓗ
Imitation rustic and horse brass,
city-centre, cosmopolitan
boozer attracting a lively,
mixed, young clientele;
welcoming landlord. Soon to
stock house beer 'Murderers
Ale'. The pub has a confusing
twin name of The Murderers
and Gardeners Arms. Children
welcome in the back bar. ☎ ◖

Golden Star

Duke Street
☎ (0603) 632447
11–11 (11–4, 5.30–11 Sat)
**Greene King XX Mild, IPA,
Rayments Special, Abbot** Ⓗ
Popular and friendly pub near
the city centre. Traditional, good
value home-cooking (vegetarian
option); no meals Sun. Q ◖ ♣

Horse & Dray

137 Ber Street
☎ (0603) 624741
11–11
**Adnams Mild, Bitter,
Broadside, Tally Ho;
Wadworth 6X** Ⓗ
Comfortable, village pub in the
city centre, well worth a visit.
Closes Sat afternoon when
football matches are played at
home. ♨ ☎ ◖ ♣

Jubilee

26 St Leonards Road
☎ (0603) 618734
11–11
**Fuller's London Pride;
Whitbread Boddingtons
Bitter** Ⓗ
Victorian, corner pub with two
bars and an outdoor drinking
area; games room upstairs.
Serves Woodforde's house beer
and guest beers (usually a dark
beer plus six others).
♨ ☎ ☎ ◖ ⇌ ♣

Micawbers Tavern

Pottergate ☎ (0603) 626627
11–3, 5–11
**Adnams Bitter; Draught
Bass; Hall & Woodhouse
Tanglefoot; Samuel Smith
OBB; Theakston Best Bitter;
Wadworth 6X** Ⓗ
City-centre pub with typical
local trade. Split-level bars. A
friendly atmosphere; popular
with all ages. Guest beers. ◖ ☺

Mill Tavern

2 Millers Lane, Angel Road
☎ (0603) 410268
11–3, 5.30–11
**Adnams Mild, Bitter, Old,
Broadside, Tally Ho** Ⓗ
Standard, working-class
drinking pub, representing a
Norfolk culture which is quickly
fading. Visit it before it goes
forever. Small car park.
Q ♿ ♣ P

Queens Arms

102 Magdalen Street
☎ (0603) 627667
10.30–11
**Ind Coope Burton Ale; Tetley
Bitter; Woodforde's
Wherry** Ⓗ
Large, comfortable, one-bar
pub; popular for its good value
lunches. ◖ ◗ ♣

Reindeer

10 Dereham Road
☎ (0603) 666821
11–3, 5–11 (11–11 Sat)
**Bateman XXXB; Elgood's
Bitter** Ⓗ
Recently extended, this
traditional pub always has lots
to offer the lover of real ale
(incl. six guest beers). Good
food, and live music some
nights. Note the red phone box.
The pub's own brewery is
visible through a window at the
bar (blanket pressure used).
☎ ◖ ♣ ☺ P

Ribs of Beef

24 Wensum Street
☎ (0603) 619517
10.30–11
**Adnams Bitter; Bateman
Mild; Reepham Rapier;
Theakston Best Bitter;
Whitbread Flowers IPA;
Woodforde's Wherry** Ⓗ
Up to 11 real beers are served
in this attractive, busy, city-
centre, riverside pub. Moorings
available. No food Sun.
Q ☎ ◖ ♣

Rosary

95 Rosary Road
☎ (0603) 666287
11–3, 5.30–11
**Adnams Bitter, Broadside;
Draught Bass; Marston's
Pedigree; Woodforde's
Wherry** Ⓗ
Popular pub near rail and yacht
stations. Several guest beers

served by gravity from the rear
cellar. A house beer, Rosary
Bitter, is brewed by
Woodforde's. A new
conservatory at the back
doubles as a dining room/
family room.
☎ ◖ ⇌ ♣ ☺ P

St Andrews Tavern

4 St Andrews Street (800 yds
from Blackfriars Halls)
☎ (0603) 614858
11–11 (11–3, 5–11 Mon–Thu,
Jan–March)
**Adnams Bitter, Old,
Broadside; Brains Dark** Ⓗ
Single-bar pub near the city
centre, usually offering at least
six quality real ales. Cellar bar
available for functions; a
conservatory and outdoor yard
cater for families. Folk night
Wed. Lunchtime snacks.
☎ ☎ ◖

Tap & Spile
(White Lion)

73 Oak Street
☎ (0603) 620630
11–11
Beer range varies Ⓗ
An ever-changing range of ten
real ales ensures that this pub is
a must. Although refurbished by
its new owners, it retains its
individuality. Woodforde's
White Lion house bitter is also
available. Well worth the walk
from the city centre. No food
Sun. ♨ Q ◖ ♣ ☺

Ten Bells

76 St Benedicts Street
☎ (0603) 667833
11–2.30, 5.30–11
**Greene King IPA, Rayments
Special, Abbot** Ⓗ
Smallish, city pub with regular
live music, a red phone box and
an inglenook. Part of the pub
becomes a food area/restaurant
on Wed–Sat eves. The venue
for a local chess club. No food
Sun eve. ♨ ◖ ◗ P

Wild Man

29 Bedford Street (just off
London Street pedestrian
precinct)
☎ (0603) 627686
10.30–2.30, 5.30 (7 Sat)–11 (12–2,
7.30–10.30 Sun)
**Courage Directors; Tolly
Cobbold Bitter, Original, Old
Strong** Ⓗ
One-bar, city-centre local; busy
and popular. The flagship for the
new Tolly beers in Norwich.
Good value food (eve meals:
Tue, Thu and Fri only, until
7.30). ◖ ◗

York Tavern

1 Leicester Street
☎ (0603) 620918
11–11
**Courage Best Bitter,
Directors; Everards Tiger;
Woodforde's Wherry** Ⓗ

Pleasantly spartan but refurbished, busy locals' pub comprising three distinct areas downstairs and an upstairs room. The food is inviting and varied. Bar billiards and a bowling green. Guest beer.
☎ ◑ ▶ ♣ P

Try also: **Barn Tavern**, Barn Lane (Courage); **Plough**, St Benedicts St (Courage); **Spread Eagle**, Sussex St (Brent Walker)

Old Buckenham

Ox & Plough
The Green (just off B1077)
☎ (0953) 860004
12–11
Adnams Bitter; Greene King IPA Ⅲ
Friendly, village local with a regular guest ale during the summer. ▦ ♨ ♨ ◑ ▶ ♿ ♣ P

Old Catton

Woodman
11 North Walsham Road (B1150, 2 miles N of Norwich)
☎ (0603) 426655
11–2.30, 5.30 (7 Sat)–11 (12–2.30, 7–10.30 Sun)
Marston's Pedigree; Theakston Best Bitter; Whitbread Flowers IPA, Original Ⓔ
Smart and comfortable suburban pub with a restaurant. The larger lounge has a red carpet and subdued lighting. Home of Major Wix, past landlord and celebrated trumpeter. No food Sun eve. ☎ ◑ ▶ ♿ ♣ P

Old Hunstanton

Ancient Mariner
Golf Course Road
☎ (048 53) 34411
11–3, 6–11 (11–11 summer)
Adnams Bitter, Broadside; Draught Bass; Charrington IPA Ⅲ
Part of Le Strange Arms Hotel but retaining a pub-like atmosphere. Low beams, nautical decor and intimate drinking areas. Guest beer.
▦ ♨ ☎ ⬚ ◑ ▶ ♿ ♣ P

Ormesby St Margaret

Grange Hotel
On A149, Caister bypass
☎ (0493) 731877
12–11 (may vary winter)
Adnams Bitter; Charrington IPA; Ruddles County; Woodforde's Wherry Ⅲ
Former 18th-century country house and listed building, set in two acres of grounds. Two bars: the main one has an original fireplace and spacious seating, plus many photographs of the

old house and Broadland. Regular guest beer.
▦ ♨ ☎ ⬚ ◑ ▶ Å ♣ P

Reepham

Crown
Ollands Road ☎ (0603) 870964
11–3, 6–11
Courage Directors; Reepham Granary Ⅲ
Recently refurbished, this comfortable locals' pub is also popular with visitors. Large beer garden. Traditional Yorkshire bar meals a speciality. Q ◑ ▶ ♣ P

Ringstead

Gin Trap Inn
High Street ☎ (048 525) 264
11.30–2.30, 7 (6 summer)–11
Adnams Bitter; Greene King IPA, Abbot; Woodforde's Norfolk Nog Ⅲ
Petanque is a feature of this country village pub which boasts a collection of animal traps in its split-level bar. Pleasant garden, ideal for idyllic summer eves. Woodforde's house beer. ▦ ☎ ◑ ▶ ♣ P

Rockland St Mary

New Inn
12 New Inn Hill
☎ (050 88) 395
11–11 (12–2.30, 7–11 winter)
Greene King Abbot; Tolly Cobbold Mild; Whitbread Flowers IPA Ⅲ
Comfortable, friendly local on the edge of the village; moorings for boats opposite. Games include shove-ha'penny and Shut the Box. Guest beers.
▦ Q ♨ ☎ ◑ ▶ ♣ P

Salhouse

Lodge
Vicarage Road
☎ (0603) 782828
10.30–2.30, 6–11
Greene King IPA; Theakston Best Bitter; Woodforde's Wherry Ⅲ
Eighty malt whiskies are available in this former Georgian rectory with lovely gardens and grounds. Guest beer in summer. Food ranges from snacks to a carvery.
▦ Q ☎ ◑ ▶ P

Sedgeford

King William IV
Heacham Road (B1454)
☎ (0485) 71765
11–3, 5.30 (7 winter)–11
Draught Bass; Charrington IPA; Greene King Abbot Ⅲ
A pub where a lively landlord provides gossip, entertainment and music *à la carte*. Make a detour from the coast road or

walk the Peddars Way to find him. Guest beers, and various ciders in summer.
▦ ☎ ◑ ▶ Å ♣ ⌣ P

Shouldham Thorpe

Jolly Brewers
Shouldham Gap (A134)
☎ (036 64) 7896
10.30–2.30 (3 Sat), 5.30–11
Draught Bass; Greene King IPA, Abbot; Marston's Merrie Monk, Pedigree; Wadworth 6X; Welsh Brewers Worthington BB Ⅲ
No expense has been spared in creating this excellent roadside pub; all needs are catered for in style. At least two guest beers.
▦ ☎ ⬚ ◑ ▶ ♿ Å P

Smallburgh

Crown
North Walsham Road (A149)
☎ (0692) 536314
11.30–2.30 (4 Sat), 5.30 (7 Sat)–11
Greene King IPA; Whitbread Flowers IPA, Castle Eden Ale Ⅲ
A thatched and beamed building which dates from the 15th century. Large open fire; tables and chairs made from wooden barrels and firkins. A friendly locals' pub offering good food in an attractive dining room (no meals Sun eve). Guest beers.
▦ Q ♨ ☎ ◑ ▶ ⬚ ♣ P

South Wootton

Farmers Arms
Knights Hill Village
☎ (0553) 675566
11–11
Adnams Bitter, Broadside; Draught Bass; Charrington IPA; Ruddles County; Samuel Smith OBB Ⅲ
Beautiful barn conversion on the King's Lynn ring road. A motel, conference centre and sports complex share the site. Good food. Guest beers.
▦ Q ♨ ☎ ⬚ ◑ ▶ ♿ Å ♣ P

Stalham

Kingfisher Hotel
High Street ☎ (0692) 581974
11–2.30, 6.30–11 (12–2.30, 7–10.30 Sun)
Adnams Bitter; Woodforde's Wherry Ⅲ
Modern, family-run hotel with a comfortable bar, situated in a small country town near the Broads and the sea. Local seafood a speciality.
☎ ⬚ ◑ ▶ ♿ P

Stibbard

Ordnance Arms
Guist Bottom (A1067)
☎ (032 878) 471

11–2.30, 5.30–11
Greene King IPA, Abbot Ⓗ
A friendly landlord hosts these
two bars with an additional
room off the main bar area.
Snacks available lunchtimes,
with a Thai restaurant eves at
the rear of the pub. 🚗 🛏 ♦ P

Stiffkey

Red Lion
44 Wells Road (A149, just E of
Wells) ☎ (0328) 830552
11–11 (11–2.30, 6–11 winter)
**Greene King IPA, Abbot;
Ruddles Best Bitter;
Woodforde's Wherry** Ⓖ
Superb pub, with separate bars
and open fires, in an unspoilt
village which attracts many
ramblers on the numerous
coastal walks. Re-opened Easter
1990 after 20 years as private
house – one of three former
pubs in the village which were
victims of the Watney
revolution. Excellent food.
🚗 Q 🏃 🛏 ♦ ⓓ 🍴 ઢ P

Stokesby

Ferry Inn
Ferry Lane (2 miles from
A1064) ☎ (0493) 751096
11–3, 6.30–11
**Adnams Bitter; Whitbread
Wethered Bitter** Ⓗ
Pleasant, riverside pub in a
picturesque village. Occasional
guest beers. Meals available in
summer only. 🚗 Q 🏃 🛏 ♦ ⓓ 🍴 P

Swaffham

Kings Arms Hotel
Market Place ☎ (0760) 721495
11–11
**Courage Directors;
Whitbread Flowers
Original** Ⓗ
Old, unspoilt, one-roomed pub
with a lively but relaxed
atmosphere. Just right for a pint
after visiting the fine Saturday
market. ⓓ ♦ P

Swanton Abbot

Weavers Arms
Aylsham Road (2 miles from
B1150 at Westwick)
☎ (0692) 69655
11–3.30 (5 Sat), 7–11
**Whitbread Castle Eden Ale,
Flowers Original** Ⓗ
Quiet, country pub with beams
and an open fire. Old
agricultural implements adorn
the walls. Guest beers.
🚗 Q 🏃 🛏 ♦ ⓓ ⓔ P

Try also: **Jolly Farmers** (Free)

Swanton Morley

Darby's
Elsing Road (at B1147 jct)
☎ (0362) 637647

11–2.30, 6–11
**Adnams Bitter, Broadside;
Hall & Woodhouse
Tanglefoot; Woodforde's
Wherry** Ⓗ
Pub constructed from two
derelict cottages; has a genuine
local feel, a warm welcome and
great quality (and value) food.
Guest beer and a mild.
Children's playground in the
garden.
🚗 Q 🏃 🛏 ♦ ⓓ ઢ 🄰 ♣ ⓕ P

Tasburgh

Countryman
Ipswich Road (A140, 7 miles S
of Norwich) ☎ (0508) 470946
11–2.30, 6.30–11
**Adnams Bitter; Greene King
IPA** Ⓗ
Large roadside pub where food
is a major consideration. Guest
beers in summer. 🛏 ⓓ ♦ P

Terrington St Clement

County Arms
Marshland Street
☎ (0553) 828511
12–11
**Greene King IPA, Rayments
Special, Abbot** Ⓗ
Village pub with olde-worlde
charm, close to a renowned
African Violet centre.
🚗 Q 🛏 ⓓ ઢ P

Thetford

Albion
Castle Street ☎ (0842) 752796
11–2.30, 6–11 (12–2, 7–10.30 Sun)
Greene King IPA, Abbot Ⓗ
Small, comfy, friendly, flint-
faced pub close to Castle Hill
ancient monument. By far the
cheapest ale in the area.
Q 🛏 ⓓ ♣ P

Thompson

Chequers Inn
Griston Road OS923969
☎ (095 383) 360
11–3, 6–11
**Adnams Bitter; Draught
Bass; Greene King IPA;
Welsh Brewers Worthington
BB** Ⓗ
Unspoilt, 16th-century,
thatched pub, well off the
beaten track, which has a fine
reputation amongst the locals
and is very busy all year round.
Three bars, two with very low
ceilings. Guest beer.
Q 🏃 🛏 ♦ ⓓ ♣ ⓕ P

Thornham

Lifeboat Inn
Ship Lane ☎ (048 526) 236
11–3, 6–11 (11–11 summer)
**Adnams Bitter; Greene King
XX Mild, IPA, Abbot** Ⓗ

Original, 16th-century
smugglers' inn, still lit by oil
lamps and complemented by
recent extensions. Very busy in
summer. Mild is kept in the
kitchen – ask. Guest beers.
Penny in Hole played.
🚗 Q 🏃 🛏 ♦ ⓓ ♣ P

Thorpe St Andrew

Gordon
88 Gordon Avenue (off
Norwich ring road, Harvey
Lane section) ☎ (0603) 34658
11–2.30, 7–11
**Greene King IPA, Abbot;
John Smith's Bitter** Ⓗ
Popular estate pub with an
interesting mock Tudor facade.
Friendly atmosphere. Guest
beer. 🚗 🛏 ⓓ ♣ P

Tibenham

Greyhound
The Street (2 miles E of B1113)
OS136895 ☎ (037 977) 676
12–2, 6.30–11
Beer range varies Ⓗ
Popular with locals and keenly
sought by others. Three rooms;
lots of games; dog, cat and
library. Imaginative, good value
food. Guest beers and K9, a
Woodforde's house beer.
🚗 Q 🏃 🛏 ♦ ⓓ ઢ 🄰 ♣ P

Tivetshall St Mary

Old Ram
Ipswich Road (A140)
☎ (0379) 608228
11–11
**Adnams Bitter; Greene King
Abbot; Ruddles County;
Webster's Yorkshire Bitter** Ⓗ
Much-renovated, rambling,
roadside pub, retaining great
character: stripped beams, real
fires and stone-tiled floors. The
strongly featured food is always
available and accommodation
has recently been added. Guest
beer. 🚗 🏃 🛏 ♦ ⓓ ઢ P 🏵

Toft Monks

Toft Lion
The Street (A143)
☎ (050 277) 702
11.30–2.30, 6.30–11
**Adnams Bitter, Old;
Woodforde's Wherry** Ⓗ
Friendly local, modernised but
comfortable; a former Morgan's
house called the White Lion,
renamed to avoid confusion
with a nearby pub at
Wheatacre.
🚗 Q 🏃 🛏 ♦ ⓓ ♣ P

Walcott

Lighthouse
Coast Road (B1159)
☎ (0692) 650371
11–3, 6.30–11

Norfolk

Ind Coope Burton Ale; Tetley Bitter Ⓗ
Genuine locals', rural pub on a lonely stretch of coast road. Events are always in the pipeline. The pub's camping space is often full in summer.
🏕 ⛺ 🍴 🍺 ◗ ⏺ Å P

Walpole Cross Keys

Woolpack
Sutton Road ☎ (0553) 828327
12–3, 7–11
Adnams Bitter, Broadside Ⓗ
Pleasant, country inn on the old A17. 🏕 Q ⛺ 🍺 ◗ ⏺ ♣ P

Warham

Horseshoes
Bridge Street ☎ (0328) 710547
11–2.30, 7–11 (12–2.30, 7–10.30 Sun)
Greene King IPA Ⓗ, Abbot; Woodforde's Wherry Ⓖ
Old, unspoilt, gas-lit pub with a 1921 electric pianola and an old gramophone. Good, home-cooked food lunchtimes and Thu–Sat eves.
🏕 Q ⛺ 🍴 🍺 ◗ ⏺ ♣ P

Weasenham All Saints

Ostrich Inn
On A1065 ☎ (032 874) 221
11–3, 7–11
Adnams Bitter, Extra Ⓗ
Friendly, roadside pub with basic furnishings, but a warm welcome and a fire. Get your fruit and veg here!
🏕 Q ⛺ 🍺 ◗ Å ♣ P

Wells

Crown Hotel
The Buttlands
☎ (0328) 710209
11–2.30, 6–11
Adnams Bitter; Marston's Pedigree; Tetley Bitter Ⓗ
A coaching inn since the 18th century, this fine hotel, facing the tree-lined green, is a Tudor building with a Georgian facade.
🏕 🍺 🍴 ◗ ⏺ P

Try also: Golden Fleece (Brent Walker)

Welney

Lamb & Flag
Main Street ☎ (035 471) 242
11–2.30, 7–11 (12–2.30, 7–10.30 Sun)
Elgood's Bitter, GSB Ⓗ
Cosy, Fenland pub covered by Boston creepers in summer. This area is noted for its fishing and a huge pike is displayed in the pub's restaurant.
🏕 Q ⛺ 🍴 ◗ ⏺ 🍴 Å ♣ P

Try also: Three Tuns (Elgood's)

Weston Longville

Parson Woodforde
Off A1067
☎ (0603) 880106
11–3, 6–11
Adnams Bitter; Draught Bass; Ind Coope Burton Ale; Tetley Bitter; Woodforde's Wherry Ⓗ
Roomy brick and beam bar with two fine, large, brick fireplaces, one with a log fire.
🏕 ⛺ 🍺 ◗ ⏺ 🍴 ♣ P

West Rudham

Dukes Head
Lynn Road (A148)
☎ (048 522) 540
11–3, 5.30–11
Adnams Bitter; Greene King Abbot; Woodforde's Wherry Ⓗ
A flint and carrstone pub beside the main road, popular with locals and busy with summer tourists. Good selection of games, but no facilities for children.
🏕 Q 🍺 ◗ ⏺ ♣ P

West Somerton

Lion
Martham Road (B1159/B1152 jct) ☎ (0493) 393289
11–3, 6–11
Greene King XX Mild, IPA, Abbot Ⓗ
Friendly, village pub with a separate public bar. Basic, and unspoilt by refurbishment.
Q ⛺ 🍺 ◗ 🍴 Å ♣ P

Try also: Nelson Head, Horsey (Free)

West Walton

King of Hearts
School Road
☎ (0945) 584785
11–2.30, 6.30–11 (12–2.30, 7–10.30 Sun)
Elgood's Bitter Ⓗ
Village pub with a plush bar and a separate restaurant. Good local reputation for food.
🏕 Q 🍺 ◗ ⏺ P

Wimbotsham

Chequers
7 Church Road OS622050
☎ (0366) 387704
11.45–2.30, 7–11
Greene King IPA, Abbot Ⓗ
Long, low, one-bar pub off the usual tourist track; pleasant and friendly. Q 🍺 ◗ ⏺ ♣ P

Try also: Hare Arms, Stow Bardolph (Greene King)

Winterton

Fisherman's Return
The Lane (off B1159)
☎ (0493) 393305
11–11 (11–2.30, 7–11 winter)
Adnams Bitter; Ruddles Best Bitter; Webster's Yorkshire Bitter Ⓗ
300 year-old building with real beams and panelling. Two distinct rooms, games and music in one, the other a quiet lounge. Popular with locals and tourists. Extensive, interesting menu.
🏕 Q ⛺ 🍴 ◗ ⏺ ♣ P

Wreningham

Bird in Hand
Church Road (B1133)
☎ (0508) 41438
11–3, 5.30–11
Adnams Bitter; Marston's Pedigree; Whitbread Castle Eden Ale, Flowers Original; Woodforde's Wherry Ⓗ
Well-tiled floor and wooden raftered roof in a pub with a brickwork bar and room dividers. Pleasant pictures and mirrors add to the atmosphere and there are landscaped gardens. Up to three guest beers. 🍺 ◗ ⏺ 🍴 P

Wymondham

Cross Keys
Market Street
☎ (0953) 602152
10.30–2.30, 5.30–11
Ruddles County; Webster's Yorkshire Bitter Ⓗ
Pub boasting a very old exterior, near the market cross. Much of the interior is devoted to food. Guest beer. 🛏 ◗ ⏺ 🚆

Feathers
Town Green ☎ (0953) 605675
11–2.30, 7–11
Adnams Bitter; Greene King Abbot; Marston's Pedigree Ⓗ
Popular, local free house which has now lost its car park (but there is a public one very close by). Regularly has three or four guest beers, as well as a Woodforde's house beer (Feathers Tickler). 🍺 🚆 ⏺

ONLY A REAL COAL FIRE WILL DO.

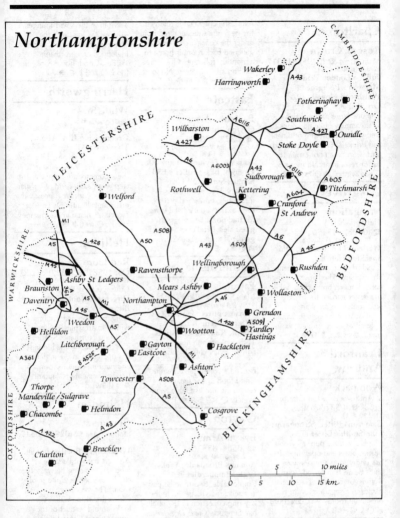

Northamptonshire

(map showing:)
CAMBRIDGESHIRE
LEICESTERSHIRE
WARWICKSHIRE
BEDFORDSHIRE
BUCKINGHAMSHIRE
OXFORDSHIRE

Wakerley
Harringworth
Fotheringhay
Southwick
Wilbarston
Oundle
Stoke Doyle
Rothwell
Sudborough
Kettering
Titchmarsh
Welford
Cranford St Andrew
Ravensthorpe
Wellingborough
Rushden
Ashby St Ledgers
Mears Ashby
Wollaston
Braunston
Daventry
Northampton
Grendon
Hellidon
Weedon
Wootton
Yardley Hastings
Litchborough
Gayton
Hackleton
Eastcote
Ashton
Towcester
Thorpe Mandeville
Sulgrave
Helmdon
Cosgrove
Chacombe
Charlton
Brackley

0   5   10 miles
0   5   10   15 km

Ashby St Ledgers

Old Coach House Inn
☎ (0788) 890349
12–2.30, 6–11
**Everards Tiger, Old Original;
Marston's Pedigree;
Whitbread Flowers
Original** Ⓗ
Perhaps the quintessential
country pub: a small snug bar
and a games room which have
many interesting features. The
main bar has a large wood fire
and an old range for winter.
Two guest beers.
🏛 ⬥ ⊞ ⬥ ⬥ P

Ashton

Old Crown
Stoke Road ☎ (0604) 862268
12–2.30 (3 Sat), 7–11
**Adnams Broadside; Wells
Eagle, Bombardier** Ⓗ

Large, village-centre local,
dating from 1772. Large garden
with play area; separate bar
with pool table and darts. The
pub's history is documented in
the lounge. *A la carte* dining.
🏛 ⬥ ⊞ ⬥ P

Brackley

Plumbers Arms
Manor Road
☎ (0280) 702495
10.30–11
**Draught Bass; Hook Norton
Best Bitter** Ⓗ
Two-roomed, back-street local.
The homely lounge has a real
fire. Guest beers; a real drinker's
pub. 🏛 ⬥ ⬥ ⬥

Braunston

Old Plough
High Street ☎ (0788) 890000
11–2.30, 6.15–11

**Ansells Mild, Bitter; Ind
Coope Burton Ale** Ⓗ
Smart, semi-timbered bar with a
real fire and darts. The lounge
has what appears to be a tree
trunk in the middle; plenty of
leather seating. A pub since
1672, and in this guide for the
past 12 years. 🏛 🏛 ⬥ ⬥ ⊞ ⬥ P

Chacombe

George & the Dragon
Silver Street ☎ (0295) 710602
12–2.30, 5.30–11 (12–11 Thu–Sat)
**Adnams Bitter; Brains SA;
Jennings Bitter; Thwaites
Bitter** Ⓗ
Unchanged, three-roomed,
country pub, with a gem of a
snug where the wall is made
from the backs of the settles.
Stone-mullioned windows and
stone flags abound.
🏛 Q ⬥ 🏛 ⊞ ⬥ P

Northamptonshire

Charlton

Rose & Crown
Main Street ☎ (0295) 811317
12–3, 5 (6.30 Sat)–11
**Fuller's London Pride;
Marston's Pedigree;
Whitbread Flowers IPA,
Original** Ⓗ
The one large room of this
17th-century building copes
well with the mixture of diners
and drinkers. Guest beer. Food
(incl. vegetarian option) in the
bar or restaurant. No meals Sun
eve in winter. ▲ Q ➳ ✿ Ⓖ 🅙 ▶ P

Cosgrove

Navigation
Thrupp Wharf
☎ (0908) 543156
11–11 (12–2.30, 7–11 winter)
**Morland Old Masters, Old
Speckled Hen** Ⓗ
Canalside pub with a pleasant
atmosphere. The bar and lounge
contain much breweriana, whilst
the larger garden to the rear
leads onto the canal and is
popular with families in summer.
Specialises in guest ales (six in
total). ▲ ✿ Ⓖ 🅙 ▶ ♣ P

Cranford St Andrew

Woolpack
St Andrews Lane (off Grafton
Road) ☎ (053 678) 256
11–2.30, 6–11
**Camerons Bitter, Strongarm;
John Smith's Bitter** Ⓗ
Classic, country pub; all wood
beams, brass and open fires. It
has undergone a renaissance
since being transferred from
Manns' ownership. Traditional
games in a separate room; real
fires in all rooms. Ask directions.
▲ Q ✿ Ⓖ ♣ P

Daventry

Coach & Horses
Warwick Street
☎ (0327) 76692
11–2.30 (3 Sat), 5 (7 Sat)–11
**Ind Coope Burton Ale;
Marston's Pedigree; Tetley
Bitter** Ⓗ
Old coaching inn with a village
inn feel, despite its town
location. Fortnightly live jazz in
the Stables Bar. Pool table at the
back; conversation in the wood-
boarded front end. Children's
play area in the garden. No
food Sun. ▲ Q ✿ Ⓖ ♣

Dun Cow
61 Brook Street
☎ (0327) 71545
10.30–2.30 (4 Sat), 5.30 (6.30 Sat)–11
(10.30–11 Fri)
**Greenalls Davenports Bitter,
Thomas Greenall's Bitter** Ⓗ
Old coaching inn whose recent

refurbishment has not changed
the gem of a snug, entered from
under the coach arch. The
galleried back room is home to
a monthly folk club. Only three
landlords this century. No food
Sun. ▲ Q ➳ ✿ Ⓖ 🅙 ♣ P

Eastcote

Eastcote Arms
Gayton Road
☎ (0327) 830731
12–2.30 (not Mon), 6–10.30 (11 Fri &
Sat; 12–2, 7–10.30 Sun)
**Banks & Taylor Eastcote Ale;
Draught Bass; Fuller's ESB;
Samuel Smith OBB** Ⓗ
Small, village pub with
interesting prints and pictures.
One of the county's stalwarts
for traditional beers; regular
guest ales. Excellent, large
garden. Lunches Tue–Sat.
▲ Q ✿ Ⓖ 🅙 P

Fotheringhay

Falcon
Main Street ☎ (083 26) 254
11.30 (10 in public bar)–2.30, 7–11
**Adnams Bitter; Greene King IPA,
Abbot; Ruddles County** Ⓗ
18th-century pub near
Fotheringhay church and the
site of the castle. Small public
bar and a comfortable lounge.
Good food in the separate
restaurant (not available Mon
eve). ▲ Q ✿ 🅙 ▶ ♣ P

Gayton

Eykyn Arms
☎ (0604) 858361
11–2.30, 6–11
**Adnams Broadside; Wells
Eagle, Bombardier** Ⓗ
Comfortable, two-roomed pub
in a secluded village. Note the
key ring collection in the public
bar. Supports *Guide Dogs for the
Blind.* ▲ Ⓖ 🅙 ♣ P

Grendon

Crown
Manor Road ☎ (0933) 663995
12–2.30, 6 (6.30 Sat)–11
**Adnams Bitter; Marston's
Pedigree** Ⓗ
Listed, stone-built local, sold off
by Manns in 1982. Now a
thriving local for all age groups:
a lively bar, and a cosy, quieter
lounge. Guest beers.
▲ Q ✿ Ⓖ 🅙 ♣ P

Try also: Half Moon (Wells)

Hackleton

White Hart
Main Road ☎ (0604) 870271
11–3 (3.30 Fri & Sat), 6–11
**Ruddles Best Bitter, County;
Webster's Yorkshire Bitter** Ⓗ
Stone-built pub whose first
landlord was way back in 1739,

as listed in the smart lounge. A
40ft well is built into the
lounge bar; the other bar has an
inglenook and Northants
skittles. Good, home-cooked
food. Q ✿ Ⓖ 🅙 🅔 ♣ P

Harringworth

White Swan
Seaton Road
11.30–2.30, 6–11
**Greene King IPA, Abbot;
Theakston XB** Ⓗ
16th-century, stone-built
coaching inn. The stairs up to the
accommodation have a 'trip
step' – an early form of burglar
alarm. Two drinking areas and a
restaurant. Walter De La Mare
carved his name in the chimney
breast. Q ⇌ 🅙 ♣ ♣ P

Hellidon

Red Lion
OS519581 ☎ (0327) 61200
12–3, 7–11
**Courage Best Bitter,
Directors; Hook Norton Best
Bitter** Ⓗ
Long, two-roomed, country pub
with a smart, split-level bar,
featuring Northants Skittles.
The dimly-lit, beamed lounge
has open fires in the inglenook
and hunting/country prints and
brasses. Separate restaurant.
▲ ✿ Ⓖ 🅔 ♣ P

Helmdon

Chequers
Station Road ☎ (0295) 768175
11–3, 7–11
Wells Eagle, Bombardier Ⓗ
A single bar with a large
fireplace, standing between the
children's room and the pool
room. The very large garden,
with a dry stone wall, overlooks an old viaduct of the
former Great Central Railway.
Ideal for families. Guest beers.
No food Sun eve, or Mon.
▲ ➳ ✿ Ⓖ 🅙 P

Kettering

Cordwainer
Bath Road ☎ (0536) 518578
11–3, 6–11 (11–11 Fri)
**Home Bitter; Theakston
XB** Ⓗ
Friendly, estate pub, with a
large bar and a smart lounge,
near North Park. It takes its
name from the local leather
tanning industry. ✿ 🅔 ♣ P

Try also: Bakers Arms
(Banks's)

Litchborough

Old Red Lion
Banbury Road
11–2.30 (3 Sat), 6.30–11
Banks's Bitter Ⓔ

Warm and welcoming, village local on the Knightly Way public footpath. Good value bar snacks available, except Sun.
🍴 🕳 🕯 ♣ P

Mears Ashby

Griffins Head
Wilby Road ☎ (0604) 812945
12–2.30, 5.30 (7 Sat)–11
Adnams Bitter; Bateman XXXB; Greene King IPA; Whitbread Flowers IPA Ⓗ
Impressive, brick-built pub set back from the road and offering good food. Basic bar with Northants skittles and a cosy lounge with a real fire. Home-cooked food (not served Sun or Mon eves). 🍴 Q 🕯 🕳 🌂 🕳 ♣ P

Northampton

Barn Owl
Olden Road, Rectory Farm
☎ (0604) 416483
11–3, 6–11
Greene King IPA, Rayments Special, Abbot Ⓗ
A great estate pub – the only Greene King pub in Northampton. Winner of CAMRA's *Best New Pub* award in 1986: one large bar on two levels. No food Sun. 🕳 🌂 ♿ P

Brewers Arms
Gas Street ☎ (0604) 36900
12–2.30, 5.30–11
Banks & Taylor Shefford Bitter, SOD, SOS, 2XS (winter) Ⓗ
Formerly a Manns pub, this listed building is the only Banks & Taylor tied house in the county. Live music last Wed in the month and every Sun. No keg beer; occasional guest beers. 🍴 🕯 🕳 🍺

Garibaldi
19 Bailiff Street (off Campbell Square) ☎ (0604) 30356
11.30–11
Draught Bass; Welsh Brewers Worthington BB Ⓗ
Easy-going, local in a side-street near the police station. Boxing gym on the first floor. 🌂 ♣

King Billy
4 Commercial Street
12–11
Banks's Bitter; Everards Old Original; Ruddles County; Theakston XB, Old Peculier; Younger IPA Ⓗ
Extended, street-corner local, popular with a young, but far from yuppy, clientele. Regular rock bands or discos. Guest beers. 🕯 🍺 ♿

Lamplighter
66 Overstone Road (400 yds E of main bus station)
☎ (0604) 31125
11–3, 6 (7 Sat)–11

Courage Best Bitter, Directors Ⓗ
Comfortable, small, side-street local done up as a high-class London pub, with real wood and an expensive decor: leaded-glass screens and brewery knick-knacks. No food Sat or Sun.
🕯 🕳 ♣

Old House at Home
216 Wellingborough Road
11–2.30 (3 Fri & Sat), 6–11
Ansells Mild; Everards Tiger; Ruddles Best Bitter, County; Webster's Yorkshire Bitter Ⓗ
Deservedly popular, town pub whose landlord is a very keen real ale supporter. Games include the increasingly rare Northants hood skittles. A function room upstairs provides varied entertainment. 🕯 ♣

Queen Adelaide
50 Manor Road, Kingsthorpe
☎ (0604) 714524
11–3, 5.30–11
Banks's Bitter; Ruddles Best Bitter; Webster's Yorkshire Bitter, Choice Ⓗ
Popular pub with old photos and original ceiling panelling in the bar and a nostalgic games room (Northants skittles). Children's playthings on the patio. Meals Mon–Fri.
Q 🕯 🕳 ♣ P

Road to Morocco
Bridgewater Drive
11–2.30 (3 Sat), 6–11
Courage Best Bitter Ⓗ
Good estate pub with a mixed clientele. The small bar is dominated by a pool table, while the smart, quiet lounge is decorated in Moorish style.
Q 🕯 🕳 ♣ P

Oundle

Ship
West Street ☎ (0832) 273918
11–3, 6–11 (11–11 Sat)
Draught Bass; Greene King IPA; Marston's Pedigree; Theakston XB Ⓗ
Large, three-roomed pub in an attractive, small town. Live music some Fri nights. Guest beer. 🍴 Q 🕯 🕳 🌂 🕳 ♣ P

Ravensthorpe

Chequers
Chequers Lane
☎ (0604) 770379
11–3, 6–11
Adnams Broadside; Bateman XB; Moorhouse's Pendle Witches Brew; Samuel Smith OBB Ⓗ
Friendly, village local with good food. The lounge has a collection of reference books; a separate games room across the yard offers skittles; and the large garden has a play area.

Lunches served weekends only; eve meals Mon–Sat.
Q 🌂 🕯 🕳 ♣ P

Rothwell

Red Lion Hotel
Market Hill
☎ (0536) 710409
11–2, 5–11
Wells Eagle, Bombardier Ⓗ
Impressive, ironstone building, claiming to be the last purpose-built coaching inn in England (1903). Three different drinking areas. Guest beer. No food Sun.
🛏 🕳 ♣ P

Rushden

Feathers
High Street
☎ (0933) 50251
11–2.30 (3 Fri & Sat), 5.30–11
Wells Eagle, Bombardier Ⓗ
Traditional-style pub with tasteful decor and comfortable furniture. Good bar snacks. Quiz night Sun. Guest beers 🕯 🕳 ♣ P

King Edward VIII
Queen Street
☎ (0933) 53478
11–11
Wells Eagle Ⓗ, **Bombardier** Ⓖ
Fine, traditional drinking pub with a good atmosphere, home cooking and comfortable seating. Quiz night Sun. Food all day Sat. 🍴 🕳 ♣ 🌂

Southwick

Shuckburgh Arms
Main Street
☎ (0832) 274007
11.30–2.30, 6–11
Adnams Bitter, Broadside; Hook Norton Best Bitter, Old Hooky; Taylor Landlord Ⓖ
Classic, unspoilt, village local dating from the 16th century. A basic bar and cosy lounge with bar billiards. Situated by the cricket pitch and opposite Southwick Hall. Popular with all sections of the community. Local CAMRA *Pub of the Year* in 1984 and 1990. Guest beers.
🍴 Q 🕯 🕳 ⚲ P

Stoke Doyle

Shuckburgh Arms
☎ (0832) 272339
12–2.30 (not Mon), 7–11
Draught Bass; Hook Norton Old Hooky; Marston's Border Bitter, Pedigree Ⓗ
17th-century, stone-built inn. The wood-panelled bar boasts Chesterfields and an inglenook. Northants skittles and occasional jazz nights. Home-cooked food in the separate dining room and summer barbecues. No food Mon lunch. Guest beer.
🍴 Q 🌂 🕯 🛏 🕳 ♣ P

Northamptonshire

Sudborough

Vane Arms
Main Street ☎ (080 12) 3223
11.30–3, 5.30–11
Moorhouse's Pendle Witches Brew; Theakston Old Peculier Ⓗ
Deservedly popular, old, thatched, village pub with stonework and beams throughout the good, basic public and the plusher lounge. At least seven guest beers; ask for the sample tray. No eve meals Sun or Mon.
🏠 Q 🛏 ⍾ ⌷ ⊞ ♣ P

Sulgrave

Star Inn
Manor Road ☎ (0295) 76389
11–2.30, 6–11
Hook Norton Best Bitter, Old Hooky Ⓗ
Stone-built, country pub with a single, beamed, stone-flagged bar, a small dining room, and a function room. The skeleton in the corner belies the size of the Desperate Dan pies. No food Sun eve. Follow the signs to Sulgrave Manor.
🏠 Q 🛏 ⍾ ⌷ P

Thorpe Mandeville

Three Conies
☎ (0295) 711025
11–2.30, 6.30–11
Hook Norton Best Bitter, Old Hooky Ⓗ
Impressive, three-storey, stone-built pub. A small public bar has a pool table while the larger lounge, with its impressive fireplace, is more comfortable. Separate restaurant (bookings only Sun lunch). 🏠 Q ⍾ ⌷ ⊞ P

Titchmarsh

Dog & Partridge
High Street ☎ (080 12) 2546
12–3, 6.30(7)–11
Adnams Broadside; Wells Eagle, Bombardier Ⓗ
18th-century, village pub. Much improved by the recent addition of a public bar. Two real fires to keep the local quiz fanatics warm. Northants skittles.
🏠 ⊛ ⍾ ♣ P

Towcester

Plough
Market Square ☎ (0327) 50738
11–2.30, 5–11
Adnams Broadside; Wells Eagle Ⓗ
A long bar to the rear of the pub complements the smaller lounge which fronts onto the market square. Excellent value food at all times. 🏠 ⌷ ⊞ ♣

White Bear
London Road ☎ (0327) 51486
11–2.30 (3.30 Fri), 6–11 (11–11 Sat)
Ind Coope ABC Best Bitter; Wadworth 6X Ⓗ
Street-corner local with a large, basic bar and a cosy lounge. Home to several traditional pub teams. 🏠 ⍾ ♣ P

Try also: Peacock Inn
(Camerons)

Wakerley

Exeter Arms
Main Street ☎ (057 287) 817
12–2.30 (not Mon), 6 (7 Sat)–11
Adnams Broadside; Bateman XB Ⓗ
Reputedly haunted, 300-year-old pub near Wakerley Woods: a public bar and a comfortable lounge with a wood-burning stove. No food Mon.
🏠 ⍾ ⌷ ⊞ ♣ P

Weedon

Globe Hotel
Watling Street ☎ (0327) 40336
11–11
Marston's Pedigree; Ruddles County Ⓗ
Lively and friendly lounge bar in a small hotel, with a separate restaurant. Live music Mon nights. Guest beer.
🏠 Q ⍾ 🛏 ⌷ P

Welford

Shoulder of Mutton
High Street ☎ (0858) 575375
12–2.30, 7–11
Bateman XB; Ruddles Best Bitter Ⓗ
Welcoming, 17th-century local well renovated into a single room, split by arches. The large garden offers plenty of play equipment and a skittle room provides family shelter in inclement weather. Good value food (menu caters for vegetarians and children).
🏠 ⍭ ⊛ ⌷ ♣ P

Wellingborough

Cannon
Cannon Street ☎ (0933) 29629
11–4, 5.30 (6 Fri, 6.30 Sat)–11
Banks & Taylor SOS; Wells Eagle Ⓗ
Very popular, town-centre pub for all ages, which has two rooms around a U-shaped bar. Guest ales are a feature with always seven to choose from.
🏠 ⊛ ♣ P

Horseshoe
Sheep Street ☎ (0933) 222015
11–4.30, 7–11
Draught Bass Ⓗ
Busy pub near the Arndale Centre. Crowded at weekends.

Separate games bar with bar billiards and pool. Guest beers. Lunchtime snacks. 🏠 ⊞ ♣ P

Vivian Arms
Knox Road ☎ (0933) 223660
11–2.30 (3 Sat), 6–11
Wells Eagle Ⓗ
Friendly, back-street local with a games room, plus a quiet room. Jazz every Tue eve. Snacks lunchtimes. Floodlit petanque piste in the garden. Guest beers.
🏠 Q ⊛ ⌷ ⊞ ♣ P

Wilbarston

Fox Inn
Church Street
☎ (0536) 771270
12–3, 6.30–11
Marston's Burton Best Bitter, Pedigree Ⓗ
Excellent, village local, parts of which date back to the 14th century. A good basic public and a large split-level lounge. Numerous pub game teams – trophies abound. High quality food (no eve meals Sun).
⊛ 🛏 ⌷ ⌷ ♣ P

Wollaston

Boot
High Street ☎ (0933) 664270
12–2.30 (3 Sat), 6–11
Courage Best Bitter; Tolly Cobbold Original Ⓗ
Busy, friendly local at the centre of the village. Whitewashed and thatched, with a small bar, cosy lounge and a games room (Northants skittles). Bar snacks. Landlady is a formidable nines dominoes player. 🏠 Q ⊞ ♣ P

Wootton

Wootton Workingmen's Club
High Street ☎ (0604) 761863
12–2.30, 7–11 (12–2, 7–10.30 Sun)
Banks's Bitter; Greene King IPA; Mansfield Riding Mild; Wells Eagle Ⓗ
Formerly the Old Red Lion, this club has been refurbished to bring back a pub atmosphere. Specialises in guest ales. The pleasant bar, with an adjoining games room, has exposed stonework; the smart concert room doubles as a lounge. Guest beers. CIU entry regulations apply. ⊞ ♣ P

Yardley Hastings

Red Lion
☎ (060 129) 210
Adnams Broadside; Wells Eagle Ⓗ
Small, village pub. The bar has brassy bits and pieces; the locals frequent the lounge. Separate skittles room. No food Sun.
Q ⊛ ⌷ ⊞ ♣ P

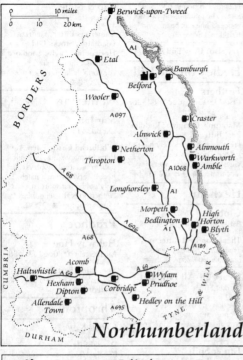

Longstone, *Belford*

Acomb

Miners Arms Inn
Main Street ☎ (0434) 603909
11.30–3, 5.30–11 (11–11 Fri & Sat)
**Big Lamp Prince Bishop Ale;
Federation Best Bitter;
Morrells Varsity** ⊞
Popular, village pub with good
food, incl. vegetarian option.
Big Lamp house beer,
Easter–Oct. Guest beers.
🏚 Q 🍴 🕯 🍺 ♣ ♣

Allendale Town

Golden Lion
On B6303
11–11
Beer range varies ⊞
Pleasant, friendly, town-centre
pub. Good food at affordable
prices. Guest beers. 🏚 🍴 🕯 🍺

Alnmouth

Red Lion Inn
Northumberland Street
☎ (0665) 830584
12–2.30, 7–11 (may vary)
**Tetley Bitter; Theakston Best
Bitter** ⊞
Friendly pub in a picturesque
village. Good food; self-
catering flat.
🏚 Q 🍴 🕯 🍺 & ♣ P

Alnwick

Market Tavern
Fenkle Street ☎ (0665) 602442
11–3, 6–11
**Vaux Lorimers Best Scotch,
Samson** ⊞
Crowded in the evenings,
unhurried at lunchtime; an ex-
Tetley pub. ⊟

Oddfellows Arms
Narrowgate ☎ (0665) 602605
11–3, 7–11
Vaux Samson ⊞
Characterful pub next to the
Castle. Fishing tackle and animal
heads in the bar. ⊟

Queens Head
Market Street
☎ (0665) 602442
11–11
**Vaux Samson; Wards
Sheffield Best Bitter** ⊞
Comfortable, popular local in
the county town. Lively in the
evenings. Q 🍴 🕯 🍺 🕯 🍺 & ♣ P

Tanners Arms
Hotspur Street
12–3 (not Mon & Tue), 7–11
Belhaven 70/-, 80/- ⊞
Excellent, seemingly ever-
improving pub with a
welcoming licensee; one of
Northumberland's finest pubs.
Occasional guest beers. 🏚

Amble

Masons Arms
Woodbine Street
☎ (0665) 710360
11–11 (12–3, 6–11 winter)
**Hoskins & Oldfield Heroes
Bitter; Ruddles Best Bitter;
Taylor Landlord** ⊞
Friendly, seaside pub with a
small bar, pool room and
lounge. Good food (book Sun
lunch). Guest beers.
🍴 🕯 🍺 🕯 & 🏕 ♣

Bamburgh

Castle Hotel
Front Street ☎ (066 84) 351
12–3, 6–11
**Vaux Lorimers Best Scotch,
Samson** ⊞
In winter, a cosy locals' pub; in
summer, a tourist's dream, with
basic family facilities, good food
and a warm welcome. 🏚 🍴 🕯

Victoria Hotel
The Grove ☎ (066 84) 431
11–11
Tetley Bitter ⊞
Imposing, main-street hotel, in
sight of the castle. Guest beers.
🏚 🍴 🕯 🕯 🍺 & 🕯

Bedlington

Northumberland Arms
Front Street East
11–3, 7–11 (11–11 Thu–Sat, &
summer)
Beer range varies ⊞
Established, real ale pub in the
town centre. Guest beers. 🍺 ♣

Belford

Salmon
High Street ☎ (0668) 213245
11–3, 6–11 (11–11 Sat)
Vaux Lorimers Best Scotch ⊞
Friendly, welcoming pub with a
lounge bar and games room.
⊟ ♣ P

Berwick-upon-Tweed

Barrels
Bridge Street
12–2.30, 7–11
**McEwan 80/-; Theakston
Best Bitter** ⊞
Welcome addition to the
Tweedside real ale scene: a
compact, street-level bar and a
cellar bar with a pool table.
Guest ales. ⇌ ♣ ☺

Free Trade
Castlegate ☎ (0289) 806498
12–3, 7–11
Vaux Lorimers Best Scotch ⊞
Magnificent, unspoilt interior,
eccentric time-keeping and a
rare unhurriedness. A gem. ⊟ ⇌

Hen & Chickens
Sandgate ☎ (0289) 306314
11–3, 6–11
McEwan 70/-, 80/- ⊞
Welcoming, basic pub with pine
cladding. Friendly staff. ♨ Q

Try also: Brown Bear (Vaux)

Blyth

Kitty Brewster
549 Cowpen Road, Bebside (off
A189) ☎ (0670) 352732
11–3 (2.30 Mon & Tue), 5 (6 Fri &
Sat)–11
**Courage Directors; John
Smith's Bitter, Magnet** ⊞
Well-run, large, stone pub on
the outskirts of town. Good
value meals. ⇄ ◖ ♣ P

Oddfellows Arms
Bridge Street
11–11 (11–3, 6–11 winter)
**Ruddles County; Stocks Old
Horizontal; Theakston Best
Bitter** ⊞
Traditional local with a small
lounge off a tiny bar. Eccentric
toilets! Guest beers. ঊ ♣

Corbridge

Wheatsheaf Hotel
St Helen's Street
11–11
**Vaux Double Maxim; Wards
Sheffield Best Bitter** ⊞
Splendidly imposing pub in the
market square. ♨ ⛺ ⊛ ◖ ◗ ঊ ⇄

Craster

Jolly Fisherman
11–3, 6–11
Wards Sheffield Best Bitter ⊞
Welcoming, split-level pub in a
tiny village, once famous for
kippers. Snacks include fresh
crab sandwiches. ♨ ⊛ ঊ ♣ P

Dipton

Dipton Mill Inn
12–3, 6–11
**Hadrian Gladiator; Webster's
Yorkshire Bitter; Yates Bitter,
Premium** ⊞
Warm, welcoming, country pub
in pleasant surroundings. Oak
beams; plenty of knick-knacks.
Guest beers. ♨ Q ⛺ ⊛ ◖

Etal

Black Bull
12–3, 6–11
Vaux Lorimers Best Scotch ⊞
Country pub with a thatched
roof in a tiny, picturesque
village. Castle and working
watermill nearby. Q ◖ ◗ ♣ P

Haltwhistle

Black Bull
Market Square
11–3, 6–11 (11–11 Fri & Sat)
Tetley Bitter ⊞

Friendly, stone-built, village
local. The unimposing exterior
conceals fine oak beams and
traditional decor. ⊛

Try also: Grey Bull (Free)

Hedley on the Hill

Feathers
OS078592 ☎ (0661) 843268
12–3 (Sat only), 6–11 (12–2.30,
7–10.30 Sun)
**Marston's Pedigree; Ruddles
Best Bitter** ⊞
Friendly pub in a lovely hill-top
village. Food at weekends only.
Guest beers. Closed weekday
lunchtimes. ♨ Q ⛺ ◖ ◗ ♣ P

Hexham

Globe
Battle Hill ☎ (0434) 603742
11–11
Theakston Best Bitter ⊞
Traditional hostelry: wood,
brass and *bonhomie*. ♨ ঊ ⇄

Heart Of All England
Market Street
11–11
Theakston XB ⊞
A once-great traditional local,
now at last striving to recapture
former glories. ⇄

Tap & Spile
Battle Hill ☎ (0434) 602039
11–11
**Camerons Bitter; Everards
Tiger; Jennings Mild** ⊞
Bustling pub with two rooms in
traditional style. Guest beers.
No food weekends.
Q ◖ ⊟ ♨ ⇄ ♣

High Horton

Three Horse Shoes
Hathery Lane
11–3, 6–11
**Tetley Bitter; Theakston Best
Bitter** ⊞
Large, comfortable pub, local
CAMRA *Pub of the Year*
1987/1988. ♨ ⊛ ◖ P

Longhorsley

Linden Pub
Linden Hall Hotel (on A697)
11–3, 6–11
**Ruddles County; Theakston
Best Bitter** ⊞
Comfortable, converted granary
in hotel grounds. ⊛ ◖ ◗ ♣ P

Morpeth

Joiners Arms
Wansbeck Street
12–3 (11–4 Wed, 11–3 Fri), 5.30–11
(11–11 Sat)
**Draught Bass; Taylor
Landlord; Theakston XB** ⊞
Recently refurbished, friendly,
two-roomed pub. Guest beers.
⊛ ◖ ◗ ⊟ ⇄

Tap & Spile
Manchester Street
11–11
**Camerons Bitter; Hadrian
Gladiator; Stocks Old
Horizontal; Taylor Landlord** ⊞
Small, traditional bar;
comfortable lounge. Guest
beers. Q ◖ ⊟ ⇄ ⏚

Netherton

Star Inn
On B6341
11–2, 7–11
Whitbread Castle Eden Ale Ⓖ
Remote, marvellous, unspoilt
pub, in beautiful countryside.
Beer is served from a hatch. The
only public transport to
Netherton is the school bus
from Thropton. ♨ Q ⊛ ⊟

Prudhoe

Halfway House
Main Street ☎ (0661) 32688
11–3, 6–11
Theakston Best Bitter ⊞
Pleasant, two-roomed pub with
modern furnishings.

Thropton

Cross Keys
11–11
Draught Bass ⊞
Lovely, two-roomed pub. Good
food. ♨ ⊛ ◖ ◗ P

Warkworth

Masons Arms
Dial Place ☎ (0665) 711398
11–3, 6–11
**Theakston Best Bitter;
Younger No. 3** ⊞
Traditional, village inn with
low-beamed ceilings, backing
onto the river and dating back
600 years. Popular, very
friendly and cosy; historic in its
own right. Q ⊛ ◖ ◗ ⊟ ঊ ⏚ ♣

Wooler

Ryecroft Hotel
Ryecroft Way ☎ (0668) 81459
11–11
**Marston's Pedigree; Tetley
Bitter; Yates Bitter** ⊞
Popular, well-run, family hotel
with a reputation for good food.
The lounge has a conservatory
extension. Guest beers.
♨ Q ⊛ ⇄ ◖ ঊ ⏚ ♣ P

Wylam

Boathouse Inn
Station Road ☎ (0661) 853431
11–3, 6–11 (11–11 Fri & Sat)
**Bateman XXXB; Taylor
Landlord; Tetley Bitter;
Theakston Best Bitter;
Whitbread Boddingtons
Bitter; Younger No. 3** ⊞
Friendly, welcoming pub. Guest
beers. ♨ ⊛ ◖ ◗ ⊟ ⇄ ♣ P

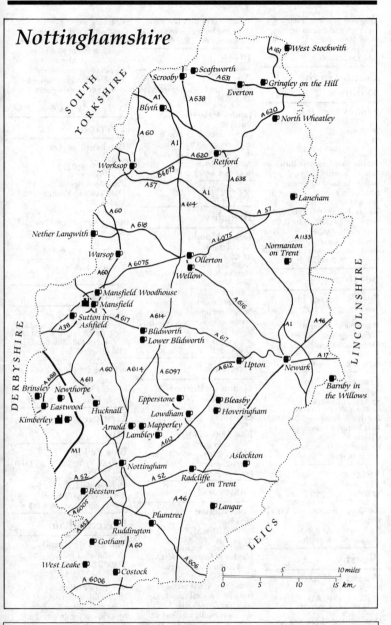

Nottinghamshire

West Stockwith · *Scaftworth* · *Scrooby* · *Gringley on the Hill* · *Everton* · *Blyth* · *North Wheatley* · *Worksop* · *Retford* · *Laneham* · *Nether Langwith* · *Normanton on Trent* · *Warsop* · *Ollerton* · *Wellow* · *Mansfield Woodhouse* · *Mansfield* · *Sutton in Ashfield* · *Blidworth* · *Lower Blidworth* · *Upton* · *Newark* · *Brinsley* · *Newthorpe* · *Eastwood* · *Hucknall* · *Epperstone* · *Bleasby* · *Hoveringham* · *Barnby in the Willows* · *Kimberley* · *Lowdham* · *Mapperley* · *Arnold* · *Lambley* · *Nottingham* · *Aslockton* · *Radcliffe on Trent* · *Beeston* · *Langar* · *Plumtree* · *Ruddington* · *Gotham* · *West Leake* · *Costock*

SOUTH YORKSHIRE · *DERBYSHIRE* · *LINCOLNSHIRE* · *LEICS*

Hardys & Hansons, *Kimberley*; **Mansfield**, *Mansfield*

Arnold

Horse & Jockey
71 Front Street (Croft Road jct)
☎ (0602) 267123
10.30–3 (3.30 Fri & Sat), 5.30–11
Home Mild, Bitter Ⓔ
Homely town-centre pub with
separate pool room. Piano in
lounge; large function room

upstairs; skittle alley outside.
Q ❀ ⊞ ♣ P

Aslockton

Cranmer Arms
Main Street ☎ (0949) 50362
11–3.30, 5.30–11 (11–11 Sat)
Home Mild, Bitter Ⓗ
Friendly locals' pub with
children's play area in large

garden. Named after Thomas
Cranmer who was a native of
the village. Long alley skittles.
No food Mon/Tue.
🏠 Q ❀ ⊞ ⇆ ♣ P

Old Greyhound
Main Street ☎ (0949) 50957
11–3, 6–11 (11–11 Sat)
**Home Bitter; Theakston
XB** Ⓗ

235

Convivial pub with a single bar serving various small drinking areas. Large indoor skittle alley doubles as a family room. Pool table. ⌖ ⌗ ⌲ ♣ P

Barnby in the Willows

Willow Tree Inn

Front Street (off A17 3 miles E of Newark)
☎ (0636) 626613
11.30–3, 6.30 (10.45–3 Sat), 6.30 (7 winter)–11
Wards Sheffield Best Bitter Ⓗ
Late 17th- early 18th-century, heavily-beamed village inn, situated in a conservation area. James Hole, a former local brewer, bought this as his first pub in 1874. The centre of village activities. Friendly landlord – a warm welcome is always assured. Regular guest beers. Q ⌖ ⌗ ⌯ ⌲ (♣ P

Beeston

Boat & Horses Inn

Trent Road ☎ (0602) 258589
11–3 (4 Sat), 7–11
Home Mild, Bitter Ⓔ
Welcoming, two-roomed local. Close to canal and nature reserve. Eve meals to order only. ⌗ ⌖ (⌲ ⌵ ♣ P

Commercial Inn

19 Wollaton Road
☎ (0602) 254480
11–2.30, 7–11 (11–11 Sat)
Hardys & Hansons Best Mild, Best Bitter, Kimberley Classic Ⓔ
Comfortable town-centre local.
⌗ (⌲ ⌵ ♣ P

Victoria

85 Dovecote Lane
☎ (0602) 254049
11–3.30, 7–11 (11–11 Fri & Sat)
Ind Coope Burton Ale; Tetley Bitter Ⓗ
Back-street local opposite maltings. ⌗ (⌲ ⌵ ♣ P

Bleasby

Wagon & Horses

Gypsy Lane (opp. church)
☎ (0636) 830283
12–2 (2.30 Sat), 6.30–11 (12–2.30, 7–10.30 Sun)
Home Bitter; Theakston XB Ⓗ
Pretty, whitewashed and pantiled country inn enjoying a fine view of the village church. The interior has nice wood panelling and a pleasant rural charm. ⌗ Q ⌗ ⌗ ⌯ ⌲ ♣ P

Blidworth

Bird in Hand

Main Street ☎ (0623) 792356
11–4, 5.30–11 (11–11 Fri & Sat)
Mansfield Riding Bitter, Old Baily Ⓗ

Village local with a fine view. An island bar serves one multi-level room. ⌗ Q ⌗ (♣ P

Blyth

Angel

Bawtry Road (⅓ mile from A1)
☎ (0909) 591213
11–3, 6–11
Hardys & Hansons Best Bitter Ⓔ
An inn much older than it appears: dating from coaching days, it has huge fires and a busy food trade.
⌗ Q ⌗ ⌗ ⌯ ⌲ ♣ P

Try also: White Swan (Whitbread)

Brinsley

Robin Hood

17 Hall Lane
☎ (0773) 713604
12–3, 6.30 (7 winter)–11
Hardys & Hansons Best Mild, Best Bitter Ⓔ
Characterful local in DH Lawrence country, rumoured to be haunted upstairs by former licensee. Collection of colliery plates. Disco Fri; guest singers Sat. Two skittle alleys.
Q ⌗ ⌲ ♣ P

Costock

Generous Briton

14 Main Street (50 yds off A60 towards East Leake)
☎ (0509) 852347
11–2.30, 6.30–11
John Smith's Bitter Ⓗ
Two-roomed village local with a friendly atmosphere. Home-cooked lunches incl. traditional fare Sun. ⌗ (⌲ ♣ P

Eastwood

Lord Raglan

Newthorpe Common
(off B6010/A610)
☎ (0773) 712683
11.30–3, 5.30 (6.30 Sat)–11
Hardys & Hansons Best Mild, Best Bitter Ⓔ, **Kimberley Classic** Ⓗ
Welcoming estate pub, a focal point for the local community with friendly, talkative hosts. Wed quiz night; weekend sing-along with traditional musicians, plus guest artists, in the warm, inviting, olde-worlde lounge. Good quality food. Children's play garden. ⌗ ⌗ (⌲ ♣ P

Epperstone

Cross Keys

Main Street (off A6097)
☎ (0602) 663033
11–2.30 (12–2.30 Sun), 6–11
Hardys & Hansons Best Mild, Best Bitter Ⓔ, **Kimberley Classic** Ⓗ

Charming, white-painted village local with a well-deserved reputation for its bar meals (no food Sun eve or Mon). The cosy, individual rooms have so far mercifully escaped the brewery's tendency towards characterless, open-plan renovations.
⌗ Q ⌖ ⌗ (⌯ ⌲ ⌵ ♣ P

Everton

Blacksmiths Arms

Chapel Lane
☎ (0777) 817281
12–3, 7 (6 Fri & Sat)–11
Theakston Best Bitter, XB, Old Peculier; Younger Scotch Ⓗ
Converted blacksmith's shop still retaining original beams. Several real fires. One room used as a *crêperie*.
⌗ Q ⌖ ⌗ (⌯ ⌲ ♣ P

Try also: Sun Inn (John Smith's)

Gotham

Sun Inn

The Square ☎ (0602) 830484
11.30–2.30 6–11 (12–2, 7–10.30 Sun)
Everards Mild, Beacon, Tiger, Old Original Ⓗ
Comfortable and friendly local in a small village. Food served in the lounge, with the bar reserved for conversation and games. Guest beers. ⌗ (⌲ P

Gringley on the Hill

Blue Bell Inn

High Street ☎ (0777) 817406
11–3 (not Mon–Thu in winter or Mon/Tue in summer), 6.30–11
Draught Bass; Stones Best Bitter; Tetley Bitter Ⓗ
Lively village local. ⌗ ⌗ (⌵

Hoveringham

Marquis of Granby

Main Street (1 mile off A612)
☎ (0602) 663080
12–2.30, 6.30–11 (12–2.30, 7–10.30 Sun)
Marston's Pedigree Ⓗ
Traditional, family-run free house in an unspoilt village, once famous for its gravel pits. A short walk from the River Trent, the pub is popular with both locals and tourists. Good reputation for bar meals (no food Sun). Guest beers.
⌗ Q ⌗ (⌲ ♣ P

Reindeer

Main Street ☎ (0602) 663629
11.30–3, 5.30–11
Marston's Burton Best Bitter, Pedigree Ⓗ
Old and genuine country pub: two separate rooms, beautifully furnished, with beamed ceilings.

Food is a highlight – the splendid intimate restaurant is a feature (no food Sun eve or Mon). Guest ales. Drinkers-only bar. ♨ Q ⊛ ◐ ▶ ⊕ ♣ P

Hucknall

Red Lion
High Street
10.30–2.30, 6–11
Home Mild, Bitter Ⓔ
Traditional alehouse with through passage and four inter-connecting rooms. Can be crowded at weekends. ⊕ ♣ P

Kimberley

Cricketers Rest
Chapel Street (off Main Street, B6010)
☎ (0602) 380894
11–3.30 (4 Sat), 6.30–11
Hardys & Hansons Best Mild, Best Bitter, Kimberley Classic Ⓗ
Comfortable, well-appointed, open-plan pub with discreet dartboard area. Reputedly haunted by former landlady. Mon night disco; Thu night quiz. ⊛ ◐ ♣

Lord Clyde
Main Street ☎ (0602) 384907
10.30–11
Hardys & Hansons Best Mild, Best Bitter, Kimberley Classic Ⓗ
A video jukebox always attracts a congregation of young people in this open-plan pub. Especially hectic at weekends. Thu eve disco. ⊛ ◐ ♣

Nelson & Railway
Station Road (off B6010)
☎ (0602) 382177
10.30–3, 5–11 (10.30–11 Fri, Sat & bank hols)
Hardys & Hansons Best Mild Ⓔ, **Kimberley Classic** Ⓗ & Ⓔ
Impressive pub of character in a pleasant location next to the brewery. Wood-panelled bar and an attractively restored, beamed lounge with adjoining dining area. Excellent quality food (till 9pm; no meals Sun eve). Low cost B & B; cheap beer 5–7, Mon–Fri. Garden with swings. ⊛ ◐ ▶ ⊕ ♣ P

Queens Head
Main Street (B6010)
☎ (0602) 382117
10.30–4, 6–11
Hardys & Hansons Best Mild, Best Bitter Ⓔ, **Kimberley Classic** Ⓗ
Prominent, street-corner local of proven quality. Busy with young people at weekends; small, quieter snug in top corner upstairs. Lounge bar features live music from local artists.
⊛ ◐ ⊕ ♣

Lambley

Nags Head
Main Street ☎ (0602) 312546
11–3, 5.30–11
Home Mild, Bitter; Theakston XB Ⓗ
Spacious village inn, understandably popular with families (safe play area and separate games room). The raised patio fronting the road is very pleasant in fine weather.
⛄ ⊛ ◐ ▶ ⊕ ♣ P

Robin Hood
Main Street ☎ (0602) 312531
11–3 (3.30 Sat), 6–11
Home Bitter Ⓔ
A village local over 100 years old. Formerly a Hutchinson & Sons pub. Well-known for beer and skittles parties. The separate private function room accommodates 40. Interesting collection of water jugs over the bar. ⊛ ⊕ ♣ P

Laneham

Butchers Arms
Main Street ☎ (077 785) 255
12–3, 7–11
Marston's Pedigree Ⓗ
Popular village pub with small lounges and a new refurbished bar area, retaining the old pub atmosphere. For those needing to work up a thirst, the pub also incorporates a fitness centre. Guest beers.
♨ Q ⊛ ◐ ⊕ ⅄ ♣ P

Langar

Unicorns Head
Main Street (near Bingham-Harby/Cropwell Bishop Road jct) ☎ (0949) 60460
11–3, 6–11
Home Mild, Bitter Ⓔ
Welcoming village local well-known for its games and entertainment. Sat eve sing-alongs; guest artists Sun eve; regular darts, pool and skittles events. ♨ ⊛ ◐ ⊕ ♣ P

Lowdham

Old Ship
Main Street ☎ (0602) 663049
11.30–2.30, 5.30–11
Courage Best Bitter, Directors; John Smith's Bitter Ⓗ
Youngsters' bar with satellite TV, pool table and CD player. The comfortable lounge acts as fine contrast and is popular with all ages. Home-cooked food a speciality (no meals Sun eve).
Q ⛄ ⊛ ◐ ▶ ⊕ ♣ P

Worlds End
Plough Lane (just off A6097)
☎ (0602) 663857
11.30–3, 5.30–11

Marston's Burton Best Bitter, Pedigree Ⓗ
Popular village pub formerly known as the 'Plough', smart but unpretentious; a welcome find out-of-town. Easily located – look for flagpole in the garden. ♨ ⊛ ⊕ ⅄ ⇌ ♣ P

Lower Blidworth

Fox & Hounds
Calverton Road
OS590548 ☎ (0623) 792383
11–3.30, 6–11.30 (11–11.30 Sat in summer)
Hardys & Hansons Best Mild, Best Bitter Ⓗ & Ⓔ
Multi-roomed country inn. Rallying photos and tropical fish adorn lounge walls. No meals Wed eve. ♨ Q ⛄ ⊛ ◐ ▶ ⊕ ♣ P

Mansfield

Kings Arms
Ratcliffe Gate (Newark road, just out of centre)
☎ (0623) 24077
11–11
Camerons Bitter, Strongarm Ⓗ
Small, one-roomed, street-corner local. Separate pool area; quiz nights. Free beer draw Fri eve.
◐ ♣

William IV
Stockwell Gate (opp. Victoria Hospital) ☎ (0623) 21283
11–11
Mansfield Riding Mild, Riding Bitter, Old Baily Ⓗ
Comfortable and well-furnished pub. Large tap room with two pool tables. Spacious family room and small garden with swing and slide. A popular pub and deservedly so; just off town centre. ⛄ ⊛ ◐ ⊕ ♣ P

Yew Tree Inn
Woodhouse Road (near cinema and theatre) ☎ (0623) 23729
11–11
Camerons Bitter; Everards Old Original; Tolly Cobbold Bitter Ⓗ
Popular pub just off town centre. One room with separate pool area. Regular quiz nights; Karaoke Sat eve. Lively landlady. Eve meals to order only. ⊛ ◐ ♣ P

Mansfield Woodhouse

Portland Arms
2 High Street
☎ (0623) 422903
11.30–3, 7–11 (11–11 Sat)
Courage Directors; John Smith's Bitter, Magnet Ⓗ
Popular pub: a meeting place for local hockey teams. Landlord plays organ for sing-along Sun night. Eve meals till 9pm. Large function room. ◐ ▶ ⊕ ♣ P

Nottinghamshire

Star Inn

Warsop Road
☎ (0623) 24145
11–3, 7–11 (may vary in summer)
**Wards Thorne Best Bitter,
Sheffield Best Bitter, Kirby** ⊞
One of the oldest buildings in
the area; a low-beamed, three-
roomed pub, tastefully
decorated. Excellent play
facilities for children in the
garden. Good food till 9pm.
Colourful licensee! ❀ ◐ ▶ P

Mapperley

Travellers Rest

Mapperley Plains
☎ (0602) 264412
11–11
**Home Bitter; Theakston XB;
Younger IPA** ⊞
Popular roadhouse with award-
winning food (incl. vegetarian)
and well-geared to the needs of
families. The separate 'Pop Inn'
family room is open every eve
and lunchtime when there is no
school. Probably the highest
pub in the county. Other S&N
beers sometimes replace the IPA
and XB. No-smoking area at
lunchtime only. ❀ ⇞ ❀ ◐ ♣ P ⍻

Nether Langwith

Jug & Glass

Queens Walk (off A632)
☎ (0623) 742283
11.30–3.30, 7–11
**Hardys & Hansons Best Mild,
Best Bitter** ⒠**, Kimberley
Classic** ⊞
Stone-built pub set on village
green, with River Poulter
meandering by. Very popular in
summer. ❀ ❀ ⊟ ⅙ ♣ P

Newark

Castle & Falcon

London Road
☎ (0636) 703513
11–3, 7–11
**Courage Directors; John
Smith's Bitter, Magnet** ⊞
Three-roomed, 19th-century
local. Lounge is decked out in
Royal Navy memorabilia.
Popular for pub games, incl.
long alley skittles, pool, darts
and dominoes. No food Sun.
Public car park opposite.
Q ❀ ◐ ⊟ ⇌ (Castle) ♣

Crown & Mitre

53 Castlegate (50 yds from
castle)
☎ (0636) 703131
11–3, 6–11
**Courage Directors; John
Smith's Bitter; Wards
Sheffield Best Bitter** ⊞
Smartly-furnished, oblong bar
on a split level; separate room
upstairs for pool, darts,
dominoes, etc.
❀ ⅞ ◐ ⊟ ⇌ (Castle) ♣ P

Mail Coach

Beaumond Cross, 13 London
Road
☎ (0636) 605164
11–2.30 (3 Wed, Fri & Sat), 5.30–11
**Ansells Mild; Hoskins &
Oldfield Tom Kelly's Stout;
Ind Coope Benskins Best
Bitter, Burton Ale; Tetley
Bitter** ⊞
Very pleasant town pub; a
mainly Georgian building, but
some parts are older. Cellar
reputedly contains part of old
town hall. Very varied clientele
keeps pub quite busy. Charity
'frog' racing in the summer.
Guest ales. Board games
available.
❀ ❀ ⋈ ◐ ⇌ (Castle) ♣ P

Old Malt Shovel

25 Northgate
☎ (0636) 702036
11.30–3, 7 (5 Fri)–11
**Taylor Landlord; Wards
Sheffield Best Bitter** ⊞
Well-decorated single bar,
rightly popular. Good food.
Regular guest beers: usually
Adnams Broadside plus one
other. ❀ ❀ ◐ ⇌ (Castle &
Northgate)

Newthorpe

Ram Inn

Beauvale (old B6010, off B600)
☎ (0773) 713312
11–4, 6–11 (11–11 Sat)
**Hardys & Hansons Best Mild,
Best Bitter** ⒠**, Kimberley
Classic** ⊞
Friendly roadside pub, popular
with locals. Good selection of
food at reasonable prices.
❀ ◐ ▶ ⊟ ♣ P

Normanton on Trent

Square & Compass

Eastgate (3 miles E of A1)
☎ (0636) 821439
12–3, 6–11
Adnams Extra ⊞
Popular, low-beamed pub on
the edge of the village. Cosy feel;
small restaurant; regular guest
beers.
❀ Q ❀ ⋈ ◐ ▶ ⅄ ♣ P

North Wheatley

Sun Inn

Low Street (off A620)
☎ (0427) 880210
11.30–3, 6.30–11 (11–11 Sat)
Bass Special ⊞
Popular village pub with
organised events, including live
rock music on Thu nights.
Separate pool room. Guest
beers.
❀ ❀ ◐ ▶ ⊟ ⅄ ♣ P

Nottingham

Boat Inn

Priory Street, Old Lenton
☎ (0602) 786482
11–2.30 (3 Sat), 6 (6.30 Sat)–11
(12–2.30, 7–10.30 Sun)
Home Mild, Bitter ⒠
One-roomed local with a
friendly atmosphere. Attractive
wood panelling with inlaid
mirrors. ◐ ♣

Castle

202 Lower Parliament Street
(next to ice stadium)
☎ (0602) 504601
11.30–2.30, 6–11 (12–2.30, 7–10.30
Sun)
**Ansells Bitter; Ind Coope
ABC Best Bitter, Burton Ale;
Tetley Bitter** ⊞
One large room with alcoves
and split-level areas, and a
summerhouse, built half-in and
half-out of the pub. Unusual
floral light fittings. Lots of pine
and open brickwork. No food
Sun. ❀ ◐ ♣ ♣

Coopers Arms

3 Porchester Road,
Thorneywood (20 yds from
Carlton Rd jct)
☎ (0602) 502433
11–2.30 (3.30 Mon & Fri; 11.30–4.30
Sat), 6 (5.30 Fri; 6.30 Sat)–11
Home Mild, Bitter ⒠
A friendly local dating from the
1850s with an interior that has
not been drastically changed.
Separate pool bar. Skittle alley.
⊟ ♣ P

Crown Inn

Crocus Street, The Meadows
☎ (0602) 866152
11–11 (11–3, 5.30–11 Tue–Thu)
Home Mild, Bitter ⒠
A typical, traditional, street-
corner locals' pub, built nearly
200 years ago. Comfortable
lounge; pool table in the bar.
Friendly atmosphere. Discos
most Fri and weekend eves.
❀ ⊟ ♣ ♣

Fox

17 Dale Street, Sneinton (next
to Greens Windmill)
☎ (0602) 504736
11–3, 6–11
**Bateman XXXB; Ind Coope
ABC Best Bitter, Burton
Ale; Taylor Landlord; Tetley
Bitter** ⊞
Deservedly-popular pub on the
fringe of Nottingham. A
separate upstairs pool room
complements the two
downstairs rooms. Guest beers.
❀ ⊟ ♣

Lincolnshire Poacher

161–163 Mansfield Road (400
yds from Victoria Centre)
☎ (0602) 411584
11–3, 5 (6 Sat)–11
**Bateman Mild, XB, XXXB;
Marston's Pedigree** ⊞

A must for serious beer drinkers, with over 400 guest ales last year. Twinned with an Amsterdam bar. Notorious for bar staff banter — you have been warned! Arrive early; ask to see pub mascot! Eve meals till 8pm, no food Sun. Q ⚙ ◑ ◖ ⊟ ♣

Magpies

Meadow Lane (500 yds from Notts County FC)
☎ (0602) 863851
11–3, 5 (7 Sat)–11 (11–11 Fri)
Home Mild, Bitter Ⓔ
Friendly town pub on eastern edge of city. Handy for Trent Bridge cricket and Nottingham Racecourse, as well as football. A haunt of sports enthusiasts, with pool particularly popular. No meals Sat/Sun eve or Sun lunch. ⚙ ◑ ◖ ⊟ ♣ P

March Hare

248 Carlton Road, Sneinton (A612) ☎ (0602) 504328
10.30–2.30, 6–11
Courage Directors; John Smith's Bitter Ⓗ
Typical 'just post-war' brick exterior; a friendly local within. Its reputation attracts many customers from outside the area. The landlord is the longest serving in the city. ◖ ⊟ ♣ P

New Market Inn

38 Lower Parliament Street
☎ (0602) 411532
11–4, 5.30 (7 Sat)–11 (12–2.30, 7–10.30 Sun)
Home Mild, Bitter; Theakston XB, Old Peculier; Younger Scotch, IPA Ⓗ
Excellent ale house, full of character. Bar is adorned with railway memorabilia; three comfortable lounge areas. Varied home-cooked food (eve meals to order only). Guest beers. Q ❧ ◖ ⊟ ♣ P

Norfolk Hotel

66 London Road (400 yds from Trent Bridge)
☎ (0602) 863003
12–11 (may close Sat afternoon in football season; 12–2.30, 7–10.30 Sun)
Home Mild, Bitter Ⓔ
A fine, redbrick, Victorian local. The traditional bar has darts and pool, but the table is removed for skittles matches. The small, quiet and comfortable lounge has the original settles with bell pushes (no longer working). Handy for football grounds. Eve meals till 8pm; no food Sun. Q ◑ ◖ ⊟ ♣ P

Plainsman

149 Woodthorpe Drive, Mapperley (Woodborough Road jct, 3 miles from centre)
☎ (0602) 622020
10.30–2.30, 5.30–11 (12–2.30, 7–10.30 Sun)
Hardys & Hansons Best Mild Ⓔ**, Best Bitter,**

Kimberley Classic Ⓗ
Quiet suburban pub with a lounge several steps higher than the ground-floor bar. ⊟ ♣ P

Portland Arms

Portland Road (off A610 Alfreton road near Canning Circus) ☎ (0602) 782429
11.30–3, 7–11
Hardys & Hansons Best Bitter, Kimberley Classic Ⓗ
Friendly local on edge of city centre. Single, open-plan bar with distinct areas. Cheap cobs. In improved Victorian area. ⚙ ♣

Sir Charles Napier

North Sherwood Street (N of centre near polytechnic)
☎ (0602) 474223
12–2.30 (3 Thu), 5–11 (12–11 Wed, Fri & Sat)
Marston's Pedigree; Whitbread Boddingtons Bitter, Castle Eden Ale, Flowers Original Ⓗ
A comfortable, cosy pub, handy for the city centre. One divided room with games area at the rear. Guest beers. Mainly vegetarian cuisine. ◖ ◑

Trip to Jerusalem ♣

1 Brewhouse Yard, Castle Road (foot of Castle Rock)
☎ (0602) 473171
11–3 (4 Sat), 5.30 (6 Sat)–11 (11–11 Sat in summer)
Hardys & Hansons Best Mild, Best Bitter, Kimberley Classic; Marston's Pedigree Ⓗ
Claiming to be the oldest inn in England (1189), the 'Trip' is a must for any visitor to Nottingham and has become even more attractive since being bought by Hardys & Hansons and offering their full range of ales in excellent condition.
🏯 Q ⚙ ◖ ❧ ♣

Vine

25 Handel Street, Sneinton
☎ (0602) 504233
11–3 (2.30 Tue–Thu), 6.30–11
Home Mild, Bitter; Theakston XB Ⓗ
Lively 120-year old, two-roomed pub near open market. A sensitively-renovated local with a rare corner door. The pick of the bunch in a well-pubbed area of the city. ⊟ ♣

Ollerton

White Hart

Station Road
☎ (0623) 822410
11.30–4, 7–11
Samuel Smith OBB Ⓗ
Tucked-away in the centre of the old village, this pub is popular with both locals and tourists from nearby Sherwood Forest. Pleasant lounge and traditional bar. ❧ ⚙ ◑ ◖ ⊟ ♣ P

Plumtree

Griffin Inn

1 Main Road
☎ (0602) 335743
11–2.30 (12–2 Sun), 5.30–11
Hardys & Hansons Best Mild, Best Bitter Ⓔ**, Kimberley Classic** Ⓗ
Large Victorian village local, built in 1843. The modernised interior has a long, central bar. Gas log fire and TV in lounge; separate bar. Pleasant and upmarket. Excellent lunch menu.
Q ⚙ ◖ ⊟ ♣ P

Radcliffe on Trent

Black Lion

Main Road (¼ mile off A52)
☎ (0602) 332138
11–2.30, 6–11
Home Mild, Bitter Ⓔ
Large mock-Tudor pub at the centre of the village, with a friendly bar and lounge. Charity steam fair held first Sat in October. No meals weekends.
⚙ ◖ ❧ ♣ P

Retford

Market Hotel

West Carr Road, Ordsall (off A620, W of railway line)
☎ (0777) 703278
11–3.30, 6–11 (11–11 Sat)
Adnams Broadside; Everards Tiger; Marston's Pedigree; Taylor Landlord; Tetley Bitter; Theakston Best Bitter Ⓗ
Recently-extended to offer a large function room. A total of 14 real ales on offer, incl. regular guest beers.
Q ⚙ ◑ ◖ ❧ P

Turks Head

Grove Street
☎ (0777) 702742
11–3, 7–11
Wards Sheffield Best Bitter Ⓗ
Friendly town pub close to the market place. Attractive façade and panelled interior. Popular with pub games enthusiasts. Good lunches. 🏯 ⋈ ◖ ⊟ ♣ P

Try also: **Black Boy**, Moorgate (Wards)

Ruddington

Red Lion

1 Easthorpe Street (crossroads in centre of village)
OS573331 ☎ (0602) 844654
11–2.30 (3.30 Sat), 5.30–11 (12–2.30, 7–10.30 Sun)
Home Mild, Bitter; Theakston XB; Wells Bombardier Ⓗ
An excellent village locals' pub with a white-painted exterior, and a cosy, mock-beamed lounge. The wide passage has

tables and chairs (where children are allowed); function room upstairs. Two guest beers each week. Q ✿ ⊞ ♣ P

Scaftworth

King William
Off A631 ☎ (0302) 710292
12–2.30 (not Mon–Wed), 7–11
**Everards Old Original;
Marston's Pedigree; Tolly
Cobbold Original; Whitbread
Castle Eden Ale** ⊞
An unspoilt country pub with many small rooms for hiding away in. Good home-cooked food (vegetarian option; no chips!). No eve meals Mon. Garden down to river features play area and pets.
⚶ Q ⅏ ✿ ⓓ ▶ P ⅍

Scrooby

Pilgrim Fathers
Great North Road (A638)
☎ (0302) 710446
11–3, 7–11
John Smith's Bitter ⊞
A popular, 18th-century coaching inn on the old A1. Pleasant and friendly cottage-style interior; good quality food to appeal to most tastes (vegetarian included). ✿ ⓓ ▶ Å P

Sutton in Ashfield

Market Inn
Market Place
☎ (0623) 552961
11–3, 7–11
**Home Mild, Bitter;
Theakston XB, Old
Peculier** ⊞
Old Victorian pub, superbly renovated into one of a growing number of Home's 'ale houses'. Traditionally-furnished; exposed brick and stonework; wooden floors and furnishings – a mecca for real ale in a poor area for good beer. Two guest beers each week. Eve meals on request only. Limited parking.
ⓓ ♣

Railway Inn
High Pavement
☎ (0623) 555476
11.30–3, 7–11 (may extend Fri & Sat in summer)
John Smith's Bitter ⊞
Pleasant local with small, unusually-shaped interior. Good food at all times. ✿ ⓓ ▶ ♣

Upton

Cross Keys
Main Street ☎ (0636) 813269
11.30–2.30, 6–11
**Bateman XXXB; Marston's
Pedigree; Whitbread
Boddingtons Bitter, Castle
Eden Ale** ⊞
Friendly old pub in conservation area. Upstairs restaurant is open Thu–Sat eves and Sun lunch. Meals in the bar at all times. Live music Sun eves. Guest beers. ⚶ ✿ ⓓ ▶ ♣ P

Warsop

Hare & Hounds
Church Street
☎ (0623) 842440
11–3, 6–11 (11–11 Fri & Sat)
**Hardys & Hansons Best Mild,
Best Bitter, Kimberley
Classic** ⊞
Traditional and lively, mock-Tudor pub in the centre of town. Busy tap room.
⚶ Q ⅏ ✿ ▶ ♣ ♣ P

Try also: Gate, Mansfield Road (Courage)

Wellow

Red Lion
The Green ☎ (0623) 861000
11 (11.30 Fri & Sat)–2.30, 5.30 (6.30 Sat)–11
**Marston's Pedigree; Ruddles
Best Bitter, County;
Webster's Choice; Whitbread
Castle Eden Ale** ⊞
Pub opposite the maypole, with several cosy rooms. Good food lunch and eves. Guest beers.
Q ✿ ⓓ ▶ P

Try also: Durham Ox (John Smith's)

West Leake

Star
Melton Lane (3 miles E of M1 jct 24)
OS523261 ☎ (0509) 852233
12–2.30, 6–11 (12–2, 7–10.30 Sun)
Draught Bass ⊞
A gem of an olde-worlde pub, well worth the small trouble a stranger might have in finding it. Good value and excellent quality weekday lunchtime cold table (no meals Sat/Sun). Pub known locally as the 'Pit House'. Guest beers.
⚶ Q ✿ ⓓ ♣ P

West Stockwith

Waterfront Inn
Marina (jct of River Trent and Chesterfield Canal)
☎ (0427) 891223
12–3, 6–11
**Ruddles Best Bitter;
Theakston XB; Webster's
Yorkshire Bitter** ⊞
Refurbished pub with interesting historical connections, overlooking marina on River Trent. Popular with the boating fraternity. Buffet-style food.
Q ⅏ ✿ ⓓ ▶ ⊞ Å ♣ P

Worksop

Newcastle Arms
Carlton Road (A60, 50 yds from station)
☎ (0909) 485384
11–3, 5.30–11
**Marston's Burton Best Bitter,
Pedigree; Ruddles County;
Webster's Yorkshire Bitter** ⊞
Popular free house catering for all ages; comfortable and friendly atmosphere. Busy at weekends. Regular, varied guest beers. ⅏ ✿ ⓓ ▶ Å ⇌ ♣

Try also: Lion, Bridge Street (Stocks)

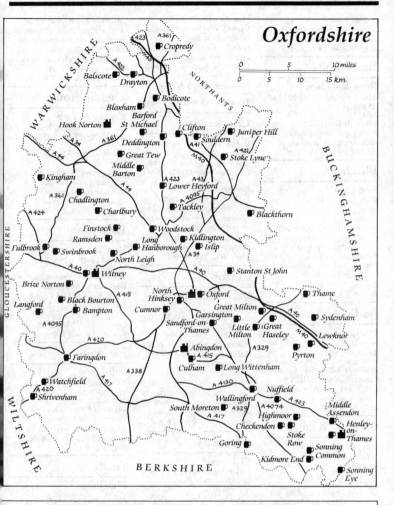

Oxfordshire

Brakspear, Henley-on-Thames; **Glenny**, Witney; **Hook Norton**, Hook Norton; **Morland**, Abingdon; **Morrells**, Oxford

---

Balscote

Butchers Arms
Shutford Road (off A422, 2 miles W of Banbury)
☎ (0295) 73750
11–3, 7–11
Hook Norton Best Bitter Ⓗ
Classic, one-roomed village pub. No food but conversation. Occasionally sells Hook Norton Mild from a polypin for two locals! 🏠 Q 🅂 ♣ P

Bampton

Romany
Bridge Street
☎ (0993) 850237
11–3 (4 Sat), 6–11

Archers Best Bitter; Hook Norton Best Bitter Ⓗ
Pleasant and friendly, small town inn. Weekly guest beers; extensive menu, incl. vegetarian and children's choices.
🏠 Q 🅂 🅂 ⇆ ◖ ▶ P

Barford St Michael

George Inn
Lower Street (off B4031)
☎ (0869) 38226
12–2.30, 6–11 (12–3, 7–10.30 Sat)
Adnams Bitter; Hall & Woodhouse Tanglefoot (summer); **Wadworth 6X, Old Timer** (winter) Ⓗ
300 year-old stone and thatch; beamed ceilings and open fires. Set in Swere Valley close to

trout fishing. Home-cooked food (not served Sun/Mon eves); big beer garden. Live blues bands Mon eve; morris dancing festival in summer. A multi-purpose pub!
🏠 Q 🅂 🅂 ◖ ▶ ⇆ 🅐 ♣ P

Black Bourton

Horse & Groom
Burford Road
☎ (0993) 842199
12–3 (not Mon), 7–11
Morland Bitter; Wadworth 6X Ⓗ
Large village pub with extensive grounds available for caravanning and camping. The large family room leads into the garden with swings. Home-

Oxfordshire

cooked food includes vegetarian option; separate restaurant. Regular guest beers.
🏠 Q ⌂ ⚲ 🛏 ◖ ◗ ＆ ♿ ♣ P

Blackthorn

Rose & Crown
300 yds from A41/B4011 jct
☎ (0869) 252534
12–2.30, 7–11
Morrells Bitter Ⓗ
Basic Victorian pub with a friendly parlour atmosphere. Interesting jukebox. 🏠 ⌂ P

Bloxham

Red Lion
High Street (A361)
☎ (0295) 720352
11–2.30, 7–11
Adnams Bitter; Wadworth 6X Ⓗ
Pleasant, friendly, two-bar village pub with a large garden. Food available seven days (roast Sun lunch Oct–April). Ample parking. Guest beers.
🏠 Q ⚲ ◖ ◗ ⚲ ＆ ♿ P

Bodicote

Plough
High Street (off A41)
☎ (0295) 262327
11–2.30, 5–11 (12–2.30, 7–10.30 Sun)
Bodicote Bitter, Old English Porter, No. 9, Triple X Ⓗ
Lively and friendly brew pub. Good food all week.
🏠 Q ⚲ ◖ ◗ ⚲ ♣ P

Brize Norton

Carpenters Arms
Station Road
☎ (0993) 842568
11–2.30, 6–11
Morland Bitter Ⓗ
Good, old-fashioned, basic but vibrant village local. No food but lots of conversation. Likely to close in a year, so hurry!
🏠 Q ⚲ ♣ P

Chadlington

Tite Inn
Mill End (close to A361)
☎ (060 876) 475
12–2.30, 6.30 (7 winter)–11 (closed Mon, except bank hols)
Adnams Bitter; Glenny Dr Thirsty's Draught; Wadworth 6X Ⓗ
16th-century free house and restaurant on the edge of the village, overlooking rolling countryside. Delightful gardens. No jukebox, slot machines or games. Children welcome. Guest beers. 🏠 Q ⚲ ◖ ◗ ♿ P

Charlbury

Rose & Crown
Market Street
☎ (0608) 810103

11.30–3, 6–11 (11.30–11 Sat)
Glenny Wychwood; Hook Norton Best Bitter Ⓗ
Friendly, town-centre local with a small beer garden. Good rotation of guest beers. Home-cooked bar meals (incl. vegetarian). ⚲ ◖ ◗ ＆ ♣

Try also: White Hart (Free)

Checkendon

Black Horse
Between Stoke Row and Checkendon, up narrow track
OS667841 ☎ (0491) 680418
11–2.30, 6.30–11
Brakspear Bitter Ⓖ
No food; no music; no indoor loos; not even a proper address! An unspoilt gem of a basic pub, off the beaten track. The landlady has run it for 60 years. Difficult to find but worth the effort. 🏠 Q ⚲ ⚲ ♿ ♣ P

Clifton

Duke of Cumberland's Head
On B4031 ☎ (0869) 38534
12–2.30, 6–11
Donnington BB; Hook Norton Best Bitter; Jennings Bitter; Ruddles Best Bitter; Wadworth 6X Ⓗ
Thatched, 17th-century Hornton-stone building with beams, an inglenook and an intimate restaurant. Vibrant atmosphere. No food Sun eves in winter. 🏠 Q ⚲ 🛏 ◖ ◗ ＆ P

Cropredy

Red Lion
8 Red Lion Street (off A423)
☎ (0295) 750224
11 (11.30 winter)–3, 5 (6 winter)–11
Arkell's 3B; Tetley Bitter; Wadworth 6X Ⓗ
Pleasant village local overlooking the churchyard and popular with canal folk. Dates back to the 15th century and has Civil War connections. Home-cooked food always available. 🏠 ⌂ ◖ ◗ ♣ P

Culham

Lion
44 High Street
☎ (0235) 520327
11–3, 6–11
Morrells Bitter, Varsity Ⓗ
Village local near Thames lock; popular with fishermen and boaters. 🏠 ⚲ ♣ P

Cumnor

Bear & Ragged Staff
Appleton Road (off A420, left after village)
☎ (0865) 862329
11–2.30 (3 Sat), 5.30 (6 Sat)–11

Morrells Bitter, Varsity Ⓗ
16th-century inn. Previously a farmhouse, with some original parts intact. One main bar with open fires at both ends. Stone floors; neat comfy settees. Good food. 🏠 Q ⚲ ◖ ◗ P ⚲

Deddington

Crown & Tuns
New Street/Oxford Road (A423) ☎ (0869) 38343
11–4, 6–11
Hook Norton Mild, Best Bitter Ⓗ
Friendly coaching inn. A haven of peace from jukeboxes and slot machines. Knock if apparently closed when it should be open. 🏠 Q ＆ ♣

Drayton

Roebuck
On A422 ☎ (0295) 730542
11–2.30, 6–11
Adnams Extra; Hook Norton Best Bitter; Marston's Pedigree; Ruddles County Ⓗ
Early 17th-century, picturesque village inn with a split-level bar. No eve meals Mon or winter Sun. 🏠 Q ⚲ ◖ ◗ ♣ P

Faringdon

Folly
54 London Street
☎ (0367) 240620
11–2.30, 5.30–11
Morrells Bitter, Varsity Ⓗ
Charming little town pub with no frills. Beer is served in lovingly polished glasses.
🏠 Q ⚲ ◖ ♣

Finstock

Plough Inn
The Bottom (off B4022, Witney–Charlbury road)
OS362162 ☎ (0993) 868333
12–2.30, 6–11 (12–11 Sat)
Adnams Broadside; Draught Bass; Hook Norton Best Bitter Ⓗ
Traditional, thatched pub, built in 1772 with inglenook and exposed beams. Warm welcome, fine fare and guest beers. Real cider available in summer.
🏠 Q ⚲ 🛏 ◖ ◗ ＆ ⚲ ⚲ ♣ ◐ P

Fulbrook

Masons Arms
Shipton Road (A361, Burford–Chipping Norton road)
☎ (0993) 822354
12–3 (not Mon; 11.30–3 Sat), 6.30–11
Hook Norton Best Bitter; Wadworth 6X Ⓗ
200 year-old, friendly, Cotswold stone, village pub with original beams and open fires. 🏠 Q ⚲ ◖ ◗ ♣ ◐

Garsington

Plough Inn
1 Oxford Road
☎ (086 736) 395
11–11
**Courage Best Bitter,
Directors** ⊞
Popular, well-run village local.
The large, enclosed, attractive
garden has a well-equipped
children's play area and an Aunt
Sally alley. Basket meals eves;
snacks only Sun lunchtime.
🏠 ⑧ ◐ 🌢 ⊞ ♣ P

Goring

John Barleycorn
Manor Road (off B4009 at
Miller of Mansfield pub jct)
☎ (0491) 872509
10–2.30, 6–11
Brakspear Bitter, Special ⊞
Attractive, 16th-century, low-
beamed inn with cosy saloon
and good food. Close to River
Thames and the Ridgeway long
distance footpath.
Q ⑧ ⋈ ◐ 🌢 ⊞ ♣

Great Haseley

Plough
Rectory Road (off A329, close
to M40 jct 7)
☎ (0844) 279283
11.30–2.30, 6.30–11
Greene King IPA ⊞
Friendly, old local in picturesque
village. The public bar is full of
character, with stone walls, low
beams and a large inglenook.
Quiet garden where Aunt Sally
can be played. Snacks available
at lunchtimes. 🏠 ⑧ ⊞ ♣ P

Great Milton

Bell Inn
The Green (off A329)
☎ (0844) 279270
12–2.30, 7–11 (12–2, 7–10.30 Sun;
closed Wed)
**Brakspear Bitter; Marston's
Pedigree; Uley Old Spot** ⊞
Welcoming, 17th-century
country pub with good home-
made food. Occasional food
theme nights and beer festivals.
Guest beers. 🏠 Q ⑧ ◐ 🌢 ⊞ ⅄ ♣

Great Tew

Falkland Arms
Off B4022 ☎ (060 883) 653
11.30–2.30 (not Mon), 6–11 (12–2,
7–10.30 Sun)
**Donnington BB; Hall &
Woodhouse Tanglefoot;
Hook Norton Best Bitter;
Wadworth 6X** ⊞
Outstanding, 16th-century,
classic pub in preserved village.
Oak panels, settles, flagstones,
oil lamps, clay pipes, snuff and a
thatched roof – a gem. Guest
beers; home-made food. Four

bedrooms, one with a four-
poster bed. No-smoking area at
lunchtime only.
🏠 Q ⑧ ⋈ ◐ 🌢 ♣ ⅄

Henley-on-Thames

Saracen's Head
129 Greys Road (½ mile SW of
central crossroads)
☎ (0491) 575929
11–2.30, 5.30–11
Brakspear XXX Mild, Bitter ⊞
Popular, busy local with an
emphasis on pub games. Teams
in local leagues for darts and
dominoes. Limited range of
food (especially Sun lunchtime),
but all home-cooked.
🏠 ⑧ ⋈ ◐ 🌢 ⅄ ⋈ ♣ P

Try also: Three Tuns

Highmoor

Dog & Duck
On B481, S of Nettlebed
☎ (0491) 641261
11 (11.30 winter)–3, 6–11
**Brakspear XXX Mild
(summer), Bitter, Special, Old
(winter)** ⊞
Cosy, two-bar, roadside pub in
Chiltern woodland. Small,
separate, no-smoking dining
room. Large enclosed garden
with barbecues on summer
weekends. Good value, home-
made food includes vegetarian
option (no meals Mon or winter
Sun eve). 🏠 Q ⑧ ◐ 🌢 ♣ P

Islip

Swan Inn
Lower Street ☎ (086 75) 2590
11–2.30, 6–11
**Morrells Bitter, Graduate,
College (winter)** ⊞
Comfortable, one-bar, village
local overlooking River Ray.
Growing collection of cheeky
postcards. No meals Sun/Mon
eves. Q ⋈ ⑧ ◐ 🌢 ⅄ P

Juniper Hill

Fox Inn
600 yds off A43
OS579325 ☎ (0869) 810616
11–2.30, 6–11
Hook Norton Best Bitter ⊞,
Old Hooky Ⓖ
Quiet, friendly pub in the centre
of a hamlet described in *Lark
Rise to Candleford*. 🏠 Q ⑧ ♣ P

Kidlington

Wise Alderman
Station Approach, Banbury
Road (A423) ☎ (086 75) 2281
11–2.30, 5.30–11
**Tetley Bitter; Wadworth
6X** ⊞
Comfortable and friendly pub at
the northern end of a growing
commuter village. ⑧ ◐ 🌢 ♣ P

Kidmore End

New Inn
Chalkhouse Green Road (off
B481 at Sonning Common)
☎ (0734) 723115
11–2.30, 6–11
Brakspear Bitter, Special ⊞,
Old Ⓖ
Comfortable, two-bar pub with
beams, wood panelling and a
large garden. Near a pretty
church and the village pond.
Good cooking; imaginative
menu. Family room is no-
smoking. ⅄ ⑧ ◐ 🌢 P ⅄

Kingham

Plough
Main Street (off B4450)
☎ (0608) 658327
10.30–2.30, 5.30–11
Draught Bass; Glenny Bitter ⊞
Lively locals' pub opposite the
village green. Guest beers.
🏠 ⑧ ⊞ ⅄ ♣ P

Langford

Bell
Off A361 through Filkins, bear
right, then first right
☎ (036 786) 281
11–2.30, 6.30–11
**Archers Village; Morland
Bitter; Wadworth 6X** ⊞
Quiet, 17th-century inn and
village local, difficult to find but
worth the effort. Unpretentious,
conventional, but genuinely
home-cooked pub menu (no
food Sun lunchtime or Mon
eve). 🏠 Q ⑧ ◐ 🌢 ♣ P

Lewknor

Olde Leathern Bottel
1 High Street (off B4009, close
to M40 jct 6)
☎ (0844) 51482
11–2.30, 6–11
**Brakspear Bitter, Special,
Old** ⊞
Comfortable and inviting,
family-run, village pub with a
friendly atmosphere. Large,
well-kept garden. Food is good
quality, home made and
reasonably priced. Pleasant
family area. 🏠 ⅄ ⑧ ◐ 🌢 ♣ P

Little Milton

Plough
Thame Road (A329)
☎ (0844) 278180
11–11 (11–3, 5–11 winter)
**Morrells Dark, Bitter,
Varsity, Graduate** ⊞
17th-century, stone-walled and
timber-beamed pub with a
village atmosphere. Good value
food. Large, enclosed play area
and a garden with a pets' corner;
small function room. Discount
for senior citizens on beers and
spirits. 🏠 ⅄ ⑧ ◐ 🌢 ♣ P

Oxfordshire

Long Hanborough

Swan
Millwood End (Combe Road, off A4095) OS417144
☎ (0993) 881347
11–2.30, 6–11
Morrells Bitter 🅗
Old-fashioned, cosy village pub with inglenook. Garden has pets and a children's play area. Barbecues at weekends in fine weather. 🏠 🅒 🅑 🚹 ⇌ (Long Hanborough/Combe) ♣ P

Long Wittenham

Machine Man
Off High Street (A415), 200 yds towards Little Wittenham
☎ (086 730) 7835
11–3, 6–11
Crown Buckley Best Bitter; Eldridge Pope Royal Oak; Exmoor Gold 🅗
Genuine village locals' pub with good value, home-made food – try the game hotpot (no meals Sun eve). Aunt Sally on Wed in summer. Two guest beers always available. ETB-approved accommodation.
🛏 Q 🚫 🏠 🚹 🅒 🅑 ♿ ♣ P

Try also: **Plough**, High Street (Ushers)

Lower Heyford

Bell
21 Market Square (off B4030, back of village)
☎ (0869) 47176
11.30–2.30, 7–11
Adnams Bitter; Ind Coope Burton Ale; Tetley Bitter 🅗
Warm, friendly, 16th-century village pub with separate children's room. Snacks in summer. 🛏 Q 🚫 🏠 🛡 ⇌ P

Middle Assendon

Rainbow
On B481, 1 mile from A423 jct
☎ (0491) 574879
11.30–2.30, 6–11
Brakspear XXX Mild, Bitter, Special, Old (winter) 🅔
Friendly, old, low-beamed local in beautiful Chiltern dry valley. Popular with walkers and cyclists in the summer. The handpulls operate electric pumps. 🏠 🅒 🔄 ♿ ♣ P

Middle Barton

Carpenters Arms
North Street (off A423 at Hopcrofts Holt, and A44 from Enstone)
☎ (0869) 40378
11–2.30, 6–11
Ind Coope ABC Best Bitter; Wadworth 6X 🅗
Comfortable, thatched, 16th-century pub, popular with

walkers. Good varied menu. Two bars. 🏠 🚹 🅒 🅑 🔄 P

North Hinksey

Fishes Inn
Oxford RFC sign from church, 100 yds ☎ (0865) 249796
10.30–2.30, 6–11
Morrells Bitter, Varsity, Graduate 🅗
Spacious, village pub with public bar at front and large, comfortable lounge at rear. Recent additions are the conservatory and patio, overlooking the huge garden. Two Aunt Sally pitches. Hosts the annual village flower show and fete. 🏠 🅒 🅑 ♿ ♣ P

North Leigh

Woodman Inn
New Yatt Road (off A4095, Witney–Woodstock road)
OS384132 ☎ (0993) 881790
11.30–3, 7 (may be earlier in summer)–11
Glenny Bitter; Hook Norton Best Bitter; Wadworth 6X 🅗
Small village pub. Large garden (with Aunt Sally) is safe for children. Guest beers; jazz; home-made food. The bar has a well. 🏠 🚹 🅒 ♿ ♣ P

Nuffield

Crown
On A423, 2 miles W of Nettlebed ☎ (0491) 641335
11–3, 6–11
Brakspear Bitter, Special, Old 🅗
17th-century, beamed coaching inn with a large inglenook fireplace. The wide range of excellent home-made food includes vegetarian dishes. Children allowed in dining area at lunchtime. Conveniently situated on the Ridgeway footpath. 🛏 Q 🏠 🅒 🅑 🛡 ♿ P

Oxford

Black Boy
91 Old High Street, Headington ☎ (0865) 63234
11–3, 6–11 (11–11 Sat)
Morrells Bitter, Varsity, Graduate 🅗, **College** (winter) 🅖
Large, three-bar local frequented by everybody from the postboy to a peer of the realm.
Q 🏠 🅒 🔄 ♣ P

Dewdrop Inn
258 Banbury Road, Summertown (A4165)
☎ (0865) 59372
11–3, 5.30–11 (12–2, 7–10.30 Sun)
Courage Best Bitter, Directors 🅗
Two 1820s cottages, much rebuilt and enlarged over the years into a comfortable pub.

Serves the needs of local business people and residents (very busy lunchtimes).
🏠 🅒 🅒 ♣ ❀

Eagle & Child
49 St Giles
☎ (0865) 58085
11–2.30, 5.30 (6 Sat)–11 (12–2.30, 7–10.30 Sun)
Ind Coope Burton Ale; Tetley Bitter; Wadworth 6X 🅗
Multi-alcoved pub, which was frequented by CS Lewis and Tolkien. A good place for a convivial chat, but, being justifiably popular, can get a little crowded. Be prepared to stand. No-smoking food area.
Q 🏠 🅒 🅑 ⇌

Fir Tree Tavern
163 Iffley Road (A4158)
☎ (0865) 247373
12–3, 6–11
Morrells Bitter, Varsity, Graduate 🅗
Small, split-level pub, popular with locals and students. Home-made pizzas a speciality. Pavement drinking area. 🏠 🅒 🅑

Gardeners Arms
39 Plantation Road
☎ (0865) 59814
11–11
Morrells Bitter, Graduate 🅗
Friendly, one-bar pub, attracting students and locals. Meals served in new garden room at the rear where children are welcome. 🚫 🏠 🅒 🅑 ♿ ♣

Hollybush
106 Bridge Street, Osney (off Botley Road)
☎ (0865) 723454
10.30–2.30, 5.30 (6 Sat)–11
Courage Best Bitter, Directors 🅗
Busy local near the river. Home-cooked meals (no food Mon eve). Guest beers usually include Glenny Wychwood.
Q 🏠 🅒 🅑 🔄 ⇌ ♣ P

King's Arms
Holywell Street
☎ (0865) 242369
10.30–3, 5–11 (10.30–11 Sat & summer)
Morland Bitter; Wadworth 6X; Younger No. 3; Young's Bitter, Special, Winter Warmer 🅗
Pub dating from 1607 but with an 18th-century frontage. The oldest part includes a room known as the 'Don's Bar'. Popular with students, tourists and business people. Opens 10.30 Sun for breakfasts.
Q 🚫 🏠 🅒 🅑 🍽

Marlborough House
60 Western Road, Grandpont (off A4144)
☎ (0865) 243617
11.30–2.30, 6–11 (11.30–11 Sat)

Oxfordshire

Ind Coope ABC Best Bitter,
Burton Ale; Mansfield Riding
Mild; Tetley Bitter Ⓗ
Back-street, locals' pub, popular
with students. Folk music every
other Mon; pianist every other
Wed. Pool room upstairs.
🖛 🕻 🕮 ♣

Old Tom
101 St Aldates
☎ (0865) 243034
10.30-3, 5-11 (12-2.30, 7-10.30 Sun)
Morrells Bitter, Varsity Ⓗ
Long, thin, one-bar, city-centre
pub, popular with Town and
Gown, musicians and non-
musicians. Eve meals finish
early. No-smoking area
lunchtimes only. Q 🕮 🕻 🕨 ⇌ ⅋

Osney Arms
45 Botley Road
☎ (0865) 247103
11-2.30, 6-11 (11-11 Sat)
Greene King IPA, Abbot Ⓗ
Friendly locals' pub, a short
walk from the station. 🕮 ⇌ ♣

Prince of Wales
80 Cowley Road (B480)
☎ (0865) 241382
10.30-2.30 (3 Mon & Fri; 4 Sat), 7-11
Morrells Dark, Varsity Ⓗ
Homely, split-level, street-
corner local. Open for breakfast
each weekday morning
(9-10.30). No food weekends.
🕻 ♣ P

Temple Bar
21 Temple Street (off B480)
☎ (0865) 243251
12-2.30, 7-11
Draught Bass; Hall &
Woodhouse Tanglefoot;
Wadworth 6X, Old Timer Ⓗ
Popular, two-bar local. Folk
music sessions every Sun –
bring an instrument! Wheelchair
access from Stockmore Street.
🕮 🕮 🕭 ♣ P

Victoria Arms
Mill Lane, Old Marston
☎ (0865) 241382
11.30-2.30, 6-11
Hall & Woodhouse
Tanglefoot; Wadworth IPA,
6X, Farmer's Glory, Old
Timer Ⓗ
Popular riverside pub at the end
of a long drive off Mill Lane
(beware the sleeping policemen).
Regularly used in summer by
punters from the Cherwell
boathouse. Regular guest beers.
Q 🕮 🕻 🕨 P

Pyrton

Plough
Off B4009 N of Watlington
OS687961 ☎ (049 161) 2003
11.30-2.30, 6-11 (closed Mon eve)
Adnams Bitter; Brakspear
Bitter; Fuller's ESB Ⓗ
Attractive, 17th-century,
thatched pub in a quiet country

village. Popular for its home-
made food, served in the bar or
the separate restaurant (no food
Mon eve). 🕮 🕮 🕻 🕨 🕭 🕈 ♣ P

Try also: Fox & Hounds,
Watlington (Brakspear)

Ramsden

Royal Oak
1 mile off B4022, opp. war
memorial
OS357153 ☎ (0993) 868213
11-2.30, 6.30-11
Banks's Bitter; Hook Norton
Best Bitter, Old Hooky Ⓗ
Friendly, 17th-century coaching
inn. One room, but separate
restaurant (vegetarian option).
Guest beers. Accommodation in
converted stable block.
🕮 Q 🕮 🖾 🕻 🕨 🕭 P

Sandford-on-
Thames

Fox
29 Henley Road
☎ (0865) 777803
11-2.30, 6-11
Morrells Dark, Bitter Ⓖ
Good, basic pub, with the
cheapest beer for miles.
🕮 Q 🕮 🕮 🕭 P

Shrivenham

Prince of Wales
High Street
☎ (0793) 782268
11-3, 6-11
Hall & Woodhouse
Tanglefoot; Wadworth IPA,
6X Ⓗ
Warm and cosy country pub
with a split-level, comfortable
lounge and a basic bar. Good
food includes a selection of
home-cooked pizzas and decent
bread (no meals Sun eve).
Limited parking.
🕮 Q 🖛 🕮 🕻 🕨 🕮 P

Sonning Common

Bird in Hand
Reading Road (B481)
☎ (0734) 723230
11-2.30, 6-11
Courage Best Bitter;
Wadworth 6X Ⓗ
Low-beamed pub with a large
inglenook and traditional pub
furnishings. Very popular
restaurant (standard pub menu)
and meals also served in the bar
(not Sun eve). The attractive,
enclosed garden backs onto
woodland, ideal for children.
Q 🕮 🕻 🕨 🕭 P

Sonning Eye

Flowing Spring
Henley Road (A4155, 2 miles E
of Caversham)
☎ (0734) 693207

12-2.30 (3 Fri & Sat), 5.30 (6 Sat)-11
Fuller's Chiswick, London
Pride, Mr Harry, ESB Ⓗ
Comfortable, roadside pub with
a cosy atmosphere. A wrought
iron staircase leads down to a
huge garden. Occasional events
include a national Mamod and
Meccano steam rally (April), a
Fun Day (June) and a steam
engine rally (July). No food
Mon/Tue eves, or Sun.
🕮 🕮 🕻 🕨 P

Souldern

Fox
Off B4100, 2 miles S of Aynho
☎ (0869) 345284
11-3, 7-11
Draught Bass; Hook Norton
Best Bitter Ⓗ
Friendly, Cotswold-stone pub in
village centre. The small
restaurant offers home-cooked
food. Guest beers.
🕮 Q 🕮 🖾 🕻 🕨 🕭 ♣ P

South Moreton

Crown Inn
Off A4130 ☎ (0235) 812262
11-3, 5.30-11
Adnams Bitter; Hall &
Woodhouse Tanglefoot;
Wadworth IPA Ⓗ, 6X Ⓖ
Popular, traditional village local
with a spacious single bar.
Interesting decor: floorboards,
rugs and deep red walls and
ceiling generate a warm and
cosy atmosphere. Good value,
home-cooked food. Guest beers
frequently available. Interesting
games. 🕮 Q 🕮 🕻 🕨 ♣ P

Stanton St John

Star Inn
Off B4027 ☎ (086 735) 277
11-2.30, 6.30-11 (12-2.30, 7-10.30
Sun)
Hall & Woodhouse
Tanglefoot; Wadworth IPA,
6X, Farmer's Glory, Old
Timer Ⓗ
17th-century inn still retaining
some original features. Tasty
home-cooked, reasonably priced
food, with vegetarian option, is
served every day. Children may
bring well-behaved parents to
the family room (no-smoking)
and walled beer garden.
🕮 Q 🖛 🕮 🕻 🕨 🕮 ♣ P ⅋

Stoke Lyne

Peyton Arms
500 yds off A41
☎ (0869) 345285
10.30-2.30 (not Mon), 6-11
Hook Norton Mild, Best
Bitter, Old Hooky Ⓖ
Small, basic, village local,
unchanged by time – a real rural
gem. Aunt Sally played.
🕮 Q 🖛 🕮 🕮 ♣ P

Oxfordshire

Stoke Row

Cherry Tree
Off B481 ☎ (0491) 680430
10–2.30, 6–11
Brakspear XXX Mild, Bitter,
Special, Old Ⓖ
Picturesque, low-beamed village
local. Games room with pool;
swings and slide in garden.
Plays host to Velocette owners
club. ▲ ⑧ ♣ P

Swinbrook

Swan
1 mile off A40, 2 miles E of
Burford
☎ (099 382) 2165
11.30–2.30, 6–11
Morland Bitter; Wadworth
6X Ⓗ
Characterful, 17th-century,
riverside country inn, a former
watermill. Good, home-cooked
food. Darts and dominoes in the
old tap room. ▲ Q ⑧ ( ) ♣ P

Sydenham

Plough & Harrow
Emmington (on B4445)
☎ (0844) 51367
12–2.30 (3 Sat), 6.30–11
Brakspear Bitter; Fuller's
London Pride; Hook Norton
Old Hooky; Morland Old
Speckled Hen Ⓗ
250 year-old drovers' pub now
a modern eating and drinking
house in typical Oxfordshire
countryside, with views of the
Chilterns. Excellent walking and
riding country, within easy
reach of Oxford.
▲ Q ⑧ ᚐ ( ) ♣ P

Try also: Crown (Morrells)

Tackley

Kings Arms
3 Nethercote Road (off A423)
☎ (086 983) 334
11.30–3 (3.30 Sat), 6.30–11
Morrells Bitter, Varsity Ⓗ
Lively, basic, village pub. Very
games-oriented, with strong
darts, pool and Aunt Sally
teams. ▲ ⑧ ᚐ ⇌ ♣ P

Thame

Rising Sun
26 High Street
☎ (084 421) 4206
11–2.30, 6–11
Hook Norton Best Bitter;
Marston's Pedigree;
Wadworth 6X Ⓗ
Attractive, 16th-century, oak-
beamed building with an
overhanging first floor. The
cosy atmosphere is enhanced by
low ceilings. Guest beers. Board
games. ▲ ⑧ ( ) ♣

Swan Hotel
9 Upper High Street
☎ (0844) 261211
11–11
Brakspear Bitter; Hook
Norton Best Bitter Ⓗ
Popular, town-centre inn
overlooking the market place.
Many unusual fittings and
furniture. Constantly-changing
selection of guest beers from
around the country; fine
restaurant and bar meals
(vegetarian and children's
choices).
▲ Q ⇌ ⑧ ᚐ ( ) ᚐ P

Try also: Six Bells (Fuller's)

Wallingford

Cross Keys
48 High Street (A4130, 400
yds W of centre)
☎ (0491) 37173
11–3, 6–11
Brakspear XXX Mild, Bitter,
Special, Old Ⓗ
Unspoilt, three-roomed, 17th-
century town pub. Small,
comfortable lounge; public bar
with separate darts room.
Children's play area in garden.
Reputedly haunted – ask the
locals about 'Charlie'. Eve meals
till 8.30; no food Sun.
Q ⑧ ( ) ᚐ ♣ P

Watchfield

Royal Oak
Oak Road (off A420, between
Swindon and Oxford)
☎ (0793) 782668
11–2.30, 7–11
Courage Best Bitter,
Directors Ⓗ
Lively, friendly local with
atmosphere. An ivy-covered
building in the old part of the
village. Guest beers are Young's
Special, Wadworth 6X and
Everards Tiger, in rotation.
Skittle alley. ⑧ ( ) ♣ P

Witney

Carpenters Arms
132 Newland (E end of Witney,
on Oxford road)
☎ (0993) 702206
10.30–2.30, 6–11
Morrells Bitter Ⓗ
Comfortable, one-bar pub,
popular with all ages.
Worthington White Shield
available. ⑧ P

Court Inn
Bridge Street
☎ (0993) 703228
10.30–3, 6–11
Courage Best Bitter; John
Smith's Bitter Ⓗ
17th-century coaching inn, with
a large lounge and a small
bar/games room. The landlord
hails from Bradford and is
fanatical about his beer; his John

Smith's is the best in the area.
▲ ⇌ ( ) ᚐ ♣ P

House of Windsor
31 West End
☎ (0993) 704277
12–3.30 (not Mon), 6 (7 Sat)–11
Felinfoel Double Dragon;
Hook Norton Best Bitter, Old
Hooky; Marston's Pedigree;
Wadworth 6X Ⓗ
A homely and lively, popular
local in a suburban area of town.
No food Mon eve.
▲ ⑧ ( ) ᚐ P

Three Pigeons
Woodgreen
☎ (0993) 702803
10.30–3, 6–11
Courage Best Bitter,
Directors Ⓗ
Cosy, Cotswold-stone pub
dating back to the 15th century.
Overlooks the village green and
has a children's play area. No
eve meals Sun.
Q ⑧ ( ) ᚐ ♣

Woodstock

Queens Own
59 Oxford Street
☎ (0993) 812414
11–2.30, 6–11
Hook Norton Mild, Bitter,
Old Hooky Ⓗ
Friendly local in a tourist town.
♣

Rose & Crown
81 Manor Road, Old
Woodstock
☎ (0993) 812009
11–3, 6–11
Morrells Bitter, Varsity Ⓗ
Large, friendly pub at the
northern end of town.
⑧ ( ) ᚐ ᚐ ♣ P

Help keep real ale
alive by joining
CAMRA. Your voice
helps encourage
brewers big and small
to brew cask beer and
offer all beer drinkers
a better choice. For
membership details
see page 480.

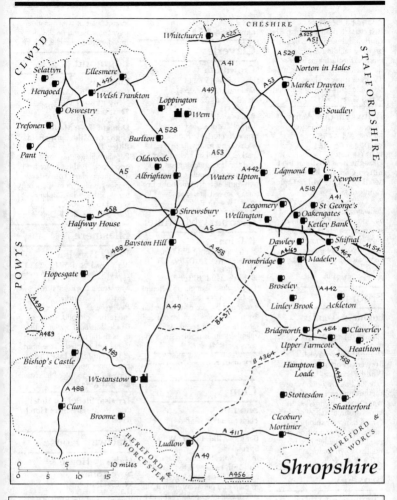

CHESHIRE

CLWYD

STAFFORDSHIRE

POWYS

HEREFORD & WORCESTER

HEREFORD & WORCS

Shropshire

Whitchurch · Norton in Hales · Market Drayton · Soudley · Selattyn · Ellesmere · Hengoed · Welsh Frankton · Loppington · Wem · Oswestry · Trefonen · Pant · Burlton · Oldwoods · Albrighton · Waters Upton · Edgmond · Newport · Shrewsbury · Leegomery · St George's · Oakengates · Wellington · Ketley Bank · Halfway House · Bayston Hill · Dawley · Shifnal · Hopesgate · Ironbridge · Madeley · Broseley · Bishop's Castle · Linley Brook · Ackleton · Wistanstow · Bridgnorth · Claverley · Heathton · Upper Farmcote · Clun · Broome · Hampton Loade · Stottesdon · Shatterford · Cleobury Mortimer · Ludlow

0 5 10 15 | 10 miles

⌂ *Hanby*, Wem; **Wood** Wistanstow

Ackleton

Folley Inn
On B4176, 6 miles S of Telford
☎ (074 65) 225
12–2.30 (3.30 Sat), 6.30 (7 Sat)–11
Banks's Mild, Bitter Ⓔ
Situated on a road locally
known as the 'Rabbit-Run', at
the end of the village; a large,
single-bar pub with a small,
intimate ante-room. A large
feature fireplace is adorned with
copper and brass. ⍟ ♣ P

Albrighton

Crown Inn
High Street (old A41)
☎ (0902) 372204
11.30–2.30, 5.30–11 (11–11 Sat)
Banks's Mild, Bitter Ⓔ
Large, multi-roomed inn in the
town centre: comfortable

lounge and snug, and a basic
bar. The garden has a children's
play area. ⌂ Q ⍟ ⇔ Ⓓ ⇄ ♣ P

Bayston Hill

Compasses Inn
Hereford Road (A49)
☎ (0743) 722921
12–2.30 (3 Fri), 5–11 (11–11 Sat)
**Draught Bass; M&B
Highgate Mild, Brew XI** Ⓗ
Friendly, main road local with a
lounge and a separate public bar
with a decor which reflects its
nautical connection. Note, too,
the fascinating collection of
carved wooden elephants. Guest
beers. ⌂ ⍟ Ⓓ ♣ P

Bishop's Castle

Three Tuns Hotel
Salop Street
☎ (0588) 638797

11.30–2.30, 6.30–11
**Three Tuns Mild, XXX, Castle
Steamer, Old Scrooge** Ⓗ
Classic home-brew pub with a
brewing tradition going back
many years; one of the four
remaining in the early 1970s.
Its coal-fired tower brewery
proclaims its lineage. Changes
in ownership over recent years
have, however, led to changes
in its products.
⌂ Q ⍟ Ⓓ ⇔ ♣ ⟲ P

**Try also: Crown & Anchor
Vaults** (Free)

Bridgnorth

Bell & Talbot Inn
2 Salop Street (B4364, old
A458) ☎ (0746) 763233
11.30–3, 6 (7 winter)–11
**Batham Best Bitter; Younger
IPA** Ⓗ

247

Shropshire

A Grade II listed free house with two character-laden rooms. The courtyard, housing the old brewery building at the rear, is reached through a passage decorated with a 'real ale' mural. Two guest beers always available, plus cider in summer. ▲ 🏠 🍺 ⊕ ≉ (SVR) ○

Railwayman's Arms
Severn Valley station (off B4364, old A458)
☎ (0746) 764361
11–11 (11–2.30, 7–11 winter)
Draught Bass; Batham Best Bitter; Courage Best Bitter; M&B Highgate Mild; Taylor Landlord Ⓗ
Pub located in a Severn Valley Railway building, overlooked by Bridgnorth Castle. Full of steam memorabilia, it is almost a museum in its own right. A huge decorative mirror dominates the fireplace. Regular guest beer.
▲ Q ≉ (SVR) ♣ ○ P

Broome

Engine & Tender
Off Clun-Craven Arms road (B4367/8) ☎ (058 87) 275
12–3, 7–11
Draught Bass; Welsh Brewers Worthington BB; Wood Parish Ⓗ
Extended railway pub whose interlinking rooms display mementoes which reflect its name. Broome Halt platform has a small railway exhibition; the train stops by request only. A guest beer is added in busy months. Own campsite.
Q 🍺 ▲ ♣ P

Broseley

Cumberland Hotel
Jackson Avenue (off B4375)
☎ (0952) 882301
10–11
Ansells Mild; Ruddles Best Bitter; Webster's Yorkshire Bitter Ⓗ
An old house that has become a very comfortable hotel, located behind a housing area and close to Ironbridge Gorge. Lively bar and a quiet well-furnished lounge; good, home-made food.
▲ 🏠 🛏 🍺 ♣ ♣ P

Burlton

Burlton Arms
Ellesmere Road
☎ (093 922) 284
12–2.30, 7 (earlier in summer)–11
Hanby Drawwell; Wadworth 6X (summer) Ⓗ
Once a Wem Brewery pub so it is fitting that Hanby beers from Wem are now available here. Tastefully extended; once multi-roomed now all interconnected.

Guest beer. Has its own campsite. ▲ 🏠 🍺 ▲ ♣ P

Claverley

Crown Inn
High Street (5 miles E of Bridgnorth, off A454)
☎ (074 66) 228
12–3, 7–11
Banks's Mild, Bitter Ⓔ
Large, Tudor-styled inn with three comfortable rooms. Set in a charming rural village. The car park is behind an arched barn, and the beer garden is set well back from the pub. Children welcome at lunchtime only. Eve meals served Thu–Sat.
▲ 🏠 🍺 ⊕ ♣ P

Cleobury Mortimer

Bell Inn
8 Lower Street (A4117, near town centre) ☎ (0299) 270305
11–3, 7 (6 Fri & Sat)–11
Banks's Mild, Bitter Ⓔ
Large, plush lounge, on different levels, and a small, old-fashioned bar are complemented by many rooms, incl. a pool and private snooker room (day membership available). Cider in summer. ▲ ⊕ ♣ ○

Try also: King's Arms Hotel (Free)

Clun

Sun Inn
High Street ☎ (058 84) 559
11–3, 6–11 (12–2.30, 7–10.30 Sun)
Banks's Mild, Bitter; Wood Special Ⓗ
In a remote, timeless village, this 15th-century listed, Cruck-built pub has all the ingredients to help you get away from it all. A stone-flagged public bar and a cash register set of handpumps enhance its character.
▲ Q 🏠 🛏 🍺 ▲ ♣ P

Dawley

Crown Inn
High Street ☎ (0952) 505015
11–4, 7–11 (11–11 Fri & Sat in summer)
Draught Bass; M&B Highgate Mild, Brew XI Ⓗ&Ⓔ
Large, comfortable pub with a lounge and separate rooms for pool and darts. A good, friendly town pub for all age groups. 🏠 🍺 ♣ ○ P

Three Crowns Inn
Hinkshay Road (off B4373 at Finger Road garage)
☎ (0952) 590868
11–3 (4 Fri & Sat), 6.30–11
Marston's Burton Best Bitter, Pedigree Ⓗ
Recently modernised, small, town pub with U-shaped

lounge, part of which is given over to darts and pool. Good friendly atmosphere. 🏠 🍺 ▲ ♣ P

Edgmond

Lion Inn
Chetwynd Road (off B5062 at Newport Road jct)
☎ (0952) 810346
12–2.30 (3 Sat), 7–11
Draught Bass; M&B Highgate Mild, Springfield Bitter Ⓔ
Popular village pub noted for its good food; barbecues are held in summer. Has a comfortable lounge/dining room and a busy bar: worth a visit. Sun lunch served to order only and no food Sun eve. 🏠 🍺 ♣ P

Ellesmere

White Hart Inn
Birch Road ☎ (0691) 622333
12–3 (not Wed, or Mon–Thu in winter), 7–11
Marston's Border Mild, Burton Best Bitter, Pedigree Ⓗ
Interesting old pub which is Grade II listed. Popular with users of the nearby Llangollen Canal and situated at the heart of the Shropshire Lake District. Pedigree is not available in winter. No food Wed lunchtime.
🏠 🍺 ♣ P

Try also: Black Lion Hotel (Marston's); **Ellesmere Hotel** (Free)

Halfway House

Halfway House & Seven Stars
☎ (0743) 884387
11.30–3, 7–11 (may vary)
Burtonwood Best Bitter (summer), **Forshaw's** Ⓗ&Ⓖ
Two pubs under the same roof which complement each other well. The first consists of three rooms: a well-appointed lounge, a games room and a public bar. Go next door and step back in time to a tiled floor, a high-backed settle and beer served by gravity. 🏠 🍺 ▲ ♣ P

Hampton Loade

Lion Inn
Signed off A442 S of Quatt
OS748862 ☎ (0746) 780263
12–2.30 (not Mon–Fri), 7 (7.30 winter)–11 (12–2.30, 7–10.30 Sun)
Hook Norton Best Bitter, Old Hooky Ⓗ
A multi-roomed country pub, with a separate restaurant, built in the 17th century as a cider house. Original beams and horse brasses in all five rooms and real fires throughout. Large selection of country wines;

guest beers in summer. No food Mon. Note restricted lunchtime opening. ▣ ▣ ◖ ▌ ◗ ▲
≉ (SVR via chain ferry) P

Heathton

Old Gate Inn
One mile NW of Halfpenny Green Airfield; off B4176, 8 miles W of Dudley
OS813924 ☎ (074 66) 431
12–3, 6–11
HP&D Bitter, Entire; Taylor Landlord Ⓗ
A country inn dating back to around 1600, off the beaten track but well worth finding. Has a relaxing atmosphere, good food (incl. vegetarian choice), and a barbecue and sandpit in the garden. The only Holts (HP&D) pub in Shropshire. ▣ Q ▣ ◖ ▌ ◗ ▣ P

Hengoed

Last Inn
3 miles N of Oswestry, off
B4579 ☎ (0691) 659747
12–3, 7–11
Marston's Border Bitter, Pedigree; Wood Special Ⓗ
Country pub with separate games and family rooms. Regular guest beers. ▣ ▙ ◖ ▌ ◗ ▣ ◔ ◔ P

Hopesgate

Stables Inn
Off A488, turn right in Hope
OS343019 ☎ (0743) 891344
11–11 (closed Mon; 12–2.30, 7–10.30 Sun)
Ansells Mild; Hanby Drawwell; Ind Coope Burton Ale; Marston's Pedigree; Wood Special Ⓗ
Small, friendly, traditional country pub, situated on high ground with excellent views. Warm up by the massive log fire in winter. Excellent range of modestly-priced, home-cooked dishes. No food Sun–Wed eves. ▣ Q ▣ ◖ ▌ ◔ ◔ P

Ironbridge

Crown Inn
10 Hodge Bower (off B4373)
☎ (0952) 433128
12–3, 7–11
Banks's Mild, Bitter Ⓔ
Situated high above historic Ironbridge, this pub offers panoramic views over the Severn Gorge to Broseley. A popular locals' pub away from the tourist area. ▣ ◔ P

Ketley Bank

Lord Hill Inn
Main Road (off A442/B5061 at Greyhound interchange)
☎ (0952) 613070

12–2.30 (3 Sat; not Tue–Thu) 7–11 (12–2.30, 7–10.30 Sun)
Draught Bass; Hook Norton Best Bitter; M&B Highgate Mild Ⓗ
A family conservatory fronts this well-frequented free house which also has a basic public bar and an L-shaped lounge. The village bakery and mortuary were once housed in the pub cellar. Has been the local CAMRA *Pub of the Year* more than once. Three guest beers plus Worthington White Shield. ▣ ▙ ▣ ◖ ▌ ◗ ▣ ◔ P

Leegomery

Malt Shovel Inn
Hadley Park Road (100 yds S of Leegomery roundabout on A442) ☎ (0952) 242963
12–2.30, 5–11 (12–2.30, 7–10.30 Sun)
Marston's Pedigree Ⓗ
A plain, compact bar and a comfortable and pleasant lounge with brass decorations; this traditional pub is favoured by more mature imbibers. ▣ Q ▣ ◖ ▣ ◔ P

Linley Brook

Pheasant Inn
¼ mile off B4373 OS680978
☎ (0746) 762260
12–2.30, 6.30 (7 winter)–11
Banks's Mild Ⓗ
An unspoilt, traditional free house, run by a traditional landlord with traditional values. Set in an attractive rural location and well worth finding. Two guest beers always available. No children. ▣ Q ▣ ◖ ▌ ◗ ▣ ◔ P

Loppington

Blacksmiths Arms
On B4397 ☎ (0939) 33762
12–3, 7–11
Draught Bass; Wood Special Ⓗ
A cosy country pub making the best of its olde-worlde appeal of wooden beams and snug nooks and crannies. Trout pool and horse riding facilities nearby.
Q ▙ ▣ ◪ ◖ ▌

Try also: Dickin Arms (Free)

Ludlow

Church Inn
Buttercross ☎ (0584) 872174
11–11
Draught Bass; Ruddles Best Bitter, County; Webster's Yorkshire Bitter Ⓗ
Tucked away in the heart of Ludlow, behind Buttercross and away from the traffic on one of the town's most ancient sites. The nearby parish church of St Laurence is the largest and most majestic in Shropshire.
Q ◪ ◖ ▌ ≉

George Hotel
Castle Square
☎ (0584) 872055
11–11
Ansells Mild, Bitter Ⓗ
Genuine, town-centre, drinkers' pub – reputedly haunted. Across the square is the castle, one of the earliest built of stone, and a major venue for the annual Ludlow Festival. ◪ ◖ ▣ ≉ ◔

Madeley

All Nations Inn
Coalport Road (off Legges Way)
☎ (0952) 585747
12–3, 7–11
All Nations Pale Ale Ⓗ
A long-established, one-roomed brew pub, a listed building. The basic bar serves the only draught drink in the pub. It is close to Blists Hill, site of the Ironbridge Gorge Museum.
Q ▣ ▲ ◔ P

Anchor Inn
Court Street
☎ (0952) 585790
11–11
Banks's Mild; M&B Springfield Bitter Ⓗ
In the centre of Madeley, a popular locals' pub with a maritime theme. ▣ ▲ ◔ P

> Join CAMRA —
> see page 480!

Market Drayton

King's Arms
Shropshire Street
☎ (0630) 652417
11–3 (5 Wed & Fri; 11–11 Sat)
Marston's Mercian Mild, Burton Best Bitter, Pedigree Ⓗ
Ancient former coaching inn, built in 1674. Now a friendly, two-roomed, locals' pub: a boisterous bar with a jukebox and a smaller snug-cum-lounge cater for all ages. Good selection of whiskies. Local CAMRA *Pub of the Year 1991.*
▣ ◔ P

Newport

King's Head Inn
Chetwynd End (A519, at Forton Road jct)
☎ (0952) 812860
11.30–3, 6.30–11
Marston's Burton Best Bitter, Pedigree Ⓗ
Friendly pub at the north end of town, comprising three rooms: lounge, bar and dining room. All home-cooked, fresh food is served, with barbecues and pig roasts in summer. No meals Sun eve. ▣ Q ▣ ◖ ◖ ▌ ▣ ▲ ◔ ◔

249

Shropshire

Norton in Hales

Hinds Head
Main Road (1½ miles W of
B5415, Woore–Market
Drayton road)
OS703387 ☎ (0630) 43014
12–3, 6–11
**Draught Bass; M&B Mild,
Springfield Bitter** H
Welcoming village local, off the
beaten track but well worth a
visit. Large comfortable lounge;
a small games-oriented bar and
a restaurant. Over 30 malt
whiskies are on offer and a
guest beer may be available.
Note the old etched-glass door
advertising Joules Stone Ales.
🏚 🌣 🕻 🍴 🛏 🌿 ♣ P

Oakengates

Rose & Crown Inn
Holyhead Road (B5061)
☎ (0952) 614348
12–2.30, 7–11 (12–2, 7–10.30 Sun)
**Ansells Mild, Bitter; Ind
Coope Burton Ale** H
Very pleasant roadside local
with a small, comfortable
lounge and a larger, L-shaped
bar. Friendly atmosphere;
excellent lunches. Arrive early if
you want to eat. Guest beers.
🌣 🕻 🛏 ≠ ♣ P

Oldwoods

Romping Cat
½ mile E of B5067 at Walford
Heath
☎ (0939) 290273
12–3 (not Fri), 7–11 (12–2, 7–10.30
Sun)
Whitbread Castle Eden Ale H
A guest beer is always available
in this neat country pub near
Bomere Heath. Well-known
locally for its efforts for charity.
🏚 Q ♣ P

Oswestry

Black Lion
59 Salop Road
☎ (0691) 652745
12–11 (may close if quiet)
**Marston's Border Exhibition,
Pedigree** H
Popular, if modest, traditional
local, a few minutes from the
town centre. 🛏 ♣

Golden Lion
Upper Church Street
☎ (0691) 653747
12–3, 7 (6 Fri & Sat)–11
**Marston's Border Bitter,
Merrie Monk, Pedigree** H
A lively bar contrasting nicely
with a comfortable lounge.
Q 🌣 🕻 🛏 P

Sun Inn
Church Street
☎ (0691) 653433
12–3 (not Tue–Thu), 7.30–11

**Thwaites Best Mild;
Wadworth 6X** H
Street-corner pub,
sympathetically renovated as a
genuine free house. The dining
area serves home-cooked food.
Clog Iron Bitter, the house beer,
is available, alongside a regular
guest beer. Note the original
Walker's windows. Q 🕻 🛏 🕻 ♣

Pant

Cross Guns Inn
On A483
☎ (0691) 830821
11.30–3.30, 7–11
**Marston's Border Exhibition,
Burton Best Bitter,
Pedigree** H
Pleasantly-situated, Welsh
border pub with a small stone-
flagged bar.
🏚 Q 🌣 🕻 🛏 🕻 🏕 ♣ P

St George's

Albion Inn
Station Hill (between
Oakengates and St George's
centres) ☎ (0952) 614193
12–2.30, 6–11
**Marston's Burton Best Bitter,
Pedigree, Owd Rodger**
(winter) H
Town pub with a lovely
Victorian atmosphere; a single
room with coal fires, pleasantly
decorated with pictures,
stencilled ceiling and period
furnishings. Good value, simple
food. 🏚 🌣 🛏 🛏
≠ (Oakengates) ♣ P

Selattyn

Cross Keys
Ceiriog Road (B4579)
☎ (0691) 650247
11–11 (may close afternoons)
Banks's Mild, Bitter H
17th-century gem of a village
pub, just off Offa's Dyke.
🏚 Q 🌣 🕻 ♣ P

Shatterford

Red Lion Inn
Bridgnorth Road (A442, at
county boundary)
☎ (029 97) 221
11.30–2.30, 6.30–11
Banks's Mild, Bitter E;
Batham Best Bitter H
Small bar on two levels, with
exposed beams, and a large
dining room at the rear. Two
car parks – one in Shropshire,
one in Worcestershire! Good
selection of guest beers.
🏚 🌣 🕻 ▶ 🏕 P

Shifnal

Plough Inn
Broadway (B4379)
☎ (0952) 460678
7–11 (closed Mon; 11–11 Thu–Sat)
Beer range varies H

Long, oak-beamed pub in the
centre of Shifnal. The large
garden offers barbecue facilities.
Up to three guest beers
available. 🌣 ≠

White Hart Inn
4 High Street (B4379)
☎ (0952) 461161
12–2.30 (3 Sat; not Mon), 6–11
**Ansells Mild, Bitter; Ind
Coope Burton Ale; Premier
Pitfield Dark Star** H
This 16th-century coaching inn
was a recent winner of the
CAMRA West Midlands *Pub of
the Year*. Three guest beers, and
good food (Tue–Sat) – German
meals are a speciality.
🌣 🕻 🛏 ≠ P

Try also: Anvil Inn (Banks's)

Shrewsbury

Castle Vaults
Castle Gates
☎ (0743) 358807
11.30–3, 6–11 (12–3 Sun, closed Sun
eve)
**Marston's Border Mild,
Pedigree** H
A free house in the shadow of
the castle where the landlord
exercises discretion over the
customers he admits. Mexican
food is a speciality in the
smoke-free dining area.
Unusually, the pub has a roof
garden. Regular guest beers.
🏚 Q 🌣 🛏 🕻 ≠

Dog & Pheasant
20 Severn Street, Castlefields
(300 yds from station)
☎ (0743) 352835
12–3 (5 Fri & Sat), 7–11
**Ansells Mild, Bitter; Ind
Coope Burton Ale** H
Pub with a lively bar at the
front and a quieter saloon,
displaying wartime RAF
memorabilia. The outside
seating faces the world's first
iron-framed houses. Holder of
Allied's *Master Cellarman* award.
Guest beers. Q 🌣 🕻 🛏 ≠ 🍀

Dolphin
48 St Michaels Street
☎ (0743) 350419
12–3, 5.30–11 (12–11 Fri & Sat)
Beer range varies
Late-Georgian pub with a
porticoed entrance. No keg beer
or lager but a choice of up to
six guest beers from a
constantly changing range. No
under-21 year-olds admitted.
Q 🌣 🛏

Nags Head
Wyle Cop ☎ (0743) 362455
11.30–11
**Ansells Bitter; Ind Coope
Burton Ale; Tetley Bitter** H
Historic house with jetty at
rear; reputed to be haunted.
Regular guest beer. ≠ ♣

250

Station Hotel
Castle Foregate
☎ (0743) 344716
11–4, 6–11
**Draught Bass; M&B Mild,
Brew XI** E
The mild is worth missing a few
trains for in this very popular
pub across the road from the
station. Pool room. ⊞ ≠ ♣

Try also: Albert, Smithfield Rd
(Banks's)

Soudley

Wheatsheaf Inn
Off A41, 1 mile S of
Cheswardine OS725288
☎ (063 086) 311
12–3, 7 (7.30 winter)–11
**Marston's Border Mild,
Burton Best Bitter, Pedigree,
Owd Rodger** (winter) H
Friendly but remote village pub
on the Staffordshire border,
dating back to 1784. Visitors
include users of the Shropshire
Union Canal, which runs a mile
south of the pub. Games include
bar skittles. A good range of
home-cooked meals is served.
🏠 ⊛ ◖ ▶ ⊞ ♣ P

Stottesdon

Fox & Hounds
High Street ☎ (074 632) 222
11–3, 6–11 (11–11 Sat)
Dasher's Bitter H
Brew pub in a small village in
the heart of Shropshire. Both
pub and landlord are full of
character (like the beer). Skittle
alley at the rear can be hired.
🏠 Q ⊛ ▲ ♣ P

Trefonen

Efel Inn
☎ (0691) 659840
12–3, 7–11
**Marston's Border Exhibition,
Border Bitter, Pedigree** H
Small, country pub in Welsh
border village. Adjacent to
Offa's Dyke footpath.
Q ⊛ ⊞ ♣ P

Upper Farmcote

Red Lion O'Morfe
3 miles from Bridgnorth on
A458; turn left towards
Claverley OS770919
☎ (074 66) 678
11.30–2.30 (3.30 Sat), 7–11
Banks's Mild, Bitter E; **Wood
Special** H
Large, country pub with lounge,
no-smoking conservatory for
families, a small bar and a pool
room. The excellent food helps
to make this a very popular pub
all year round (eve meals
Mon–Thu until 9pm). Boules
played. 🏠 ⛟ ⊛ ◖ ▶ ⊞ ▲ ♣ P ⅍

Waters Upton

Lion Inn
On A442
☎ (0952) 83317
12–3, 6–11
M&B Highgate Mild E
Multi-levelled pub with three
separate drinking areas and a
front room which is used as a
post office and general store.
Note the many pictures of the
Lion steam engine. Regular
guest beer. ⊛ ◖ ▶ ⊞ ▲ ♣ P

Wellington

Plough Inn
King Street (ring road near
centre) ☎ (0952) 255981
12–2.30, 7–11
**Ansells Mild, Bitter; Ind
Coope Burton Ale** H
Comfortable local, popular with
lunchtime diners. A basic,
uncarpeted bar with a pool table
contrasts with the good, cosy
lounge. Guest beer. Landlord
holds the *Master Cellarman*
award for his Burton Ale. Eve
meals Thu–Sat. ⊛ ◖ ▶ ⊞ ≠ ♣ P

Welsh Frankton

Narrowboat Inn
Ellesmere Road (A495)
☎ (0691) 661051
11.30–3 (may extend summer and
weekends), 7–11

Wadworth 6X H
Modern pub at the side of the
Shropshire Union (Llangollen)
Canal. Boats for hire at the pub.
Normally has up to three other
beers on handpump. ⊛ ◖ ▶ ♣ P

Wem

Horse & Jockey
High Street ☎ (0939) 34891
12–11
**Burtonwood Mild, Best
Bitter, Forshaw's** H
Presently a robust, one-roomed
pub, intended for expansion into
buildings at the rear. ≠ ♣ P

Try also: Dickin Arms
(Marston's); **Station**, Yorton
(Wood)

Whitchurch

Old Town Hall Vaults
St Marys Street
☎ (0948) 2251
10.30–11
**Marston's Border Bitter,
Pedigree** H
Neat pub down a side-street.
Opens at 10am for coffee, so
giving more time to study the
mementoes of Edward German,
who was born at the pub.
Whitchurch is also known as the
home of Joyce, who was famous
for his tower clocks.
⊛ ◖ ▶ ⊞ ≠ ♣

Try also: Star (Marston's)

Wistanstow

Plough
Off A489, W of A49
☎ (0588) 672523
12–2.30, 7–11
**Wood Parish, Special,
Wonderful** H
As this is ostensibly the Wood
brewery tap, all its beers (when
brewed) are available. The high-
vaulted lounge boasts a large
bottle collection; the lower
public bar stands in the original
part of the building. Locally-
produced food served.
🏠 ⊛ ◖ ▶ ⊞ ♣ P

◖ **Meals** ▶

Pubs featured which serve lunchtime or evening meals are given the
◖ or ▶ sign respectively.

For more detailed information about real ale pubs which serve quality
food, consult CAMRA's **Good Pub Food** by Susan Nowak, now in
its second edition. Copies are available, priced £7.99, from all good
book stores or direct from CAMRA, 34 Alma Road, St Albans, Herts,
AL1 3BW (post free).

Somerset

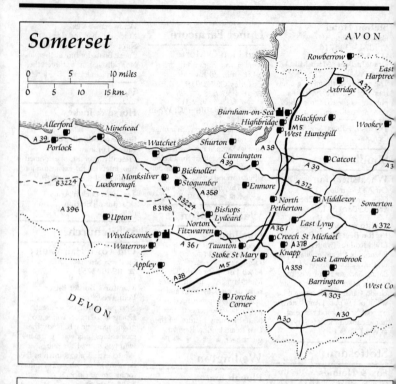

AVON

Rowberrow

East Harptree

Axbridge

A371

Blackford

Wookey

Burnham-on-Sea

Highbridge

West Huntspill

M5

Catcott

A39

A371

Allerford

Minehead

Watchet

Shurton

A38

Porlock

A39

Cannington

A39

Bicknoller

Monksilver

Stogumber

Enmore

A372

Middlezoy

Somerton

Luxborough

A358

North Petherton

B3224

B3188

B3224

Bishops Lydeard

East Lyng

A372

Upton

Norton Fitzwarren

A361

Creech St Michael

A318

Wiveliscombe

Knapp

East Lambrook

Waterrow

A361

Taunton

Stoke St Mary

A358

Appley

M5

Barrington

West Co

A38

A303

DEVON

Forches Corner

A30

A30

0   5   10 miles
0   5   10   15 km

🏭 **Ash Vine**, Trudoxhill; **Berrow, Royal Clarence**, Burnham-on-Sea; **Cotleigh**, **Exmoor**, Wiveliscombe; **Oakhill**, Oakhill

---

Allerford

Victory Inn
First left past Norton Fitzwarren, then left across railway
☎ (0823) 461282
11–2.30 (3 Sat), 6–11
Cotleigh Tawny; Exmoor Ale; Fuller's London Pride; Hall & Woodhouse Tanglefoot; Marston's Pedigree; Young's Special Ⓗ
Large, multi-roomed pub currently being renovated and upgraded. It offers a long list of permanent beers, good food and a comfortable atmosphere. Excellent garden (with animals) for children.
🏨 Q ❀ ⛄ ◑ ▮ 🍴 ♣ P

Appley

Globe Inn
Off A38, through Greenham
☎ (0823) 672327
11–2.30, 6.30–11
Cotleigh Tawny Ⓗ
Thriving, country pub with a traditional corridor serving area and a variety of rooms. Guest beer. 🏨 Q ❀ ⛄ ◑ ▮ ♣ P

Axbridge

Lamb Inn
The Square
☎ (0934) 732253
11–2.30 (3 Sat), 6.30–11 (12–2.30, 7–10.30 Sun)
Butcombe Bitter; Wadworth 6X Ⓗ
Rambling pub opposite King John's hunting lodge and now owned by Butcombe brewery. It features a large, terraced garden and an unusual bar made out of bottles. No food winter Sun eves. Guest beer.
Q ❀ ⛄ ◑ ▮ ♣ ◔

Barrington

Royal Oak
Off B3168 at Westport
☎ (0460) 53455
12–2.30, 7–11 (12–11 Sat)
Ash Vine Bitter; Exmoor Ale Ⓗ
Old, stone-built pub in a pretty village; two bars, a skittle alley and an upstairs function room. Normally at least two guest beers from a good range.
🏨 Q ⛄ ◑ ▮ 🍴 ♣ ◔ P

Bicknoller

Bicknoller Inn
32 Church Lane (2 miles E of Williton on A358, Taunton road)
☎ (0984) 56234
11–3.30 (may vary), 5.30–11
Draught Bass; Charrington IPA Ⓗ
Late 14th-century, traditional, thatched, country inn at the foot of the Quantocks; well situated for walkers. Large children's room with skittle alley, pool and darts. Guest beer.
🏨 Q ❀ ⛄ ◑ ▮ 🍴 ♣ ◔ P

Bishops Lydeard

Bell Inn
West Street (off A358)
☎ (0823) 432968
10.30–2.30, 6–11
Exmoor Ale; Wadworth 6X; Webster's Yorkshire Bitter Ⓗ
Village pub, popular with all ages: a large public bar with tiled floor and an adjoining children's games room; carpeted lounge and conservatory dining area, with a wide menu choice. Ten minutes' walk from West

Butcombe Bitter; Royal
Clarence Pride, Regent;
Wadworth 6X Ⓗ
Large, hotel bar on the seafront,
with a side pool/games area,
and a separate, quiet lounge bar.
Has its own brewery in the old
skittle alley. Always three guest
beers. Q ❧ ⇥ ◖ ▶ ⊕ ♣ P

Cannington

Maltshovel
Blackmoor Lane (off A39)
☎ (0278) 653432
11.30–3, 6.30 (7 winter)–11
Butcombe Bitter; Wadworth
6X Ⓗ
Thatched, country pub on a
secluded road at the back of the
village. Separate restaurant;
children's room and a tiny, cosy
public bar. Worth finding for a
quiet drink. Guest beer.
▥ Q ❧ ⇥ ◖ ▶ ⊕ ❧ Å ♣ ⇗ P

Castle Cary

White Hart
Fore Street ☎ (0963) 50255
11–3, 5.30–11 (11–11 Sat)
Courage Best Bitter; John
Smith's Bitter Ⓗ
Big, popular, modernised pub
with separate drinking areas.
▥ Q ⑧ ⇥ ◖ ▶ ♣ ⇗ P

Try also: Countryman (Free)

Catcott

King William
Off A39 ☎ (0278) 722374
11.30–3, 6–11
Eldridge Pope Dorchester,
Hardy Country, Royal Oak;
Palmers IPA Ⓗ
Village pub with a restaurant
extension. Small public bar with
dartboard and a traditional
lounge bar. The food area has
an old well, discovered during
building work.
Q ❧ ⑧ ◖ ▶ ⊕ ♣ ⇗ P

Cranmore

Strode Arms
Off A361 ☎ (074 988) 450
11.30–2.30, 6.30–11
Bunces Best Bitter;
Wadworth IPA, 6X Ⓗ
Attractive, country inn, in part
dating back to the 14th century.
Situated opposite the village
duck pond and near the East
Somerset railway. Guest beer
and Wilkins cider. No eve meals
Sun in winter. ▥ Q ⑧ ◖ ▶ ⇗ P

Creech St Michael

Bell Inn
St Michael Road
☎ (0823) 442881
12–2.30, 6.30–11
Oakhill Bitter; Ruddles Best
Bitter; Ushers Best Bitter Ⓗ

Active, village pub with a
games area/skittle alley and a
separate eating area on a higher
level (children's portions and a
vegetarian option).
▥ ❧ ⑧ ◖ ▶ Å ♣ P

East Harptree

Castle of Comfort
On B3134
☎ (0761) 221321
12–2.30, 7–11
Draught Bass; Butcombe
Bitter Ⓗ
Remote, stone-built, former
coaching inn on the site of the
Roman road. A real ale ghost in
residence – ask the landlord.
Live music Fri. Well worth a
visit. Good food and guest
beers. ⑧ ◖ ▶ ⊕ ♣ P

East Lambrook

Rose & Crown
Silver Street (off A303, N of S
Petherton)
☎ (0460) 40433
11.30–2.30, 7.30 (7 summer)–11
Ash Vine Bitter; Hook
Norton Best Bitter; Ind
Coope Burton Ale Ⓗ
Cosy, oak-beamed pub with
two bars and an attractive
garden. Guest beers. Bus stop
outside.
▥ ❧ ⑧ ◖ ▶ ⊕ ♣ ⇗ P

East Lyng

Rose & Crown
On A361, Taunton–
Glastonbury road
☎ (082 369) 235
11–2.30, 6.30–11
Butcombe Bitter; Eldridge
Pope Hardy Country, Royal
Oak Ⓗ
Comfortable pub with a stone
fireplace and wooden beams.
The well-tended garden offers
fine views across Sedgemoor.
Wheelchair access at the rear.
Skittle alley.
▥ Q ⑧ ⇥ ◖ ▶ ⇗ ≈ ♣ P

East Woodlands

Horse & Groom
1 mile E of A361/B3092 jct
OS792445 ☎ (0373) 462802
12–2.30 (not Mon), 6–11
Draught Bass; Butcombe
Bitter; Exmoor Ale; Fuller's
London Pride; Marston's
Pedigree; Wadworth 6X Ⓖ
Well worth finding; a 17th-
century inn at the edge of
Longleat Estate. Two
contrasting bars, one with a fine
open fireplace and a flagstoned
floor. The other is the more
recent, no-smoking Woodlands
bar, all traditional pine and
tranquillity. Cider in summer.
▥ Q ⑧ ◖ ▶ ⊕ Å ♣ ⇗ P ⅋

Somerset railway. Two skittle
alleys. Guest beer.
▥ Q ❧ ⑧ ◖ ▶ ⊕ ♣ P

Blackford

Sexeys Arms
On B3139, W of Wedmore
☎ (0934) 712487
11–2.30, 7–11
Courage Bitter Ale, Best
Bitter Ⓗ
13th-century, village inn with a
cosy, oak-beamed lounge,
warmed by a real log fire. The
basic bar has a dartboard and an
unusual roof. Meals in the bar
or restaurant, except Tue and
Wed eves (book restaurant,
especially at weekends).
▥ ❧ ⑧ ◖ ▶ ⊕ ♣ P

Bruton

Blue Ball
2 Coombe Street (A359)
☎ (0749) 812315
11.30–3 (2.30 winter), 6.30–11
Wadworth 6X Ⓗ
Dating from 1650: two
contrasting bars. John Steinbeck
reputedly wrote *Grapes of
Wrath* in the traditional Forge
Bar. ▥ ⇥ ◖ ▶ ⊕ ≈ ♣

Burnham-on-Sea

Royal Clarence Hotel
The Esplanade
☎ (0278) 783138
11–11

Somerset

Emborough

Old Down Inn
At A37/B3139 crossroads
☎ (0761) 232398
12–3, 7–11
Draught Bass Ⓗ&Ⓖ
Atmospheric coaching inn,
c. 1640, with a diversity of
rooms and old furniture. Burnt
down in 1886, but fortunately
rebuilt. Occasional guest beer in
summer. No meals Sun
lunchtime or winter eves.
🏠 Q ⬤ 🕸 🕽 🖳 ♣ ⌂ P

Enmore

Enmore Inn
☎ (0278) 422052
11–2.30, 6–11 (12–2.30, 7–10.30 Sun)
**Butcombe Bitter; John
Smith's Bitter; Whitbread
Flowers Original** Ⓗ
Large pub in a rural setting, yet
close to town. Attracts a mix of
local trade and outsiders. Guest
beer. 🕸 ⬤ 🕽 🖳 P

Try also: **Tynte Inn** (Free)

Faulkland

Tuckers Grave Inn
On A366, ½ mile N of village
☎ (0373) 834230
11–2.30, 6–11
**Draught Bass; Butcombe
Bitter** Ⓖ
The burial place of a 1747
suicide, this former farm cottage
has doubled as an inn for over
200 years. The story of Tucker
can be found above the parlour
fire. 🏠 Q ⬤ 🕽 ♣ ⌂ P

Forches Corner

Merry Harriers
OS083171 ☎ (0823) 42270
12–2.30, 6.30–11
**Cotleigh Tawny; Exmoor
Ale** Ⓗ
Isolated pub at a crossroads on
top of the Blackdown Hills, with
interconnected, low-ceilinged
rooms and open fires; large
garden and children's play area.
Guest beer.
🏠 🕸 ⬤ 🕽 🖳 ▲ ♣ ⌂ P

Frome

Sun
6 Catherine Street
☎ (0373) 73123
11–3, 6–11 (11–11 Sat)
**Felinfoel Double Dragon;
Hall & Woodhouse
Tanglefoot; Marston's Merrie
Monk, Pedigree; Wadworth
6X; Whitbread Flowers
Original** Ⓗ
Lively, former coaching inn in
an historic part of town. An
impressive oasis, well worth
finding. No food Sun. Guest
beer. 🏠 ⬤ 🖂 🕽 ♣ ⌂

Highbridge

Coopers Arms
Market Street (B3139, off A38,
near station)
☎ (0278) 783562
11–3, 5.30–11
**Cotleigh Old Buzzard;
Greene King Abbot; Palmers
IPA** Ⓔ
Large, modernised pub with
two lounge bars, a public bar
and a skittle alley/darts bar.
Guest beers in the cellar are
listed on a blackboard; ask
which ones are on (always at
least four). Q ⬤ 🖳 🚆 ♣ P

Knapp

Rising Sun
Off A361 OS301254
☎ (0823) 490436
11.30–2.30, 6.30–11
Draught Bass; Exmoor Ale Ⓗ
Country, food pub: plush bar
and a separate dining area
(supper licence). Close to the
Somerset Levels walking routes.
Meeting/children's room to the
side of the bar; campsite
opposite. Cider in summer.
🏠 Q ⬤ 🕸 🕽 🖳 ▲ ⌂ P

Luxborough

Royal Oak of
Luxborough
OS304257 ☎ (0984) 40319
11–2.30, 6 (7 winter)–11
**Cotleigh Tawny; Eldridge
Pope Royal Oak; Exmoor
Gold** Ⓖ; **Whitbread Flowers
IPA** Ⓗ
Locally known as the 'Blazing
Stump', this unspoilt, quaint inn
was voted the best in the South
West CAMRA region 1989/
1990. Folk music Fri. Guest
beers and cider in summer.
🏠 Q 🕸 🖂 🕽 🖳 ▲ ♣ ⌂ P

Middlezoy

George Inn
Main Street (just off A372)
☎ (0823) 69215
12–3 (not Mon, except bank hols),
7–11
Cotleigh Harrier, Tawny Ⓗ
Somerset CAMRA *Pub of the
Year* 1988 and 1990: a
flagstoned bar, a comfortable
lounge, a separate pool room
(where children are welcome)
and a skittle alley. Always a
choice of four guest beers and
often many more, especially at
the impromptu beer festivals.
Good food and an extensive
range of bottled beers.
🏠 ⬤ 🖂 🕽 🖳 ♣ P

Milborne Port

Queens Head
High Street ☎ (0963) 250314
11–2.30, 6–11

**Butcombe Bitter; Fuller's
London Pride; Hook Norton
Best Bitter; Ringwood
Fortyniner** Ⓗ
Historic, village pub with
character, a large courtyard,
separate restaurant and a skittle
alley. Excellent food and guest
beers.
🏠 Q ⬤ 🕸 🖂 🕽 🖳 🖳 ♣ ⌂ P

Minehead

Old Ship Aground
Quay Street ☎ (0643) 702087
11–2.30, 7–11 (may extend in summer)
Ushers Best Bitter Ⓗ
Large inn overlooking the
harbour, with a small public bar
and a comfortable lounge. The
patio (fronting a summer-only
bar) is suitable for children.
Handy for the West Somerset
railway.
🏠 🕸 🖂 🕽 🖳 ▲ ♣ P

Try also: **Haywards Bars**
(Ushers); **Wellington Hotel**
(Free)

Join CAMRA —
see page 480!

Monksilver

Notley Arms
☎ (0984) 56217
11–2.30, 6–11 (12–2.30, 7–10.30 Sun)
**Ruddles County; Theakston
Best Bitter; Ushers Best
Bitter** Ⓗ
Historic, village local with an
award for the best pub food in
the South West. A good family
room and facilities, and a large
garden. 🏠 Q ⬤ 🕸 🕽 🖳 ♣ P

North Petherton

Lamb Inn (Carvey's
Free House)
Fore Street ☎ (0278) 662336
11–3, 7–11
Cotleigh Tawny Ⓗ
Friendly, roadside pub with a
larger interior than it promises
from outside. Cosy sunken
dining area and split-level
lounge. Guest beers. ⬤ 🖂 🕽 ♣

Try also: **Walnut Tree** (Free)

Norton Fitzwarren

Ring of Bells
On B3227, near Taunton Cider
☎ (0823) 275995
11–2.30, 6–11
Cotleigh Tawny Ⓗ
A lively pub with two carpeted
bars plus a good skittle alley,
where children are welcome at
lunchtime. Good value food and
three guest beers.
🏠 ⬤ 🕽 ▲ ♣ ⌂ P

Nunney

George Inn
Church Street ($\frac{1}{2}$ mile N of A359/A361 jct)
☎ (0373) 84458
11 (12 winter)–3, 6 (6.30 winter)–11
Mole's Bitter; Ruddles County; Ushers Best Bitter Ⓗ
A comfortable former court-house and coaching inn, opposite the remains of moated Nunney Castle. Guest beer.
🏠 Q ⏰ 🍴 ◑ ◐ ♣ P

Oakhill

Oakhill Inn
Fosse Road (A367)
☎ (0749) 840442
11–3 (4 summer), 6.30–11
Eldridge Pope Hardy Country, Royal Oak; Oakhill Bitter Ⓗ
Recently-renovated, two-bar pub. The public is split into a cosy snug and a games area, with pool, darts and shove-ha'penny, popular with the young. Over 30s patronise the more food-oriented lounge (no food Mon eve). 🏠 🍴 ◑ ◐ ♣ P

Oldford

Ship
On B3090, 1½ miles N of Frome ☎ (0373) 462043
11–3.30, 6–11 (11–11 Sat)
Ruddles Best Bitter; Ushers Best Bitter; Websters Yorkshire Bitter Ⓗ
A warm welcome is enjoyed in this pleasantly modernised pub with three areas leading off a central bar. Good garden for children. Reasonably-priced food. Guest beer.
🏠 ⏰ 🍴 ◑ ♣ P

Porlock

Ship Inn
High Street (bottom of Porlock Hill)
10.30–3, 5.30–11
Draught Bass; Cotleigh Old Buzzard; Courage Best Bitter Ⓗ
13th-century, thatched inn within walking distance of the sea and moor. An old bar with a stone floor and a log fire in winter. A pub for conversation – there is no piped music and the games room is separate. The restaurant has vegetarian and children's menus. Guest beers.
🏠 Q ⏰ 🍴 ◑ ◐ ♠ ⏰ P

Rode

Cross Keys
20 High Street ($\frac{1}{2}$ mile N of A36/A361 jct)
☎ (0373) 830354
11–2.30, 6–11
Draught Bass; Charrington IPA Ⓗ
Traditional, two-bar pub in an old village, the former Fussell's brewery tap. Skittle alley.
🍴 ◐ ♣ P

Rowberrow

Swan Inn
Off A38 at Churchill
☎ (0934) 852371
12–2.30, 6–11
Draught Bass; Butcombe Bitter; Wadworth 6X Ⓗ
Former cider house converted from three stone cottages: two bars. Guest beers. 🏠 Q ⏰ 🍴 ◑ ◐ ♣ P

Rudge

Full Moon
1 mile N of A36 at Standerwick
☎ (0373) 830936
12–2.30 (not Mon), 6–11
Draught Bass; Butcombe Bitter; Wadworth 6X Ⓗ
A step back in time; a pub with flagged floors and small rooms where recent changes have not spoilt the traditional character. The garden has a children's play area. No lunches Mon.
🏠 Q ⏰ 🍴 ◑ ◐ ◐ ♣ P

Shepton Mallet

Horseshoe Inn
Bowlish (A371, $\frac{3}{4}$ mile W of centre) ☎ (0749) 342209
12–2.30 (not Tue; 11.30–3.30 Sat), 6–11 (12–2.30, 7–10.30 Sun)
Felinfoel Double Dragon; Wiltshire Stonehenge Bitter, Old Grumble Ⓗ
Spacious public bar with pool, darts and shove-ha'penny, and a pleasant, comfortable lounge, warmed in winter by two blazing wood fires. Guest beer.
🏠 🍴 ◐ ◐ P

Kings Arms
Leg Square (near B3136)
☎ (0749) 343781
11–2.30, 6–11
Ansells Bitter; Ind Coope Burton Ale; Wadworth 6X Ⓗ
17th-century pub of character, in the northern part of town, known locally as the 'Dust Hole'. *Beware the Addlestones cider, dispensed using CO_2.* No eve meals Sun. ⏰ 🍴 ◑ ◑ ♣ P

Shepton Montague

Montague Inn
$\frac{1}{4}$ mile off A359, near A371 jct
☎ (0749) 813213
12–2, 5.30 (6 winter)–11
Butcombe Bitter; Marston's Pedigree Ⓖ
Attractive, country inn with a friendly atmosphere and traditional comforts. Small snug to the rear of the main bar.

Guest beer and Sandford cider. Lunches served weekends only in winter. 🏠 Q ⏰ 🍴 ◑ ◐ ♣ P

Shurton

Shurton Inn
Follow signs for Hinkley Point
☎ (0278) 732695
11–2.30, 6–11
Exmoor Ale, Stag; Hall & Woodhouse Badger Best Bitter Ⓗ
Comfortable, village pub close to Hinkley Point power station. Regular live music and functions, incl. Xmas party on Midsummer's Day! Guest beers.
🏠 Q ⏰ 🍴 ◑ ◐ ◑ ♣ ♣ ⏰ P

Somerton

Unicorn at Somerton
West Street ☎ (0458) 72101
11–2 (4 occasionally), 5.30–11
Draught Bass; Oakhill Bitter Ⓗ
16th-century coaching inn with an original fireplace. The comfortable and relaxing bar always has at least five real ales available – over 50 different ones each year. Local farmhouse cider; boules and skittles. A pub which complements the historic town. No meals Sun eve.
🏠 Q 🍴 ◑ ◐ ◐ ♣ ⏰ P

Stogumber

White Horse
☎ (0984) 56277
11–2.30, 6–11
Cotleigh Tawny; Exmoor Ale Ⓗ
Traditional pub opposite the 12th-century church in a pretty village. Restaurant and accommodation available in an old market house now joined to the pub. Excellent home-made food and an extensive bar menu. Children not admitted. Cider in summer. 🏠 ⏰ 🍴 ◑ ◐ ♣ ⏰

Stoke St Mary

Half Moon
Off A358 at Henlade
☎ (0823) 442271
11.30 (11 Wed–Sat)–2.30, 6–11
Marston's Pedigree; Whitbread Boddingtons Bitter, Flowers IPA Ⓗ
Popular, renovated, country pub with a stone-flagged bar area and separate dining areas.
Q ⏰ 🍴 ◑ ◐ ◑ ♣ P

Taunton

Black Horse
Bridge Street ☎ (0823) 272151
11–3, 7–11
Exmoor Ale; Whitbread Boddingtons Bitter, Castle Eden Ale Ⓗ

Somerset

Popular, friendly and well-run, town pub. Tastefully-refurbished, it extends a long way back from the entrance.
🏠 🕾 🍴 ◑ 🚻 ♣

Masons Arms
Magdalene Street (next to St Mary's church)
🕾 (0823) 288916
10.30–3, 5 (6 Sat)–11
Draught Bass; Exmoor Ale; Goldfinch Tom Brown's Ⓗ
Comfortable, back-street pub in the town centre. Guest beers in winter and always the best range of independent beers in town. Q 🛏 ◑ ◗ 🚲

Minstrels (Castle Hotel)
Castle Bow, North Street
🕾 (0823) 272671
11–3, 7–11
Draught Bass; Eldridge Pope Hardy Country Ⓗ
L-shaped bar at the rear of Castle Hotel: tastefully renovated with lots of dark woodwork and panelling. Live music Wed and Sun eves. Guest beer. 🛏 ◑ ◗

Wood Street Inn
Wood Street 🕾 (0823) 333011
11–3, 6–11 (11–11 Thu, Fri & Sat)
Courage Directors; John Smith's Bitter Ⓗ
Busy, friendly, back-street local; an L-shaped bar with a separate pool room. Yard/garden at the rear. 🕾 🛏 ◑ 🚻 🚲 ♣

Trudoxhill

White Hart
½ mile S of A361 at Nunney Catch 🕾 (0373) 84324
12 (11.30 Sat)–2.30, 7 (6.30 Fri & Sat)–11
Ash Vine Bitter, Challenger, Tanker; Butcombe Bitter Ⓗ
A comfortable atmosphere in a village pub with a purpose-built brewery at the rear.
🏠 🕾 ◑ ◗ 🚲 P

Upton

Lowtrow Cross Inn
12–3 (not Tue in winter), 6–11
Draught Bass; Cotleigh Tawny Ⓗ
Unspoilt, rural village local in a remote part of the Brendon Hills. Has own camping and caravan site. Large skittle alley/games room for children, and swings outside.
🏠 🕾 ◑ 🚲 A ♣ P

Watchet

West Somerset Hotel
Swain Street 🕾 (0984) 34434
11–3, 6–11 (11–11 Sat)
Ushers Best Bitter Ⓗ
Large hotel in the centre of town, offering good value accommodation. Conveniently

situated near West Somerset railway station. Guest beers.
🕾 🛏 ◑ ◗ 🚲 ♣

Try also: **Bell** (Free)

Waterrow

Rock Inn
On B3227
🕾 (0984) 23293
11–2.30, 6–11
Cotleigh Tawny; Exmoor Gold; Ushers Best Bitter Ⓗ
Old pub set in a pretty, little valley and built against a rock face, which forms part of the fireplace. One end of the bar serves as the public, the other the lounge, which leads to the restaurant.
🏠 Q 🚲 🕾 🛏 ◑ ◗ A ♣ ○ P

West Coker

Royal George
11 High Street (A30)
🕾 (0935) 862334
11–2.30, 6–11 (12–2, 7–10.30 Sun)
Draught Bass; Hall & Woodhouse Tanglefoot; Welsh Brewers Worthington BB Ⓗ
Character pub with oak-beamed ceilings and a friendly atmosphere. Separate games room with bar billiards and a superb skittle alley/function room, the latter a recent addition built in sympathetic style. Extended opening for food Sun (6–11).
🏠 Q 🕾 ◑ ◗ ♣ ○ P

West Huntspill

Royal Artillery
On A38
🕾 (0278) 783553
11–2.30, 7–11
Butcombe Bitter; Courage Best Bitter Ⓗ
Cosy locals' pub with a small lounge area and a dartboard. Lunchtime snacks. Q 🕾 🚲 P

Wincanton

Bear Inn
Market Place 🕾 (0963) 32581
11–2.30, 5.30–11 (11–11 Sat)
Draught Bass; Marston's Pedigree; Smiles Best Bitter Ⓗ
Comfortable, oak-beamed hotel with a collection of Toby jugs. Guest beers. No eve meals Sun.
🏠 🛏 ◑ ◗ A ♣ P

Dolphin Hotel
High Street 🕾 (0963) 32215
11–3, 6–11
Courage Best Bitter; Oakhill Bitter, Yeoman Ⓗ
Lively, convivial, High Street hotel bar, where the landlord is the chef. Guest beers.
🏠 Q 🕾 🛏 ◑ ◗ 🚲 ♣ ○ P

Witham Friary

Seymour Arms
OS745409
11.30–2.30, 6–11
Ushers Best Bitter Ⓗ
Old village local, unspoilt by progress. Central serving hatch and a fine garden. Taunton and Bulmers cider available.
🏠 Q 🕾 🚲 ♣ ○

Wiveliscombe

Courtyard Hotel
High Street 🕾 (0984) 23737
11.30–3, 7–11
Exmoor Ale, Gold, Stag; Ringwood Old Thumper Ⓗ
Small bar area with the atmosphere of a lounge; a friendly, quiet pub. Monthly folk music in downstairs cellar bar. Q 🛏

Wookey

Burcott Inn
On B3139, 2 miles W of Wells
🕾 (0749) 73874
11–2.30 (3 Sat), 6–11
Butcombe Bitter Ⓗ
Deservedly popular, roadside pub with a friendly atmosphere. Over 40 different guest beers per year and always two available (mid and high gravity). An L-shaped bar with a copper serving top and a small games room; children are welcome in the dining room. The good-sized garden boasts an old cider press. No eve meals Sun or Mon. 🏠 Q 🕾 ◑ ◗ ♣ P

Yeovil

Alexandra
Southwestern Terrace (next to old station car park)
🕾 (0935) 23723
11–11
Gale's XXXD, Best Bitter, HSB Ⓗ
Traditional, town pub offering the Gale's range of country wines, as well as its excellent beer. ◑ 🚲 ♣ ○

Armoury
1 The Park (A30 opp. hospital)
🕾 (0935) 71047
11–2.30 (3 Fri & Sat), 6 (6.30 Mon & Tue)–11
Adnams Broadside; Butcombe Bitter; Hall & Woodhouse Tanglefoot (summer); **Wadworth 6X, Farmer's Glory, Old Timer** Ⓗ
A lively, simply furnished, town pub, converted from an old armoury. HQ of *Real Ale: The Armoury Society* (RATAS).
Q 🕾 ◑ 🚲 ♣ ○

Try also: **Fleur de Lys**, Mudford Rd (Bass)

THE BEER BOOKSHOP

CAMRA and its publishing subsidiary, Alma Books, produce the most extensive and authoritative list of titles on the subject of beer and pubs. Here is a selection of the best beer books around.

Susan Nowak's *Good Pub Food* sold out in its first edition. The second edition, completely revised, will take you to pubs whose the food rivals the finest restaurant's at a fraction of the cost, with the added attraction of offering a decent pint of real ale to accompany your meal. But if it's a roof over your head that you're after, you need *Beer, Bed & Breakfast* by Roger Protz, now in its third edition. This indispensable guide to reasonably-priced accommodation in some of the country's best hostelries is an ideal holiday planner and, in conjunction with Roger's *Real Ale Drinker's Almanac* – a handy, pocket-sized hardback guide to the breweries and beers of Britain – livens up any business trip.

Roger is also co-editor of *CAMRA's 21st Birthday Book*. This chronicle of the life and times of the best known and probably the best loved pressure group in the country features items on the movement's foundation and its many campaigns, and an evaluation of CAMRA's influence on the brewing industry to date and in the future. It's a commemorative volume no dedicated real ale drinker will want to miss (available from spring 1992).

Another book which extols the pleasures (and sometimes pitfalls) of beer drinking is Barrie Pepper's *Bedside Book of Beer*, an anthology of writings connected with beer, pubs and breweries, with contributions from Shakespeare, Joyce and Orwell, to name but a few. For the more practically-minded, the *CAMRA Guide to Home Brewing*, by Graham Wheeler, is the definitive work on the subject. It includes essential tips on techniques and problem solving, as well as a good selection of recipes.

Alma's regional guides, in depth pub selections for Devon & Cornwall, East Anglia, Lakeland, London, North Wales and Yorkshire, carry the kind of extra detail on classic, real ale pubs which it is impossible to include in the *Good Beer Guide*. Ideal for holidays, they are now available at a reduced price, so buy yours while stocks last.

Other publications to look out for include Jill Adam's *The Best Pubs for Families*, which pinpoints over 400 pubs around the country where children are genuinely made welcome and where harrassed parents can enjoy a good pint of ale. David Kitton's *Good Cider Guide*, now in its third edition, is another national guide, offering an exhaustive listing of real cider producers and outlets, and a title to look out for in 1992 is Alma's *The Best Waterside Pubs*, which will prove to be an invaluable companion for users of the country's canals and rivers. All the above titles are available post-free from CAMRA. Use the order form on page 477.

Staffordshire

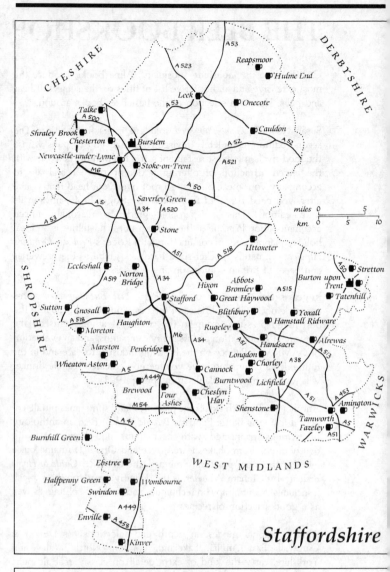

Staffordshire

🏠 **Burton Bridge, Heritage, Marston's**, *Burton upon Trent*; **Titanic**, *Burslem*

Abbots Bromley

Baggot Arms
Baggot Street (B5234, N end of village) ☎ (0283) 840371
11–2.30, 6–11
Marston's Pedigree Ⓗ
18th-century coaching inn – a meeting place for Blithfield Reservoir traditionalists.
🏠 ◖ P

Royal Oak
Main Street ☎ (0283) 840117
12–3, 6.30–11 (12–2, 7–10.30 Sun)
Courage Directors; Marston's Pedigree Ⓗ
Former 17th-century farmhouse, much-beamed. Full bar menu and an excellent restaurant.
🏠 Q ◖ P

Alrewas

George & Dragon
Main Street ☎ (0283) 790202
11–2.30 (3 Sat), 6–11 (12–2.30, 7–10.30 Sun)
Marston's Pedigree Ⓗ

Popular, friendly, village-centre pub. 'Claymore' restaurant and a motel next door.
🏠 ✱ ⇥ ◖ ♣ P

Amington

Pretty Pigs
Shuttington Road
☎ (0827) 63129
11–3, 5–11
Draught Bass; M&B Mild, Brew XI Ⓔ
Large, roadside pub well furnished and comfortable with

beamed ceilings. Good food always available in the dining area and upstairs carvery.
🍴🛏🍺◖◗♣ P

Blithbury

Bull & Spectacles
Uttoxeter Road (B5014)
☎ (088 922) 201
12–3, 6–11
Ind Coope Burton Ale; Marston's Pedigree ℍ
15th-century, country pub close to Blithbury Reservoir. Popular for food. 🍺🍴◖◗🍺♣ P

Brewood

Admiral Rodney
21 Dean Street (on Coven road out of village centre)
OS859089 ☎ (0902) 850853
11–3, 5.30–11
HP&D Mild, Bitter, Entire, Plant's Progress ℍ
Black Country-style pub, adapted to its rural Staffs setting. Collection of Staffordshire dogs. No meals Sun eve. Booking advisable at busy times. 🍺🍴◖◗♣ P

Burnhill Green

Dartmouth Arms
Snowden Road OS787006
☎ (074 65) 268
12–2.30, 7–11 (12–2.30, 7–10.30 Sun)
Ansells Mild, Bitter; Ind Coope Burton Ale ℍ
Popular, village pub, renowned for its home-made bar meals/snacks. Children's meals may be taken in the garden only. No food Sun eve or Mon lunchtime. Well worth finding. Allied guest beer. 🍺 Q 🍴◖◗ P

Burntwood

Trident
166 Chase Road (off B5190 Cannock–Lichfield road)
12–2.30 (4 Sat), 7–11
Marston's Pedigree ℍ
Popular local whose small lounge is adorned with model planes and pictures – distinctly different. The large bar has a pool table. Q 🍺🍺♣ P

Burton upon Trent

Anglesey Arms
104 Bearwood Hill Road, Winshill (off A50, Ashby Road) ☎ (0283) 64791
10.30–2.30 (3.30 Sat), 5.30–11
Marston's Burton Best Bitter, Pedigree, Owd Rodger ℍ
Popular local with a traditional lounge. Renovations have included provision of a family room in the conservatory. Boasts the oldest bowling green in Burton. Good value snacks.
🍴🍺🍺◖◗♣ P

Beacon Hotel
277 Tutbury Road (off A50)
☎ (0283) 68968
11–3, 6–11
Draught Bass ℍ
Comfortable, spacious, three-roomed hostelry. Excellent bar snacks and meals. Purpose-built family room. Guest beer.
Q 🍴🍺🍴◖◗🍺♣ P

Burton Bridge Brewery
24 Bridge Street (A50, 250 yds W of river) ☎ (0283) 36596
11.30–3, 5.30–11
Burton Bridge XL, Bridge Bitter, Porter, Top Dog Stout (winter) ℍ
Brewery tap where a friendly welcome is assured. Bar has spartan furnishings, including wooden pews. Upstairs function room and skittle alley. Guest beer on Sun. 🍺 Q ◖◗♣

Prince Alfred
Derby Street ☎ (0283) 62178
11–3, 6–11
Courage Directors; John Smith's Bitter ℍ
Pub run by the longest-serving landlord in Burton: 32 years. The smart lounge has a CD jukebox; the public bar has darts and a pool table. Separate children's room with video games. 🍴🛏◖◗🍴♣ P

Roebuck
Station Street ☎ (0283) 68660
11–11 (11–3, 6–11 Sat; 12–3, 7.30–10.30 Sun)
Ansells Mild, Bitter; Ind Coope ABC Best Bitter, Burton Ale; Tetley Bitter ℍ
Single room used by brewery workers and decorated with unusual ornaments. Fun quiz Sun (fortnightly). Only one guest beer pump, but at least 30 different beers have been served. 🛏◖◗♣ ↻

Cannock

Unicorn
62 Church Street, Hendsford
12–2.30 (3 summer), 7–11
Ansells Mild, Bitter; Marston's Pedigree ℍ
Basic pub with a busy bar and a quiet lounge where food is served. 🍺🍺◖◗🍺♣ 🍴 P

Cauldon

Yew Tree
Off A52/A523
11–3, 6–11
Draught Bass; Burton Bridge XL; M&B Mild ℍ
One of the finest pubs in the country, dating back to the 17th century. Its superb collection of assorted antiques includes working polyphonia, a pianola, grandfather clocks and sundry Victoriana. Note the old yew tree in the car park.
Q 🛏🍺🍴🏕♣ P

Cheslyn Hay

Mary Rose
Moon Lane
12–2.30, 6.30–11 (12–2.30, 7–10.30 Sun)
Ansells Mild, Bitter; Ind Coope Burton Ale; Tetley Bitter ℍ
A converted farmhouse with a display of Mary Rose memorabilia. Excellent food (not available Sun eve). 🍺◖◗🍴 P

Chesterton

Black Horse
Castle Street
☎ (0782) 561313
12–3 (4 Sat), 7–11
Ind Coope Burton Ale; Tetley Bitter ℍ
Recently-modernised, locals' pub, sporting a traditional bar and a lounge. The outdoor patio is part-covered. Guest beers.
◖◗♣ ↻

Chorley

Malt Shovel
1 mile N of B5190 Lichfield–Cannock road OS112070
12–2.30, 7–11 (12–2.30, 7–10.30 Sun)
Ansells Mild, Bitter; Ind Coope Burton Ale; Tetley Bitter ℍ
Village pub hidden in a maze of country lanes. Cosy lounge and down-to-earth bar; regular sing-alongs. 🍺 Q 🍺🍺♣ P

Ebstree

Holly Bush
Ebstree Road OS854959
☎ (0902) 895587
12.30–2.30 (11.30–3 Sat), 6–11 (12–2.30, 7–10.30 Sun)
Ansells Mild, Bitter; Ind Coope Burton Ale; Tetley Bitter ℍ
Pleasant, country pub, half a mile west of the Staffs and Worcester Canal. Barbecues on summer weekends. Beware of the spider! 🍺🍺◖◗🍺♣ P

Eccleshall

Bell
High Street ☎ (0785) 850378
11.30–3 (4 Fri, 5 Sat), 6–11
Draught Bass; Welsh Brewers Worthington BB ℍ
Popular pub in the town centre: the lounge fireplace is a feature.
🍺🛏🍺◖◗🍺🍴♣ P

Royal Oak
High Street ☎ (0785) 850230
11–3, 6.30–11
Burtonwood Best Bitter, Forshaw's ℍ
Large, town-centre free house with a restaurant, a comfortable lounge and a small, cosy snug.
🛏🍺◖◗🏕♣ P

Staffordshire

St George Hotel
Castle Street
☎ (0785) 850300
11–11
Banks's Bitter; Ind Coope Burton Ale; Tetley Bitter Ⓗ
Enterprising central hotel offering restaurant and conference facilities. The site has been occupied at various times by a coaching inn, a draper's shop and an undertaker's – one area is still referred to as the Coffin Room. ♨ ⓦ ⋈ ◖ ◑ ♣ P

Enville

Cat
Bridgnorth Road (A458)
☎ (0384) 872209
11–3, 6–11 (closed Sun)
Holden's Special; Hook Norton Old Hooky; Marston's Pedigree; Theakston XB, Old Peculier; Younger IPA Ⓗ
Part 16th-century country inn with a games room at the rear and a restaurant upstairs. Boules in summer. Beer range varies. ♨ Q ⓦ ◖ ◑ ⊟ & ♣ P

Fazeley

Three Horseshoes
New Street (off the Birmingham road) ☎ (0827) 289754
12–2.30 (3 Fri & Sat), 7–11 (12–2.30, 7–10.30 Sun)
Draught Bass Ⓗ
Small, back-street pub with a comfortable lounge bar. Ask about the Bass Club. ⓦ ♣

Four Ashes

Four Ashes
Station Drive (A449, Stafford road) ☎ (0902) 790229
11–3, 5–11 (11–11 Sat)
Banks's Mild, Bitter Ⓔ
Large, comfortable roadside pub with a rural vista (apart from the chemical works!). Bowls played. No food Sun. ♨ ⓦ ◖ ♣ P

Gnosall

Horns
High Street ☎ (0785) 822441
11–3 (3.30 Sat), 6–11
Draught Bass; M&B Springfield Bitter Ⓔ
Convivial, village-centre pub. Ask the landlord about the 'carved' bar front. Small car park. ⊟ ♣ P

Royal Oak
Newport Road (A518)
☎ (0785) 822362
12–3, 6–11
Ansells Bitter; Ind Coope Burton Ale; Tetley Bitter Ⓗ
Hospitable, two-roomed, village local: a narrow, basic bar and a larger, more comfortable lounge. ♨ ⓦ ◖ ◑ ⊟ ♣ P

Great Haywood

Fox & Hounds
Main Road ☎ (0889) 881252
12–11
Ansells Bitter; Ind Coope Burton Ale; Marston's Pedigree; Tetley Bitter Ⓗ
Extended, open-plan pub near the Trent and Mersey Canal.
♨ ⓦ ◖ ◑ & ♣ P

Halfpenny Green

Royal Oak
OS825920 ☎ (0384) 88318
11.30–3, 6–11
Banks's Mild, Bitter Ⓔ
Popular, old country local on the crossroads near the aerodrome. ♨ ⓦ ◖ ◑ ♣ ◔ P

Hamstall Ridware

Shoulder of Mutton
Yoxall Road ☎ (088 92) 389
11–3, 6 (7 winter)–11
Beer range varies
An oasis for real ale lovers in the Staffs countryside, close to the Ridware Art Centre. Regular guest beers from Lloyds and Burton Bridge. ♨ ⓦ ◖ ◑ ♣ P

Handsacre

Crown Inn
24 The Green
11–3, 6–11
Draught Bass; M&B Highgate Mild Ⓗ
Picturesque and friendly canalside pub. Lunchtime snacks.
Q ⓦ ⊟ ♣ P

Haughton

Bell
Newport Road (A518)
☎ (0785) 780301
11–3, 6–11
Banks's Mild; Courage Best Bitter, Directors Ⓗ
One-roomed, village pub with a vast collection of book matches on display. ♨ ⓦ ◖ ◑ ♣ P

Hixon

Green Man
Lea Road ☎ (0889) 270931
12–3 (11.30–4 Sat), 6–11
Draught Bass; Welsh Brewers Worthington BB Ⓗ
Village pub, north of the high street, with a keen fundraising clientele. Home-cooked food (incl. vegetarian dishes); eve meals Tue–Sat.
♨ ⓦ ◖ ◑ ⊟ & ▲ ♣ P

Hulme End

Manifold Hotel
10 miles E of Leek on B5054
☎ (028 84) 537
11–3, 7–11
Wards Mild, Thorne Best

Bitter, Sheffield Best Bitter Ⓗ
Formerly the 'Light Railway', an impressive stone-built hotel in open countryside by the River Manifold. A friendly welcome, excellent accommodation and food. Occasional live folk or jazz. Guest beers in summer.
♨ Q ⓦ ⋈ ◖ ◑ & ▲ ♣ P

Kinver

Plough & Harrow
High Street ☎ (0384) 872659
12–2.30 (3 Sat), 7–11
Batham Mild, Best Bitter, XXX Ⓗ
Three-roomed pub, known locally as the 'Steps'. Handy for the Staffs and Worcs Canal. Meals Tue–Sat. ♨ ⋈ ◖ ◑ ⊟ ♣ P

Leek

Abbey Inn
Abbey Green Lane (1 mile out of Leek, off the Macclesfield road) ☎ (0538) 382865
11–3, 7–11
Draught Bass Ⓗ
Delightful, three-storey, stone-built pub. A central bar serves all rooms which have a good atmosphere. Good food lunch and early eve. Excellent value. Guest beer. ♨ Q ⓦ ⋈ ◖ ◑ P

Blue Mugge
17 Osborne Street (400 yds from bus station)
11–3 (4 Sat), 6 (7 Sat)–11
Draught Bass Ⓗ
Friendly, four-roomed pub with a central bar. Excellent value food and beer. The young landlord is popular with locals. No meals weekends. ⓦ ◖ ♣

Dyers Arms
Macclesfield Road
☎ (0538) 382321
11.30–3, 7–11
Draught Bass Ⓗ
Two-roomed pub, just out of town. A good welcome is assured from the landlord, a former Stoke City FC player. Limited parking. ♨ ◖ ⊟ ♣ P

Wellington
104 Strangman Street
11–3, 7–11
Marston's Mercian Mild, Burton Best Bitter, Pedigree Ⓗ
Popular, good, old-fashioned, street-corner local with two rooms. All beer is served from the lounge. Note the unusual pump sleeves. Q ⊟ ♣

Wilkes Head
St Edward Street
☎ (0538) 383616
11.30–3, 7–11
Ind Coope Burton Ale; Tetley Bitter Ⓗ
Small, three-roomed pub with

old stables to the rear; dates from c.1730. Live music upstairs. Guest beers. No food Sun. ♨ Q ◖ ♣ P

Lichfield

Carpenters Arms
Christchurch Lane (off A461)
☎ (0543) 262098
12–3 (4 Fri & Sat), 7–11
Banks's Mild, Bitter Ⓗ
Friendly local in a residential area, west of the city. Close to Pype Green and Leomensly Woods. ♣ P

City Frog
Frog Lane
11–3, 5.30–11 (11–11 Fri & Sat)
Draught Bass; Stones Best Bitter Ⓗ
Lively, city pub, convenient for local Indian and Chinese eating houses. ◖ ⇌ (City) ♣

Little Barron Hotel
Beacon Street
☎ (0543) 414500
11–3, 5–11
Theakston Best Bitter, XB, Old Peculier Ⓗ
Family-run hotel close to the park. The banqueting suite also has a bar. ⇔ ◖ ▸ P

Queens Head
Queens Street
11–3, 7–11
Marston's Pedigree Ⓗ
A traditional pub: friendly, no frills, but good company. ⊞ ♣

Longdon

Swan with Two Necks
Brook End ☎ (0543) 490251
12–2.30, 7–11
Ansells Mild, Bitter; Ind Coope ABC Best Bitter, Burton Ale Ⓗ
400 year-old, village pub with a low ceiling, authentic beams and a stone slab floor. Excellent restaurant (eves). ♨ Q ⬛ ◖ ▸ ⊞ P

Marston

Fox
1 mile NW of Wheaton Aston
OS835140 ☎ (0785) 840729
12–4, 7–11
Hall & Woodhouse Tanglefoot; Lloyds Country; Marston's Pedigree, Owd Rodger (winter); **Wood Special** Ⓗ
Somewhat isolated rural free house, especially popular with cyclists; well worth seeking out. Snacks available. Guest beers. ♨ Q ⬛ ⊞ ▲ ♣ ⇨ P

Moreton

Rising Sun
2 miles E of A41 OS799168
☎ (0952) 70251

11.30–5, 7–11
Marston's Burton Best Bitter, Pedigree Ⓗ
Friendly, rather isolated, country pub. Bar billiards in the snug, which also serves as a family room.
♨ ⇖ ⬛ ◖ ▸ ⊞ ♣ P

Newcastle-under-Lyme

Castle Mona
Victoria Street (off A34 S)
☎ (0782) 612849
12–3 (may vary), 7–11
Greenalls Davenports Bitter, Thomas Greenall's Bitter Ⓗ
Two-roomed, street-corner local, well worth the few minutes' walk from the town centre. Attracts a thriving sports and social fraternity. Occasionally closed weekday lunchtimes. Q ⊞ ♣

Crossways
Nelson Place
☎ (0782) 616953
11–3, 7–11
Courage Directors; John Smith's Magnet Ⓗ
Large pub opposite Queens Gardens on the outskirts of town. Disco music some eves. No food Sun. ◖ ▸ ♣

Victoria
62 King Street (A53 to Hanley)
☎ (0782) 615569
11–3 (4.30 Sat), 5 (7 Sat)–11
Draught Bass; Stones Best Bitter Ⓗ
Two-roomed, corner pub, a few minutes' walk from the town centre. Handy for the Victoria Theatre. Strong games and quiz following. Now offers an extended range of lunchtime food. Q ⬛ ◖ ⊞ ♣

Norton Bridge

Railway
Station Road (off A520)
☎ (0785) 760289
11–4, 7–11
Draught Bass Ⓗ
Tastefully renovated pub, a few yards from the west coast main line railway junction.
♨ ⬛ ⊞ ▲ ⇌ ♣ P

Onecote

Jervis Arms
6 miles E of Leek on B5054
☎ (0538) 304206
12–3, 7–11
Draught Bass; Ruddles County; Theakston XB, Old Peculier Ⓗ
Popular, country inn, noted for its hospitality, fine food and large garden, good for families.
Q ⇖ ⬛ ◖ ▸ ⊞ ♿ ▲ ♣ P

Penkridge

Cross Keys
Filance Lane (by Staffs & Worcs Canal bridge 86, 400 yds off A449) OS925134
☎ (0785) 712826
11–3 (4 Sat), 6.30–11
Draught Bass Ⓗ; **M&B Highgate Mild, Springfield Bitter** Ⓔ
Modernised pub, attracting much canal trade in summer. Barbecue in the garden, but no food Sun eve. ⬛ ◖ ▸ ♣ P

White Hart
Stone Cross (A449, 20 yds from B5012 jct) ☎ (0785) 712242
11.30–4, 6–11
Draught Bass; M&B Highgate Mild, Springfield Bitter, Brew XI Ⓔ
Excellent, village-centre hostelry with a brook running through its beer garden. Eve meals till 9pm.
♨ ⬛ ◖ ▸ ⊞ ⇌ ♣ P

Reapsmoor

Butchers Arms
8 miles E of Leek, on Longnor road ☎ (029 88) 4477
12–3, 7–11
Marston's Pedigree Ⓗ
Welcoming, rural pub, popular with the locals. Can be isolated in winter. Guest beers. Bar snacks. ♨ Q ▲ P

Rugeley

Albion
Albion Street
11–4, 5.30–11 (11–11 Fri & Sat)
Banks's Mild, Bitter Ⓔ
Lively, town-centre local, catering for all tastes. ⬛ ♣

Saverley Green

Hunter
Sandon Road
☎ (0782) 392067
12–3, 7–11
Ind Coope ABC Best Bitter, Burton Ale; Tetley Bitter Ⓗ
Cosy, country pub with great hospitality. Occasional beer festivals and guest beers.
♨ ⇖ ⬛ ⊞ ▲ ♣ P

Shenstone

Railway
Main Street (off A5127, 200 yds S of A5)
☎ (0543) 480503
11.30–2.30, 5.30–11
Marston's Merrie Monk, Pedigree Ⓗ
A true village pub with a locals' bar and a split-level lounge. No food Sun. ⬛ ◖ ⇌ ♣ P

Staffordshire

Shraley Brook

Rising Sun Inn
Knowle Bank Road (off A52)
☎ (0782) 720600
12–3.30, 6.30–11 (11–11 Sat)
**Rising Sun Sunlight, Rising,
Setting, Sun Stroke, Total
Eclipse, Solar Flare** Ⓗ
Very popular free house which
has undergone many changes
over the years yet still retains
its character. Has brewed its
own beers since 1989. Guest
beers; good selection of food.
🏠 ⌛ ◖ ▶ & Å ⌒ P

Stafford

Bird in Hand
Mill Street ☎ (0785) 52198
11–11 (11–4, 7–11 Sat)
**Courage Best Bitter,
Directors** Ⓗ
Popular and enterprising, town-
centre pub with a bar, a snug, a
lounge and a games room.
Guest beer. 🍴 ◖ 🍺 ♣

Coach & Horses
Mill Bank ☎ (0785) 223376
11–3.30 (4.30 Sat), 7–11
**Draught Bass; M&B
Springfield Bitter** Ⓗ
Straightforward pub near the
main post office and Victoria
Park. Lunchtime snacks. 🍺 ≢ ♣

Cottage by the Brook
Peel Terrace ☎ (0785) 223563
12–3.30, 7–11 (12–11 Fri & Sat)
**Ind Coope ABC Best Bitter,
Burton Ale; Marston's
Pedigree; Tetley Bitter** Ⓗ
Large, lively, four-roomed pub
warmed by real fires in the
lounge and club room – where
children are welcome. Bar
snacks. 🏠 🍴 🍺 ♣

Holmcroft
Holmcroft Road (100 yds off
A5013) ☎ (0785) 52634
11–3, 6–11 (11–11 Sat)
Banks's Mild, Bitter Ⓔ
Popular, estate pub run by a
long-established landlord. No
food Sun. 🍴 ◖ 🍺 ♣ P

Railway Inn
23 Castle Street, Castletown
☎ (0785) 42890
12–2.30 (not Sat), 6 (7 Sat)–11
**Ansells Bitter; Ind Coope
Burton Ale** Ⓗ
Victorian, street-corner local
which boasts a large whisky
selection. The menu caters for
vegetarians. Home of the
Osprey International Powerboat
Rescue Team. Guest beer.
🏠 Q ◖ ▶ 🍺 ≢ ♣

Rifleman
Common Road ☎ (0785) 40515
12–3, 5–11
**Ansells Bitter; Ind Coope
Burton Ale; Marston's
Pedigree** Ⓗ

Comfortable, one-room pub
next to Stafford Common. Guns
feature in the decor. Live music.
🏠 🍴 ◖ ▶ P

Stafford Arms
Railway Street
☎ (0785) 53313
11.30–2 (not Sat), 7.30–11
Beer range varies Ⓗ
Fine, one-roomed pub whose
beers have attracted a strong
following: at least five at all
times. No food Sun. ◖ ≢ P

Sun
7 Lichfield Road
☎ (0785) 42208
11–3, 6–11
**Draught Bass; M&B
Highgate Mild** Ⓗ
Pleasant, multi-roomed, town-
centre pub with an 'olde-
worlde' restaurant. Regular
guest beers. ⌛ 🍴 ◖ ▶ 🍺 ♣ P

Stoke-on-Trent: *Burslem*

Foaming Quart
Greenhead Street
☎ (0782) 834941
12–3, 7–11 (11–11 Fri)
**Burtonwood Mild,
Forshaw's** Ⓗ
One large room with a raised
lounge area and a small,
separate pool room. Parking
easy, except on Port Vale match
days, when the pub is very
busy. 'Guests' are made to feel
at home. Burtonwood house
beer on sale. 🍴 ♣

Fenton

Malt 'n' Hops
295 King Street (A50)
☎ (0782) 313406
12–3, 5.30–11
Burtonwood Mild Ⓗ
Main road, single-roomed free
house in an area dominated by
the big brewers. Ever-changing
guest beers, usually at least five,
and a guest beer from
Burtonwood. Former local
CAMRA *Pub of the Year*.
≢ (Longton) ♣

Hanley

Coachmakers Arms
Lichfield Street
12–3, 7.30–11
Draught Bass; M&B Mild Ⓗ
Small, mid-terraced, traditional
local: three rooms incl. a tiny
public bar and a drinking
corridor. 🏠 Q 🍺 ♣

Highland Laddie
69 Wellington Road (off
Bucknall New Road)
12–3, 7–11
**Ansells Mild, Bitter; Draught
Bass** Ⓗ

Friendly, back-street local,
recently refurbished. Live music
Sat nights. 🏠 🍺 ♣

Rose & Crown
Etruria Road (opp. Festival Park
entrance) ☎ (0782) 280503
12–3 (not Sat or Sun), 7–11
**Ansells Mild, Bitter; Ind
Coope Burton Ale** Ⓗ
Traditional bar and a larger
lounge (called the Parlour),
which is given over to food.
Always a friendly welcome.
Guest beers. Children welcome
if dining.
🏠 Q 🍴 ◖ ▶ 🍺 ≢ (Etruria) P

Hartshill

Jolly Potters
296 Hartshill Road
11–3, 6 (7 Sat)–11
Draught Bass; M&B Mild Ⓗ
Old pub of immense character
in the conservation area, next to
a church. Four small rooms, plus
a central drinking corridor: a
classic town pub. Q 🍺 ♣

Northwood

Cross Guns
19 Vincent Street
☎ (0782) 268520
1 (12 Sat)–3.30, 7.30–11 (12–2.30,
7–10.30 Sun)
Draught Bass; M&B Mild Ⓗ
Smart, comfortable lounge and
a traditional bar: an absolute
gem, tucked away in side-streets.
It has its own bowls team. 🍴 ♣

Norton

Norton Arms
1 Endon Road
11.30–3, 7–11 (12–2, 7–10.30 Sun)
Draught Bass Ⓗ
Basic, no-frills, drinkers' pub
with a similarly large bar and
lounge; separate pool room.
🍺 & ♣ P

Stoke

Blacks Head
16 North Street (just off A500,
Queensway)
☎ (0782) 415594
12–3 (4 Sat), 5.30 (7 Sat)–11
**Draught Bass; Theakston
Old Peculier** Ⓗ
Terraced free house, over 200
years old and formerly owned
by Joule's brewery. Wide range
of guest beers: a total of six
beers always on draught. No
food Sun. Cider in summer.
◖ 🍺 ≢ ♣ ⌒

Glebe
Glebe Street
11–11
Banks's Mild, Bitter Ⓔ
Large pub of character next to
the town hall, dwarfed by new
council offices. Small, somewhat
basic bar, with pool and darts;

larger lounge, popular with students and locals. ◖ ⊞ ≋ ♣

Staff of Life

Hill Street (off Campbell Place)
11–3 (4 Fri & Sat), 7–11
Draught Bass Ⓔ
Old, popular, street-corner boozer of a type becoming hard to find. Three rooms off a central drinking corridor; atmosphere and character aplenty. Q ⊞ ≋ ♣

Tunstall

White Hart

43 Roundwell Street
☎ (0782) 835587
11–5, 7–11 (11–11 Fri & Sat)
Marston's Border Bitter, Pedigree Ⓗ
No-nonsense, corner local at the edge of the town centre. Friendly atmosphere; full of characters. Q ⊛ ◖ ♣

White Horse

143 Brownhills Road (bottom end of High Street)
11–3.30, 7–11
Draught Bass; M&B Mild; Welsh Brewers Worthington BB Ⓗ
An increasingly rare find – a traditional, basic, locals' pub: a simple bar heated by a central stove, a pool room and a small snug, used for meetings. Enjoy it while you can! ⌂ Q ⊞ ≋ (Longport) ♣

Stone

Pheasant

Old Road ☎ (0785) 814603
11.30–3.30, 6–11
Draught Bass; Welsh Brewers Worthington BB Ⓗ
Friendly local, immaculately maintained for ten years by the present landlord. Eve meals Fri and Sat only. ⊛ ◖ ◗ ⊞ ≋ ♣

Stretton

Beech Inn

Derby Road (A5121, N of Burton) ☎ (0283) 61811
11.30–3, 5.30–11
Marston's Pedigree, Owd Rodger (winter) Ⓗ
A no-frills, drinkers' local which is popular for club meetings. Pet sheep in the garden. Coaches welcomed. ⇔ ⊛ ⊞ ◖ ♣ P

Sutton

Red Lion

Newport Road (A519)
☎ (0952) 811048
11–3, 6–11
Banks's Mild, Bitter Ⓔ
Lively, country pub, with a roaring fire in winter. Children's adventure playground and a family room (not Sun lunch). ⌂ ⇔ ⊛ ◖ ◗ ▲ ♣ P

Swindon

Green Man

High Street ☎ (0384) 400532
11–11
Banks's Mild, Bitter Ⓔ
Popular local with a friendly atmosphere. Near the Staffs and Worcs Canal and once a butcher's shop. The landlord's boxing memorabilia is much in evidence. Live music Tue and Fri. No food Sun eve.
◖ ◗ ⊞ ⑆ ♣ P

Talke

Swan Inn

Swan Bank ☎ (0782) 782722
11–3, 6–11 (11–11 Fri & Sat)
Burtonwood Best Bitter, Forshaw's Ⓗ
Lively, village local which suits most age groups. Large lounge and a smaller bar with a pool table. The enterprising landlord tries to keep the atmosphere buzzing by holding quiz nights, karaoke, etc. ⊛ ◖ ◗ ⊞ ♣ P

Tamworth

Albert Hotel

Albert Road ☎ (0827) 64694
11–2.30, 7–11
Bateman Mild; Hoskins Beaumanor, Penn's Ale, Premium, Old Nigel Ⓗ
Friendly local, a short distance from the town centre: a mock-beamed lounge and a small public bar. Roadside tables. No eve meals before 8pm.
⊛ ⇔ ◖ ◗ ⊞ ⑆ ≋ ♣ P

Boot

Lichfield Road
☎ (0827) 68824
11–3, 7–11
Marston's Mercian Mild, Pedigree Ⓗ
Modernised, one-bar pub on the edge of the town centre. Tables outside in summer. ⊛ ◖ ≋ ♣

Hamlets Wine Bar

13–15 Lower Gungate
☎ (0827) 52277
11–2.30, 7–11 (11–11 Sat)
Marston's Merrie Monk, Pedigree; Samuel Smith OBB Ⓗ
Basic, central free house with a good atmosphere; popular with students. Guest beer. ◖ ≋ ♣

Tamworth Arms

Lichfield Street
☎ (0827) 67056
11.30–2.30 (3 Sat), 5.30 (5 Thu, 7 Sat)–11 (11.30–11 Fri)
Draught Bass; M&B Mild Ⓗ
Small local, with complicated opening hours designed to suit the local factory trade. Open-plan layout, with lounge and bar areas. Known locally as the 'Bottom House'. ≋ ♣

Tatenhill

Horseshoe Inn

Main Street ☎ (0283) 64913
11–3, 5.30–11
Marston's Pedigree, Owd Rodger Ⓗ
18th-century village pub internally altered but retaining simple, beamed features. Well known for food (not served Mon eve). ⇔ ⊛ ◖ ◗ ⑆ P

Uttoxeter

Black Swan

Market Street
☎ (0889) 564657
11–3.30, 5.30–11 (11–11 Wed, Fri & Sat; 12.30–3, 7–10.30 Sun)
Draught Bass Ⓔ
17th-century, listed building of great character. Visitors are made welcome. ⊞ ≋ ♣ P

Vaults

Market Place
☎ (0889) 562997
11–2.30 (3.30 Wed), 5.30–11
Draught Bass Ⓗ
Busy, unspoilt hostelry with a friendly atmosphere. Bar snacks. ⇔ ⊞ ≋ ♣

Wheaton Aston

Hartley Arms

56 Long Street (by Shropshire Union Canal bridge 19)
☎ (0785) 840232
12 (11 Sat)–3, 6.30–11
Banks's Mild, Bitter Ⓔ
Modern, canalside pub, handy for Weston Park. The menu offers vegetarian and children's options. No food Sun eve.
⊛ ◖ ◗ ⊞ ♣ P

Wombourne

Old Bush

High Street ☎ (0902) 893509
11.30–3, 6–11 (12–2.30, 7–10.30 Sun)
Banks's Mild, Bitter Ⓔ
Two-roomed pub with a small bar (mainly used by locals), and a large lounge. ⌂ Q ◖ ⊞ ⑆ ♣ P

Red Lion

Old Stourbridge Road (off A449) ☎ (0902) 892270
11–11
Banks's Mild; Draught Bass; Stones Best Bitter Ⓗ
17th-century coaching inn on the original main road, now bypassed. ⌂ ⊛ ◖ ◗ ⊞ ⑆ ♣ ⏝ P

Yoxall

Crown Inn

Main Street ☎ (0543) 472551
11–3, 5.30–11
Marston's Pedigree Ⓗ
Large, stone-built pub. The bar contains a snug and the lounge has an eating area (daily specials). ⇔ ◖ ◗ ⊞ ⑆ ♣ P

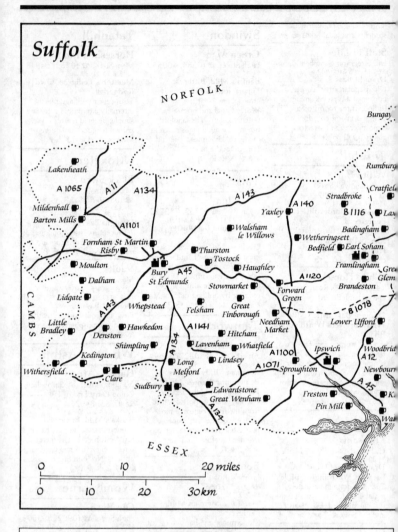

Suffolk

Adnams, Southwold; **Earl Soham**, Earl Soham;
Forbes, Oulton Broad; **Greene King**, Bury St
Edmunds; **Mauldons**, Sudbury; **Nethergate**,
Clare; **Scotties**, Lowestoft; **Tolly Cobbold**, Ipswich

Aldeburgh

Cross Keys
Crabbe Street ☎ (0728) 452637
11–2.30, 6–11
Adnams Mild (summer),
Bitter, Old, Extra (summer),
Broadside Ⓗ
Superbly cosy, friendly, Grade II
listed building, between the
main street and the seafront. Its
attractive frontage has steps
down to the entrance. Seafood a
speciality.
🏠 Q ⛽ ⋈ ◖ ▲

Railway Hotel
Leiston Road ☎ (0728) 453864
11–3, 6–11
Adnams Mild, Bitter Ⓗ
Friendly main bar with a large
show of wood. The dartboard is
said to be the only one in
Aldeburgh (which makes the
pub team the best in the town!).
Fine pictures of trains although
the station is long gone. No
food Mon. ⛽ ⋈ ◖ ▲ ♣

White Hart
High Street ☎ (0728) 453205
11–11 (may vary)
Adnams Bitter, Old,

Broadside Ⓗ
Compact, wood-panelled local
with a nautical theme.
🏠 ⛽ ⋈ ◖ ▲ ♣

Badingham

White Horse
On A1120 ☎ (072 875) 280
10.30–3, 6–11 (10.30–11 Sat)
Adnams Mild (summer),
Bitter, Old, Broadside Ⓗ
Small public bar with pool and
sporting trophies; a more
spacious lounge/dining area
with a grandfather clock.
⛽ ⋈ ◖ ⛽ ♣ P

Barton Mills

Bell
Bell Lane (follow signs off A11)
11–3, 5–11 (11–11 Sat)
Greene King IPA, Abbot Ⓗ
Friendly, village local, where
recent refurbishment has
allowed space for enthusiastic
games teams. Collection of old
photos of village life. ❽ ♣

Bull Inn
☎ (0638) 713230
11–11
**Adnams Bitter; Draught Bass;
Greene King IPA** Ⓗ
Fine, old, family-run coaching
inn, offering all facilities to
travellers. Guest beer. ❽ ⋈ ◑ P

Bedfield

Crown
Church Lane ☎ (072 876) 431

11–11 (may close 3–6 if quiet)
Greene King IPA Ⓗ
Village green local retaining old,
exposed beams and a tiled floor.
Warm welcome; guest beer.
🏠 ⋊ ❽ ◑ ▲ ♣ ⌂ P

Bramfield

Bell
The Street
11–2.30, 6.30–11
Adnams Mild, Bitter Ⓖ
Good, basic, two-bar pub with
exposed beams. A cask is built
into the bar in the smaller room.
Ring the Bull in the public bar.
Q ❽ ◑ ▣ ▲ ♣ P

Brandeston

Queens Head
☎ (072 882) 307
11.30–2.30, 5.30 (6 Mon)–11
**Adnams Mild, Bitter, Old,
Broadside** Ⓗ
Excellent all-round pub.
Children may play in the award-
winning garden or children's
room until early eve. Adults
amuse themselves in the 'drinks
only' back bar or tuck into
good value, home-made food in
the comfortable lounge.
🏠 Q ⋊ ❽ ⋈ ◑ ▣ ▲ ♣ ⌂ P

Bungay

Chequers
23 Bridge Street
12–3, 5.30–11 (12–11 Sat)
**Adnams Bitter; Greene King
IPA, Abbot** Ⓗ
400 year-old building with a
covered patio area at the back.
Four ever-changing guest beers
bring variety to the area.
❽ ◑ ♣ P

Bury St Edmunds

Elephant & Castle
2 Hospital Road
☎ (0284) 764792
11–2.30 (3 Sat), 5–11
**Greene King XX Mild, IPA,
Rayments Special, Abbot** Ⓗ
Homely, two-bar pub where the
landlady makes tasty well-
priced meals. ❽ ◑ ▣ P

Flying Fortress
Great Barton ☎ (028 487) 665
12–3, 5–11
**Adnams Bitter; Greene King
IPA, Rayments Special,
Abbot; Mauldons Bitter** Ⓔ
Friendly free house on an old
WWII airfield and featuring
artefacts connected with the
Flying Fortress bomber. Good
choice of home-cooked food.
Petanque played; the garden at
the rear is safe for children.
Regular eve jazz sessions.
❽ ◑ ♣ ⌂ P

Masons Arms
14 Whiting Street (off

Abbeygate Street)
11–3, 5–11 (11–11 Sat)
**Greene King XX Mild, IPA,
Rayments Special, Abbot** Ⓗ
Bustling, town pub, at least 250
years old. An unusual, timber
exterior has an Essex board
front. The yard is a suntrap. Eve
meals from 7.30. Q ❽ ◑ ◑

Rising Sun
98 Risbygate Street
☎ (0284) 701460
11–11 (12–2.30, 7–10.30 Sun)
**Greene King XX Mild, IPA,
Rayments Special, Abbot** Ⓗ
Reputedly the oldest pub in the
town (1606). Especially popular
on market days. In former times,
cattle drovers slept in the loft.
No-smoking area in the dining
room (no food Sun eve). ◑ P

Clare

Bell Hotel
Market Hill ☎ (0787) 277741
11–3, 5–11
**Greene King Abbot;
Nethergate Bitter, Old
Growler** Ⓗ
Expensive, antique-laden, small
town hotel at the Western end
of Constable Country.
Restaurant and pub food.
🏠 ⋈ ◑ P

Cratfield

Poacher
Bell Green ☎ (098 798) 206
11–11 (may vary in winter)
**Adnams Bitter; Greene King
IPA, Abbot** Ⓗ
Classic, rural pub with murals
outside. The inside is full of
original beams and fixtures.
Bottle collection (1300
miniatures); stuffed birds and
animals. 🏠 ⋊ ❽ ◑ ▣ ▵ ▲ ♣ P

Dalham

Affleck Arms
Brookside ☎ (0638) 500306
11–2.30, 6.30–11
**Greene King XX Mild, IPA,
Abbot** Ⓗ
Elizabethan, thatched, village
pub with a friendly atmosphere.
Food all week, incl. a Sunday
roast. 🏠 Q ❽ ◑ ▣ P

Denston

Plumbers Arms
Wickham Street
☎ (0440) 820350
11–2.30, 5–11
**Greene King XX Mild, IPA,
Abbot** Ⓗ**, Winter Ale** Ⓖ
Large, friendly, country pub,
dating back to the 1700s; an
original stopping-point for
horse traffic between Bury and
Haverhill. Book for eve meals
after 7pm. 🏠 Q ❽ ◑ ▣ ♣ P

Dunwich

Ship
St James Street
☎ (072 873) 219
11–3, 6–11 (11–11 summer)
Adnams Bitter, Old, Broadside; Greene King Abbot Ⓗ
Inn with a nautical theme in an historic village, featuring a timbered bar with back handpumps. Close to the beach and bird reserves.
🏠 Q ♿ ⚓ ⛄ ◖ ♣ ⚘ ♣ ⏏ P

Earl Soham

Victoria
On A1120 ☎ (0728) 82758
11–2.30, 5.30–11
Earl Soham Gannet Mild, Victoria, Albert Ale, Old Cyril Ⓗ
Pub with genuine wooden fixtures and no plastic. Real fare, too, with both beer and food made on the premises. Can get crowded. 🏠 Q ♿ ◖ ◗ ♣ P

Edwardstone

White Horse
Mill Green (off A1071)
☎ (0787) 211211
11.30–2, 6.30–11
Greene King XX Mild, IPA, Abbot Ⓗ
Traditional Suffolk pub offering a good selection of games incl. quoits. Excellent value bar food all week; full menu Thu–Sun (book for Sun lunch). Note the large collection of enamel signs.
🏠 Q ♿ ◖ ◗ ◖ ⚘ ♣ ⏏ P

Felsham

Six Bells
11–2.30 (not Mon–Thu), 5–11
(11–2.30, 5–10.30 Sun)
Greene King XX Mild, IPA, Abbot Ⓗ
Basic but comfortable, village local in an interesting, 16th-century building. Still displays the rules to the Felsham Jolly Boys Society c. 1930. Original beer engines are fitted at the rear of the bar. 🏠 Q ♿ ⚙ ♣ P

Fornham St Martin

Woolpack
On A134, 3 miles N of Bury St Edmunds ☎ (0284) 753380
11–3, 5.30–11 (11–11 Sat)
Greene King IPA, Rayments Special, Abbot Ⓗ
Well-appointed pub with a quiet lounge and a lively public bar, popular with local sports clubs.
Q ♿ ◖ ◗ ⚙ P

Forward Green

Shepherd & Dog
On A1120 ☎ (0449) 711361

10.30–2.30, 5.30–11
Greene King IPA, Abbot Ⓗ
As always, a good, honest ale house. 🏠 Q ♿ ◖ ◗ ⚙ ♣ ⚘ P

Framlingham

Railway Inn
9 Station Road
☎ (0728) 723693
11–3, 5.30–11 (12–2.30, 7–10.30 Sun)
Adnams Mild (winter), **Bitter, Old, Extra** (summer), **Tally Ho** Ⓖ
Plush lounge bar boasting a Victorian fireplace and fine decor. The friendly public bar has basic wood tables, settles, and a beer barrel seat. Fine country pub; good prices, quality and atmosphere.
🏠 Q ◖ ◗ ⚙ ♣ ♣ P

Freston

Boot
Main Road (B1456, up Freston Hill) ☎ (0473) 780277
11–2.30, 6–11
Tolly Cobbold Mild, Bitter, Original Ⓗ
Comfortable lounge bar with a separate dining room serving good value, home-cooked food.
♿ ◖ ◗ P

Great Finborough

Chestnut Horse
High Road (B1115)
☎ (0449) 612298
11–3, 6–11
Greene King XX Mild, IPA, Abbot Ⓗ
Good, friendly, village local attracting a mixed clientele. No eve meals Tue or Sun; try the 'huffers'. Working sewing machine table bases, and an open, brick fireplace.
🏠 Q ♿ ◖ ◗ ⚙ ♣ ♣ ⚘ ♣ P

Great Glemham

Crown Inn
Off A12 ☎ (072 878) 693
11–3 (not Mon), 7–11
Adnams Bitter, Old, Broadside (summer); **Greene King IPA, Abbot** Ⓗ
Attractive exterior; the inside is comfortable with basic wood tables and an adjoining lounge area. Quiet music; good menu. Will stay open all day if busy.
🏠 ♿ ◖ ◗ ♣ ♣ P

Great Wenham

Queens Head
The Row (Capel St Mary road)
☎ (0473) 310590
12–2.30, 6 (6.30 Sat)–11
Adnams Bitter; Greene King IPA, Abbot Ⓗ
Victorian, cottage-style, one-bar house with exposed wood beams, now sympathetically

modernised. Piped CD music; live music most Thu eves. Local guest beers. 🏠 ♿ ◖ ◗ ♣ ♣ ⚘ ♣ P

Haughley

Railway Tavern
Old Street ☎ (0449) 673577
11–2.30, 5.30 (6.30 Sat)–11
Adnams Old; Greene King XX Mild, IPA, Abbot; Woodforde's Wherry Ⓗ
19th-century, comfortable railside tavern with a friendly welcome; 11 years in this guide. Landlord breeds champion Labradors. Good, home-cooked food (not served Mon eve). 🏠 Q ♿ ⚙ ◖ ◗ ♣ P

Hawkedon

Queens Head
12–2.30, 7–11 (closed Mon, and some lunchtimes in winter)
Greene King IPA; Nethergate Bitter Ⓗ
Village bar with an unusual, quality menu. Large fireplace; quietly warring pub pets. Parties of 12 collected by 1930s motorcoach if dining. 🏠 ♿ ◖ ◗ P

Hitcham

White Horse
The Street ☎ (0449) 740981
11.30–2.30, 7–11 (closed Mon)
Greene King XX Mild, (summer), **IPA, Rayments Special, Abbot** Ⓗ
Attractive, beamed, village pub: good local trade in the public bar; popular restaurant in the lounge (no lunches Sun).
🏠 ◖ ◗ ⚙ ♣ P

Ipswich

County Hotel
29 St Helens Street (opp. County Hall)
☎ (0473) 255153
11–11 (11–2.30, 7–11 Sat)
Adnams Mild, Bitter, Old, Extra, Broadside, Tally Ho Ⓗ
Large pub near the town centre with a choice of 'Green' or 'Burgundy' drinking areas: the former is quiet and plush; the latter more boisterous. Good value food. Guest beer. ◖ ◗ ♣ ♣

Duke of York
212 Woodbridge Road
11–2.30 (may extend), 7–11
Adnams Bitter, Broadside Ⓗ
A family local with a quiet lounge; darts, jukebox, etc. in the bar. Q ⚙ ♣ P

Lord Nelson
Fore Street ☎ (0473) 254072
11–11
Adnams Mild, Bitter, Broadside Ⓗ
Lively public bar with a quiet lounge, close to the dockside.

Small room for meetings or functions. Pub dates back to 1663 but is not olde-worlde; rather a pub that has evolved. ⊞ ♣

Trafalgar
Spring Road
☎ (0473) 725276
11–2.30 (3 Fri & Sat), 5.30–11
Theakston Best Bitter, XB Ⓗ
Popular free house, a short walk from the town centre, with a superb selection of guest ales. Friendly atmosphere. Shove-ha'penny is played, but beware – the landlord plays Pass the Pigs for pints. The Mauldons house beer is called 'Baldrick'. ⌂ ⊛ ◑ Ⓖ & ♣ P

Water Lily
100 St Helens Street
11.30–2.30, 7.30–11
Tolly Cobbold Mild, Bitter, Original, Old Strong Ⓖ
The only Ipswich pub with gravity dispensed beer. As unchanging as ever, with its basic but comfortable bar and tiny snug. No food Sun. ⌂ Q ⊛ ◑ ⊞ ♣

Woolpack
1 Tuddenham Road (B1077)
☎ (0473) 253059
11–2.30, 5.30–11 (12–2.30, 7–10.30 Sun)
Courage Directors; Tolly Cobbold Mild, Bitter, Original, Old Strong Ⓗ
16th-century building: a comfortable, medium-sized lounge, a small bar and smoke room, plus a games room with billiards. Quiet in week, lively at weekends. Q ⊛ ⊞ ♣ P

Kedington

White Horse
Sturmer Road
☎ (0440) 63564
11–11
Greene King XX Mild, IPA, Abbot Ⓗ
Very popular, village pub near a Saxon church. Large garden (summer barbecues); excellent bar food, incl. vegetarian dishes. Q ⊛ ⋈ ◑ ▶ ⊞ ♣ ⌂ P

Kirton

White Horse
Bucklesham Road
☎ (039 48) 615
12–4, 7–11 (11–11 Thu)
Tolly Cobbold Mild, Bitter Ⓗ
Traditional, village pub, the hub of community life. Guest beers. ⊛ ◑ ▶ ⊞ Å ♣ P

Lakenheath

Half Moon
High Street ☎ (0842) 861484
11–2.30, 6–11
Greene King XX Mild, IPA Ⓗ

Popular local on the outskirts of the village; a fine flint building which retains the classic Victorian layout of two bars and centre servery for off-sales. Inexpensive, good quality food, Mon–Sat. Q ⊛ ◑ ▶ ♣ P

Plough
Mill Road ☎ (0842) 860285
11–2.30, 6–11
Greene King XX Mild, IPA Ⓗ
Fine Victorian flint building in the centre of a busy village. Two bars – one a pool room. No snacks Sun. ⊛ ⊞ ♣ P

Lavenham

Angel
Market Place
☎ (0787) 247388
11–3, 6–11
Nethergate Bitter; Ruddles County; Webster's Yorkshire Bitter Ⓗ
Impressive, 14th-century coaching inn overlooking the Market Cross and Guildhall. Pick a quiet time and ask to see the medieval, vaulted cellars. ⌂ ⊛ ⋈ ◑ ▶ ♣ P

Laxfield

Kings Head (Low House)
Gorams Mill Lane (off B1117)
☎ (098 683) 395
11–3, 6–11
Adnams Bitter, Old; Ind Coope Burton Ale; Wadworth 6X Ⓖ
15th-century alehouse with a roaring log fire in winter around which large settles are arranged. Beer comes straight from casks in the back room, there being no bar. Bowls at the rear. Small dining area. Guest beers. ⌂ Q ⊛ ◑ ▶ ⊞ ♣ ⌂ P

Lidgate

Star
The Street ☎ (0638) 500275
11–2.30, 7–11
Greene King IPA, Abbot Ⓗ
Centre of activity in an almost unchanged village. Spit-roast beef is a speciality; barbecues every summer weekend. Beware of ducks crossing the road near the village pond. ⌂ ⊛ ◑ ▶ ♣ P

Lindsey

Red Rose
Lindsey Tie ☎ (0449) 741424
11–2.30, 6 (5 Fri)–11
Adnams Broadside; Greene King IPA, Abbot Ⓗ
Interesting old building with a large inglenook in the bar and a miniature zoo in the beer garden. Good, home-cooked food in the lounge restaurant. Mauldons house beer also on sale. ⌂ Q ⊛ ◑ ▶ ⊞ P

Little Bradley

Royal Oak
Bury Road ☎ (044 083) 229
11.30–3, 6–11
Adnams Bitter; Greene King IPA, Rayments Special; Nethergate Bitter Ⓗ
Main road pub which gets very busy at weekends. The welcoming landlord is dismissive of keg beer. ⊛ ◑ ▶ ⊞ P

Long Melford

Swan Inn
Hall Street (A134)
☎ (0787) 78740
11–3, 5–11
Greene King XX Mild, IPA, Abbot Ⓖ
A pub with no gimmicks! A good locals' public bar and a lounge at the rear with a separate restaurant area. Eve meals Fri and Sat only. Q ◑ ▶ ⊞ ♣

Try also: **George & Dragon**, High St (Greene King)

Lower Ufford

White Lion
☎ (0394) 460770
11.30–2.30, 6.30–11
Tolly Cobbold Mild, Bitter Original, Old Strong Ⓗ
Very friendly local on the edge of the village. The main drinking area is separated from a smaller back area by an imposing fireplace. Extensive menu. Jazz and kippers Thu night! No food Sun eve or Mon. ⌂ Q ⊛ ◑ ▶ ♣ P

Middleton

Bell
The Street ☎ (072 873) 286
11–11 (may vary)
Adnams Mild (summer), **Bitter, Old, Broadside** Ⓖ
Attractive, listed building on the edge of the marshes. Handy for Minsmere RSPB Reserve and the Suffolk Heritage Coast. ⌂ Q ⊛ ◑ ▶ ♣ P

Mildenhall

Queens Arms
Queensway ☎ (0638) 713657
11–2.30, 7–11
Greene King XX Mild, Abbot Ⓗ
Homely pub on the outskirts of a small town, attracting a local trade of all ages. Small range of food but all home-made. Q ⊛ ⋈ ◑ ♣ P

Try also: **Half Moon** (Greene King)

Suffolk

Moulton

Kings Head
Bridge Street ☎ (0630) 750156
11–3, 5–11
Greene King IPA, Abbot ⊞
Lively, welcoming local facing
the green and near the
packhorse bridge. Newmarket is
three miles away. Lunches
Wed–Sun; eve meals Mon–Sat.
🏠 🍽 ① ①

Needham Market

Swan
High Street ☎ (0449) 720280
11–11
**Greene King XX Mild, IPA,
Rayments Special, Abbot** ⊞
500 year-old, beamed,
traditional, family pub with a
relaxed atmosphere. Food
served in the bar or restaurant
(no-smoking area). No food Sun
eve. 🏠 🍽 ① ① ♦ ⩽ ♣ P

Newbourn

Fox
The Street
11–2.30, 6 (7 winter)–11
Tolly Cobbold Bitter Ⓖ
14th-century inn with original
beams throughout. Note the old
Tolly enamel signs on the walls.
Good outside drinking area.
🏠 Q ⩽ 🍽 ① ♦ ♣ P

Orford

Jolly Sailor
Quay Street ☎ (0394) 450243
11–2.30, 6–11 (12–2.30, 7–10.30 Sun)
Adnams Bitter ⊞
16th-century, quayside inn,
long deserted by the sea.
Unusual collection of stuffed
miniature dogs. Live music most
Sat eves. The family room is
suitable for older children. Fresh
Orford cod sometimes served.
Eve meals till 8.45.
🏠 ⩽ 🍽 ① ① ♣ P

Oulton Broad

Forbes Brewery Bar
Harbour Road Ind. Estate
☎ (0502) 587905
5.30–11 (11–11 Sat; closed Sun)
Beer range varies ⊞
Spit and hops (the local fire
brigade won't allow sawdust)-
type bar attached to the
brewery, serving excellent value
Forbes beers. Due for
enlargement. ⟳ P

Pin Mill

Butt & Oyster
Off B1456 ☎ (0473) 780764
11–3, 7–11 (11–11 summer)
Tolly Cobbold Mild ⊞,
Bitter Ⓖ, **Original, Old
Strong** ⊞

Internationally-known,
unchanging, riverside inn with a
family room and restaurant.
Busy in summer but quiet in
winter. Shove-ha'penny and
Connect Four played.
🏠 Q ⩽ 🍽 ① ① ① ♣ P

Risby

Crown & Castle
South Street ☎ (0284) 810393
11.30–2.30, 7–11
**Greene King XX Mild, IPA,
Abbot** ⊞
Pleasant, two-bar pub with a
spacious public bar and an
alcoved lounge. Vegetarian
main meals served as well as
standard pub fare, Mon–Sat.
🏠 🍽 ① ① ① ♣ P

Rumburgh

Buck
Mill Road ☎ (098 685) 257
11–11
**Adnams Bitter, Old; Greene
King IPA, Rayments Special;
Webster's Yorkshire Bitter** ⊞
Pub full of interlinked rooms,
incl. games and dining areas,
each retaining its original
boarded walls and flagged floor.
Thought to have been the guest
house for the priory.
🏠 ⩽ 🍽 ① ① ① Å ♣ P

Shimpling

Bush
Shimpling Street (off A134)
☎ (0284) 828257
11–3, 5.30–11
**Greene King XX Mild, IPA,
Abbot** ⊞
16th-century, timbered building
with a good, friendly public bar
and a separate restaurant. Note
the photographic display of
village history. 🏠 🍽 ① ① ① P

Sibton

White Horse
Halesworth Road (off A1120
by garage in Peasenhall)
☎ (072 879) 337
11.30–2.30 (not Mon, except bank
hols), 7–11
Adnams Bitter ⊞
16th-century free house with a
very pleasant dining room. A
second handpulled beer is
usually available. Well-behaved
children welcome. Camping for
CC members only. No food Sun
eve. 🏠 Q ⩽ 🍽 ① ① ♦ Å ♣ P

Southwold

Lord Nelson
East Street ☎ (0502) 722079
11–11 (may vary)
**Adnams Mild, Bitter, Old,
Broadside, Tally Ho** ⊞
A good, solid refurbishment has
left the pub much larger than

before, whilst retaining all its
old atmosphere. Suntrap patio
garden. 🏠 🍽 ① ① ♣ ♣

Red Lion
South Green
☎ (0502) 722385
11–3, 7–11 (11–11 summer)
Adnams Mild (summer),
Bitter, Old, Extra (summer),
Broadside, Tally Ho ⊞
Pub with a front bar adorned
with local artefacts. The back
rooms are used as a dining area.
🏠 ⩽ 🍽 ① ① Å P

Sproughton

Beagle
Old Hadleigh Road
☎ (047 386) 455
11–2.30, 5–11
**Adnams Mild, Bitter,
Broadside; Greene King IPA,
Abbot; Mauldons Bitter** ⊞
Large free house converted from
a row of whitewashed cottages;
comfortable lounge and a
friendly bar, beamed
throughout. Varied menu of
home-cooked food (not served
Sun). Guest beers.
🏠 Q 🍽 ① ① ① P

Stowmarket

Royal William
53 Union Street (off
Stowupland St)
☎ (0449) 674553
11–3, 6–11
**Greene King IPA, Abbot,
Winter Ale** Ⓖ
Fine, old pub with background
music and a good, friendly
atmosphere; just a walk from
the station. Come and see
Abbot the dog. 🍽 ① ① ⩽ ♣

Try also: Little Wellington

Stradbroke

Queens Head
☎ (0379) 384384
11–3 (may vary), 6.30–11
**Adnams Bitter, Old; Greene
King IPA, Rayments Special,
Abbot** ⊞
Good, village local, its bar area
divided by a huge brick
fireplace. Pergola beer garden,
and cook-your-own barbecue in
summer. Occasional jazz. Guest
beer. 🏠 🍽 ① ① ① ♦ Å ♣

Sudbury

Wagon & Horses
Acton Square, Church Walk
☎ (0787) 312147
11–3, 6–11
**Greene King XX Mild, IPA,
Rayments Special, Abbot** ⊞
Revitalised, back-street pub with
a public bar, games room,
restaurant and snug. Interesting
architecture incorporates
different styles and ages.

Entrance is through the courtyard. Next to the site of the old Phoenix brewery.
Q ⑧ ◖ ⬗ ⇄ ♣ P

Thurston

Black Fox
Barrels Road ☎ (0359) 30636
12–2.30 (Sat & Sun only, may vary), 7–11
Adnams Bitter; Greene King IPA; Hook Norton Old Hooky; Mauldons Bitter Ⓖ
The most traditional pub in West Suffolk, with all beers on gravity dispense in a back room. In the same family since time immoral! Well worth finding, but phone first, as hours vary. ⬛ Q ♣ ⌂ P

Tostock

Gardeners Arms
Church Road ☎ (0359) 70460
11–2.30, 7–11
Greene King IPA, Abbot Ⓗ
Old, original-beamed building near the village green; basic public bar and a fine, comfortable lounge with an open fire. The restaurant also offers vegetarian meals. Quoits played. No lunches Sun; no eve meals Mon/Tue. ⬛ ⑧ ◖ ⬗ P

Walberswick

Bell
Ferry Road ☎ (0502) 723109
11–4, 6–11
Adnams Bitter, Extra, Broadside Ⓗ
600 year-old, Grade II listed building with open fires, beamed ceilings and worn stone and brick floors. High-backed settles and views to the River Blyth and the sea, too. Essentially unchanged for years. Eve meals in the restaurant.
⬛ Q ✕ ⑧ ◖ ⬗ ⬗ Å ♣ P

Walsham le Willows

Six Bells
High Street ☎ (0359) 259726
11.30–2.30, 6.30 (6.30 Sat)–11
Greene King XX Mild, IPA, Abbot Ⓗ
Fine, old, beamed pub in a pleasant village. Accommodation only in summer. ⬛ Q ⑧ ⬗ ♣ P

Walton

Tap & Spile (Half Moon)
High Street ☎ (0394) 282130
11–4, 5.30–11 (11–11 Thu & Fri)
Adnams Bitter; Nethergate Bitter Ⓗ
One of the newest Tap & Spiles, on the edge of Felixstowe. Typical 'T&S' decor, with a

separate bar and lounge, and a small snug area. Watch out for Charlie the horse – or his deposits! Four guest beers. No food weekends.
⬛ ⑧ ◖ ♣ P

Wenhaston

Star
Between A12 and Wenhaston village ☎ (050 270) 240
11–3, 6–11
Adnams Mild (summer), **Bitter, Old** Ⓖ
Out-of-the-way pub with beer direct from the cooling cupboards behind the bar. The back room serves as a lounge-cum-dining area. Close to 'Toby's Walks' – the reputed stalking ground of the Devil. ⬛ Q ⑧ ◖ ♣ P

Wetheringsett

Cat & Mouse Inn
Pages Green (A140, Park Green, up Wetherup Street) OS145652 ☎ (0728) 860765
11–2, 5–11
Adnams Bitter Ⓗ&Ⓖ; **Greene King IPA; Nethergate Bitter; Tolly Cobbold Mild; Whitbread Boddingtons Bitter; Woodforde's Wherry**
Hard-to-find, traditional, rural pub with a cottage-like interior and low, beamed ceilings. Home-made food with vegetarian option (eve meals require 24-hours' notice). Always 15 ales on; ten on hand pull, five from the cellar by gravity dispense.
⬛ Q ⑧ ◖ Å ♣ ⌂ P

Whatfield

Four Horseshoes
The Street ☎ (0473) 827971
11.30–2.30 (not Mon), 7–11
Adnams Bitter, Broadside; Greene King IPA Ⓗ
Traditional, two-bar, village local, a haven for war-gamers. Caravan in the grounds for hire. Occasional guest beers.
⬛ Q ⑧ ◖ ⬗ Å ♣

Whepstead

White Horse
Rede Road ☎ (0284) 488542
11.30–3, 6.30–11
Greene King IPA, Abbot Ⓗ
Two very separate bars serving beer drinkers and foodies respectively. Strong on single-plate oriental dishes. Detached from the main village, it can be spotted from the distant main road by its orange light.
⬛ ⑧ ◖ ⬗ ♣ P

Withersfield

White Horse
Hollow Hill ☎ (0440) 706081
12–2.30, 5–11
Greene King IPA; Nethergate Bitter Ⓗ
17th-century, thatched, country inn, popular for business lunches. Attracts local trade eves and weekends; summer brings tourists. Oak beams and a log fire feature in the bar. *À la carte* restaurant (no food Sun lunch). ⬛ Q ⑧ ◖ ⌂ P

Woodbridge

Olde Belle & Steelyard
New Street ☎ (0394) 382933
11–2.30, 6–11 (11–11 Sat)
Greene King IPA, Rayments Special, Abbot Ⓗ
Traditional, Grade I listed building, with an unusual weighbridge over the road. Generally smoke-free atmosphere, with a no-smoking family room. Vast range of pub games. Pizzas only on the menu (no food Wed).
⬛ Q ✕ ⑧ ◖ ⬗ ⬗ ♣ ✗

Seckford Arms
Seckford Street ☎ (0394) 384446
11–11
Adnams Bitter, Broadside; Draught Bass; Whitbread Castle Eden Ale Ⓗ
Genuine, family-run free house, with regular guest beers. Superb Mayan wood carvings feature throughout. Exposed beams in the lounge; heated foot-rail in the bar. Caters for families in a no-smoking extension.
✕ ⑧ ◖ ⬗ ♣ ✗

Yaxley

Bull
Ipswich Road (crossroads off A140/B1117)
☎ (037 983) 604
11–3, 5.30–11 (11–11 Sat & bank hols)
Adnams Bitter, Broadside; Mauldons Porter; Woodforde's Wherry Ⓗ
Genuine free house; a 16th-century, high-beamed pub with a large garden and children's play area. On a busy road near the Thornham Estate, a thatched church and public walks. Bar billiards. Summer guest beers; home-made food.
Q ⑧ ◖ Å ♣ P

Join CAMRA — see page 480!

Surrey

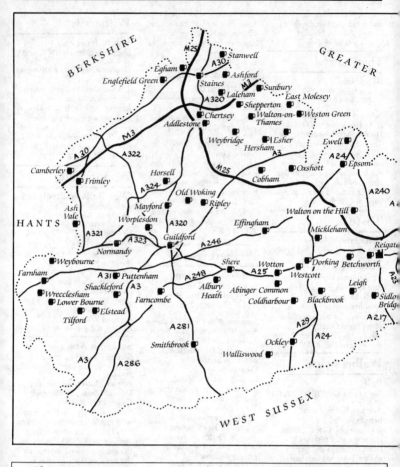

BERKSHIRE · GREATER · HANTS · WEST SUSSEX

Stanwell · Egham · Englefield Green · Ashford · Staines · Sunbury · Laleham · East Molesey · Shepperton · Chertsey · Walton-on-Thames · Weston Green · Addlestone · Weybridge · Esher · Ewell · Hersham · Epsom · Camberley · Frimley · Horsell · Cobham · Oxshott · Old Woking · Mayford · Ripley · Ash Vale · Worplesdon · Effingham · Walton on the Hill · Mickleham · Normandy · Guildford · Reigate · Weybourne · Puttenham · Shere · Wotton · Dorking · Betchworth · Farnham · Shackleford · Albury Heath · Abinger Common · Westcott · Leigh · Wrecclesham · Lower Bourne · Farncombe · Coldharbour · Blackbrook · Sidlow Bridge · Tilford · Elstead · Smithbrook · Ockley · Walliswood

---

🏠 · *Pilgrim*, *Reigate*

Abinger Common

Abinger Hatch
Abinger Lane OS115460
☎ (0306) 730737
11–2.30, 6–11
**Gibbs Mew Bishop's Tipple;
Hall & Woodhouse Badger
Best Bitter, Tanglefoot; King
& Barnes Sussex; Ringwood
Fortyniner; Wadworth 6X** Ⓗ
17th-century inn set opposite
the village green and pond.
Large central fireplace and
flagstoned floor. Food is all
home-cooked and features daily
specials. 🏠 ✿ ◑ ▶ ▲ ♣ P

Addlestone

Queens Arms
107 Church Road (B3121)
☎ (0932) 847845
11–3, 5.30–11
**Courage Best Bitter,
Directors; Wadworth 6X** Ⓗ

Small pub built in the 1860s,
simply decorated within.
✿ ◑ ♣ P

Albury Heath

William IV
Little London ($\frac{1}{2}$ mile S of Shere
village) OS066467
☎ (0486) 412685
11–3, 5.30–11
**Courage Best Bitter; Greene
King Abbot; Ind Coope
Benskins Best Bitter; Pilgrim
Surrey; Tetley Bitter;
Wadworth 6X** Ⓗ
Wonderfully characterful village
local; completely unspoilt.
Three distinct sections include
an eating area, a public bar and
a comfortable front lounge with
a large open fireplace.
Beautifully situated with a lovely
garden. In summer, can get a bit
touristy. Excellent food. Difficult
to find (ask for directions), but

well worth the effort.
🏠 Q ✿ ◑ ▶ ⊕ ▲ ♣ ◔ P

Ashford

Ash Tree
Convent Road (B378)
☎ (0784) 252362
11–3, 5.30–11
Fuller's London Pride, ESB Ⓗ
Fairly typical estate-style pub
from the outside but with a
comfortably furnished lounge.
Public bar is quiet except for
darts nights. Cellar is reputedly
haunted by a ghost from the old
convent. Patio for outdoor
drinking.
✿ ◑ ▶ ⊕ & ♣ P

Ash Vale

Old Ford
Lynchford Road (A3011)
☎ (0252) 544840
11–11

Surrey

LONDON

● Warlingham

● Caterham

M25

A25   ● Oxted

M23

● Outwood   A22

B2028

KENT

● Felbridge

EAST SUSSEX

0   5 miles
0   5   10 km

**Courage Best Bitter,
Directors; Wadworth 6X** Ⓗ
Built in the 1850s and virtually
part of the station whose
platform was once extended for
General Gordon. If he arrived
now, he would almost walk into
the pub's dining area. Separate
pool room at rear; garden
(summer barbecues) has a pets
corner.
🏠 ◐ ▶ ≠ (North Camp) ♣ P

Betchworth

Dolphin
The Street OS211498
☎ (0737) 842388
11–3, 5.30–11
**Young's Bitter, Special,
Winter Warmer** Ⓗ
17th-century, listed pub with
original stone-flagged floor and
inglenook. Although only one
bar, there are three distinct
drinking areas. Situated in a
charming village, opposite its
ancient church. Vegetarian
meals available. 🏠 Q 🏠 ◐ ♣ P

Blackbrook

Plough
Blackbrook Road OS181466
☎ (0306) 886603
11–2.30, 6–11 (12–2.30, 7–10.30 Sun)
**King & Barnes Sussex,
Broadwood, Old, Festive** Ⓗ
A rural, two-bar pub with an
excellent menu, including
vegetarian option (eve meals
Tue–Sun). Old sewing machine
tables in the public bar, which
also houses a collection of over
500 ties — contributions
welcome. Note, too, the unusual
display of saws. A regular in
this guide. 🏠 ◐ ▶ ⊞ P

Camberley

Ancient Foresters
23 Park Street (off A30)
☎ (0276) 64830
11–3 (4 Sat), 5.30 (6 Sat)–11
(12–2.30, 7–10.30 Sun)
**Draught Bass; Stones Best
Bitter** Ⓗ
Unpretentious, town-centre pub
with horseshoe bar. Quiet
during the week but bustling
and sometimes boisterous at
weekends. A haven for foot-
sore shoppers. Best-kept and
best value Bass for miles. Small
front patio for outdoor drinking.
No food Sun. 🏠 ◐ ≠ ♣

Bridgers
299 London Road (A30)
☎ (0276) 670160
11.30–3, 5–11
**Gibbs Mew Wiltshire, Local
Line, Salisbury, Bishop's
Tipple** Ⓗ
Completely restored,
traditionally-furnished town
pub, named after a founder of
Gibbs brewery. Attractive, solid,
balustraded bar with brass
fittings. Victorian pottery, prints
and brasses reflect the period
well. Bar billiards in separate
sports area. Comfortable and
friendly. A brisk lunchtime/
early eve business trade gives
way to the younger crowd mid
eve. 🏠 ◐ ▶ ◔ ≠ ♣

Lamb
593 London Road, Blackwater
(A30 by Blackwater Bridge
roundabout)
☎ (0276) 33832
11–3, 5.30 (5 Fri, 7 Sat)–11
**Morland Bitter, Old Masters,
Old Speckled Hen** Ⓗ
A fresh and airy atmosphere is
achieved from a modern, stone-
paved floor and liberal use of
light-coloured wood. Profuse
plant life helps segregate the
restaurant section from the bar.
Excellent food.
🏠 ◐ ▶ ≠ (Blackwater) P

Try also: Royal Standard
(Morland)

Caterham

King & Queen
34 High Street (B2030)
11–2.30, 6–11
**Charrington IPA; Fuller's
London Pride; Young's
Special** Ⓗ
Much larger than it would
appear from the outside.
Originally three cottages which
became a pub in the 1840s. The
400 year-old building retains
an olde-worlde atmosphere
with separate, interconnecting
rooms. Taxi firm attached.
🏠 ♣ P

Try also: Clifton Arms,
Chaldon Road (Charrington)

Join CAMRA —
see page 480!

Chertsey

Golden Grove
St Anns Hill Road (off
A320/B388 roundabout)
☎ (0932) 562132
11.30 (11 Sat)–3, 5.30 (6 Sat)–11
**Ind Coope Friary Meux Best
Bitter, Burton Ale; Young's
Special** Ⓗ
A 16th-century, former
coaching inn which still has
stabling. The low, beamed
ceiling adds character, and there
is an attractive garden. Handy
for visitors to St Anns Hill Park.
Q 🏠 ◐ P

Vine
5 Bridge Road (B375)
☎ (0932) 563010
11–3, 5–11 (11–11 Sat)
**Courage Best Bitter,
Directors** Ⓗ
Dating back 400 years, this
popular local is well run by an
enthusiastic landlady. Regular
quiz night and, among other
attractions, an interesting
collection of cameras. Guest
beer. Q 🏠 ◐ ▶ Å ♣ P

Cobham

Running Mare
45 Tilt Road, (just off Stoke
Road, A245, between Cobham
and Stoke D'Abernon)
☎ (0932) 862007
11–2.30, 6–11
**Hall & Woodhouse Badger
Best Bitter; Ruddles Best
Bitter, County** Ⓗ
Recently refurbished, olde-
worlde-style pub, divided into
two drinking areas. Fresh flowers
usually decorate tables.
Overlooks triangular green
known locally as 'the Tilt'.
Entertainment on Thu and Fri
nights (singer or disco). No food
Sun eve. 🏠 ◐ ▶ ◔ P

Surrey

Silvermere Tavern

Silvermere Golf Club, Redhill Road (B366)
☎ (0932) 864988
11–11
Wadworth 6X; Whitbread Boddingtons Bitter Ⓗ
Large, single-storey, modern bar, part of a golf and leisure complex open to all. Patio overlooks the lake where the bouncing bomb was first tested. No meals Sun eve. ⚑ ◖ ▶ P

Coldharbour

Plough Inn

Coldharbour Lane OS152441
☎ (0306) 711793
11.30–3, 6 (7 winter)–11
Adnams Broadside; Crown Buckley Best Bitter; Gibbs Mew Bishop's Tipple; Hall & Woodhouse Badger Best Bitter; Ringwood Old Thumper; Theakston Old Peculier Ⓗ
In popular walking country, this pub prides itself on the range of beers and traditional cooking (no eve meals winter Sun/Mon). Children welcome weekends at lunchtime. The public bar area has pool and darts. Guest beers and Churchwards medium dry cider. ⚑ ⛺ ⚞ ◖ ▶ ♣ ◔

Dorking

Cricketers

81 South Street (A25, one-way system)
☎ (0306) 889938
11–3, 5.30 (6 Sat)–11
Fuller's Chiswick, London Pride, ESB Ⓗ
Popular town-centre pub with good value lunches. Also serves Fuller's occasional brew, Mr Harry. Small, but sheltered and attractive patio garden at the rear. Chess and backgammon available. No weekend meals. ⚑ ♣

Old House At Home

24 West Street (A25, one-way system)
☎ (0306) 889664
11–3, 5.30 (6 Sat)–11
Young's Bitter, Special Ⓗ
Pub which dates from the 15th century and is decorated with brasses and other artefacts. Eve meals till 8.30. Sometimes sells Winter Warmer from a pin on the bar. ⚑ ⚑ ◖ ▶ ⇌ (West)

Star

36 West Street (A25, one-way system)
☎ (0306) 889734
11–2.30, 6–11
Greene King IPA, Rayments Special, Abbot Ⓗ
Street-corner locals' pub which, although small, offers a variety

of activities, often finding space for live music on Sun night.
◖ ⇌ (West) ♣

Try also: Queen's Head, Horsham Rd (Fuller's)

East Molesey

Bell Inn

4 Bell Road (off B369)
☎ (081) 941 0400
11–3, 5.30–11 (11–11 Sat)
Courage Best Bitter, Directors; John Smith's Bitter Ⓗ
An historic coaching inn, complete with stables, known as the 'Crooked House' and dating from 1460. A former customer was the 18th-century highwayman, Claude Duvalier. Originally Molesey's first post office. Q ⚑ ♣ P

Europa

171 Walton Road (B369)
☎ (081) 979 5183
11–2.30, 5–11 (11–11 Sat)
Courage Best Bitter, Directors; John Smith's Bitter; Young's Bitter Ⓗ
Three distinctive bars incl. a no-nonsense public with a pool table and darts. Happy hour 5–7 weekdays, 7–8 Sun.
Q ⚑ ◖ ♣

Try also: Prince of Wales, Bridge Rd (Courage)

Effingham

Plough

Orestan Lane (off A246 via 'The Street')
☎ (0372) 58121
11–2.45 (3 Sat), 6–11
Young's Bitter, Special Ⓗ
Friendly oasis for good beer in a poorly served area. In early eve food often dominates but quickly gives way to bitter drinkers. Landlord has always opposed electronic intrusions of any kind. Extensions planned.
Q ⚑ ◖ ⬧

Egham

Crown

38 High Street (off A30)
☎ (0784) 432608
11–3, 5.30 (6 Sat)–11
Courage Best Bitter, Directors; John Smith's Bitter Ⓗ
Thriving town-centre pub with prize-winning garden. A closure attempt a few years ago was thwarted by a locals' petition.
⚑ ◖ ⚌ ⇌ P

Elstead

Woolpack

The Green (B3001)
☎ (0252) 703106
11–2.30, 6–11

Ind Coope Friary Meux Best Bitter, Burton Ale Ⓖ
Pleasant, spacious, open-plan pub dating from 1650. Food oriented but presenting a splendid array of casks behind the bar. A good children's room is well integrated into the pub. Guest beers. ⚑ Q ⛺ ⚑ ◖ ▶ P

Try also: Star (Courage)

Englefield Green

Beehive

34 Middle Hill (off A30)
☎ (0784) 431621
12–2.30, 5.30–11
Brakspear Special; Gale's XXXD, Best Bitter, HSB Ⓗ
Long-established, ex-free house which still maintains an impressive range of beers under the Gale's ownership. The mild is especially welcome. Guest beers and Bulmers Traditional cider. ⚑ Q ◖ ▶ ◔ P

Epsom

Barley Mow

12 Pikes Hill (off Upper High Street, A2022)
☎ (0372) 721044
11–3, 5.30–11
Fuller's London Pride, ESB Ⓗ
Popular locals' pub of unusual construction. The conservatory at the rear has now thankfully had the piano removed. The pub is not overly large so, in summer, the pleasant garden is a bonus. ⚑ ◖ ▶

Try also: Kings Arms, East St (Young's)

Esher

Claremont Arms

2 Church Street (A244 westbound)
☎ (0372) 464083
10.30–11
Courage Best Bitter, Directors Ⓗ
Fine side-street local with good value meals (no food Sun). Handy for Sandown Park racecourse. ◖ ♣

Ewell

King William IV

17 High Street (off A24)
☎ (081) 393 2063
11–11
Ind Coope Friary Meux Best Bitter, Burton Ale; Tetley Bitter Ⓗ
A friendly, 19th-century local with original etched windows. Pool table in the large public bar; live music Thu and Sat eve in front bar. Meals served from midday till 7pm.
⚑ ⚑ ◖ ▶ ⚌ ⇌ (East/West) ♣ P

Farncombe

Cricketers
37 Nightingale Road
☎ (0483) 415435
11–3, 5.30–11 (11–11 summer)
Fuller's Chiswick, London Pride, ESB Ⓗ
Formerly a run-down and under-utilised 'Big Six' pub, now revitalised by a change of beer. The result is a crowded and lively establishment for all ages. Likely to be extended in near future. Always a good atmosphere. ⌂ ❀ ◖ ◗ ⇌ ♣

Try also: Freeholders, St Johns St (Fuller's).

Farnham

Hop Blossom
Long Garden Walk, Castle Street (off A287)
☎ (0252) 710770
11–3, 6–11
Fuller's London Pride, ESB Ⓗ
A small, L-shaped bar which can be 'cliquey' yet is cosy and comfortable. ⇌

Lamb
43 Abbey Street (off A287)
☎ (0252) 714133
11–2.30, 6–11
Shepherd Neame Master Brew Bitter, Master Brew Best Bitter, Bishops Finger Ⓗ
Squeeze through the tiny double doors to meet mine host, Rod, presiding over this earthy establishment. It is dominated by a large dog, pool and darts enthusiasts. Parking difficult.
⌂ ❀ ◖ ◗ ♿ ⇌ ♣

Queens Head
9 The Borough (A287/A325, one-way system)
☎ (0252) 726524
11–11
Gale's BBB, Best Bitter, 5X, HSB Ⓗ
One of Farnham's few remaining classic pubs, mostly consisting of the original 16th-century structure. Excellent, bustling proper public bar (with Georgian reproduction prints). The wonderful pub sign is one of Gale's' finest. A cosmopolitan mix of clientele. No meals Sun. Parking difficult. ⌂ Q ❀ ◖ ⊟

Felbridge

Woodcock
Woodcock Hill (A22)
☎ (0342) 325859
11–2.30, 5.30–11 (11–11 Sat)
Harveys Armada; Larkins Best Bitter; Pilgrim Surrey; Ringwood Old Thumper Ⓗ
A good selection of beer, as well as food, in this bar which is attached to an upmarket restaurant. Beams and leaded windows; reasonably priced accommodation. Real cider in summer. ⌂ ❀ ⛿ ◖ ◗ ◌ P

Frimley

Railway Arms
78 High Street (off A325)
☎ (0276) 23544
11–2.30, 6–11 (12–2, 7–10.30 Sun)
Ind Coope Burton Ale; Taylor Walker Best Bitter; Tetley Bitter; Young's Bitter Ⓗ
The restful decor and busy conversation in the saloon, and the darts in the real public bar combine to make this a fine, traditional pub. ◖ ⊟ ♿ ⇌ ♣

Guildford

Clavadel Hotel
Epsom Road (A246)
☎ (0483) 572064
11–2.30, 5.30–11
Cains Bitter; Exmoor Ale; Hook Norton Best Bitter; Mansfield Riding Bitter; Morland Bitter; Premier Maiden's Ruin Ⓗ
Excellent hotel bar: Guildford's only free house, offering over 90 different beers throughout the year. Live jazz third Fri in every third month. Eve meals in restaurant.
Q ❀ ⛿ ◖ ⇌ (London Rd) ♣ P

Royal
132 Worplesdon Road (A322)
☎ (0483) 575173
11–11
Courage Best Bitter, Directors Ⓗ
Large street-corner local with friendly service, a comfortable lounge and a traditional public bar. ❀ ⛿ ◖ ⊟ ♣ P

Spread Eagle
46 Chertsey Street (A320)
☎ (0483) 35018
10.30–2.30 (3 Fri, 3.30 Sat), 5–11
Courage Best Bitter, Directors; John Smith's Bitter, Magnet Ⓗ
Close to town centre and usually crowded, especially with lunchtime food trade (no meals Sun). Tenanted pub with proper guest beers changed at least monthly; stronger guests some weekends. ⛿ ❀ ◖ ⇌ ♣ P

Try also: Prince Albert (Courage)

Hersham

Royal George
130 Hersham Road (off A244)
☎ (0932) 220910
11–2.30 (3 Sat), 5.30–11
Young's Bitter, Special, Winter Warmer Ⓗ
Popular post-war local with naval mementoes in the lounge, as well as photos of guide dogs bought by pub regulars.
⌂ Q ❀ ◖ ◗ ⊟ ♣ P

Horsell

Plough
Cheapside, South Road
☎ (0483) 714105
11–2.30 (3 Sat), 5.30 (6 Sat)–11
Gale's HSB; Ind Coope Friary Meux Best Bitter, Benskins Best Bitter; King & Barnes Sussex; Tetley Bitter; Young's Special Ⓗ
Being situated on commonland on the edge of the village, a rural atmosphere prevails. Good outdoor drinking and handy for country walks. Not easy to find without local knowledge. Worth seeking out.
Q ❀ ◖ ◗ P

Laleham

Turks Head
The Broadway (B377)
☎ (0784) 469078
10.30–3, 4.30–11 (11–11 Sat)
Courage Best Bitter, Directors Ⓗ
Friendly, little, one-bar pub, not far from River Thames. Plate on wall declares 'no strangers here – only friends we have yet to meet'. Guest beer is usually Wadworth 6X or Young's Special. No meals Sun.
◖ ♿ ⛺ ♣

Leigh

Plough
Church Road OS224468
☎ (0306) 78348
11–2.30, 6–11 (11–11 Sat)
King & Barnes Sussex, Broadwood, Old, Festive Ⓗ
15th-century inn, beautifully situated by the village green. Good food is available in the lounge and restaurant (no meals Mon eve or Sun), while the public bar is for games. Happy hour 6–7.30pm.
❀ ◖ ◗ ⊟ ♣ P

Lower Bourne

Fox
21 Frensham Road (A287, S side of village)
☎ (0252) 716395
11–3, 6–11
Courage Best Bitter, Directors Ⓗ
Split-level horseshoe bar, divided into a traditional public bar and food-oriented lounge (no eve meals Sun/Mon). Good walking country. Guest beers.
❀ ◖ ◗ ⊟ ♣ P

Try also: Spotted Cow, B3001 (Courage)

Surrey

Mayford

Mayford Arms
Guildford Road (off A320 near
B380 jct) OS997560
☎ (0483) 761018
11.30–2.30, 5.30–11 (11–11 Sat)
**Greene King IPA, Rayments
Special, Abbot** Ⓗ
A friendly pub with a layout
that leads to a natural
segregation of customers: three
bars of different character.
Cricket, golf and quiz teams.
Excellent family facilities in
summer, incl. garden fort.
Q 🏠 🍴 🍺 🛏 ♣ P

Mickleham

King William IV
Byttom Hill (off A24
southbound) OS174538
☎ (0372) 372590
12–2.30, 7–10.30 (11–2.30, 6–11
summer)
Adnams Bitter, Old (winter);
**Hall & Woodhouse Badger
Best Bitter; Wadworth 6X** Ⓗ
Charming pub perched on a
rocky hillside. The cosy, old-
fashioned public bar features a
grandfather clock; the lounge is
tiny. The splendid garden can
be a real suntrap. Guest beers in
summer. 🏠 Q 🏠 🍺 ♣

Normandy

Duke of Normandy
Guildford Road (A323)
☎ (0483) 235157
11.30–2.30, 6 (6.30 Sat)–11
Greene King IPA, Abbot Ⓗ
A friendly, two-bar, roadside
locals' inn. Good outside games
area for children. 🏠 🍺 🛏 ♣ P

Ockley

Cricketers
Stane Street (A29)
☎ (0306) 79205
11–2.30, 6–11
**Fuller's London Pride; Hall &
Woodhouse Badger Best
Bitter; Ringwood Best
Bitter** Ⓗ
An attractive pub dating from
1542, with Horsham flagstones
on the floor and, unusually, the
roof. Large inglenook. The
cheapest pint in the area. Patio
for summer drinking. 🏠 🏠 🍺 P

Old Woking

White Hart
High Street (off A247)
☎ (0483) 763202
11–3, 5–11 (11–11 Sat)
**Courage Best Bitter,
Directors; John Smith's
Magnet** Ⓗ
Close enough to Woking to be
a suburban pub but retaining a
village atmosphere. Good

contrasting bars: the public is
small and lively; the saloon
more spacious and quiet. No
meals Sun. Boules played.
🏠 🍺 🛏 ♣ P

Outwood

Dog & Duck
Prince of Wales Road
OS313460
☎ (034 284) 2964
11–11
**Everards Old Original; Hall
& Woodhouse Badger Best
Bitter, Tanglefoot; Wadworth
6X; Wells Eagle** Ⓗ
Friendly rural pub serving good
food (vegetarian option and
children's menu). Impressive
range of traditional games incl.
Ringing the Bull. Frequent guest
ales. 🏠 🏠 🍺 ♣ P

Oxshott

Bear
Leatherhead Road (A244)
☎ (0372) 842747
11–3, 5.30–11
**Young's Bitter, Special,
Winter Warmer** Ⓗ
A medium-sized, open-plan pub
with a small restaurant area;
comfortably appointed. Children
allowed in conservatory. Good
value, home-cooked food (no
meals Sun eve).
🏠 🏃 🍺 🛏 ♣ P

Oxted

Crown
53 High Street, Old Oxted (off
A25) ☎ (0883) 717853
12–2.30, 6–11
**Adnams Bitter, Broadside;
Fuller's London Pride;
Pilgrim Progress** Ⓗ
Pub on the crown of a hill,
hence the name. Bars on two
levels: the upper bar has a good
quality restaurant and features
fine Victorian panelling and
'Play School' windows. The
large garden has a children's
adventure playground and a
petanque pitch. Guest beers.
🏃 🍺 ≠ ♣

Puttenham

Good Intent
62 The Street (off B3000)
☎ (0483) 810387
11–2.30 (3.30 Sat), 6–11
Courage Best Bitter Ⓗ
A classic country pub with
beamed saloon, featuring a huge
fireplace. Also a good public bar
in the best tradition. Handy for
the North Downs Way and
Cuttmill Pond. No food Sun.
Interesting guest beers always
available.
🏠 Q 🏠 🍺 ♣ P

Reigate

Yew Tree
99 Reigate Hill (A217, off
M25 jct 8)
11–11
**Courage Best Bitter,
Directors; John Smith's
Bitter; Wadworth 6X** Ⓗ
A comfortable, wood-panelled
lounge, halfway up Reigate Hill.
The best Courage beer for miles
ensures that the pub is very
popular with businessmen
'working late in the office'!
🏠 🏠 🍺 P

Try also: **Home Cottage**,
Redhill (Young's)

Ripley

Seven Stars
Newark Lane (B367, ½ mile W
of village)
☎ (0483) 225128
11–3, 5.30–11
**Ind Coope Friary Meux Best
Bitter, Benskins Best Bitter,
Burton Ale; Mansfield Old
Baily; Tetley Bitter** Ⓗ
An imposing 1930s-style
building in a rural setting, close
to Wey Navigation. Handy for
a drink, a meal and a river walk.
Can be busy in the summer.
🏠 🏠 🍺 P

Try also: **Talbot Hotel** (Ind
Coope)

Shackleford

Cyder House
Peperharrow Road (off A3)
OS935453
☎ (0483) 810360
11–2.30, 5.30–11
**Gale's HSB; Greene King
IPA; Hook Norton Old
Hooky; Ringwood
Fortyniner, Old Thumper** Ⓗ
Deservedly-popular with a
varied clientele – drivers, walkers
and drinkers; also caters for
children. Can be crowded on
Sun and in summer with diners.
Worth trekking through the
lanes to find.
🏃 🏠 🍺 ◌

Shepperton

Barley Mow
67 Watersplash Road (off
B376)
☎ (0932) 225580
11–3, 5.30–11 (11–11 Fri & Sat)
**Ruddles Best Bitter, County;
Webster's Yorkshire Bitter** Ⓗ
Busy, out-of-the-way pub, not
far from Shepperton Studios.
Meals highly recommended;
snacks only eves. Guest beer
changes every week.
🏠 🏠 ♣ P

Shere

Prince of Wales
Shere Lane
☎ (0486) 412313
11–2.30, 6–11
Young's Bitter, Special, Winter Warmer Ⓗ
Situated in a delightful village with a pretty stream: ideal for a Sun afternoon stroll or as a stop-over for more serious walking. The small public bar is dominated by a pool table and contrasts with a more sedate lounge. Eve meals Wed–Sat.
🏠 Q ⊱ ❀ ◖ ▮ ╬ ₲ ♣ P

Sidlow Bridge

Three Horseshoes
Ironsbottom (off A217)
OS249463 ☎ (0293) 862315
12–2.30 (3 Sat), 7–11
Fuller's London Pride, ESB; Greene King IPA; Hall & Woodhouse Tanglefoot Ⓗ
A small, rural, 17th-century coaching inn with a fine range of ales. No noisy machines. Welcomes those arriving by helicopter (phone in advance) but not motorcyclists. Guest beers. Q ❀ ◖ ♣ P

Smithbrook

Leathern Bottle
On A281
☎ (0483) 274117
11–2.30 (3 Sat), 6–11
King & Barnes Sussex, Broadwood, Old, Festive Ⓗ
An 18th-century imposing roadside inn and popular stopping-off point. Also serves as a tourist information centre. Good for local walking. No coaches. Public bar is quiet.
🏠 Q ❀ ◖ ▮ ╬ ₲ ⏎ P

Staines

Bells
124 Church Street (off B376)
☎ (0784) 454240
11–11
Courage Best Bitter, Directors Ⓗ
Lively town pub offering a selection of good food and a guest beer (eve meals finish at 6.30). Riverside walks nearby.
Q ⊱ ❀ ◖ ▮

Blue Anchor
High Street (A308)
☎ (0784) 452622
11–11
Ruddles Best Bitter; Wadworth 6X; Webster's Yorkshire Bitter Ⓗ
This Grade I listed pub enjoys a prime, town-centre location. Regular eve music ranges from 60s to country and western.

Nine Men's Morris played. Rightly popular with all ages.
🏠 ❀ ⋈ ◖ ▮ ₲ ╬ ♣ P

Wheatsheaf & Pigeon
Penton Road (off B376)
☎ (0784) 452922
11–3, 5–11 (11–11 Sat)
Courage Best Bitter, Directors Ⓗ
Well-run pub close to the river on the southern outskirts of the town. A blaze of floral displays in summer. Guest beers.
Q ❀ ◖ ▮ ₲

Stanwell

Wheatsheaf
Town Lane (B378)
☎ (0784) 253372
11–11 (11–4, 7–11 Sat)
Courage Best Bitter, Directors Ⓗ
A small village pub with a friendly atmosphere; a former tripe house, though, unfortunately, this dish is no longer served. Don't be put off by the proximity of Heathrow Airport, this remains a good, traditional public house. Guest beer. No food Sun. ❀ ◖ ♣ P

Sunbury

Flower Pot Hotel
Thames Street
☎ (0932) 780741
11–3, 5–11
Draught Bass; Brakspear XXX Mild; Charrington IPA; King & Barnes Sussex; Tetley Bitter; Young's Special Ⓗ
Tastefully-refurbished after three years of closure and decay. Pleasantly situated, close to the Thames, and providing a rare, welcome outlet for real mild.
⋈ ◖ ▮

Tilford

Barley Mow
Tilford Green OS873435
☎ (025 125) 2205
11–2.30 (3 Sat), 6 (5.30 Sat in summer)–11
Courage Best Bitter, Directors; John Smith's Bitter Ⓗ
A classically-situated, village pub on the cricket green, complete with riverside garden (summer barbecues) and ghost. An 18th-century building converted to a pub by cricketing hero Billy Beldham. Tea room in garden summer weekends. No meals winter Sun. Guest beer. 🏠 Q ❀ ◖ ▮ ▲ ♣

Walliswood

Scarlett Arms
Walliswood Green Road
OS120381 ☎ (030 679) 243
11–2.30, 5.30–11
King & Barnes Mild, Sussex,

Broadwood, Old, Festive Ⓗ
A classic country pub, dating from 1620, featuring a stone-flagged floor and a large inglenook. Note the mis-spelt name on the sign. Home-cooked food and daily specials.
🏠 ❀ ◖ ▮ ♣ P

Walton-on-Thames

Ashley Arms
Halfway Green (off A244)
☎ (0932) 223322
11–3, 5 (6 Sat)–11
Draught Bass; Theakston Best Bitter; Webster's Yorkshire Bitter Ⓗ
Small pub, dating from 1842, situated on Ashley Park Estate village green. Friendly, welcoming atmosphere. Pianist Sat and Sun eves; trad. jazz once a month. No food Sun.
🏠 ❀ ◖ ▮ ╬ ♣ P

Walton on the Hill

Fox & Hounds
Walton Street (B2220)
☎ (0737) 812090
11–11
Draught Bass; Charrington IPA; M&B Highgate Mild; Wadworth 6X Ⓗ
Excellent village inn which serves food and ale of the same high quality. The good atmosphere is enhanced by the very efficient service and the absence of any music. Food available all day. 🏠 Q ❀ ◖ ▮ P

Try also: Bell (Charrington)

Warlingham

White Hart
3 Farleigh Road (B269)
☎ (088 32) 4106
11–3, 5.30 (6 Sat)–11
Draught Bass; Charrington IPA; Young's Special Ⓗ
15th-century farmhouse which became a pub 200 years later. Inside a warren of inter-connecting drinking areas is served from a small bar. Beware of the very low beams. By far the best pub in a village which is known for the first-ever reading of the *New English Prayer Book* in 1549. No food Sun. 🏠 Q ❀ ◖ ♣ P

Westcott

Cricketers
Guildford Road (A25)
☎ (0306) 883520
11–3, 5.30–11
Adnams Bitter; Fuller's London Pride; Hall & Woodhouse Badger Best Bitter, Tanglefoot; Pilgrim Surrey Ⓗ

Surrey

Competitively-priced free house with darts and pool. The raised area is usually used for eating (no eve meals Mon or Wed). Outside drinking is restricted to a small pavement area. 🏠 ◖ ▶ ♣

Weston Green

Alma Arms
Alma Road (off A309)
☎ (081) 398 4444
11–2.30 (3 Fri & Sat), 6–11
Courage Best Bitter, Directors Ⓗ
Former hunting lodge with an oak-beamed interior. Overlooks a picturesque green and pond, and features mementoes of a Crimean War battle, from which the pub takes its name.
Q 🏠 ◖ ⇌ (Esher) ♣ P

Weybourne

Running Stream
66 Weybourne Road (B3007)
☎ (0252) 23750
11.30–2.30, 6–11
Courage Best Bitter, Directors; John Smith's Bitter Ⓗ
Comfortable roadside local: you can always hear yourself talk over the background music. A friendly pub with a landlord of 15 years' standing. Patio for summer drinking. ◖ P

Weybridge

Old Crown
83 Thames Street (off A317)
☎ (0932) 842844
10.30–2.45 (3.30 Sat), 5–11
Courage Best Bitter, Directors; Wadworth 6X Ⓗ

A 16th-century pub with an attractive, weatherboarded façade. Several rooms with differing atmospheres. Food always available; fresh fish is a speciality. Q 🏠 ◖ ▶ ♣ P

Prince of Wales
11 Cross Road, Oatlands (off A3050) ☎ (0932) 852082
11–11
Adnams Bitter; Fuller's London Pride; Ind Coope Burton Ale; Tetley Bitter; Whitbread Boddingtons Bitter Ⓗ
Cosy pub with traditional decor; no fruit machines or noisy games to spoil the atmosphere. Good value restaurant (no meals Sun eve). Guest beers. Q 🏠 ◖ P

Worplesdon

Fox
Fox Corner (B380, 200 yds from A322 jct)
☎ (0483) 232520
11–2.30 (3 Sat), 5–11
Courage Best Bitter, Directors Ⓗ
A traditional rural drinking house with a lively public bar and a quiet intimate lounge. Still retains its original Surrey wooden slats and marvellous outside gents. Long may it and the general atmosphere survive. Garden play area for summer.
Q 🏠 ⊟ P

Wotton

Wotton Hatch
Guildford Road (A25)
☎ (0306) 885665

11–2.30, 5.30–11 (11–11 Sat)
Fuller's Chiswick, London Pride, ESB Ⓗ
The small, cosy public bar is mainly used by locals, while walkers, and those wanting food, usually frequent the saloon bar. Large restaurant with a cocktail bar. Situated on an old pilgrim route, in attractive countryside facing the North Downs. 🏠 🏠 ◖ ▶ ♣ P

Wrecclesham

Bat & Ball
Bat & Ball Lane, Boundstone OS833445 ☎ (025 125) 2108
11–11
Ballard's Best Bitter; Exmoor Gold; Fuller's London Pride; Greene King Abbot; Hook Norton Best Bitter; Young's Special Ⓗ
Out-of-the-way free house with good family facilities. Excellent meals available all week. Worth the hunt. 🏠 ⥥ 🏠 ◖ ▶ P

Sandrock
Sandrock Hill Road (off B3384)
☎ (0252) 715865
11–2.30, 5.30–11 (11–11 Sat)
Batham Mild, Best Bitter; Brakspear Bitter; Exmoor Gold; Holden's Bitter; Taylor Landlord; Whitbread Boddingtons Bitter Ⓗ
One of the greatest. Why else would the local CAMRA branch hold their Christmas parties here? Always a good selection of Black Country beers. A must for serious beer drinkers. No food Sun. 🏠 Q 🏠 ◖ ♣ P

'Bloody hell, if it's not passive smoking it's stubble burning!'

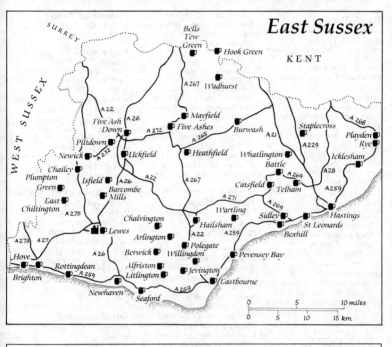

East Sussex

🏭 **Harveys**, *Lewes*

Alfriston

Market Cross/ Smugglers
Waterloo Square
☎ (0323) 870241
11–3, 6.30–11
Courage Best Bitter, Directors Ⓗ
Smart, 12th-century, village pub with two ghosts and two names. Lots of drinking areas create a warm, intimate atmosphere, and there is an attractive conservatory and a small garden area. Note the large collection of early kitchen aids. Q ⑧ ◖ ▶ Å

Try also: Star (Free)

Arlington

Old Oak Inn
Cane Heath ($\frac{1}{2}$ mile off the Hailsham–Upper Dicker road)
☎ (0323) 482072
11–2.30, 6–11 (12–2.30, 7–10.30 Sun)
Hall & Woodhouse Badger Best Bitter; Harveys BB Ⓖ
Oak beams, inglenook and log fires in a cosy pub which is comfortable without being overdone. Handy for Abbots Wood and Michelham Priory. Good reputation for food (no meals Sun/Mon eves). Regular

guest beers, all from the cask. Sells Xmas trees in season.
🏭 Q ⑧ ◖ ▶ ♿ P

Barcombe Mills

Anglers Rest
1 mile W of A26, N of Lewes
OS428150 ☎ (0273) 400270
Hours vary
Harveys BB, Old; Wadworth 6X Ⓗ
Single-bar pub in a rural location by a renovated railway station and the River Ouse. Popular and extensive menu. Children's games in the garden.
⑧ ◖ ▶ Å ♣ P

Battle

Chequers
Lower Lake (A2100, just S of Battle)
☎ (042 46) 2088
10–3, 6–11
Marston's Pedigree; Whitbread Boddingtons Bitter, Fremlins Bitter, Flowers Original Ⓗ
Smart, attractive, well-kept pub on the site of the Battle of Hastings. Dating from the 15th century, its oak beams add atmosphere and there is a resident ghost. Note the copper bar top. Caters equally well for

locals and tourists and is handy for the abbey. 🏭 ⑧ ⋈ ◖ ▶ Å ≈

Try also: Kings Head (Courage)

Bells Yew Green

Brecknock Arms
☎ (089 275) 237
Harveys XX Mild, Pale Ale, BB, Old Ⓗ
Unpretentious, village pub with hop memorabilia in the public bar. Views from the beer garden across the fields to the old George Ware brewery.
🏭 Q ⑧ ◖ ⊟ ♿ ♣ P

Berwick

Cricketers Arms
300 yds W of Alfriston roundabout on A27, then left
☎ (0323) 870469
11–3, 6–11
Harveys BB, Old Ⓖ
Timeless, country pub, untouched by modernists in any way; an ideal walking base. Stone floor in the public bar; good views of the South Downs. All draught beer comes direct from the cask. Very highly recommended.
🏭 Q ⑧ ◖ ▶ Å ≈ ♣ P

East Sussex

Bexhill

Bell Hotel
Church Street ☎ (0424) 21965
10.30–11 (12–2, 7–10.30 Sun)
**Courage Best Bitter,
Directors; Young's Special** Ⓗ
Large, rambling, old hotel in the
heart of the old town. Adjacent
to the parish church and the old
manor barn. Various drinking
areas to choose from; visit the
garden bar to experience indoor
thunderstorms and marvel at the
famous giant goldfish.
⊛ ⊨ ◑ ≷ ♣

Sportsman
15 Sackville Road
☎ (0424) 214214
10.30–3, 5–11 (10.30–11 Fri, Sat &
summer)
**Adnams Bitter; King &
Barnes Festive; Webster's
Yorkshire Bitter** Ⓗ
Welcoming and friendly, town-
centre pub, with a jovial
atmosphere created by an
outgoing landlady and sociable
locals. Sunny and secluded beer
garden. Frequent eve functions
and competitions throughout
the year. An oasis in a desert of
choice. Guest beers. ⊛ ◑ ≷ ♣

Try also: **Traffers** (Free)

Brighton

Albion
28 Albion Hill (behind former
Tamplins brewery)
☎ (0273) 604439
10.30–11
**Whitbread Boddingtons
Bitter, Best Bitter, Flowers
Original** Ⓗ
Friendly, two-bar, split-level
local with two bar billiards
tables. 10p per pint off for card
carrying CAMRA members.
Gale's XXXD is a 'permanent'
guest beer. A *Good Beer Guide*
regular. ⊛ ♣ ⏣

Basketmakers Arms
12 Gloucester Road (½ mile SE
of station) ☎ (0273) 697014
11–3, 5.30–11 (11–11 Fri & Sat)
**Gale's XXXD, BBB, 5X,
HSB** Ⓗ
Lively local tucked away in the
back-streets but worth seeking
out. The interior is adorned
with a collection of tins and
other ephemera. Live music Sun
lunch and eve. Another *Good
Beer Guide* regular. ◑ ≷ ♣

George Beard
125 Gloucester Road
☎ (0273) 607765
11–3, 5.30–11
**Adnams Mild, Broadside;
Harveys BB, Old** Ⓗ
Comfortable and stylish, town
pub with a relaxing atmosphere.
Interesting Victorian prints;

good value lunches (Mon–Sat).
Mini beer festival in Nov and a
varied range of guest beers.
◑ ≷ ♣

Greys
105 Southover Street
☎ (0273) 680734
11–2.45, 5.30–11 (11–11 Sat)
**Adnams Bitter; Whitbread
Boddingtons Bitter, Flowers
Original** Ⓗ
Small, lively, popular pub – a
microcosm of society. Strong
interest in the local music scene:
live music Sun lunch and Mon
eve. Recommended for its
excellent lunches (Mon–Sat).
⊛ ◑

Hand in Hand
33 Upper St James Street,
Kemptown
☎ (0273) 602521
11–11
**Hall & Woodhouse Badger
Best Bitter, Tanglefoot;
Kemptown Mild, Bitter,
Celebrated Staggering Ale,
SID** Ⓗ
Small, corner pub with its own
'tower' brewery (Kemptown).
The decor defies description!
Always popular and often very
busy. Vegetarian meals are
available, as are guest beers. ◑ ◗

Lamb & Flag
9 Cranbourne Street
☎ (0273) 26415
11–11
**Charrington IPA; Fuller's
London Pride** Ⓗ
Local town pub, popular at
lunchtimes. Its proximity to the
main shopping area leads to a
good passing trade. Lunchtime
snacks available. Q ≷ ♣

Leconfield Arms
116 Edward Street (440 yds E
of Royal Pavilion)
☎ (0273) 687515
11–11
**Courage Best Bitter; John
Smith's Bitter** Ⓗ
True town local, thankfully
missed by the modernisation hit
squad, hence the small wood-
panelled bars and leaded-glass
windows. A pub with no frills
but a warm welcome. Take care
on the steep stairs to the toilets.
⊟ ♣

Lord Nelson
36 Trafalgar Street (200 yds E
of station)
☎ (0273) 682150
10.30–3, 5.30–11
**Harveys XX Mild, Pale Ale,
BB, Old, Armada** (summer) Ⓗ
Town pub with two separate
drinking areas, both devoid of a
jukebox. Original settles and
fireplaces; note the snob-screen
between the drinking areas.
Busy for good, lunchtime food.
◑ ≷ ♣ ⏣

Pedestrian Arms
Foundry Street (SE of station)
☎ (0273) 697014
11–11
**King & Barnes Festive;
Ruddles Best Bitter;
Webster's Yorkshire Bitter** Ⓗ
Small, back-street local, popular
at all times with Royal Mail
workers from the nearby sorting
offices. Decorated with many
old photographs of the area.
Look for the CAMRA logo on
the outside! Regular Pilgrim
guest beers. ◑ ≷ ♣

Robin Hood
3 Norfolk Place
11–11
**Fuller's London Pride; Hall &
Woodhouse Badger Best
Bitter; Harveys BB;
Ringwood Fortyniner; Taylor
Landlord; Wadworth 6X** Ⓗ
Large, popular, two-bar local,
off Western Road. Quiet
drinking area away from the
main bar; bar billiards and darts
played. Good selection of guest
beers regularly available.
◑ ♣

Royal Standard
59 Queens Road (100 yds S of
station)
☎ (0273) 29813
11–11
**Adnams Broadside; Draught
Bass; Harveys BB; Mitchell's
Best Bitter** Ⓗ
Extremely popular pub with
good value food; fish dishes are
a speciality. At least one guest
mild is always available and
beer festivals are held regularly
during the year. Up to 15 guest
beers on gravity dispense in the
'Vestry' alcove. ◑ ◗ ≷

Sir Charles Napier
50 Southover Street
☎ (0273) 601413
11–3, 6–11
Gale's XXXD (summer), **BBB,
5X, HSB** Ⓗ
Busy, deceptively spacious,
corner local. The full range of
Gale's country wines is also
available. No food Sun.
⛷ ⊛ ◑ ♣ ⏣

Burwash

Bell
High Street (A265)
☎ (0435) 882304
11–2.30, 6–11
Harveys XX Mild (summer),
BB, Old Ⓗ
Superbly-kept pub and
restaurant dating from the early
17th century and mentioned in
Puck of Pooks Hill. Marvellous
collection of barometers and
mulling irons. Known for its
warm welcome. Regular guest
beers.
⌂ Q ⛷ ⊛ ⊨ ◑ ◗ ♣ ⏣ P

Catsfield

White Hart
On A261
☎ (0424) 892650
10–3, 6–11
Draught Bass; Charrington IPA; Harveys BB Ⓗ
Village local with a deceptive interior: very large, comfy and welcoming. A good centre for walking and an ideal bolt-hole on wet winter nights, with its big fireplace. No meals Sun, but hot snacks. ⌂ ⊜ ⊛ ◑ ▶ ♣ P

Chailey

Horns Lodge
South Street, South Chailey (A275)
☎ (0273) 400422
Hours vary
Greene King IPA; Hall & Woodhouse Badger Best Bitter; Harveys BB Ⓗ
Family-run pub with separate restaurant and family areas. Good local trade; winner of pub games trophies. ⌂ ⊛ ◑ ♣ P

Try also: Kings Head (Beards chain)

Chalvington

Yew Tree Inn
Chalvington Road, off A22 at Golden Cross OS525099
☎ (032 183) 326
11–3, 6–11
Harveys BB Ⓗ
Remote, rural pub, off the beaten track, but well worth finding. Exposed beams, low ceilings, stone floors and one of the oldest cricket pitches in the country. Active cricket and soccer teams. No food Sun. ⌂ Q ⊛ ◑ ▶ ♣ P

Eastbourne

Black Horse
220 Seaside (½ mile E of centre)
☎ (0323) 23143
11–3, 5.30–11
Draught Bass; Charrington IPA Ⓗ
A rarity in these parts – a traditional, street-corner local. Home of a championship-winning dominoes team. Regular quiz nights; much fund-raising for guide dogs. Good value lunches. Tables on the street. Q ⊛ ◑ ▶ ♣

Hurst Arms
76 Willingdon Road (1¼ miles N of centre, on A22)
☎ (0323) 21762
11–3, 6–11
Harveys XX Mild (summer), **BB, Old, Armada** Ⓗ
Popular, red-brick, Victorian local, named after a former windmill: a busy public bar and

a quieter saloon. A continuous *Good Beer Guide* entry since 1978. Good value hot and cold snacks available at all times. ⊛ ◑ ♣

Lamb Inn
High Street (A259, 1 mile N of centre)
☎ (0323) 20545
10.30–3, 5.30–11
Harveys XX Mild (summer), **BB, Old, Armada** Ⓗ
Harveys' old-town showpiece: a half-timbered pub, full of antique furniture. Rumours exist of a secret passage connecting the pub's 12th-century crypt with a nearby church. Handy for the art gallery, museum and Gildredge Park. Popular with locals, students and visitors alike. Q ⊜ ⊛ ◑ ▶ ⊕ P

East Chiltington

Jolly Sportsman
Chapel Lane (off B2116)
OS372153 ☎ (0273) 890400
11.30–2.30 (not Mon), 6 (7 winter)–11
Harveys BB Ⓗ
A true centre of village life. A pub well off the beaten track, with good views of the South Downs and Sussex Weald; popular with ramblers. Separate areas for dining and pool. Meals served Wed–Sun. Guest beers in summer. ⊛ ◑ ▶ ♣ P

Five Ash Down

Firemans Arms
On old A26, N of A272 crossroads OS477237
☎ (082 581) 2191
Hours vary
Harveys BB; Theakston Best Bitter, Old Peculier; Younger IPA Ⓗ
Two-bar pub run by a steam railway enthusiast and attracting a good local trade. Traction engine meet on New Year's Day. The beer range varies. ⌂ ⊜ ⊛ ◑ ▶ ♣ ♧ P

Five Ashes

Five Ashes Inn
On A267, near Mayfield
☎ (082 585) 485
11–3, 6–11
Courage Directors; Harveys BB; Hook Norton Old Hooky Ⓗ
Small, country inn with an inglenook and oak beams: a small saloon and a tiny public – not recommended for the claustrophobic. Guest beers and a house bitter. ⌂ ⊜ ⊛ ◑ ▶ ♣

Hailsham

Grenadier
High Street ☎ (0323) 842152
11–3, 6–11

Harveys XX Mild, BB, Old Ⓗ
Popular, two-bar, town pub with a classic, Victorian facade, a genuine public bar and an intimate saloon, often full. Look for the original gas lamp fittings. Strong on charity fund-raising – the bar is lined with pictures of guide dogs bought by the pub. ⊛ ◑ ⊕ ♣ P

Kings Head
146 South Road
☎ (0323) 843880
11–2.30 (3 Sat), 6–11
Harveys BB, Old Ⓗ
Two-bar local in the Cacklebury area of Hailsham. A genuine pub with a lively public bar and a loyal clientele. Known locally as the 'Kings-Head-South-Road', to distinguish it from a Courage pub of the same name. No food Sun eve. ⌂ ⊛ ◑ ▶ ⊕ ♣ P

Hastings

First In, Last Out
14–15 High Street, Old Town
☎ (0424) 425079
12–3.30 (not Mon in winter), 7–11
Adnams Broadside; St Clements Crofters, Cardinal Ⓗ
Small, friendly brew pub (St Clements brewery); a window in the bar overlooks the full mash production. Open, central fireplace; alcove-style seating. The cheapest beer in the area; a home-brew gem, not to be missed. Guest beers. ⌂ Q ▲ ♣ ♧

Royal Standard
East Beach Street, Old Town (A259) ☎ (0424) 420163
10 (12 winter)–11
Shepherd Neame Master Brew Bitter, Spitfire, Bishops Finger Ⓗ
Compact, two-bar pub on the seafront, with naval and military decoration. Handy for the tourist attractions. A warm welcome, but watch out for the door-operated spider on the bar. ⌂ ⊛ ⊕ ♣

Stag Inn
14 All Saints Street, Old Town
☎ (0424) 425734
11.30–3, 7–11
Marston's Pedigree; Whitbread Fremlins Bitter Ⓗ
Ancient pub in the Old Town's most picturesque street. Discover the smugglers' tunnel, the unique game of 'Loggits', the small collection of mummified cats and the beer-mat catching dogs! Varied guest beers at reasonable prices; always a friendly atmosphere. ⌂ Q ⊜ ⊛ ◑ ◑ ⊕ ♣

Try also: Pump House (Fremlins)

East Sussex

Heathfield

Star Inn
Church Street, Old Heathfield (off B2096) ☎ (0435) 863570
11–3, 6–11
Gale's HSB; Harveys Pale Ale; King & Barnes Sussex; Ruddles Best Bitter Ⓗ
14th-century, village local actually in the churchyard. A comfortable saloon with an inglenook; cosy public bar with militaria. The award-winning gardens offer superb views. Look out for the cider-drinking ghost! A pub with a record of serving beer for 600 years. No eve meals Sun/Mon.
🏚 Q 🍴 🍺 🌳 ♣ P

Hook Green

Elephants Head
On B2169, near Frant
OS655359 ☎ (0892) 890279
11–3, 6–11
Harveys XX Mild, Pale Ale, BB, Old, Armada Ⓗ
Country pub of true character, set back off the road and close to the hop gardens of Kent. Solid stone and sturdy timbers make this a comfortable resting spot for a pint. A rare outlet for the entire Harveys range.
🏚 Q 🍴 ♣ P

Hove

Hedgehog & Hogshead
100 Goldstone Villas (next to station) ☎ (0273) 733660
11–2.30, 5.30–11 (11–11 summer; may close football match days)
Ruddles Best Bitter Ⓗ
Former plastic Phoenix pub, now the first in a new chain of David Bruce brew pubs, its full name being 'Bertie Belcher's Brighton Brewery at the Hedgehog & Hogshead, in Hove Actually'! Bare floorboards, church pews and old brewery pictures make a bright and cheerful atmosphere which is appreciated by a wide selection of drinkers. Changing guest beer. Blanket pressure on the house brews. 🍴 ⇌ 🍺

Try also: **Hove Place**, First Ave (Free)

Icklesham

Queens Head
Parsonage Lane (off A259, just past Oasthouse pub)
☎ (0424) 814552
11–3, 6–11 (11–11 Sat)
Cotleigh Tawny; Greene King Abbot; Ringwood Old Thumper; Taylor Landlord Ⓗ
Hard-to-find, tile-hung, quiet, country pub with a magnificent, long, mahogany serving counter in the public bar. Walls are decorated with old farming implements and there are superb views from the garden. Warm, friendly atmosphere. Beer range often changes; cider in summer.
🏚 Q 🍴 🍺 ⚲ 🌳 ♣ ⇌ P

Isfield

Laughing Fish
Isfield Station (off A26)
OS452172 ☎ (082 575) 349
11–3, 6–11
Harveys Pale Ale, BB, Old, Armada Ⓗ
Village inn, next to the 'Lavender Line' converted station and near Bentley Motor Museum and Wildfowl Park. Beer range varies. No meals Mon eve.
🏚 🍴 🍺 ♣ P

Jevington

Eight Bells
High Street (B2101, Friston–Polegate road)
☎ (032 12) 4442
11–2.30, 6–11 (12–2, 7–10.30 Sun)
Courage Best Bitter, Directors; Harveys BB; John Smith's Bitter Ⓗ
600 year-old, locals', village pub, complete with oak beams and window seats. Warm welcome; excellent home cooking. Paintings by local artists and locally grown produce for sale. Attractive, safe garden. Q 🍺 🍴 ♣ P

Lewes

Black Horse Inn
55 Western Road (old A27, opp. County Hall)
☎ (0273) 473653
11–2.30, 6–11
Brakspear Special; Harveys BB, Old Ⓗ
Traditionally furnished public bar, awash with pictures of old Lewes; usually crowded and lively, with a smaller, more sedate saloon at the rear. Originally a coaching inn, built in 1810. Q ⇌ 🍴 ♣

Gardeners Arms
46 Cliffe High Street
☎ (0273) 474808
11–11 (11–3, 5.30–11 winter)
Adnams Bitter; Butcombe Bitter; Eldridge Pope Dorchester, Royal Oak; Hook Norton Mild; Palmers IPA Ⓗ
Comfortable, friendly free house, almost opposite Harveys' brewery, offering an ever-changing range of beers. Church-style seating is an interesting feature. Occasional live music. A must for real ale drinkers. 🍴 ♣ 🍺

Royal Oak
8 Station Street
☎ (0273) 474803
11–2.30, 5 (6 Sat)–11
Adnams Broadside; Brakspear Special; Harveys BB, Old; Wadworth 6X Ⓗ
Lively and thriving, single-bar pub, emerging from a renovated, quiet local. Particularly busy at weekends. Many reminders of the old pub and historic Lewes adorn the walls. 🏚 🍺 🍴 ⇌

Litlington

Plough & Harrow
On Exceat–Alfriston road
☎ (0323) 870632
11–2.30 (12–3 Sat), 6.30–11
Hall & Woodhouse Badger Best Bitter, Tanglefoot; Harveys BB Ⓗ
There are always six beers available in this smart, busy, village pub which enjoys a huge food trade in its separate restaurant area. A railway theme extends to models in the bar. There is a children's servery and an aviary. Guest beers.
🏚 Q 🍴 P

Mayfield

Railway Inn
Stone Cross OS579266
☎ (0435) 872529
11–3, 6–11
Draught Bass; Charrington IPA; Larkins Bitter; Welsh Brewers Worthington BB Ⓗ
Old-fashioned pub which has retained two rooms with distinct characteristics; an oak-panelled saloon and a bustling public bar. 🏚 Q 🍺 🍴 ♣ P

Rose & Crown
Fletching Street (⅛ mile E of village) ☎ (0435) 872200
11–3, 6–11
Adnams Bitter; Harveys BB Ⓗ
Superbly atmospheric pub with varied rooms at different levels and an inglenook. Rare guest beers and good food combine to make this an excellent, village local, well worth finding.
🏚 Q 🍺 ⇌ 🍴 🍺 ♣ P

Try also: **Carpenters Arms** (Free)

Newhaven

Engineer
76 Railway Road, East Side (400 yds from A259)
☎ (0273) 514460
11–11
Charrington IPA Ⓗ
Cheerful pub near the harbour, used by workmen and dockers. Quiz nights popular; euchre played. No food Sun. Guest beers being sought.
🏚 🍺 🍴 ⇌ ♣

Jolly Boatman

135 Lewes Road (Elphick Road
jct) ☎ (0273) 514457
3, 6–11
Harveys BB, Old ⏣
Friendly, edge-of-town local;
one-bar with typical town decor
and nautical paraphernalia.
Harveys Mild is kept under
blanket pressure. Upstairs room
with pool and darts. No food
Sun. ◖ ♣

Try also: **Ark** (Grand Met);
Riverside (Free)

Newick

Royal Oak

Church Road (turn S off A272)
☎ (082 572) 2506
Hours vary
**Harveys BB; Whitbread
Boddingtons Bitter, Strong
Country, Flowers Original** ⏣
Traditional, oak-beamed public
bar in what used to be the
village manor house;
comfortable saloon with music.
See the wattle and daub wall
panel between the bars. Small
garden. ⌂ ❀ ◖ ◗ ⊞ ♣ P

Try also: **Crown** (Beards
chain)

Pevensey Bay

Castle Inn

76 Eastbourne Road (A259)
☎ (0323) 764970
11–3, 6–11
**Draught Bass; Charrington
IPA** ⏣
Attractive, whitewashed pub
converted from a row of
cottages (see the old picture in
the lounge). Warm and
comfortable atmosphere; varied
menu. ⌂ Q ❀ ◖ ◗ ⊞ ▲ ⇌ ♣ P

Piltdown

Peacock

Shortbridge (B2102, off A272)
☎ (0825) 762463
Hours vary
**Harveys BB; Larkins Bitter;
Whitbread Flowers
Original** ⏣
Picturesque, upmarket, oak-
beamed pub with an inglenook,
separate restaurant and pleasant
gardens, front and back. Near
the site of the Piltdown Man
hoax. ⌂ ❀ ◖ ◗ P

Playden

Peace & Plenty

On A268
☎ (079 78) 342
11–3, 6.30 (5.30 Sat, 6 summer)–11
**King & Barnes Sussex;
Young's Special** ⏣
Hospitable, roadside free house
which welcomes families in its
large beer garden. Varied food
available at all sessions; cosy,

pleasant atmosphere. The beer
range varies and may expand in
summer. ⌂ Q ❀ ◖ ◗ ♿ P

Plumpton Green

Fountain

Station Road
☎ (0273) 890294
10.30–2.30, 6–11 (may vary)
Young's Bitter, Special ⏣
Young's only tied house in
Sussex and deservedly popular;
a *Good Beer Guide* perennial with
a locally well-known landlord.
Note the large inglenook.
Unfortunately, Young's Winter
Warmer is no longer sold.
⌂ ◖ ♣ ♣ P

Polegate

Dinkum

54 High Street
☎ (032 12) 2029
10.30–11
Harveys BB, Old, Armada ⏣
Two-bar, traditional pub. The
plush saloon bar has a superb,
dark wood counter which
complements the furnishings.
There is also a large games
room and a garden. The pub
name derives from WWII when
Australian servicemen stationed
nearby frequented it.
Q ❀ ❀ ◖ ◗ ⇌ ♣ P

Rottingdean

Queen Victoria

54 High Street
☎ (0273) 302121
10.30–2.30, 6–11
**Harveys BB; Marston's
Pedigree** ⏣
Two-bar pub with a mock
Tudor frontage, decorated
inside with many old
photographs, one showing a
delivery by a steam dray. Note
the old United Ales
advertisement by the fireplace.
Bar billiards played. ◖ ◗ ♣

Try also: **Plough** (Bass)

Rye

Ypres Castle Inn

Gun Gardens (off A259)
☎ (0797) 223248
11–11 (11–3, 7–11 winter)
**Marston's Pedigree;
Whitbread Fremlins Bitter,
Pompey Royal** ⏣
Excellent, unspoilt pub which
appeals to all tastes, tucked
away behind the castle but well
worth seeking out. Magnificent
views of the harbour and fishing
port; safe garden. Jazz/blues Fri
and Sun eves. Handy for Rye's
tourist attractions. Morning
coffee from 10am.
⌂ Q ❀ ❀ ◖ ⇌ ♣

Try also: **Standard** (Free)

St Leonards

Duke

48 Duke Road, Silverhill (off
A2100) ☎ (0424) 436241
11–11
**Ind Coope Friary Meux Best
Bitter, Burton Ale; Tetley
Bitter** ⏣
Traditional, corner local with
contrasting bars: a bustling,
locals' public bar and a quiet,
1960s lounge. Successful trivia
team. An excellent pub with
great customer loyalty. Varied
guest beers at reasonable prices.
Q ❀ ◖ ◗ ❀ ⚲

Horse & Groom

Mercatoria (off A259)
☎ (0424) 420612
11–3, 5.30–11
**Courage Directors; Harveys
Pale Ale, BB, Old** ⏣
Smart, comfortable pub,
decorated with sporting prints.
Popular and often busy, with a
friendly, pleasant atmosphere;
tucked away in the heart of St
Leonards. Q ❀ ◖ ◗ ♿ ⇌ ♣

Seaford

Beachcomber

Marine Parade (on seafront)
☎ (0323) 892719
11–11
**Charrington IPA; Harveys
BB** ⏣
Spacious pub with good range
of beers, recently restored after
a fire. Live entertainment Thu
and Sat nights. Sun eve meals in
summer only. Adventure
playground in the garden. No-
smoking family room.
❀ ❀ ◖ ◗ ♿ ♣ P ✗

Old Plough

20 Church Street
☎ (0323) 892379
11–3, 6–11 (11–11 Fri & Sat)
**Draught Bass; Charrington
IPA** ⏣
Small, cosy and very old;
probably the best pub in
Seaford. Reckoned to have the
best-kept cellar and noted for its
Bass. A real connoisseur's pub.
No food Sun.
⌂ ❀ ❀ ◖ ⇌ ♣ P

White Lion Hotel

74 Claremont Road (600 yds
W of station)
☎ (0323) 892473
11–2.30 (3 Sat), 6–11
**Harveys BB, Old; Young's
Special** ⏣
Pub with comfortable, up-to-
date bars, incl. a games room off
the saloon. Extensive menu;
children's dishes in the
restaurant; no food Sun eve.
Guest beers.
❀ ⇤ ◖ ◗ ⊞ ▲ ⇌ ♣ P

Try also: **Cinque Ports**, High
St (Charrington)

Sidley

New Inn
32 Ninfield Road (A269)
☎ (0424) 210581
10.30–3, 6–11 (10.30–11 Sat)
Draught Bass; Harveys BB Ⓗ
Attractive, weatherboarded pub in an elevated position in the village centre. Despite the name, the building dates from 1629. A warren of small rooms and bars, featuring attractive woodwork. The traditional public bar has a bare, wooden floor. Eve meals Tue–Sat.
Q ⛵ ❀ ◐ ◗ ⊟ ♣ P

Staplecross

Cross Inn
On B2165
☎ (0580) 830217
11–2.30, 6–11
Adnams Bitter; Fuller's London Pride; Harveys BB; Whitbread Fremlins Bitter Ⓗ
15th-century, village local with low ceilings and an inglenook large enough to hold a party. Lots of oak beams and a ghost. Relaxed atmosphere; connections with the old wool trade, hence the village name. Guest beers. ⌂ Q ⛵ ♿ ♣ P

Telham

Black Horse
Hastings Road (A2100)
☎ (042 46) 3109
11–3, 6–11
Marston's Pedigree; Whitbread Fremlins Bitter, Flowers Original Ⓗ
Pleasant, rural pub with a friendly, welcoming atmosphere, lots of oak beams and an attractive, half-weatherboarded exterior. Unusually, it has a pool table on the first floor and a skittle alley on the second – in the roof! Boules played in summer.
⌂ Q ❀ ◐ ◗ ♿ ♣ P

Uckfield

Alma Arms
Framfield Road (B2102, E of centre) ☎ (0825) 762232
11–2.30, 6–11
Harveys XX Mild, Pale Ale, BB, Old Ⓗ
Traditional, town pub, unspoilt by recent extension work. In the same family for generations and a rare mild outlet. An oasis in a poor town for drinking. Meals Mon–Fri. No smoking in the family room.
Q ⛵ ❀ ◐ ⊟ ♿ ♣ P ⚔

Wadhurst

Greyhound
St James Square (B2099)
☎ (089 288) 3224
11–2.30, 6.30–11
Draught Bass; Charrington IPA; Fuller's London Pride Ⓗ
An inn since 1502, haunt of the locally-famous Hawkhurst Gang in the 18th century. Cosy, welcoming atmosphere; impressive inglenook; large garden with play area; separate restaurant. The beer range may be expanded.
⌂ Q ❀ ◐ ◗ ♿ ♣ P

Wartling

Lamb in Wartling
On minor road N of roundabout E of Pevensey village OS658092
☎ (0323) 832116
11–2.30 (3 Sat & summer), 7 (6.30 Sat & summer)–11
King & Barnes Sussex, Broadwood, Old Ⓗ
Cosy pub in the centre of a small village. Log fires in both bars; separate snooker room (children admitted). Quality carvery/*à la carte* restaurant in a converted outhouse. Very friendly welcome; slightly off the beaten track, but worth finding. ⌂ Q ❀ ◐ ◗ ♣ P

Whatlington

Royal Oak
On A21
☎ (0424) 870492
11–3, 6–11
Harveys Pale Ale; Marston's Pedigree; Whitbread Fremlins Bitter; Young's Special Ⓗ
Attractive, country inn dating from 1490 and displaying a list of landlords since 1509. Beams and hop festoons add to the welcoming atmosphere. Look out for the 80ft well in the bar and the resident ghost. The landlord also owns a butcher's, so food is of a high standard.
⌂ Q ⛵ ❀ ◐ ◗ ♣ P

Willingdon

Red Lion
99 Wish Hill (off A22)
☎ (0323) 502062
11–2.30 (3 Sat), 5.30–11 (12–2.30, 7–10.30 Sun)
King & Barnes Sussex, Broadwood, Old, Festive Ⓗ
Village local at the foot of the downs. Recently upgraded and modernised after escaping the grip of Watney, but still retains a friendly atmosphere. Served as the model for the pub in *Animal Farm*, written by Orwell when he stayed in the village. No food Sun. ❀ ◐ ◗ ♣ P

'Oh no, it's even worse than I thought'

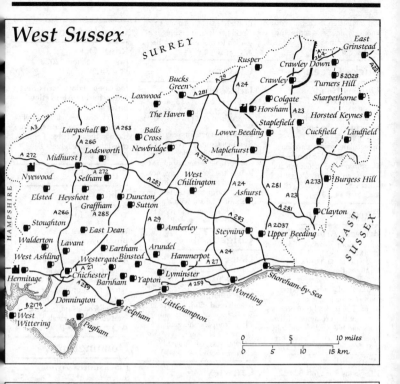

West Sussex

Ballard's, Nyewood; **King & Barnes**, Horsham; **Sussex**, Hermitage

Amberley

Sportsman
Rackham Road (off B2139)
☎ (0798) 831787
11–2.30, 6–11
Adnams Bitter; Gale's BBB Ⓗ
Friendly pub, off the beaten
track, commanding a panoramic
view from the rear patio. Inch's
cider; guest beers in summer.
🏠 Q ⊛ ◖ ▷ ⧖ ⅙ ♣ ☞ P

Arundel

Swan Hotel
High Street ☎ (0903) 882314
11–11
**Courage Directors; Hall &
Woodhouse Badger Best
Bitter, Tanglefoot** Ⓗ
Pleasant, one-bar hotel in the
historic town centre. Three
guest beers available.
Q ⊱ ◖ ▷ ⅙ ▲ ⇌

White Hart
3 Queen Street
☎ (0903) 882374
11–3, 5.30–11 (11–11 Sat)
**King & Barnes Sussex,
Festive** Ⓗ
Deservedly popular, town pub
where a small frontage belies a
roomier interior. The large
collection of pump clips testifies
to the extensive range of guest
ales (usually a choice of three).
Upstairs rooms are used by the
Drip Action Theatre Co.
🏠 Q ⊛ ◖ ▷ ▲ ⇌ ♣

Ashurst

Fountain
On B2135, just S of Partridge
Green ☎ (0403) 710219
11–2.30, 6–11
Marston's Pedigree Ⓖ;
**Whitbread Fremlins Bitter,
Strong Country** Ⓗ, **Flowers
Original** Ⓖ
Delightful, 16th-century pub
with a stone floor, oak beams
and inglenook. Good food (incl.
vegetarian and children's).
Voted *Best Country Pub* in West
Sussex by the Brewers Society
and the local newspaper. Up to
three guest beers available.
🏠 Q ⊱ ⊛ ◖ ▷ ⅙ ▲ ♣ P

Balls Cross

Stag
Off A283, near Kirdford
☎ (0403) 77241
11–3, 6–11

**King & Barnes Sussex,
Broadwood** Ⓗ
Friendly and popular, old,
village local with a stone floor,
low ceilings and an inglenook:
an unspoilt gem. Serves as a
polling station. No food Sun.
🏠 Q ◖ ▷ ⧖ ⅙ ▲

Barnham

Murrell Arms
Yapton Road (under rail bridge
from centre) ☎ (0243) 553320
11–2.30, 6–11 (11–11 Sat)
Gales BBB, 5X, HSB Ⓗ
Three-bar local, laden with
drinking memorabilia. Antique
auctions are held alternate
Weds. Live music every Thu
night and the penultimate Sun
of the month. Ring the Bull
played. A pub with its own
vineyard. 🏠 Q ⊱ ⊛ ◖ ▷ ▲ ♣ P

Binsted

Black Horse
Binsted Lane (off A27/B2132)
OS980064 ☎ (0243) 551213
11–3, 6–11
**Draught Bass; Gale's BBB,
Best Bitter, HSB** Ⓗ; **Pilgrim
XXXX Mild** Ⓖ

West Sussex

Off the beaten track, but worth finding. Fine views across the valley from the garden.
🏠 Q ⦿ ◐ ♣ P

Bucks Green

Queens Head
On A281 ☎ (0403) 722202
11–3, 6–11
Courage Best Bitter, Directors; John Smith's Bitter Ⓗ
Immaculate, oak-beamed pub with a comfortable family room. Good food, incl. children's and vegetarian options. Occasional guest beers. No motorcycles.
🏠 Q ⛄ ⦿ ⛵ ◐ P

Burgess Hill

Brewers Arms
251 London Road (A273)
☎ (0444) 232153
11–2.30, 6–11 (11 Fri & Sat)
Draught Bass; Charrington IPA Ⓗ
A true locals' pub, built from local materials. The old Kemp Town (Brighton) brewery logo can be seen amongst the brick and tile work. Regular live music; bar billiards. Guest beer.
◐ ⊟ ♣

Watermill
1 Leylands Road (off B2112, 100 yds E of Wivelsfield station) ☎ (0444) 235517
11–11
Ruddles Best Bitter, County; Webster's Yorkshire Bitter Ⓗ
Comfortable pub in the 'World's End' area of the town. Although converted to single bar design some years ago, there is still very much a local, public bar area at one end. Regular, varying guest beers.
⦿ ◐ ▶ ≠ (Wivelsfield) ♣ ○ P

Chichester

Cathedral Tavern
29 Southgate
☎ (0243) 781352
10.30–3, 6–11 (10.30–11 summer & Dec)
Ind Coope Burton Ale; King & Barnes Sussex; Ruddles Best Bitter, County; Tetley Bitter Ⓗ
Much-changed, city-centre pub, now back to a traditional appearance. Guest beer, usually from an independent brewery.
⦿ ◐ ▶ ≠ P

Rainbow
56 St Pauls Road (B2178, 100 yds N of fire station)
☎ (0243) 785867
10–11
Ind Coope Friary Meux Best Bitter, Burton Ale; Tetley Bitter Ⓗ
Friendly and spacious local offering good value meals, with

---

monthly special food eves. Good family area and patio garden to the rear. Guest beers.
🏠 Q ⛄ ⦿ ◐ ⚄ ♣ P

Clayton

Jack & Jill
Brighton Road (A273, near B2112 jct) ☎ (0273) 843595
11–2.30, 6–10.30 (11 Fri & Sat; 11–11 summer)
King & Barnes Sussex; Ruddles County; Webster's Yorkshire Bitter Ⓗ
Comfortable, friendly pub at the foot of the South Downs, near the windmills after which it is named. Farming bric-a-brac on the walls; garden with a play area. Guest beers. No food Sun eve. 🏠 ⛄ ⦿ ◐ ♣ P

Colgate

Dragon
Off A264, Horsham–Crawley road ☎ (0293) 851206
11–3, 5.30–11 (12–2, 7.30–10.30 Sun)
King & Barnes Sussex, Broadwood, Old, Festive Ⓗ
Small, two-bar, country inn with a large car park and garden. Lunchtime snacks; shove-ha'penny played. Situated in St Leonards Forest. 🏠 Q ⦿ ♣ P

Crawley

Maid of Sussex
89 Gales Drive, Three Bridges
☎ (0293) 525404
11–3 (3.30 Sat), 6–11
Courage Best Bitter, Directors Ⓗ
Large and friendly, well-run, estate pub with a comfortable lounge bar. Simple food Mon–Sat. Imperial Russian Stout stocked. Has been in the *Guide* for over ten years.
⛄ ⦿ ◐ ⊟ ≠ (Three Bridges) ♣ P

Plough Inn
Ifield Street, Ifield
☎ (0293) 524292
11–3 (4 Sat), 6–11
King & Barnes Sussex, Broadwood, Old, Festive Ⓗ
Traditional, village local, now on the edge of town, next to the old church and Ifield Barn Theatre. Food is basic but very good value (not served Sun lunch). Q ⦿ ◐ ▶ ≠ (Ifield) ♣

White Hart
High Street ☎ (0293) 524292
10–11
Harveys XX Mild (summer), **Pale Ale, Sussex, Old, Armada** Ⓗ
Bustling, town-centre pub in traditional style. Good value lunches Mon–Fri. Strong Irish flavour. ◐ ⊟ ≠ P

Try also: Plough, Three Bridges (Whitbread)

Crawley Down

Royal Oak
Grange Road (off B2028)
☎ (0342) 713170
11–11
Ind Coope Friary Meux Best Bitter, Burton Ale; Tetley Bitter Ⓗ
Quality, two-bar, village local with a good atmosphere. Games room in the public bar. Formerly called the 'Prizefighters'.
Q ⛄ ⦿ ◐ ▶ ♣ P

Cuckfield

White Harte
South Street
☎ (0444) 413454
11–3, 6–11
King & Barnes Sussex, Broadwood, Old, Festive Ⓗ
Friendly, two-bar pub with an olde-worlde atmosphere; genuine oak beams and an inglenook in the saloon bar. Family room open in the summer only. Winner of a *Healthy Food* award from the local council. No meals Sun.
🏠 Q ⛄ ⦿ ◐ ▶ ♣ P

Donnington

Blacksmiths Arms
Selsey Road (B2201, 2 miles S of Chichester)
☎ (0243) 783999
11–2.30, 6–11
Draught Bass; Gale's HSB; Hall & Woodhouse Badger Best Bitter; Marston's Burton Best Bitter, Pedigree; Ringwood Old Thumper Ⓗ
An intriguing collection of antique bric-a-brac festoons the interior of this rural free house. Noted for its food, with an enterprising menu, it can be busy. Guest beers; Ringwood Best is sold as 'Blacksmiths Bitter'. Good family facilities in summer. No meals Sun eve.
🏠 ⦿ ◐ ▶ ⚄ ♣ P

Duncton

Cricketers
Main Road (A285)
☎ (0798) 42473
11–3, 6–11
Ind Coope Friary Meux Best Bitter, Burton Ale; Young's Special Ⓗ
Friendly, country pub, built in 1600 as a brewery. In 1860 it was owned by John Wisden, the cricket publisher. Guest beer.
🏠 Q ⦿ ◐ P

Eartham

George
OS938094 ☎ (024 365) 340
11–3, 6–11
Beer range varies Ⓗ

Downland, country pub with a restaurant. Apart from the house beer (Eartham Ale; not brewed here), three other real ales are available, changed at regular intervals. Families are made welcome. ♨ Q ❀ ◖ ❻ ♿ ♣ P

East Dean

Hurdlemakers
☎ (0243) 63318
11–2.30, 6–11
Adnams Bitter; King & Barnes Sussex; Mansfield Old Baily; Ruddles County; Webster's Yorkshire Bitter Ⓗ
Fine, flint-built, village pub with easy access to Goodwood. An excellent garden caters for all. Previously named the 'Star & Garter'. ♨ Q ❄ ❀ ◖ ◗

East Grinstead

Dunnings Mill
Dunnings Road (West Hoathly road, 1 mile S of centre)
☎ (0342) 326341
11–3, 6–11 (11–11 Fri & Sat)
Draught Bass; Charrington IPA; Harveys BB Ⓗ
400 year-old water mill converted to a pub and restaurant. Two, low-beamed bars cater for different clienteles. ♨ ❄ ❀ ◖ ◗ ◖ ♣ P

Ship
Ship Street ☎ (0342) 323197
11–3, 5.30–11 (11–11 Sat)
Harveys BB, Old; King & Barnes Sussex, Festive; Ruddles Best Bitter; Webster's Yorkshire Bitter Ⓗ
Family-run, town-centre pub, catering for all tastes. The landlord is the town's longest serving licensee. The old ale is sometimes from King & Barnes; the function room only sells keg beer. A pub well worth finding.
Q ❀ ◖ ❻ ❷ ⇌

Elsted

Elsted Inn
Elsted Marsh, near Midhurst (3 miles SW of A272)
☎ (0730) 813662
11–3, 5.30–11
Ballard's Trotton, Best Bitter, Wassail; Marston's Pedigree Ⓗ
Welcoming, tastefully refurbished, Victorian pub. The sign on the wall shows one of its former names and provides a clue to the origins of the pub. Up to three guest beers.
♨ Q ❀ ◖ ◗ ♣ ♣

Try also: Three Horseshoes

Felpham

Old Barn
Off A259 ☎ (0243) 821564
11–11

Ballard's Wassail; Greene King Abbot; King & Barnes Festive; Marston's Merrie Monk, Pedigree; Pitfield Dark Star Ⓗ
Single-bar pub equidistant from the village centre, sea and Butlins. Features strong ales and guest beers. ♨ ◖ ❻ P

Try also: Southdowns (Ind Coope)

Graffham

White Horse
Heyshott Road
OS926176 ☎ (079 86) 331
11–3, 6–11
Bateman XXXB; Eldridge Pope Dorchester, Hardy Country; Palmers IPA Ⓗ
Friendly, good value, village free house. The large garden and conservatory restaurant at the rear both offer downland views. Walkers welcomed. Guest beers. Book for Sun lunch. ♨ Q ❄ ❀ ◖ ◗ ▲

Hammerpot

Woodmans Arms
On A27, Arundel–Worthing road ☎ (090 674) 240
10–3, 5.30–11
Gale's BBB, Best Bitter, HSB Ⓗ
16th-century, roadside pub, with low beams, stone floor and inglenook. Good food; main meals must be booked. Large car park. ♨ Q ❀ ◖ ◗ ❻ P

The Haven

Blue Ship
2 miles W of A29
OS083306 ☎ (0403) 722709
11–3, 6–11
King & Barnes Sussex, Broadwood, Old Ⓖ
Classic, country inn, c. 1400. No cellar and no locals propping up the bar – as there isn't one! Beer is served to several drinking areas from a central servery. Good food. Limited parking.
♨ Q ❄ ❀ ◖ ◗ ❷ ♣ P

Hermitage

Sussex Brewery
36 Main Road (A259)
☎ (0243) 37155
11–11
Eldridge Pope Dorchester, Hardy Country; Hall & Woodhouse Badger Best Bitter, Tanglefoot; Wells Eagle Ⓗ
Friendly local just like all pubs used to be! Guest beers always available.
♨ Q ❄ ❀ ◖ ◗ ⇌ (Emsworth)♣ P

Heyshott

Unicorn Inn
1¼ miles E of A286
OS898180
☎ (0730) 813486
11–2.30 (3.30 summer), 7 (6.30 summer)–11 (supper licence)
Ballard's Best Bitter; Marston's Burton Best Bitter, Pedigree Ⓗ
Pleasant, one-bar, country pub by the South Downs; walkers welcomed. Good food with vegetarian options (no meals Mon eve). Guest beers.
♨ Q ❀ ◖ ◗ ♣ P

Horsham

Dog & Bacon
North Parade (1 mile N of centre on B2237, old A24)
11–2.30, 6–11
King & Barnes Mild, Sussex, Broadwood, Old Ⓗ
Friendly, edge-of-town pub with a small room for families, or hire. Awaiting refurbishment, but cosy enough at present. Bar billiards. No food Sun.
♨ ❄ ❀ ◖ ❷ ♣ P

Stout House
29 Carfax ☎ (0403) 67777
10–4 (3 Tue & Wed), 7.30–11
King & Barnes Sussex, Broadwood, Old, Festive Ⓗ
Good, town-centre pub. One of the best of King & Barnes's houses. Old, friendly and traditional in style, with low beams. Lunchtime snacks.
Q ❷ ❻ ❀ ♣

Tanners Arms
Brighton Road (A281)
☎ (0403) 50527
11–2.30 (3 Sat), 6–11
King & Barnes Mild, Sussex, Old Ⓗ
Friendly, serious drinkers' pub with a small lounge bar. Many active teams; King & Barnes Pentathlon champions two years running. Bar skittles, bar billiards and shove-ha'penny; karaoke nights.
♨ Q ❀ ◖ ◗

Try also: Boars Head Tavern, Worthing Rd (Free)

Horsted Keynes

Green Man
☎ (0825) 790656
11–2.30, 6–11
Harveys BB, Old Ⓗ
Pleasant, village pub on the green, with railwayania in the public bar; a mile from the Bluebell Line station. Guest beers.
♨ Q ❀ ◖ ◗ ❷ ❻ ♣ P

Try also: Victorian Bar, at the station (Free)

West Sussex

Lavant

Earl of March
Lavant Road (A286, 2 miles N of Chichester)
☎ (0243) 774751
10.30–2.30, 6–11
Ballard's Best Bitter; Courage Directors; Ringwood XXXX Porter, Old Thumper; Ruddles Best Bitter, County Ⓗ
Deceptively large, roadside pub, specialising in home cooking (particularly game in season). The open-plan arrangement allows for a quiet dining area and space for families. Dogs welcome. Consistently the best value pub in the area. Guest beers. Q ⏱ ⊜ 🕮 ◑ 🕽 ⅙ ♣ P

Lindfield

Linden Tree
47 High Street
☎ (0444) 482995
11–3, 6–11
Harveys BB, Old; Hook Norton Old Hooky; Marston's Pedigree; Ringwood Old Thumper; Wadworth 6X Ⓗ
Small, upmarket free house with subdued lighting and shop-like, bay windows; sited in a picturesque village. A friendly welcome is assured, although it can get very busy and rather smoky in winter. A *Good Beer Guide* regular. The beer range may vary. No food Sun. ⏱ Q ◑

Littlehampton

Foresters Arms
31 Horsham Road (A259)
☎ (0903) 716570
11–2.30, 6–11 (11–11 Fri & Sat)
Ind Coope Friary Meux Best Bitter; Tetley Bitter Ⓗ
Two-bar, edge-of-town pub; a cosy saloon with a small bar, featuring live music on Fri, and a public bar for games. A guest beer is available and always varied. ⊜ 🕮 🕽 ⅙ ⅄ ♣ P

New Inn
5 Norfolk Road (near seafront)
☎ (0903) 713112
11 (12 winter)–11
Fuller's London Pride; Harveys BB; Young's Special Ⓗ
A welcome, free trade addition in a town dominated by tied estates. Four guest beers regularly available.
⏱ ⊜ 🕮 🕽 ♣

Lodsworth

Hollist Arms
The Street (1 mile N of A272, between Midhurst and Petworth) ☎ (079 85) 310

Ballard's Trotton; King & Barnes Sussex, Festive Ⓖ
Traditional and welcoming, village-centre pub with several, contrasting drinking areas around a central bar. Separate restaurant. Occasional guest beers.
⏱ Q ⏱ ⊜ 🕮 ◑ 🕽 ⅙ ⅄ ♣ P

Lower Beeding

Plough
Leechpole Hill Road (A279)
☎ (0403) 891277
11–3, 6–11 (11–11 Fri & Sat)
King & Barnes Sussex, Festive, Old Ⓗ
Friendly, very relaxed local, probably the cheapest in the area. ⏱ Q ⊜ 🕮 ◑ 🕽 ⅄ P

Loxwood

Onslow Arms
High Street (B2133)
☎ (0403) 752452
11–2.30, 4.30–11 (11–11 Fri & Sat and some summer weekdays)
King & Barnes Sussex, Broadwood, Old, Festive Ⓗ
Two-roomed, low-ceilinged, village local on the banks of the Wey and Arun Canal.
⏱ ⊜ 🕮 ◑ 🕽 ⅄ P

Lurgashall

Noahs Ark
The Green (1 mile W of A283, 5 miles N of Petworth)
OS937273 ☎ (042 878) 346
11–2.30, 6–11
Greene King IPA, Abbot Ⓗ
Wooden-tiled pub in an idyllic village green setting: a traditional locals' bar and a small saloon bar. Open-air theatre is performed in July each year. Food highly recommended (not served Sun). ⏱ Q ⏱ ⊜ 🕮 ◑ 🕽 ⅄ P

Lyminster

Six Bells
Lyminster Road (A284)
☎ (0903) 713639
10–3, 6–11
Ind Coope Friary Meux Best Bitter, Burton Ale; Tetley Bitter Ⓗ
Large, well patronised coaching inn, with an inglenook and oak beams. A single-bar pub with a step through to a restaurant. Large car park at the rear.
⏱ Q ⊜ 🕮 ◑ ⅙ ⅄ P

Maplehurst

White Horse
Park Lane (between A281 and A272, S of Nuthurst)
☎ (0403) 891208
12–2.30, 6–11
Adnams Broadside; Brakspear Special; King & Barnes Sussex Ⓗ

Pleasant pub in the Sussex Weald; its large garden offers excellent views. Boasts a collection of heraldic shields and the widest bar top in Sussex. Regular guest beers. Children welcome in the new conservatory (no-smoking at lunchtime). ⏱ Q ⏱ ⊜ 🕮 ◑ 🕽 P ⅞

Midhurst

Crown
Edinburgh Square (behind old fire station) ☎ (0730) 813462
11–11
Fuller's London Pride, ESB; Gale's HSB; Shepherd Neame Master Brew Bitter; Theakston Best Bitter Ⓗ
Welcoming, traditional, old pub with a separate restaurant. Guest beers. ⏱ ⊜ 🕮 ◑ 🕽 ⅄ ♣ P

Royal Oak
Chichester Road ($\frac{1}{2}$ mile S of Midhurst, by A286)
☎ (0730) 814611
11–11
Ballard's Best Bitter; Marston's Pedigree; Ringwood Old Thumper; Wadworth 6X; Whitbread Boddingtons Bitter, Flowers Original Ⓗ
Large, single bar with small partitions forming individual areas. A large car park to the front of the pub is surrounded by a long, sloping lawn and garden with plenty of benches and tables. Look out for Dwile Flonking days in July.
⏱ ⊜ 🕮 ◑ 🕽 ♣ P

Swan
Red Lion Street
☎ (0730) 812853
10–11 (supper licence)
Harveys XX Mild, Pale Ale, BB, Armada Ⓗ
15th-century, split-level, town-centre local with a restaurant where children are welcome. Food available all day, except 4–5pm; vegetarian options. Note the mural in the upstairs bar. ⏱ Q ⊜ 🕮 ◑ 🕽 ⅄ ♣

Wheatsheaf
Wool Lane (A272)
☎ (0730) 813450
11–11
King & Barnes Sussex, Broadwood, Old, Festive Ⓗ
Smart, one-roomed pub with an oak-beamed interior. Parking can be interesting; the pub is best approached on foot (there is a large car park 150 yards to the north). ⏱ ⊜ 🕮 ◑ 🕽 ♣

Newbridge

Limeburners
Near Billingshurst, signed at A272/B2133 jct
☎ (0403) 782311
11–3, 6–11

Gale's BBB, Best Bitter, HSB 🄷
Old pub, formed in 1805 from three cottages, after the closure of the Wey and Arun Canal. Named after lime kilns once nearby. The one drinking area is popular with a younger clientele. Guest beers. No eve meals Wed. ⌂ ❀ ◖ ◗ ⛺ ♣ P

Pagham

Lion Hotel & Country Club
Nytimber Lane
☎ (0243) 262149
11–3, 5–11 (11–11 Fri & Sat)
Courage Best Bitter, Directors; Ringwood Best Bitter, Old Thumper; John Smith's Bitter 🄷
Original, 15th-century inn with beams a-plenty; very popular and comfortable. Food is good value. 40 malt whiskies available. Q ❀ ⊨ ◖ ◗ ⊟ ♣ P

Rusper

Royal Oak
Friday Street (left fork in road past church going N; follow signs) OS186369
☎ (0293) 871393
11–3, 6–11
King & Barnes Sussex, Broadwood, Old, Festive 🄷
Compact, rural local, outside the village and well off the beaten track; well worth finding. Split levels and low beams are a feature. ⌂ Q ⚘ ❀ ◖ ◗ ♣ P

Selham

Three Moles
¾ mile S of A272, at Halfway Bridge OS935206
☎ (079 85) 303
11–2.30, 5.30–11
King & Barnes Mild, Sussex, Broadwood, Old 🄷
Small, isolated, country pub definitely worth finding. Ploughman's lunches only, even at night. Table skittles; sing-song nights first Sat, and folk nights second Fri, each month.
⌂ Q ❀ ⛺ ♣ P

Sharpethorne

Bluebell
Station Road
☎ (0342) 810264
12–2.30, 6–11
Courage Best Bitter, Directors; Fuller's ESB; Harveys BB; Marston's Pedigree; Wadworth 6X 🄷
Friendly, welcoming local offering regular, varied guest beers at low prices for the area. The emphasis is not on food – for a change! No meals Mon eve. ⌂ Q ❀ ◖ ◗ ♣ P

Shoreham-by-Sea

Ferry Inn
East Street ☎ (0273) 454125
11–3, 5–11
Courage Best Bitter, Directors 🄷
Unusually designed pub with three bars (quiet one downstairs), situated opposite the footbridge to the beach. Takes its name from the old ferry which plied this route to the beach. Q ◖ ⊟ ⇌ ♣

Marlipins
38 High Street (A259)
☎ (0273) 453369
10–3.30, 5.30–11
Draught Bass; Charrington IPA 🄷
Old pub with very low beams, next door to the town museum which is even older. Good value food, now including take-away pizzas. Always busy and very popular with customers of all ages. Q ❀ ◖ ⇌

Staplefield

Victory Inn
Warninglid Road (B2114)
☎ (0444) 400463
11–11 (11–3, 5–11 winter)
Gale's HSB; King & Barnes Sussex; Ruddles Best Bitter, County; Webster's Yorkshire Bitter 🄷
Village pub dating back to 1848, opposite the cricket green and within one mile of Nymans Gardens. Serves over 70 different kinds of ploughman's! Games include Shuttlebox and Monkey in the Tailors. Beware karaoke nights.
⌂ Q ⚘ ❀ ◖ ◗ ⛺ ♣

Steyning

Norfolk Arms
18 Church Street
☎ (0903) 812215
11–3, 6–11
Fuller's London Pride; Marston's Pedigree; Whitbread Strong Country, Flowers Original 🄷
Traditional, two-bar, town-centre pub, with oak beams and wood panels. Friendly welcome; good food. Q ❀ ◖ ⊟ ♣

Stoughton

Hare & Hounds
Off B2146, through Walderton OS791107 ☎ (0705) 631433
11–3, 6–11 (11–11 Fri & Sat in summer)
Brakspear Bitter; Fuller's London Pride; Gibbs Mew Bishop's Tipple; Mansfield Old Baily; Taylor Landlord; Whitbread Boddingtons Bitter 🄷
Fine, Sussex flint building. A warm welcome awaits at this popular, remote pub, nestling in the South Downs. Humorous posters advertise the guest beers. Local seafood often features on a menu which also caters for children. 17th year in the *Guide*. ⌂ Q ❀ ◖ ◗ ⊟ ♣ P

Sutton

White Horse
5 miles SW of Petworth, off A285 OS979152
☎ (079 87) 221
11–3, 6–11
Bateman XB; Fuller's London Pride; Ruddles County; Young's Bitter 🄷
Recent refurbishment has done nothing to spoil the character of this Georgian village inn. A comfortably furnished saloon; bare boards in the welcoming village bar. Popular in summer with walkers and visitors to the nearby Roman villa at Bignor.
⌂ Q ❀ ⊨ ◖ ◗ ⊟ ♣ P

Turners Hill

Red Lion
Lion Lane (200 yds from crossroads on B2028)
11–3, 6–11
Harveys BB, Old 🄷
Friendly, village local which has been in the *Guide* for many years. Occasional live music in the upstairs club room, but access to it can be hair-raising! Fine collection of bottled beers in the upper lounge.
⌂ Q ❀ ◖ ⛺ ♣ P

Upper Beeding

Bridge
High Street ☎ (0903) 812773
11–2.30 (3 Sat), 5.30–11
King & Barnes Mild (summer), **Sussex, Broadwood, Old** 🄷
Friendly, two-bar local in a pleasant location on the banks of the River Adur; not destroyed by recent renovation. Parking can be difficult. ❀ ◖ ⊟ ♣

Walderton

Barley Mow
250 yds E of B2146
OS789106 ☎ (0705) 631321
11–2.30 (3 summer), 6–11
Gale's HSB; Ind Coope Burton Ale; King & Barnes Sussex; Whitbread Boddingtons Bitter 🄷
Pleasant, downland pub in good walking country. Recent renovation has made extra space for diners. Popular skittle alley (must book); garden with a stream alongside. Home-cooked food includes game in season and a vegetarian option.
⌂ Q ❀ ◖ ◗ ♣ P

West Sussex

West Ashling

Richmond Arms
Mill Lane (¼ mile W of B2146)
OS805073 ☎ (0243) 575730
11–3, 5.30–11 (11–11 summer; hours may vary)
Harveys XX Mild; King & Barnes Festive; Marston's Pedigree; Taylor Landlord; Thwaites Bitter; Whitbread Boddingtons Bitter Ⓗ
Excellent, one-bar, village local with a separate skittle alley. Good selection of home-cooked food, incl. vegetarian; ten handpumps, with four guest beers always available, plus cider in summer. Can be smoky on busy winter eves.
🏠 Q ⊛ ℂ ⓓ Å ♣ ⤢ P

West Chiltington

Five Bells
Smock Alley OS093172
☎ (0798) 812143
11–3, 6–11
King & Barnes Mild Ⓖ, Sussex Ⓗ
Spacious, one-bar pub near the village with an imaginative selection of three guest beers always available. Trad. jazz first Sun eve of the month.
🏠 Q ⊛ ℂ ⓓ ♣ ⤢ P

Queens Head
The Hollows (2 miles SW of B2139/B2133 jct)
☎ (0798) 813143
11–3, 6–11
Marston's Pedigree; Whitbread Fremlins Bitter, Flowers Original Ⓗ
400 year-old, village-centre, two-bar pub, now run by a former King & Barnes brewhouse manager. Collections of coins, banknotes and bottles everywhere. Clog and morris dancing a speciality.
🏠 Q ⊛ ℂ ⓓ ⊟ ♣ P

Westergate

Labour in Vain
Nyton Road (A29, 1½ miles S of A27) ☎ (0243) 543173

11–2.30 (3 Sat, may extend), 6–11
Ballard's Best Bitter Ⓗ, Wassail Ⓖ; Harveys BB; Young's Bitter, Special Ⓗ
Fine, village local, warmed by a large, log fire. Extensive, good value menu, incl. a vegetarian option, in the bar and a small, no-smoking restaurant. Regular Thai food eves a speciality. Convenient for Fontwell racecourse and named after a famous scandal.
🏠 Q ⊛ ℂ ⓓ ♣ P

West Wittering

Lamb Inn
Chichester Road (B2179, 1 mile N of centre) ☎ (0243) 511105
11–2.30, 6–11
Ballard's Best Bitter, Wassail; Bunces Benchmark, Best Bitter, Old Smokey; Harveys Old Ⓗ
Old, roadside inn with a welcoming atmosphere and an excellent range of beers. Diners delight in the extensive range of good value, home-made food, yet adequate elbow room remains for the drinkers. Guest beers. No eve meals Sun in winter.
🏠 Q ⊛ ℂ ⓓ ⧖ Å P ✗

Worthing

Chapmans
27 Railway Approach
☎ (0903) 30690
10.30–11
Gale's HSB; Hall & Woodhouse Tanglefoot; Harveys BB; Ruddles County; Wadworth 6X; Whitbread Flowers Original Ⓗ
Busy free house crammed with various antiquities – even a red phone box. The family room is available until 8pm.
⛌ ⋈ ℂ ⓓ ⤢ P

Old House at Home
77 Broadwater Street East
☎ (0903) 32661
10.30–2.30, 5.30 (6.30 Sat)–11
Draught Bass; Charrington IPA; Young's Special Ⓗ

Genuine, unspoilt, Sussex flint-faced pub in Broadwater village. Dating from the 17th-century and once a smuggler's inn, it comes complete with a ghost. The comfortable, warm saloon bar is full of curios; lively public bar. Good selection of games. No food Sun.
🏠 Q ⊛ ℂ ⓓ ♣ P

Pawn & Castle
21 Rowlands Road
☎ (0903) 36232
11–2.30, 6–11 (11–11 Sat)
Harveys BB; Whitbread Flowers Original Ⓗ
Small free house with two bars, near the town centre and popular with shoppers. Friendly welcome; five guest beers always available. ℂ ⓓ ⧖ ♣

Vine
27–29 High Street, Tarring
☎ (0903) 202891
11–2.30 (3 Sat), 6–11
Adnams Bitter; Hall & Woodhouse Badger Best Bitter; Hop Back Summer Lightning; Wadworth 6X Ⓗ
Popular local, in a well-preserved village street. The former Parsons brewery stands at the rear. The large garden is used for the pub's own beer festival each October. Lunches served Mon–Sat.
Q ⊛ ℂ ⧖ ≢ (West) P

Try also: George & Dragon (Grand Met)

Yapton

Maypole Inn
Maypole Lane (off B2312)
OS977042 ☎ (0243) 551417
11–2.30, 5.30–11 (11–11 Sat)
Bateman XB; Crown Buckley Best Bitter; Mansfield Riding Mild; Ringwood Best Bitter, XXXX Porter; Younger IPA Ⓗ
Excellent, welcoming pub; hard to find but worth the effort. Holder of the local CAMRA *Mild Trophy*. Beer range varies. No food Tue eve or Sun.
🏠 Q ⊛ ℂ ⓓ ⧖ ♣ P

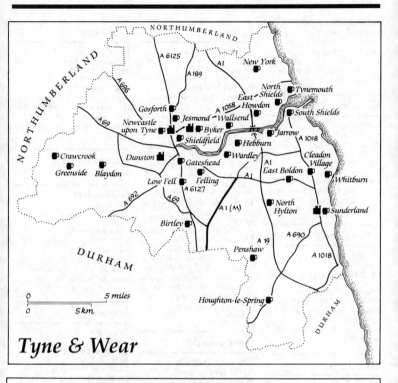

Tyne & Wear

🏭 **Big Lamp**, Newcastle upon Tyne; **Federation**, Dunston; **Hadrian**, Byker; **Vaux**, Sunderland

---

Birtley

Coach & Horses
Durham Road (A6127)
☎ (091) 410 2756
11–3, 6–11
Bass Light; Stones Best Bitter Ⓗ
Large roadhouse with a varied clientele and a good quality restaurant with vegetarian options. A rare chance to sample Bass Light in the North East. 🍴 🍺 🍽 🌭 ♣ P

Blaydon

Black Bull
Bridge Street
☎ (091) 414 2846
11.30–3, 6–11
Camerons Bitter, Strongarm; Everards Old Original Ⓗ
Friendly pub offering consistently good ales. Quiet public bar; skittles played.
🛏 Q 🍴 ⊕ ⇌ ♣ P

Byker

Cumberland Arms
Byker Buildings (off A193 by Byker bridge)
☎ (091) 265 6151

11–11
Hadrian Gladiator Ⓖ
A gem for spit and sawdust devotees: two downstairs rooms, one with a jukebox, one for whiling away the mellow afternoon. Upstairs is the evocative Haymarket Bar – the remains of Newcastle Breweries' finest pub (now a car park). Regular live music. Various guest ales. 🍴 ⊖ (Manors/Byker)

Free Trade Inn
St Lawrence Road (off A186, near Glasshouse Bridge)
☎ (091) 265 5764
11–11
McEwan 80/-; Theakston Best Bitter, XB; Younger No. 3 Ⓗ
Split-level, basic pub whose large windows give an excellent view of the river and quayside. Local artists' work on display. Live music each week. Popular with theatrical and musical types. A building featured in a little known Lowry work can be seen from here. 🛏 🍴

Glendale Hotel
Potts Street
☎ (091) 265 5174
11–11 (11–3, 5.30–11 Wed & Thu)

Draught Bass; Stones Best Bitter Ⓗ
Two-roomed pub attracting a friendly, mixed clientele. Note the photographs of the area in days gone by. Staff contribute to a happy atmosphere. Former local CAMRA *Pub of the Year.*
🍺 ⊕

Ship Inn
Stepney Bank (under Byker bridge, near City Farm)
☎ (091) 232 4030
11–11
Marston's Pedigree; Whitbread Boddingtons Bitter, Castle Eden Ale Ⓗ
Small, friendly local with regulars from the arts, craft and music world. Live folk music in impromptu sessions. Can be very busy at weekends. Comfortable and unspoilt, although the talking pinball machine can be distracting. Keen pool team.
🍴 ⊕ ⊖ (Manors) ♣

Tap & Spile
33 Shields Road
☎ (091) 276 1440
11.30–3, 6–11 (11–11 Fri & Sat)
Hadrian Gladiator; Taylor Landlord Ⓗ

Two-roomed pub with exposed brickwork and old wood, giving a turn-of-the-century appearance. Friendly atmosphere and a mixed clientele. Up to ten guest ales.
Q ◁ ⊞ ❂ ♣ ⌂ P

Cleadon Village

Cottage
North Street
☎ (091) 536 7883
11–3, 5.30–11
Vaux Samson ⊞
Small, corner local with farmhouse-style decor, in an ever-expanding village. Always busy, especially early eves. Pleasant walks on nearby hills. ⊛ ♣

Crawcrook

Rising Sun
Bank Top
☎ (091) 413 3316
11.30–11
Marston's Pedigree; Whitbread Boddingtons Bitter, Castle Eden Ale ⊞
Popular local offering good value food. Busy at weekends.
⊛ ◁ ▮ ♣ P

East Boldon

Black Bull
98 Front Street (A184)
☎ (091) 536 3969
11–3, 5.30–11
Vaux Samson ⊞
Comfortable, roadside pub serving quality meals; Sun lunches a speciality. Children welcome in the conservatory until 9pm.
⌕ ⊛ ◁ ▮ ♣ P

Grey Horse
Front Street (A184)
☎ (091) 536 4186
11–11
Vaux Samson ⊞
Mock-Tudor, roadside inn with an impressive facade: a traditional bar and a pleasant lounge, incorporating a small eating area. Guest beers.
🏚 ⊛ ◁ ▮ ⊞ ♣ P

East Howdon

Duke of Wellington
Northumberland Dock Road
☎ (091) 262 3079
11–11
Ruddles Best Bitter; Theakston XB ⊞
A spacious lounge in traditional style with wooden floorboards, crystal chandeliers and a handsome bar. Ceramic tiling graces the exterior. Exceptional value, home-cooked food. Big Lamp house beer; guest ales.
🏚 ⌕ ◁ ⅋ ♣ ⅍

Felling

Old Fox
Carlisle Street
☎ (091) 438 0073
12–4, 6–11 (12–11 Fri & Sat)
Ruddles Best Bitter; Webster's Yorkshire Bitter, Choice ⊞
Friendly local with a good range of guest ales. A warm welcome is assured. The landlord also holds the licence for the Tyneside CAMRA beer festival. Excellent value bed and breakfast. Guest beers.
🏚 ⋈ ◁ ❂ ♣

Wheatsheaf
26 Carlisle Street
☎ (091) 438 6633
11–3, 6–11 (may vary)
Big Lamp Bitter, Prince Bishop Ale, Old Genie ⊞
Big Lamp's only tied house. A former local CAMRA *Pub of the Year*, it is still decidedly quixotic in character but now forging ahead and deserving a place in this book. Guest beers.
🏚 ❂ ♣

Gateshead

Borough Arms
80–82 Bensham Road
☎ (091) 478 1323
11–4, 6–11
Ruddles County; Theakston XB ⊞
Pleasant, two-roomed pub near the town centre, serving consistently good ales and well-priced meals. Guest beers.
◁ ⅋ ❂ P

Gosforth

Gosforth Hotel
High Street
☎ (091) 285 6617
11–3, 6–11
Everards Old Original; Marston's Pedigree ⊞
The same, unhurried service in all the well-refurbished areas, each with a seemingly different character. No food Sun. Guest beers. ◁

Greenside

White Swan
Main Street (B6315)
☎ (091) 413 4255
11–3, 6–11
Marston's Pedigree; Theakston Best Bitter; Webster's Choice ⊞
A warm welcome is assured at this many-roomed pub with a country feel. Toasted sandwiches available at lunchtime.
Q ⌕ ⊛ ⅋ P ⅍

Hebburn

New Clock
Victoria Road East
☎ (091) 489 3556
11–3, 6–11
Vaux Samson ⊞
Open-plan pub on a main through road; very popular at weekends. Note the unusual, red-felt pool table. No food Sun.
◁ ♣ P

Houghton-le-Spring

Golden Lion
The Broadway
☎ (091) 384 2460
11–3, 6–11
Vaux Samson ⊞
Small, town pub with separate rooms from a main bar area. Previously in the *Good Beer Guide* for 10 years and now reinstated with its new landlord. No food Sun. ⌕ ◁ ♣ ♣

Jarrow

Western
Western Road
☎ (091) 489 6243
11–11
Camerons Strongarm; Everards Old Original; Tolly Cobbold Original ⊞
Friendly, no-frills boozer in a revitalisation area, adjacent to a former steelworks. Named after a famous ship built on the Tyne.
⅋ ❂ ♣

Jesmond

Legendary Yorkshire Heroes
Archbold Terrace, Sandyford Road
☎ (091) 281 3010
11–11
Theakston XB; Webster's Choice ⊞
Formerly the 'Royal Archer', now the flagship of the new Legendary Yorkshire Heroes chain. Features live music most eves and a quiz night on Wed. Guest beers. The family room is a no-smoking area.
⌕ ◁ ❂ ⅍

Lonsdale
Lonsdale Terrace, West Jesmond (opp. Metro station)
☎ (091) 281 0039
11–11
McEwan 80/-; Theakston Best Bitter ⊞
Spacious lounge with a smaller public bar catering for a varied clientele, incl. many students in term-time. Upstairs function room. No food Sat.
◁ ⅋ ❂ (W Jesmond) ♣

Low Fell

Aletaster
Durham Road
☎ (091) 487 0770
11–3, 5.30–11 (11–11 Sat)
**McEwan 80/-; Theakston
Best Bitter, XB; Younger
No. 3** Ⓗ
L-shaped bar in traditional style
with ten handpumps. Shove-
ha'penny and bar skittles
played. Guest beers. ♣ P

Newcastle upon Tyne

Bacchus
High Bridge
☎ (091) 232 6451
11.30–11 (11.30–4, 7–11 Sat; 7–10.30
Sun; closed Sun lunch)
**McEwan 80/-; Stones Best
Bitter; Tetley Bitter;
Theakston XB** Ⓗ
Comfortable, friendly pub with
a wood-panelled lobby and two
rooms: one boasts fine, old
advertising mirrors. Popular
with business people at
lunchtimes; very busy at
weekends. Guest beers.
Q ◖ ⊖ (Monument)

Baltic Tavern & Baltic Vaults
11–17 Broad Chare (off
Quayside, opp. law courts)
☎ (091) 261 7385
11–11
**Marston's Pedigree;
Whitbread Castle Eden Ale,
Flowers Original** Ⓗ
Recent conversion of an old pub
and warehouse, providing two,
one-roomed pubs, each
comfortable and well decorated:
welcome additions to the
Quayside drinking area.
Wheelchair access to the Tavern
bar only. ◖ ⅙

Bridge Hotel
Castle Square
☎ (091) 232 7780
11.30 (11 Fri & Sat)–3, 5.30 (5 Fri, 6
Sat)–11 (12–2.40, 7–10.30 Sun)
Theakston Best Bitter, XB Ⓗ
Large, comfortable pub: a quiet
lounge with superb bar fittings,
and a more boisterous bar with
a pool table. Holds regular mini
beer festivals. Its folk club is the
oldest in country (Thu); the
blues club (Tue) features
international acts. Guest beers.
Q ▣ ▤ ⇌ ⊖ (Central) ♣

Broken Doll
Blenheim Street
☎ (091) 232 1047
11–11
**Theakston Best Bitter, XB,
Old Peculier** Ⓗ
Towering monument to
Novocastrian culture: Gothic
splendour mingles with the
finest in live music. The XB is

the best in town but is out of
place beneath the Matthew
Brown lion. The Doll itself is
living on borrowed time
(threatened by a road scheme).
▣ ⇌ ⊖ (Central)

Cooperage
32 The Close, Quayside
☎ (091) 232 8286
11–11
**Ind Coope Burton Ale;
Marston's Owd Rodger;
Tetley Bitter** Ⓗ
14th-century, beamed building
comprising a pub, restaurant
and function rooms. Excellent
food. Economiser in use behind
the bar. Guest beers.
◖ ⇌ ⊖ (Central) ♣ ♨

Crown Posada
33 The Side ☎ (091) 232 1269
11–3 (4 Sat), 5.30 (7 Sat)–11 (11–11
Fri)
**Hadrian Gladiator; Stones
Best Bitter; Taylor Landlord;
Theakston Best Bitter** Ⓗ
Superb, Victorian pub with
impressive, stained-glass
windows. A former winner of
the CAMRA *Joe Goodwin Pub
Preservation Award*. Guest beers.
Q ⅙ ⇌ ⊖ (Central)

Duke of Wellington
High Bridge
☎ (091) 261 8852
11–11 (7–10.30 Sun; closed Sun
lunch)
**Alloa Arrol's 80/-; Ind
Coope Burton Ale; Jennings
Bitter; Marston's Pedigree;
Tetley Bitter** Ⓗ
Single-roomed pub on the
fringe of a trendy drinking area;
busy at weekends. Friendly staff
and much passing trade produce
a good atmosphere. Guest
beers. ◖ ⊖ (Monument)

Forth Hotel
Pink Lane (opp. Central Station)
☎ (091) 232 6478
11–3, 5–10.30
**Ind Coope Burton Ale;
Jennings Bitter; Tetley
Bitter** Ⓗ
L-shaped pub, characterful and
cosy, where the landlord
ensures a warm welcome and
serves some of the best Tetley
in the county. An interesting
machine provides a treat for
pinball fans. ⇌ ⊖ (Central)

Newcastle Arms
St Andrews Street (near
Gallowgate bus station)
☎ (091) 232 3567
11–11
**Ind Coope Burton Ale;
Taylor Landlord; Tetley
Bitter** Ⓗ
Comfortable, single-room pub,
split into three sections,
attracting a varied clientele. Its
walls sport interesting prints
and a fine Arrol's mirror.
⊖ (St James's)

Old George Inn
Old George Yard (off Cloth
Market) ☎ (091) 232 3956
11–11
**Draught Bass; Stones Best
Bitter** Ⓗ
One of the most historic pubs in
Newcastle. Entered from a
cobbled courtyard, the King
Charles room (Charles I drank
here) has a modern, split-level
extension. Wooden panels and
exposed beams add to the
atmosphere. Comfortable and
cosy; it can get very busy.
◖ ⊖ (Monument)

Rose & Crown Hotel
166 City Road (opp. Tyne Tees
TV studio) ☎ (091) 232 4724
11–11 (11–4, 6.30–11 Sat; 12–2,
7–10.30 Sun)
**Draught Bass; Hadrian
Gladiator; Theakston XB** Ⓗ
Friendly, two-roomed pub
overlooking the river;
temporarily reprieved from
demolition as part of the
Quayside redevelopment.
▤ ⊖ (Manors) ♣

Rosies Bar
2 Stowell Street (next to
Gallowgate bus station)
☎ (091) 232 0339
11–11
**Alloa Arrol's 80/-; Ind
Coope Burton Ale; Tetley
Bitter** Ⓗ
An over-ambitious
refurbishment is now happily
losing its polish. Handy for
football, the Irish club and
Chinatown, hence its varied
clientele. ⊖ (St James's)

Villa Victoria
144 Westmorland Road (near
Newcastle College)
☎ (091) 232 2460
12–3, 6–11
**Draught Bass; Stones Best
Bitter** Ⓗ
An attractive building standing
on a bend in the road: a single
room with a central bar. Look
for the decorated (former)
fireplace near the pool table.
Wood-panelling, with a good
use of mirrors, makes the room
look larger. Mainly local
customers (students lunchtime).

New York

Shiremoor House Farm
Middle Engine Lane
☎ (091) 257 6302
11–11
**Stones Best Bitter; Taylor
Landlord; Theakston Best
Bitter, Old Peculier** Ⓗ
Well renovated farm buildings,
retaining a rustic appearance.
Highly commended in
CAMRA's *Pub Design Awards*
1990. Guest ales and regular
mini beer festivals. High quality
restaurant. Q ▣ ◖ ▶ Å P

Tyne & Wear

North Hylton

Shipwrights
Ferryboat Lane (off A1231, under A19 Wear Bridge)
☎ (091) 549 5139
11–3, 7–11 (supper licence)
Vaux Samson; Wards Sheffield Best Bitter Ⓗ
Riverside pub in a secluded location, but under a main trunk road bridge. The first-floor carvery enjoys extended views to the River Wear. Eleven years in this guide. ♨ ◖ ♣

North Shields

Chainlocker
New Quay (opp. ferry landing)
☎ (091) 258 0147
11.30–3.30, 5.30–11 (11–11 Fri & Sat)
Ind Coope Burton Ale; Taylor Landlord; Tetley Bitter Ⓗ
Small, but spacious pub with a mixed clientele. Seafood dishes are a speciality. Guest beers. ♨ Q ◖ ◗

Magnesia Bank
1 Camden Street
☎ (091) 257 4831
11–11
Butterknowle Bitter, Conciliation Ale; Ruddles County; Taylor Landlord; Tetley Bitter; Yates Bitter Ⓗ
A former club, offering some of the best quality beers in the area. Guest ales. ♨ ◖ ◗ ⊖ ♣ P

Tap & Spile
184 Tynemouth Road
☎ (091) 257 2523
11.30–3, 5.30–11 (11–11 Fri & Sat)
Old Mill Bullion; Taylor Landlord Ⓗ
Homely, L-shaped pub with a comfortable lounge area. Tyneside CAMRA *Pub of the Year* in 1989 and 1990. Guest beers. ◖ ◗ ♣ ○

Wolsington House
Burdon Main Row (opp. gates to Smith's Dock)
☎ (091) 257 8487
11–11
Stones Best Bitter; Theakston Best Bitter Ⓗ
Edwardian free house, now a popular venue for local bands. Fires in the lounge, where children are admitted. Guest beers. ♨ ◖ ⊟

Wooden Doll
103 Hudson Street
☎ (091) 257 3747
11–11
Taylor Landlord; Tetley Bitter; Theakston Best Bitter; Wards Sheffield Best Bitter Ⓗ
Pleasant, comfortable pub with views of the Tyne estuary. No food Sun eve. Q ◖ ◗ ⊟ ⅍ ⊖ P

Penshaw

Grey Horse
Village Green
☎ (091) 584 4882
11–3 (4 Sat), 6 (5.30 Sat)–11
Tetley Bitter Ⓗ
Popular pub on the village green, just off the main A183 through road. Near Penshaw Monument – famous for the Lambton Worm legend. Celebrating 10 years in the guide. No food Sun. ♨ ◖

Shieldfield

Globe Inn
Barker Street
☎ (091) 232 0901
11–11
Draught Bass; Stones Best Bitter Ⓗ
Two-roomed pub near the polytechnic, attracting mainly local drinkers. Friendly regulars, who are keen on sports. Basic but comfortable.
Q ♨ ⊟ ⊖ (Jesmond/Manors) ♣ P

Queen's Arms
1 Simpson Terrace (near Manors cinema)
☎ (091) 232 4101
12–11
McEwan 80/–; Theakston Best Bitter, XB, Old Peculier Ⓗ
Comfortable pub in two main sections, with fine, old prints, displays of work by local artists, bric-a-brac and atmospheric lighting. Friendly staff and a mixed clientele ensure a happy bar, even when full. No meals Tue or Sun. ♨ Q ♨ ◖ ⊟ ⊖ (Manors)

South Shields

Chichester Arms
1 Laygate Lane (next to Metro)
☎ (091) 456 1711
11–3, 5–11 (11–11 Sat)
Ind Coope Burton Ale; Tetley Bitter Ⓗ
Smartly refurbished, corner pub on the town-centre outskirts, with a typical Tetley interior. Allied guest beers.
◖ ◗ ⅍ ⊖ (Chichester)

Dolly Peel
137 Commercial Road (B1302/B1301 jct)
☎ (091) 427 1441
11–11
Bateman XXXB; Taylor Landlord; Theakston XB; Younger No. 3 Ⓗ
Extremely well-run, corner pub on the town's outskirts. Always well patronised and rightly so. Two guest ales available. Q ⅍ ⊖ (Chichester) ♣

Holborn Rose & Crown
East Holborn (Middle Dock gates)
☎ (091) 455 2379
11–11
McEwan 80/–; Theakston XB; Younger No. 3 Ⓗ
Pleasant, old pub in a dockside location. Now open-plan but retaining much of its character, incl. a superb bar and backfitting. Varied clientele. ♨ ⊖ ♣

Railway
9–11 Mill Dam
☎ (091) 455 5227
11–3, 6–11 (11–11 Fri & Sat)
Courage Directors; Fuller's London Pride, ESB; Taylor Landlord Ⓗ
Old pub on the route to the revitalised riverside, just out of the main market square. Lively bar and a quiet lounge. Guest beers. Q ⊟ ⊖ ♣

Steamboat
12–14 Mill Dam
☎ (091) 454 0134
11–11
Vaux Lorimers Best Scotch, Samson, Double Maxim; Wards Sheffield Best Bitter Ⓗ
Interesting, old pub with a history of press gangs and royalty! Award-winning restored frontage; winner of a recent local *Pub of the Year* award. One of only a handful of pubs offering the full range of Vaux ales. ⇔ ⊟ ⊖ ♣

Sunderland: *North*

Pilot Cutter
Harbour View, Roker (A183, coast road)
☎ (091) 567 1402
12–3, 7–11 (11–11 Fri & Sat matchdays)
Theakston Best Bitter, XB, Old Peculier Ⓗ
Basic, open-plan, corner pub near the football club, with views over the river mouth. Match days tend to be busy. Guest beers. ♨ ♣

St Hilda's Parish Centre
Beaumont Street, Southwick (opp. library)
☎ (091) 549 4999
7–10.30 (11–2.30, 7–10.30 Sat & Sun; closed Tue)
McEwan 70/–, 80/–; Theakston Best Bitter, XB, Old Peculier; Younger No. 3 Ⓗ
Multi-roomed community centre in a former Labour Exchange building, catering for numerous sports and social clubs. Voluntary staff and management mean restricted opening hours. CAMRA *National Club of the Year* runner-up. Beers available in rotation. Q ♨ ⊟ ⅍ ♣ ⅋

Sunderland: *South*

Brewery Tap
Dunning Street
☎ (091) 567 7472
11–11
Vaux Double Maxim Ⓗ
Lovely, little pub on the
brewery doorstep; sadly the
beer range is limited.
Comfortable surroundings and
extensive photographic records
of the old town. ⊞ ⇌ ♣ P

Ivy House
Worcester Street
☎ (091) 567 3399
11–11
**Vaux Samson; Wards
Sheffield Best Bitter** Ⓗ
Popular, dimly-lit pub; noisy
and brash, serving mainly the
student population. Tucked
away in side-streets behind Park
Lane bus station. Guest beers.
◖ P

Greensleeves
12 Green Terrace (behind
leisure centre)
☎ (091) 567 0852
11.30–2.30, 5 (7 Sat)–11
**Draught Bass; Theakston
Best Bitter, XB** Ⓗ
Popular bar near the
polytechnic, scheduled for major
refurbishment. Regular guest
beers. ◖ ⇌

Saltgrass
Hanover Place, Ayres Quay,
Deptford

11.45–3, 5.30–11 (11.30–11 Fri & Sat)
**Vaux Samson, Double
Maxim; Wards Sheffield Best
Bitter** Ⓗ
Classic drinking house in the
former shipbuilding heartland.
Roaring fire in the cosy, front
bar; relaxed and friendly
atmosphere throughout. Wide
range of customers; children
welcome. Rightly celebrating its
tenth year in the guide.
⊞ ⊛ ◖ ⊞ ♣ ♣

Tap & Spile
Salem Street, Hendon
☎ (091) 514 2810
12–3, 6–11 (12–11 Thu; 11–11 Fri &
Sat)
**Camerons Bitter, Strongarm;
Stocks Old Horizontal** Ⓗ
Formerly the 'Salem' and
birthplace of the local CAMRA
branch, now renovated as one
of the chain of Brent Walker
traditional ale houses, selling a
wide range of independent
breweries' ales. Popular with
students. Brent Walker's 1991
Warmest Welcome winner. Guest
beers. ♣ ♣

Tynemouth

Tynemouth Lodge
Hotel
Correction House Bank,
Tynemouth Road
☎ (091) 257 7565
11–11
**Draught Bass; Belhaven 80/-;
Stones Best Bitter;
Theakston Best Bitter** Ⓗ

Pub with good beer, good cheer
and good measures; warm
welcome assured. Guest beers.
⊞ Q ⊖ P

Wallsend

Hadrian Lodge Hotel
Hadrian Road
☎ (091) 262 7733
11–3, 6.30–11
**Ind Coope Burton Ale; Tetley
Bitter; Theakston Best
Bitter** Ⓗ
Attractive bar in a new hotel.
Q ⇔ ◖ ⊞ ⅄ ⊖ P

Wardley

Green
Whitemare Pool
☎ (091) 495 0171
11.30–3, 5.30–11 (11–11 Sat)
**Draught Bass; Ruddles
County; Theakston Best
Bitter** Ⓗ
Pleasant, new pub with a bar,
lounge and separate restaurant.
⊞ ⊛ ◖ ▶ ⅄ P

Whitburn

Jolly Sailor
1 East Street
☎ (091) 529 3221
11–11
Bass Light, Draught Bass Ⓗ
Three-roomed, corner pub in a
pleasant, coastal village. Huge,
locally-caught fish are a
speciality at lunchtime. Children
welcome. ⊞ Q ⊛ ◖ ⊞ ♣

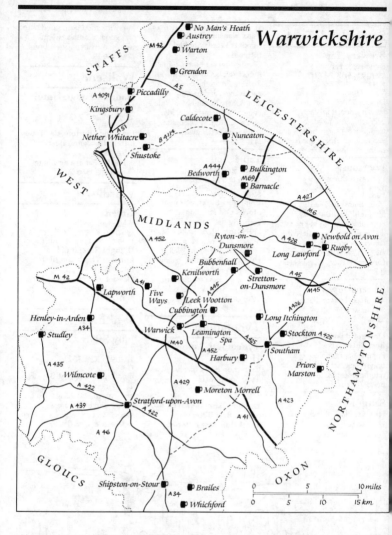

Warwickshire

Austrey

Bird in Hand
Church Lane (off main road)
☎ (0827) 830260
12–2, 6.30–11
Marston's Pedigree Ⓗ
Splendid, listed, historic hostelry
opposite the village church.
Smoking prohibited around the
bar.
🏠 Q ⊛ ⊕ 📶 ♣ P

Barnacle

Red Lion
Lower Road
11–2.30, 7–11
M&B Mild, Brew XI Ⓗ
Village local with a respectable
lounge and a lively bar.
◑ ▶ ⊕ ♣ P

Bedworth

Newdigate
Newdigate Road
☎ (0203) 314867
12–2.30 (3 Fri, 3.30 Sat), 5–11
**Ansells Mild, Bitter; Draught
Bass; Ind Coope Burton Ale;
Tetley Bitter** Ⓗ
Estate pub with separate games
and dining areas. Family room
leads out to the garden.
🕭 ⊛ ◑ ▶ ⊕ ♣ P

Old Goose
Orchard Street, Colleycroft (off
B4113) ☎ (0203) 313266
12–3, 7–11
**Ansells Mild, Bitter; Banks's
Bitter** Ⓗ
Single-room pub with a
conservatory which also acts as
a family room. Children's play
area. Q 🕭 ◑ ▶ ⊕ ♣

Brailes

Gate Inn
Upper Brailes (B4035)
☎ (0608) 85212
12–3 (4 winter Sat), 7 (6 Fri & summer
Sat)–11
**Hook Norton Mild, Best
Bitter, Old Hooky** Ⓗ
Friendly, old village local, next
to the site of the former Brailes
brewery. Children are made
very welcome; Aunt Sally in
garden. No food Sun eve.
🏠 ⊛ ◑ ▶ ⊕ ⅄ Ⓐ ♣ P

Bubbenhall

Malt Shovel
Lower End (off a side road, off
A445) ☎ (0203) 301141
11.30–2.30, 6–11
**Ansells Mild, Bitter; Draught
Bass; Tetley Bitter** Ⓗ

Very friendly country pub, exceedingly popular for meals. Expatriate Italian landlord has a passion for good beer and good, home-cooked food, but food does not take precedence over drinkers. Bowling green.
⌂ Q ❀ ◖ ◗ ⊞ ♣ P

Bulkington

Rule & Compass
Leicester Street (off B4109)
11–3, 5–11
Draught Bass; M&B Mild, Brew XI [H]
Village pub with an upstairs restaurant and a garden with playthings. ❀ ◖ ◗ ⊞ ♣

Caldecote

Royal Red Gate
Watling Street (A5/A444 jct)
11–3, 6–11
Marston's Burton Best Bitter, Pedigree [H]
Two-roomed pub with a bar billiard table. Richard III passed here on his way to Bosworth Field. Q ❀ ◖ ⊞ ♣ P

Cubbington

Queens Head
Queen Street ☎ (0926) 429949
11.30–2.30, 5.30–11
Ansells Mild, Bitter; Marston's Pedigree [H]
Popular village local with a quiet, relaxing lounge and a busy bar with the emphasis on games. Q ❀ ⊞ ♣ P

Five Ways

Case is Altered
Rowington Road (just off old A41) OS225700
11–2.30, 6–11 (12–2, 7–10.30 Sun)
Ansells Mild, Bitter [G]**; Ind Coope Burton Ale** [G]&[E]**; Samuel Smith OBB** [H]**; Whitbread Flowers Original** [G]
Rural pub in a timewarp, even down to the sixpenny piece-operated bar billiards. Very rare cask pumps used to dispense some beers. Lounge only open at weekends. Children welcome in the games room.
⌂ Q ❀ ⊞ ♣ P

Grendon

Black Swan
Watling Street
☎ (0827) 713640
11–2.30, 6–11
Ruddles Best Bitter; Webster's Yorkshire Bitter [H]
Open-plan pub with bar, games and lounge areas; a friendly locals' house. Good choice of food incl. home-made specials.
❀ ◖ ◗ ♣ P

Harbury

Gamecock
Chapel Street
☎ (0926) 612374
11.30–3, 6.30–11
Banks's Bitter [H]
Friendly, basic village local; busy on games nights (Tue and Wed) when teams are at home. Regulars are involved in prize-winning carnival floats, Victorian street fairs and other fundraising events for the village. No food Sun. ⌂ Q ◖

Try also: Dog (Ansells)

Henley-in-Arden

Three Tuns
103 High Street
11–3, 6–11
M&B Brew XI; Marston's Burton Best Bitter, Pedigree [H]
Small, two-roomed pub, or is it one room split into two? Left-hand side is a bit 'posher'. Q ❀

Try also: Golden Cross (Ansells)

Kenilworth

Clarendon Arms
44 Castle Hill (opp. castle)
☎ (0926) 52017
11–3, 5.30–11
Courage Best Bitter, Directors [H]
Food-oriented, pleasantly renovated old pub; drinkers still very welcome in the bar.
Q ≍ ❀ ◖ ◗

Clarendon House Hotel
High Street (A452/A459 jct)
☎ (0926) 57668
11.30–2.30, 6–11
Hook Norton Best Bitter, Old Hooky; Whitbread Best Bitter, Flowers Original [H]
Plush hotel bar but with a welcoming atmosphere. Idiosyncratic dress code – jeans and T shirt OK, sleeveless shirt/vest is not. Dress sensibly and reward your taste buds.
⊨ ◖ ◗

Earl Clarendon
Warwick Road (lower end of town) ☎ (0926) 54643
11–2.30, 6–11
Marston's Burton Best Bitter, Pedigree [H]
Another 'Clarendon' – there are three in town. This one is a friendly locals' pub with sing-songs at weekends. Q ❀ ◖ ♣

Kingsbury

Royal Oak
Coventry Road (main street, near Kingsbury Water Park)
☎ (0827) 872339
12–2.30 (3.30 Sat), 6–11 (12–2.30, 7–10.30 Sun)
Marston's Burton Best Bitter, Merrie Monk, Pedigree [H]
Tastefully modernised in traditional style with a split-level lounge and an almost separate public bar. Good quality cheap food available most of the time (no meals Sun eve). ≍ ❀ ◖ ◗ ⊞ Λ ♣ P

Try also: White Swan (M&B)

Lapworth

Navigation
Old Warwick Road (B4439)
☎ (0564) 783337
11–2.30, 5.30–11 (11–3, 6–11 Sat)
Draught Bass; M&B Mild, Brew XI [H]
An excellent two-roomed traditional pub with a popular garden, alongside the canal – one of the best pubs for miles around. Good value food and an ever-changing range of guest beers. ⌂ Q ❀ ◖ ◗ ⊞ ⇌ P

Leamington Spa

Red House
113 Radford Road
11.30–3, 5.30–11 (11–11 Fri & Sat)
Draught Bass; M&B Highgate Mild, Springfield Bitter [H]
Welcoming, Victorian town pub which has managed to retain separate bar and lounge areas, despite removing part of the dividing wall. Unusual handpulls. The only outlet for Springfield in the area. The safe, walled garden to the rear is good for young children.
Q ❀ ⊞ ♣

Somerville Arms
Campion Terrace
11–2.30 (3 Fri & Sat), 5.30 (6 Sat)–11
Ansells Mild, Bitter; Ind Coope Burton Ale; Marston's Pedigree; Tetley Bitter [H]
Excellent Victorian local now in the *Guide* for 15 consecutive years. Busy front bar and small cosy lounge at the rear. Always friendly. The motto above the bar says it all: 'Real ale for your health. You'll get no better'.
Q ⊞ ♣

Leek Wootton

Anchor
Warwick Road
☎ (0926) 53355
11–3, 6 (7 Mon & Sat)–11 (11.30–2.30, 7–10.30 Sun)
Draught Bass; M&B Brew XI [H]
Excellent village pub with a basic bar and a comfortable lounge. Well-known for its lunches (not available Sun) from the servery in the lounge.
⌂ Q ❀ ◖ ⊞ ♣ P

Warwickshire

Long Itchington

Harvester
Church Lane
☎ (0926) 812698
11–3, 6–11
Hook Norton Best Bitter, Old Hooky 🄷
Good village pub: a comfortable lounge with an aquarium, and an excellent restaurant. Guest beers.
👶 ◖ ◗ ⊟ P

Long Lawford

Sheaf & Sickle
Coventry Road (A428)
☎ (0788) 544622
12–3 (4 Sat), 6–11
Ansells Mild, Bitter 🄷
Victorian, roadside, ex-coaching inn. Bar has a games room leading off, as well as an excellent family room; the lounge is small and comfortable. Good garden with its own cricket pitch. Northants skittles played. Weekly guest beers.
👶 ❀ ◖ ⊟ ⛺ ♣ P

Moreton Morrell

Black Horse
2 miles from M40
12–2.30 (3 Sat), 7–11
Everards Old Original 🄷
Fairly basic village pub, popular with students from the local agricultural college. Pleasant, peaceful garden with good views. Q ❀ ⛺

Nether Whitacre

Dog Inn
Dog Lane (off B4098)
☎ (0675) 81318
12–2.30, 6–11 (12–2.30, 7–10.30 Sun)
Draught Bass; M&B Mild, Brew XI 🄷
Friendly, country pub, popular during summer when children can use the garden. Q ❀ ◖ ⊟ P

Try also: Gate

Newbold on Avon

Barley Mow
Main Street (B4112)
☎ (0788) 544174
11–2.30 (4 Sat), 6–11
M&B Mild, Brew XI 🄷
Vibrant pub next to the Oxford Canal. The bar is on two levels and is often crowded; a smaller lounge has a pianist on Sun eve. The large garden slopes down to the road and is well stocked with swings. ❀ ◖ ◗ ⊟ ⛺ ♣ P

No Man's Heath

Four Counties
☎ (0827) 830243
11–2.30, 6.30–11
Ansells Mild; Ind Coope Burton Ale; Marston's Pedigree 🄷
Traditional, friendly and cosy, roadside inn, situated near the point where Derbyshire, Leicestershire, Warwickshire and Staffordshire meet. The large, varied menu of excellent, home-cooked food matches the quality of the beer. 🏠 ❀ ◖ ◗ P

Nuneaton

Hayrick
Meadowside (off B4114, 3 miles E of centre)
☎ (0203) 348181
11–3, 7–11
Courage Best Bitter, Directors 🄷
Modern estate pub with see-through toilets (glass walled).
👶 ❀ ◖ ♣ P

Piccadilly

Sportsmans Arms
Perryman Drive (between Kingsbury and the M42/A5 jct) ☎ (0827) 873560
12–2.30, 6.30 (6 Sat)–11
M&B Mild; Marston's Pedigree 🄷
Despite its plain, modern exterior, this comfortable and popular pub has a deservedly high reputation for food. Friendly, conscientious landlord; private snooker room. No food Sun lunch. 👶 ❀ ◖ ◗ ⊟ ♿ ♣ P

Priors Marston

Falcon Inn
Left off A361 at Byfield
☎ (0327) 60562
12–3, 6.30–11
Everards Beacon, Tiger; Moorhouse's Pendle Witches Brew; Wiltshire Old Grumble 🄷
Pleasant village pub, a former coaching house, dating back to the 15th century. Oak beamed ceilings. Very busy pub at weekends. Barbecues held on the patio. Guest beers.
🏠 Q ❀ ◖ ◗ ♿ ♣ P

Rugby

Alexandra Arms
72 James Street
11–2.30, 5.30 (7 Sat)–11 (12–2.30, 7–10.30 Sun)
Webster's Yorkshire Bitter, Choice 🄷
Cosy, town-centre pub near the new car park and local theatre; large, well-equipped games room and an L-shaped lounge.
Q ❀ ◖ ♿ ≠ ♣

Engine
1 Bridget Street (off Lawford Rd, at corner of Plowman St)
11–11
M&B Mild 🄴**, Brew XI; Marston's Pedigree** 🄷
Traditional Victorian corner local now in the middle of a new housing development. This Grade II listed building has two lounges, a corner bar and a small snug. 🏠 Q ❀ ⊟ ♣

Half Moon
28–30 Lawford Road (A428)
11–2.30, 5.30–11 (11–11 Fri; 10–11 Sat; 12–3, 7.30–10.30 Sun)
Ansells Mild, Bitter; Ind Coope Burton Ale 🄷
Wonderful, terraced pub close to the town centre; very friendly and welcoming to locals and outsiders. A single L-shaped room with darts in one corner. Guest beers. ♣

London House
Chapel Street
☎ (0788) 575981
11–2.30 (3 Fri, 4 Sat), 7–11
Marston's Mercian Mild, Burton Best Bitter, Pedigree, Owd Rodger (winter) 🄷
A single-roomed pub on two levels, situated in the centre of the town's pedestrian shopping area. Caters for a cross-section of society and is very busy at weekends. An essential part of a Rugby pub crawl. ◖ ♣

Peacock
69 Newbold Road (A426)
☎ (0788) 567923
11.30–2.30 (3 Sat), 7–11
Bateman Mild; Hoskins Beaumanor, Penn's Ale, Premium, Old Nigel (winter) 🄷
Large, Victorian, corner pub near police station. Small snug bar is separate from the lounge and large games room. Home of the local CAMRA branch. Always friendly. Ever-changing range of guest beers. ◖ ◗ ≠ ♣

Victoria
1 Lower Hillmorton Road
11–2.30 (4 Sat), 7–11
Draught Bass; M&B Highgate Mild 🄷**, Brew XI** 🄴
Victorian corner pub near the town centre. The bar is dominated by pool and darts; warm and friendly lounge with CD jukebox. Interesting, original interior fittings. Trad. jazz Mon eves. No weekend food. ◖ ⊟ ≠ ♣

Ryton-on-Dunsmore

Blacksmiths Arms
High Street (200 yds off A45)
☎ (0203) 301818
12–2.30, 6–11 (12–2.30, 7–10.30 Sun)
Draught Bass; M&B Brew XI 🄷
Quiet lunchtime pub which becomes a very busy restaurant-pub in the eves. Constantly-growing brass and copperware collection. 🏠 ◖ ◗ ♣ P

Shipston-on-Stour

Black Horse
Station Road (just off A3400, behind old school)
☎ (0608) 61617
12–2.30, 7–11
Home Bitter; Theakston XB, Old Peculier; Webster's Yorkshire Bitter 🄷
Dates back 100 years and was originally a row of cottages for Cotswold sheep farmers; thatched roof and an interesting interior. An excellent family room leads into the garden. Regular guest beers. No eve meals Mon or Sun.
⌂ Q ♉ ❀ ◐ ◑ ⊟ ♿ ♣ P

Shustoke

Griffin Inn
On B4114, ½ mile E of village, off M6 jct 4
☎ (0675) 81205
12–2.30, 7–11 (12–2.15, 7–10.30 Sun)
M&B Mild; Marston's Pedigree; Theakston Old Peculier; Wadworth 6X 🄷
Popular free house which has been recently extended. Ever-changing variety of guest beers, and Weston's Old Rosie cider (in summer). No food Sun.
⌂ Q ♉ ❀ ◐ ♿ ⛺ ♁ P

Plough Inn
The Green (B4114, 2 miles from Coleshill, off M6 jct 4)
☎ (0675) 81557
12–2.30 (3 Sat), 7 (6.30 Thu–Sat)–11
Draught Bass; M&B Mild, Brew XI 🄷
Excellent, traditional village pub with friendly service. Popular with locals. Eve meals Thu–Sat; no food Sun. Skittles available.
⌂ Q ❀ ◐ ◑ ♿ ♣ P

Southam

Old Mint
Coventry Street
☎ (0926) 812339
11–2.30 (3 Sat), 6.30 (6 Sat)–11
Draught Bass; Hook Norton Best Bitter; Marston's Pedigree; Wadworth 6X; Whitbread Castle Eden Ale, Flowers Original 🄷
Characterful, 15th-century building of local stone; reputedly a mint in the Civil War. Two cosy bars are adorned with copper, brassware and a collection of weaponry. A very busy pub. Guest beers.
⌂ ❀ ◐ ◑ ⊟ P

Stockton

Crown
High Street (S off A426, bear right) ☎ (0926) 812255
12–3, 7 (5.30 Fri)–11 (12–11 Sat)
Ansells Mild, Bitter 🄷
Friendly, country pub with a basic bar and comfy, homely lounge boasting two real fires, plenty of brasses and a piano. Major building works in hand to create a restaurant and a large bar area. Up to four guest beers regularly available. Petanque played.
⌂ ❀ ◐ ◑ ⊟ ♣ ♁ P

Stratford-upon-Avon

Lamplighter
42 Rother Street
☎ (0789) 293071
11–11
Ansells Bitter; Courage Best Bitter, Directors; John Smith's Bitter; Tetley Bitter 🄷
Popular, lively pub with a reputation for good food. Gaslit interior and a stone-flagged floor in the lower room.
⌂ ❀ ◐ ⇌

Queens Head
54 Ely Street (just off Market Square) ☎ (0789) 204914
11.30–4, 6–11 (11.30–11 Fri & Sat; 12–2.30, 7–10.30 Sun)
Draught Bass; M&B Brew XI; Younger No. 3 🄷
L-shaped bar with two real fires. Beer garden open in the summer. ⌂ ❀ ◐ ◑ ⇌

Shakespeare Hotel
Chapel Street
☎ (0789) 294771
11–2.30, 5.30–11
Courage Directors; Donnington SBA; Hook Norton Old Hooky 🄷
Real ale is served in the Froth & Elbow bar of this beautiful, half-timbered, Tudor building. Comfortable, spacious lounge. Popular with locals and tourists alike. Guest beers.
⌂ Q ❀ ⛟ ◑ ⇌ ♣ P

White Swan Hotel
Rother Street
☎ (0789) 297022
11–2.30, 5.30–11
Marston's Pedigree; Wadworth 6X 🄷
Another beautiful Tudor building, with wood-panelled walls. Cosy, small bar and a large, comfortable lounge; no smoking restaurant. Guest beers on a monthly basis.
⌂ Q ♉ ⛟ ◐ ◑ ⇌ P

Stretton-on-Dunsmore

Shoulder of Mutton
Village green
12–2.30 (not Wed), 7.30–11 (12–2.30, 7–10.30 Sun)
M&B Mild, Brew XI 🄷
Superbly unspoilt, 19th-century village local with an added 1940s lounge. Small wood-panelled snug and a tiled bar with bentwood furniture. Lunchtime snacks; keen beer prices. Camping by prior arrangement. In a complete timewarp. ⌂ Q ♉ ❀ ⊟ ⛺ ♣ P

Studley

Little Lark
108 Alcester Road
☎ (052 785) 3105
11–3, 6–11
Ind Coope Burton Ale; Lumphammer 🄷
Member of the Little Pub Company chain of ten pubs, sporting a newspaper and printing theme. Home of the *Little Lark*, the LPC newspaper.
⌂ ❀ ◐ ◑

Warwick

Avon Tavern
27 Pickard Street (off A445)
11–3.30 (4 Fri & Sat), 7–11
Marston's Mercian Mild, Burton Best Bitter, Pedigree 🄷
A friendly welcome in an enthusiastically-run pub, tucked away in a Victorian back street, near St Nicholas Park. Comfortably furnished, with plenty of alcoves for quiet conversation. Separate room for darts players. ❀ ♣ P

Old Fourpenny Shop Hotel
27–29 Crompton Street
☎ (0926) 491360
12–2.30 (11.30–3 Sat), 6–11
Draught Bass; M&B Brew XI 🄷
Attractive, three-storey, Georgian building, close to the racecourse. The comfortable, split-level bar is popular with both locals and visitors. Enclosed garden at the rear. Regular guest beers. ❀ ⛟ ♣ P

Whichford

Norman Knight
12–2.30 (3 Sat), 7–11
Hook Norton Best Bitter, Old Hooky 🄷
Undeveloped little local facing the village green.
⌂ Q ❀ ⊟ ⛺ ♣ P

Wilmcote

Swan House Hotel
The Green ☎ (0789) 267030
11–11
Hook Norton Best Bitter; Theakston XB 🄷
A listed, part 18th-century, small hotel close to Mary Arden's house. With its friendly, lively atmosphere, the Swan is deservedly popular with nearby canal users. Excellent food. Children welcome.
⌂ ❀ ⛟ ◐ ◑ ♿ ⇌ P

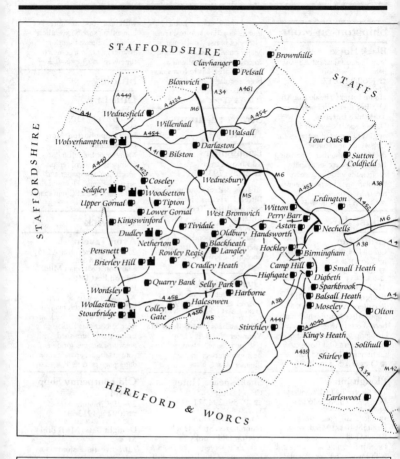

Banks's, Wolverhampton; **Batham**, Brierley Hill;
British Oak, Hanson's, Dudley; Holden's,
Woodsetton; **Sarah Hughes**, Sedgley; **Premier**,
Stourbridge

Bilston

Trumpet
58 High Street (A4039)
☎ (0902) 493723
12–3 (4 Sat), 8–11 (12–3, 8–10.30
Sun)
**Holden's Mild, Bitter,
Special** Ⓗ
Popular, one-roomed jazz
centre; live groups nightly and
Sun lunchtime (no food Sun).
☸ ◖ P

White Rose
20 Lichfield Street, Swan Bank
(A41 opp. town hall)
☎ (0902) 492497
12 (11 Sat), 3–7, 7–11
**M&B Highgate Mild,
Springfield Bitter** Ⓔ
Spotlessly clean and friendly,
with the quality of beer and
pool games equally high. Seep
(Indian card game) is played.
◖ ♣

Try also: George & Dragon,
Bradley (Banks's); **Greyhound
& Punchbowl** (Banks's)

Birmingham: Aston

Manor Tavern
6 Portland Street (¼ mile from
Aston Cross)
☎ (021) 326 8780
11–2.30, 6.45–11 (11–11 Fri; 12–2.30,
7–10.30 Sun)
**Ansells Mild, Bitter;
Marston's Pedigree** Ⓗ
Old inner city, two-roomed pub
which can be spotted from
Lichfield Road. Recent modest
refurbishment has left it clean,
tidy and popular. ◖ ⊟ ♣

Reservoir
469 Lichfield Road (Cuckoo
Road jct) ☎ (021) 327 3376
11.30–2.30, 4.30–11 (11–11 Fri;
11.30–3, 7–11 Sat)
M&B Mild, Brew XI Ⓔ
Pub with a modern interior
which belies its external
appearance. A U-shaped bar
with a separate pool and darts
area, plus a nice lounge. Brew XI
is a big seller. Good value,
home-made food. ◖ ⊟ ⇌ ♣

Balsall Heath

Old Moseley Arms
53 Tindall Street
☎ (021) 440 1954
11–3, 5.30–11 (11–11 Fri & Sat)
**Ansells Mild, Bitter; Ind
Coope Burton Ale; Marston's
Pedigree** Ⓗ

West Midlands

West Midlands

0 — 5 miles
0 — 5 — 10km

M 42

WARWICKSHIRE

M 6

A 45

A 444

A 4114 — A 46

Hampton in Arden

Coventry

Knowle
A 41 — A 452 — A 46 — A 423

WARWICKSHIRE

Coope Burton Ale; Marston's
Pedigree; Tetley Bitter Ⓗ
A much-loved local institution,
nestling behind the new
convention centre. 1990 local
CAMRA *Pub of the Year*,
frequented by players and
celebrities from the nearby rep,
CBSO and Central TV.
◖ ⧉ ⇌ (New St) ♣

Woodman
106 Albert Street
☎ (021) 643 1959
11–2.30, 5 (7 Sat)–11
**Ansells Mild, Bitter; Tetley
Bitter** Ⓗ
Good, old, unspoilt local with a
friendly landlord and good
value bar snacks.
⧉ ⧖ ⇌ (Moor St) ♣

Digbeth

Adam & Eve
Bradford Street
☎ (021) 772 8390
11–11
**Banks's Bitter; Eldridge Pope
Royal Oak; Marston's
Pedigree; Theakston Best
Bitter, XB; Wadworth 6X** Ⓗ
Friendly pub where regular live
music includes big-name bands.
Guest beers. ⚏ ◖ ▮ ⧉

Erdington

Lad in Lane
Bromford Lane (main outer
circle)
☎ (021) 377 7184
11–2.30, 6–11 (12–2.30, 7–10.30 Sun)
**Ansells Mild, Bitter; Ind
Coope Burton Ale** Ⓗ
Black and white pub, long
established. ⚏ ◖ ⧉ ⧖ ⇌ ♣ P

Handsworth

Woodman
375 Holyhead Road (in front of
West Brom. football ground)
☎ (021) 525 3532
11–3, 5 (6 Sat)–11 (12–2.30, 7–10.30
Sun)
**M&B Highgate Mild,
Springfield Bitter, Brew XI** Ⓔ
A well-kept, large lounge with a
very small bar at the side. The
door is locked at Sat lunchtime
when football is on; only
regulars gain access during this
session. ◖ ⧉

Harborne

White Horse
York Street (off High Street)
☎ (021) 427 6023
11–3, 6–11
**Ansells Mild; Ind Coope
Burton Ale; Tetley Bitter** Ⓗ
Two-roomed, village-type pub;
bustling and friendly especially
at weekends. ⚏ ◖ ♣ P

Friendly, two-roomed, old-
fashioned pub in a quiet part of
Balsall Heath – worth hunting
out. ◖ ♣

Camp Hill

Brewer & Baker
Old Camphill
☎ (021) 772 8185
11–11
Banks's Mild, Bitter Ⓔ
Pub sympathetically re-built on
an old site, catering for all age
groups. Lunches served
Mon–Fri. ⚏ ◖ ⧖ ♣ P

City Centre

Atkinsons Bar
Midland Hotel, Stephenson
Street
☎ (021) 643 2601
11–3, 5 (5.30 Sat)–11 (closed Sun)
Beer range varies Ⓗ&Ⓖ
Hotel bar renowned for above-
average prices and obtuse entry
regulations. However, it does
stock up to nine real ales at any
time.

Fox Inn
17 Lower Essex Street

☎ (021) 622 1210
12–2.30, 6–11 (12–11 Fri & Sat)
**Ansells Mild, Bitter; Burton
Bridge Porter; Ind Coope
Burton Ale** Ⓗ
Small, two-roomed local which
has had a chequered career of
name changes and closures. The
present tenant has turned it
round with good beer and great
value food of eye-popping
proportions and very low
prices. Only the brave, or
foolish, will attempt the
'Honeymonster'.
◖ ▮ ⧉ ⇌ (New St)

Gough Arms
Upper Gough Street
☎ (021) 643 0081
11–3, 7–10.30 (11–11 Mon)
**Courage Best Bitter,
Directors; M&B Mild** Ⓗ
Friendly, back-street local, lately
popular with staff from
Davenports. Lunchtime snacks
available. ⧉ ⇌ (New St) ♣

Prince of Wales
Cambridge Street
☎ (021) 643 9460
11.30–3, 5 (7 Sat)–11
Ansells Mild, Bitter; Ind

West Midlands

Highgate

Queens Arms
Macdonald Street
☎ (021) 692 1960
11–3, 5.30–11
Banks's Mild; M&B Mild, Brew XI Ⓗ
Basic corner pub with a welcoming landlord and a good atmosphere. 🕯 ♣ ♁

White Swan
Bradford Street
☎ (021) 622 2586
11–3, 6–11
Ansells Mild; Tetley Bitter Ⓗ
Good, unspoilt pub where the mild is well worth trying.
🕯 ⇌ ♣

Hockley

Black Eagle
16 Factory Road
☎ (021) 523 4008
11–3 (4 Sat), 7–11
Ansells Mild, Bitter Ⓗ
A century-old, four-roomed pub, situated on the site of an old brewery. Warm welcome assured. Guest beer. 🌣 ◖ ▶ 🕯 ᵹ

King's Heath

Station
High Street ☎ (021) 444 1257
11–11 (11–2.30, 6–11 Sun)
Ansells Mild, Bitter; HP&D Entire; Ind Coope Burton Ale; Tetley Bitter Ⓗ
Still popular and smart, two years on from complete renovation. An original tiled wall has been retained in the passage to the back room. Burgers are a speciality. ◖ ♣

Moseley

Prince of Wales
118 Alcester Road
☎ (021) 449 4198
11–3 (3.30 Sat), 5.30 (6 Sat)–11
Ansells Mild; Ind Coope Burton Ale Ⓗ
Lively, high street pub: the bar and two back rooms are served through a hatch. Has the largest throughput of Burton Ale in Birmingham, hence its consistent, good quality. Hot snacks available both sessions.
Q 🌣 🕯 ᵹ

Nechells

Villa Tavern
307 Nechells Park Road
☎ (021) 328 9831
11–2.30 (3.30 Fri & Sat), 5.30 (6.30 Sat)–11
Ansells Mild, Bitter; Marston's Pedigree; Tetley Bitter Ⓗ
Old, terracotta pub of two

rooms: a spartan bar and a recently redecorated lounge.
◖ 🕯 P

Perry Barr

Wellhead Tavern
76 Franchise Street (just off A34, on outer ring)
☎ (021) 331 4554
12–3, 5 (7 college holidays)–11
(12–2.30, 7–10.30 Sun)
Ansells Mild, Bitter; Ind Coope Burton Ale; Tetley Bitter Ⓗ
Twice local CAMRA *Pub of the Year*. The licensee's own brewery company, offers up to three guest beers brewed by Aston Manor (range varies). Reputedly serves the cheapest beer in Brum. Very good value lunches. A must. 🌣 ◖ ⇌ ♣ ♁

Selly Park

Hibernian
Pershore Road
11–2.30 (3 Fri & Sat), 5.30–11
Ansells Mild, Bitter; Ind Coope Burton Ale; Tetley Bitter Ⓗ
Four-roomed former hotel incorporating a restaurant and a live music room (where the landlord himself entertains). Guest beer.
Q 🌣 ◖ ▶ 🕯 ᵹ ⇌ ♣ ♣ P

Small Heath

Black Horse
Green Lane (200 yds from A45) ☎ (021) 773 7271
11–11 (11–3.30, 6.30–11 Sat)
M&B Mild, Brew XI Ⓔ
Very friendly Irish/Brummie pub near the Islamic Centre.
🌣 ◖ 🕯

White Lion
151 Muntz Street
☎ (021) 772 8668
11–11 (11–3, 7–11 Sat)
M&B Mild, Brew XI Ⓔ
Popular, locals' pub. 🕯 ♣

Sparkbrook

Rose Tavern
Henley Street
☎ (021) 771 0600
11–11
Ansells Mild, Bitter; Tetley Bitter Ⓗ
Basic bar and a pleasant lounge, ideal for functions. Reasonably-priced wholesome lunches served. ◖ 🕯 ♣

Stirchley

Lifford Curve
Fordhouse Lane
☎ (021) 451 1634
11–3, 5–11 (11–11 Sat)
Banks's Mild, Bitter Ⓔ
Typically functional Banks's boozer with a large, airy bar and

lounge. Karaoke sessions.
🌣 🕯 ᵹ ♣ P

Witton

Safe Harbour
Moor Lane (between A4040 & A453) ☎ (021) 356 4257
11–2.30 (3 Fri & Sat), 5 (6 Sat)–11
Ansells Mild, Bitter; Tetley Bitter Ⓗ
Pub known as the 'Diggers', opposite the main cemetery gate. A basic bar and a comfortable lounge cater for local factory workers and residents. 🌣 ◖ 🕯 ♣ P

Blackheath

Bell & Bear
71 Gorsty Hill Road
☎ (021) 561 2196
11–11 (11–3, 6–11 Sat; 12–2.30, 7–10.30 Sun)
HP&D Mild, Bitter, Entire; Taylor Landlord Ⓗ
Pleasantly refurbished pub providing various drinking and eating areas around a central bar. No eve meals Sun.
🌣 ◖ ▶ ⇌ (Old Hill) P

Waterfall
Waterfall Lane, Cradley Heath
☎ (021) 561 3499
11–3, 6–11
Batham Best Bitter; Everards Tiger, Old Original; Hook Norton Old Hooky; Marston's Pedigree; Theakston Old Peculier Ⓗ
Revitalised former tied house perched on a bank, with a waterfall in the back garden. The function room frequently hosts quizzes. Two guest beers.
🌣 ◖ ▶ 🕯 ᵹ ⇌ (Old Hill) ♣ ♁ P

Bloxwich

Romping Cat
97 Elmore Green Road (B4210)
12–11
Banks's Mild, Bitter Ⓔ
Small, basic, three-roomed pub with a round-cornered bar and a tiny smoke room. 🌣 🕯 ⇌ ♣

Saddlers Arms
Fishley Lane, Lower Farm Estate, Little Bloxwich
☎ (0922) 405839
11–3, 6–11 (11–11 Sat)
Banks's Mild, Bitter Ⓗ
Modern estate pub with a nice lounge and a friendly atmosphere. ᵹ 🌣 🕯 ♣ P

Brierley Hill

Bell
72 Delph Road (B4172)
☎ (0384) 72376
11–3, 5–11 (11–11 Fri & Sat)
HP&D Mild, Bitter, Entire, Deakin's Downfall Ⓗ
Traditionally decorated, Victorian pub at the bottom of

the Delph flight of locks on the Dudley Canal. Quiz Wed nights. ▨ ▩ ◖ ♣ P

Black Horse

Delph Road (B4172)
☎ (0384) 79142
11.30–3, 5.30–11 (11.30–11 Sat; 12–2.30, 7–10.30 Sun)
Banks's Mild; Courage Directors Ⓗ
Popular hostelry on the famous Delph Crawl. Beware the keg bitter. Quizzes every other Mon. ▨ ▩ ◖ ▶ ♣ ⌂ P

Roebuck

Amblecote Road
☎ (0384) 79137
12–3, 5.30 (7 Sat)–11 (12–2, 7–10.30 Sun)
Ansells Bitter; Ind Coope Burton Ale; Marston's Pedigree Ⓗ
Friendly, roadside pub, near the Merry Hill shopping complex. Games-oriented charity nights are always popular. No food Sun. ◖ ♣ P

Vine (Bull & Bladder)

10 Delph Road (¾ mile off A461) ☎ (0384) 78293
12–4, 6–11 (12–11 Fri & Sat)
Batham Mild, Best Bitter XXX Ⓗ
Boisterous, Black Country brewery tap, its brightly painted frontage featuring a Shakespearian quotation. Live jazz Mon. ▨ ▩ ◖ ♣ P

Woodside

67 Pedmore Road (A4036, near Merry Hill centre)
☎ (0384) 77550
12–2.30, 6–11 (7.30–10.30 Sun; closed Sun & bank holiday lunch)
Adnams Broadside; Banks's Mild; Hanby Drawwell; Taylor Landlord Ⓗ
Smart free house near Europe's largest shopping complex. Good value menu (incl. vegetarian dishes) served in a separate restaurant. Guest beers changed on a regional basis monthly; cider in summer. ▨ Q ⋈ ◖ ♣ ⌂ P

Brownhills

Prince of Wales

98 Watling Street (A5)
☎ (0543) 372551
12–3 (not Mon–Fri), 7.30–11
Ansells Mild, Bitter; Banks's Mild Ⓗ
Small, one-roomed pub on the main road between two north entry roads to Brownhills. ⊟

Wheel Inn

96 Lindon Road (B4152, halfway between Walsall Wood and Brownhills)
☎ (0543) 378408
11.30–3, 6.30–11 (11–11 Fri & Sat)
Banks's Mild, Bitter; M&B Highgate Mild Ⓔ
Popular, urban pub which

features occasional cheap beer nights. Function room. ▨ ⌂ ⊟ ♣

White Horse

White Horse Road (off A5)
☎ (0543) 374053
11–3, 6–11
Banks's Mild, Bitter Ⓔ
Friendly, three-roomed pub, close to Chasewater. ▩ ◖ ▶ ⊟ ♣ P

Clayhanger

George & Dragon

Church Street (off A4124)
☎ (0543) 372047
12–3 (not Mon–Fri), 7–11
Ansells Mild, Bitter Ⓗ
Basic bar and a pleasant lounge, enjoying a good community atmosphere. Popular games room. Note: closed weekday lunch. Limited parking.
⌂ ⊟ ♣ P

Colley Gate

Little Chop House

Windmill Hill (A458)
☎ (0384) 635089
11–2.30, 6–11
Ansells Mild; Ind Coope Burton Ale; Lumphammer Ⓗ
Recently renamed and refurbished hostelry of the Little Pub Company chain, well-known for its steaks, 'sizzlers' and Desperate Dan pies. Live music Tue eve. Only Lumphammer is visible on the pumps so ask for other beers. The company's own fun newspaper is also available.
▨ Q ◖ ▶ P

Why Not

Whynot Street
☎ (0384) 61019
12–2.30, 6–11 (12–11 Sat; supper licence)
Wiltshire Stonehenge Bitter, Old Grumble, Old Devil Ⓗ
Three areas around a bar, including a dining section, with a games area at the rear. Tucked up a short lane on the edge of town. Four guest beers. Yard outside for summer drinking.
▨ ▩ ◖ ▶

Coseley

White House

1 Daisy Street, Daisy Bank (B4163) ☎ (0902) 402703
11–3, 6–11
HP&D Mild, Bitter, Entire Ⓗ
Friendly, two-roomed pub dominating the crossroads. The enterprising landlord has introduced a wide variety of guest beers. ▨ ▩ ◖ ⊟ ⇌ ♣

Coventry

Admiral Lord Rodney

Short Street, Parkside (just off

ringroad, A423 jct)
☎ (0203) 551738
11–11
Draught Bass; M&B Mild, Brew XI Ⓗ
Increasingly popular free house in a refurbished, old wooden-beamed, ex-M&B pub. 'Happiness is handpulled' is part of the pub logo. Regular Wed night gathering place for the local branch of CAMRA. Guest beers. Q ▩ ◖ ♣ ⌂ P

Boat Inn

Black Horse Road, Exhall (off A444) ☎ (0203) 361438
11–3 (may close earlier), 6–11
Ansells Mild, Bitter; Ind Coope Burton Ale; Marston's Pedigree; Tetley Bitter Ⓗ
A Heritage inn: the old wood-panelled bar area is the original bar; the semi-plush area is the old lounge; the newest area is smartest. All one room, but not obviously so. ▨ ⌂ ▩ ◖

Biggin Hall Hotel

214 Binley Road, Copsewood
☎ (0203) 451056
11–3 (4 Sat), 4 (6 Sat)–11 (11–11 Fri)
Marston's Mercian Mild, Burton Best Bitter, Pedigree, Owd Rodger Ⓗ
Not a hotel, despite the name: a smart bar and plush lounge with a large, central table. All decor is turn of century. Games room/family room to the rear and a large function room upstairs. Good food.
▨ Q ⌂ ▩ ◖ ⊟ ♣ P

Black Horse

Spon End ☎ (0203) 677360
10–3, 4.30–11
Draught Bass; M&B Mild, Brew XI Ⓗ
Old pub, very popular with the locals and the Irish community. Has been threatened with demolition for a couple of years. ▨ Q ⊟ ♣ P

Elastic Inn

Lower Ford Street (behind bus station) ☎ (0203) 227039
11–3, 5.30 (6.30 Sat)–11
Ansells Mild, Bitter; Tetley Bitter Ⓗ
Small, corner pub near the cinema, offering a limited lunchtime menu. ◖

Greyhound Inn

Sutton Stop, Longford (road/track leading to canal)
☎ (0203) 363046
11–11
Draught Bass; M&B Mild Ⓗ
Old, canalside pub in the Hawkesbury conservation area, with outside drinking on the canal bank. Well known for its food, particularly the pies; infamous for its idiosyncratic licensee! Guest beer.
▨ ▩ ◖ ▶ ⊟ P

West Midlands

Malt Shovel

Spon End ☎ (0203) 220204
11–2.30 (later on request), 7 (6 Sat)–11
**Ansells Mild, Bitter; Tetley
Bitter** Ⓗ
Small, but exceedingly popular,
one-roomed pub with many
nooks and crannies. The original
Heritage pub, straight opposite
M&B's Coventry depot (they
should take a hint). Very few
alterations and excellent beer –
a gem. Guest beer. ▲ ❀ ◖ ♣ P

Miners Arms

Aldermans Green Road,
Aldermans Green
☎ (0203) 360457
11–2.30, 7–11
**Ansells Mild, Bitter; Tetley
Bitter** Ⓗ
Friendly, estate-type pub on a
main road on the north side of
town. Close to the motorway
(M6), but no access. ❀ ◖ ♣ P

Nursery Tavern

Lord Street, Chapelfields
☎ (0203) 674530
11.30–2 (3 Sat), 7–11
**Ruddles Best Bitter, County;
Webster's Yorkshire Bitter,
Choice** Ⓗ
Pleasant pub in an inner city
residential area where the
housing design often reflects its
former status as a watch-making
district. Lunches served
Mon–Fri. Guest beer.
Q ❀ ◖ ⊟ ♣ ◔

Old Windmill

22 Spon Street
☎ (0203) 252183
11–2.30, 5.30 (6 Mon & Fri, 7 Sat)–11
(12–2, 7–10.30 Sun)
**Ruddles Best Bitter, County;
Webster's Yorkshire Bitter,
Choice** Ⓗ
16th-century building altered in
recent years to take in the
courtyard and brewhouse as
indoor drinking areas. The
whole street is full of restored
and original timber-framed
buildings. A tourist stop in an
area with an outdoor drinking
ban. Guest beer. ▲ Q ◖ ♣ ◔

Prince William Henry

Foleshill Road
☎ (0203) 687776
11.30–11
**Draught Bass; M&B Brew
XI** Ⓗ
Large, lively pub close to the
canal and Courtaulds main
Coventry works. Specialises in
Indian cuisine. ◖ ▶ P

Red House

Stoney Stanton Road
☎ (0203) 637929
11–3, 7–11
**Bateman Mild; Hoskins
Beaumanor, Premium, Old
Nigel** Ⓗ
Large, ex-M&B roadhouse built
during the war (note the carving

on the pub front). Tastefully
refurbished twice before re-
opening – once after a fire.
Wood-panelled lounge; similar
bar games room to the rear.
Guest beers. ◖ ⊟ ♣ P

Rose & Woodbine

North Street, Upper Stoke
11–3, 6–11
**Ansells Mild; Ruddles Best
Bitter; Webster's Yorkshire
Bitter** Ⓗ
Back-street local, an A–Z
needed to find it. The bar is
effectively a games room; the
lounge has smarter decor.
Regular entertainment nights.
⊟ ♣

Cradley Heath

Wagon & Horses

100 Reddall Hill Road (A4100)
☎ (0384) 636035
11.15–3, 7–11
Banks's Mild, Bitter Ⓔ
Boisterous, Black Country local.
The bar features photos and
paintings of Staffordshire bull
terriers, together with
miscellaneous 'souvenirs'.
⊟ ⇌ ♣ P

Try also: Swan (Holden's)

Darlaston

Fallings Heath Tavern

Walsall Road (A4038)
☎ (021) 526 3403
12–2.30 (3 Sat and if busy), 7–11
**Draught Bass; M&B
Highgate Mild; Welsh
Brewers Worthington BB** Ⓗ
Two-roomed, main road local
which has a pig collection above
the bar. Bar snacks available.
⇞ ❀ ⊟ ♣ P

Green Dragon

55 Church Street (500 yds N of
A4038/A462 jct)
☎ (021) 526 3674
11–2.30, 7–11
**M&B Highgate Mild;
Springfield Bitter** Ⓗ
Small and lively, two-roomed
local with a strong darts
emphasis. Guest beer. ❀ ⊟ ♣

Dudley

Lamp Tavern

116 High Street (A459, near
Hanson's Brewery)
☎ (0384) 254129
11–11
**Batham Mild, Best Bitter,
XXX** Ⓗ
Welcoming, Black Country local
on the edge of the town centre.
The garden has a children's
climbing frame. ▲ ❀ ◖ ⊟ ♣ P

Old Vic

King Street (A461/New Mill
Street jct) ☎ (0384) 236082
11–11

**Home Mild, Bitter;
Theakston Old Peculier;
Younger IPA, No. 3** Ⓗ
Lively, town-centre pub with
regular guest beers; a single
room around an island bar.
Weston's Old Rosie cider.
◖ ⇞ ♣ ◔

Try also: Old Priory (HP&D)

Earlswood

Bulls Head

Lime Kiln Lane (off B4102)
☎ (021) 728 2335
12–2.30, 6–11
**Ansells Mild, Bitter; Ind
Coope Burton Ale; Tetley
Bitter** Ⓗ
The bar area has a tiled floor
and a separate darts throw. The
rambling lounge has an
unusually high bar. Popular with
Sunday cyclists. Swings and
slides in the garden.
▲ Q ❀ ◖ ⊟ ♣ P

Four Oaks

Crown

Walsall Road
☎ (021) 308 1258
11–11
**Ansells Mild, Bitter; Ind
Coope Burton Ale; Marston's
Pedigree; Tetley Bitter** Ⓗ
Pub with a warm, friendly
atmosphere and olde-worlde
character, featuring leather
Chesterfields and antique fire
surrounds. Tasty food, home-
made at lunchtime, plus
authentic American, Mexican,
Italian and Indian cuisine. Live
entertainment every night.
◖ ▶ ⊟ ⇞ ⇌ (Butlers Lane) P

Halesowen

Beehive

Hagley Road (B4183, 800 yds
from town) ☎ (021) 550 1782
11–11
**Banks's Bitter; Hanson's
Mild** Ⓔ
Cosy lounge and rear function
room, serving a varied and low-
priced food menu. The bar is
popular with locals for its beer,
pool, and Sun eve sing-alongs.
▲ ❀ ◖ ▶ ⊟ ♣ P

Rose & Crown

Hagley Road, Hasbury (B4183,
1 mile from centre)
☎ (021) 550 2757
12–2.30 (3 Sat), 5.30 (6 Sat)–11
**HP&D Mild, Bitter, Entire,
Deakin's Downfall** Ⓗ
Always busy Holts' pub with
various drinking areas radiating
from a central bar. Many
interesting and unusual
artefacts. Good lunchtime food
selection (no food Sun).
Occasional quiz nights are
increasingly popular. ▲ ♣ P

Hampton in Arden

White Lion
On B4102 ☎ (067 55) 2833
12–2.30, 5.30–11
**Draught Bass; M&B
Highgate Mild, Brew XI** Ⓗ
Traditional, village inn with a
small public bar and a larger,
well furnished lounge. No eve
meals Sun. ⌂ Q ◑ 🍴 ⌂ ৬ ♿ P

Kingswinford

Old Court House Hotel
High Street (A4101)
☎ (0384) 271887
11–2.30, 5–11
Banks's Mild Ⓔ**; Courage
Directors; John Smith's
Bitter; Wards Sheffield Best
Bitter** Ⓗ
Large, comfortable pub on the
Dudley road, opposite the
church. 🍴 ☙ ◑ ▶ P

Park Tavern
187 Barnett Lane (500 yds
from A4101)
☎ (0384) 287178
12–11
**Ansells Bitter; Batham Best
Bitter; HP&D Entire; Ind
Coope Burton Ale** Ⓗ
Pleasant local near Broadfield
House Glass Museum. 🍴 ⌂ ♣ P

Knowle

Red Lion
High Street ☎ (0564) 772461
11–2.30 (3 Sat), 5 (5.30 Sat)–11
**Ansells Mild; Ind Coope
Burton Ale; Tetley Bitter** Ⓗ
Pub featuring a basic bar with
an original grate; large lounge
and wine bar. Function room
available for hire. No food Sun.
⌂ ◑ ⌂ ♣ P

Langley

New Navigation
Titford Road (A4123, ¼ mile
from M5 jct 2)
☎ (021) 552 2525
11.30–3, 6–11 (11.30–3.30, 7–11 Sat)
**HP&D Mild, Bitter, Entire,
Deakin's Downfall** Ⓗ
Welcoming pub, with a pleasant
atmosphere, on the Titford
Canal. ⌂ 🍴 ◑ ♣ P

Lower Gornal

Black Bear
Deepdale Lane
☎ (0384) 253333
11.30–3, 6 (6.30 Mon)–11
**Premier Pitfield Bitter, Old
Merlin Mild, Knightly** Ⓗ
Lively pub on a steep corner
slope overlooking the Black
Country and Worcestershire
beyond. A former 17th-century,
Gornal stone cottage with an
interesting history. Live
entertainment Fri eve. Varied

range of beers, incl. guests and
Whitbread's Old Grizzly house
beer. ⌂ 🍴 🛏 ◑ ♣ ♿

Red Cow
84 Grosvenor Road (off
B4176) ☎ (0384) 253760
12–4.30, 6.30 (7 Sat)–11
**Banks's Bitter; Hanson's
Mild** Ⓔ
Old Black Country local of
character, a pub since 1835. A
traditional oasis in an area of
redevelopment. Comfortable,
snug lounge. 🍴 ⌂ ৬ ♣ P

Netherton

Elephant & Castle
250 Cradley Road (B4173)
☎ (0384) 636849
12–2.30, 5.30–11 (11.30–4, 7–11 Sat;
12–2.30, 7–10.30 Sun)
**Banks's Mild; HP&D Bitter,
Entire, Deakin's Downfall** Ⓗ
Comfortable, Black Country
local with occasional impromptu
pianola recitals by the landlord.
Summer barbecues. Good value
lunchtime specials cooked on
the solid fuel Aga. ⌂ Q 🍴 ◑
৬ ♿ (Cradley Heath) ♣ P

White Swan
45 Baptist End Road (400 yds
off A459) ☎ (0384) 256101
12–3.30, 7–11
**Banks's Mild; HP&D Bitter,
Entire, Deakin's Downfall** Ⓗ
Welcoming, 18th-century,
former home-brew house
(Roe's), with a contrasting bar
and lounge. Good value, home-
cooked food. ⌂ 🍴 ◑ ⌂ ♣ P

Oldbury

Waggon & Horses
Church Street (off A4034,
Oldbury ringway)
☎ (021) 552 5467
12–2.30 (3 Fri), 5.30 (5 Fri, 6 Sat)–11
**Draught Bass; Batham Best
Bitter; Everards Old
Original; Hanson's Mild;
Marston's Pedigree** Ⓗ
Listed, Victorian town pub with
original tiles, a copper ceiling
and Holt's (of Aston) brewery
window. Popular with drinkers
and diners (book for Sun lunch).
⌂ Q 🛏 🍴 ◑ ▶ ♿ (Sandwell &
Dudley)

Olton

Lyndon
Barn Lane ☎ (021) 743 2179
12–2.30, 6–11 (12–2.30, 7–10.30 Sun)
**Ansells Mild, Bitter; Tetley
Bitter** Ⓗ
Small bar and a large, split-level
lounge. The conservatory
overlooks the garden and there
is a well-appointed smoke room.
Lunches served Mon–Fri; eve
meals Tue–Sat; good quality
and reasonably priced.
🛏 🍴 ◑ ▶ ⌂ ৬ ♣ P

Pelsall

Old House at Home
Walsall Road
11–3, 5–11 (11–11 Fri & Sat)
Banks's Mild, Bitter Ⓔ
Popular pub near the common.
Bar snacks available.
⌂ ♣ P

Pensnett

Holly Bush
Bell Street (just off High Street,
A4101)
☎ (0384) 78711
1–4, 7–11
**Batham Mild, Best Bitter,
XXX** Ⓗ
Bright and welcoming, modern
estate pub. 🛏 🍴 ⌂ ♣ P

Quarry Bank

Church Tavern
36 High Street (A4100)
☎ (0384) 68757
10–2.30, 6–11 (10–11 Sat)
**HP&D Mild, Bitter, Entire,
Deakin's Downfall** Ⓗ
Cheerful, welcoming pub with
Black Country Society
connections and traditional,
local cooking (book for Sun
lunch). Wed is quiz night. ⌂ ◑
▶ ⌂ ৬ ♿ (Cradley Heath) ♣ P

Rowley Regis

Sir Robert Peel
1 Rowley Village (B4171, 400
yds from Blackheath town
centre) ☎ (021) 559 2835
12–4, 7–11
**Ansells Mild, Bitter; British
Oak Eve'ill** Ⓗ
Welcoming remnant of the old
hilltop village. The cheerfully
decorated bar and lounge are
separated by a central passageway with framed cartoons
and its own servery. Regular
guest beers. ⌂ 🍴 ⌂ ♿ ♣

Sedgley

Beacon Hotel
129 Bilston Street (A463, ¼
mile E of High Street)
☎ (0902) 883380
12–2.30, 5.30–10.45 (11 Fri; 11–3,
6–11 Sat; 12–2.30, 7–10.30 Sun)
**M&B Springfield Bitter;
Sarah Hughes Sedgley
Surprise, Ruby Mild** Ⓗ
Superb example of a lovingly
restored, Victorian hostelry. The
three-tier brewery at the rear
was re-opened in 1987 after 30
years' closure. The new bitter
was added to the established
Ruby Mild in 1990. Regular
guest beers.
⌂ Q 🛏 🍴 ⌂ ♣ P

West Midlands

Shirley

Bernie's Real Ale Off-Licence
266 Cranmore Boulevard (off A34, 1 mile N of M42 jct 4)
☎ (021) 744 2827
12–2 (not Mon), 5.30–10
Batham Best Bitter; Fuller's ESB; Taylor Landlord; Titanic Premium; Wadworth 6X Ⓗ
A veritable emporium for the connoisseur of offerings from small breweries near and far: an ever-changing selection. Guest real ciders, too. 'Try before you buy' system. ☼

Solihull

Golden Lion
727 Warwick Road (opp. Mell Square) ☎ (021) 704 9969
10.30–3 (3.30 Sat), 5.30 (7 Sat)–11
Courage Best Bitter, Directors; John Smith's Bitter Ⓗ
Welcoming, town-centre local with three, distinct rooms; a large and popular lounge, a busy public bar (the only one left in the town centre), plus a snug (open on request). A traditional pub.
🏠 ◖ ▶ 🍴 ♣ P

Stourbridge

Gladstone
High Street, Audnam (A461)
☎ (0384) 442703
11–3, 6–11
HP&D Mild, Bitter, Entire Ⓗ
Recent acquisition of the HP&D chain. A one-roomer with a lively and friendly atmosphere; several alcoves and many artefacts. À la carte meals served until 9.30, Mon–Sat eves, and lunchtimes, incl. Sun. ◖ ▶ P

Longlands Tavern
Western Road
☎ (0384) 392073
11.30–3, 6–11 (11–11 Sat)
Banks's Mild, Bitter Ⓔ
Smart, back-street pub where the local CAMRA branch was formed; still as popular as ever.
◖ ♣ P

Old Crispin
Church Street (off A491, by old library) ☎ (0384) 377581
11–2.30, 7–11 (may vary; 12–3, 8–10.30 Sun)
Marston's Burton Best Bitter, Pedigree Ⓗ
A tavern popular with students and lovers of Cordon Bleu standard food – vegetarians included. A good supply of newspapers can be read in the airy conservatory; the cosy, upstairs restaurant can be booked. No food Sun eve. Guest beers. Q ◖ ▶ ≠

Red Lion
Lion Street (just off ring road)
☎ (0384) 397563
11.30 (11 Sat)–2.30 (3 Fri & Sat), 7–11 (12–2.30, 7–10.30 Sun)
Draught Bass; M&B Brew XI Ⓗ
Popular, two-roomed pub with an additional parlour for functions or meals. Good value, award-winning food includes vegetarian and Indian dishes. No meals Sat eve or Sun.
🏠 ◖ ▶ ≠ ♣

Robin Hood
196 Collis Street (off A461, near football ground)
☎ (0384) 440281
11–3, 6–11
Batham Best Bitter; Everards Tiger, Old Original Ⓗ
Deservedly popular, terraced hostelry offering varied à la carte meals in its two, distinctly separate drinking areas (vegetarians well catered for). The two or three guest beers usually include a mild. No food Sun eve. Q ◖ ▶

Shrubbery Cottage
Heath Lane, Oldswinford (200 yds from B4186/A491 jct)
☎ (0384) 377598
12–2.30, 6–11
Holden's Mild, Bitter, Special Ⓗ
Friendly, popular local with always a lively atmosphere. A much needed extension is being added. Occasional guest beer.
🏠 ◖ ≠ (Stourbridge Junction) P

Sutton Coldfield

Duke Inn
Duke Street (off Birmingham Road) ☎ (021) 355 1767
11.30–3, 5.30–11
Ansells Mild, Bitter; Ind Coope Burton Ale; Tetley Bitter Ⓗ
Unspoilt, traditional local with an old wooden bar, and etched mirror and windows. Friendly, basic, L-shaped public bar and a cosy, homely lounge. Bar snacks available. Q 🏠 ≠ ♣ P

Laurel Wines Off-Licence
63 Westwood Road (just off Chester Rd, A452)
☎ (021) 353 0399
12–2, 5.30 (5 Sat)–10.30 (12–2 Sun)
Batham Best Bitter; Burton Bridge Festival; Marston's Pedigree Ⓖ
Friendly and popular off-licence which sells a wide range of real ales, in any quantity, direct from the cask. Five guest beers from all over the country.

Station
Station Street
☎ (021) 355 3640
11–11

Draught Bass; M&B Mild, Brew XI; Marston's Pedigree Ⓗ
Very popular, lively, hub of activity with satellite TV, frequent live music and summer barbecues. A lounge and two public bars; function room upstairs with a pool table.
🏠 ◖ ◖ Å ♣

Three Tuns
19 The High Street (A5127)
☎ (021) 355 2996
11–2.30, 5–11 (11–11 Sat)
Ansells Mild, Bitter; Ind Coope Burton Ale; Marston's Pedigree Ⓗ
Listed coaching inn with a haunted cellar, log fire and a friendly atmosphere. 🏠 🏠 ◖ ≠ ☼

Tipton

Prince Regent
190 Horseley Heath (A461)
☎ (021) 557 2156
11–4 (4.30 Sat), 6 (7 Sat)–11
Banks's Mild, Bitter Ⓔ
Plain, compact, Black Country local with a friendly atmosphere.
🏠 🏠 ≠ (Dudley Port) ♣

Tividale

Wonder
94 Dudley Road West (A4033)
☎ (021) 557 1024
11–3, 6–11 (11–11 Fri & Sat)
Banks's Mild, Bitter Ⓔ
Comfortable, 19th-century local, its original four rooms now opened up into a single area and refurbished in Victorian style. 🏠 🚶 🏠 ◖ ♣ P

Upper Gornal

Crown
Holloway Street, Ruiton (off A459) ☎ (0902) 884035
12–3.30, 7–11
Banks's Bitter; Hanson's Mild Ⓔ
Popular, friendly, old local at the top of the 'Bonk'. Windows indicate it was a home-brew house at the turn of the century.
🏠 🚶 🏠 🚶 ♣ ☼ P

Old Mill
Windmill Street (off A459)
☎ (0902) 887707
12–3, 6.30–11 (12–11 Sat)
Holden's Mild, Bitter, Special, XL Ⓔ
Comfortable and welcoming, two-roomed hostelry serving good value bar meals (separate restaurant upstairs). Old Mill house beer from Holden's.
🏠 ◖ ▶ 🏠 ♣ ☼ P

Walsall

Duke of Wellington
Birmingham Street (off A34)
☎ (0922) 25604

11–11
**M&B Highgate Mild,
Springfield Bitter, Brew XI** Ⓔ
Traditional, popular local: a
bright, busy bar and a
comfortable lounge. No food
Sun. ⊛ ◖ ♣ P

Duke of York
Lumley Road ☎ (0922) 27593
11.30–3, 6–11
**M&B Highgate Mild, Brew
XI** Ⓗ
Plush, Tudor-style bar, and a
large, Spanish-style lounge,
which is popular with young
people in the evening. Bar
skittles played. Lunches served
on Fri only. ⊛ ◖ ♣

Hamemaker's Arms
87 Blue Lane West (A454)
☎ (0922) 28083
11.30–3, 6–11 (11–11 Sat)
Banks's Mild, Bitter Ⓔ
Pleasantly modernised 30s pub,
handy for the town centre: a
large, well laid-out bar and a
very comfortable, farmhouse-
style lounge. Paved barbecue
area outside; no food Sun.
Q ⊛ ◖ ◖ ≢ ♣ P

New Fullbrook
West Bromwich Road (southern
part of ring road)
☎ (0922) 21761
11.30–11 (11–3.30, 5.30–11 Sat)
**M&B Highgate Mild,
Springfield Bitter, Brew XI** Ⓔ
Large and relatively original,
30s pub with a quiet,
comfortable lounge and a huge
trade in mild. No food Sun.
Tables at front for summer
drinking. Q ⊛ ⊛ ◖ ♣ P

New Inns
5 John Street ☎ (0922) 27660
12–3, 5.30 (7 Sat)–11 (12–3, 8–10.30
Sun)
**Ansells Mild, Bitter; Ind
Coope Burton Ale** Ⓗ
Small-roomed, Victorian, back-
street local with a cosy lounge.
Traditional, warm and
comfortable; a rare haven from
jukeboxes and fruit machines.
Beautifully cooked, interesting
food; sumptuous Sunday roasts
(no eve meals Sun or Mon).
≢ Q ⊛ ◖ ≢ ♣

Oak Inn
336 Green Lane (A34)
☎ (0922) 645758
12–2.30 (11.30–3 Sat), 7–11 (closed
Sun lunch)
**Wiltshire Ma Pardoe's Mild,
Stonehenge Bitter, Old
Grumble, Old Devil** Ⓗ
Pleasant, one-roomed pub with
an unusual island bar. Guest
beers. ◖ ▶ ≢ ♣ P

Walsall Arms
Bank Street (behind Royal
Hotel, off A34)
☎ (0922) 26660
12–3, 5–11

Banks's Mild, Bitter Ⓔ;
Draught Bass Ⓗ; **M&B
Highgate Mild** Ⓗ; **Marston's
Burton Best Bitter,
Pedigree** Ⓗ
A restrained, well-designed
modernisation of a Victorian
local. Small, separate rooms and
a passageway drinking area
make this busy pub very social
and conversational. The skittle
room is popular for functions.
No food at weekends.
Q ⊛ ◖ ≢ ♣

White Lion
Sandwell Street
☎ (0922) 28542
12–3, 7–11
**Ansells Mild, Bitter; Ind
Coope Burton Ale** Ⓗ
Large, popular, back-street local.
Beware sloping floor in the bar.
Separate pool room. Guest
beers. ◖ ◖ ♣

Wednesbury

Old Blue Ball
Hall End
☎ (021) 556 0197
12–3, 7–11
M&B Highgate Mild Ⓔ
Small, three-roomed, traditional
local. ⊛ ◖ ♣

Rosehill Tavern
80 Church Hill
☎ (021) 556 0850
12–3, 7–11
Ansells Mild, Bitter Ⓗ
Friendly, welcoming local with a
traditional bar and a comfortable snug room off. ≢ ⊛ ◖ ♣ P

Woodman
Wood Green Road (500 yds
from M6 jct 9, opp Wood
Green College)
☎ (021) 556 1637
11–11 (11–4, 6–11 Sat)
**Courage Directors; John
Smith's Bitter** Ⓗ
Large, roadside pub: a basic bar
and a pool/games room; cosy
smoke room. Currently under
threat of redevelopment. Guest
beers. Children welcome in
games room. ◖ ♣ P

Wednesfield

Broadway
Lichfield Road (A4124)
☎ (0922) 405872
11.30–2.30, 5–11 (12–3, 6–11 Sat)
**Ansells Mild, Bitter; HP&D
Entire; Ind Coope Burton
Ale** Ⓗ
Pleasant, multi-roomed pub with
wood panelling in the lounge.
The back lounge has ornate
plaster coving, stained-glass
partitions, wooden-framed
mirrors and a plate rack. No
meals Sun. Ramp entrance for
wheelchairs.
⊛ ◖ ◖ ♿ ♣ P

Pyle Cock
Rookery Street
☎ (0902) 732125
10.30–4, 6–11 (10.30–11 Sat)
Banks's Mild, Bitter Ⓔ
Excellent, locals' boozer with
lovely etched windows
depicting a pyle cock.
Q ≢ ◖ ♣ P

Spread Eagle
Broad Lane South (off A4124)
☎ (0902) 606890
11–2.30, 5–11 (11–11 Fri & Sat)
Banks's Mild, Bitter Ⓔ
Large, post-war estate pub:
three spacious rooms, all usually
lively and popular. ◖ P

West Bromwich

Old Hop Pole
High Street, Carter's Green (just
off NW end of expressway)
☎ (021) 525 6648
11.30–2.30, 5–11 (11.30–11 Fri & Sat)
**HP&D Mild, Bitter, Entire,
Deakin's Downfall** Ⓗ
19th-century local, refurbished
in Victorian style, in an area
offering a wide choice of beers.
⊛ ♣

Try also: New Hop Pole
(Courage); **Railway**
(Camerons)

Willenhall

Brewers Droop
44 Wolverhampton Street (200
yds from centre)
☎ (0902) 607827
12–3, 6–11
**Batham Best Bitter; Everards
Old Original; Hook Norton
Old Hooky** Ⓗ
Former coaching house on the
Wolverhampton–Walsall road.
A comfortable, two-roomed pub
with folk music every Thu in an
upstairs room. At least two
guest beers usually available.
Eve meals Fri and Sat only.
⊛ ⊛ ◖ ♣

Falcon
Gomer Street West (50 yds
from Brewers Droop)
☎ (0902) 633378
12–11
Banks's Mild, Bitter Ⓔ;
**Ruddles Best Bitter,
County** Ⓗ
Two-roomed, locals' pub with a
strong darts following in the
traditional bar. Built in 1936, on
the site of an older pub dating
from 1841. A variety of guest
beers and Weston's Old Rosie
cider available. ⊛ ◖ ♣ ▭

Robin Hood
54 The Crescent
☎ (0902) 608006
12–3, 7 (5.30 Fri)–11
**Ansells Mild; HP&D Entire;
Ind Coope Burton Ale; Tetley
Bitter** Ⓗ

West Midlands

Welcoming, one-roomed pub with a very warm and friendly atmosphere. Walsall CAMRA *Pub of the Year* 1989 and 1990. Entire may be replaced by guest beers. Snacks available at all times. ♨ ♣ ♣ P

Three Tuns
8 Walsall Road
11–3, 5–11
M&B Highgate Mild E
Traditional, mild-only, working class local run by a long-standing licensee. Q ✦ ♣

Wollaston

Plough
Bridgenorth Road (A461)
☎ (0384) 393414
12–2.30 (3 Sat), 7–11
M&B Mild, Springfield Bitter E; **Draught Bass** H
Popular, two-roomed pub with an additional pool room; nice collection of china plates. Large garden. Eve meals Fri and Sat only. ♨ ♢ ▶ ✦ ♣ P

Stourbridge Lion
Bridgenorth Road (A461)
☎ (0384) 442119
12–3, 5.30 (7 Sat)–11
Ind Coope Burton Ale; Taylor Landlord; Tetley Bitter; Whitbread Boddingtons Bitter H
Pleasant, two-roomed pub with a separate, no-smoking restaurant. Guest beers. ♢ ▶ ✦ P

Wolverhampton

Clarendon
Chapel Ash (A41)
☎ (0902) 20587
11–11
Banks's Mild, Bitter E
Imposing, Victorian, multi-roomed brewery tap with a rare corridor bar. The quiet snug is open lunchtimes only; the public bar opens at 7pm. No food Sat or Sun. Q ♢ ✦ ♣ P

Combermere Arms
Chapel Ash (A41)
☎ (0902) 21880
11–2.30, 6–11
Draught Bass; Stones Best Bitter H
Pub cunningly disguised as a terraced house, with an interesting tree growing in the gents. Wheelchair access at the rear. ♨ ✦ ♣

Great Western
Sun Street (off A4124)
☎ (0902) 351090
11–11 (11–2.30, 5.15–11 Sat; 12–2.30, 7–10.30 Sun)
Batham Best Bitter; Holden's Stout, Mild, Bitter, Special, XL H
Revitalised pub next to an old, low-level station; railway memorabilia. Excellent value

Black Country food. Eve meals for parties with advance notice. Pleasant garden and patio area. ♨ ♨ ♢ ⇌ ♡ P

Homestead
Lodge Road, Oxley (off A449)
☎ (0902) 787357
11.30–3, 6–11
Ansells Mild, Bitter; Ind Coope Burton Ale; Marston's Pedigree H
Large, pleasant, suburban pub with an excellent children's playground. Plush lounge and a basic bar. ♨ ♢ ▶ ✦ ♣ P

Lewisham Arms
Prosser Street, Park Village (off A460) ☎ (0902) 53505
11.30–3, 6–11 (11–11 Sat)
Banks's Mild, Bitter E
Gloriously unspoilt, Victorian ale house. ✦ ♣

Mitre
Lower Green, Tettenhall (off A41) ☎ (0902) 753487
12–3, 6 (7 Sat)–11
Draught Bass; Stones Best Bitter E
Pleasant, old pub by the village green, with various rooms. No food Sun. Weston's Special Vintage cider. ♨ ♢ ✦ ♣ ♡

Newhampton Inn
Riches Street, Whitmore Reans (off A41) ☎ (0902) 745773
11–11
Courage Best Bitter, Directors; John Smith's Bitter H
Busy, street-corner local attracting a cosmopolitan clientele to its three, distinctly different rooms. Large beer garden next to the bowling green. Regular live music. Barbecue summer weekends. The smoke room is quiet. Guest beer (changes daily). ♨ Q ♨ ✦ ♣

Old Ash Tree
Dudley Road (A459)
☎ (0902) 342218
11–11
Banks's Mild, Bitter E
Cosy, locals' pub with a surprisingly large garden and a floodlit bowling green at the rear. ♨ ✦ ♣ P

Posada
Lichfield Street (opp. art gallery)
☎ (0902) 710738
11–2.30, 5–10.30 (11–10.30 Fri & Sat)
HP&D Mild, Bitter, Entire H, **Deakin's Downfall** G
Town-centre, Victorian pub with a tiled frontage. Lively, and popular with students, but usually closes when Wolves are at home. No food at weekends. ♢ ⇌ ♣

Queens Arms
13 Graiseley Row (off A449, Penn Road) ☎ (0902) 26589

12–3, 5 (8 Sat)–11 (12–3, 8–10.30 Sun)
Ansells Mild, Bitter; Ind Coope Burton Ale H
Small, one-room pub which had its own brewery until the 1960s. No food Sun.
♨ ♢ ✦ ♣ P

Royal Oak
School Road, Tettenhall Wood, (½ mile uphill from Compton roundabout)
☎ (0902) 754396
11–3 (4 Sat), 6–11
Banks's Mild; M&B Brew XI, Springfield Bitter E
A rare outlet for Brew XI in a village pub absorbed by suburban Wolverhampton. Multi-roomed, with a large games/children's room and an extensive garden at the rear.
♒ ♨ ✦ ♣

Stamford Arms
Lime Street, Penn Fields (off Lea Road) ☎ (0902) 24172
12–3, 6–11 (11–11 Sat)
Banks's Mild, Bitter E
Turn-of-the-century, multi-roomed pub with an upstairs function room. Q ♨ ✦ ♣

Yew Tree
44 Pool Street (5 mins' walk from ring road)
☎ (0902) 21195
11–2.30 (4 Sat), 5.30 (8 Sat)–11 (11–11 Fri; 12–3, 8–10.30 Sun)
Banks's Mild; M&B Highgate Mild, Springfield Bitter E
Friendly, Victorian pub in an industrial area. Opens at 8.30am for breakfasts. ♒ ♢ ♣

Try also: **Brewery Tap**, Dudley Rd (HP&D); **Halfway House**, Tettenhall Rd (M&B); **Swan**, Compton (Banks's)

Woodsetton

Park Inn
George Street (just off A457/A4123)
☎ (0902) 882843
12–2.30 (6 Sat), 6 (7 Sat)–11
Holden's Mild, Bitter, Special H&E, **XL** H
Friendly and comfortable brewery tap with regular summer barbecues. Brewery visits can be arranged. No food Sun. ♨ ♨ ♢ ♿ ⇌ (Tipton/ Owen St) P

Wordsley

Samson & Lion
140 Brierley Hill Road (B4180, ½ mile from village centre)
☎ (0384) 77796
12–3, 6–11 (12–11 Fri & Sat)
Banks's Mild E; **Batham Best Bitter** H
Sympathetically restored, canalside hostelry still undergoing development. Facilities for boaters provided. Guest beers. ♨ ♨ ♢ ♿ ✦ ♣ P

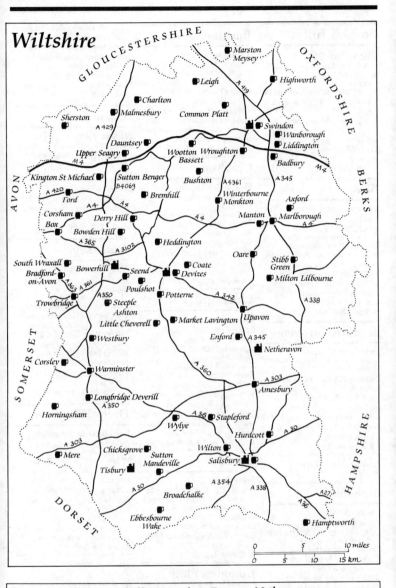

Wiltshire

Archers, Arkell's, Swindon; **Bunces**, Netheravon; **Gibbs Mew, Hop Back**, Salisbury; **Mole's**, Bowerhill; **Wadworth**, Devizes; **Wiltshire**, Tisbury

Amesbury

Antrobus Arms Hotel
15 Church Street
☎ (0980) 623163
10.30–2.30, 6–11
Draught Bass; Wadworth IPA, 6X Ⓗ
Georgian hotel with displays of coaching memorabilia. Pretty garden with cedars and a fountain. The nearest pub to Stonehenge (2 miles).
🛏 Q ❀ 🍴 ◑ ▸ P

Try also: **Kings Arms**, Church St (Courage)

Axford

Red Lion
☎ (0672) 20271
11–3, 6–11
Archers Village; Wadworth 6X Ⓗ
Flint-built, riverside pub with a low-ceilinged, pine-boarded bar. Guest beer. ❀ 🛏 ◑ ▸ ♣ P

Badbury

Bakers Arms
Off A345, near M4 jct 15
☎ (0793) 740313
11–2.30 (3 Fri & Sat), 6.30–11
Arkell's 2B, 3B Ⓗ
Small, neat pub tucked away in a side-lane. 🛏 ❀ ◑ ▸ ♣ P

Wiltshire

Bowden Hill

Rising Sun
(1 mile E of Lacock, uphill)
☎ (024 973) 363
12–3 (not Mon), 7–11
Mole's IPA, Bitter, Landlord's Choice, Brew 97; Wadworth 6X Ⓗ
Fine pub with outstanding views, good lunchtime meals and always a guest beer on tap. The landlord also owns Mole's brewery, so this is the brewery tap! ♨ Q ⊛ (⌾ P

Box

Quarrymans Arms
Box Hill OS834693
☎ (0225) 743569
11–3, 7–11 (may extend summer)
Draught Bass; Butcombe Bitter; Marston's Pedigree Ⓗ
Open-plan lounge area and small public bar in a pub with extensive views. Popular with locals and visitors, and busy in summer. Guest beer.
♨ ⊛ ⋈ ( ) ⊕ & ♣ P

Bradford-on-Avon

Bunch of Grapes
Silver Street ☎ (022 16) 3877
11–2.30, 6.30–11
Bateman XXXB; Smiles Best Bitter Ⓗ
Small, friendly, town pub with a cosy front lounge and a lively public, offering a wide range of guest beers. Excellent food; live jazz occasionally.
( ) ⊕ ≠ ♣ ⌾

Try also: Canal Tavern (Wadworth)

Bremhill

Dumb Post
Dumb Post Lane
OS975727 ☎ (0249) 813192
11.30–2.30 (not Wed), 7–11
Archers Best Bitter; Hall & Woodhouse Tanglefoot; Wadworth 6X Ⓗ
Good value free house with a pleasant view eastwards. Parrot in residence. ♨ ⊛ (⊕ P

Broadchalke

Queens Head
Off A354 via Coombe Bissett
☎ (0722) 780344
11–3, 7–11
Exmoor Ale; Ringwood Best Bitter; Ruddles Best Bitter; Wadworth 6X Ⓗ
15th-century pub in a quiet rural setting with exposed flint walls and a large inglenook. Formerly a bakehouse and stables on the Pembroke estate. Guest beers.
♨ Q ⌀ ⊛ ⋈ ( ) ▲ ♣ ⌾ P

Bushton

Trotting Horse
OS063778 ☎ (0793) 731338
11–2.30, 7–11
Ind Coope Burton Ale; Tetley Bitter; Wadworth 6X Ⓗ
Pub of character, full of nooks and crannies and with a huge malt whisky collection. Guest beers; food recommended (no-smoking dining room). Worth finding. ♨ ⊛ ⋈ ( ) & ♣ P

Charlton

Horse & Groom
On B4040 ☎ (0666) 823904
12–3, 7–11
Archers Village; Mole's Bitter; Wadworth 6X Ⓗ
Three hundred year-old country inn in traditional Cotswold stone, set well back from the road: small saloon, large public. Weekly guest beers and good restaurant. ♨ Q ⊛ ( ) ⊕ & P

Chicksgrove

Compasses Inn
Lower Chicksgrove (small winding lane 1 mile off A30 – signposted) ☎ (0722) 70318
12–3 (2.30 winter), 7–11
Adnams Bitter; Draught Bass; Wadworth 6X Ⓗ
16th-century picturesque inn with the bar in the cellar area of a cottage. Flagstone floor, low beams, large fire and interesting pub games. Children welcome. Idyllic setting. Guest beers.
♨ Q ⊛ ⋈ ( ) ▲ ♣ ⌾ P

Coate

New Inn
OS040616 ☎ (038 086) 644
12–2 (not Tue & Thu), 5 (6.30 Sat)–11
Wadworth IPA, 6X Ⓖ
Friendly, traditional pub. Landlord is a member of the Society for Preservation of Beer from the Wood (SPBW).
♨ Q ⋇ ⊛ ( ) & ♣ P

Common Platt

Foresters Arms
OS110868 ☎ (0793) 770615
11–2.30, 6–11
Courage Best Bitter, Directors; John Smith's Bitter Ⓗ
Friendly, traditional, locals' pub with a hunting theme in the public bar. Spacious lounge with a high, barn-style ceiling. Guest beer. ⊛ ( ) & ♣ P

Corsham

Two Pigs
38 Pickwick (A4, 80 yds NE of B3353 jct) ☎ (0249) 712515
12–3 (not Mon–Thu), 7–11
Beer range varies Ⓗ
Old pub for over-21s. An ale buff's utopia, with always three guest beers and a house beer from Bunces. Wooden clad walls; stone floor; friendly warm atmosphere. Blues background music. Live music Mon. ♨ ⊛ ⌾

Corsley

Cross Keys
Lye's Green (⅓ mile N of A362, near Longleat) OS821462
11.30–2.30 (not Mon & Tue; 12–3 Sat), 6.30–11
Draught Bass; Butcombe Bitter; Mole's Bitter Ⓗ
Welcoming and characterful pub with grand log fires in winter. No lunches Sun.
♨ ⊛ ( ) ⊕ ▲ ♣ ⌾ P

Dauntsey

Peterborough Arms
B4069, Chippenham Road, 2 miles W of Lyneham
11–3, 6–11 (closed Mon)
Ansells Bitter; Hook Norton Best Bitter, Old Hooky; Ind Coope Burton Ale; Tetley Bitter; Wadworth 6X Ⓗ
Welcoming, friendly pub serving meals in both bars. Large garden with children's play equipment; skittle alley. Guest beers.
♨ Q ⋇ ⊛ ( ) ⊕ ▲ ♣ P

Derry Hill

Lansdowne Arms Inn
On A342, 1 mile from A4
11–2.30, 6–11
Wadworth IPA, 6X, Farmer's Glory Ⓗ**, Old Timer** Ⓗ&Ⓖ
Comfortable, country pub with a large garden, children's playground and lovely view. Excellent restaurant and bar snacks of the same quality. Home of the formation drinking team. Cider in summer only.
♨ Q ⊛ ( ) ♣ ⌾ P

Try also: Soho Inn, Studley (A4)

Devizes

Cavalier
Eastleigh Road
☎ (0380) 723285
11–3, 7 (6 Sat)–11
Wadworth IPA, 6X Ⓗ
Basic, 1960s, two-bar estate pub, with a new skittle alley-cum-function room. ⊛ ( ) ⊕ ♣ P

Hare & Hounds
Hare & Hounds Street
11–2.30, 7–11
Wadworth IPA, 6X Ⓗ
Friendly, tucked-away pub with a relaxed atmosphere. Mainly used by locals. No food Sun.
⊛ (♣ P

Ebbesbourne Wake

Horseshoe Inn
OS242993 ☎ (0721) 780474
11.30 (12 Mon)–2.30, 6.30 (7 Mon)–11
Adnams Bitter; Ringwood Best Bitter (summer), XXXX Porter; Wadworth 6X G
Remote, 18th-century inn at the foot of an old ox drove. Formerly hatch-door service; now converted into two small bars with a fine display of working tools. Most ales are served from wooden casks. Guest beers. No food Mon eve.
🏠 Q 🍴 ⚬ ( ) ⊟ ♣ ⌂ P

Enford

Swan
Longstreet ☎ (0980) 70338
11.30 (12 winter)–2.30, 6.30 (7 winter)–11 (11–6, 7–11 Sat)
Hop Back Special H
Cosy, unspoilt, thatched free house with an unusual gantry sign straddling the road. Good value for money. Children welcome in the small bar at lunchtimes. Usually two guest beers. 🏠 ⚬ ( ) ♣ ⌂ P

Ford

White Hart
Off A420 ☎ (0249) 782213
11–3, 6–11 (11–11 Sat)
Fuller's London Pride, ESB; Hall & Woodhouse Badger Best Bitter, Tanglefoot; Marston's Pedigree; Wadworth 6X H
Excellent pub which regularly has ten ales on sale. A trout stream runs beside the beer garden. 🏠 Q 🍴 ⚬ ( ) ⌂ P

Hamptworth

Cuckoo
Hamptworth Road (off B3079)
OS243197 ☎ (0794) 390302
11–2.30, 6–11 (11–11 Sat)
Draught Bass; Bunces Best Bitter; Hall & Woodhouse Badger Best Bitter, Tanglefoot; Wadworth IPA, 6X G
Popular, basic pub in a quiet rural setting on the edge of the New Forest. Three small, interlinked rooms of public bar standard maintain a nice, cosy atmosphere. Very good garden.
🏠 Q 🐟 🍴 ⚬ ⌂ P

Heddington

Ivy Inn
Off A3102 ☎ (0380) 850276
11–3.30, 6.30–11
Wadworth IPA, 6X, Old Timer G
Idyllic, thatched, country pub.
🏠 Q 🐟 ⚬ ♣ ⌂ P

Highworth

Saracens Head
Market Place ☎ (0793) 762284
11–11 (11–2.30, 6–11 Sat)
Arkell's 2B, 3B, Mash Tun Mild H
Busy, smart (no T-shirts), beamed and oak-panelled bar of character in a typical market-town hotel. Q 🍴 ⚬ ( ) P

Try also: Globe (Courage)

Horningsham

Bath Arms Hotel
Off B3092 OS809416
11–11 (12–2.30, 7–10.30 Sun)
Draught Bass; Eldridge Pope Dorchester; Wadworth 6X H
Fine, country hotel in an idyllic setting on the edge of Longleat Park. Guest beer and 50 malt whiskies on sale.
🏠 Q 🍴 ⚬ ( ) ⊟ ♣ ⌂ P

Hurdcott

Black Horse
Black Horse Lane (off A338)
11–2.30, 6–11
Gibbs Mew Wiltshire, Salisbury H
Old building at the end of a country lane, formerly three cottages and a forge. Wattle and daub upstairs; beamed bar below. Jovial company. Eve meals Wed–Sat. 🍴 ⚬ ( ) 🐾 ♣ P

Kington St Michael

Jolly Huntsman
☎ (0249) 75305
11.30–2.30, 6.30–11
Draught Bass; Hall & Woodhouse Tanglefoot; Marston's Pedigree; Tetley Bitter; Wadworth 6X H
Roomy, one-bar, village-centre pub with a dining area serving a good range of meals.
🏠 🍴 ⚬ ( ) ⌂ P

Leigh

Foresters Arms
Malmesbury Road (B4040)
☎ (0793) 750901
12–2.30 (not Mon–Fri), 7–11
Wadworth 6X G
Intimate bar with a tiled floor. C&W music Wed. Guest beer.
🏠 🍴 ⚬ ( ) 🐾 ♣ P

Liddington

Village Inn
Off B4192 ☎ (0793) 790314
12–2.30, 6–11
Fuller's ESB; Marston's Pedigree; Wadworth 6X; Whitbread Flowers IPA, Original H
Cosy, carpeted, split-level lounge bar with red-brick facings and fireplace. Guest beer. Eve meals Tue–Sat.
🏠 Q 🍴 ⚬ ( ) P

Little Cheverell

Owl
Low Road (off B3098)
12–2.30, 6.30 (7 Sat & winter)–11
Wadworth IPA, 6X H
One-bar local with a separate dining area (no food Mon). Pleasant, steep-sloping, wooded garden with a stream. Regular guest beer. 🏠 🍴 ⚬ ( ) ♣ P

Longbridge Deverill

George
At A350/B3095 jct
10.30–2.30, 6–11 (12–2.30, 7–10.30 Sun in winter)
Gale's Best Bitter, HSB H
18th-century, traditional pub with a riverside garden. Three separate bars cater for both the local and heavy summer trades.
🏠 Q 🍴 ⚬ ( ) ⊟ ♣ ⌂ P

Malmesbury

Red Bull
Sherston Road (B4040, 1 mile W of town) ☎ (0666) 822108
11–2.30, 6–11
Archers Best Bitter; Draught Bass; Whitbread WCPA, Boddingtons Bitter H
Country pub, ideally suited to families. Now in the fourth generation of family ownership.
🏠 Q 🐾 🍴 ⚬ ( ) ⊟ ♣ P

Manton

Up The Garden Path
High Street ☎ (0672) 512677
11.30–2.30, 6.30–11
Archers Best Bitter; Hook Norton Best Bitter; Wadworth 6X H
Pub at the top of a steep path, with cosy corners in a carpeted bar. No meals Mon eve.
🏠 🍴 ⚬ ( ) ♣ P

Market Lavington

Drummer Boy
25 Church Street (B3098)
12–2.30, 6.30–11
Wadworth IPA, 6X H
Popular, locals' pub. See the back of the menu for the history of its name. Guest beer.
🏠 🍴 ⚬ ( ) ⌂ ♣ P

Marlborough

Green Dragon
High Street ☎ (0672) 512366
11–2.30, 7–11
Wadworth IPA, 6X H
Ancient building with a busy bar and rooms below: bare brick walls and pottery. Popular with younger people in the eve. No eve meals Sun. 🍴 ⚬ ( ) ♣

Wiltshire

Marston Meysey

Spotted Cow
2½ miles from A419/A417
☎ (0285) 810264
11–3, 6–11
**Eldridge Pope Royal Oak;
Wadworth 6X; Whitbread
Boddingtons Bitter** ℍ
Hospitable, farmhouse-style,
Cotswold-stone pub. Guest
beer. ♨ ⚄ ⦿ ◖ Å ♣ P

Mere

Butt of Sherry
Castle Street (B3095)
☎ (0747) 860352
11.30–2.30, 5–11 (11–3, 6–11 Sat)
**Gibbs Mew Wiltshire,
Premium, Bishop's Tipple** ℍ
Traditional pub with a lively
local trade. Unusual collection
of cameras. Pot-bellied, cast iron
stove in the lounge area.
♨ ⦿ ⋈ ◖ ◗ ♣

Milton Lilbourne

Three Horseshoes
On B3087 ☎ (0672) 62323
11–3, 6.30–11
**Adnams Bitter; Wadworth
6X** ℍ
Smart, open-plan bar featuring a
30ft-deep well. Guest beer. No
food Mon; no-smoking
restaurant. ♨ ⚄ ⦿ ◖ Å ♣ P

Oare

White Hart
On A345 ☎ (0672) 62273
11–2.30 (3 Sat), 6.30 (7 Sat)–11
Wadworth IPA, 6X ℍ
Genuine, unspoilt, village
roadside local. No food Mon
lunch or Sun eve.
♨ ⦿ ◖ ◗ ⊟ ♣ P

Potterne

George & Dragon
High Street ☎ (0380) 722139
12–2.30, 6–11 (12–2, 7–10.30 Sun)
Wadworth IPA, 6X ℍ
Coaching inn with Civil War
connections, built by the Bishop
of Salisbury, c. 1500. An
agricultural museum and a
licensed shooting gallery are
incorporated. Snuff for sale. No
food Mon. Q ⦿ ⋈ ◖ ◗ ♣ P

Poulshot

Raven
Poulshot Road (off A361)
☎ (0380) 828271
11–3, 6.30–11
**Wadworth IPA, 6X, Old
Timer** ℂ
Welcoming, village pub,
deservedly popular. Grade II
listed (early 1700s), with a
walled garden. The Wadworth
dray-horses holiday home is
nearby. ♨ ⦿ ◖ ◗ P

Salisbury

City Arms
Ox Row (Market Place)
☎ (0722) 329623
Draught Bass; Gale's HSB ℍ
18th-century, city-centre pub
with an oak-panelled bar and
pleasant, secluded alcoves. Busy
on market days. ♨ ◖ ◗ ♣ ♣

Haunch of Venison
Minister Street (opp. Poultry
Cross) ☎ (0722) 22024
11–11
**Courage Best Bitter,
Directors; Wadworth 6X** ℍ
Old-English chop house,
c. 1320; now a busy, city-
centre pub with many historic
and unusual features, incl. a
mummified hand, a pewter-
topped bar and rows of taps
formerly used to dispense
fortified wines and spirits. No
meals Sun eve. ♨ Q ◖ ◗ ⇒

Queens Arms
Ivy Street ☎ (0722) 334144
11–2.30, 5.30–11 (11–11 Sat)
**Ushers Best Bitter; Webster's
Yorkshire Bitter** ℍ
A Grade II listed building which
has held a licence since the 16th
century. One L-shaped lounge
bar, lively at weekends. Good
food. ♨ ⦿ ◖ ⇒

Red Lion Hotel
Milford Street ☎ (0722) 32224
11–2.30, 6–11
**Draught Bass; Ushers Best
Bitter; Wadworth 6X** ℍ
Old coaching inn, dating in part
from the 13th century. Its
clocks are world famous; the
case of the skeleton/organ clock
was reputedly carved by
prisoners captured from the
Spanish Armada. Guest beers.
♨ Q ⚄ ⦿ ⋈ ◖ ◗ ⇒ P

Village
33 Wilton Road (off St Pauls
roundabout) ☎ (0722) 329707
11–11 (11–3.30, 5.30–11 Mon–Wed in
winter)
**Ash Vine Bitter; Oakhill
Bitter, Yeoman; St Austell
XXXX Mild; Taylor
Landlord** ℍ
Convivial pub with a cosy cellar
bar featuring occasional live
music. Royal Wedding ale
collection. Popular with railway
enthusiasts: Class 33 loco'
horns in use. Guest beers. ⇒ ♣

Wyndham Arms
27 Estcourt Road (off Churchill
Way E ring road)
4.30 (4 Fri, 12 Sat)–11
**Hop Back GFB, Special,
Summer Lightning** ℍ
Wiltshire's only pub-brewery: a
pleasantly refurbished, Victorian
corner pub with one bar and
two adjoining rooms – Dennis

and Gnasher abound! Excellent
value. Jovial atmosphere.
Lunches Sat only. Q ◖ ♣

Try also: Oddfellows, Milford
St (Hall & Woodhouse)

Seend

Bell
Bell Hill ☎ (0380) 828338
11–3, 6–11 (11–11 Sat)
Wadworth IPA, 6X ℍ
Two rooms with a cosy lounge,
and an imposing, old brewhouse
outside. Very popular for its
home-cooked weekday lunches.
♨ Q ⚄ ⦿ ⊟ Å ♣ ◠ P

Sherston

Rattlebone Inn
Church Street
☎ (0666) 840871
12–2.30, 7–11 (12–11 Sat)
**Butcombe Bitter;
Moorhouse's Pendle Witches
Brew; Wadworth 6X** ℍ
Lively public bar with a range
of pub games; quieter lounge
and dining area. Good food.
Small garden with boules. Guest
beers. ♨ Q ⦿ ◖ ⊟ ⅋ ♣ P

South Wraxall

Longs Arms
Upper South Wraxall (off
B3109) ☎ (022 16) 4450
12 (11 Sat)–2.30, 5.30 (6.30 Sat)–11
Wadworth IPA, 6X ℍ
Relaxed, friendly, village pub
with a spacious, comfortable
lounge and a snug, locals' public
bar. Good food (no eve meals
Sun–Tue). Guest beers.
♨ Q ⦿ ◖ ⊟ ♣ ◠ P

Stapleford

Pelican Inn
Warminster Road (A36)
☎ (0722) 790241
11–3, 5.30–11 (11–11 Sat)
**Ringwood Best Bitter,
Fortyniner** ℍ
250 year-old coaching inn of
flint and stone. The restaurant
area is a former stables and
mortuary. Large garden at the
rear with swings. Children
welcome in the dining area.
Guest beers. ♨ ⦿ ◖ ⊟ ⅋ P

Steeple Ashton

Longs Arms
High Street ☎ (0380) 870245
11–2.30, 6–11 (12–2.30, 7–10.30 Sun)
**Gibbs Mew Wiltshire, Local
Line, Premium, Salisbury** ℍ
Quiet, old coaching inn in a
pretty village: once a
magistrates court. The lounge has
now been designated a
restaurant. Wheelchair access to
Ladies WC only.
♨ ⦿ ◖ ◗ ⊟ ⅋ ♣ ◠ P

Stibb Green

Three Horseshoes
On A346 ☎ (0672) 810324
11–3, 6–11
Wadworth IPA, 6X Ⓗ, Old Timer Ⓖ
Pretty, thatched pub with a cosy, beamed bar and a tiny, intimate lounge/diner (no food Sun eve). ▣ ▧ ⓘ ▸ ⊕ ♣ P

Sutton Benger

Wellesley Arms
High Street ☎ (0249) 720251
11–3, 6–11
Wadworth IPA, 6X, Old Timer Ⓗ
Welcoming, comfortable, roadside pub with Duke of Beaufort connections. Collection of Toby jugs. Genuine home-cooked food. Q ▣ ⓘ ▸ ⊕ ♣ ⚲ P

Sutton Mandeville

Lancers Inn
On A30 ☎ (072 270) 220
11–3, 6–11
Fuller's London Pride; Wadworth 6X Ⓗ
Large pub in quiet surroundings with a good view of the Fovant Badges on the nearby drove. One large bar; darts and pool table in a separate area. Skittle alley. Cider in summer. Good wholesome food. Guest beers.
▣ ▧ ▣ ⓘ ▸ ⚲ ♣ ○ P

Swindon

Beehive
Prospect Hill ☎ (0793) 523187
12–11
Morrells Dark, Varsity Ⓗ
Unusual, lively pub with a bar on five levels. Just behind the college. ▣ ⓘ ♣

Glue Pot
Emlyn Square ☎ (0793) 523935
11–11
Archers Village, Best Bitter, Golden Ⓗ
Imposing, listed, stone building in Brunel's Railway Village. One busy bar. Guest beer. No food Sun. ⓘ ▸ ♣

Wheatsheaf
Newport Street
☎ (0793) 523188
11–2.30, 5.30–11
Wadworth IPA, 6X, Farmer's Glory, Old Timer Ⓗ
Good, plain front bar with bare floorboards; mercifully sound-insulated from the decibel-loaded lounge. Guest beer. Q ▣ ▨ ⓘ ▸ ⊕

Trowbridge

Lamb Inn
Mortimer Street
11.30–2.30, 7–11 (11–11 Sat)

Wadworth IPA, 6X, Old Timer Ⓗ
A modern lounge and a contrasting public bar with multiple pool tables. Live music. ▣ Q ▧ ⓘ ⊕ ♣ P

Try also: Rose & Crown (Bass)

Upavon

Antelope
At A342/A345 jct
11–2.30, 6.30–11
Wadworth IPA, 6X, Old Timer Ⓗ
Smart, comfortable lounge bar with a cosy atmosphere. Separate games room. Family snug. ▣ ▧ ▧ ⓘ ▸ ♣ P

Upper Seagry

New Inn
Off A429
11–2.30, 6.30–11
Adnams Bitter; Draught Bass; Wadworth 6X Ⓗ
Quiet, village local: a large, long bar with two open fires.
▣ Q ▧ ⓘ ▸ ⚲ P

Wanborough

Black Horse
Bishopstone Road (former B4507) ☎ (0793) 790305
11–3, 5.30–11 (11–11 Sat)
Arkell's 2B, 3B, Mash Tun Mild Ⓗ, Kingsdown (winter) Ⓖ
The collection of personalised mugs testifies to the drinkers' loyalty to an unspoilt local. Garden, aviary, animals, games and a fine view. No food Sun.
▧ ⓘ ▸ ⚲ ♣ P

Warminster

Masons Arms
East Street ☎ (0985) 212894
11–2.30, 6–11 (10.30–3, 6.30–11 Sat)
Draught Bass; Welsh Brewers Worthington BB Ⓗ
Traditional, two-bar pub; one of a dying breed. No food Sun.
Q ▧ ⓘ ⊕ ♣ ○ P

Try also: Old Bell (Free)

Westbury

Oak Inn
Warminster Road (A350)
11–2.30, 6–11
Draught Bass; Welsh Brewers Worthington BB Ⓗ
A mock-Tudor exterior conceals a 16th-century, purpose-built inn with more recent additions. Guest beers.
▣ ▧ ⓘ ⊕ ♣ P

Try also: Crown (Wadworth); **Ludlow Arms** (Free)

Wilton

Bear Inn
West Street ☎ (0722) 742398
11–2.30, 5.30–11
Hall & Woodhouse Badger Best Bitter Ⓗ
Small, 16th-century pub with one public bar; quiet during the week but noisy and busy at weekends. ▣ ▧ ⓘ ♣

Winterbourne Monkton

New Inn
Off A4361 ☎ (067 23) 240
11–3, 6–11
Adnams Bitter; Wadworth 6X Ⓗ
Small, friendly local near Avebury stone circle. Guest beer. ▣ ▧ ⋈ ⓘ ♣ P

Wootton Bassett

Old Nick
Station Road ☎ (0793) 848102
11–2.30, 6–11 (11–11 Fri & Sat)
Gibbs Mew Bishop's Tipple; Ind Coope Burton Ale; Tetley Bitter; Wadworth 6X Ⓗ
Formerly the police station, now an extensive bar. The adjoining courthouse is a disco bar with a pool table. Live music Wed. Guest beers. ▣ ▧ ⓘ ▸ ○ P

Wroughton

Fox & Hounds
Markham Road
11–3, 5.30–11
Arkell's 2B, 3B, Mash Tun Mild, Kingsdown Ⓗ
Neat, single-bar motel.
▣ ▧ ⋈ ⓘ ▸ ♣ P

Wylye

Bell
High Street ☎ (098 56) 338
11 (11.30 winter)–2.30, 6–11
Gibbs Mew Local Line; Hall & Woodhouse Badger Best Bitter; Wadworth 6X Ⓗ
14th-century inn in a peaceful setting. The Wily Association vigilante group was formed here in 1798 and operated for 70 years. Regular guest beers.
▣ ▧ ⋈ ⓘ ▸ ⚲ ♣ P

ONLY A REAL COAL FIRE WILL DO.

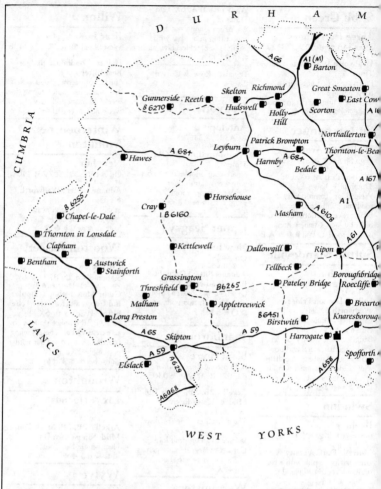

North Yorkshire

Big End, Harrogate; **Cropton**, Cropton;
Franklin's, Bilton; **Malton**, Malton; **Marston
Moor**, Kirk Hammerton; **Selby**, Selby; **Samuel
Smith**, Tadcaster; **Whitby's**, Whitby

Acaster Malbis

Ship Inn
At foot of Acaster Lane, SW of
Bishopthorpe OS591455
☎ (0904) 705609
11.30–5, 7–11
**Taylor Landlord; Tetley Mild,
Bitter** Ⓗ
18th-century pub, tastefully
extended, on the riverside at the
village centre. Popular with
boaters and campers.
🏠 🍴 ⚓ ( ) 🅰 P

Try also: **Sun Inn**, Colton

Allerston

Cayley Arms
On A170
☎ (0723) 859338
12–2.30, 7–11
**Bass Special; Camerons
Bitter** Ⓗ

On the main road, yet in the
heart of the country, by Dalby
Forest with a trout stream
outside. Warm welcome.
🏠 ♿ 🍴 ⚓ ( ) ⚘ 🅰 ♣ P

Ampleforth

White Horse
West End (off B1363, 5 miles N
of Easingwold) ☎ (043 93) 378
11–2.30, 6–11
Tetley Bitter Ⓗ

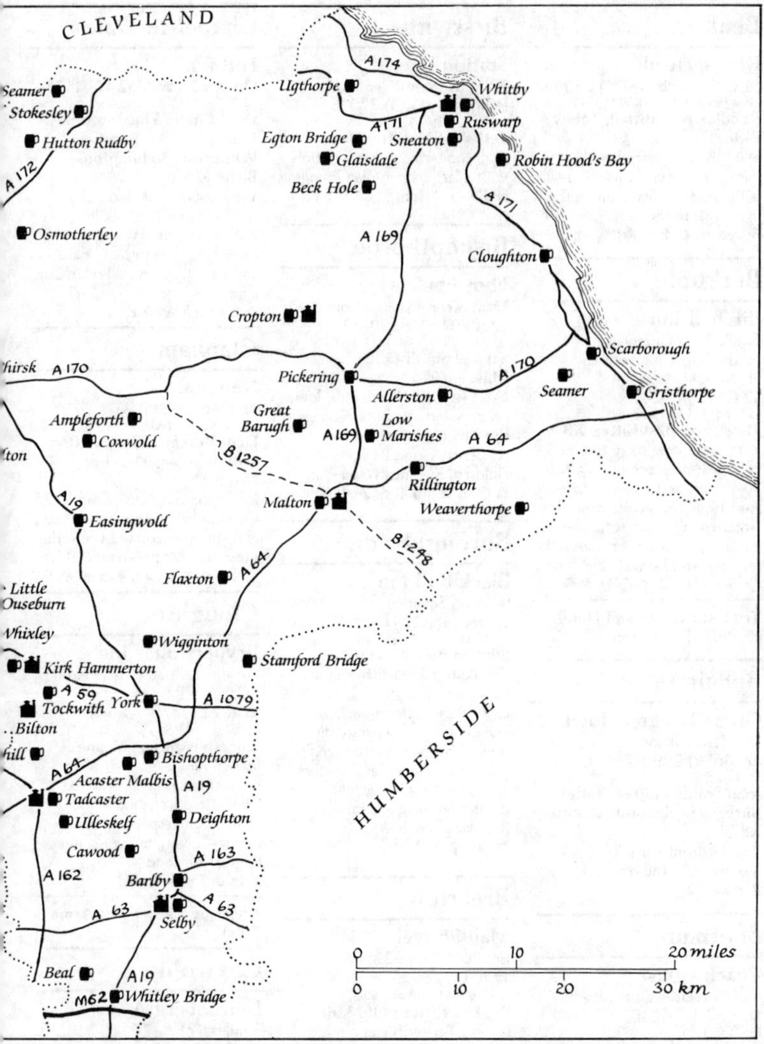

Deservedly popular and cosy, village pub. Comfortable, oak-beamed interior with settle seating. One main bar and a separate dining room.
⌂ ❀ ⊨ ☾ ◗ ♣ P

Appletreewick

New Inn
Main Street (back road, between Barden Tower and Burnsall) ☎ (075 672) 252
11.30–3 (not Mon in winter), 7–11
John Smith's Bitter; Younger Scotch, IPA Ⓗ
Welcoming and friendly pub where the emphasis is on drink rather than food. The bar is in an L-shaped room with another room across the hall. Gated beer garden over the road. Large range of foreign bottled beers. No. 3 may appear in place of IPA. ⌂ Q ⛽ ❀ ⊨ ☾ ⛺ ♣ ⌓ P

Austwick

Game Cock
On road to Horton
☎ (046 85) 226
Lunchtime varies, 6–11
Thwaites Bitter Ⓗ
Old-fashioned little bar, conservatory and restaurant. No food winter Mon.
⌂ ⛽ ❀ ⊨ ☾ ◗ ⊟ ♣ P

Barlby

Bay Horse Inn
York Road (off A19, 2 miles W of Selby) ☎ (0757) 703878
12–11
Courage Directors; John Smith's Bitter Ⓗ
Popular, village pub with open-plan bars. Successful darts team. Camping in an adjacent field. Meals until 7pm. ⛽ ☾ ⛺ ♣ P

Barton

King William IV
Silver Street ☎ (032 577) 256
11.30–3 (4 Sat), 7–11
John Smith's Bitter, Magnet Ⓗ
Roadside local with one main room and a couple of separate areas just off. Children welcome until 9pm. Excellent, screened garden with play equipment. No lunches Tue; eve meals summer only. ⌂ ❀ ☾ ◗ ♣ P

North Yorkshire

Beal

King's Head
Main Street ☎ (0977) 673487
12–3 (Fri & Sat only), 7–11
**Ruddles Best Bitter; Tetley
Bitter** Ⓗ
With its time-warp bar and
numerous rooms, this pub really
is the hub of village life in the
evenings. In the same family for
47 years. 🏚 ⊛ ♣ ♣ P

Beckhole

Birchall Inn
1 mile from Goathland;
footpath to Grosmont and
NYM railway
☎ (0947) 86245
11–11 (11–3, 7–11 winter)
Theakston Best Bitter, XB Ⓗ
Rural gem, originally two
cottages; now combines a pub,
post office and a general store.
Aquarium in a small, front bar;
larger room to the rear. The
garden is on a terrace above the
pub. Bar snacks available.
Quoits played. 🏚 Q ⊛ ♣

Try also: **Goathland Hotel**,
Goathland (Camerons)

Bedale

Green Dragon Hotel
16 Market Place
☎ (0677) 22902
11–11
**John Smith's Bitter; Tetley
Bitter; Theakston Best Bitter,
XB** Ⓗ
Popular front bar with a
restaurant to the rear.
🏚 ⊛ 🛏 ◖ ◗

Bentham

Coach House
Main Street, High Bentham
☎ (052 42) 62305
11–2.30, 7–11
**Hartleys XB; Robinson's Best
Bitter** Ⓗ
Pub where a fine, 17th-century
exterior overlooks a small
cobbled square with seats. The
1985 interior has a single large
bar, with the usual amenities,
and a restaurant to the rear.
🏚 ⊛ ◖ ◗ ≱ ♣ P

Punch Bowl
Low Bentham (B6480, road to
Wray) ☎ (052 42) 61344
11.30–2.30, 6–11
Mitchell's Best Bitter Ⓗ
18th-century, old-time, village
inn, extended in 1986 into a
barn to form a restaurant (open
weekends), but small, real
rooms remain. No food Mon.
Angling available.
🏚 Q ☕ ⊛ 🛏 ◖ ♣ P

Try also: **Sun Dial** (Thwaites)

Birstwith

Station Inn
500 yds from River Nidd
bridge ☎ (0423) 770254
11.30–3, 6.30–11
Tetley Mild, Bitter Ⓗ
Old, converted railway station
with a large, open-plan lounge
and a small snug. Q ⊛ ◖ ◗ P

Bishopthorpe

Ebor Inn
Main Street (3 miles from York)
☎ (0904) 706190
10.30–3.30, 6–11 (11–11 Sat)
**Samuel Smith OBB,
Museum** Ⓗ
Olde-worlde, village pub: low
ceilings and lots of brass; near
the Archbishop of York's
residence. Good facilities for
children. Eve meals Thu–Sat.
🏚 Q ☕ ⊛ ◖ ◗ 🛏 ☕ ♣ P

Boroughbridge

Black Bull Inn
St James Square
☎ (0423) 322413
11–11 (11–3, 7–11 winter)
**John Smith's Bitter;
Theakston Best Bitter** Ⓗ
Attractive, historic, 13th-
century pub offering a snug,
lounge, bar and separate dining
room. This quaint and friendly
pub attracts locals and visitors
alike and has an excellent
reputation for good food.
Regular guest beer.
🏚 🛏 ◖ ◗ ♿ ♣

Brearton

Malt Shovel
Off B6165 OS322608
☎ (0423) 862929
12–3, 6.45–11 (closed Mon)
**Big End Piston; Old Mill
Bitter; Tetley Bitter;
Theakston Best Bitter, XB** Ⓗ
16th-century pub with stone
walls and original oak beams.
Reputation for good food (not
served Mon). 🏚 Q ⊛ ◖ ◗ ♣ P

Cawood

Ferry Inn
King Street (off B1222)
☎ (0757) 268515
11–11
**Mansfield Riding Mild,
Riding Bitter, Old Baily;
Tetley Bitter; Webster's
Yorkshire Bitter; Younger
Scotch** Ⓗ
16th-century pub on the river
bank, with low ceilings and
original beams. Quiet and
friendly. Menu caters for
children and vegetarians.
🏚 Q ☕ ⊛ 🛏 ◖ ◗ ♣ ♣ P

Chapel-le-Dale

Hill Inn
On B6255 ☎ (052 42) 41256
12–3, 7–11 (11–11 Sat)
**Dent Bitter; Theakston Best
Bitter, XB, Old Peculier;
Whitbread Boddingtons
Bitter** Ⓗ
Well-known, isolated pub on
the Three Peaks Walk in
potholing country. Utility
furnishings; varnished boards
and bare stonework. Folk music
alternate Sats.
🏚 ⊛ 🛏 ◖ ♣ P

Clapham

New Inn
☎ (046 85) 203
11.30–3, 7–11 (supper licence)
**Dent Bitter; McEwan 80/-;
Tetley Bitter; Younger
No. 3** Ⓗ
Large coaching inn, dated 1776.
One bar has leather bench seats
and stucco-decorated walls, the
other has oak panelling (1990
vintage). 🏚 ⊛ 🛏 ◖ ◗ ♣ P

Cloughton

Bryherstones Inn
Newlands Road (1 mile N of
village on Ravenscar road)
☎ (0723) 870744
11.30–3, 7–11
**Camerons Bitter; Younger
Scotch No. 3** Ⓗ
Popular, country inn where
families are welcome in the
lower room, especially during
the day. Lively in the evenings.
Popular for food.
🏚 ☕ ⊛ ◖ ◗ 🛏 ♣ P

Try also: **Blacksmiths Arms**
(Bass)

Coxwold

Fauconberg Arms
3 miles S of A170
☎ (034 76) 214
11–3, 6–11
**Tetley Bitter; Theakston Best
Bitter; Younger Scotch** Ⓗ
In an idyllic setting, on the main
street of a lovely village; a
beautifully appointed, old inn
with a lounge bar, oak room
and restaurant. Generally busy,
but packed at mealtimes.
🏚 🛏 ◖ ◗ 🛏 ♣ P

Cray

White Lion
On B6160 N of Buckden
☎ (075 676) 262
11–11
**Moorhouse's Premier;
Younger Scotch** Ⓗ
Traditional Dales pub with
original beams and stone flags.
The adjoining barn has been
converted to pleasant, five-

bedroomed accommodation. Ideally situated for walkers, at the head of Wharfedale by Buckden Pike. Dogs welcome. Two other beers usually available.

🏚 ☎ 🍴 ⬅ ◖ ➤ Å ♣ P

Cropton

New Inn
Rosedale turn off A170 at Wrelton OS756890
☎ (075 15) 330
11–3, 5.30–11 (12–2.30, 7–11 winter)
Cropton Two Pints, Special Strong; Tetley Mild, Bitter Ⓗ
Brew pub producing distinctive beers using local malt and well water; a large lounge with a separate restaurant and pool room. Children are welcome in the large garden and well-equipped family room.
🏚 ☎ 🍴 ◖ ➤ Å ♣ P

Dallowgill

Drovers
On the moor road between Pateley Bridge and Kirby Malzeard
☎ (0765) 658510
12–2, 7–11 (closed Mon, except bank hols)
Old Mill Bitter; Younger Scotch Ⓗ
One-bar, stone-built, rural pub. Scrupulously clean and very welcoming.
🏚 Q ☎ 🍴 ◖ ➤ Å ♣ P

Dalton

Jolly Farmers of Olden Times
Between A19 and A1, just S of A168, near Thirsk OS431762
☎ (0845) 577359
12–2 (4 Sat, not Mon–Thu), 7.30–11
Ruddles Best Bitter; Webster's Yorkshire Bitter, Choice Ⓗ
200 year-old, beamed, village pub, tastefully modernised with a comfortable lounge area, quiet bar, games room and a small dining room (book, especially for bargain three-course Sun lunches). Regular guest beers. Note restricted lunchtime opening.
🏚 ☎ 🍴 ◖ ➤ ⬅ Å ♣ P

Deighton

White Swan Inn
On A19, 6 miles S of York
☎ (0904) 87287
11.30–2.30 (3 Sat), 7 (6.30 Sat)–11
Theakston XB, Old Pecurier; Younger Scotch, No. 3 Ⓗ
Roadside inn which is popular for meals. Separate bars but open-plan rooms.
Q ☎ ◖ ➤ ⬅ Å ♣ P

Easingwold

Station Hotel
Crankley Lane
☎ (0347) 22635
11 (3 winter)–11
Tetley Bitter; Whitbread Castle Eden Ale Ⓗ
Originally part of the Easingwold railway terminus, built in 1892. Alterations have retained the Victorian/Edwardian theme in a large, pleasant lounge bar and a separate pool room. ☎ ◖ ➤ ♣

East Cowton

Beeswing
☎ (0325) 378349
12–3 (not Mon), 7–11
Marston's Pedigree; Tetley Bitter Ⓗ
Modernised country eating house which retains a cosy, traditional bar. Named after the oldest horse ever to win the Ascot Gold Cup.
🏚 ⬅ ◖ ➤ ⬅ ♣ P

Egton Bridge

Postgate Inn
7½ miles W of Whitby, next to station OS805054
☎ (0947) 85241
11–11 (11–3, 7–11 winter)
Camerons Bitter, Strongarm; Everards Old Original (summer) Ⓗ
Attractive hotel, overlooking the rustic railway station. Quoits played. The menu caters for children and vegetarians.
🏚 Q ☎ ☎ ◖ ➤ ⬅ ⬅ ♣ P

Try also: Horseshoe Hotel (Free)

Elslack

Tempest Arms Hotel
50 yds off A56
☎ (0282) 842450
11.30–3, 6.30 (7 Sat)–11
Tetley Mild, Bitter; Thwaites Bitter; Younger Scotch Ⓗ
Friendly, cosily partitioned, one-roomed pub with a separate restaurant, decorated with small china frogs. Good-value food includes a vegetarian option and a range of fresh fish dishes.
🏚 ☎ ⬅ ◖ ➤ P

Fellbeck

Half Moon
On B6265 ☎ (0423) 711560
12–3, 6.30–11
Taylor Landlord; Theakston Best Bitter; Younger Scotch Ⓗ
Pleasant, roadside inn close to the local beauty spot of Brimham Rocks. Traditional bar and large, sunny lounge.
🏚 Q ☎ ☎ ◖ ➤ ⬅ ♣ ⬅ P

Flaxton

Blacksmiths Arms
Main Street ☎ (0904) 86210
12–3, 7–11 (12–11 Sat in summer)
Theakston Best Bitter, XB, Old Pecurier; Younger No. 3 Ⓗ
Superb, little, multi-roomed pub recently sold off by Bass, and opened as a free house. Creole-cookery a speciality. Guest beers in summer.
🏚 ☎ ☎ ⬅ ◖ ➤ ⬅ Å ♣ P

Glaisdale

Anglers Rest
Off A171, top of hill from station OS779053
☎ (0947) 87261
11–3 (may vary Sat & summer), 7 (6.30 Sat, 6 summer)–11
Tetley Bitter; Theakston Best Bitter, Old Pecurier Ⓗ
Very popular, old hilltop pub, formerly called the 'Three Blast Furnaces'. Popular with walkers and campers. Home-cooked food incl. vegetarian option; gourmet eves Fri and Sat. Children welcome. Live music.
🏚 ☎ ☎ ⬅ ◖ ➤ ⬅ Å ⬅ ♣ P

Grassington

Black Horse
Garrs Lane (off the square)
☎ (0756) 752770
11–3, 6.30–11
Ruddles Best Bitter; Tetley Mild, Bitter; Theakston Best Bitter, XB, Old Pecurier Ⓗ
Comfortable and welcoming, L-shaped hotel bar with a large fireplace. Dining room attached.
🏚 Q ☎ ☎ ◖ ➤ Å ♣

Great Barugh

Golden Lion
OS749790 ☎ (065 386) 242
12–2, 7–11 (12–2.30, 6.30–11 summer)
Malton Double Chance; Tetley Bitter Ⓗ
Pub dating from 1630, with Royalist connections during the Civil War. A cosy, country pub of character and charm, with a friendly atmosphere. Two rooms: one used for pool in winter and as a diner in summer. No meals Sun eve.
🏚 Q ☎ ◖ ➤ Å P

Great Smeaton

Bay Horse
On A167 ☎ (060 981) 466
12–3 (not Mon or Tue), 6.30–11
Courage Directors; John Smith's Bitter Ⓗ
Small free house in the middle of a row of roadside cottages. Lounge to one side, bar to the other; neat rear garden. Guest beers. 🏚 ☎ ◖ ➤ ⬅ ♣

North Yorkshire

Gristhorpe

Bull Inn
Off A165 ☎ (0723) 512359
11.30–4, 7–11
Younger Scotch, IPA, No. 3 Ⓗ
Enlarged, old, village local specialising in home-cooking. Children, five years and over, welcome for meals.
🏠 🅰 🅹 🅳 🌟 🅰 ♣ P

Try also: **Foords Hotel**, Filey (Camerons)

Gunnerside

Kings Head
On B6270, 5 miles W of Reeth
☎ (0748) 86261
11.30–3, 6.30–11
Theakston Best Bitter, XB (summer), **Old Peculier** (summer) Ⓗ
A pub retaining much stonework, incl. floors, fireplace and mantelpiece. Small, homely bar. Snacks lunchtime and eve. The king in question is Gunnar, an ancient Norse chieftain.
🏠 Q 🌟 🅰

Harmby

Pheasant
On A684, 1 mile E of Leyburn
☎ (0969) 22223
12–6 (not winter), 8–11
Tetley Bitter Ⓗ
Popular, rural inn at the gateway to Wensleydale. Note restricted winter opening.
🏠 Q 🅰 🅱 🅰 P

Harrogate

Coach & Horses
16 West Park (A61)
☎ (0423) 568371
11–11
John Smith's Bitter Ⓗ
Welcoming pub within walking distance of the town centre, commanding excellent views over the Stray. No lunches Sun.
Q 🅹 🅰 🅴 ♣ P

Dragon
Skipton Road (A59, 1½ miles from centre) ☎ (0423) 503405
11–11
John Smith's Bitter, Magnet Ⓗ
Very popular, large, corner local with a roomy lounge and conservatory, plus a small, wood-panelled snug.
Q 🌟 🅱 🅹 🅴 🅴 ♣ P

Hales Bar
1 Crescent Road
☎ (0423) 569861
11–11
Draught Bass; Stones Best Bitter Ⓗ
A gem in the true sense of the word: a gas-lit lounge with

unusual, gas cigar lighters. Old barrels and stuffed birds add to the atmosphere. Q 🅹 🅴

Muckles
11 West Park (A61)
☎ (0423) 504463
11–3, 5–11 (11–11 Sat)
Tetley Bitter Ⓗ
Busy pub within walking distance of the town centre and overlooking the Stray. 🅹 ♣ P

Tap & Spile
31 Town Street (off West Park Stray) ☎ (0423) 526785
11–11
Camerons Strongarm Ⓗ
Traditionally furnished pub: three rooms with exposed brick and stonework and wooden floors. Up to ten constantly-changing guest beers make it a mecca for real ale drinkers. Note: no wheelchair access to the ladies' WC. Next to a municipal car park.
🏠 🅹 🅴 ♣ ♣

Woodlands
Wetherby Road (A59, 1½ miles from centre)
11.30–3, 5.30–11
Ruddles Best Bitter; Webster's Yorkshire Bitter, Choice Ⓗ
Spacious, open-plan bar and conservatory with an unusual ceiling. Next to the Yorkshire Showground. Q 🌟 🅹 🅴 🅴 ♣ P

Hawes

Crown Hotel
Market Place (A684)
☎ (0969) 667212
11–11
Theakston Best Bitter, XB, Old Peculier Ⓗ
Early 19th-century hotel with two rooms: a simple wood-furnished bar and a modernised lounge. 🏠 🅰 🅹 🅳

Holly Hill

Holly Hill Inn
Top of Sleagill OS172003
☎ (0748) 822192
12–2.30, 4.30–11 (12–11 Sat & bank hols)
Theakston Best Bitter, XB, Old Peculier; Younger Scotch Ⓗ
Pub with a great enthusiasm for traditional beer and a continuous guest beer policy.
Q 🅰 🅹 🅴 ♣ ♣

Horsehouse

Thwaite Arms
8 miles SW of Leyburn
OS047812 ☎ (0969) 40206
12–3 (not winter), 7–11
Theakston Best Bitter, Old Peculier (summer) Ⓗ
Built in 1808, this is the most remote real ale pub in the Dales.

Stone-flagged floors, cushioned church pew seating and a piano – it has the lot. Note restricted winter opening. 🏠 🐱 🅰 🅿

Hudswell

George & Dragon
2 miles SW of Richmond
☎ (0748) 823082
12–2 (not Mon), 7–11
Ruddles Best Bitter (summer); **Webster's Yorkshire Bitter, Choice** Ⓗ
Well worth seeking out: a locals' bar on the right, with another, small room on the left. Fine views to the rear.
🏠 Q 🌟 🅰 🅹 🅳 🅴 🅰 ♣ P

Hutton Rudby

King's Head
36 North Side
☎ (0642) 700342
12–3 (Sat only), 6.30–11 (12–2, 7–10.30 Sun)
Camerons Bitter, Strongarm Ⓗ
Warm and cosy, village pub with a beamed ceiling. Popular in the evenings. 🏠 Q 🌟 🅴 ♣

Kettlewell

Kings Head
☎ (075 676) 242
11.30–3 (may extend summer), 6–11 (11.30–11 Sat)
Taylor Landlord; Tetley Mild (summer), **Bitter** Ⓗ
Friendly, three-storey pub frequented by locals and hikers. Still retains a traditional atmosphere, with an inglenook and bench seating, despite its opened-out interior.
🏠 Q 🌟 🅰 🅹 🅳 🅰 ♣ P

Kirk Hammerton

Crown Inn
Station Road (100 yds from A59, York–Harrogate road)
OS472559 ☎ (0423) 330341
11.30–3 (not Mon–Fri), 7–11
Marston Moor Cromwell, Brewers Pride Ⓗ
Old, village pub much used by visiting anglers. The home of Marston Moor brewery. Eve meals Sat and Sun only.
🏠 Q 🅰 🅹 🅴 ♣ P

Knaresborough

Groves
Market Place
☎ (0423) 863022
11–11
Theakston Best Bitter; Younger Scotch, No. 3 Ⓗ
Popular pub in the corner of the historic market place; a deserved entry in all previous *Good Beer Guides*. Q 🅹 🅴 ♣ ♣

316

Marquis of Granby

31 York Place (A59 to York)
☎ (0423) 862207
11–3, 6–11
Samuel Smith OBB Ⓗ
Recently refurbished pub in
Victorian style, close to the
newly-opened swimming pool.
Municipal car park adjacent.
🏠 Q ⊕ ⅄

Old Royal Oak

7 Market Place
☎ (0423) 863139
11 (10 Wed)–11
**Courage Directors; John
Smith's Bitter** Ⓗ
Prominently situated pub with
twin, lounge-style bars.
Excellent value Sun lunches.
Beware – landlord operates a
charity swear box! Small
outdoor drinking area.
🍴 ⊠ ◖ ⅀ ♣

Leyburn

Golden Lion

Market Place ☎ (0969) 22161
11.30–3, 6.30–11
Theakston Best Bitter, XB Ⓗ
Comfortable hotel with bay
windows fronting the market
place. One, pleasant bar with a
panelled dining area (where
children are admitted).
🏠 🍴 ⊠ ◖ ▮ P

Little Ouseburn

Green Tree Inn

On B6265 ☎ (0423) 330930
11.30–3, 6–11 (11–11 Sat)
**John Smith's Bitter; Taylor
Landlord** Ⓗ
Roadside, country pub with
wood panelling and a friendly,
local atmosphere. Well-behaved
children welcome. One bar with
a dining area adjoining. One
guest beer. No meals Tue eve or
winter Mon lunchtimes.
🏠 🍴 ◖ ▮ ♣ P

Long Preston

Maypole

On A65 ☎ (072 94) 219
11–3, 6 (5.30 Sat)–11
Marston's Pedigree (summer);
**Taylor Best Bitter; Whitbread
Castle Eden Ale** Ⓗ
Comfortable, village local with
lounge and public bars. Recently
refurbished but retaining a
traditional feel. Meals include
a vegetarian option and are
usually served in the dining
room (where children are
welcome). 🏠 🍴 ⊠ ◖ ▮ ⊕ ⤚ ♣ P

Low Marishes

School House Inn

3 miles N of A64/A169 jct
☎ (0653) 86247
11–3 (may extend), 6.30–11 (supper
licence)

Malton Double Chance;
Marston's Pedigree; Tetley
Bitter Ⓗ

Tidy pub with good food and
excellent facilities for all the
family, both inside and out.
Guest beers. Ukers, a violent
form of ludo, is a local favourite.
🏠 ⊠ 🍴 ◖ ▮ ⊕ ⅄ ♣ P

Malham

Listers Arms

☎ (072 93) 330
12–3 (2 winter; not Tue), 7–11
**Ind Coope Burton Ale;
Younger Scotch** Ⓗ
Large, stone-built pub just over
the bridge on the way to
Goredale Scar. Three separate
drinking areas, plus a sizeable
dining room. Usually two guest
beers. Note: closed Tue
lunchtime. 🏠 ⊠ 🍴 ◖ ▮ ⅄ ♣ ⊖ P

Malton

Blue Bell

14 Newbiggin
☎ (0653) 692236
11–2.30, 5.30–11 (11–11 Tue, Fri &
Sat)
**Draught Bass; Stones Best
Bitter; Tetley Bitter** Ⓗ
Multi-roomed symphony in
brown featuring good food
(vegetarian option), guest beers
and a worldwide range of 180
bottled beers. Q 🍴 ◖ ▮ ⤚ P

Crown Hotel
(Suddaby's)

Wheelgate ☎ (0653) 692038
11–3 (4 Sat), 5.30–11 (11–11 Fri)
**Malton Pale Ale, Double
Chance, Pickwick's Porter,
Owd Bob; John Smith's
Bitter** Ⓗ
Neat hotel offering a full range
of local beers. The functional
bar is complemented by a
conservatory-style extension,
where children are welcome.
Guest beers. The menu includes
three vegetarian options, but
eve meals are only for residents.
🏠 Q ⊠ 🍴 ◖ ⅀ ♣ P

Try also: Spotted Cow
(Tetley)

Masham

Bay Horse

Silver Street ☎ (0765) 89236
11–11
**John Smith's Bitter; Tetley
Bitter; Theakston Best Bitter,
XB** Ⓗ
Typical market town pub with a
public bar and a comfortable
lounge. 🏠 🍴 ◖ ▮ ⊕ ♣ ⊖

Northallerton

Golden Lion Hotel

112 High Street (A167)
☎ (0609) 777411
10.30–2.30 (5 Wed), 6–11

Tetley Bitter Ⓗ

Historic posting house, now a
THF hotel, with real ale
available in the plush
Coachman's Bar. Occasional live
music. 🏠 ⊠ 🍴 ◖ ▮ P

Osmotherley

Golden Lion

6 West End ☎ (060 983) 526
11–3, 6–11
**Courage Directors; John
Smith's Bitter, Magnet** Ⓗ
Attractive, old pub in the centre
of the village. Strong emphasis
on food. Candles and fresh
flowers make for a cosy and
welcoming interior. Children
welcome at lunchtime.
🏠 ⊠ 🍴 ◖ ▮ ⅄ ♣ P

Pateley Bridge

Crown Hotel

High Street ☎ (0423) 711348
11.30–3, 6 (7 winter)–11 (11–11 Sat)
John Smith's Bitter Ⓗ
Small, popular hotel on the main
street of a beautiful Nidderdale
market town. Open-plan lounge
with an adjoining restaurant.
🏠 ⊠ 🍴 ◖ ▮ ⅄ ♣

Patrick Brompton

Green Tree

On A684 ☎ (0677) 50262
12–2, 6–11
**Ind Coope Burton Ale; Tetley
Bitter; Theakston Best Bitter,
XB** or **Old Peculier** Ⓗ
Traditional, country two-roomer
with the bar reserved for darts
and good conversation.
Separate dining room.
🏠 ⊠ 🍴 ◖ ▮ ⊕ P

Pickering

Station Hotel

Park Street (opp. station)
☎ (0751) 72171
11 (12 winter)–4, 6–11
Younger Scotch, IPA Ⓗ
Popular, two-roomed pub: a
games-oriented bar and a
comfortable lounge,
complemented by a restaurant
where children are welcome.
Limited parking.
🏠 🍴 ◖ ▮ ⊕ ⤚ (NYM) ♣ P

Try also: Black Bull (Free);
Black Swan (John Smith's)

Reeth

Kings Arms

On B6270 ☎ (0748) 84259
11–4, 6–11 (11–11 Sat)
**Theakston Best Bitter, XB,
Old Peculier** Ⓗ
On an excellent, village green
site, the 'Middle House' (as
it is known locally), has a
welcoming, comfortable interior.
🏠 ⊠ 🍴 ◖ ▮

North Yorkshire

Richmond

Oak Tree
Budge Street
☎ (0748) 822363
11.30–3, 7.30–11
**John Smith's Bitter,
Magnet** H
The quaintest pub in town, with
low beams, wood panelling and
an open fire. Sometimes offers
music. 🏚 🍽 ♣

Rillington

Coach & Horses
Low Moorgate
☎ (094 42) 373
11–3, 6–11
**McEwan 80/-; Younger
Scotch** H
Popular pub situated
prominently on the A64 and
offering good food. Cat-
bedecked, multi-roomed interior.
Children very welcome in the
restaurant and garden.
🏚 🍽 ◑ ▶ 🍽 ♣ P

Ripon

Golden Lion
69–70 Allhallowgate
☎ (0765) 602598
11–3, 7–11 (11–11 Sat)
**Marston Moor Cromwell;
John Smith's Bitter;
Theakston Best Bitter** H
16th-century town pub: a
lounge bar, pool room, and a
dining room. One regular guest
beer (changes monthly).
🍽 🍽 ◑ ▶

One Eyed Rat
Allhallowgate
☎ (0765) 707704
12–3, 5.30–11
**Big End Piston; Marston's
Pedigree; Taylor Landlord** H
Small, terraced pub with a large
garden. Very popular with
students. Four guest beers are
changed regularly. Bar billiards
table. 🏚 🍽 ♣ ⊘

Station
North Road ☎ (0765) 602140
11–11
Tetley Mild, Bitter H
Large, three-roomed pub with
traditional decor and a friendly
atmosphere.
Q 🍽 🍽 ◑ ▶ 🍽 🍽 ♣ P

Robin Hood's Bay

Dolphin Hotel
King Street (50 yds from dock
area) ☎ (0947) 880337
12–3, 7–11 (11–11 Sat & summer)
**Courage Directors; John
Smith's Bitter, Magnet** H
Grade II, rambling, old pub.
Pool and family rooms are
connected by many stairs (the
pub is on three levels). The

menu specialises in locally-
caught seafood (eg shark).
🏚 🍽 🍽 ◑ ▶ 🍽 ♣

Laurel Inn
☎ (0947) 880400
11.30 (12 winter)–3 (may vary), 7
(7.30 winter)–11
**Old Mill Bitter; John Smith's
Bitter; Tetley Bitter;
Theakston XB** H
Small, friendly local in a
picturesque, cliffside village.
Guest beers available, but not
usually in the holiday season.
The landlord plans to start
brewing. 🏚 Q 🍽 🍽 ♣

Roecliffe

Crown Inn
On main street, opp. village
green ☎ (0423) 322578
11.30–3, 6–11
**Tetley Bitter; Theakston Best
Bitter** H
Multi-roomed pub, run by the
same family for 30 years. A
friendly local, with a plush
lounge and wooden beams.
Children welcome. Coach house
available for functions.
🏚 Q 🍽 🍽 ◑ ▶ 🍽 🚹 Å ♣ P

Ruswarp

Bridge Inn
1 mile from Whitby, opp.
station ☎ (0947) 602780
12–2 (3 summer, 4 Wed), 7–11
Courage Directors (summer);
**John Smith's Bitter,
Magnet** H
Old, riverside pub by the
railway station level crossing
and the sharply-angled Esk
road bridge; an attractively
simple bar with a smoke room
and dining room. Ruswarp cattle
mart held each Wed.
Q 🍽 🍽 ◑ ▶ 🍽 Å 🍽 ♣

Scarborough

Alma Inn
Alma Parade (near Northway
traffic lights)
☎ (0723) 385587
11–3 (4.30 Fri & Sat), 6.30–11
**McEwan 80/-; Tetley Bitter;
Younger Scotch, IPA,
No. 3** H
Traditional free house with an
eye-catching exterior, and
pleasant, snug, drinking alcoves
around one, semi-circular bar.
Much bric-a-brac on view.
Lunchtime snacks. 🏚 🍽 🍽

Angel Inn
North Street
☎ (0723) 365504
11–3, 5.30–11 (11–11 Fri & Sat)
Camerons Bitter H
Cosy local; games oriented,
with photographic mementos
of the landlord's international
rugby league career. 🍽 ♣

Cask
Cambridge Terrace
☎ (0723) 500570
11–2.30 (3 Fri & Sat), 6–11
**McEwan 80/-; Tetley Bitter;
Younger Scotch, No. 3** H
Popular, especially with the
young, but welcoming to all.
Attractions include regular
guest beers, a function room, a
children's room and child-
friendly, self-catering flats. Eve
meals finish early.
🍽 🍽 🍽 ◑ ▶ 🍽

Highlander
Stresa Hotel, 15 The Esplanade
(on South Cliff)
☎ (0723) 365627
11–11
**Wm Clarke's Thistle Mild,
Bitter, EXB, 68; Tetley
Bitter; Younger IPA** H
Large hotel with a public bar
overlooking the South Bay, and
its own brewery. Its distinctive
Scottish flavour is enhanced by
a huge whisky collection.
🏚 Q 🍽 🍽 🍽

Hole in the Wall
26 Vernon Road
☎ (0723) 373746
11.30–2.30 (3 Sat), 7–11
**Malton Double Chance;
Theakston Best Bitter, XB,
Old Peculier** H
Thriving ale house just off the
town centre. Guest beers always
available. Vegetarian option on
the menu (no food Sun).
Q 🍽 ◑ 🍽 ♣ ♣

Leeds Arms
St Marys Street (old town)
☎ (0723) 361699
12–3, 7–11
Draught Bass H
Subdued, old town gem with a
nautical atmosphere. 🏚

Tennyson Arms
Dean Road ☎ (0723) 363912
11–3 (4 Fri & Sat), 7–11 (11–11
summer)
Ind Coope Burton Ale
(summer); **Tetley Mild, Bitter;
Younger Scotch** H
Friendly two-roomer with a
lively, games-oriented bar and
lounge. Regular live
entertainment, function facilities
and guest beers. Pavement
tables for summer. Snacks
available. 🍽 🍽 ♣

Trafalgar Hotel
Trafalgar Street West (5 mins
from Northway roundabout)
☎ (0723) 372054
11–11
**Camerons Bitter,
Strongarm** H
Smart, busy, games-oriented
local, attracting a varied
clientele, especially at weekends.
Note the large picture of the
famous battle in the lounge.
🍽 🍽 ♣

Scorton

Royal
Northside ☎ (0748) 818608
12.30–3.30, 5.30–11 (11–11 Fri & Sat)
**Camerons Bitter,
Strongarm** Ⓗ
Attractive, traditional, panelled
bar, with a separate dining
room. Overlooks the unusual,
raised village green. ⌂ ⊛ ◖ ▶ ♣

Try also: White Heifer (Free)

Seamer
(Scarborough)

Londesborough
Main Street ☎ (0723) 863230
11–3, 6–11
**Camerons Bitter; Tetley
Bitter; Younger Scotch** Ⓗ
Open-plan pub with one bar
serving the old bar, a large
lounge with alcoves and a pool
room. Regular live
entertainment; new 'Loft'
restaurant. ⌱ ◖ ▶ ♣ P

Seamer (Stokesley)

King's Head
12 Hilton Road
☎ (0642) 710397
12–3 (not Mon–Fri), 7–11
**McEwan 80/-; Theakston
XB; Younger Scotch** Ⓗ
Four cosy rooms built round a
central bar: ideal for a quiet
evening drink and chat. Note:
no lunchtime opening
weekdays. ⌂ Q ⊱ ⊕ ♣ P

Selby

Abbey Vaults
James Street (300 yds from
abbey) ☎ (0757) 702857
11–4, 6.30–11 (11–11 Mon, Fri & Sat)
Mansfield Riding Bitter Ⓗ
Busy pub, especially on market
day (Mon). Opens at 10am for
coffee. Separate pool room and
function room. ⊛ ◖ ⊕ ⥲ ♣ P

Blackamoor
6 Finkle Street (100 yds N of
market place)
☎ (0757) 702987
11–11
Tetley Bitter Ⓗ
Busy, town pub, refurbished in
Edwardian style. Popular with
young people, especially at
weekends. ⌱ ⥲

Cricketers Arms
Market Place
☎ (0757) 702120
11–3.30, 5.30–11 (11–11 Mon, Fri &
Sat)
Samuel Smith OBB Ⓗ
Comfortable, busy pub with
traditional decor; popular at
weekends and on market day
(Mon). Freshly cooked lunches
served. ◖ ⥲

New Inn
Gowthorpe (100 yds W of
market place)
☎ (0757) 703429
11–11
Tetley Bitter Ⓗ
Traditional town pub with a
separate snug bar. Q ⊛ ⊕ ⥲

Skelton

Blacksmiths Arms
On A19 ☎ (0904) 470425
12–2.30, 7–11
Samuel Smith OBB Ⓗ
Detached pub on the edge of
the village. Two rooms with
unusual names: 'Mares Nest'
and 'Loose Box'. ⌂ ◖ ▶ ⊕ ♣ P

Skipton

Craven Hotel
Craven Street (over canal
footbridge from bus station)
☎ (0756) 792595
11.30–4, 7–11
Thwaites Best Mild, Bitter Ⓗ
Large building near the railway,
popular with locals and away
from the hurly-burly of the
town centre. A spacious, high-
ceilinged bar with a separate
room for darts and
entertainment, plus a small pool
room. One of Thwaites' most
easterly outlets. Small outdoor
drinking area. ⊱ ⊛ ⅙ ⥲ ♣ P

Royal Shepherd
Canal Street ☎ (0756) 793178
11–4, 5–11 (11–11 Sat)
**Hartleys XB; Marston's
Pedigree; Whitbread Castle
Eden Ale** Ⓗ
Friendly, back-street, canalside
pub, most easily approached on
foot via an alleyway from the
high street. The small, award-
winning beer garden to the side
is a suntrap. New stained-glass
window and many photos of
old Skipton.
⌂ Q ⊱⊛ ◖ ⥲ ♣

Try also: Inn Between,
Snaygill (Free)

Sneaton

Wilsons Arms
Beacon Way (B1416, 2 miles
from Ruswarp)
☎ (0947) 602552
12–3, 7–11 (may vary summer)
**Theakston Best Bitter, XB,
Old Peculier** Ⓗ
Reputedly haunted, this Grade II
listed, large, extended pub
caters for families. Roast on
Sun; no eve meals Mon. Quoits
played. Regular bus service from
Whitby. ⌂ ⊱ ⊛ ◖ ▶ ▲ ♣ P

Spofforth

Railway Inn
Main Street (A661)
☎ (0937) 590257

11.30–3, 5.30–11
Samuel Smith OBB Ⓗ
Very small, cosy, stone-built,
village pub. No food Sun.
⌂ ⊛ ◖ ▶ ⊕ P

Stainforth

Craven Heifer
Off B6479 ☎ (072 92) 2599
11–3, 6 (6.30 winter)–11
Thwaites Best Mild, Bitter Ⓗ
18th-century inn with four
public rooms, next to the
packhorse bridge, surrounded
by classic Dales limestone
scenery. ⌂ ⊱ ⊛ ◖ ◖ ▲ ♣

Stamford Bridge

Three Cups Inn
Stamford Bridge West (A166)
☎ (0759) 71396
11–2.30, 6.30 (6 summer)–11
**Draught Bass; Stones Best
Bitter** Ⓗ
Historic inn with origins as far
back as 1215. The large, open-
plan interior features exposed
beams, an ancient well and
1960s photos of the pub.
Separate restaurant (booking
essential weekends); large beer
garden with children's
playground. Guest beer.
⌂ ⊛ ⌱ ◖ ▲ P

Stokesley

Station
Station Road ☎ (0642) 710436
12–4, 7–11
**Theakston Best Bitter, XB,
Old Peculier** Ⓗ
Built in 1861 to serve the now-
defunct railway: a light and airy
bar and a small snug, with a
bar/function room at the rear
(weekly live blues music). No
food Sun; eve meals by
arrangement only.
⌂ Q ⊛ ◖ ⅙ ♣ P

White Swan
1 West End ☎ (0642) 710263
11.30 (11 Sat)–3, 5.30 (7 Sat)–11
Younger No. 3 Ⓗ
Small and cosy, village pub with
a warm welcome. Shows an
impressive commitment to real
ale with a choice of six at any
time and guest beers always
available. ⌂ Q ⊛ ◖ ▶ ◷

Tadcaster

Angel & White Horse
Bridge Street (A659)
☎ (0937) 835470
11–2.30, 5 (7 Sat)–11
**Samuel Smith OBB,
Museum** Ⓗ
Large, town pub next to Sam's
brewery, displaying brewery
photographs in the wood-
panelled bar. The shire horses
are stabled in the coachyard
which also serves as an outdoor
drinking area. ⌂ Q ⊛ ◖

North Yorkshire

Thirsk

Olde Three Tuns
15 Finkle Street (just off market place) ☎ (0845) 23291
11–3, 6–11
Tetley Bitter Ⓗ
16th-century pub which has undergone complete, but sympathetic, restoration. No food Sun. ⌂ ⓐ ◖ ⊞ P

Thornton in Lonsdale

Marton Arms
Off A65/A687 jct
☎ (052 42) 41281
12 (7 winter)–11 (may vary)
Dent Bitter; Moorhouse's Premier; Theakston Best Bitter Ⓗ
Pre-turnpike coaching inn, dated 1679 but reputedly older, with a large, comfortable, oak-beamed lounge. Good home cooking and up to 13 guest beers. ⌂ ⓐ ◄ ◖ ♣ ⌆ P

Thornton-le-Beans

Crosby
Off A168, 3 miles S of Northallerton
☎ (0609) 772776
11–3 (not Tue in winter), 6–11
Webster's Yorkshire Bitter Ⓗ
Large, well-appointed, village pub. The horseshoe-shaped partitions were installed by a former jockey owner. Ring the Bull game played.
⌂ Q ⓐ ◖ Å ♣ P

Threshfield

Old Hall Inn
On B6265
☎ (0756) 752434
11–3, 5.30–11
Taylor Best Bitter, Landlord; Theakston Best Bitter; Younger Scotch Ⓗ
Opened-out pub with an attractive L-shaped room and conservatory. The main room has a splendid Yorkshire range. Good quality, upmarket food usually served in a small dining room.
⌂ Q ⌣ ⓐ ◖ Å ♣ P

Tockwith

Spotted Ox
Main Street (B1224, 2 miles from Wetherby racecourse)
☎ (0423) 358387
11.30 (11 Sat)–11
McEwan 80/-; Tetley Bitter; Younger Scotch Ⓗ
Neat, open-plan pub at the village centre. The monument to the battle of Marston Moor is a local feature. No eve meals Sun. ⌂ Q ⌣ ⓐ ◖ Å ♣ ⌆ P

Ugthorpe

Black Bull
Off A171, 6 miles W of Whitby ☎ (0947) 840286
Tetley Bitter; Theakston Best Bitter, XB, Old Peculier Ⓗ
Excellent, village pub set in a group of 19th-century cottages. Live music Sun lunchtimes. Children welcome in the pool room. Menu includes vegetarian and children's choices. Occasional guest beers. Quoits played. ⌂ ⓐ ◄ ◖ ♣ ⌆ P

Try also: Ellerby Hotel, Ellerby (Free)

Ulleskelf

Ulleskelf Arms
Church Fenton Lane (by station) OS518401
☎ (0937) 832136
11–3 (not Mon–Fri), 7–11
John Smith's Bitter, Magnet; Tetley Bitter Ⓗ
Large, village pub, closed weekday lunchtimes. An open-plan bar with a separate pool room (darts and doms also played). Try the meat and potato pie. Q ⓐ ◖ Å ≉ ♣ P

Weaverthorpe

Star Inn
☎ (094 43) 273
12–3 (not Mon–Fri), 7–11
Old Mill Bitter; Taylor Landlord; Tetley Bitter; Webster's Yorkshire Bitter Ⓗ
Country inn with a bar for everyone. The front lounge is comfortable and popular with diners while the more functional bar is popular with the local younger generation. Separate pool area. ⌂ ⌣ ⓐ ◄ ◖ Å ♣ P

Whitby

Buck Inn
11 St Annes Staithe
☎ (0947) 601378
11–3, 6–11 (11–11 summer)
John Smith's Bitter, Magnet Ⓗ
Busy, quayside pub, popular with locals and visitors. It offers views of the abbey and church across the harbour. Sky TV. The family room is also used for functions. Eve meals summer only. ⌣ ◄ ◖ ≉ ♣

Duke of York
Church Street
☎ (0947) 601378
11–3 (may vary), 7–11 (11 summer)
Courage Directors; John Smith's Bitter, Magnet Ⓗ
Harbourside pub with magnificent views, situated at the foot of 199 steps leading up to the abbey and church. Acts as a folk centre during Folk Week. ◄ ◖ ≉ ♣

Plough Hotel
Baxtergate
11–4, 6–11 (11–11 summer)
Samuel Smith OBB Ⓗ
Busy, town-centre pub with varied rooms, near rail and bus stations and a public car park. Focal point for Folk Week in August, and has its own folk club. ⌂ ⌣ ⓐ ◄ ◖ ⊞ ♣ ♣

Try also: Black Horse, Church St (Tetley); **Cutty Sark,** Newquay Rd (Camerons); **Dolphin Hotel,** Bridge St (Camerons)

Whitley Bridge

George & Dragon
Doncaster Road (A19)
☎ (0977) 661319
11.30–3.30, 5–11 (11.30–11 Fri & Sat)
John Smith's Bitter Ⓗ
Eye-catching, roadside pub standing in extensive grounds: a locals' tap room and a comfortable lounge. Excellent value meals. ⌂ ⓐ ◖ ♣ ♣ P

Whixley

Bay Horse
Stonegate (main road, off A59)
12–3 (not Mon–Fri), 7–11
John Smith's Bitter; Tetley Bitter Ⓗ
Pub with a multi-roomed layout around a small bar, creating a friendly yet intimate atmosphere. A true village local. The restaurant has easy access for wheelchairs. Families welcome. No meals Mon eve.
Q ⓐ ◖ ♣ ♣ P

Wigginton

Black Horse
Front Street (off B1363, 5 miles N of York) ☎ (0904) 765218
11.30–3 (4 Sat), 5.30 (7 Sat)–11
Bass Special; Stones Best Bitter Ⓗ
Pleasant pub in the village centre. Recent changes have resulted in a series of linked drinking areas, with much use of wood panelling. ⓐ ◖ ♣ P

Wighill

White Swan
3 miles N of Tadcaster
OS475470 ☎ (0937) 832217
12–3, 6–11
Stones Best Bitter; Tetley Bitter; Theakston Best Bitter, Old Peculier; Younger No. 3 Ⓗ
Old-style, stone-built, country village pub: small bars, low ceilings and plenty of racing memorabilia. Popular and busy on York and Wetherby race days. ⌂ Q ⌣ ⓐ ◖ ⊞ Å ♣ P

York

Brown Cow Inn

36 Hope Street (off Walmgate, just inside city walls)
☎ (0904) 634010
11–11 (11–4, 6–11 Tue)
Taylor Best Bitter, Landlord Ⓗ
Small, friendly, two-roomed local, pleasantly decorated and surrounded by modern housing. Two large aquaria house a colourful variety of fish. Convenient for the city walls and local shops. Pool played.
⊛ ≈

Golden Ball

Cromwell Road, Bishophill (inside Victoria Bar)
☎ (0904) 652211
11.45–3, 7–11
Courage Directors ; Malton Double Chance ; John Smith's Bitter, Magnet Ⓗ
Unspoilt, traditional pub consisting of two rooms and a small snug in a residential part of the walled city. The authentic, well-preserved exterior features glazed bricks and etched windows. Q ⊛ ⊟ ≈

Hole in the Wall

High Petergate
☎ (0904) 634468
11–11
Mansfield Riding Mild, Riding Bitter, Old Baily Ⓗ
Formerly the 'Board Inn', a pub almost entirely rebuilt in the early 1980s but retaining some traces of its original fabric. Mixed clientele, but with a young emphasis at times. Very busy Fri and Sat eves. Eve meals in summer only. ⚏ ◖ ▮

John Bull

Layerthorpe (off Foss Islands Road) ☎ (0904) 621593
11–11
Taylor Best Bitter, Landlord Ⓗ
Bustling free house with much 1930s memorabilia: enamel signs, old bottles and tins.

Regular live music adds to the atmosphere. Guest beers.
⚏ Q ⊛ ⊟ ○

Minster Inn

24 Marygate (off Bootham)
☎ (0904) 624499
11–3 (4 Sat), 5.30–11
Bass Light, Draught Bass ; Old Mill Bitter ; Stones Best Bitter Ⓗ
Excellent, terraced pub with a traditional layout, situated in a pleasant side-street near the ruins of St Mary's Abbey. A bar with two lounges and a meeting room. Q ⊟ ⚍

Other Tap & Spile

15 North Street
☎ (0904) 656097
11.30–3, 5–11 (11–11 Fri & Sat)
Big End Piston Ⓗ
Known until 1989 as the 'Yorkshire Hussar', but re-opened in 1990 as part of the Tap & Spile chain. Three rooms, one of which is regularly used for meetings. The selection of beers varies, but usually eight are available. Good value bar meals. ≿ ◖ ▮ ⊟ ≈ ♣

Royal Oak Inn

Goodramgate (near Minster)
☎ (0904) 653856
11–11
Camerons Bitter ; Everards Old Original Ⓗ
Excellent, three-roomed pub which specialises in home cooking (including the bread). Meals available until 7.30. The family room is no-smoking.
≿ ◖ ▮ ⊟ ≈ ⚍

Spread Eagle Inn

98 Walmgate
☎ (0904) 635868
11–11
Taylor Best Bitter, Landlord ; Theakston XB, Old Peculier Ⓗ
Popular free house, the subject of a recent, sympathetic refurbishment. At least three guest beers always available. Bar meals 12–8 Mon–Sat ; live music Sun lunch. Restaurant upstairs. ≿ ⊛ ◖ ▮ ≈

Tap & Spile

Monkgate (200 yds through Monk Bar)
☎ (0904) 656158
11.30–3, 5–11 (11.30–11 Sat)
Camerons Bitter ; Hadrian Gladiator ; Old Mill Bitter ; Stocks Horizontal Ⓗ
Large, traditional ale house with a raised games area to the rear. Good selections of home-cooked bar meals and guest ales (occasional draught cider). Beer festivals from time to time.
⊛ ⚍ ◖ ≈ ○ P

Waggon & Horses

Lawrence Street (100 yds from Walmgate Bar)
☎ (0904) 658788
11–11
Courage Best Bitter ; John Smith's Bitter, Magnet Ⓗ
Plain, three-roomed pub with mainly local trade. Disco Sun nights ; pool table. Swings and a slide in the outdoor drinking area. ⊛ P

York Arms

High Petergate (100 yds from Bootham Bar)
☎ (0904) 624508
11–11
Samuel Smith OBB, Museum Ⓗ
Olde-worlde, town pub comprising three bars ; popular with young people and students. The restaurant has a no-smoking area.
Q ⚍ ◖ ▮ ⊟ ≈

York Beer Shop

28 Sandringham Street (off Fishergate)
☎ (0904) 647136
11 (4.15 Mon, 10 Sat)–10 (12–2, 7–10 Sun)
Bateman XXXB ; Malton Owd Bob ; Old Mill Bitter ; Taylor Best Bitter, Landlord Ⓗ
Busy real-ale off-licence with other specialist products, incl. foreign bottled beers (nearly 200 varieties), wine and cheeses. Also boasts three ciders and the occasional perry. The ultimate offy! ○

○
Real Cider

Where a pub serves traditional cider – as different from keg cider as traditional ale is from keg beer – we include the apple symbol.

For more information on real cider, and a comprehensive directory of where to find it, you should pick up David Kitton's **Good Cider Guide**, priced £5.95 and available from all good book stores or direct from CAMRA, 34 Alma Road, St Albans, Herts, AL1 3BW (post free).

South Yorkshire

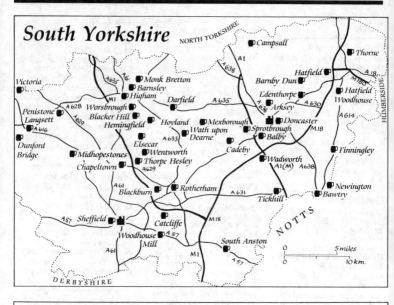

South Yorkshire map showing NORTH YORKSHIRE, Campsall, Thorne, Victoria, Monk Bretton, Barnsley, Higham, Darfield, Hatfield, Barnby Dun, Edenthorpe, Hatfield Woodhouse, HUMBERSIDE, Penistone Langsett, Worsbrough, Blacker Hill, Hemingfield, Hoyland, Mexborough, Arksey, Doncaster, Dunford Bridge, Midhopestones, Elsecar, Wentworth, Dearne, Wath upon Dearne, Sprotbrough, Balby, Finningley, Chapeltown, Thorpe Hesley, Cadeby, Wadworth, Blackburn, Rotherham, Tickhill, Newington, Bawtry, NOTTS, Sheffield, Catcliffe, Woodhouse Mill, South Anston, DERBYSHIRE. Scale 5 miles / 10 km.

Stocks, Doncaster; **Wards**, Sheffield

Arksey

Plough
High Street
☎ (0302) 872472
12–3, 7–11
John Smith's Bitter Ⓗ
Convivial locals' pub hidden
away behind the village church.
Traditional tap room with darts
and dominoes; the larger lounge
is adorned with commemorative
plates. ⊞ ♣

Balby

Spinney
Forest Rise, Grenville Estate (off
A630)
☎ (0302) 852033
11–3.30 (4 Fri & Sat), 6.30–11
Home Bitter Ⓗ
Thriving Younger's estate pub
(formerly Home) with games-
oriented tap room and large,
comfortable lounge. Guest
beers. ⊛ ◖ ⊞ ♣ P

Barnby Dun

White Hart
Top Road (2 miles from A18, N
of Doncaster)
☎ (0302) 882959
10.30–3.30, 6–11
**John Smith's Bitter,
Magnet** Ⓗ
A modernised village pub which
has retained much of its
character. Popular with locals
and those who visit for
excellent meals (no food Sun).
Has a fascinating collection of
clocks. Guest beer. ⊞ ◖ ◗ ♣

Barnsley

Manx Arms
Sheffield Road (A61, off
roundabout on edge of centre)
☎ (0226) 293766
11–3.30, 7–11
**Ind Coope Burton Ale;
Taylor Landlord; Tetley
Bitter; Theakston Old
Peculier** Ⓗ
Popular free house catering for
all ages; very busy at weekends.
Up to six guest beers and a
cider. Pool room upstairs. Live
entertainment Sun eves; Thu
night quiz. Parking limited.
⇌ ↻ ♣ P

Old White Bear
Pontefract Road, Hoyle Mill
(A628, 1¼ miles from centre)
☎ (0226) 284947
12–3, 5.30–11
**Ind Coope Burton Ale;
Marston's Pedigree; Taylor
Landlord; Tetley Bitter** Ⓗ
Popular free house: one
comfortable lounge-style room
divided into two areas, and a
games room. Good value food:
pies with beer a speciality.
Golden oldies discos. Patio has
parkland views. Guest beers.
⊛ ⇌ ◖ ◗ ♣ P

Bawtry

Turnpike
28–30 High Street (A614/
A638)☎ (0302) 711960
11–3, 6–11
**Stocks Best Bitter, Select, Old
Horizontal** Ⓗ

Tastefully converted from a
wine bar to cater for all tastes,
and local and passing trade. The
interior is of wood, glass and
brick, with a part-concrete floor
– mind the step. Good value,
varied menu (eve meals
Mon–Thu). Regular guest beers.
⊞ ⊛ ◖ ◗

Try also: Crown Hotel (Free)

Blackburn

Crown
88 Blackburn Road (near M1 jct
34) ☎ (0709) 560498
11–3, 6–11
Tetley Bitter Ⓗ
Solid pub with all areas
comfortably decorated and walls
festooned with paraphernalia.
The garden is a real delight for
children and families.
⊛ ◖ ♣ P

Try also: Sportsman (Free)

Blacker Hill

Royal Albert
Wentworth Road (800 yds off
B6096)
☎ (0226) 742193
11–3, 7–11
**Wards Sheffield Best
Bitter** Ⓔ&Ⓗ
Attractive pub on a bend in the
road; hub of village life.
Splendid, small, wood-panelled
snug, with many horse brasses;
larger games-orientated public
bar. Pool room upstairs. Parking
at rear. Q ⊛ ⊞ ♣ P

South Yorkshire

Cadeby

Cadeby Inn
Main Street ☎ (0709) 864009
11–11 (may vary in winter)
**Courage Directors; Ind
Coope Burton Ale; John
Smith's Bitter, Magnet;
Samuel Smith OBB; Tetley
Bitter** Ⓗ
Converted farmhouse in a rural
village which has retained its
atmosphere and character. Large
lounge and cosy public bar.
Good bar meals and traditional
Sun lunch. Pleasant garden.
Guest beers. ♨ Q ⊛ ◑ ⊕ P

Campsall

Old Bells
High Street ☎ (0302) 700423
11–3, 7–11
**Webster's Yorkshire Bitter,
Choice** Ⓗ
Originally a farm, now a
rambling old pub. Four rooms,
each with its own character, and
a restaurant. ♨ ◑ ▶ ⊕ ♿ P

Catcliffe

Waverley
Brinsworth Road (B6067, off
A631 at Brinsworth)
☎ (0709) 360906
12–4, 6–11
**Ruddles County; Taylor
Landlord** Ⓗ
Unique pub with entrepreneurial
landlord. Purpose-built seven
years ago and recently
extended. Regular live music
and two guest beers.
Q ⌂ ⊛ ◑ ⊕ ♿ ⚲ ♣ P

Chapeltown

Norfolk Arms
White Lane (A6135/Warren
Lane jct, near M1 jct 35A)
☎ (0742) 468414
12–4, 7–11
Wards Sheffield Best Bitter Ⓔ
Pub very old in part – see
picture in lounge. Local hub for
footballers and anglers.
Landlord is a staunch Sheffield
Wed fan and has a keen sense of
humour. Jukebox only in pool
room. Older children welcome
in family room. ⌂ ⊛ ◑ ⇌ ♣ P

Prince of Wales
80 Burncross Road (A629, 1
mile from M1 jct 35)
☎ (0742) 467725
11–3.30 (4 Sat), 5.30 (6.30 Sat)–11
(11–11 Fri; 12–2, 7–10.30 Sun)
**Wards Sheffield Best
Bitter** Ⓗ&Ⓔ
Traditional tap room with
wood-panelled lounge. Clean air
pub with friendly clientele.
⊛ ▶ ⊕ ⇌ ♣ P

Try also: Commercial (Free)

Darfield

Hewer & Brewer
77 Snape Hill Road (B6096)
☎ (0226) 752956
12–3 (not Tue, or winter Mon), 7–11
**McEwan 80/-; Theakston
Best Bitter, XB, Old
Peculier** Ⓗ
Comfortable and cosy roadside
pub. Three separate drinking
areas plus darts alley. Good
value meals (no food Mon or
Tue). ♨ ◑ ▶ ♣ P

Try also: Bridge Inn (John
Smith's); **Longbow** (Bass)

Doncaster

Corner Pin
St Sepulchre Gate West
☎ (0302) 328213
11.30–3, 4.45–11 (11.30–11 Fri & Sat)
**John Smith's Bitter, Magnet;
Stones Best Bitter** Ⓗ
Street-corner local just away
from town centre and two
minutes' walk from station.
◑ ▶ ⇌ ♣

Masons Arms
Market Place
☎ (0302) 364391
10.30 (11 Mon, Wed & Thu)–4,
7.30–11 (12–3, 7.30–10.30 Sun)
Tetley Bitter Ⓗ
200 year-old Tetley Heritage
Inn. Many photos of old
'Donny' and a history of the
pub on display. Haunt of the
local morris men. Q ⊛ ⊕ ⇌

Railway
West Street ☎ (0302) 349700
11–11
**John Smith's Bitter, Magnet;
Theakston XB** Ⓗ
Bustling town pub with
enormous bar and tiny lounge.
Well-appointed function room
upstairs. Popular with postal
and railway workers. ◑ ⊕ ⇌ ♣

Wheatley Hotel
Thorne Road ☎ (0302) 364092
10.30–11
**Courage Directors; John
Smith's Magnet** Ⓗ
Large, well-appointed hotel just
out of the centre. Its excellent
facilities often attract coach
parties on summer eves.
Q ⌂ ⊛ ⋈ ◑ ▶ ⊕ ♿ ♣ P

White Swan
34a Frenchgate
☎ (0302) 366573
11–11
**Vaux Samson; Wards
Sheffield Best Bitter** Ⓗ
Last of 19 pubs that once
adorned Frenchgate. A tiled
passageway leads to the lounge,
while the front tap room boasts
the highest bar in Britain – 5ft
3ins. Meals till 2; sandwiches
till 6, Mon–Sat. Live music Wed
night. ◑ ⊕ ⇌ ♣

Dunford Bridge

Stanhope Arms
Windle Edge Lane (off A628)
☎ (0226) 763104
11–3 (not Mon in winter), 7–11
John Smith's Bitter, Magnet Ⓗ
Originally built as a shooting
lodge. Several rooms interlink
with a small bar; tiny snug and
separate dining room. Good,
home-made food (vegetarian
option; breakfasts available).
Sun night snuff club. Children
welcome in snug until 8pm.
Camping in grounds.
♨ Q ⊛ ◑ ▶ ♿ ⚲ ♣ P

Edenthorpe

Ridgewood
Thorne Road (A18)
☎ (0302) 882841
11–11
Samuel Smith OBB Ⓗ
Named after a famous racehorse. Comfortable, spacious
lounge and separate tap room
catering for local and passing
trade. Extensive garden with
children's playground. Eve
meals on request. ⊛ ◑ ⊕ ♣ P

Elsecar

Market Hotel
2 Wentworth Road (just off
B6097) ☎ (0226) 742240
11–4, 7–11
Stones Best Bitter Ⓔ
Built c1860 and set in Earl
Fitzwilliam's model coal-mining
village, this pub has several
unspoilt rooms. A simple
approach to innkeeping ensures
beer is preferred to food. There
is no jukebox or noisy
electronic games. Q ⊕ ⇌ ♣

Finningley

Harvey Arms
Old Bawtry Road (just off
A614) ☎ (0302) 770200
11–3, 7–11 (11–11 Sat)
Draught Bass Ⓗ
Village pub near green and duck
pond; close to RAF base famous
for its air display. Busy,
traditional bar has a collection of
Robert Taylor aircraft prints;
large lounge boasts leaded
windows. Welcoming winter
fire; good lunchtime carvery.
Eve meals Fri and Sat only.
♨ ⊛ ◑ ▶ ⊕ ♣ P

Hatfield

Green Tree
Bearswood Green (A18/A614)
☎ (0302) 840305
11–3, 6–11
**Vaux Samson; Wards Thorne
Best Bitter** Ⓗ
Very welcoming 17th-century
posting house with emphasis on
food. ♨ ⊛ ⋈ ◑ ▶ ♿ P

South Yorkshire

Hatfield Woodhouse

Robin Hood & Little John
Main Street (A614)
☎ (0302) 840213
10.30–4, 6–11
Stones Best Bitter Ⓗ
Friendly village local, very busy at weekends. ⏸ Ⓒ ⊞ ♣ P

Hemingfield

Lundhill Tavern
Beech House Road (off A633, ½ mile on Lundhill road)
☎ (0226) 752283
12–4.30, 7–11
Mansfield Old Baily; John Smith's Bitter, Magnet; Taylor Landlord Ⓗ
Off the beaten track and steeped in local coal-mining history. Unusual collection of brass blowlamps hang from wooden beams. Meals served in bar (except Mon) or restaurant. Competitively priced guest beers. Ⓒ ▶ ♣ P

Higham

Engineers Inn
Higham Common Lane (off A635) ☎ (0226) 384204
11.30–3, 7–11
Samuel Smith OBB Ⓗ
Village pub with superb, unspoilt tap room and plush lounge. Lawned beer garden with swings. Lunchtime snacks available (not Sun). ⏸ Ⓒ ⊞ ♣ P

Hoyland

Furnace Inn
Milton Road (off B6097, 500 yds from centre)
☎ (0226) 742000
11.30–3 (3.30 Sat), 5.30–11
Vaux Samson Ⓗ; Wards Thorne Best Bitter, Sheffield Best Bitter Ⓔ, Kirby Ⓗ
Welcoming stone-built inn by old forge pond. Award-winning flower displays in summer. Good value lunchtime snacks (Mon–Fri). Q ⏸ Ⓒ ♣ P

Langsett

Waggon & Horses
On A616 ☎ (0226) 763147
12–3, 7.30 (7 Sat)–11
Draught Bass Ⓗ
Ex-Water Board property with lawned garden, set in an old courtyard at the side of a large reservoir. Comfortable interior, free from music, slot machines and other distractions. Home-cooked food (no meals Sat lunch or Sun/Mon eves). B&B planned. Guest beers.
♨ Q ⏸ Ⓒ ▶ P

Mexborough

Concertina Band Club
9a Dolcliffe Road (off Main Street) ☎ (0709) 580841
12–4, 7–11 (12–2, 7–10.30 Sun)
John Smith's Bitter, Magnet; Tetley Bitter; Wards Sheffield Best Bitter Ⓗ
Small, friendly, private club steeped in history. Visitors welcome. Guest beers. ≈ ♣

Falcon
12 Main Street (near bus station) ☎ (0709) 571170
11–4, 7–11
Old Mill Bitter, Bullion Ⓗ
Recently-refurbished large lounge with raised drinking areas. Tap room with pool table; fish pond in the entrance. No meals Sun. ⏸ Ⓒ ⊞ ⅏ ♣ ≈

George & Dragon
81 Church Street
☎ (0709) 584375
12–3.30, 7–11 (12–2.30, 7–10.30 Sun)
John Smith's Bitter, Magnet; Stones Best Bitter Ⓗ
Rural-styled, one-roomed pub. Garden has children's playground. ⏸ ≈ P

Midhopestones

Club Inn
Off A616 (Bradfield sign) between Langsett and Stocksbridge
☎ (0226) 762305
11.30–3, 7–11 (12–2, 7–10.30 Sun)
Wards Sheffield Best Bitter Ⓗ
Landlord celebrates 50 years in the pub this year. Twenties pornography and saucy knickers add spice to this ancient and unique hostelry. No other frills! Even has its own card games. Locals call village 'Midup'.
♨ Q ⏸ ⊞ ♣ P

Monk Bretton

Sun Inn
Burton Road (200 yds from church) ☎ (0226) 203361
11.30–3, 5–11
John Smith's Bitter, Magnet Ⓗ
Attractive roadside local which caters for all ages. Pleasant interior; large lounge with quiet areas. Q Ⓒ ♣ P

Newington

Ship Inn
Newington Road (200 yds from A614) ☎ (0302) 710334
12–3, 7–11 (11–11 Sat)
Theakston Best Bitter, XB, Old Peculier; Younger Scotch Ⓗ
Popular village local dating back to 1700s. ⏸ Ⓒ ▶ ⊞ ♣ P

Penistone

Cubley Hall
Mortimer Road, Cubley
☎ (0226) 766086
11–3, 6–11
Ansells Bitter; Ind Coope Burton Ale; Tetley Bitter Ⓗ
Former country house with plush, multi-room interior. Fine plasterwork and mosaic-tiled floors. Wide range of excellent home-cooked food. Two children's rooms and a lawned garden with swings. Live entertainment in 200-seat function suite. ♨ ⏸ Ⓒ ▶ P

Rotherham

Bridge Inn
Greasbrough Road
☎ (0709) 363683
11–3, 6–11
Draught Bass; John Smith's Bitter; Stones Best Bitter Ⓗ
Many-roomed pub next to the well-known Chapel-on-the-Bridge. Meeting rooms are used by a variety of local groups. Much historical information about pubs in the town.
Ⓒ ⊞ ≈ ♣

Effingham Arms
Effingham Street (opp. bus station) ☎ (0709) 363353
11–11
Stones Best Bitter Ⓗ
Typical town-centre pub with four separate rooms. The stained-glass windows depict the voyage of Sir Francis Drake who was sponsored by the Duke of Effingham. ⊞ ≈ ♣

Limes
38 Broom Lane
☎ (0709) 363431
10.30–11
Theakston Best Bitter; Younger Scotch, IPA, No. 3 Ⓗ
Very comfortable bar/lounge. Emphasis on meals which are served all day, including a very cheap special dish. Well-appointed hotel with attractive weekend rates. Q ⏸ ⨝ Ⓒ ▶ P

Tabard
Herringthorpe Valley Road
☎ (0709) 364761
11–11
Courage Directors; Mansfield Riding Bitter; John Smith's Bitter Ⓗ
Large estate pub close to leisure centre. Regular oldies nights. Table football and pinball. No meals Sat or Sun.
♨ ⏸ Ⓒ ⊞ ⅏ ♣ P

Turners Arms
Psalters Lane
☎ (0709) 558937
12–3, 7–11
Wards Sheffield Best Bitter Ⓔ&Ⓗ

Smart and compact pub at
Masbrough. Three separate
rooms with lots of pub
memorabilia. Known locally as
the 'Green Bricks' due to the
external tiling. 🏠 🛇 ♣ P

Woodman

115 Midland Road
☎ (0709) 561486
12–3, 7–11
Stones Best Bitter Ⓗ
Sturdy, ex-Bentley's pub at
Masbrough. Games dominate
the tap room; quieter lounge to
the right. Snooker room
upstairs. 🏠 🍽

Sheffield : *Central*

Bath Hotel

66 Victoria Street (rear of
Glossop Road baths)
☎ (0742) 729017
12–3, 5.30 (7.30 Sat)–11 (12–2,
7.30–10.30 Sun)
**Ind Coope Burton Ale; Tetley
Bitter; Wards Sheffield Best
Bitter** Ⓗ
A Tetley Heritage Pub,
converted from Victorian
cottages to form a small,
friendly, two-roomed local. The
original ground lease prohibits
use of the site as an ale house or
for other noxious activities!
🛇 ♣

Boulogne

42 Waingate
☎ (0742) 726270
12–3, 7–11 (7–10.30 only Sun)
Beer range varies Ⓗ
Large, street-corner, ex-
Gilmour's pub due for
conversion to a 'Tap & Spile.'
Up to seven beers. Q ♿ ≠

Brown Bear

109 Norfolk Street
☎ (0742) 727744
11–3.30, 5.30–11 (12–2, 7–10.30 Sun)
**Courage Directors; John
Smith's Bitter** Ⓗ
Comfortable, two-roomed pub
decorated with thespian
memorabilia. Popular city-centre
meeting place, also patronised
by cast, musicians and audience
from nearby Crucible and
Lyceum theatres. 🏠 🛇 ♿ ♣ ♣

Fagans

69 Broad Lane
☎ (0742) 728430
11.30–3, 5.30–11 (11.30–11 Fri & Sat)
**Ind Coope Burton Ale; Tetley
Bitter** Ⓗ
Lively, popular pub with small
snug. Frequent impromptu folk
music sessions. Friendly
atmosphere. Q 🏠 🛇 ♣

Fat Cat

23 Alma Street (near Kelham
Island Museum)
☎ (0742) 728195
12–3, 5.30–11
Kelham Island Best Bitter;

**Marston's Pedigree, Owd
Rodger; Theakston Old
Peculier; Taylor Landlord** Ⓗ
Sheffield's first real ale free
house, situated in Kelham Island
conservation area. Two
comfortable rooms (one no-
smoking), corridor drinking area
and upstairs function room for
overspill (children at
lunchtimes). Pub brewhouse
recently opened. Eve meals
Mon only (8.30–9.30).
🏠 Q 🏠 🛇 ❱ ♣ ♿ ✕

Howard

53 Howard Street (opp. station)
☎ (0742) 780183
11–11 (7–10.30 only Sun)
**Mansfield Riding Mild, Bitter,
Old Baily** Ⓗ
Open-plan, lounge bar pub,
popular with students. Separate
pool area. Well-appointed with
large bar. Can be very busy.
🛇 ♿ ≠ ♣

Norfolk Arms

2 Suffolk Road
☎ (0742) 727598
11–11
**Courage Directors; John
Smith's Bitter, Magnet** Ⓗ
Triangular-shaped pub, popular
with workmen and students.
Busy tap room with pool table;
very comfortable lounge.
🍽 ≠ ♣

Red Deer

18 Pitt Street (off West Street)
☎ (0742) 722890
11.30–3, 5–11 (11.30–11 Fri; 12–3,
7.30–11 Sat; 12–2, 7–10.30 Sun)
**Ind Coope Burton Ale; Tetley
Mild, Bitter; Wards Sheffield
Best Bitter** Ⓗ
Busy, friendly, one-roomed local
with active folk club. Popular
with students and professionals.
Excellent home-cooked meals
(eves by arrangement). Children
allowed in function room for
lunchtime meals. Quiz Sun eve.
Q 🎵 🏠 🛇

Red House

168 Solly Street (near St
George's Church)
☎ (0742) 727926
11.30–3, 5 (8 Sat)–11 (12–2.30,
7–10.30 Sun)
Vaux Samson (summer);
**Wards Thorne Best Bitter,
Sheffield Best Bitter, Kirby**
(winter) Ⓗ
Comfortably-furnished local
with three separate drinking
areas around a central bar. Live
music Sun, Tue, Fri; quiz Thu.
Once known as the 'Irish
Embassy', but also popular with
students. Q 🛇 ♣

Royal Standard

156–158 St Mary's Road (inner
ring road near Bramall Lane
football ground)
☎ (0742) 722883

11.30–3, 5–11 (11.30–11 Fri & Sat;
closes 3–4.45 on football days)
**Wards Mild, Sheffield Best
Bitter, Kirby** Ⓗ
Busy pub with large lounge,
snug and tap room. Fine wood-
panelled bar. Well-patronised by
all sections of the community.
Pool and darts in both tap room
and upstairs function room.
🏠 🛇 🍺 ≠ ♣ P

Rutland Arms

86 Brown Street
☎ (0742) 729003
11–3, 5.30 (7 Sat)–11
**Ind Coope Burton Ale; Tetley
Bitter; Younger No. 3** Ⓗ
City-centre gem in a resurgent
cultural corner of the city.
Behind the distinctive Gilmour's
tiled frontage lies a comfortable
lounge, catering for a wide mix
of local customers. Eve meals till
7.30, Mon–Fri. 🏠 🍽 🛇 ❱ ≠ P

Join CAMRA —
see page 480!

Sheffield : *East*

Belfry

Eckington Road, Beighton
☎ (0742) 477309
11–2.30 (3 Sat), 5.30–11
Stones Best Bitter Ⓗ
Large, modern open-plan pub
with restaurant at rear. Pool
table and games area to left of
main entrance, with comfortable
lounge area to right.
🏠 🛇 ❱ ♿ ♣ P

Carlton

563 Attercliffe Road
☎ (0742) 443287
11.45–3 (3.45 Sat), 5 (7.30 Sat)–11
(11.45–11 Fri)
**Mansfield Riding Bitter;
Ruddles Best Bitter;
Webster's Yorkshire Bitter** Ⓗ
A warm and friendly watering
hole, attracting custom from
many parts of the city. Like the
Tardis, the interior appears
larger than the outside would
imply. Separate games room to
rear of main bar.
🏠 ≠ (Attercliffe Rd) ♣

Cocked Hat

75 Worksop Road (off
Attercliffe Road)
☎ (0742) 448332
11–11 (11–3, 7–11 Sat)
**Marston's Burton Best Bitter,
Pedigree** Ⓗ
In the Attercliffe Environmental
Corridor, this excellent
Victorian-style pub lies in the
shadow of the new Don Valley
Stadium. The warm and friendly
welcome is complemented by
the pub's noted lunches and
substantial bar snacks.
🏠 Q 🏠 🛇 ♣

South Yorkshire

Cross Keys
400 Handsworth Road,
Handsworth (A57)
☎ (0742) 694413
11–11
Stones Best Bitter Ⓗ
Popular, three-roomed local set
in the corner of the parish
church graveyard. Outstanding
example of an unspoilt and
friendly watering hole. ⊞ ♣

Milestone
12 Peaks Mount, Waterthorpe
(next to bus station)
☎ (0742) 471614
11–11
Banks's Mild, Bitter Ⓔ
Built in 1988 to serve the
Crystal Peaks shopping centre.
Tap room with pool table has
viewing glass to cellar. Large
lounge with conservatory
extension. Well-used by
shoppers lunchtimes and
cinema-goers in eves.
❀ ◖ ⊞ & ♣ P

Try also: Britannia, Worksop
Road (Stones)

Sheffield: *North*

Denison Arms
33 Watery Street
☎ (0742) 727845
11–3.45, 7–11
Stones Best Bitter Ⓔ
Splendid example of an unspoilt
local. Tastefully-decorated, bay-
windowed lounge with many
certificates won by the landlady.
Small public bar with pool table.
⊞ ♣

Foundry
111 Barrow Road
☎ (0742) 426498
11–3, 6–11
Stones Best Bitter Ⓗ**; Tetley
Bitter** Ⓔ
Renovated in 1988, but
retaining much of the original
character and wood panelling.
Separate tap room and raised
area for pool. Close to
Meadowhall complex.
❀ ◖ ⇌ (Meadowhall) ♣ P

Mill Tavern
2–4 Earsham Street
☎ (0742) 756461
11–11
**Old Mill Mild, Bitter,
Bullion** Ⓗ
A mock Tudor frontage leads
into a single bar serving all
areas of the pub. Rough
stonework and wood much in
evidence. A big charity fund-
raiser. Regular live
entertainment. Bar billiards. ♣

Robin Hood
Myers Grove Lane, Little
Matlock (right turn after
Pinegrove Country Club)
☎ (0742) 344565
11–4, 7–11

Stones Best Bitter Ⓔ
Country pub on the site of a
failed spa development. Four
interconnecting rooms; stuffed
animal collection in the bar.
Once owned by Wheatley &
Bates brewery. Picturesque
surroundings have connections
with the Robin Hood legend.
❀ Q ⇖ ⊞ ⊞ ♣ P

Sheffield: *South*

Abbey
944 Chesterfield Road
☎ (0742) 745374
11–11
**Ind Coope Burton Ale; Tetley
Bitter** Ⓗ
Busy suburban local with
separate public bar and
extensive, well-furnished
lounge. Upstairs snooker room
with dartboard. Well-patronised
bowling green at the side. Eve
meals to 8.30, except Sun.
❀ Q ❀ ◖ ⊞ & ♣ P

Earl of Arundel & Surrey
528 Queens Road (A61)
☎ (0742) 551006
11–11
**Vaux Samson; Wards
Sheffield Best Bitter, Kirby** Ⓗ
Large local on main road near
Sheffield United ground. Three
lounges and separate games
area with pool. Snooker room
and function room upstairs.
Sheffield's last remaining pound
house, which stables at the rear.
Can be very busy. ❀ ◖ & ♣

Fleur-de-Lys
Totley Hall Lane (A621, Baslow
road) ☎ (0742) 361476
11–11
**Draught Bass; Stones Best
Bitter** Ⓗ
Large suburban local on
outskirts of city. Spacious
lounge with separate carvery
area; cosy wood-panelled snug.
Large grassed garden with
children's play area. ❀ ◖ ♣ ♣ P

Old Mother Redcap
Prospect Road, Bradway (near
B6054) ☎ (0742) 360179
11–3.30, 5.30–11 (11–11 Sat)
Samuel Smith OBB Ⓗ
Popular farmhouse-style pub in
residential area. Large L-shaped,
comfortable lounge with games
area. ❀ ◖ & ♣ P

Shakespeare
106 Well Road (off A61 at
Heeley Bridge)
☎ (0742) 553995
12–3.30 (4.30 Sat), 5 (7 Sat)–11
**Stones Best Bitter; Tetley
Bitter** Ⓗ
Friendly local with three
drinking areas around one bar.
Comfortable and warm. Near
Heeley City Farm, with good
view of southern Sheffield. ❀ ♣

Sheffield: *West*

Banner Cross
971 Ecclesall Road (A625)
☎ (0742) 661479
11.30–11
**Ind Coope Burton Ale; Tetley
Bitter** Ⓗ
Busy suburban local with wood-
panelling in lounge. Large, well-
decorated tap room. Upstairs
games room has snooker and
pool. ❀ ◖ ⊞ ♣

Firwood Cottage
279 Whitehouse Lane
☎ (0742) 346057
12–4, 7–11
Tetley Bitter Ⓗ
Small, friendly local with two
neat rooms. Beamed ceilings.
Q ❀ ◖ ♣

Fox & Duck
223–227 Fulwood Road (A57)
☎ (0742) 663422
11–11
**Courage Directors; John
Smith's Bitter, Magnet** Ⓗ
Busy pub in the centre of
Broomhill shopping area. A
large bar serves several distinct
areas, each with traditional
furnishings. ❀ ◖ ▶ ♣

Old Grindstone
3 Crookes ☎ (0742) 660322
11–11
**Wards Sheffield Best Bitter,
Kirby** Ⓗ&Ⓔ**; Taylor
Landlord** Ⓗ
Spacious, Victorian-style lounge
with adjoining conservatory.
Oak-panelled games room,
modelled on a gentleman's club,
offers snooker, pool and darts.
Quiet until 7.30 when last food
orders are taken. No eve meals
Sun. Regular guest beer.
❀ ◖ ♣ ♣

Pomona
255 Ecclesall Road (A625 near
Wards brewery)
☎ (0742) 665922
11–11
**Theakston XB, Old Peculier;
Younger Scotch, No. 3** Ⓗ
Large, modern suburban local
served by a long bar, with four
well-appointed drinking areas
and a conservatory (families
welcome). Caters for all tastes,
with live music Wed/Sun and
quizzes Mon/Thu. Busy at all
times with first class meals all
day (opens at 8.30 for
breakfasts; no-smoking food area
at lunchtime). Snooker table.
❀ ⇖ ❀ ◖ & ♣

Sportsman
57 Benty Lane (A57)
☎ (0742) 660502
11–3, 5–11 (11–11 Fri & Sat)
**Draught Bass; Stones Best
Bitter** Ⓗ
Well-furnished, large, split-level
lounge; smaller games room

with sporting theme. Wide selection of home-made lunchtime food.
Q 🍴 🛏 🍺 ♣ P

South Anston

Loyal Trooper
34 Sheffield Road (off A57)
☎ (0909) 562203
12–3, 6–11 (12–11 Sat)
Tetley Bitter Ⓗ
Obviously ancient pub. Two small front rooms; larger back room with games area.
Q 🍴 ♣ P

Sprotbrough

Boat Inn
Nursery Lane, Lower Sprotbrough (between Sprotbrough and Warmsworth)
☎ (0302) 857188
11–3, 6–11 (11–11 Sat in summer)
Courage Directors; John Smith's Bitter, Magnet Ⓗ
Imaginative conversion of farm buildings in an attractive riverside setting. Bar meals (not Sat/Sun eves) and separate restaurant. Q 🍴 🍴 ▶ P

Thorne

Rising Sun
Hatfield Road (slip road off A614, just before canal bridge)
☎ (0405) 812688
11–3, 6–11
Wards Thorne Best Bitter Ⓗ
Traditional, two-roomed local on outskirts of town. Tastefully decorated and furnished lounge; pleasant restful atmosphere. Bric-a-brac and memorabilia; Victorian fireplace; magazines to browse. Eve meals by reservation only.
🛏 Q 🍴 🍴 & ♣ P

Thorpe Hesley

Horse & Tiger
Brook Hill (B6086, near A629 and M1 jct 35)
☎ (0742) 468072
11–3, 6–11 (11–11 Sat)
Stones Best Bitter; Tetley Bitter Ⓗ
Restored to its former glory, this pub stands on the site of an earlier one. Its history and plans are displayed. Bar billiards.
🍴 ♣ P

Masons Arms
Thorpe Street (off B6086)
☎ (0742) 468079
11–3, 6–11
Theakston XB; Younger Scotch, IPA, No. 3 Ⓗ
Pub dating from 1818 but much extended since. Two quiet rooms where children are welcome; lounge is much larger with central gas fire. Landlord holds the *Grandmaster*

Cellarman award, reflecting the consistently excellent beer served. Q 🍴 🍴 & ♣ P

Tickhill

Scarbrough Arms
Sunderland Street
☎ (0302) 742977
11–3, 6–11
Courage Directors; John Smith's Bitter, Magnet Ⓗ
Named after a local landowner, this welcoming hostelry stands at the centre of an historic village. Three totally different rooms: a large lounge, a games room-cum-bar and a cosy middle room with a real fire and barrel furniture. No food Sun.
🛏 🍴 🍴 ♣ P

Try also: Six out of seven Tickhill pubs sell real ale.

Victoria

Victoria Inn
Hepworth (A616)
☎ (0484) 682785
12–2, 7–11 (12–2, 7–10.30 Sun)
Tetley Bitter; Younger IPA Ⓗ
Old-fashioned and unspoilt pub, comprising basic lobby bar, intimate lounge and occasional tap room. Toasted sandwiches served from antique grill behind bar. Q P

Wadworth

Fox & Hounds
Main Street (A60)
☎ (0302) 853425
11–3, 6 (6.30 winter)–11
John Smith's Bitter, Magnet Ⓗ
18th-century village inn: two comfortable rooms and a small restaurant. Guest beer. No meals Sun eve. 🍴 🍴 🍴 ♣ P

Wath upon Dearne

New Inn
West Street (A633)
☎ (0709) 872785
11–11
John Smith's Bitter, Magnet Ⓗ
This lively, two-roomed local, once the Whitworth brewery tap, is popular with a wide cross-section of the community. Good food, including vegetarian meals, in the bar and upstairs restaurant. Guest beers.
🍴 🍴 & ♣

Sandygate
On A633, near A6023 jct
☎ (0709) 877827
11–3, 5–11
Theakston Best Bitter, XB, Old Peculier; Younger IPA, No. 3 Ⓗ
Large, imposing former hospital overlooking the Dearne Valley.

Decorated and furnished to a high standard.
🛏 🍴 🛏 🍴 🍴 ♣ P

Wentworth

George & Dragon
Main Street (B6090, 1½ miles from A6135)
☎ (0226) 742440
12–3, 7–11 (12–2.30, 7–10.30 Sun)
Oak Wobbly Bob; Taylor Best Bitter, Landlord, Porter; Tetley Bitter Ⓗ
Traditional village local full of character(s). If ever there was a traditional English country pub, it may still be here. Wide range of high-gravity guest beers – just as well it's on the Rotherham–Barnsley bus route.
🛏 Q 🍴 🍴 🛏 P

Woodhouse Mill

Princess Royal
680 Retford Road (A57, close to Sheffield city boundary)
☎ (0742) 692615
11–3.30, 7–11
Ind Coope Burton Ale; Stones Best Bitter; Tetley Bitter Ⓗ
Large, multi-roomed pub. Live jazz Tue eves. Guest beers. No food Sun.
🛏 🍴 🍴 🚆 (Woodhouse) ♣ P

Worsbrough

Edmunds Arms
Off A61 ☎ (0226) 206865
11–3 (4 Fri & Sat), 7–11
Samuel Smith OBB Ⓗ
Splendid village inn opposite a picturesque church: lounge, tap room, garden and a restaurant that opens at lunchtime (no bar meals Mon eve or Sun). Near a country park and a historic water mill.
Q 🍴 🍴 ▶ 🍴 ♣ P

Help keep real ale alive by joining CAMRA. Your voice helps encourage brewers big and small to brew cask beer and offer all beer drinkers a better choice. For membership details see page 480!

West Yorkshire

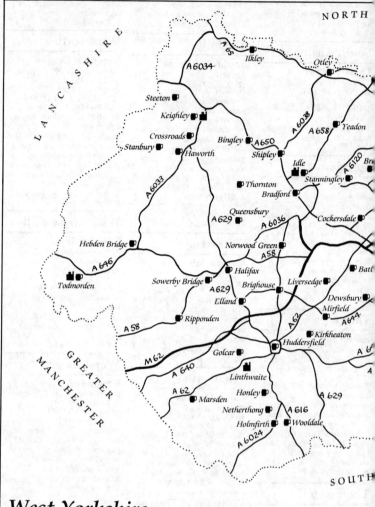

Clark's, Wakefield; **Linfit**, Linthwaite; **Taylor**, Keighley; **Robinwood**, Todmorden; **Trough**, Idle

Aberford

Arabian Horse
Main Street ☎ (0532) 813312
11–2.30, 5–11 (11–11 Sat)
**Theakston Best Bitter;
Younger Scotch, No. 3** Ⓗ
Standing on the village green and the old Great North Road: a hostelry catering for visitors and locals alike. No meals Sun.
🏠 Q ✻ ◖ ♿ ♣ P

Altofts

Poplar Inn
Church Road (½ mile from Normanton)
☎ (0924) 893416
11–11
John Smith's Bitter Ⓗ
Friendly, two-roomed, drinkers' pub. Entertainment Wed, Fri & Sat.
✻ ⊟ ≅ ♣ P

Armley

Albion Inn
86 Armley Road (old A647)
11–11
Tetley Bitter Ⓗ
Three-roomed pub with brass handpumps: a Tetley Heritage Inn and winner of a CAMRA *Pub Preservation* award. In this guide for the 19th time. Guest beer.
🏠 Q ◖ ⊟ ♣ P

Bass Mild XXXX, Light, Draught Bass; Stones Best Bitter Ⓗ
Busy, three-roomed, central meeting place. No meals Sun lunch. ⋈ ◖ ◗ ◲ ⬥ ⇌ P

Bingley

Ferrands Arms
Queen Street ☎ (0274) 563949
11.30–11
Taylor Golden Best, Best Bitter, Landlord, Ram Tam Ⓗ
Popular pub near the arts centre. Large, open-plan bar with lounge and games area (quizzes and games leagues).
◖ ⇌ ♣ P

Bradford

Albion
25 New Line, Greengates (300 yds from A657/A658 jct)
☎ (0274) 613211
11.45–3, 4.45–11 (11.45–11 Fri & Sat)
Tetley Mild, Bitter Ⓗ
Roadside local with floral decoration: a compact lounge and a busy tap room. Note the display of matchboxes featuring local public houses. ◲ ⬥ ♣

Blue Pig
Fagley Road, Fagley (down track at end of Fagley Rd)
OS193351 ☎ (0532) 560860
11.30–11
Taylor Landlord; Tetley Bitter; Theakston Best Bitter, XB; Whitbread Trophy; Younger No. 3 Ⓗ
Popular pub at the bottom of a lane, on the Leeds Country Way. Flooding necessitated the building of the low front wall and tortuous entrance way. DJ and quiz every eve. ⊛ ♣ P

Brown Cow
886 Little Horton Lane
☎ (0274) 574040
12–3, 7–11
Samuel Smith OBB Ⓗ
Two-roomed, locals' pub just off the ring road: a comfortable lounge and a basic tap room. Live entertainment Thu, Fri and Sun eves. ◲ ⬥ ♣ P

Corn Dolly
Bolton Road
☎ (0274) 720219
11–11
Stones Best Bitter; Taylor Best Bitter; Theakston Best Bitter, XB Ⓗ
Country-style pub with oak beams and a warm fire; home of the Cornucopia quiz team; pool and dominoes also played. Country & western Wed and Sun, plus a fine jukebox. Over 200 different guest beers to date; three always available.
⚿ ◖ ⬥ ⇌ (Forster Sq) ♣ P

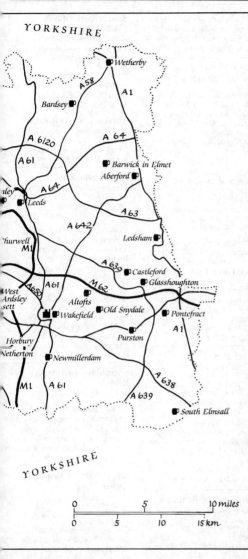

YORKSHIRE

Wetherby
A58 / A1
Bardsey
A6/20 / A64
A61
Barwick in Elmet
A64 / Aberford
...ley / Leeds
A63
A642
Ledsham
...hurwell / M1
A639
Castleford
M62 / Glasshoughton
West Ardsley sett / A650 / A61
Altofts / Old Snydale
Wakefield / Pontefract
Horbury / Purston / A1
Netherton
Newmillerdam
M1 / A61 / A638
A639
South Elmsall

YORKSHIRE

0		5		10 miles
0	5	10	15 km	

Nelson
212 Armley Road (A647)
☎ (0532) 638505
11–3, 5.30–11 (11–11 Sat)
Theakston XB; Younger Scotch, No. 3 Ⓗ
Two-roomed pub near the jail; the last home-brew pub in Leeds (ceased brewing on the death of the owner in 1952). ◖ ◲ ♣

Bardsey

Bingley Arms
Church Lane ☎ (0937) 572462
12–3, 6–11 (12–11 Fri & Sat)
Tetley Mild, Bitter Ⓗ
Ancient pub, with parts reputedly dating from the 10th century. Large garden. *A la carte* restaurant. ⚿ ⊛ ◖ ◗ ◲ ▲ ♣ P

Barwick in Elmet

New Inn
Main Street ☎ (0532) 812289
11–3, 6–11
John Smith's Bitter Ⓗ
Roadside village inn, extended into adjoining cottages. Service is from a tiny bar and hatch.
Q ◲ ♣

Batley

Wilton Arms
4 Commercial Street (off A652)
☎ (0924) 479996
11–3, 5–11 (11–11 Mon, Fri & Sat)

West Yorkshire

Drop Kick

Huddersfield Road, Low Moor
☎ (0274) 670207
11.30–3, 7–11
Thwaites Bitter Ⓗ
Modern pub near Odsal
Stadium, home of the Bradford
Northern RL team. Spacious,
open-plan lounge where lunches
are served (bar snacks only at
night); large games room with
three pool tables. ⑧ ◖ ⊞ ♣ P ⍍

Fighting Cock

21–23 Preston Street
☎ (0274) 726907
11–11
**Mansfield Riding Bitter, Old
Baily; Old Mill Bitter; Taylor
Golden Best, Landlord;
Wadworth 6X** Ⓗ
Basic and popular, back-street
ale house in an industrial area,
with real ciders and foreign
bottled beers. Famous for its
chilli and 'dockers' wedges'.
Guest beers. Live trad. jazz
Mon. ⊞ ◖ ♣ ○

Fleece

Allerton Road, Allerton (3 miles
W of centre) ☎ (0274) 542966
6–11 (12–11 Fri & Sat)
**Webster's Green Label,
Yorkshire Bitter; Stones Best
Bitter** Ⓗ
Modernised pub with music and
discos in a large lounge;
traditional pub games Tue night
in the public bar and quizzes
three times a week. ⊞ ♣ P

Hogshead

45 Haigh Hall Road,
Greengates (off New Line,
A657, 200 yds W of A658 jct)
☎ (0274) 612670
11–11 (11–3, 6.30–11 Sat)
**Trough Bitter, Wild Boar,
Hogshead** Ⓗ
Large, smart, single-roomed pub
divided into two areas by a
large, central bar. Formerly a
Conservative club. The games
area contains a mini ten-pin
bowling alley. ♣ P

Lancaster

Westgate ☎ (0274) 723259
11–4, 6–11 (11–11 Sat)
**Ansells Mild; Ind Coope
Burton Ale; Tetley Bitter** Ⓗ
No-nonsense, town local with a
strong regular following. Quiet
back room. Handy for dozens of
Bradford curry houses.
Q ⊞ ⇌ (Forster Sq) ♣

Macrory's Bar

Beechfield Hotel, 4 Easby Road
☎ (0274) 729524
12–3.30, 5.30–11 (12–11 Thu–Sat)
**Courage Directors; John
Smith's Bitter, Magnet** Ⓗ
Cellar bar beneath a hotel,
where solid wood furniture and
a solid fuel stove feature.
Interesting home-cooked menu
with a vegetarian option.

Popular with students. Free
bands on Mon and some other
nights. Occasional guest beers.
⑧ ⇌ ⇌ (Interchange) P

New Beehive Inn

Westgate ☎ (0274) 721784
11–11
**Caledonian Golden Promise;
Old Mill Bitter; Taylor
Golden Best, Landlord;
Tetley Bitter; Wards Sheffield
Best Bitter** Ⓗ
Well-preserved, highly
atmospheric, gas-lit, Edwardian
hostelry. Live trad. jazz every Fri
night. Regular guest beers.
⊞ ⏣ ⑧ ⇌ ◖ ⊞ & ⍍

Oakleigh

4 Oak Avenue, Manningham
☎ (0274) 544307
12–3, 6 (5 football match eves)–11
(11–11 Sat)
**Draught Bass; Marston's
Pedigree; Old Mill Bitter;
Stones Best Bitter; Taylor
Best Bitter, Landlord** Ⓗ
A long-standing classic: a free
house with a splendid garden.
Across the road from Lister
Park. A comfortable pub with a
good mix of clientele. No
jukebox. Guest beers.
⊞ Q ⑧ ⇌ ◖ ♣ P

Peel Hotel

52 Richmond Road
☎ (0274) 391739
11–3.30, 5–11 (1am Fri & Sat)
**Ruddles Best Bitter, County;
Webster's Yorkshire Bitter,
Choice** Ⓗ
Family-run pub near the
University and popular with
students. Separate disco room
with keg beer only. Good value
meals (barbecues Thu nights in
summer). Live music every Sat;
folk club Fri. ⑧ ◖ & ♣

Prospect of Bradford

527 Bolton Road (5 mins' from
Forster Square)
☎ (0274) 727018
1–4, 7–11
**Taylor Golden Best; Tetley
Bitter** Ⓗ
Spacious, Victorian pub with
panoramic views of Bradford.
Organist sing-along Fri, Sat and
Sun. Function room; excellent
buffets available. Guest beers.
⊞ ⇌ ♣ P

Red Lion

881 Manchester Road,
Bankfoot
11–11
Tetley Mild, Bitter Ⓗ
Popular local, handy for Odsal
Stadium. ⑧ ◖ & ♣ P

Red Lion

589 Thornton Road, Four Lane
Ends (B6145, 2 miles from
centre) ☎ (0274) 496684
11–3 (3.30 Thu), 5.30–11 (11–11 Fri &
Sat)

Samuel Smith OBB Ⓗ

Good, honest, main road pub,
with always a good trade.
Darts, doms, pool and quizzes.
Good lunches. Satellite TV.
⊞ ◖ ⊞ & ♣ P

Royal Oak

Sticker Lane, Laisterdyke
☎ (0274) 665265
11–3, 5.30–11
**Theakston Best Bitter, XB,
Old Peculier; Younger
Scotch, No. 3** Ⓗ
Smart, ring road local, with a
games room. ⍍ ⑧ ◖ ⊞ ♣

Royal Standard

Manningham Lane (A650, off
inner ring road)
☎ (0274) 394396
12–3, 6–11 (12 Thu, 1am Sat; 12–1am
Fri)
**Draught Bass; Marston's
Pedigree; Stones Best Bitter;
Taylor Landlord; Whitbread
Boddingtons Bitter** Ⓗ
Large, Victorian pub with fine
wood and glasswork. The small
bar, which serves the large
concert room, is closed at
lunchtime; pool table in the
main bar. Live bands Thu–Sun
nights (usually a charge). Guest
beer. £1 entrance fee after
11pm, Thu–Sat.
⊞ ◖ ⇌ (Forster Sq)

Shoulder of Mutton

Kirkgate
☎ (0274) 726038
11–11
Samuel Smith OBB Ⓗ
Small, multi-roomed pub, rebuilt
in 1825. Its surprisingly large
and high-walled beer garden is a
suntrap. High quality lunches.
⑧ ◖ ⊞ ⇌ (Forster Sq) ♣

University of Bradford Union Bars

Great Horton Road
☎ (0274) 734135
11–11 (Mainline Bar); 11.30–2.30,
4.30–11 (Biko Bar)
**Courage Directors; Tetley
Bitter; Theakston Best Bitter,
XB; Trough Wild Boar;
Younger No. 3** Ⓗ
'Mainline' and 'Steve Biko'
bars, run by the Students' Union
with full on-licences. Open
throughout the year but some
beers may only be available in
term-time. Guest beers. ○ ⍍

Bramley

Old Unicorn

Stocks Hill (A657, opp.
shopping centre)
☎ (0532) 564465
11.30–3 (4 Fri & Sat), 5.30 (7 Sat)–11
(12–2, 7–10.30 Sun)
**Tetley Mild, Bitter;
Theakston Best Bitter;
Younger No. 3** Ⓗ
Comfortable, popular, 200 year-
old free house; much extended,

with an opened-out interior. The beer garden is very popular with families. Good home-cooked food, with a vegetarian option. Q ▦ ◖ ♣ P

Old Vic
17 Whitecote Hill
11–3 (4 Sat), 7–11
Draught Bass; Taylor Golden Best, Landlord; Tetley Mild, Bitter; Trough Wild Boar Ⓗ
Formerly a vicarage, then a social club; now a popular free house, set back from the road in its own grounds. Two lounges, a games room and a function room. Seven beers on sale. Q ♣ P

Brighouse

Crown
6 Lightcliffe Road (off A644 at the Albion) ☎ (0484) 715436
11–3, 5–11 (11–11 Thu–Sat & summer)
Tetley Bitter Ⓗ
Multi-roomed, Victorian local, which has survived redevelopment. Unusual collections, incl. plates. ♣ P

Red Rooster
123 Elland Road, Brookfoot (A6025, ½ mile from centre)
12–2 (3 Sat), 5 (6 Sat)–11
Marston's Pedigree; Old Mill Bitter; Taylor Landlord Ⓗ
Compact and friendly, roadside local. Usually five guest beers. Small car park. ▦ ▦ ♣ ◔ P

Star
29 Bridge End, Rastrick (A643)
11.30–3, 5 (7 Sat)–11
Tetley Mild, Bitter Ⓗ
Nestling next to the railway viaduct, a pub with a large, busy tap room and a comfortable, unusually-shaped lounge. Limited parking. ◖ ♣ P

Castleford

Garden House
Wheldon Road
☎ (0977) 552934
11–11
Vaux Samson (occasional); **Wards Thorne Best Bitter, Kirby** Ⓗ
Friendly, edge-of-town pub overlooking the River Aire and close to the rugby ground. RL photos and drawings adorn the walls. Good tasty food at keen prices. Q ◭ ▦ ◖ ▮ ◖ ♣

Old Mill
Lock Lane (A656, ½ mile N of town, next to canal)
☎ (0977) 557034
11–11 (may vary)
Theakston Best Bitter, XB, Old Peculier Ⓗ
L-shaped lounge with a welcoming open fire. Handy for Castleford RL ground and often full of players; busy weekends

and Sun lunchtime before matches. Other Younger's beers are rotated. Eve meals Sat only; no food Sun lunch.
▦ ▦ ◖ ▮ ◖ ◭ ♣ P

Pointer (Dog)
Marchant Street, The Potteries, Whitwood Mere (off A6032, Leeds road) ☎ (0977) 553953
11–11 (may vary)
Camerons Bitter, Strongarm (occasional) Ⓗ
Friendly, former Tetley house, comprising two lounges – one modern, one 1930s style – and a tap room. Landlord is an ex-60s RL player. The only Camerons in Castleford; occasionally has Tolly beers as guests. Q ◖ ◖ ♣ ♣

Churwell

Commercial Inn
Elland Road ☎ (0532) 532776
11.30–3, 5.30–11
Tetley Mild, Bitter Ⓗ
Beautifully-restored, 400 year-old pub, known locally as 'Top 'Ole' as it is the highest of the three pubs on Churwell Hill. Upstairs meeting/children's room. Hot snacks lunchtimes.
Q ◭ ▦ ◖ ▮ ♣ P

Cockersdale

Valley
68 Whitehall Road (A58)
☎ (0532) 852483
11–3, 5.30–11
Samuel Smith OBB Ⓗ
Offering fine views across the valley, an ideal place to start (or end) a walk on the Leeds Country Way. No food Wed or Sun. Children welcome weekend lunchtimes.
▦ Q ▦ ◖ ◭ ♣ P

Crossroads

Quarry House Inn
Bingley Road (1 mile off A629)
☎ (0535) 642239
12–3, 7–11 (11.30 supper licence)
Ind Coope Burton Ale; Taylor Landlord; Tetley Bitter Ⓗ
Family-run, converted farmhouse in open countryside. The bar is a former pulpit and is set in a small, cosy area. Good quality food, especially the mixed grill on Wed.
▦ Q ◭ ▦ ◖ ▮ ◭ ◔ ▲ P

Dewsbury

John F Kennedy
2 Webster Hill (A644, near bus station) ☎ (0924) 455828
12–4 (Sat only), 7–11
Taylor Landlord; Tetley Bitter Ⓗ

'Alternative' pub with a keen following. Unchanged for many years. Guest beers weekends. Note restricted hours. ◔ ◿ ♣

Market House
Church Street (near bus station)
☎ (0924) 457310
11–3 (4 Sat), 5 (7 Sat)–11 (11–11 Fri)
Tetley Mild, Bitter Ⓗ
A Tetley Heritage pub and a long-time legend; basic, but with character.
▦ Q ◖ ◔ ◿ ♣

Park Hotel
125 High Street, Westtown (off A644) ☎ (0924) 463819
12–3 (4 Sat), 7–11
Theakston Best Bitter; Younger No. 3 Ⓗ
Small pub, with an authentic tap room, a home to pigeon fanciers and many others. Close to Crow Nest Park. Lunches only on Sat. ▦ ◖ ▮ ♣ P

Elland

Barge & Barrel
Park Road (A6025)
☎ (0422) 373623
12–11
Marston's Pedigree, Owd Rodger; Oak Tyke; Taylor Landlord; Wards Sheffield Best Bitter Ⓗ
Spacious, Victorian-style, canalside pub, refurbished with leaded glass and polished wood. Four drinking areas, incl. a games room and a well-equipped family room. Fine fireplace in the front room. At least four guest beers.
▦ ◭ ▦ ◖ ▮ ♣ P

Colliers Arms
Park Road (A6025)
☎ (0422) 372007
11.30–3, 5.30 (5 Fri)–11 (11.30–11 Sat)
Samuel Smith OBB, Museum Ⓗ
Smart, cottage pub with two low-ceilinged rooms and a conservatory to the rear. It lies both on the main road and the canalside, and has its own moorings. Eve meals Thu–Sat.
▦ ◭ ▦ ◖ ▮ ♣ P

Glasshoughton

Rock Inn
Off Front Street, B6136 to Ferrybridge ☎ (0977) 554437
11–11
Wards Mild, Thorne Best Bitter, Kirby Ⓗ
Popular, friendly, locals' pub comprising a lounge, snug and tap room, all with open fires. Car parking very difficult and traffic wardens keen. Yorkshire CAMRA *Pub of the Year* 1990. Upstairs games room.
▦ Q ◖ ▮ ♣ P

West Yorkshire

Golcar

Golcar Lily
101 Slades Road
OS086157 ☎ (0484) 659277
12–3 (not Mon–Thu), 7–11 (closed Mon)
Ind Coope Burton Ale; Oak Old Oak; Tetley Mild, Bitter ⊞
A former Co-op building, now a smart free house with a separate restaurant. On the route of the Colne Valley Circular Walk, with a superb view. ☾ ◗ P

Halifax

Brown Cow
569 Gibbet Street, Highroad Well (1½ miles from centre)
☎ (0422) 361640
11.30–3, 5–11 (11.30–11 Fri & Sat)
Whitbread Castle Eden Ale ⊞
Unpretentious local with sporting connections. No food weekends. ☾ ♣

Clarence Hotel
Lister Lane ☎ (0422) 363266
11.30–11
Old Mill Bitter; Stones Best Bitter; Taylor Landlord; Tetley Bitter ⊞
Busy, street-corner local in a four-room, open-plan style, with an upstairs dining room. Active sports following. Happy hour every day. Occasional guest beer. ❀ ☾ ◗ ♿ ⇌ ♣ P

Dean Clough Inn
36 Lee Bridge (½ mile N of town) ☎ (0422) 346708
11.30–11 (12–3.30, 7–11 Sat)
Draught Bass; Stones Best Bitter; Tetley Bitter ⊞
Smart, Edwardian pub with a single V-shaped lounge, beneath the A629 flyover. Popular for food, specialising in pizzas; vegetarian dishes also available (eve meals finish at 7pm). ☾ ◗

Duke of York
West Street, Stone Chair, Shelf (A644) ☎ (0422) 202056
11.30–11
Taylor Best Bitter; Whitbread Castle Eden Ale ⊞
Ancient inn with a remarkable roofscape. Refurbished within, but still cosy and comfortable. Popular for food (menu includes vegetarian option).
❀ 🛏 ☾ ◗ ♣ P

Shears Inn
Paris Gates, Boys Lane (behind flats, between mills and down into mill yard)
11.45–4, 7–11 (11.45–11 Sat)
Taylor Golden Best, Best Bitter, Landlord; Younger Scotch, No. 3 ⊞
Hard to find, this tiny popular house provides a rendezvous for several sporting and cultural groups. Enjoys a sublime location, nestling in a wooded valley bottom and dominated by towering mills. No food weekends. Guest beer.
⌂ ❀ ☾ ⇌ P

Sportsman Inn
Bradford Old Road, Ploughcroft (¼ mile E of A647, 1 mile N of town) ☎ (0422) 367000
12–3, 6–11 (12–11 Sat)
Ind Coope Burton Ale; Old Mill Bitter; Ruddles County; Taylor Landlord; Tetley Mild; Theakston Old Peculier ⊞
Popular, hilltop free house with expansive views. Squash, a solarium and a sauna are all available, and an all-weather ski slope is attached. Folk club Thu; quiz nights Mon, Tue and Wed. No food Mon or Tue. Guest beer. ⌂ ♞ ❀ ☾ ◗ ♣ P

Three Pigeons
1 Sun Fold, South Parade
12–2 (3 Sat; not Tue), 7–11
Draught Bass; Stones Best Bitter; Taylor Landlord ⊞
Cosily modernised, multi-roomed, Art Deco local with an unusual octagonal drinking lobby. Hosts quizzes and local society meetings.
⌂ Q ❀ ⇌ ♣ P

Upper George
Crown Street ☎ (0422) 353614
12–11
Tetley Bitter ⊞
Very popular pub in a renovated cobbled courtyard. Frequented by many types, particularly lovers of rock music. Can get packed and noisy, especially at weekends, but a friendly, lively atmosphere is assured. Wheelchair access at the rear. ❀ ♿ ⇌ ♣

Haworth

Fleece Inn
Main Street ☎ (0535) 642172
11.30–4 (3 winter), 7–11
Taylor Golden Best, Best Bitter, Landlord, Ram Tam ⊞
Ancient coaching inn, popular with 'spirits'; a village local which welcomes visitors. Stone-flagged bar area and a quiet room which contains a spoof Brontë museum display.
⌂ ♞ ☾ ⛺ ⇌ (KWVLR) ♣

Hebden Bridge

Cross Inn
46 Towngate, Heptonstall
☎ (0422) 843833
11.30–4, 7–11
Taylor Golden Best, Best Bitter, Landlord ⊞
Comfortable, welcoming local, deep and narrow, set prominently on the steep, narrow and winding main street of an unspoilt, old hilltop town. Very limited parking.
❀ 🛏 ☾ ◗ ⛺ ♣

Fox & Goose
9 Heptonstall Road (A646)
☎ (0422) 842649
11.30–3, 7–11
Ruddles Best Bitter; John Smith's Magnet ⊞
Arched, ground-floor cellars form this distinctive local. Supper licence and small, varied food menu (no food Tue eve). Guest beers mainly from Whitbread. Parking difficult.
❀ ☾ ◗ ⇌ ♣

Nutclough House Hotel
Keighley Road (A6033)
☎ (0422) 844361
12–3 (not Mon in winter), 6–11 (11–11 Sat)
Everards Tiger; Taylor Landlord; Theakston Best Bitter; Thwaites Bitter ⊞
Spacious, comfortable, family pub with piano, quiz and folk music eves. Beware of the crisp-eating cat! Varied menu, especially vegetarian dishes. Occasional guest beer.
⌂ ❀ ☾ ◗ ⇌ ♣ P

Pack Horse
Widdop Road, Widdop
OS952317 ☎ (0422) 842803
12–3, 7–11 (12–11 Sat in summer; closed Oct–Easter)
Thwaites Bitter; Younger IPA ⊞
Isolated moorland pub near the Pennine Way. Popular with motorists. Walkers are welcome if they leave boots at the door. Good food (available Wed–Sun). Guest beer. Note winter closing. ⌂ Q ❀ ☾ ◗ ⛺ P

Shoulder of Mutton
38 New Road, Mytholmroyd (B6138) ☎ (0422) 883165
11.30–3, 7–11
Whitbread Castle Eden Ale ⊞
Very popular, roadside local with a display of Toby jugs and china. Guest beer.
☾ ◗ ⛺ ⇌ (Mytholmroyd) ♣ P

Holmfirth

Farmers Arms
Liphill Bank, Burnlee (200 yds off A635, Greenfield road)
☎ (0484) 683713
12–2 (3 Sat; not Mon), 6–11
Taylor Best Bitter; Tetley Mild, Bitter ⊞
Good all-round pub with a real fire which tends to 'kipper' you when stoked. Situated on a narrow lane so parking can be difficult. Guest beers. ⌂ ☾ ◗ ♣

Rose & Crown (Nook)
7 Victoria Square (down alley off Hollowgate, off A6024)
☎ (0484) 683960
11.30–11

Taylor Best Bitter, Landlord, Ram Tam; Tetley Mild; Theakston Best Bitter; Younger No. 3 Ⓗ
Legendary, basic boozer. Well worth the effort of finding somewhere to park. Occasional guest beers. ⌂ ❀ ⊟ Å ♣

Honley

Coach & Horses
Eastgate (200 yds from A616/A6024 jct)
☎ (0484) 666135
11.30–3, 5–11 (11.30–11 Sat)
Bass Mild XXXX, Light, Draught Bass; Stones Best Bitter Ⓗ
Busy, tastefully modernised, old coaching inn, with Luddite connections. Locally known as 'Henry's', after a former landlord. Guest beers. Lunches Mon–Fri; eve meals Mon only.
⌂ ◖ ◗ Å ⇌ P

Horbury

Shepherd's Arms
Cluntergate ☎ (0924) 274877
11–11
Theakston Best Bitter, XB, Old Peculier; Younger Scotch, No. 3 Ⓗ
Ancient inn, well-modernised in open-plan style with a bar and a large and comfortable lounge. Just outside the town centre; a friendly and well-kept pub.
⌂ ❀ ◖ ◗ ⊟ ♣ P

Huddersfield

Ale Shoppe
205 Lockwood Road, Lockwood (A616)
☎ (0484) 432479
10–7.30 (closed Sun)
Beer range varies Ⓗ
Off-licence with up to four draught beers available. Oak and Taylor's beers are regularly in stock. Over 50 bottle-conditioned beers from Belgium, Germany and Britain. A home-brewing supply shop and a beer hunter's paradise.
⇌ (Lockwood)

Rat & Ratchet
40 Chapel Hill (A616, just off ring road) ☎ (0484) 516734
11.30–11
Bateman Mild; Marston's Pedigree; Old Mill Bitter; Taylor Landlord; Thwaites Best Mild Ⓗ
Lively free house, popular with students, usually boasting 12 different real ales. Occasional live music. Guest beers.
❀ ◖ ♿ ⇌ ⌓ P

Shoulder of Mutton
11 Neale Road, Lockwood (off B6108, near A616 jct)
☎ (0484) 424835
7 (3 Sat)–11
Taylor Best Bitter, Landlord; Tetley Mild, Bitter; Thwaites Bitter Ⓗ
Old-fashioned pub at the top of a cobbled street with authentic walnut panelling, a legendary jukebox and a traditional games room. Pool room upstairs. Guest beers. ❀ ♣

Slubbers Arms
1 Halifax Old Road (off A641)
☎ (0484) 429032
11.30–4, 6.30–11
Marston's Pedigree; Old Mill Mild; Taylor Best Bitter Ⓗ
Uniquely-named, wedge-shaped pub which features a Yorkshire range, a timeclock and textile memorabilia. Guest beers.
⌂ Q ◖ ♣

Woolpack
19 Westgate, Almondbury
☎ (0484) 435702
11.30–2, 5–11 (11.30–11 Sat)
Courage Directors; John Smith's Bitter, Magnet Ⓗ
Open-plan, village local, opposite an historic church. Snacks Tue–Sat lunchtime.
❀ ◖ P

Idle

Brewery Arms
Louisa Street (off High Street)
☎ (0274) 610546
12–11
Trough Bitter, Wild Boar, Hogshead Ⓗ
Former Liberal club and restaurant, next to the brewery. Refurbished after a fire and now comprises a large lounge with a separate bar for pool. Tends to be noisy. ◖ P

Brewery Tap
Albion Road
11.30–3 (4 Sat), 6.30 (7 Sat)–11
Trough Bitter, Wild Boar Ⓗ
Converted from a bakery, but had previously been a pub. One room with a large, central bar area. Part stone walls and floor, and part wood panelling and carpet. Rock music Tue and Sat nights. ❀ ♣

Ilkley

Midland Hotel
Station Road ☎ (0943) 607433
11–11
Courage Best Bitter, Directors; John Smith's Bitter, Magnet Ⓗ
Victorian pub refurbished a few years ago with a Victorian railway theme. Guest beer.
Q ◖ ⊟ ⇌ ♣ P

Keighley

Albert Hotel
Bridge Street (Oakworth Road/Halifax Road jct)
☎ (0535) 602306
11–5, 7–11 (11–11 Fri & Sat)
Taylor Golden Best, Best Bitter, Ram Tam (winter) Ⓗ
Victorian hotel enjoying largely local trade but also a popular meeting place. One long, thin room at the front, around the corner from the bar, plus a very large pool room with an original mural. Limited parking.
⇌ ♣ P

Boltmakers Arms
East Parade ☎ (0535) 661936
11–11 (11–4.30, 7–11 Sat)
Taylor Golden Best, Best Bitter, Landlord Ⓗ
Highly popular, family-run pub with customers from all walks of life. Very handy for the railway. The smallest pub in town, it is split into two levels and can get very busy. Good range of malt whiskies. ⇌ ♣

Cricketers Arms
Coney Lane (off Worth Way)
☎ (0535) 669912
11–11 (11–4.30, 7–11 Sat)
Taylor Golden Best, Best Bitter, Ram Tam (winter) Ⓗ
Small, single-roomed, friendly local, tucked away behind Worth House. Q ♿ ⇌ ♣

Eastwood Tavern
37 Bradford Road (next to fire station) ☎ (0535) 604849
11.30–11
Taylor Golden Best, Best Bitter Ⓗ
Popular, lively local with separate games room and snug. Excellent lunches. Handy for the station. ⌂ ❀ ◖ ⊟ ⇌ ♣ P

Grinning Rat/Rat Trap
Church Street
☎ (0535) 609747
11–11 (midnight Wed, 1am Thu–Sat)
Malton Double Chance; Moorhouse's Pendle Witches Brew; Old Mill Bitter; Samuel Smith OBB; Taylor Landlord Ⓗ
Popular, central pub with three entirely different bars. Nine guest beers, incl. a mild, plus a regularly changed cider, allow a pub crawl under one roof. Live music. Bar meals usually available. ◖ ◗ ♿ ⇌ ♣ ⌓

Red Pig
Church Street
☎ (0535) 605383
11.30–2.30 (4.30 Fri & Sat), 7–11
Taylor Golden Best, Landlord; Trough Wild Boar Ⓗ
Urbane pub, very well supported by the local pool team. Official HQ of the 'Porcine Cavers'. The owner tries new brews from independent breweries. Trough brewery artefacts abound. Guest beers. ◖ ⇌ ♣

West Yorkshire

Volunteer Arms
Lawkholme Lane
☎ (0535) 600173
11–11
Taylor Golden Best, Best Bitter ⊞
Smart, two-roomed local in the town centre. Difficult to find, hidden behind a large Tetley pub in Cavendish Street.
⌑ ≠ ♣

Keighley to Oxenhope and Back

Keighley & Worth Valley Railway Buffet Car
Stations at Keighley, Ingrow, Damens, Oakworth, Haworth and Oxenhope
☎ (0535) 645214
Sat & Sun only, March–Oct; Sun only, Oct–Dec
Beer range varies ⊞
Railway buffet car giving changing views of the Worth Valley as it travels the line. One or two guest beers served from polypins refilled several times a day. Talking timetable (0535) 643629. Train available for hire with beer of your choice.
Q P ⍓

Kirkheaton

Beaumont Arms
Church Lane ☎ (0484) 543502
12–3.30, 7–11
Taylor Best Bitter; Tetley Mild, Bitter ⊞
In a quiet hamlet in the hollow below Kirkheaton Village, linked to St John's church by a medieval tunnel. A haven of quiet drinking in oak-panelled surroundings; a Tetley Heritage pub with a children's playground. Better known locally as the 'Kirkstile'.
⌂ Q ⌑ ▲ ♣ P

Ledsham

Chequers
Claypit Lane ☎ (0977) 683135
11–3, 5.30–11 (11–11 Sat; closed Sun)
John Smith's Bitter; Theakston Best Bitter; Younger Scotch, No. 3 ⊞
Classic, busy, country pub with several low-beamed rooms and a cosy, intimate atmosphere, warmed by open fires. Fine upstairs restaurant and an enclosed beer garden at the rear.
⌂ Q ↶ ⊛ ⌑ ♣ P

Leeds

Adelphi
1 Hunslet Road, Leeds Bridge
11–11 (11–3, 7.30–11 Sat)
Tetley Mild, Bitter ⊞
Multi-roomed pub with fine woodwork, glass panels and tiles. Live music Sat eve; function rooms. No food weekends. ⌑ ⊞ ♣

Ale House
79 Raglan Road (opp. Leeds University) ☎ (0532) 455447
12 (4 Mon)–10.30 (10–10.30 Sat; 12–3, 7–10 Sun)
Ale House Hyde Park Best, Monster Mash, No. 9, White Rose Ale ⊞
Real ale off-licence/brewery, started in 1987, selling three or four guest beers as well as cider, foreign bottled beers, wines, spirits and snacks. Brews occasional special beers. ⌕

Chemic Tavern
9 Johnston Street, Woodhouse
☎ (0532) 440092
11–3, 5.30–11 (11–11 Sat)
Ind Coope Burton Ale; Tetley Bitter ⊞
Cosy, wood-panelled bar, lively but without music; notable collection of jugs. Nice tap room. Q ⊞ ♣ P

City of Mabgate
45 Mabgate (3 mins' walk from W Yorkshire Playhouse)
☎ (0532) 457789
11.30–11
Whitbread Boddingtons Bitter, Trophy, Castle Eden Ale, Flowers Original ⊞
Very popular, two-room pub, in Edwardian style; a lively tap room and a lounge area displaying many photos of old Leeds. Two guest beers every week, also cider and organic wine. A mini beer festival is held annually. House beer, Mabgate Old Ale, is brewed by Burton Bridge. Meals Mon–Fri.
⌂ Q ⊛ ⌑ ⊞ ♣ ⌕

Duck & Drake
Kirkgate ☎ (0532) 465806
11–11
Home Bitter; Marston's Pedigree, Owd Rodger; Old Mill Bitter; Taylor Dark Mild, Landlord; Theakston Best Bitter, XB, Old Peculier; Younger No. 3 ⊞
No-frills ale house, frequented by all walks of life. Live music Tue, Thu and Sun. Up to four guest beers. No meals weekends. ⌂ ⌑ ⊞ ♣ ♣ ⌕

Eagle Tavern
North Street (A61, at Sheepscar interchange) ☎ (0532) 457146
11.30–3, 5.30–11
Taylor Golden Best, Dark Mild, Best Bitter, Landlord, Ram Tam ⊞
White, Georgian building with two rooms and a great atmosphere. Live music four nights a week. Two guest beers and real cider. The landlord has won Leeds CAMRA *Pub of the* *Year* three years running, the last two years in this pub.
⊛ ⋈ ⌑ ⊞ ♣ ⌕ P

Fox & Newt
9 Burley Road, Burley
☎ (0532) 432612
11–11
Theakston XB, Old Peculier; Whitbread Castle Eden Ale ⊞
One-roomed, bare-boarded brew pub in period style; busy with students from the college opposite. Whitbread malt-extract brewery on site. No meals weekends. ⌑

Gardeners Arms
33 Beza Street, Hunslet
☎ (0532) 712971
11–11
Tetley Mild, Bitter ⊞
Classic local, nestling between factories. Three small, original rooms; a Tetley Heritage pub.
⌂ Q ⌑ ⊞ ♣ P

Garden Gate
37 Waterloo Road, Hunslet
☎ (0532) 700379
11–11
Mansfield Riding Bitter; Tetley Mild, Bitter ⊞
Splendid, totally unspoilt, Victorian palace: a feast of glass tiles and wood in four rooms off a central corridor. Well worth a visit. ⌂ Q ⌑ ⊞ ♣ P

Grove Inn
Back Row, Holbeck
☎ (0532) 439254
11.30–11 (11.30–3, 5.30–11 Mon & Tue, 11.30–4, 7–11 Sat)
Courage Directors; John Smith's Bitter, Magnet; Taylor Landlord ⊞
Basic pub, nestled by the new ASDA offices. Home of the legendary Grove Folk on Fri; music on other nights, too. Guest beers planned.
⌂ Q ⌑ ⊞ ♣ ♣

Hanover Arms
Lower Wortley
☎ (0532) 630508
11.30–3, 6.30–11 (11.30–11 Fri & Sat)
Courage Best Bitter; Mansfield Riding Bitter; John Smith's Bitter ⊞
Large pub with three completely different rooms: a basic tap, a wonderful panelled lounge and a large modern, draped music lounge. Live music four times a week. Wheelchair access to the tap room. Q ⊞ ⌑ ⊞ ⅙ ♣ P

Mulberry
Hunslet Road
11–3, 6.30–11 (11–11 Sat)
Theakston Best Bitter, XB; Younger IPA, Scotch ⊞
Roadside pub busy at lunchtime with workers from local factories and attracting people from further afield in the eves. P

West Yorkshire

Mustard Pot
20 Stainbeck Lane, Chapel Allerton ☎ (0532) 696284
11–11
Mansfield Riding Mild, Riding Bitter, Old Baily Ⓗ
Recently redecorated (not spoiled) conversion of a listed, 18th-century house. One large room with comfy, low settees and a friendly atmosphere. Large garden. Food till 7pm.
🅱 ◖ ▶ ♣ P

Nags Head
Town Street, Chapel Allerton ☎ (0532) 624938
11–3.30, 5.30–11 (11–11 Fri & Sat)
Samuel Smith OBB Ⓗ
Old, village-centre coaching inn: a large, L-shaped room with a cosy no-smoking area; busy tap room with darts and dominoes. Quiz night Tue. No food Sun. Q 🅱 ◖ 🄴 ♣ P ✗

New Roscoe
Bristol Street, Sheepscar (5 mins from bus station along Regent Street) ☎ (0532) 460778
11–11
Tetley Mild, Bitter Ⓗ
Large, three-roomed pub. The lounge area has bric-a-brac and mementoes from the Old Roscoe. Winner of *Pub in Bloom* 1990. Regular guest beers.
⅚ 🅱 ◖ ♣ P

Station
Hillidge Road ☎ (0532) 700707
11.30–3, 5.30–11 (11.30–11 Fri & Sat)
Samuel Smith OBB Ⓗ
Friendly, two-roomed local, named after the long-defunct Hunslet station. ◖ 🄴 ♣

Viaduct
Briggate (under railway, by Swinegate) ☎ (0532) 454863
11–3, 5.30–11 (11–11 Thu & Fri)
Tetley Mild, Bitter Ⓗ
Unchanged, basic, drinkers'-only pub. ⇌

Victoria Family & Commercial
Great George Street (back of Town Hall) ☎ (0532) 451386
11–11 (12–2, 7–10.30 Sun)
Tetley Mild, Bitter Ⓗ
Large, Victorian-style pub; three rooms with lots of brass and leather seating. Separate food bar in the main lounge. Serves a mixed clientele from students to lawyers. No food Sun.
Q ◖ ⇌

Whitelocks
Turks Head Yard, Briggate ☎ (0532) 453950
11–11
McEwan 80/-; Younger Scotch, No. 3 Ⓗ
Famous, popular pub, worth a visit just to admire its charm. Hardly touched in the last 150

years, it boasts fine brewery mirrors and a tiled bar. The restaurant is open lunchtimes and early eves. Alley drinking area outside. Children welcome lunchtimes in the top bar.
🅱 Q 🅱 ◖ ▶ ⇌

Wrens
61a New Briggate ☎ (0532) 458888
11–3, 5–11 (11–11 Fri & Sat)
Ansells Mild, Bitter; Ind Coope Burton Ale; Tetley Mild, Bitter Ⓗ
Popular pub opposite the Grand Theatre. Three rooms; the Theatre Bar is no-smoking. Piano and quiet piped music; no games. Popular with CAMRA members. Guest beers.
Q ◖ 🄴 ♣ ✗

Liversedge

Black Bull
37 Halifax Road, Millbridge (A649, 400 yds from A62)
11.30–3.30, 5.30–11
Clark's Bitter; Old Mill Bitter; Stones Best Bitter; Taylor Golden Best; Tetley Bitter; Trough Wild Boar Ⓗ
Welcoming no-frills local, retaining a separate front bar, with the rest of the pub open plan. Guest beers. 🅱 ♣

Marsden

Hare & Hounds
Mount Road ☎ (0484) 844478
12–2, 7–11 (11–11 Sat)
Tetley Mild, Bitter; Theakston Best Bitter Ⓗ
Welcoming pub close to the Pennine Way. Pool room and a horseshoe bar. Note the fine plate collection in the lounge.
🅱 🅱 Å ♣ P

Mirfield

Flowerpot Inn
65 Calder Road, Lower Hopton (½ mile from centre, via Station Road) ☎ (0924) 496939
11–4, 7–11
Taylor Best Bitter; Tetley Mild, Bitter Ⓗ
Multi-roomed, 300 year-old building with windows from the former Ramsden brewery. Traditional tap room.
Q 🅱 ⅙ ⇌ ♣ P

Netherthong

Cricketers Arms
Off Haig Lane, Deanhouse (off A6024) ☎ (0484) 682993
7–11 (11–11 Sat)
Taylor Best Bitter; Tetley Mild, Bitter Ⓗ
Stone-built, village pub with a cricketing theme. Away from the tourist honeypot of

Holmfirth and worth the effort to find it. On the Holme Valley Circular Walk. 🅱 🅱 ◖ ▶ P

Netherton

Star Inn
211 Netherton Lane (B6117, off A642) ☎ (0924) 274496
11.30–3 (4 Fri & Sat), 6.30–11
Samuel Smith OBB Ⓔ
Friendly and well-kept, village local with a lively tap room, a small lounge and a large function room. No food Sun–Wed. 🅱 ◖ 🄴 ♣ P

Newmillerdam

Pledwick Well Inn
Barnsley Road (A61) ☎ (0924) 255088
11.30–3, 5.30–11
Camerons Bitter, Strongarm Ⓔ
Quaint, 200 year-old coaching inn with a large garden. Both bars are adorned with Victoriana. Over 100 malt whiskies. Some tables are no-smoking. Eve meals not always available. Q 🅱 ◖ 🄴 ♣ P ✗

Norwood Green

Old White Beare
Village Street (½ mile NW of A58/A641) ☎ (0274) 676645
11.30–3 (4 Fri & Sat), 6–11
Whitbread Castle Eden Ale Ⓗ
16th-century inn named after an English ship which sailed against the Spanish Armada. Now modernised and extended, but retaining many of its oldest features. No meals Sun.
Q 🅱 ◖ ♣ P

Old Snydale

Cross Keys
New Road ☎ (0924) 892238
12–3, 7–11
Theakston XB; Younger Scotch Ⓗ
Impressive, whitewashed pub with a notable sign, on the edge of a country hamlet. Two well-furnished lounge areas cater for all ages. Ask about the local ghost. Quiz night Wed. Monthly clay pigeon shooting. No food weekends.
🅱 🅱 ◖ ♣ P

Ossett

Boons End
Low Mill Road (off Healey Road, 1 mile W of centre) ☎ (0924) 273865
12–3 (not Tue), 5.30–11 (12–11 Fri & Sat)
Clark's Bitter, Hammerhead; Taylor Landlord; Tetley Bitter Ⓗ

335

West Yorkshire

Old, stone pub near the river and railway. Summer barbecues and regular live music inside and out. Edwardian-style interior with added breweriana. Strong local following despite its out of the way location. Folk club Thu. Two guest beers. No food Tue. 🏠 ⬧ ◖ ◗

Horse & Jockey
18 Dale Street (near bus station)
☎ (0924) 274061
11–4, 7–11
Samuel Smith OBB Ⓗ
Smart, recently refurbished, listed building: a two-roomed, split-level pub with attractive stained-glass windows and interesting prints in the tap room. Popular with the young at weekends. ◖ ♣ P

Little Bull
99 Teal Street (¼ mile off Queens Drive)
☎ (0924) 273569
12–3 (4 Sat), 7–11
Thwaites Best Mild, Bitter Ⓗ
Very friendly local which holds regular charity quiz nights. Lively but insulting tap room! 🏠 P

Otley

Junction Inn
Bondgate ☎ (0943) 463233
11–3, 5.30–11 (11–11 Thu–Sat)
Taylor Best Bitter, Landlord; Tetley Bitter; Theakston XB, Old Peculier Ⓗ
One-roomed, stone, corner pub with many small, private areas. Lively atmosphere; popular with younger people. A Tetley free house. 🏠 ◖

Red Lion
Kirkgate ☎ (0943) 462226
11–11
Courage Directors; John Smith's Bitter, Magnet Ⓗ
Very well-kept pub near the market place. Quite small, with three separate drinking areas served by a single bar. Menu includes vegetarian option.
Q ⬧ ◖

Pontefract

Greyhound Inn
Front Street ☎ (0977) 791571
11–4, 7–11 (11–11 Fri & Sat)
Ruddles Best Bitter, County; Theakston Best Bitter Ⓗ
Lively, three-roomed pub in the town centre. Regular live R&B music. Comfortable, traditional bar, and a lounge with a collection of local pub memorabilia. 🏠 ⬧ ◖ ⊟ ♣

Tap & Spile
28 Horsefair (opp. bus station)
☎ (0977) 793468
11–11 (may vary)
Camerons Bitter, Strongarm;

Everards Old Original; Stocks Old Horizontal Ⓗ
Traditional style alehouse with one long bar and three separate drinking areas. A mecca for real ale drinkers in an area dominated by the big brewers. Up to nine guest beers.
Q ◖ ⊟ ⬧ ♣ P

White Rose
Cobblers Lane (A645, 1 mile from centre) ☎ (0977) 702254
11.30–3, 5–11
Mansfield Riding Bitter, Old Baily Ⓗ
Modern pub and restaurant, recently refurbished in traditional style.
⬧ ◖ ◗ ⊟ ⬧ ♣ P

Purston

White House
Pontefract Road (A645)
11–4, 7–11
Samuel Smith OBB Ⓗ
Excellent, one-roomed pub, catering for all ages and a mainly local trade. ◖ P

Queensbury

Pineberry
On Brighouse–Denholme road
☎ (0274) 882168
12–4.30, 6 (7 Sat)–11 (supper licence)
Ruddles Best Bitter; John Smith's Bitter; Taylor Landlord; Webster's Green Label, Yorkshire Bitter Ⓗ
Friendly and popular, food-oriented pub. 🏠 Q ⬧ ◖ ◗ ⬧ ♣ P

Ripponden

Blue Ball
Blue Ball Lane, Soyland (off A58) ☎ (0422) 823603
12–3 (not Tue), 7–11
Courage Directors; John Smith's Bitter, Magnet; Taylor Golden Best, Dark Mild, Landlord; Theakston Old Peculier Ⓗ
Welcoming, moorland inn, dating from 1672. Wonderful views of the surrounding moors and nearby reservoir. Folk music and sing-alongs.
🏠 Q ⬧ ⬧ ◖ ◗ ⬧ ♣ P

Bridge
Priest Lane ☎ (0422) 822595
11.30–4, 5.30–11 (11–11 Sat)
Taylor Golden Best, Best Bitter; Ruddles County or Webster's Yorkshire Bitter; Younger Scotch Ⓗ
Ancient hostelry with a splendid timber structure; full of interesting ornaments. Most of the beer pumps are unlabelled. 🏠 Q ⬧ ◖ ◗ ⬧ P

Shipley

Oddfellows Hall
Otley Road ☎ (0274) 584568

11–11
Courage Directors; John Smith's Bitter Ⓗ
Friendly 19th-century local with a refurbished, L-shaped lounge and a separate public bar. Good value, home-made lunches. Live music Fri. Guest beer.
⬧ ◖ ⊟ ⬧ ♣ P

South Elmsall

Chequers Inn
Barnsley Road (off A638)
☎ (0977) 645805
11–4, 7–11 (11–11 Fri & Sat)
Mansfield Riding Bitter Ⓗ
Large, mock-Tudor pub, in the centre of a mining town, with a spacious, comfortable lounge. Disco Fri, Sat and Sun nights in the function room. Separate games room with pool and snooker.
⬧ ◖ ◗ ⊟ ⬧ ♣ P

Sowerby Bridge

Moorings
No 1 Warehouse, Canal Basin (off A58) ☎ (0422) 833940
11.30–3, 5.30 (7 Mon, 6 Sat)–11
McEwan 80/-; Moorhouse's Premier; Theakston XB; Younger Scotch Ⓗ
Smartly converted canal warehouse at the head of the Calder and Hebble Navigation. An open bar and separate eating areas. Wide range of bottled foreign beers; extensive range of single malts. Guest beer. No-smoking family room.
⬧ ⬧ ◖ ◗ ⊟ ⬧ P ⊠

Puzzle Hall
21 Hollins Mill Lane (off A58)
☎ (0422) 835547
12–11
Vaux Double Maxim; Wards Mild, Thorne Best Bitter, Sheffield Best Bitter, Kirby Ⓗ
Characterful, old, former home-brew pub, nestling between the canal and the river. The Vaux group beer range may vary, but Thorne and Sheffield are regulars.
🏠 ⬧ ◖ ⬧ ♣ P

Stanbury

Friendly
Main Street ☎ (0535) 642098
11–11 (12–4, 7–11 winter)
Stones Best Bitter Ⓗ
Three-roomed, small, comfortable local with a welcome for visitors. All food is home cooked (eve meals in summer only). The cellar, with stained-glass windows, used to be the bar but is now four feet below ground. Winner of a *Best-Kept Cellar* award 1990. Quiz night Tue. Guest beers.
Q ⬧ ⬧ ◖ ◗ ⊟ ⬧ ⬧ P

West Yorkshire

Stanningley

Fleece Hotel
116 Town Street (A647)
☎ (0532) 577832
12–11
Taylor Landlord; Tetley
Bitter; Theakston Best Bitter,
XB, Old Peculier Ⓗ
Busy roadside pub with a large
lounge and separate public bar,
now extended into the barbers
shop next door. Lunches
Mon–Fri. Guest beers.
Q ⋈ ◖ ♣ ♠

Steeton

Old Star
Skipton Road (at A6034/old
A629 jct) ☎ (0535) 652246
11–3, 5–11
Courage Directors; John
Smith's Bitter, Magnet Ⓗ
Pleasant, single-roomed pub
with a cosy atmosphere and a
lively landlord. ⌂ Q ⇌ P

Thornton

Blue Boar
354 Thornton Road (4 miles
from Bradford centre)
12–3, 5.30–11 (11–11 Mon, Fri & Sat)
Taylor Best Bitter,
Landlord Ⓗ
Roadside, locals' pub with an
open-plan and a separate
pool room. Live music every
Sun night; quiz Wed. ♣

Great Northern
528 Thornton Road (5 miles
from Bradford centre)
☎ (0274) 833400
12–3, 6.30–11
Thwaites Mild, Bitter Ⓗ
Large, open-plan, old coaching
inn, with an emphasis on
excellent food (restaurant
upstairs). Disco and quiz Wed.
⌂ ◖ ▮ ⅃ & P

Todmorden

Masons Arms
1 Bacup Road, Gauxholme
(A6033/A681 jct)
☎ (0706) 812180
12–3, 7 (7.30 Sat)–11
John Smith's Bitter, Magnet;
Thwaites Best Mild, Bitter Ⓗ
Small, cosy free house with a
triangular snug, a fine fireplace,
and double-pedestal, fixed,
scrubbed tables (one once used
as a mortuary slab). Varied food
(lunches weekends only).
⌂ ▮ ◖ ▯ & ⇌ (Walsden) ♣

Queen Hotel
Rise Lane ☎ (0706) 812961
11–11
Draught Bass; Stones Best
Bitter Ⓗ
Elegant hotel, originally linked
to the adjacent station platform

by a footbridge. Occasional
guest beer. Quizzes.
▮ ⋈ ◖ ▯ ⇌ ⅋

Woodpecker
224 Rochdale Road, Shade
(A6033) ☎ (0706) 816088
12–2.30, 5–11 (11–11 Sat)
Lees GB Mild, Bitter Ⓗ
Family-run, active locals' pub
with a long, L-shaped bar. Near
the canal, it is the only Lees pub
in Yorkshire. ◖ & ♣ ♠

Wakefield

Albion
Stanley Road (take Peterson
Road from Kirkgate
roundabout) ☎ (0924) 376206
11–3 (4 Fri), 6–11 (11–11 Sat)
Samuel Smith OBB Ⓗ
Imposing but homely, 1920s
estate pub on the edge of the
town centre. Impressive
collection of coloured glassware.
Friendly, local clientele.
▮ ◖ ▮ ⇌ (Kirkgate) ♠ P

Beer Engine
77 Westgate End (400 yds
from station)
☎ (0924) 375887
12–11
Taylor Landlord Ⓗ
Very popular, traditional ale
house with gas lighting, a
stone-flagged floor, brewery
memorabilia and no jukebox.
Wakefield's only true free
house. Unrivalled guest beers –
up to 15 a week.
⌂ ▮ ⇌ (Westgate) ♣ ◔

Cock Inn
180 Batley Road, Alverthorpe
(1 mile from Wakefield)
☎ (0924) 373649
11.45–4, 7–11
Stones Best Bitter; Tetley
Bitter Ⓗ
Cheerful, 1930s pub retaining
separate rooms and a friendly,
local atmosphere. No food Sun.
Q ◖ ▮ ♣ P

Inns of Court
22 King Street (by Town Hall)
☎ (0924) 375560
11–11 (11–4, 7–11 Sat)
John Smith's Magnet Ⓗ
Recently refurbished, central
pub with a lively, comfortable
atmosphere, which attracts a
cross-section of clientele. Shares
a long history with the city law
courts. ▮ ◖ ⇌ (Westgate)

Poste Haste
Brunswick Street, Kirkgate
☎ (0924) 374455
11.30–3, 6.30–11 (11–11 Fri & Sat)
Taylor Landlord; Webster's
Yorkshire Bitter Ⓗ
Comfortable, 1960s estate pub.
The landlord is a keen supporter
of live music; bands Fri/Sat
nights (small charge).
▮ ◖ ▯ ▮ ⇌ (Kirkgate) ♣ P

Three Houses Inn
379 Barnsley Road, Sandal
(A61) ☎ (0924) 255642
11.30–3, 5.30–11
Courage Directors; John
Smith's Bitter Ⓗ
Former coaching inn with
highwaymen connections, in a
fashionable suburb. Cosy, old-
fashioned interior with four
rooms around the bar. Dining
room. ⌂ ▮ ◖ ▯ P

Vine Tree
82 Leeds Road, Newton Hill
(A61, 10 mins' walk from town)
☎ (0924) 290151
11–11
John Smith's Bitter, Magnet Ⓗ
Twin lounge with a pool room
at the back of the bar and a
large garden play area. Ask
about the ghost. ▮ ◖ & ♣ P

West Ardsley

British Oak
407 Westerton Road (off
A653) ☎ (0532) 534792
12–3, 6–11
Whitbread Boddingtons
Bitter, Trophy, Castle Eden
Ale, Flowers Original Ⓗ
Friendly pub: open-plan, with a
large, central, oak bar, an
extensive 'tasteless tie'
collection and oil paintings for
sale. Live entertainment on Sat
night. Many different guest
beers. Summer barbecues (no
food Sun). ▮ ◖ ♣ P

Wetherby

George & Dragon
High Street ☎ (0937) 582888
11–4, 6–11
John Smith's Bitter,
Magnet Ⓗ
Large, popular pub with three
airy rooms. Enjoys a riverside
setting and has a large, safe beer
garden. Guest beers planned.
Eve meals Mon–Thu until 8pm.
Q ▮ ◖ ▯ ▮ & ▲ ♣ P

Wooldale

Wooldale Arms
Wooldale Road (off A635)
11–3 (not Mon–Fri), 6–11
Vaux Lorimers Best Scotch;
Wards Thorne Best Bitter,
Sheffield Best Bitter Ⓗ
Village local, now an open-plan
free house, situated in a
conservation area above New
Mill. Guest beers. Q P

Yeadon

Oddfellows
The Green ☎ (0532) 503819
11–11
Tetley Mild, Bitter Ⓗ
Excellent tap room with a long,
narrow lounge. Known locally
as 'the Rag'. ▮ ♣ P

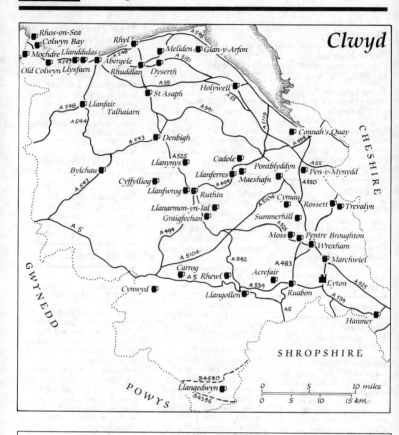

Clwyd

🏠 *Plassey*, Eyton

Abergele

Gwindy
Market Street
☎ (0745) 833485
11–11 (may vary)
**Marston's Burton Best Bitter,
Pedigree** Ⓗ
Old market town pub with a
modernised public bar and pool
room. Small, comfortable lounge
at the rear. The family room is a
new addition.
Q ☻ ⑧ ◐ ● ⊕ Å ≈ ♣ P

Try also: **Bull Hotel** (Lees);
George & Dragon (Allied)

Acrefair

Hampden Arms
Llangollen Road (A483)
☎ (0978) 821734
11–4, 7–11
Banks's Mild, Bitter Ⓔ
Large public house situated on
the main road near to a large
housing estate and leisure
centre. Small, cheerful lounge
and a spacious, busy bar with a
TV for racing fans. ⊕ ♣

Try also: **Duke of Wellington**
(Marston's)

Bylchau

Sportsmans Arms
(Tafarn y Heliwr)
Bryntrillyn (halfway between
Denbigh and Pentrefoelas on
A543)
☎ (074 570) 214
12–3, 7–11 (not Mon or Tue; 11–11
summer all week)
Lees GB Mild, Bitter Ⓗ
The highest pub in Wales: an
oasis on a desert moorland, a
traditional pub with a small bar
and a good size lounge. Organ
sing-songs at weekends in
summer, with traditional Welsh
singing by the locals.
🏠 Q ⑧ ◐ ● ⊕ Å ♣ P

Cadole

Colomendy Arms
Gwernaffield Road (off A494, 2
miles W of Mold)
☎ (0352) 85217
12–3 (not winter), 7–11 (11–11 Sat)
Burtonwood Best Bitter Ⓗ
Friendly, unspoilt, village local,
consisting of a welcoming main
bar and a small, adjoining
lounge where children are
welcome. 🏠 ⑧ ♣ P

Carrog

Grouse Inn
On B5437, ¾ mile off A5
12–4, 7–11
Lees GB Mild, Bitter Ⓗ
Simple, pleasant inn alongside
the River Dee with good views
of the valley. Well worth the
short detour off the A5.
🏠 ⑧ ⇥ ◐ ● ♣ P

Colwyn Bay

Park Hotel
128 Abergele Road
☎ (0492) 530661
11–11
**M&B Mild, Bitter; Stones
Best Bitter** Ⓗ
Newly refurbished, large,
single-room bar with the recent
addition of three real ales. Pool,
darts and quizzes most nights.
≈ ♣

Sir Robert Peel

43 Station Road
☎ (0492) 534630
11–3, 5–11 (11–11 summer)
Ind Coope Burton Ale; Tetley Bitter Ⓗ
Old police station which was to become a wine bar but has been developed into a good, town-centre pub. Large selection of traditional bottled beers. Tables outside in summer. Back-gammon played. ⑧ ◖ ▮ ≈ ♣

Try also: **Taylors** (Free); **Toad Hall** (Free)

Connah's Quay

Sir Gawain & The Green Knight

Golftyn Lane
☎ (0244) 812623
11.30–3, 5.30–11 (11–11 Sat)
Samuel Smith OBB Ⓗ
Converted former farmhouse with a split-level interior. Frequented by college students at lunchtimes. No meals weekends. ⚉ ⑧ ◖ ▮ ⊖ ♣ P

Cyffylliog

Red Lion Hotel

Off B5105, 4 miles W of Ruthin ☎ (082 46) 664
12–3, 6.30–11
Lees GB Mild, Bitter Ⓗ
Genuinely attractive pub in idyllic, rural surroundings with good value accommodation and food. Brimming with atmosphere.
⚉ Q ⑧ ⇔ ◖ ▮ ⊖ ᴅ Å ♣ P

Cymau

Olde Talbot Inne

Cymau Road (off A541)
OS297562 ☎ (0978) 761410
11–4, 7–11
Hydes' Anvil Mild, Bitter Ⓔ
Hilltop pub in pleasant surroundings and enjoying good views: a busy, village local with a quiet and relaxing lounge. Q ◖ ▮ ⊖ ᴅ ♣ P

Cynwyd

Prince of Wales

On B4401 1½ miles S of A5
12–3, 6.30–11
Burtonwood Mild Ⓗ
Unspoilt, traditional, village local with the clock and stationmaster's chair from the old Corwen station. A mild drinker's haven. ⚉ Q ⊖ P

Try also: **Blue Lion** (Marston's)

Denbigh

Masons Arms

Rhyl Road (200 yds W of roundabout) ☎ (0745) 812463
12–3, 5–11 (12–11 Sat; 12–2.30, 7–10.30 Sun)

Vaux Lorimers Best Scotch, Samson; Wards Mild Ⓗ
Small, town pub, converted to one room with lounge and bar areas separated by a central modernised bar. Rather loud jukebox, but worth a visit just to sample the ale. Simple pub fare. ⚉ ⇔ ◖ ▮ Å ♣ P

Try also: **Vaults** (Vaux)

Dyserth

New Inn (Tafarn Newydd)

Waterfall Road
☎ (0745) 570482
12–3, 5–11 (11–11 Sat; more restricted winter)
Marston's Mercian Mild, Burton Best Bitter, Pedigree Ⓗ
Typical, old-style, tasteful pub with a cosy and friendly atmosphere: a small bar and a medium-sized lounge. A hundred yards from Dyserth waterfall, a local tourist attraction. ⚉ ⦣ ⑧ ▮ Å ♣ P

Try also: **Cross Keys** (Burtonwood)

Glan-y-Arfon

White Lion

2 miles off A548 at Ffynnongroew, through Penyffordd ☎ (0745) 570280
12–3 (not Mon), 6–11
Burtonwood Forshaw's; Ruddles Best Bitter, County Ⓗ
Old-fashioned pub with a lively local trade; somewhat isolated but well worth the visit. An outpost for real cider (Thatcher's). Guest beers. Watch out for the low entrance.
⚉ Q ⑧ ▮ ⊖ ⌣ P

Graigfechan

Three Pigeons

On B5429 ☎ (082 42) 3178
12–3 (summer only), 6.30–11
Draught Bass Ⓖ
Tastefully extended, 17th-century pub with fine views over the Vale of Clwyd. Good food, with children well catered for. Beer is served from the jug. Caravan site attached. No lunchtime opening Mon–Sat in winter. ⚉ ⦣ ⑧ ⇔ ◖ ⊖ ♣ P

Hanmer

Hanmer Arms

Off A539, 6 miles W of Whitchurch ☎ (094 874) 532
11–11
Ind Coope Burton Ale; Tetley Bitter Ⓗ
Family-run hotel in a pretty mereside village, set in a peaceful, rolling landscape. Local produce features on the menu

---

(vegetarian option). Bowling green.
⚉ Q ⦣ ⑧ ⇔ ◖ ▮ ⊖ ᴅ ♣ P

Holywell

Feathers Inn

Whitford Street
☎ (0352) 714792
11–11
Draught Bass; Stones Best Bitter Ⓗ
Town-centre pub with regular entertainment, serving the best pint of Bass for miles. Friendly locals of all ages. ⇔ ◖ ▮ ⊖ ᴅ ♣

Glan yr Afon

Milwr (300 yds from old A55, by Hillcrest garage)
☎ (0352) 710052
11.30–2.30, 7–11
Ruddles Best Bitter; Webster's Yorkshire Bitter, Choice Ⓗ
17th-century pub with tasteful decor. Deer antlers collection in the public bar. Good wine list, with Spanish and Italian wines to the fore.
⦣ ⑧ ◖ ▮ ⊖ ᴅ P

Llanarmon-yn-Ial

Raven

On B5431 ☎ (082 43) 787
12–3, 6.30–11 (12–11 Mon, Fri & Sat)
Burtonwood Best Bitter, Forshaw's Ⓗ
Unspoilt, picture-postcard village pub with many small drinking areas and an excellent, low-ceilinged public bar. Set in the Clwydian Hills. Good value accommodation.
⚉ Q ⦣ ⑧ ⇔ ◖ ▮ ⊖ ᴅ ♣ P

Llanddulas

Dulas Arms Hotel

Abergele Road
☎ (0492) 515747
11–4, 6–11 (12–3, 7–11 winter)
Lees GB Mild, Bitter, Moonraker Ⓗ
Large lounge, an adjoining bar, a snug and a large family room (a *Family Pub of the Year* award-winner). Beer festival August Bank Holiday weekend. Spacious garden. Restaurant has a no-smoking area.
Q ⦣ ⑧ ⇔ ◖ ▮ ⊖ ᴅ Å ♣ P

Valentine Inn

Mill Street ☎ (0492) 518189
12–3, 5.30–11 (may vary; 12–2, 7–10.30 Sun)
Draught Bass; M&B Mild Ⓗ
Tastefully-renovated, small, village inn. The comfortable lounge features an inviting coal and log fire; the tiny public bar is popular with holiday-makers from nearby camps. Eve meals in summer only (till 8pm).
⚉ Q ⦣ ⑧ ◖ ▮ ⊖ ᴅ Å ♣

Clwyd

Llanfair Talhaiarn

Swan
Swan Square ☎ (0745) 84233
11–3, 5.30–11 (11–11 Sat)
**Marston's Mercian Mild,
Burton Best Bitter,
Pedigree** H
Traditional, village pub with a
small, cosy lounge at the front
and a medium-sized bar. Garden
at the rear.
🏠 Q ⏰ 🕳 🍴 🍺 Ⓐ ♣

Llanferres

Druid Inn
On A494 ☎ (035 285) 225
11.30–3, 5.30–11
Burtonwood Best Bitter H
Roadside inn with good views.
Real ale is available in the top
bar. Popular with visitors to the
local country walks and park.
🏠 🛏 🍴 🍺 P

Llanfwrog

Olde Cross Keys
On B5105, 1 mile from Ruthin
☎ (082 42) 5281
11.30–3, 6.30–11
Banks's Mild, Bitter H
Cosy, village pub with an
interesting, dark wood-panelled
bar serving two small lounge
areas. Large dining room (meals
in summer only); pool room.
🏠 ⏰ 🕳 🍴 🍺 ♣

Llangedwyn

Green Inn
On B4396 at Llansilin road jct
☎ (0691) 828234
11–3.30, 6.30–11
**Wadworth Farmer's Glory;
Wells Bombardier;
Whitbread Boddingtons
Bitter** H
Traditional, 17th-century pub
with a large, open fireplace in
the public bar. Horse brasses
abound in all the rooms. First
class restaurant; fishing rights
on the River Tanat.
🏠 ⏰ 🕳 🛏 🍴 🍺 P

Llangollen

Cambrian Hotel
Berwyn Street (A5)
☎ (0978) 860686
12–5 (may extend), 6.30–11
Younger Scotch H
Plain, simple hotel with a small
bar and a quiet front lounge
where children are welcome.
Eve meals weekends only in
winter. 🛏 🍴 🍺 Ⓐ ⇌ ♣ P

Wynstay Arms Hotel
Bridge Street ☎ (0978) 860710
12–4, 6.30–11
**Ind Coope Burton Ale; Tetley
Bitter** H
Unspoilt, 16th- and 17th-
century hotel with several small

eating and drinking areas (eve
meals in summer only).
🏠 ⏰ 🕳 🛏 🍴 🍺 🍺 Ⓐ ⇌ ♣ P

Llanynys

Cerigllwydion Arms
2 miles off A525, between
Ruthin and Denbigh
OS102627 ☎ (074 578) 247
11.30–3 (not Mon), 7–11
**Crown Buckley Best Bitter;
Marston's Pedigree** H
Out-of-the-way, food-oriented
house with masses of crockery
hanging from the low beams.
The only regular Buckley's
outlet in North Wales.
Occasional guest beers. Pretty
beer garden on the opposite
side of the road. No food Mon.
⏰ 🕳 🍴 🍺 Ⓐ ♣ P

Llysfaen

Semaphore Inn
Ffordd y Llan (follow signs from
Llanddulas turnoff on A55, turn
right at church)
☎ (0492) 517411
12–3, 6.30–11
**Draught Bass; Webster's
Yorkshire Bitter** H
Comfortable lounge and family
room, popular with holiday-
makers; traditional, unchanged
public bar with a good, local
atmosphere. Superb sea views,
hence the pub's name. Camping
next door. 🏠 ⏰ 🕳 🍴 🍺 Ⓐ ♣ P

Try also: **Castle** (S&N)

Maeshafn

Miners Arms
Off A494
☎ (0352) 85464
12–3, 5.30–11 (may close weekday
lunchtimes in winter)
Banks's Bitter H
Small local converted from two
former cottages in a quiet
village. Impressive open
fireplace. Separate dining area.
Youth hostel facilities nearby.
🏠 ⏰ 🕳 Ⓐ P

Marchwiel

Red Lion
Wrexham Road (A525/A528
jct) ☎ (0978) 262317
11.30–3, 5.30–11
**Marston's Border Mild,
Border Bitter, Pedigree** H
Main road pub on the outskirts
of Wrexham: a large, busy bar
and smart, quieter lounge. The
garden is popular with families.
⏰ 🕳 🍴 🍺 ♣ P

Meliden

Red Lion
100 yds off A547,
Dyserth–Meliden road
☎ (0745) 852565
11–3, 5–11

**Draught Bass; M&B Mild;
Stones Best Bitter** H
Very tasteful, old-style pub,
unspoilt by refurbishment, its
walls adorned with military
memorabilia. Cosy and friendly.
🏠 🕳 🍴 Ⓐ ⇌ (Prestatyn) ♣ P

Try also: **Melyd Arms**
(Marston's)

Mochdre

Mountain View
7 Old Conwy Road
☎ (0492) 544724
11–3, 5.30–11
**Burtonwood Mild, Best
Bitter, Forshaw's** H
Village local: a large, friendly
lounge with excellent meals (fish
a speciality; vegetarian option).
The bar has a pool table.
Q ⏰ 🕳 🍴 🍺 ♣ P ✗

Moss

Bird in Hand
Down track off B5433
OS303538 ☎ (0978) 755809
12–3 (not Mon–Fri), 7–11
Hydes' Anvil Bitter H
Friendly, open-plan pub set back
from the road. Three-quarter
size snooker table available.
Separate dining room (no eve
meals Mon). Note no lunchtime
opening weekdays. 🕳 🍴 ♣ P

Old Colwyn

Marine Hotel
Abergele Road
☎ (0492) 515484
11.30–11
**Draught Bass; M&B Mild,
Bitter** H
Large pub with a separate
lounge and restaurant (with no-
smoking area). Fish pie is a
speciality. Q 🛏 🍴 ♣ ○

Pentre Broughton

Cross Foxes
High Street (B5433)
☎ (0978) 755973
11–11
**Burtonwood Best Bitter,
Forshaw's** H
Pleasantly refurbished local with
an unusual Victorian iron
fireplace in the lounge. Children
welcome. 🏠 🕳 ♣ P

Try also: **George & Dragon**,
Brymbo (Lees)

Pen-y-Mynydd

White Lion Inn
On A5104
12–3, 7–11 (12–2, 7–10.30 Sun)
Marston's Border Bitter H
Three-roomed local, full of
character and virtually
untouched by the passage of
time. Pickled eggs are home
produced. 🏠 Q 🍺 ♣ P

Pontblyddyn

Bridge Inn
At A5104/A54 jct
☎ (0352) 770475
12–2, 6–11 (12–11 summer; supper licence)
Marston's Pedigree; Plassey Bitter; Vaux Samson Ⓗ
Fine pub with an enthusiastic landlord. The newly-opened restaurant is especially popular at weekends. Good use of old pews and refectory tables adds to the atmosphere of a traditional pub that is geared for the 90s. Jazz night Mon. Guest beer. Patio picnic and barbecue area. ♨ ♒ ♨ ◖ ► ♿ P

Try also: New Inn (Free)

Rhewl

Sun Inn
Off B5103 OS178448
☎ (0978) 861043
12–3, 6–11
Felinfoel Bitter Ⓗ
Old drovers' inn set in the beautiful Dee Valley. A 14th-century pub with stone floors; a great attraction for hikers and hill-walkers.
♨ ♒ ♨ ◖ ► ⊟ ♣ P

Rhos-on-Sea

Rhos Abbey Hotel
111 The Promenade
☎ (0492) 46601
11–3, 5–11 (11–11 Sat)
Courage Directors; John Smith's Bitter Ⓗ
Large hotel bar open to the public and popular for meals (incl. vegetarian). The public bar is available in summer only.
Q ♨ ⋈ ◖ ► ⊟ P

Rhuddlan

Castle Inn
Castle Street
☎ (0745) 590391
11–11
Marston's Burton Best Bitter, Pedigree Ⓔ
Welcoming, village local, close to Rhuddlan Castle. Eve meals till 8pm.
Q ♨ ◖ ► ⊟ Å ♣ P

Rhyl

Caskeys
Vale Road (over bridge from station, on left)
☎ (0745) 338308
12–3, 7–12 (12–12 Sat; supper licence)
Draught Bass; M&B Mild Ⓗ
Tastefully refurbished pub, popular with all ages. Good size bar and lounge area; a second, luxuriously comfortable, quiet lounge, and a separate restaurant. ♒ ◖ ► ♿ Å ⋈ ♣ P

Try also: Prince of Wales (Marston's)

Rossett

Butchers Arms
Chester Road (B5445)
☎ (0244) 570233
11.30–11
Burtonwood Mild, Best Bitter Ⓗ
Compact, roadside pub in the centre of a busy village. Small public bar and plush lounge together. Outdoor patio area.
♨ ◖ ► ⊟ ♣ P

Ruabon

Duke of Wellington
High Street (off B5606)
☎ (0978) 820381
12–4, 7–11
Marston's Border Mild, Burton Best Bitter, Pedigree Ⓗ
Nicely balanced pub with a cosy, comfortable lounge and a bright, busy bar.
Q ♨ ◖ ► ⊟ ♣ P

Try also: Wynstay Arms (Robinson's)

Ruthin

Wine Vaults
St Peters Square
☎ (082 42) 2067
12–3.30, 5–11 (11–11 Thu–Sat)
Robinson's Best Bitter Ⓗ
Cosy, two-bar local just off the main town square.
Q ♨ ⋈ ⊟ Å ♣ P

Try also: Anchor (Free)

St Asaph

Red Lion
Gemig Street
☎ (0745) 583570
11–3, 5.30–11 (11–11 Sat)
Ansells Mild; Ind Coope Burton Ale; Marston's Pedigree; Tetley Bitter Ⓗ
16th-century coach house: an attractively furnished lounge, together with a nicely decorated public bar. ♨ ♨ ◖ ► ⊟ Å ♣ P

Try also: Swan (Marston's)

Summerhill

Crown Inn
Top Road (old A541)
OS312535 ☎ (0978) 755788
11–4, 7–11
Hydes' Anvil Mild, Bitter Ⓔ
A village public bar and a comfortable, nicely furnished lounge. Good views. ♨ ⊟ ♣ P

Trevalyn

Griffin Inn
On B5102, 1 mile E of Rossett
OS382568 ☎ (0244) 570515
12–3, 5–11 (12–11 Sat)

Marston's Burton Best Bitter, Pedigree Ⓗ
Welcoming pub, off the beaten track. Originally 17th-century, with an open-plan interior and a separate pool room. Beers will be served direct from the cask on request. Food in summer only. Shove-ha'penny available.
♨ ♨ ◖ Å ♣ P

Wrexham

Golden Lion
High Street (entrance down alley) ☎ (0978) 364964
12–11
Bass Special; Stones Best Bitter Ⓗ
Old pub with low ceiling and beams. Rather noisy: a mostly locals pub.
◖ ≠ (Central) ♣

Oak Tree Tavern
Ruabon Road (A5152, downhill from High St, via Bridge St)
☎ (0978) 261450
12–3, 6.30–11
Marston's Border Bitter, Burton Best Bitter, Pedigree Ⓗ
Pub with walls and ceilings covered with brass and copper utensils and old posters.
Q ◖ ⊟ ≠ (Central) ♣ P

Turf
Mold Road (A541)
☎ (0978) 261484
11–11
Marston's Border Exhibition, Pedigree Ⓗ
Busy pub built into the side of the Wrexham football ground.
♨ ⋈ ◖ ► ⊟ ≠ (Central) P

Help keep real ale alive by joining CAMRA. Your voice helps encourage brewers big and small to brew cask beer and offer all beer drinkers a better choice. For membership details see page 480.

Dyfed

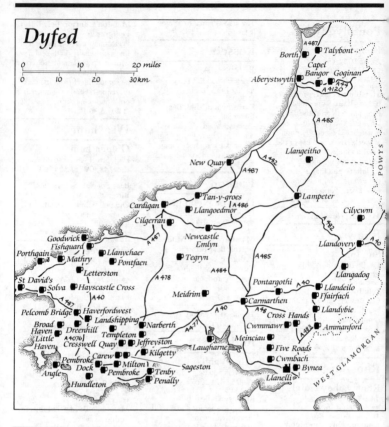

```
0        10        20 miles
0    10       20    30km
```

Talybont · Borth · Capel · Bangor · Goginan · Aberystwyth · A 487 · A 4120 · A 485 · Llangeitho · New Quay · A 482 · Lampeter · Tan-y-groes · A 486 · Cardigan · Llangoedmor · Cilycwm · Cilgerran · Newcastle Emlyn · Llandovery · A 487 · Tegryn · A 485 · Llangadog · Goodwick · Fishguard · Llanychaer · Pontfaen · Pontargothi · A 40 · Llandeilo · Porthgain · Mathry · Letterston · A 478 · A 484 · Carmarthen · Ffairfach · St David's · Solva · Hayscastle Cross · Meidrim · A 40 · Cross Hands · Llandybie · Pelcomb Bridge · Haverfordwest · A 40 · A 48 · Cwmmawr · Ammanford · Broad Haven · Landshipping · Narberth · A 477 · Meinciau · Little Haven · Dreenhill · Templeton · A 4076 · Cresswell Quay · Jeffreyston · Laugharne · Five Roads · Carew · Kilgetty · Cwmbach · Angle · Milton · Sageston · Bynea · Pembroke Dock · Pembroke · Tenby · Llanelli · Hundleton · Penally · POWYS · WEST GLAMORGAN

🏰 **Crown Buckley, Felinfoel, Llanelli**

Aberystwyth

Castle
South Road ☎ (0970) 612188
12–3, 5.30–11 (11–11 Sat)
Draught Bass Ⓗ
Large, urban pub, built by
Roberts' brewery close to the
harbour and South Marine
beach. Italian food a speciality.
🛏 ◖ 🍴 🚪 🔥 ≋ ♣

Nags Head
Bridge Street
☎ (0970) 624748
11–11
Banks's Mild, Bitter Ⓔ
Large, cheerful public bar and a
small, tidy lounge. Please use
the back entrance (High Street)
for the small family room.
🚃 ◖ 🍴 🚪 ≋ ♣

Pier Hotel
Pier Street ☎ (0970) 615126
11–4, 5.30–11
Banks's Mild, Bitter Ⓔ
Predictably near the pier and
promenade; a large public bar
and tiny lounge (side entrance,
up the alleyway). 🍴 🚪 ≋ ♣

Weston Vaults
Thespian Street
☎ (0970) 617641
11–11
Banks's Mild, Bitter Ⓔ
Popular, two-bar pub in a corner
location at the north end of the
town centre. No food Sun eve.
🚃 ◖ 🍴 🚪 🔥 ≋ ♣

Ammanford

Perrivale
Pontamman Road (A474)
☎ (0269) 593785
11.30–3.30, 5.30–11
**Felinfoel Cambrian; Welsh
Brewers Worthington BB** Ⓗ
Comfortable, main road pub.
Q 🚃 ◖ 🍴 🚪 P

Wernoleu Hotel
Off Pontamman Road (A474)
☎ (0269) 592598
11–11
Beer range varies Ⓗ
Gracious building housing a
cosy bar and an attractive
lounge. Daily papers and an
open fire; at least four real ales.
🚃 🛌 🍴 ◖ 🚪 P

Angle

Hibernia Inn
Main Street ☎ (0646) 641517
**Welsh Brewers Worthington
BB** Ⓗ
Strong naval and lifeboat
connections in a remote but
welcoming pub which caters for
all. 🚃 Q 🛌 🍴 ◖ 🚪 ♣ P

Borth

Friendship
☎ (0970) 871213
12 (11 summer)–3, 6.30 (6 summer)–11
Burtonwood Best Bitter Ⓗ
Welcoming, cottage-style free
house in the main street, where
the licence has been in the same
family for 70 years. Art gallery
in the corridor and lounge.
Lunchtime snacks.
🚃 Q 🛌 🍴 🚪 🔥 ≋ ♣

Broad Haven

Royal
200 yds from coast road up

Marine Road
☎ (0437) 781249
11–4, 6–11
Wadworth 6X G**; Welsh
Brewers Worthington BB** H
Completely renovated old pub
on the Coastal Path, close to a
sandy beach in a sheltered,
sunny position. Specialises in
seafood and Welsh produce.
Q ≿ ✿ 🏠 ◑ 🇩 ⊞ ⅄ ♣ P

Bynea

Lewis Arms
90 Yspitty Road (old A484)
11–11 (may vary)
**Felinfoel Bitter, Double
Dragon** H
Refurbished pub close to the
Loughor Estuary. ✿ ◑ ⊞ ≱ P

Capel Bangor

Tynllidiart Arms
On A44 ☎ (0970) 84248
11–2.30, 6–11 (closed Sun eve in
winter)
**Brains Dark; Whitbread
Boddingtons Bitter, Flowers
Original** H
17th-century cottage inn with
traditional settle seating around
a fire – ideal for domino players.
Historically linked to the
mailcoach trade. A rare outlet
for real cider; beer range varies.
✿ Q ◑ 🇩 ⅄ ♣ ⊙

Cardigan

Red Lion
Pwll-Hai ☎ (0239) 612782
11–11 (closed Sun eve)
Crown Buckley Best Bitter H
Ancient, back-street pub where
the large front bar has various
drinking areas; pool room at the
rear. Friendly atmosphere; large
function room. ≿ ✿ ◑ 🇩 ♣

Carew

Carew Inn
☎ (0646) 651267
11–11 (closed winter afternoons)
**Ind Coope Burton Ale; Welsh
Brewers Worthington BB** H
Extended, family pub with a
rambling garden, offering a
magnificent view of Carew
Castle. ✿ Q ✿ 🏠 ◑ 🇩 ⊞ ⅄ ♣ P

Carmarthen

Drovers Arms
Lammas Street
11–3.30, 5.30–11
**Felinfoel Bitter, Cambrian,
Double Dragon** H
Pleasant, comfortable, town-
centre pub. Q ◑ ≱

Red Lion
Priory Street
11.30–4, 6–11 (may vary)
**Crown Buckley Dark, Best
Bitter** H
Comfortable pub on the edge of
town. ◑ ⊞ ≱

Cilgerran

Pendre Inn
High Street ☎ (0239) 614223
11.30–3, 6–11
**Draught Bass; Welsh
Brewers Worthington BB** H
Ancient, stone-built pub of
character. Occasional guest
beers in summer. No Sun
lunches. ✿ Q ✿ 🇩 ♣ P

Cilycwm

Neuadd Fawr Arms
OS753400 ☎ (0550) 20361
12–3, 6.30 (7 Sat)–11
**Draught Bass; Ruddles
County** H
Friendly, rambling pub, built in
1633 as an estate manager's
house next to an old church.
Slate flagstones. A preserved
cobbled courtyard and gullies in
the street bear witness to the
drovers' era.
✿ ≿ ✿ 🇩 ⅄ ♣ ⊙ P

Cresswell Quay

Cresselly Arms
OS050066 ☎ (0646) 651210
11–11 (may close winter afternoons)
**Welsh Brewers Hancock's
HB, Worthington BB** G
Paddle, swim or boat here
during spring tides. Cricket and
hunting dominate at this pub
which resolutely defies
modernisation, except in the
sanitation department.
Worthington BB is not always
available. ✿ Q ✿ ⅄ ♣ P

Cross Hands

Cross Hands Hotel
Llanelli Road
11–11
**Felinfoel Bitter, Double
Dragon** H
Large, friendly pub with a basic
bar and a comfortable lounge.
🏠 ◑ 🇩 ⊞ P

Cwmbach

Farriers
On B4308
☎ (0554) 774256
12–3, 7 (6 Sat)–11 (closed Mon; 12–2,
7–10.30 Sun)
**Felinfoel Bitter; Marston's
Pedigree** H
Very picturesque pub in a
wooded valley. Usually a guest
beer. Q ✿ ◑ 🇩 ⊞ P

Cwmmawr

Gwendraeth Arms
Gwendraeth Road (B4310)
11.30–4, 7–11 (may vary)
Felinfoel Bitter H
Small, pleasant local. ✿ ✿ P

Dreenhill

Denant Mill Inn
Dale Road ☎ (0437) 766569
11–3, 6–11
Beer range varies H
Medieval gem and a mecca for
ale connoisseurs, set in an old,
converted mill house. No
regular draught beers, but a
carousel of weird and wonderful
ales from all over the country.
✿ Q ≿ ✿ 🏠 ◑ 🇩 ⊞ ⅄ ♣ P

Ffairfach

Torbay
Heol Cennen ☎ (0558) 822029
11–3, 5.30–11
**Draught Bass; Crown
Buckley Best Bitter** H
Popular, comfortable house
specialising in good value,
home-cooked food (over 40
choices). No meals Sun lunch.
✿ Q ✿ ◑ 🇩 ⅄ ♣
≱ (not winter Sun) ♣ P

Fishguard

Fishguard Arms
Main Street ☎ (0348) 872763
11–3, 6–11 (12–2, 7–10.30 Sun)
Felinfoel Double Dragon
(summer); **Marston's
Pedigree; Welsh Brewers
Worthington BB** H
Old, established, very small,
basic pub, where quiet
conversation and contemplation
can be enjoyed, but with
surprising entertainments from
time to time. ✿ ⊞ ♣

Old Coach House
High Street ☎ (0348) 873883
11–11
**Felinfoel Bitter, Double
Dragon** H
Renovated, old pub run by
young people for young people.
The open-plan design is clean
and light, with a family area in a
nook. Guest cider in summer. A
large patio overlooks a
play area. ✿ ◑ 🇩 ⅄ ⊙ P

Ship Inn
Newport Road, Lower Town
(A487) ☎ (0348) 874033
11–3, 7–11 (11–2, 7–10.30 Sun)
**Welsh Brewers Worthington
Dark, BB** G
Famous low-ceilinged, nautical
gem, built in 1720: a hostelry
for film stars during filming of
Under Milk Wood, Moby Dick
and so on. Mild is unusual for
the area. Next to the beautiful
Gwaun Estuary. ✿ Q ≿ ♣

Five Roads

Waunwyllt Inn
Horeb (off B4309)
12–3, 7 (6 Fri, 5.30 Sat)–11
**Felinfoel Double Dragon;
Theakston Best Bitter** H

Dyfed

Excellent free house in splendid countryside. Usually one guest beer; good food. Q ⊛ ◖ ▶ P

Goginan

Druid Inn
On A44 ☎ (0970) 84650
11–3, 5.30–11 (closed Sun)
**Banks's Mild, Bitter;
Thwaites Bitter** Ⓗ
The sole surviving pub in a former lead-mining village, set into the hillside of the Melindwr Valley. Beer range varies. Duck eggs on sale. ◖ ▶ ♣ P

Goodwick

Fishguard Bay Hotel
Quay Road ☎ (0348) 873571
11–3, 5.30–11
Crown Buckley Best Bitter Ⓗ
Pleasantly situated hotel overlooking Fishguard harbour, offering gardens, walks, a snooker room, a restaurant and a small, glazed, covered patio. TV lounge for non-smokers.
🛏 Q ⊛ ▧ ⋈ ◖ ▶
⇌ (Fishguard Harbour) ♣ ⌂ P ⅋

Glendower Hotel
The Square ☎ (0348) 872873
11–11
**Crown Buckley Best Bitter,
Rev. James** Ⓗ
Very smart pub used by nautical folk and locals: a lounge and a small breakfast room, ideal for meetings or functions.
🛏 ⊞ ⇌ (Fishguard Harbour)

Haverfordwest

Georges Inn
24 Market Street
☎ (0437) 766683
11–3, 7–11
**Ind Coope Burton Ale;
Marston's Pedigree** Ⓗ
Modernised pub retaining some originality in its nooks and settles. New restaurant with good food. Q ◖ ▶ ⊞

Pembroke Yeoman
Hill Street ☎ (0437) 762500
11–11
Ansells Bitter Ⓗ
Friendly local offering good ale, food and chat. 🛏 ⊛ ◖ ▶

Hayscastle Cross

Cross Inn
On B4330 ☎ (0348) 840216
11–3, 6–11
**Felinfoel Double Dragon;
Welsh Brewers Worthington
BB** Ⓗ
A family-owned pub since 1860: a friendly local on a crossroads, resembling an old farmhouse. The small dining room doubles as a family room; also pool room/lounge and a tiny games nook in the bar.
🛏 Q 🛏 ◖ ▶ ⊞ ♣ P

Hundleton

Speculation Inn
Follow signs for Texaco
OS947998 ☎ (0646) 661306
11.30–3 (12–2.30 winter), 6–11
**Felinfoel Bitter, Double
Dragon** Ⓗ
Two intriguing, small bars displaying an historic letter, warning a former landlord of the sins of the locality. Coarse fishing close by: a good source of information for nearby sea fishing and surfing.
🛏 Q ⊛ ◖ ▶ ⊞ Å ♣ P

Jeffreyston

Jeffreyston Inn
Sharp turn off B4586
OS088065 ☎ (0646) 651394
11–11
**Crown Buckley Best Bitter;
John Smith's Bitter; Welsh
Brewers Worthington BB** Ⓗ
Pub with a goat and a playhouse in the garden, a large restaurant area, and a 'head-banger express' minibus to ferry revellers home. Excellent variety of guest beers, some unusual for the area; cider in summer.
🛏 Q 🛏 ⊛ ◖ ▶ ⊞ Å ♣ ⌂ P

Try also: Cross Inn,
Broadmoor (Welsh Brewers)

Kilgetty

Kilgetty Arms
Carmarthen Road (opp. station)
☎ (0834) 813219
11–11
Felinfoel Bitter Ⓗ
Excellent, friendly, village pub with a strong local clientele. Its typical Welsh pub layout remains unchanged; bar to the right and lounge to the left.
🛏 Q ⊛ ⋈ ◖ ▶ ⊞ ⅋ Å ⇌ ♣ P

Lampeter

Kings Head
14 Bridge Street (A482/A485)
☎ (0570) 422598
11–3.30 (may extend), 5.30–11
**Draught Bass; Crown
Buckley Best Bitter** Ⓗ
Pleasant, unpretentious, two-bar free house in the centre of this university town. Popular with locals and students alike. The menu caters for children and vegetarians (supper licence to 12.30). Aviary in the garden.
🛏 Q ⊛ ⋈ ◖ ▶ ⊞ ⅋ Å ♣ P

Landshipping

Stanley Arms
Near the Cleddau River
OS013117 ☎ (0834) 891227
12–3, 6–11 (maybe 12–11 summer)
**Crown Buckley Best Bitter;
Welsh Brewers Worthington
BB** Ⓗ

Excellent find in an idyllic, rural area with a mooring on the nearby river for customers' use. A large beer garden surrounds this attractive, large, rambling and stone-flagged building. Live music Sat in winter, Fri in summer. No food Mon eve.
🛏 Q 🛏 ⊞ ⋈ ◖ ▶ ⅋ Å ♣ P

Laugharne

New Three Mariners
Victoria Street (A4066)
☎ (0994) 427426
11–3, 5.30–11 (11–11 summer)
Crown Buckley Best Bitter Ⓗ
Former home-brew pub built c. 1703. Two small, friendly, locals' bars and a large, comfortable pool room. Snacks available. 🛏 ⋈ ⅋ Å ♣

Letterston

Harp Inn
31 Haverfordwest Road (A40)
☎ (0348) 840061
11–3, 5.30–11
**Ansells Bitter; Ind Coope
Burton Ale** Ⓗ
Very long-established pub which has been tastefully refurbished and extended to include a large restaurant and a lounge, offering a high standard of cuisine. Sun lunches are a treat. 🛏 ⊞ ◖ ▶ ⅋ ⊞ P

Try also: Pump on the Green,
Spittal

Little Haven

Swan Inn
Off B4341
☎ (0437) 781256
11–3, 6.30–11
**Felinfoel Double Dragon;
Welsh Brewers Worthington
BB** Ⓗ
Delightful, old pub in a rocky cove approached by a footpath. Wide range of home-cooked food, incl. specials and local seafood. Restaurant open Wed–Sat eves (book).
🛏 Q ⊛ ◖ ▶ Å

Llandeilo

White Horse
125 Rhosmaen Street (A483)
11.45–3, 5.30–11 (12–2.30, 7–10.30 Sun)
**Brains Dark; Wadworth 6X;
Welsh Brewers Worthington
BB** Ⓗ
17th-century coaching inn with a courtyard and a collection of old railway photographs in its snug. Two guest beers always available – 130 different ones in 18 months. A must. No food Sun. 🛏 Q ⊛ ◖ ▶ ⊞ ⅋ ⇌ (not winter Sun) ⌂ P ⅋ (not always available)

Llandovery

Bluebell Inn
High Street ☎ (0550) 21146
11.30–11
**Draught Bass; Welsh
Brewers Worthington BB** Ⓗ
Bluebells abound hereabouts –
hence the name. Two bars with
beams, stonework and plenty of
character. The building dates
from 1810, with parts much
older. A rare survivor in a road
once lined with pubs. 🏠 🛏 ⊛ 🌙
🕪 ⊟ ♿ Å ≋ (not winter Sun) ♣

Red Lion
Market Square
11–3, 5.30–11 (closed Sun)
**Crown Buckley Dark, Best
Bitter,** Ⓖ
Basic, characterful pub where
beer is served from a hatch in
the single flagstoned bar. Hard
to find, but not to be missed: a
step back in time. 🏠 Q ≋ (not winter Sun)

Station Hotel
College View ☎ (0550) 20441
11–3, 6–11 (11–11 Fri, Sat & summer)
**Draught Bass; Welsh
Brewers Hancock's HB** Ⓗ
Built as the 'Salutation' in 1850
and renamed when the railway
arrived in 1858; a pub with a
friendly welcome, home-cooked
food (using local produce) and a
railway-theme decor. Guest
beers. ⊛ 🛏 🕪 🕪 Å ≋ (not winter
Sun) ♣ P

Llandybie

Red Lion
The Square ☎ (0269) 851202
11.30–3, 6–11 (closed Sun eve)
**Marston's Pedigree;
Whitbread Flowers
Original** Ⓗ
Regional CAMRA *Pub of the
Year*; a listed building with
much character and style in
appearance and service. Guest
beer. Q 🛏 ⊛ 🛏 🕪 🕪 ⊟ ≋ P

Llangadog

Plough
Dyrfal Road (A4069)
12–2.30, 5.30–11 (11–11 Sat)
**Draught Bass; Wadworth
6X** Ⓗ
250 year-old building once
used as a chapel: no ghost –
only a poltergeist, but still a
friendly welcome. Separate
restaurant. The sign is a genuine
plough. Guest beer. 🏠 ⊛ 🕪 Å
≋ (not winter Sun) ♣ P

Telegraph Inn
Station Road
☎ (0550) 777701
12–3, 6–11
Beer varies Ⓗ
Popular pub and noted

restaurant serving locals and
tourists alike. On the edge of
the village, by the River Towy
(famous for its fishing). No
permanent real ale, but a guest
beer at all times. ⊛ 🛏 🕪 🕪 ⊟ ♿
Å ≋ (not winter Sun) ♣ P

Llangeitho

Three Horseshoes
The Square ☎ (097 423) 244
12–3, 5.30–11 (closed Sun eve)
Tetley Bitter Ⓗ
Traditional local in a sleepy
village. Beer range varies; guest
beer (not mid winter). No food
Sun. 🏠 Q ⊛ 🕪 ⊟ ♿ Å ♣ P

Llangoedmor

Penllwyn-du
On B4570, 5 miles E of
Cardigan OS241458
☎ (023 987) 533
11–11 (may close afternoons, re-
opening 5.30; 12–2.30, 7–10.30 Sun)
**Draught Bass; Brains SA
(summer); Felinfoel Double
Dragon; Welsh Brewers
Worthington BB** Ⓗ
Remote, ex-home-brew pub and
courthouse, now a comfortable,
traditional, country pub with
fine views. Folk club alternate
Thu. 🏠 🛏 🕪 ⊟ ♣ P

Llanychaer

Bridge End Inn
On B4313, 2½ miles E of
Fishguard ☎ (0348) 872545
11–3, 5.30–11
**Draught Bass; Ind Coope
Burton Ale; Marston's
Pedigree** Ⓗ
Pub in a hidden valley, with an
enthusiastic landlord who
specialises in different ales
(over 120 beers in 15 months).
A large barn-like lounge is
decorated with country
implements. Occasional cider.
🏠 Q ⊛ 🕪 🕪 ⊟ Å ♣ ⌣

Mathry

Farmers Arms
11–11
**Draught Bass; Welsh
Brewers Worthington BB** Ⓗ
Refurbished, but unspoilt,
traditional, rural pub with an
open-plan bar. It boasts a vast
collection of Guinness prints
(cartoons). 🏠 ⊛ 🕪 Å P

Meidrim

Maenllwyd Inn
¾ mile W of village and B4299
OS278212
6–11 (closed Sun)
Crown Buckley Best Bitter Ⓖ
Rare example of an utterly
traditional, country local with a
whitewashed parlour and a

cottage-style sitting room. Beer
served by jug. No keg at all.
🏠 Q 🕪 ♿ ≋ P

Meinciau

Black Horse
On B4309
11–3, 5.30–11 (may vary)
**Crown Buckley Dark;
Felinfoel Bitter** Ⓖ
Very welcoming pub in the
countryside. 🏠 Q ⊛ 🕪 ⊟ P

Milton

Milton Brewery
On A477 ☎ (0646) 651202
11–11
**Draught Bass; Welsh
Brewers Worthington BB** Ⓗ
Rambling, 15th-century ale-
house, offering comfort and
sustenance to travellers and
locals alike.
🏠 Q 🛏 ⊛ 🛏 🕪 🕪 ⊟ ♿ Å ♣ P

Narberth

Kirkland Arms
St James Street (A478)
11–11
**Felinfoel Cambrian, Double
Dragon** Ⓗ
Lively pub, handy for the rugby
ground, with a large fish tank in
the public bar. Tables are
shaped to fit the available space;
walls are covered in artwork.
🏠 🛏 ⊛ 🕪 ⊟ ♿ Å ≋ ♣ P

Newcastle Emlyn

Bunch of Grapes
Bridge Street (A475)
11.30–11
**Courage Best Bitter,
Directors** Ⓗ
17th-century building, now
opened out, its pine floors and
furniture providing a café-bar
atmosphere. Eve meals finish at
7; no food Sun. Guest beers.
🏠 🛏 ⊛ 🕪 🕪

Coopers Arms
Station Road
☎ (0239) 710323
11.30–3 (may extend), 5.30–11
**Draught Bass; Welsh
Brewers Worthington BB** Ⓗ
Pub featuring an attractive bar
area, with stone walls and brick
arches, a separate games area
and a no-smoking dining area.
⊛ 🕪 🕪 Å ♣ P

New Quay

Seahorse Inn
Margaret Street
☎ (0545) 560736
11–11
**Crown Buckley Dark, Best
Bitter, Rev. James** Ⓗ
Victorian, one-bar pub above
the fishing harbour. 🛏 🕪 Å ♣

Dyfed

Pelcomb Bridge

Rising Sun Inn
On A478 ☎ (0437) 765171
11.30–3, 7 (6 summer)–11
Ind Coope Burton Ale; Tetley Bitter Ⓗ
Old, country inn tastefully rebuilt and retaining its original character. A family business, friendly and popular with diners.
🏠 Q 🕏 🖂 🍴 🚬 🕏 🛏 🅰 ♣ P

Pembroke

Old Cross Saws
Main Street ☎ (0646) 682475
11–11
Crown Buckley Best Bitter Ⓗ
Rugby-followers' local, larger inside than it appears from without. Well-placed for the mill pond, Norman castle and antique shops. Hillside garden.
🕏 🖂 🍴 🅰 🌉 ♣ P

Pembroke Dock

Charlton Hotel
Bush Street ☎ (0646) 682285
11–11
Draught Bass; Welsh Brewers Worthington Dark, BB Ⓗ
A gem of a beer-drinkers' local: a red-brick, turn-of-the-century, corner pub with an impressive bank of six handpumps and a large games room. 🌉 🌉 ♣

Penally

Cross Inn
11–3, 7–11 (11–11 summer)
Welsh Brewers Worthington BB Ⓗ
Pub extending a warm welcome to families, artisans, hikers et al, in the daytime, and to a strong local clientele and holiday-makers in the eve. Recently skilfully restored with slate floors, solid wooden tables and other fittings. Q 🕏 🍴 🅰 🌉 ♣

Pontargothi

Cresselly Arms
Carmarthen Road (A40)
11–3, 6–11
Marston's Pedigree; Whitbread Flowers Original Ⓗ
Attractive pub in a small village; its restaurant offers riverside views. 🏠 Q 🕏 🍴 P

Pontfaen

Dyffryn Arms
Off A487, then B4313
11–11
Draught Bass; Ind Coope Burton Ale Ⓖ
Basic pub with basic decor but good company; very popular. A

gem for the discerning enthusiast willing to search it out. Occasional cider.
🏠 Q 🕏 🖂 🕏 🍴 ♣ ◇

Porthgain

Sloop Inn
Off A487 ☎ (0348) 831449
11.30–3, 6–11 (11.30–11 Fri & Sat)
Felinfoel Double Dragon; Welsh Brewers Hancock's HB Ⓗ
Old, seafarers' pub, estd. 1743 in an historic harbour village on the Coastal Path. Original in character and a popular eating house. 🏠 🕏 🍴 ♣ P

Sageston

Plough Inn
On A477 ☎ (0646) 651557
11–3, 5.30–11
Welsh Brewers Worthington BB Ⓗ
Busy, country local offering good food and entertainment.
🏠 Q 🌉 🕏 🍴 🕏 🛏 🅰 ♣ P

St David's

Farmers Arms
Goat Street ☎ (0437) 720328
11–11
Marston's Pedigree; Whitbread Boddingtons Bitter Ⓗ
19th-century, stone-built pub with beams, flagstone floors and an original fireplace. Popular with local fishermen, farmers and lifeboatmen. Excellent, home-cooked meals and bar snacks. 🏠 Q 🌉 🕏 🍴 🕏 ♣

Solva

Cambrian Inn
Main Street ☎ (0437) 721210
11–3, 7–11
Ind Coope Burton Ale Ⓗ
18th-century, listed, village pub with a beamed bar and an attractive restaurant; near the bridge over the river and the Coastal Path. Daily specials and a roast Sun lunch (no food Sun eve). 🏠 Q 🍴 🕏 🕏 ♣ P

Ship Inn
Main Street ☎ (0437) 721247
11–11
Draught Bass; Brains SA; Felinfoel Double Dragon; Welsh Brewers Worthington BB Ⓗ
300 year-old pub in a fishing and sailing village. Free car park on the quay. The separate restaurant offers a home-cooked, full menu with daily specials.
🏠 Q 🕏 🅰 ♣

Talybont

White Lion
The Square ☎ (097 086) 245
11–4, 5.30–11

Banks's Mild, Bitter Ⓔ
Warm, slate-flagged public bar with everything available from cribbage to bus timetables; neat lounge at the rear. Well known for B&B and good value food.
🏠 Q 🕏 🖂 🍴 🕏 🛏 ♣ P

Tan-y-groes

Gogerddan Arms
On A487/B4333
12–3, 6–11 (closed Sun in winter)
Crown Buckley Best Bitter; Welsh Brewers Worthington BB Ⓗ
Large roadhouse near Aberporth, built in 1964, with a plain exterior, but attractive and comfortable inside. Two bars, a restaurant with a no-smoking area, and extensive grounds.
🕏 🍴 🕏 🛏 ♣ P

Tegryn

Butchers Arms
4 miles E of Crymych and A478 ☎ (0239) 77680
11–3, 5.30–11
Crown Buckley Best Bitter Ⓗ
Comfortable and welcoming pub in a small, isolated, hilltop village, offering fine country views. Excellent value food.
🏠 Q 🌉 🕏 🖂 🍴 🕏 🅰 ♣ P

Templeton

Boars Head
On A478 ☎ (0834) 860286
11–3, 5.30–11 (11–11 Sat & bank hols)
Ruddles Best Bitter; Webster's Yorkshire Bitter Ⓗ
Beautiful, rural, beamed and rambling pub with a very good restaurant. Children admitted to games room. 🕏 🍴 🕏 🛏 🅰 ♣ P

Tenby

Normandie Hotel
Upper Frog Street (near Five Arches) ☎ (0834) 2227
11–3, 7–11
Ruddles County; Welsh Brewers Worthington BB Ⓗ
A lively public bar, a comfortable saloon, a restaurant, and a large family room all in this old coaching inn within the town walls. Guest beers.
Q 🌉 🍴 🕏 🕏 🌉 ♣

Tenby & District Ex-Servicemen's Club
Ruabon House, South Parade
11–3, 6–11 (12–2, 7–10.30 Sun)
Welsh Brewers Worthington Dark, BB Ⓔ
Large, friendly club which welcomes temporary members. Two snooker tables and a wide range of entertainment; children welcome until 6pm. Q 🌉 🌉 ♣

Mid Glamorgan

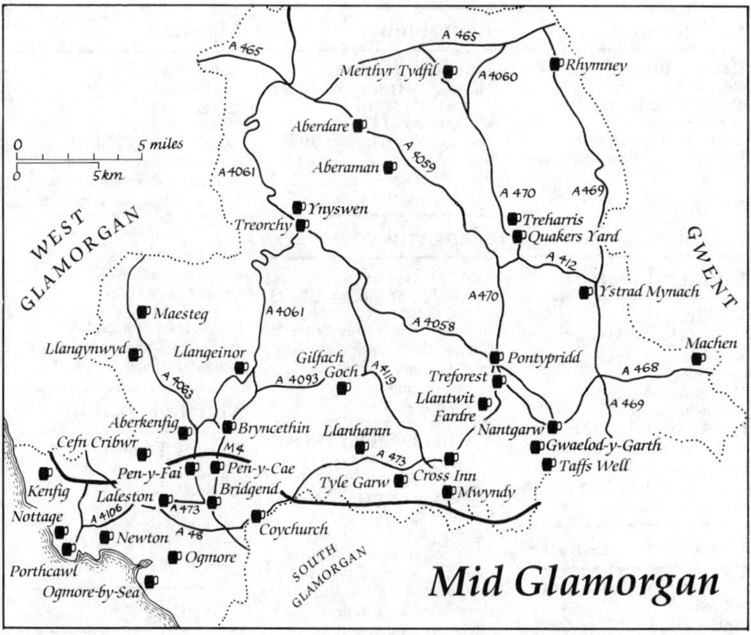

Aberaman

Temple Bar
Cardiff Road (B4275)
☎ (0685) 876137
12–4, 7–11 (may vary)
Brains SA; Felinfoel Double Dragon Ⓗ
Homely local with bric-a-brac and library in bar. Separate games room. Guest beers. Limited parking. ⌂ Q ⊞ ♣ P

Aberdare

Glandover Arms
Gadlys Road (B4275, old road to Hirwaun) ☎ (0685) 872923
12–4.30 (5.30 Sat), 6.30–11
Ansells Best Bitter Ⓗ
Convivial house with cellar restaurant. Eve meals Tue–Sat; lunches Sat only. Guest beer.
❀ ◐ ◑ ⊞ ⇌ ♣

Aberkenfig

Swan
128 Bridgend Road (1 mile from M4 jct 36)
☎ (0656) 725612
11–3.30 (4 Sat), 6–11 (12–2.30, 7–10.30 Sun)
Brains Dark, Bitter, SA; Whitbread Flowers Original Ⓗ
Pleasant, comfortable village pub. Good meals (no food Sun lunch or Sun/Mon eves).
Q ◐ ◑ ♿ P

Try also: Colliers Arms (Brains)

Bridgend

Hunters Lodge
Church Acre, Brackla
☎ (0656) 667700
11–11
Draught Bass; Welsh Brewers Hancock's HB Ⓗ
Large, friendly estate pub with pleasant decor and comfortable furnishings. Lounge restaurant is popular for lunch: children and vegetarians catered for.
Q ⛀ ❀ ◐ ◑ ⊞ ♿ ♣ P

Oldcastle
Nolton Street
☎ (0656) 652305
12–4, 6–11 (12–11 Fri & Sat)
Draught Bass; Brains SA; Welsh Brewers Worthington BB Ⓗ
Cosy, friendly town pub without an inn sign.
⌂ Q ◐ ⇌ ♣

Two Brewers
Brackla Way, Brackla (200 yds from B4181)
☎ (0656) 661788
11–11 (12.30–3, 7–10.30 Sun; 12–2.30, 5.30–11 Mon–Thu in winter)
Brains Dark, Bitter, SA Ⓗ
Large, modern estate pub with a plush lounge and family room. No meals Sun. Eve meals only if booked. Backgammon can be played. ⛀ ❀ ◐ ⊞ ♿ ♣ P

Victoria
Adare Street ☎ (0656) 667667
11–11
Courage Best Bitter, Directors; Wadworth 6X Ⓗ
Comfortable, busy town-centre pub. No lunches Sun. ◐ ♿ ⇌ ♣

Try also: Railway (Free)

Bryncethin

Masons Arms
Bridgend Road (A4061 opp. post office) ☎ (0656) 720253
12–11
Draught Bass; Brains Dark, SA; Welsh Brewers Worthington BB Ⓗ
Unspoilt bar and plush lounge. Live entertainment in the high-class restaurant Wed. ◐ ◑ ⊞ ♿ P

Cefn Cribwr

Farmers Arms
24 Cefn Road (B4281)
☎ (0656) 743648
12–11
Draught Bass; Felinfoel Cambrian Ⓗ
Unspoilt village local with mining memorabilia. Beers change regularly. Public car park across the road.
⌂ ⛀ ❀ ⊞ ♿ ⛺ ♣

Coychurch

White Horse
Main Road ☎ (0656) 652583
11.30–4, 5.30–11 (11.30–11 Fri & Sat)
Brains Dark, Bitter, SA Ⓗ
Comfortable village pub. Landlord is *Welsh Innkeeper of the Year* and *Brains Cellarman of the Year.* ❀ ◐ ◑ ⊞ ♣ P

Mid Glamorgan

Cross Inn

Cross Inn
On A473
☎ (0443) 223431
12–4.30, 6.30–11
Brains Bitter; Marston's Pedigree; Whitbread Flowers IPA Ⓗ
Bustling, small, friendly village local. Q ⊟ P

Gilfach Goch

Griffin
Hendreforgan (600 yds S of A4093 at end of narrow lane) OS988875
12–11 (may close afternoons)
Brains SA Ⓗ
Exceptional, traditional local, remotely situated in a small valley bottom. Interesting bric-a-brac and furniture. Cosy and friendly. Q ⊛ ⊟

Gwaelod-y-Garth

Gwaelod-y-Garth Inn
600 yds off Taffs Well-Pentyrch road
☎ (0222) 810408
11–11
Welsh Brewers Hancock's HB Ⓗ
Small, traditional village local, welcoming and friendly. Guest beers. Patio has valley views.
⊛ ⊟ ♣ P

Kenfig

Prince of Wales
Off B4283 near nature reserve
☎ (0656) 740356
11.30–4, 6–11
Draught Bass; Felinfoel Double Dragon; Fuller's ESB; Marston's Pedigree; Wadworth 6X Ⓖ; **Welsh Brewers Worthington BB** Ⓗ
Old pub with exposed stone walls: large main bar and two smaller rooms. Linked with historic Kenfig which lies buried under sand dunes. Beer range varies. Home cooking.
⊠ Q ⊛ ◖ ♿ ♣ P

Laleston

Laleston Inn
Wind Street (off A473, behind church)
☎ (0656) 652946
12–3, 7–11
Draught Bass Ⓖ; **Marston's Pedigree; Welsh Brewers Worthington BB** Ⓗ
15th-century free house with exposed stone walls, beams and nautical items. Jazz Sun lunchtime. Other beers often available; reasonably-priced food.
⊠ ◖ ⌂ P

Llangeinor

Llangeinor Arms
Off A4093 ☎ (0656) 870268
12–4, 7–11 (12–11 Sat)
Draught Bass; Welsh Brewers Worthington BB Ⓗ
Isolated hilltop pub with superb views. Separate, quality restaurant. ⊠ ⊛ ◖ ◗ P

Llangynwyd

Corner House
Off A4063 ☎ (0656) 732393
11.30–3.30, 6.30–11 (11–11 Sat)
Brains Bitter; Tetley Bitter Ⓗ
Comfortable, welcoming village local. Live music Thu. Restaurant and pub fare.
⊠ ⊛ ◖ ◗ ⚲ P

Yr Hen Dy (Old House)
Off A4063 ☎ (0656) 733310
11–11 (11–4, 6–11 winter)
Whitbread Flowers IPA, Original Ⓗ
Very old inn, dating back to 1147 and connected with the Cefn Ydfa legend. Thatched roof; beams; inglenook; bags of atmosphere – a real gem. Adventure playground for children. ⊠ Q ⊛ ◖ ◗ ⊟ ⚲ P

Llanharan

High Corner House
The Square (A473)
☎ (0443) 238056
11–11 (restaurant open till 12)
Courage Directors; Marston's Pedigree; Wadworth 6X; Whitbread Castle Eden Ale, Flowers Original Ⓗ
Large, plush village pub, having undergone recent Whitbread refurbishment. Evening meals and Sun lunch available in the attached restaurant. No pub meals Sun. ⊛ ◖ P

Llantwit Fardre

Crown Inn
Main Road ☎ (0443) 208531
12–2.30, 6–11
Brains Bitter, SA Ⓗ
Large, open-plan village local. Plush, but characterless decor. Eve meals; no lunches except Sun. ◗ ♣ P

Machen

White Hart
Nant y Ceisiad (100 yds N of A468, under railway bridge)
☎ (0633) 441005
11–4, 6–11
Brains SA Ⓔ
Rambling pub with interesting, windowless, wood-panelled bar. The panelling was salvaged from a luxury liner and the small restaurant resembles a ship's cabin. Enterprising guest beers. ⊠ Q ⊛ ◖ ◗ P

Maesteg

Beethovens
Castle Street
☎ (0656) 738484
11.30–4, 6.30–11 (11.30–11 Fri & Sat)
Crown Buckley SBB Ⓗ
Plush local with youngish clientele. Live entertainment Tue in upstairs function room.
⌑ ◖ ◗ ♿ ♣

Sawyers Arms
4 Commercial Street
☎ (0656) 734606
11–4.30, 6–11 (11–11 Fri & Sat)
Brains Dark, Bitter, SA Ⓗ
Pub with Victorian exterior and comfortable interior. ◖ ⊟ ♿

Merthyr Tydfil

Anchor Tavern
High Street
☎ (0685) 723840
11–11 (may close afternoons)
Draught Bass Ⓗ
Small, welcoming and full of character. ⊟ ⇌ ♣

Mwyndy

Barn
100 yds off A4119
☎ (0443) 222333
11.30–2.30, 5.30 (7 Sat)–11 (12–2.30, 7–10.30 Sun)
Felinfoel Double Dragon; Fuller's London Pride; Wadworth 6X; Welsh Brewers Hancock's HB Ⓗ
A conversion from an old barn, parts of which date back to 1570. Good reputation for food (no meals Sun). Two bars with exposed beams and stone walls; upstairs restaurant. Guest beer.
⊠ Q ⌑ ⊛ ◖ P

Castell Mynach
Llantrisant Road (A4119, 800 yds N of M4 jct 34)
11–11
Draught Bass; Welsh Brewers Hancock's HB, Worthington BB Ⓗ
Ever-popular meeting, eating and drinking house, comfortably furnished and catering for regulars and travellers alike. No food Sun. Q ⊛ ◖ P

Nantgarw

Cross Keys
Cardiff Road (A4054 just S of Treforest Ind. Est.)
☎ (0443) 843262
11–11
Brains Bitter; Whitbread Flowers IPA Ⓗ
Comfortable, open-plan house with small dining area. Successfully combines being both a lunchtime business retreat and an evening local.
◖ ◗ ♣ P

Newton

Globe
Bridgend Road (A4106)
☎ (0656) 783535
11–11 (11.30–3.30, 5.30–11 Mon–Thu
in winter)
Draught Bass Ⓖ
Welcoming local on the edge of
the village with excellent
provision for families.
🏠 ☕ 🍴 🌰 ◑ ⊟ 🅰 ♣ P

Jolly Sailor
Church Street (off A4106)
☎ (0656) 782403
11.30–11
Brains Dark, Bitter, SA Ⓗ
Village green pub with a
nautical flavour. 🏠 ☕ 🅰 ♣

Nottage

Rose & Crown
Heol-y-Capel
☎ (0656) 784850
11.30–4, 6–11 (11.30–11 Sat)
**Ruddles Best Bitter, County;
Webster's Yorkshire Bitter** Ⓗ
Smart local and carvery.
☕ ⋈ ◑ ▶ P

Ogmore

Pelican
Ewenny Road (B4524 opp.
castle) ☎ (0656) 880049
11.30–4, 6.30–11 (11–11 Fri & Sat)
**Courage Best Bitter,
Directors; John Smith's
Bitter; Wadworth 6X** Ⓗ
Smart, comfortable country pub
with restaurant. ☕ ◑ ▶ ♿ ♣ P

Ogmore-by-Sea

Craig-yr-Eos
Main Road ☎ (0656) 880388
12–4, 6.30–11
Crown Buckley Best Bitter
(summer), **SBB** Ⓗ
Seaside hotel offering fine views
over Bristol Channel.
🏠 Q ☕ 🍴 ◑ ▶ ⊟ 🅰 ♣ P

Pen-y-Cae

Tyr Isha
Off A4061, Bridgend side of
M4 services OS903827
☎ (0656) 725287
12–4, 6.30–11 (may extend in summer)
**Draught Bass; Welsh
Brewers Hancock's HB** Ⓗ
Popular converted farmhouse,
comfortably furnished with a
rustic decor. 🏠 ☕ ◑ ▶ ♿ P

Pen-y-Fai

Pheasant
Off A4063 ☎ (0656) 653614
11.30–4, 6–11 (11–11 Fri & Sat)
**Brains Dark; Courage Best
Bitter, Directors; Wadworth
6X** Ⓗ
Large village pub with luxurious
lounge. Eve meals Fri and Sat
only. 🌰 ☕ ◑ ▶ ⊟ ♿ P

Pontypridd

Bunch of Grapes
Ynysangharad Road (between
A470 Ynysybwl jct and
A4054) ☎ (0443) 402934
11–11
**Brains Bitter, SA; Welsh
Brewers Hancock's HB** Ⓗ
Comfortable pub with sun-trap
patio and a restaurant
dominated by the famous vine.
Guest beers. 🌰 ☕ ◑ ▶ ⇌ P

Greyhound
1 The Broadway (opp. station)
☎ (0443) 402350
11–11
**Draught Bass; Welsh
Brewers Worthington BB** Ⓗ
Small town pub, invariably
bustling. Guest beer. ☕ ⊟ ♣

Llanover Arms
Bridge Street (at A470
Ynysybwl jct) ☎ (0443) 403215
11.30–11
**Brains Dark, Bitter, SA;
Wadworth 6X** Ⓗ
Bustling town pub with three
bars. Broad cross-section of
drinkers and large selection of
beers. ☕ ⊟ ⇌ ♣ P

Porthcawl

Rock Hotel
98 John Street (opp. police
station) ☎ (0656) 782340
11–11
**Draught Bass; Welsh
Brewers Worthington BB** Ⓗ
Town pub with basic bar and
comfortable lounge. Generous
portions of meals.
🏠 ☕ ◑ ▶ ⊟ ♿ ♣

Quakers Yard

Glantaff Inn
Cardiff Road ☎ (0443) 410822
11–11
**Courage Best Bitter,
Directors; John Smith's
Bitter** Ⓗ
Comfortable, popular inn with a
warm, friendly atmosphere
and a separate upstairs
restaurant. Q ☕ ◑ ⊟ ⇌ P

Rhymney

Farmers Arms
Brewery Row ☎ (0685) 840257
12.30–5, 7–11
**Whitbread Flowers
Original** Ⓗ
Popular, lively and friendly.
☕ ◑ ⊟ ⇌ P

Taffs Well

Anchor
Cardiff Road (A4054, ½ mile N
of M4/A470 jct)
☎ (0222) 810104
11–11 (11–4, 6.30–11 Sat)
**Brains Bitter; Whitbread
Flowers Original** Ⓗ

Comfortable bar and pleasant
lounge with gentle nautical
theme. Outstanding bar snacks
and popular restaurant.
☕ ◑ ▶ ⊟ ⇌ ♣ P

Treforest

Otley Arms
Forest Road ☎ (0443) 402033
11–11
**Draught Bass; Brains Dark,
SA; Crown Buckley SBB** Ⓗ
Bustling suburban pub, popular
with students and locals. Guest
beers. ◑ ▶ ⊟ ⇌ ♣

Treharris

Perrott Inn
Susannah Place (A4054)
☎ (0443) 412401
3 (2 Fri)–11 (12–5, 6.30–11 Sat)
**Crown Buckley Best Bitter,
SBB; Ruddles County; Welsh
Brewers Worthington BB** Ⓗ
Lively village pub with a good
cross-section of customers. Live
music Sat night; disco Fri.
Parking limited. ☕ ♣ P

Treorchy

Red Cow
High Street ☎ (0443) 773032
12–4 (5 Sat), 6.30–11
**Welsh Brewers Hancock's
HB** Ⓗ
Smart, comfortable local with
four contrasting bars, including
a no-smoking lounge. Lunches
Sun only; eve meals Tue–Thu.
Q ◑ ▶ ⊟ ⇌ ♣ ☒

Tyle Garw

Boars Head
Coed Cae Lane (½ mile off
A473) ☎ (0443) 225400
11.30–4, 6–11
**Draught Bass; Crown
Buckley Best Bitter** Ⓗ
Small, simply-furnished, unspoilt
local. Friendly atmosphere.
Forest walks opposite. Q ☕ ⊟ ♣

Ynyswen

Crown
Ynyswen Road (A4058)
☎ (0443) 772805
11–11 (may close afternoons)
**Brains SA; Welsh Brewers
Worthington BB; Whitbread
Flowers Original** Ⓗ
Bar full of interesting artefacts;
comfortable lounge. 🏠 ⊟ ⇌ ♣

Ystrad Mynach

Olde Royal Oak
Commercial Street (A469)
☎ (0443) 814196
11–11
**Draught Bass; Welsh
Brewers Hancock's HB** Ⓗ
Unmistakable Brewers' Tudor
pub on a crossroads. No meals
Sun. Q ◑ ▶ ⊟ ⇌ P

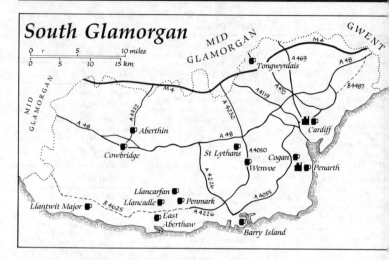

South Glamorgan

MID GLAMORGAN

GWENT

Tongwynlais

Cardiff

Aberthin

Cowbridge

St Lythans

Cogan

Wenvoe

Penarth

Llancarfan

Llancadle Penmark

Llantwit Major

East Aberthaw

Barry Island

MID GLAMORGAN

0   5   10 miles
0   5   10   15 km

Brains, *Cardiff*; **Bullmastiff**, *Penarth*

Aberthin

Hare & Hounds
On A4222 ☎ (044 63) 4892
11.30–3.30, 5.30–11 (11–11 Sat and summer if busy)
Draught Bass Ⓖ; **Brains Dark, Bitter** (summer) Ⓔ; **Welsh Brewers Hancock's HB** Ⓗ, **Worthington BB** Ⓖ
Superb, traditional village local, with two fine fireplaces. Parking limited. ⌂ Q ♿ ⛱ 🍴 🎵 ♣ P

Barry Island

Marine Hotel
Redbrink Crescent
11–11
Brains Dark, Bitter, SA Ⓗ
Comfortable local close to the fun fair. Large bar/lounge has photos of old Barry Island; children's room and small, second lounge. ⛱ 🍴 ➡ ♣ P

Cardiff

Black Lion
49 Cardiff Road, Llandaff
11–3, 5–11 (11–11 Fri & Sat; 12–2.40, 7–10.30 Sun)
Brains Dark, Bitter, SA Ⓗ
Typical Brains town pub: large lounge and traditional, basic bar. Very popular with locals. Children welcome in lounge when taking lunch (no food Sun). ◖ ⊟ ♣

Bluebell Inn
High Street ☎ (0222) 225543
11–11 (12–2, 7–10.30 Sun)
Brains Dark, Bitter, SA Ⓗ
One-bar pub opposite the castle, frequented by city-centre workers, shoppers and night-outers. ◖ ➡ (Central/Queen St)

Crown
Bute Street ☎ (0222) 463945
11–3 (may extend), 5.30–11
Ansells Dark; Tetley Bitter Ⓗ
Friendly, corner local, a short stroll from the city centre. Excellent easy-going atmosphere. A firm commitment to real ale includes a regular guest beer. Opposite the Welsh National Opera. Ansells Dark is a sales name for Crown Buckley Dark. ◖ ▶ ➡ (Central) ♣

Fox & Hounds
Chapel Row, St Mellons (off B4487) ☎ (0222) 777046
11–11
Brains Dark, Bitter, SA Ⓗ
Frequent local newspaper's *Pub of the Year*. Part of the lounge converts into a dining room to serve award-winning lunches. Well-equipped children's play area in the large garden.
Q 🍴 ◖ ▶ ♣ P

Golden Cross
283 Hayes Bridge Road (opp. Ice Rink) ☎ (0222) 394556
12–3, 5–11 (11–11 Sat; 7–10.30 only Sun)
Brains Dark, Bitter, SA Ⓗ
Wonderfully preserved pub behind the Holiday Inn. Beautiful tiled pictures in the bar and entrance depict old Cardiff. Ornate tiled bar front. Outdoor area in summer. Eve meals on request. ⛱ 🍴 ◖ ⊟ ♣ (Central/Queen St) ♣

Grange
Penarth Road, Grangetown ☎ (0222) 230681
11–11
Brains Dark, Bitter, SA Ⓗ
Thriving local near a busy road junction. Comfortable, large lounge with access to outdoor area. Skittle alley. Early eve meals on request.
🍴 ◖ ⊟ ➡ (Grangetown) ♣

Millers Mate
Thornhill Road, Thornhill (A469, 4 miles from centre)
11–11
Banks's Mild, Bitter Ⓗ
Former farmhouse converted to a pub in the last ten years. The building is much older than the surrounding estate. Steakhouse-type diner on first floor. A welcome new outlet for Banks's beers in the area. Lunches Mon–Fri. Q ◖ P

Old Arcade
Church Street (off High Street next to covered market)
11–11 (7–10.30 alternate Suns)
Brains Dark, Bitter, SA Ⓗ
Busy city-centre pub with various sporting mementos. Handy for shops and St David's Centre. Lounge open lunchtimes and Fri/Sat eves only.
◖ ⊟ ➡ (Central/Queen St)

Old Cottage
Cherry Orchard Road, Lisvane (1 mile E of A469)
☎ (0222) 747582
11.30–11 (11.30–3.30, 5.30–11 Mon & Tue; 11–11 summer)
Ansells Bitter; Ind Coope Burton Ale; Tetley Bitter Ⓗ
Converted 200 year-old farmhouse in semi-rural area. Next to Cefn Onn Park. Good value home-cooked food. Q 🍴 ◖
▶ ♿ ➡ (Lisvane & Thornhill) P

Plough Inn
1 Merthyr Road, Whitchurch
☎ (0222) 623017
11–11 (11–4, 7–11 Sat)

Brains Dark, Bitter, SA Ⓗ
Friendly, village-style pub with four separate bars off a central corridor. Large skittle alley. Bar meals cater for children and vegetarians (no food Sun). In centre of Whitchurch shopping area.
Q ❀ ◖ ⊟ ≠ (Whitchurch) ♣

Quarry House

St Fagans Rise, Fairwater
☎ (0222) 565577
11–3, 6–11 (11–11 Sat; 12–2, 7–10.30 Sun)
Courage Best Bitter, Directors Ⓗ
Comfortable suburban pub at the end of a cul-de-sac. Converted old manor house with children's play area in the garden. ❀ ◖ ⊟ ♣ P

Royal Oak

200 Broadway, Roath
(Newport Road jct)
11–3, 5.30–11
Brains Dark, Bitter Ⓗ, **SA** Ⓖ
Large corner local with lots of sporting memorabilia. Frequent live music. The only Brains tied house with beer on gravity. Splendid stained-glass windows feature men of literary renown.
Q ❀ ◖ ♣

Three Arches

Heathwood Road, Llanishen
☎ (0222) 752395
11–11
Brains Dark, Bitter, SA Ⓗ
One of Brains's largest pubs: three public bars and an upstairs function room, overshadowed by the railway line on the embankment above.
Q ❀ ◖ ⊟ ≠ (Heath) ♣ P

Ty Mawr Arms

Graig Road, Lisvane (1 mile N of B4562) OS183842
☎ (0222) 754456
12–3, 6–11
Draught Bass; Bullmastiff Best Bitter; Felinfoel Double Dragon; McEwan 80/-; Samuel Smith OBB; Summerskills Best Bitter Ⓗ
300 year-old listed building in extensive gardens with panoramic views. Ceiling beams were originally ship's timbers. Aviary and roaming peacock. Former S. Glamorgan CAMRA *Pub of the Year*. Beer range constantly varies.
🏛 Q ❀ ◖ ⊟ ♣ P

Cogan

Cogan Hotel

Pill Street ☎ (0222) 704280
12–11
Brains Bitter; Welsh Brewers Hancock's HB Ⓗ
Classic suburban local, enhanced by Brains guest beer. Splendid

public bar has bar billiards, a rarity in South Wales. Lounge is dimly-lit but cosy. ❀ ◖ ⊟ ≠ ♣

Cowbridge

Bear Hotel

High Street ☎ (044 63) 4814
11.30–11
Brains Bitter, SA; Crown Buckley Best Bitter; Felinfoel Double Dragon; Welsh Brewers Hancock's HB Ⓗ
Large, popular, well-appointed town-centre hotel. Widely-listed restaurant. Guest beers.
Q ❧ 🛏 ◖ ⊟ ♣ P

East Aberthaw

Blue Anchor

Off B4265 ☎ (0446) 750329
11–11
Brains SA; Crown Buckley Best Bitter; Marston's Pedigree; Theakston Old Peculier; Wadworth 6X; Whitbread Flowers IPA Ⓗ
Award-winning 14th-century thatched inn: six inter-connecting rooms around a central bar. Beware low oak beams and narrow gangways. Excellent pub food; separate restaurant. One changing guest beer. 🏛 Q ❧ ❀ ◖ ⊟ P

Llancadle

Green Dragon

Off B4265 ☎ (0446) 750367
11–11
Bullmastiff Ebony Dark; Felinfoel Double Dragon; Welsh Brewers Hancock's HB; Whitbread Flowers IPA Ⓗ
Recently extended to blend with the original thatched village pub. Children welcome in back lounge. Two guest beers. 🏛 Q ❀ ◖ ⊟ P

Llancarfan

Fox & Hounds

Off A48 from Bonvilston
☎ (0446) 781297
11–3.30, 6.30–11 (11–11 Sat)
Brains SA; Felinfoel Cambrian; Ruddles Best Bitter Ⓗ
16th-century village inn with quality restaurant. Guest beers.
🏛 Q ❧ ❀ ◖ P

Llantwit Major

Old White Hart

Wine Street ☎ (0446) 793549
11.30–11
Welsh Brewers Worthington BB Ⓗ
Converted 14th-century terrace of three cottages in the town square. Two bars; large garden

with children's play area. Summer barbecues.
🏛 Q ❀ ◖ ⊟ Å ♣

Penarth

Pilot

Queens Road ☎ (0222) 702340
11.30–11
Brains Dark, Bitter, SA Ⓗ
Two-bar locals' pub: smart, often quiet lounge and plain public. The gently nautical theme reflects its position overlooking bay and marina.
⊟ & ≠ (Dingle Rd) ♣

Penmark

Six Bells Inn

Off A4226 near airport
☎ (0446) 710229
12–11
Welsh Brewers Hancock's HB Ⓗ
Friendly village pub with much Hancock's memorabilia in the bar. The landlord from 1966–69 wrote a book featuring the pub. No eve meals Sun. 🏛 Q ❀ ◖ ◗ ⊟ & Å ♣ P

St Lythans

Horse & Jockey

Twyn-yr-Odyn (behind HTV studios)
☎ (0222) 593396
11–3.30, 5.30–11
Draught Bass; Welsh Brewers Hancock's HB Ⓗ
Pub with central bar. Panoramic view over the Cardiff area (on a clear day across the Channel). No food Sun. ❀ ◖ Å ♣ P

Tongwynlais

Lewis Arms

1 Mill Road
☎ (0222) 810330
11–3.30, 5.30–11
Brains Dark, Bitter, SA Ⓗ
Friendly locals' pub with a village atmosphere. Named after Col. Henry Lewis whose picture hangs in the lounge. No food Sun. Historic Castell Coch is nearby. Q ◖ ⊟ ♣ P

Wenvoe

Wenvoe Arms

18 Old Port Road (off A4050)
☎ (0222) 591129
11.30–3.30, 5.30–11 (11.30–11 summer)
Brains Dark, Bitter, SA Ⓗ
Comfortable, welcoming, traditional village local. Family room is separate from the pub. Meals in eve and on Sun in restaurant only (book). Car park access is via side road.
🏛 Q ❧ ❀ ◖ ⊟ ♣ P

West Glamorgan

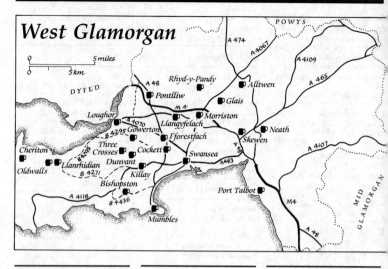

Alltwen

Butchers Arms
Alltwen Hill (off A474)
12–3, 6.30–11
Everards Old Original H
Comfortable free house with at least three guest beers. Restaurant overlooks Swansea Valley. 🏵 ◖▮ P

Bishopston

Joiners Arms
50 Bishopston Road (off B4436)
☎ (044 128) 2658
11–3.30, 5.30–11 (11–11 Thu–Sat)
Draught Bass; Welsh Brewers Worthington BB H
Attractive village pub with a somewhat dark interior. Guest beers.
🛏 🏵 ◖▮ ♣ P

Cheriton

Britannia
Llanmadoc Road, Llanmadoc
OS450930 ☎ (0792) 336624
12–3.30 (not Tue), 7–11
Draught Bass (summer);
Marston's Pedigree; Welsh Brewers Hancock's HB H
A handy halfway stopping point on the round-Gower cycle ride. Excellent restaurant. Guest beers in summer.
🏨 🏵 🛏 ◖▮ 🍴 ♣ P

Cockett

Cockett Inn
Waunarlwydd Road (A4216)
11.30–3.30, 5.30–10.30 (11.30–11 Fri & Sat; 12–3, 7–10.30 Sun)
Crown Buckley Dark, Best Bitter H
Village local with a spacious bar and games area. 🏵 ◖▮ 🍴 ♣

Dunvant

Found Out
Killan Road ☎ (0792) 203596
11.30–3, 5.30–11 (11–11 Thu–Sat)
Whitbread Flowers IPA, Best Bitter, Flowers Original, Wethered Winter Royal H
Popular suburban pub. ◖▮ ♣ P

Fforestfach

Star Inn
1070 Carmarthen Road
11.30–3.30, 5.30–11 (may vary)
Crown Buckley Dark, Best Bitter E
Popular local serving a nearby industrial estate. Lunchtime bar snacks. 🏵 🍴 ♣ P

Glais

Old Glais
On B4291 ☎ (0792) 843316
12–4, 6–11 (may vary)
Ruddles Best Bitter, County; Webster's Yorkshire Bitter H
Comfortable and friendly village pub. 🏵 ◖▮ 🍴 ♣ P

Gowerton

Berthlwydd
Berthlwydd ☎ (0792) 873454
12–3.30, 6–11
Courage Directors; Felinfoel Double Dragon H
Beautifully renovated and extended free house overlooking Loughor Estuary. Excellent meals. Guest beers.
🏵 ◖▮ P

Welcome to Gower
Mount Street ☎ (0792) 872611
11.30–3.30, 5.30–11 (11.30–11 summer)
Crown Buckley Dark, Best Bitter H
Very well-appointed pub at the gateway to Gower. 🏵 ◖▮ 🍴 ♣ P

Killay

Railway Inn
Gower Road ☎ (0792) 203946
11.30–3.30 (4 Sat), 5.30–11
Draught Bass; Welsh Brewers Worthington Dark, Hancock's HB H
Pub situated by an old railway with assorted memorabilia. Convenient for Clyne Valley walk and cycle track. 🏵 🍴 ♣ P

Llangyfelach

Plough & Harrow
Llangyfelach Road (off M4 jct 46) ☎ (0792) 771816
11.30–4, 6–11 (12–2, 7–10.30 Sun)
Courage Best Bitter, Directors; John Smith's Bitter H
Large, comfortable pub; outdoor area overlooks Penllergaer Forest. 🏵 🍴 ♣ P

Llanrhidian

Welcome to Town
Off B4295 ☎ (0792) 390015
12–3, 6–11
Younger IPA H
Pleasant pub opposite village green and overlooking estuary.
Q 🏵 ◖▮

Loughor

Red Lion
Glebe Road ☎ (0792) 892983
11.30–11
Felinfoel Bitter, Double Dragon H
Friendly, no-frills bar and spacious, comfortable lounge.
🏵 ◖▮ 🍴 ♣ P

Reverend James
180 Borough Road
☎ (0792) 892943
11.30–11

352

Crown Buckley Dark, Best Bitter ⊞
Welcoming local with an excellent adjoining restaurant.
🏠 🕯 ◖ ◗ ⊟ ⅃ P

Morriston

Lamb & Flag
3 Sway Road (on Morriston Cross) ☎ (0792) 771663
11.30–3.30, 5.30–11 (11–11 Fri & Sat)
Bateman XXXB; Courage Best Bitter ⊞
Spacious, wood-panelled bars. Live entertainment most Fris and Suns. Good value. ⊟ ♣

Mumbles

Antelope
628 Mumbles Road
11.30–3.30, 7–11
Courage Directors; John Smith's Bitter ⊞
Intimate bar with separate lounge area upstairs. ⊟ ♣

Oystercatcher
510 Mumbles Road
11.30–3, 6–11
Ruddles Best Bitter; Wells Bombardier ⊞
Friendly bar overlooking the seafront. Excellent food. ◖

Park Inn
23 Park Street (100 yds off main road) ☎ (0792) 366338
11.30–3.30, 5.30–11 (11.30–11 Fri & Sat)
Ruddles Best Bitter, County ⊞
Small, friendly local away from the busy seafront. 🏠 Q ◖

William Hancock
Western Lane (near seafront)
11–11
Draught Bass; Welsh Brewers Hancock's HB ⊞
Formerly the Waterloo, its name changed for no apparent reason. However, landlord and beer quality remain the same. ◖

Neath

Greyhound
Water Street ☎ (0639) 637793
11–11
Ruddles County ⊞
Large, comfortable pub with good food. ◖ ⇌

Oldwalls

Greyhound
☎ (0792) 390146
11–11
Draught Bass; Welsh Brewers Hancock's HB ⊞
Large pub, popular with locals, tourists and cyclists, on the quieter north side of Gower. Excellent food (seafood a speciality). Guest beers.
🏠 Q ♨ 🕯 ◖ ◗ ⊟ P

Pontlliw

Castle Inn
On A48 ☎ (0792) 882961
11–4, 6–11
Felinfoel Bitter ⊞
Pleasant, rural pub between Penllergaer and Pontardulais. ⊟

Port Talbot

Accolade
Green Park Ind. Est. (left out of station) ☎ (0639) 891467
11.30–3.30, 6–11 (11–11 Fri & Sat)
Brains Dark, SA; Courage Best Bitter, Directors; Ruddles Best Bitter, County ⊞
Large, recently-built town pub. ◖ ⇌ P

St Oswalds
Station Road ☎ (0639) 899200
12–4, 6–11
Crown Buckley Best Bitter ⊞
Distinctive pub with adjoining restaurant. ◖ ◗ ⇌

Rhyd-y-Pandy

Masons Arms
2 miles N of M4 jct 46
☎ (0792) 842535
11.30–4, 6–11
Courage Best Bitter, Directors ⊞
Rural pub, popular at lunchtimes. 🏠 🕯 ◖ P

Skewen

Crown Hotel
216 New Road (B4291)
11.30–4, 6–11 (may vary)
Brains Dark, MA, SA ⊞
Regulars' bar and comfortable lounge. The only outlet for MA – a brewery mix of Dark and Bitter. Snooker table. ⊟ ♣

Swansea

Adam & Eve
High Street ☎ (0792) 655913
11–4, 5.30–11 (11–11 Thu–Sat)
Brains Dark, Bitter, SA ⊞
A welcome Brains outlet: a traditional three-roomed local.
◖ ⊟ ⇌

Bryn-y-Mor Hotel
Bryn-y-Mor Road
11–3.30, 5.30–11 (11–11 Thu–Sat)
Ansells Bitter; Crown Buckley Dark; Ind Coope Burton Ale; Tetley Bitter ⊞
Locals' bar with games area; comfortable lounge with live music most Sun nights. 🕯 ◖ ⊟ ♣

Builders Arms
Oxford Street
☎ (0792) 476189
11–3.30, 7–11 (closed Sun)
Crown Buckley Dark, Best Bitter ⊞

Unusual, split-level bar offering excellent cuisine (book for eve meals). Closed on Sun unless booked. Parties catered for. ◖ ◗

Cricketers
83 King Edward Road
11–11
Ansells Bitter; Ind Coope Burton Ale; Tetley Bitter ⊞
Extremely popular and lively pub serving good food. Barbecues in summer. 🕯 ◖

Duke of York
Princess Way
☎ (0792) 653830
11–11
Draught Bass; Welsh Brewers Worthington Dark, BB ⊞
Home of 'Ellington's' blues/jazz venue: live acts Tue–Fri and occasionally on Sat. ◖ ⊟ ⇌ ♣

Queens Hotel
Gloucester Place (near Marina)
☎ (0792) 643460
11–11
Theakston Best Bitter, Old Peculier ⊞
Pleasantly refurbished pub with a large bar displaying old photographs on a nautical theme. Good food; occasional live music. 🛏 ◖ ◗ ♿

Rhyddings
Brynmill (near east entrance to Singleton Park, up the hill)
☎ (0792) 648885
11–11
Ansells Bitter; Ind Coope Burton Ale; Tetley Bitter ⊞
Spacious bar and lounge, popular with students. 🕯 ◖ ⊟ ♣

Vivian Arms
Sketty Cross, Sketty (on the Cross) ☎ (0792) 203015
11–11
Brains Dark, Bitter, SA ⊞
Solidly-comfortable, suburban mecca with good food. Large lounge; unusual bar with wood panelling. 🕯 ◖ ⊟

Westbourne Hotel
Bryn-y-Mor Road
11.30–3.30, 6–11 (11.30–11 Fri & Sat)
Draught Bass; Welsh Brewers Worthington Dark, Hancock's HB ⊞
Popular pub with a comfortable lounge. Excellent menu. 🕯 ◖ ⊟

Three Crosses

Joiners Arms
Joiners Road
☎ (0792) 873479
12–4, 6–11 (12–11 Fri & Sat)
Ruddles Best Bitter, County; Webster's Yorkshire Bitter ⊞
Popular village local with pool and darts in the bar. ◖ P

Gwent

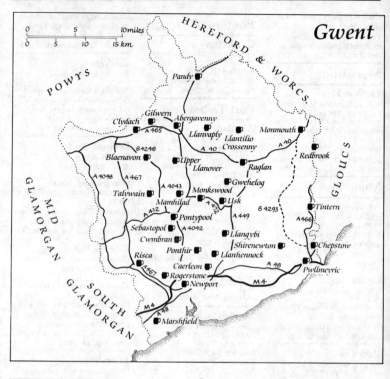

Abergavenny

Great Western Hotel
Station Road (off Monmouth Road)
☎ (0873) 3593
11.30–3, 6 (7 winter)–11
Draught Bass; Ruddles Best Bitter H
Comfortable, family-run pub with bar, lounge and pool room. As befits its name and proximity to the BR station, it has a strong railway theme which features much memorabilia of local interest. Good value food. Garden and patio. 🏠 ⊗ ⊯ ◑ ▶ ⧖ ≉ ♣ P

Hen & Chickens
Flannel Street (off High Street)
☎ (0873) 3613
10.30–4, 7–11 (10–11 Tue; 10.30–11 Fri & Sat)
Draught Bass; Welsh Brewers Hancock's HB H
A superb, unspoilt town pub with bar and snug. A must on any town crawl, the cosy and friendly atmosphere of the 'Chicks' has charmed many a visitor. Lunches, served in the 'Chicks Parlour', cater for most tastes. 🏠 Q ◑ ♣

Malthouse
Newmarket Close, Lion Street (off Market Street, behind town hall) ☎ (0873) 77842

11–11
Ind Coope Burton Ale H
An interesting mix of bistro, café bar and pub, housed in an attractive old stone building in a quiet town-centre location. Has wide appeal. Tasty food from an imaginative menu. Guest ales at weekends. Function room. Bar billiards. ⊗ ◑ ▶ ♣ P

Somerset Arms
Victoria Street (Merthyr Road jct) ☎ (0873) 2158
12–3, 7–11
Draught Bass; Welsh Brewers Hancock's HB H
A homely pub with a spruce interior featuring interesting bric-a-brac, especially in the lounge. The public bar has fitted wooden bench seating and a built-in trophy cabinet. Growing reputation for good food (no lunches Sun). Guest beer. Function/dining room.
🏠 Q ⊗ ◑ ▶ ⧖ ♣

Blaenavon

Cambrian Inn
Llanover Road
☎ (0495) 790327
6–11 (12–11 Sat)
Brains Bitter, SA H
Traditional, well-used local with a pool and darts room separate from the bar and new lounge. Horse racing paraphernalia. Guest beers. ⧖ ♣

Caerleon

Kings Arms
Belmont Hill (towards Christchurch area of Newport)
☎ (0633) 420329
11–3, 5.30–11
Draught Bass; Welsh Brewers Worthington BB H
Popular 17th-century inn and restaurant, an ex-flour mill. Old low beams, much original stone-work and woodfittings lend a cosy atmosphere. Small public lounge and 'Sundowner' bar with fireplace. Good reputation for food (no lunches Sun). Garden play area.
🏠 ⊗ ◑ ▶ ♣ P

Tabard Brasserie
9 High Street
☎ (0633) 422822
12–3, 7–11 (closed Sun)
Beer range varies H
Takes its name from the heraldic name for a knight's vest. Primarily a restaurant but has an excellent range of real ales from many breweries, served in the cosy bar. Wide variety of highly recommended meals at competitive prices. A must if you're in the area. Parking at side. Q ⊗ ◑ ▶ P

White Hart Inn
High Street (town square)
☎ (0633) 420255

11.30–3, 5–11 (11.30–11 Thu & Fri; 11–11 Sat)

Brains SA; Courage Best Bitter, Directors Ⓗ

Deservedly-popular pub in a prime drinking area. Very busy at weekends, especially in summer. Frequented by students during term-time. No food Sat.
🍺 ◑ ♣ P

Chepstow

Bridge Inn

Bridge Street (near old iron bridge)
☎ (0291) 625622
11–3, 6–11

Beer range varies

A fine old pub in a scenic riverside setting. Formerly the 'Ship & Castle', it took its present name in 1813 when the iron bridge opened. Open-plan interior; slate floor in the 'Watermans' bar. Beer details displayed by the handpumps. Good food. 🍺 Q ◑ ▶ ≉ P

Castle View Hotel

Bridge Street
☎ (029 12) 70349
12–2.30, 6–11 (12–2.30, 7–10.30 Sun)

Butcombe Bitter; Ind Coope Burton Ale Ⓗ

Aptly-named, 18th-century hotel with a splendid view of Chepstow Castle. A charming base for touring the surrounding area. The comfortable, spacious lounge has a fireplace at each end and an old grandfather clock. Good home-made food. Public car park opposite. The beers listed alternate.
Q 🍺 ⋈ ◑ ≉

Coach & Horses

Welsh Street (near Town Arch)
☎ (0291) 622626
11–3, 6–11

Draught Bass; Brains SA; Felinfoel Cambrian; Webster's Yorkshire Bitter Ⓗ

A long-time favourite haunt of real ale drinkers in the area: a split-level bar with wooden beams. The story of how Guinness is brewed is displayed on the lower bar walls. The large TV screen is handy for major sporting events. Venue of Chepstow Beerex in July. No food weekends. 🍺 ⋈ ◑ ≉ ♣

Clydach

Rock & Fountain

Old Blackrock Road (A465, between Brynmawr and Gilwern) ☎ (0873) 830393
12–4 (3 winter), 7–11 (11–11 Sat in summer)

Ruddles Best Bitter, County; Webster's Yorkshire Bitter Ⓗ

Open-plan pub with a comfortable snug. The separate restaurant has a natural waterfall and is open until midnight. Nine

Men's Morris and shove-ha'penny played. Guest beer.
🍺 Q ⋈ 🍺 ◑ ◑ ♿ ⅄ ♣ P

Cwmbran

Blinkin' Owl

The Oxtens, Hellys Way, Coed Eva (1 mile past Cwmbran Stadium)
☎ (063 33) 4749
11.30–3.30 (4.30 Sat), 5.30 (6.30 Sat)–11

Brains Dark, Bitter, SA Ⓗ

A well-established estate pub, popular with Brains drinkers from all over Cwmbran. The genial landlord has won many awards for his cellar. Spacious public bar and comfortable lounge with adjoining dining area. No lunches Sun.
Q ◑ ◑ ▶ ♣ P

Bush Inn

Graig Road, Upper Cwmbran (off Upper Cwmbran Road)
☎ (063 33) 3764
11–3, 7 (6 Fri & Sat)–11

Courage Best Bitter; John Smith's Bitter Ⓗ

A very popular pub, especially at weekends. Comfortably-furnished with armchairs and settees. No lunches Fri-Sun — order eve meals in advance. Regular discos. Parking is limited. 🍺 🍺 ◑ ◑ ♣ P

Rose & Crown

Victoria Street
☎ (063 33) 66700
11–11

Brains SA; Courage Best Bitter Ⓗ

Lively, down-to-earth local in the heart of the village which gave the new town its name. Regular disco eves in lounge; 'Karaoke Krazy' on Sun eves. Occasional guest beers. A short walk from Cwmbran Stadium and town centre. 🍺 ▶ ♣ P

Gilwern

Bridgend Inn

Main Road (off A465, next to canal) ☎ (0873) 830939
12–5, 7–11 (12–11 Fri & Sat)

Hall & Woodhouse Tanglefoot Ⓗ

Olde-worlde pub right on the side of the canal. Popular with walkers, cavers and canal people. Reasonably priced pub food. Guest beers.
🍺 ◑ ◑ ♿ ⅄ ♣ P

Gwehelog

Hall Inn

Old Raglan Road
☎ (029 13) 2381
12–3, 6–11

Tetley Bitter Ⓗ

Roadside inn: comfortable lounge and stone-flagged public bar with pool table and darts.

Separate restaurant and spacious garden. Guest beer.
🍺 🍺 ◑ ◑ ♣ P

Llangybi

White Hart

Main Road (B4596)
☎ (063 349) 258
11–3, 6–11

Marston's Pedigree; Theakston Best Bitter Ⓗ

Comfortable, 12th-century coaching inn with interesting historical features and connections. Good food. Draught Bass is a regular guest beer. 🍺 🍺 ◑ ▶ 🍺 P

Llanhennock

Wheatsheaf Inn

(1 mile off Caerleon–Usk road)
OS353929 ☎ (0633) 420468
11–3, 5.30–11 (11–11 Sat)

Draught Bass; Samuel Smith OBB; Welsh Brewers Worthington BB Ⓗ

Traditional old country inn. Chickens and ducks provide entertainment in the pleasant beer garden. Cricket and French boules in summer. Doorstep sandwiches a speciality.
🍺 Q 🍺 ◑ ▶ ♣ P

Llantilio Crossenny

Hostry Inn

On B4233 between Monmouth and Abergavenny
☎ (060 085) 278
12–3, 6.30–11

Smiles Best Bitter Ⓗ

Thriving village pub with lots of atmosphere. Landlord has a teddy bear collection. Popular for its unusual pub games and good food (incl. vegetarian). Live music Sun lunchtime; folk or piano on Thu eves. Two guest beers usually available.
🍺 ⋈ ◑ ▶ 🍺 ♣ P

Llanvapley

Red Hart Inn

On B4233 ☎ (0600) 85227
12–3, 6–11 (11–11 some Sats in summer)

Draught Bass Ⓗ

Large country pub with separate downstairs eating area. Spacious garden with many birds and animals. Two guest beers usually available. Camping by arrangement. Skittles can be booked. 🍺 🍺 ⋈ ◑ ▶ ⅄ ♣ P

Mamhilad

Horseshoe Inn

(2 miles off A4042, near Pontypool)
☎ (0873) 880542
11–11 (11–3.30, 6.30–11 winter)

Felinfoel Double Dragon; Whitbread Flowers Original Ⓗ

Gwent

Former Royal Mail staging post, near the Monmouthshire and Brecon Canal. Garden play area for children; several footpaths for energetic adults. Separate restaurant with a wide and good value menu. Guest beer – usually on gravity dispense.
🏰 ⏰ ⊛ ◑ ▶ P 🍴

Marshfield

Port O'Call
(2 miles S of A48, next to railway line)
☎ (0633) 680171
11.30–3, 5.30–11
Courage Best Bitter 🅷, **Directors** 🅶 & 🅷; **John Smith's Bitter** 🅷
Country pub with a split-level lounge. Excellent bar meals. Family room in summer.
⊠ ⊛ ◑ ▶ ⊟ ♣ P

Try also: **Masons Arms** (Allied)

Monkswood

Beaufort Arms
Usk Road (A472)
☎ (049 528) 215
11.30–3.30 (4.30 Fri), 6–11 (11–11 Sat)
Courage Best Bitter, Directors; John Smith's Bitter 🅷
Welcoming roadside pub with a separate dining area, offering a varied, good-value menu. The spacious outdoor area overlooks a cricket pitch. Guest beers. Gwent CAMRA *Pub of the Year* 1990. Q ⊛ ◑ ▶ ⊟ P

Monmouth

Punch House
Agincourt Square
☎ (0600) 3855
10.30–3 (4 Mon), 5–11 (11–11 Fri & Sat)
Draught Bass; Wadworth 6X; Welsh Brewers Hancock's HB, Worthington BB 🅷
Well-known, historic pub with an impressive display of hanging baskets in summer. The comfortable bar is decorated with rural trappings. Renowned for its home-produced food, served in the bar or upstairs restaurant. ⊛ ◑ ▶

Newport

Globe Inn
132 Chepstow Road, Maindee (A48)
☎ (0633) 213062
11–3 (4 Sat), 6–11
Courage Best Bitter 🅷
Quiet local in the heart of Maindee shopping area. The front bar has a cosy adjoining snug; public bar at the rear. Guest beer. Q ⊛ ⊟ ♣

Greyhound Inn
Christchurch
☎ (0633) 420306
11.30–4, 6 (7 winter)–11
Courage Best Bitter; John Smith's Bitter; Wadworth 6X 🅷
Traditional, out-of-town local in the village of Christchurch, next to the memorial cross. A very warm welcome is always assured. Excellent views of Bristol Channel and South Gwent nearby. Lunches Tue–Sat; eve meals Fri only.
Q ⊛ ◑ ▶ ♣ P

Ivy Bush Inn
65 Clarence Place (300 yds from town bridge and castle)
☎ (0633) 267571
11–11
John Smith's Bitter 🅷
Lively, traditional local in a popular dining-out area close to Newport RFC. Good mix of clientele in rooms which seek to use every inch of space. Pool table in the bar; piano in the lounge. Function room. No food Sun. ⊛ ◑ ⊟ ⇌ ♣

Lamb
6 Bridge Street
☎ (0633) 266801
11–11
Courage Best Bitter, Directors; John Smith's Bitter 🅷
Busy town-centre bar, popular with people from all walks of life. Handy for shops or nightclubs. A regular watering-hole for those doing the Newport circuit. Floral decoration and pictures of old Newport on the walls. ⇌

Queen's Hotel
Bridge Street
☎ (0633) 262992
11–11 (Tudor Bar); 11–3, 7–11 (Queen's Bar)
Draught Bass 🅴; **Brains Dark, SA** 🅷
Two-bar hotel: Tudor Bar is a lounge bar for mixed age groups and includes an aquarium and pool table; Queen's Bar is noisy and lively, mainly for young people.
⇎ ◑ ▶ ⊟ ♣ ⇌

Royal Mail
31 Mill Street
☎ (0633) 263339
11–11
Courage Best Bitter; John Smith's Bitter; Wadworth 6X 🅶
Spacious locals' pub just off the town centre, behind the station. Very popular with local Post Office workers. Lively public bar. Occasional live music. Meals till 7pm (book Sun).
⊛ ◑ ▶ ⊟ ⇌ ♣

Pandy

Old Pandy Inn
Hereford Road
☎ (0873) 890208
11 (11.30 winter)–3, 6 (6.30 winter)–11
Brains Dark; Courage Directors; Felinfoel Double Dragon; Smiles Best Bitter 🅷
Lovely country inn with something to please almost everybody. An adjacent barn has been converted to a restaurant catering for all tastes, except children's. Choice of over 30 whiskies. The beer garden has a play area for the youngsters.
🏰 ⊛ ◑ ▶ ⚲ 🅰 ♣ P

Ponthir

Star Inn
Caerleon Road
☎ (0633) 420582
11–3, 5.30–11 (11–11 Sat; 12–2.30, 7–10.30 Sun)
Ansells Bitter; Ind Coope Burton Ale 🅷
Traditional village local with a cosy public bar. The comfortable lounge features types of locally-produced brickwork, each having a descriptive plate. Licensee has won several cellarmanship awards.
⊛ ◑ ▶ ⊟ ♣ P

Pontypool

Prince of Wales
Prince of Wales Terrace, Lower Cwmynyscoy (200 yds past viaduct, up small lane)
☎ (0495) 756737
11.30–11
Courage Best Bitter; John Smith's Bitter 🅷
Small, cosy and very friendly pub. Various entertainments arranged. Note the wall-mounted cribbage board. Separate games room. Guest beer(s) available at weekends. Children welcome. Short stroll to Pontypool RFC. Limited parking. 🏰 ⊛ ♣ P

Wellington Inn
Tranch Road (off Albion Road, above High Street)
☎ (0495) 753477
12–11 (12–3.30, 6–11 winter)
Ruddles Best Bitter, County 🅷
The 'Sally' (as it is known) dates back some 600 years and was put to various uses until it became a pub in 1834. The bar area has a low, beamed ceiling and exposed stonework around the fireplace. Subdued lighting enhances the cosy atmosphere in the split-level rooms. Pool room. 🏰 ⊛ ◑ ▶ ♣

Pwllmeyric

New Inn
On A48, 2 miles from
Chepstow ☎ (0291) 622670
12–11
Draught Bass Ⓔ**; Marston's
Pedigree; Whitbread Flowers
IPA** Ⓗ
A fine roadside inn where the
rural-style bar contrasts with the
almost stately lounge. The
wood panelling in the latter was
salvaged from the ocean liner
Empress of France, which is
pictured in several photographs.
Good food (no meals Sun).
🏚 ⑧ ◖ ▮ ⊟ ♣ P

Raglan

Ship Inn
High Street ☎ (0291) 690635
11.30–3.30, 5.30–11
**Draught Bass; Hook Norton
Best Bitter** Ⓗ
Old coaching house dating from
the 16th century. Cobbled
forecourt with an old water
pumping device. Convenient for
Raglan Castle. ⑧ ◖ ▮ ⊟ ♣

Redbrook

Bush Inn
Main Road (A466)
☎ (0600) 3237
11–3 (4 Sat), 6–11 (supper licence)
Hook Norton Best Bitter Ⓗ
Recently-renovated, open-plan
pub just inside the Gwent
border, near the site of old
Redbrook station. Regular guest
beer. ⑧ ◖ ▮ ♣ P

Risca

Risca House
Commercial Street (old main
road) ☎ (0633) 614918
11.30–11
**John Smith's Bitter;
Wadworth 6X** Ⓗ
Busy, basic, friendly local. Live
music on Wed eve. Regular
guest beer. ⑧ ♣ P

Try also: **Fox & Hounds**
(Courage)

Rogerstone

Tredegar Arms
Cefn Road ☎ (0633) 893417
11 (12 Sat)–3, 6–11 (12–2, 7–10.30
Sun)

**Courage Best Bitter,
Directors** Ⓗ
Well-appointed pub on the old
main valleys road. Guest beers.
⑧ ◖ ▮ ⊟ P

Sebastopol

Open Hearth
Wern Road (off B4244 & South
Street)
OS294985 ☎ (0495) 763752
11.30–3, 6–11
**Draught Bass; Courage Best
Bitter; Fuller's London
Pride** Ⓗ
Popular, canalside pub with
separate restaurant. Always a
wide range of guest beers.
Hidden away in a pleasant
location – ask any local for
directions. Good value bar
meals.
Q ⑧ ◖ ▮ ⊟ ♣ P

Shirenewton

Carpenters Arms
On B4235, Usk–Chepstow
road, N of village
☎ (029 17) 231
11–2.30, 7–11
**Draught Bass; Courage Best
Bitter; Hook Norton Best
Bitter; Ruddles County;
Wadworth 6X** Ⓗ
Old country inn with flagstone
floors. Several rooms in a
variety of styles and sizes.
Guest beers.
🏚 Q ⑧ ◖ ▮ ⊟ Å P

Tredegar Arms
☎ (029 17) 274
11–3, 7–11
Smiles Best Bitter Ⓗ
Welcoming inn at the centre of
the village, boasting a large
collection of malt whiskies.
Guest beers.
🏚 Q ⑧ ◖ ▮ ⊟ ♣ P

Talywain

Globe Inn
Commercial Road (main
Abersychan–Varteg road)
☎ (0495) 772053
6–11 (11–11 Sat)
**Brains Bitter; Crown Buckley
Best Bitter** Ⓗ
Friendly, busy local with
separate pool room. Guest beer.
🏚 ♣ ♣

Tintern

Cherry Tree
Devauden Road (off A466)
☎ (0291) 689292
11–3, 6–11
**Welsh Brewers Hancock's
HB** Ⓖ
Small, friendly, single-roomed
pub where beer is brought up
from the cellar. Bar billiards.
Rare Toastmaster sign outside.
Bulmers medium cider. Situated
in a popular walking area.
🏚 Q ⑧ ♣ ⊙ P

Try also: **Rose & Crown**

Upper Llanover

Goose & Cuckoo
Off A4042 OS291073
☎ (0873) 880277
11.30–3, 7–11
**Brains SA; Bullmastiff Best
Bitter** Ⓗ
Very hard-to-find pub, but well
worth the effort. A small, cosy
hostelry where mainly
vegetarian food is served. Guest
beer in summer. 🏚 Q ◖ ▮ ♣ P

Usk

Kings Head
Old Market Street
☎ (029 13) 2963
11–11
**Brains Bitter; Hall &
Woodhouse Tanglefoot;
Whitbread Flowers
Original** Ⓗ
Large pub with contrasting
bars: a comfortable, stone-
walled lounge with an
impressive fire, and a traditional
public bar, with darts and a pool
table. Guest beer.
🏚 Q ⋈ ◖ ▮ ⊟ ♣ P

Royal Hotel
New Market Street
☎ (029 13) 2931
11–3, 7–11
**Draught Bass; Felinfoel
Double Dragon; Welsh
Brewers Hancock's HB** Ⓗ
Well-loved, Victorian-style
local. Notable for its large
collection of china, flat irons and
old bottles. Note the billiard
chalk dispenser at the bar. Food
very popular. 🏚 ◖ ▮ ⊟

Try also: **Cardiff Arms** (Free)

Beer Listings

Beers are listed in alphabetical order of brewery name, then in
increasing order of strength. Only the pub's traditional ales are given.
For full details of all the beers listed in the pub entries, refer to the
Breweries Section, beginning on page 390.

Gwynedd

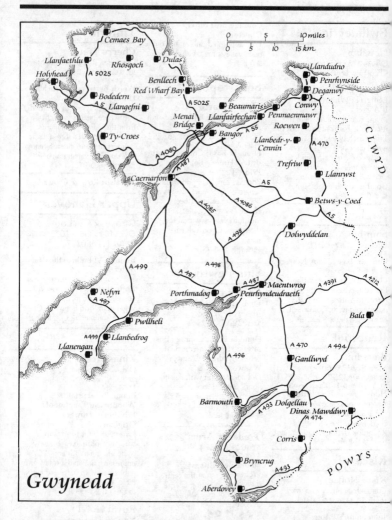

Gwynedd

Aberdovey

Penhelig Arms
On A493 ☎ (065 472) 215
11–3, 6–11
**Ind Coope Burton Ale;
Marston's Pedigree** Ⓗ
Small, 19th-century, seaside
town hotel with an excellent
restaurant and a wood-panelled
'Fisherman's Bar'. ⋈ ◖ 🍴🍺⇌

Try also: Dovey Inn (Banks's)

Bala

White Lion Royal Hotel
High Street ☎ (0678) 520314
11–11
**Ind Coope Burton Ale; Tetley
Walker Bitter** Ⓗ
Black and white hotel, reputedly
one of Wales's oldest coaching
inns: a small 'Poachers Bar', a
pool room and a beamed

lounge. A Welsh-speaking
favourite with hill-walkers.
🏠🎿🍴⋈◖◗🍺🚻♿⛵P

Try also: Goat Hotel
(Marston's)

Bangor

Ship Launch
Garth Road ☎ (0248) 364067
11–11
Draught Bass Ⓗ
Small, friendly pub near the
Victorian pier. A central bar
serves several different rooms –
one has a magnificent brewery
mirror. Q ◖ ♣ ♠

Union
Garth Road ☎ (0248) 362462
11–11
**Burtonwood Best Bitter,
Forshaw's** Ⓗ
Pub where one bar serves a
number of separate rooms

containing a display of
photographs, prints and nautical
artefacts. Overlooks a bay.
Q🍺⋈◖⇌♣P

Barmouth

Tal y Don
High Street ☎ (0341) 280508
11–11
**Burtonwood Mild, Best
Bitter, Forshaw's** Ⓗ
Typical, town-centre pub
adorned with brass from floor to
ceiling. ⋈◖◗🍺🚻♿Ⓐ⇌♣

Beaumaris

Olde Bulls Head
Castle Street ☎ (0248) 810329
11–11
Draught Bass Ⓗ
Historic inn (Grade II listed), full
of character. Its main, beamed
bar is packed with antique

358

weapons, and copper and brass. Smaller 'china' bar. No food Sun. 🏛 Q ⋈ ◖ P

Benllech

Glanrafon Hotel
Bangor Road ☎ (0248) 852687
11–3.30, 6–11
Lees Bitter Ⓗ
Large, black and white, village-centre hotel, handy for the shops and beach. A quiet, comfortable lounge and a noisier, more spartan bar.
Q ⋩ 🏮 ⋈ ◖ ◗ ⊞ ♣ P

Betws-y-Coed

Pont-y-Pair Hotel
On A5 ☎ (0690) 710407
11–11
Tetley Walker Bitter Ⓗ
Large, granite building; a meeting place for mountaineers and walkers. ⋈ ◖ ◗ Å ⋨ ♣

Bodedern

Crown Hotel
On B5109 ☎ (0407) 740734
12–3.30, 6–11 (11–11 Sat & bank hols)
Burtonwood Best Bitter Ⓗ
Popular, village pub with a comfortable lounge, more spartan bar, and a separate pool room doubling as a children's room. Very reasonably priced food and accommodation. A good base for touring Anglesey.
🏛 🏮 ⋈ ◖ ◗ ⊞ ♣ P

Bryncrug

Peniarth Arms
12–3, 6–11
Welsh Brewers Hancock's HB Ⓗ
Busy, village pub whose landlord is an ex-Allied brewer. Traditional decor.
🏛 🏮 ◖ ◗ ⊞ Å ♣ P

Caernarfon

Y Gordon Fach
Hole in Wall Street
11–11
Draught Bass; Tetley Walker Dark Mild, Bitter Ⓗ
Modernised pub used by friendly locals, not far from the castle. ◖ ◗ ⊞ Å

Cemaes Bay

Stag
High Street ☎ (0407) 710281
11–3.30, 6 (7 winter)–11 (11–11 Sat & summer)
Burtonwood Best Bitter, Forshaw's Ⓗ
Friendly, village pub, popular with locals and summer visitors. Interesting pictures of the old village contrast with colour photographs. The most northerly pub in Wales.
🏛 Q 🏮 ◖ ◗ ⊞ ♣

Conwy

Albion Vaults
Upper Gate Street
11–11
Ind Coope Burton Ale; Tetley Walker Dark Mild, Bitter Ⓗ
Traditional, multi-roomed local. Guest beers. 🏛 ⋩ ⊞ Å ⋨ ♣

Corris

Slater's Arms
Bridge Street ☎ (0654) 761324
11.30–3, 6–11 (11–11 Sat & bank hols)
Banks's Mild, Bitter Ⓔ
Old-fashioned, two-roomed pub in a former slating village. YHA hostel nearby. 🏛 Q ◖ ◗ ⊞ Å

Deganwy

Castle Hotel
☎ (0492) 583555
11–11
Webster's Choice, Wilson's Bitter Ⓗ
Hotel bar serving as a popular local. Attractive gardens with estuary views.
🏛 Q 🏮 ⋈ ◖ ◗ ⊞ Å ⋨ P

Try also: Farmers Arms (Allied)

Dinas Mawddwy

Red Lion
Off A470 ☎ (065 04) 247
11–3, 6–11 (11–11 summer)
Draught Bass; Welsh Brewers Worthington BB Ⓗ
Well worth the visit to see the brass bar. A friendly locals' pub with a large lounge, popular with hill-walkers and fishermen.
🏛 ⋩ 🏮 ◖ ◗ ⊞ ⊞ Å ♣ P

Dolgellau

Stag Inn
Bridge Street
☎ (0341) 422533
10.30–11
Burtonwood Mild, Best Bitter, Forshaw's Ⓗ
Characterful, one-roomed, town pub, an ever-present in this guide. ⋩ 🏮 ◖ ◗ ⊞ ♣

Dolwyddelan

Y Gwydyr
☎ (069 06) 219
11.30–3, 6.30–11 (11–11 Sat & summer)
Tetley Walker Bitter Ⓗ
Cosy, village pub where Welsh is spoken as a matter of course. Visitors are made very welcome. Sun lunch in summer only. 🏮 ⋈ ◖ ◗ ⊞ Å ⋨ P

Dulas

Pilot Boat
On A5025 ☎ (024 888) 205
11 (11.30 winter)–3.30, 6 (7 winter)–11 (11–11 Sat & bank hols)

Robinson's Mild, Best Bitter Ⓔ
Interesting, old, country pub. The bar is made from a clinker-built boat. Small lounge and a separate pool room, both accommodating children.
🏛 🏮 ◖ ◗ ⊞ Å ♣ P

Ganllwyd

Tyn y Groes
On A470 ☎ (034 140) 275
11–3, 6.30–11
Marston's Pedigree; Whitbread Boddingtons Bitter Ⓗ
Valley inn situated in a forest, its decor in keeping with the situation. Other Whitbread beers, incl. mild, sometimes sold.
🏛 Q 🏮 ⋈ ◖ ◗ ⊞ P

Holyhead

Boston
London Road
☎ (0407) 762449
11–3.30, 6–11
Ansells Mild; Tetley Walker Bitter Ⓗ
Busy, open-plan local with a central bar, areas for pool and darts, and a small lounge. Handy for the Irish ferry.
⊞ ⋨ ♣

Llanbedrog

Ship Inn
Bryn-y-Gro ☎ (0758) 740270
11–3, 5.30–11 (11–11 summer; closed Sun)
Burtonwood Mild, Best Bitter Ⓗ
Cosy, friendly pub, popular with visitors. Unusually-shaped family room.
🏛 Q 🏮 ◖ ◗ ⊞ ⊞ Å ♣ P

Try also: Glyn-y-Weddw (Robinson's)

Llanbedr-y-Cennin

Olde Bull Inn
Off B5106 ☎ (049 269) 359
12–3, 6.30–11
Lees GB Mild, Bitter Ⓗ
Pub in the Conwy Valley, with breathtaking views; part of the community.
🏛 Q 🏮 ⋈ ◖ ◗ Å ♣ P

Llandudno

Cottage Loaf
Market Street
11–11
Ruddles County; Webster's Yorkshire Bitter, Choice Ⓗ
Very popular eating house at lunchtime; busier at night with drinkers. Built from a ship's timbers on top of an old bakehouse, with a stone and wood floor. 🏛 Q 🏮 ◖ ⋨ P

Gwynedd

London Hotel

Mostyn Street
☎ (0492) 876740
11.30–11 (11.30–4, 7–11 winter)
Burtonwood Mild, Best Bitter, Forshaw's Ⓗ
Busy, town-centre pub with a London theme, incl. an old red phone box in the folk club. Good food. ➰ ⑧ ⇔ ⟨ 🌓 ♣ ♣

Olde Victoria

Church Walks
☎ (0492) 860949
11–11
Ansells Mild; Ind Coope Burton Ale; Marston's Pedigree; Tetley Walker Bitter Ⓗ
Popular and cosy, town-centre pub/restaurant, thoughtfully refurbished on a Victorian theme. Q ⑧ ⟨ 🌓

Try also: **Kings Head** (Allied); **Gresham** (Allied); **Claries** (Courage)

Llanengan

Sun Inn

11–11 (closed Sun)
Ind Coope Burton Ale; Tetley Walker Bitter Ⓗ
Popular pub near Hell's Mouth Beach. Excellent food.
➰ Q ⑧ ⟨ 🌓 ⊟ ⑇ ♣ ♣ ⌣ P

Llanfaethlu

Black Lion

On A5025 ☎ (0407) 730209
11–3.30 (12–2.30 winter), 6–11 (12–11 Sat)
Burtonwood Best Bitter Ⓗ
Old pub with a large lounge and a pool room separated by a small bar. Popular with visitors.
➰ ⟨ 🌓 ⊟ ♣ P

Llanfairfechan

Llanfair Arms

Mill Road ☎ (0248) 680521
11–11
Draught Bass Ⓗ
Multi-roomed local in the uphill part of town. ➰ ⑧ ⑇ Å ⇌ ♣

Llangefni

Railway

High Street ☎ (0248) 722166
11–3.30 (5 Sat), 6.30–11 (12–2, 7–11 Mon–Wed, Xmas–Easter)
Lees GB Mild, Bitter Ⓗ
Friendly, town pub, now opened out, but still retaining different drinking areas, incl. a games room. Q ⑧ ♣

Llanrwst

New Inn

Denbigh Street
11–11
Marston's Burton Best Bitter, Merrie Monk, Pedigree Ⓗ
Modernised but not spoiled; a popular local. ➰ Å ⇌

Maentwrog

Grapes

On A496 ☎ (076 685) 208
11–11
Draught Bass; Stones Best Bitter Ⓗ
Old inn, with parts from the 13th century; three rooms and a restaurant. ➰ ➰ ⇔ ⟨ 🌓 ⊟ ♣

Menai Bridge

Liverpool Arms

St George's Pier (100 yds off A545) ☎ (0248) 712453
11–3.30, 5.30–11
Greenalls Bitter, Thomas Greenall's Bitter Ⓗ
Interesting, comfortable, old pub, near the Strait. Several rooms full of nautical artefacts. One small, central servery. Good food. Q ⑧ ⟨ 🌓 ⊟

Nefyn

Sportsman

Stryd Fawr ☎ (0758) 720205
11–11 (closed Sun)
Ind Coope Burton Ale; Tetley Walker Bitter Ⓗ
Friendly pub. Huge wood fire.
➰ Q ⑧ ⟨ 🌓 ⊟ ⑇ Å ♣ ♣

Penmaenmawr

Alexandra Hotel

High Street ☎ (0492) 622484
11–11
Ind Coope Burton Ale; M&B Mild; Tetley Walker Bitter Ⓗ
Warm and friendly working-man's pub, unspoilt by redecoration and retaining its traditional snug. ➰ ⇌ ♣

Penrhyndeudraeth

Royal Oak

High Street ☎ (0766) 770501
11–3, 6–11
Burtonwood Mild, Best Bitter Ⓗ
1930s pub with modern decor and sporty locals: dominoes played. ➰ ⟨ 🌓 ⊟ ⑇ Å ♣ ♣

Penrhynside

Cross Keys

Pendre Road ☎ (0492) 46415
5.30–11 (11–11 Sat)
Ind Coope Burton Ale; Tetley Walker Mild, Bitter Ⓗ
Traditional local and a focal point in this old quarrying village. ⑧ Å ♣

Porthmadog

Ship

Lombard Street (off High Street)
11–11 (closed Sun)
Ind Coope Burton Ale; Tetley Walker Dark Mild, Bitter Ⓗ
Popular, town pub overlooking the local park and near the

Ffestiniog Railway. Known for its oriental cuisine. Guest beers.
➰ ⇔ ⟨ 🌓 ⊟ ⑇ ♣ P

Pwllheli

White Hall

Gaol Street ☎ (0758) 613239
11–3.30, 5.30–11
Ind Coope Benskins Best Bitter, Burton Ale Ⓗ
Unspoilt, town pub with four rooms of polished floors and original decor. Few pubs of this type survive in the area.
➰ ⇔ ⑧ ⟨ 🌓 ⊟ ⑇ Å ⇌ ♣

Red Wharf Bay

Ship

Off A5025 ☎ (0248) 852568
11–11 (11.30–4, 7–11 winter)
Ansells Mild; Ind Coope Benskins Best Bitter; Tetley Walker Bitter Ⓗ
Pub of real character – a long, white building facing the sea, with low-beamed ceilings, flag floors, exposed stone walls and huge fireplaces. A pub food award-winner. Guest beers.
➰ Q ⇔ ⑧ ⇔ ⟨ 🌓 ⊟ ⑇ ♣ P

Rhosgoch

Rhosgoch Hotel (Ring)

Off B5111 ☎ (0407) 830720
12–3 (not Mon–Thu in winter), 6–11 (11–11 Fri & Sat)
Draught Bass; Stones Best Bitter Ⓗ
Small, country pub with a very friendly atmosphere: an L-shaped room served by a central bar. Guest beers. ➰ ⑧ ⟨ 🌓 Å ♣ P

Roewen

Ty Gwyn

11–11
Lees GB Mild, Bitter Ⓗ
Village pub in an idyllic setting, much changed internally but keeping its atmosphere.
➰ Q ⑧ ⟨ 🌓 ⊟ ⑇ ♣ P

Trefriw

Olde Shippe

On B5106 ☎ (0492) 640013
12–11
Burtonwood Mild, Best Bitter, Forshaw's Ⓗ
Popular, village local in an historic spa area. ➰ ⑧ ⇔ ⟨ 🌓
⑇ Å ⇌ (Llanrwst) ♣ P

Ty-Croes

Queens Head

Bryn-Du (1 mile off A4080)
OS345725 ☎ (0407) 810806
11–11
Burtonwood Best Bitter Ⓖ
Largely unspoilt, country pub with three rooms off a central servery (casks behind the bar). Large garden. Eve meals in summer. ➰ Q ⑧ ⟨ 🌓 ⊟ ⇌ ♣ P

facilities for children and a petanque pitch. ⑧ ◖ ▮ ♣ P

Bulls Head

The Struet ☎ (0874) 622044
11.30-3, 7-11 (11-11 Fri)
Brains Bitter; Felinfoel Double Dragon; Tetley Bitter; Wadworth 6X Ⓗ
Friendly, comfortable pub with a small bar and a lounge area. Two of the above ales available at any one time. Good quality bar snacks, reasonably priced. A small outdoor drinking area overlooks the river and cathedral. ⑧ ⋈ ◖ ▮ ♣ ♣

Olde Boars Head

Ship Street
☎ (0874) 622856
11-3, 5.30-11 (11-11 Fri & Sat)
Brains SA; Everards Old Bill; Fuller's ESB Ⓗ
Pub where the small, but busy, front bar has a real boar's head on display and the very large lounge has ample seating and standing room. Good variety of beers, incl. some locally casked ales and a Hanby house beer.
⑧ ◖ ⊟ ♣ ◠ P

Caersws

Red Lion

Main Street
☎ (068 684) 646
11-3, 6.30-11 (12-11 Fri; 11-11 Sat)
Marston's Pedigree; Tetley Bitter Ⓗ
Two-bar, village local, popular with tourists.
◖ ▮ ⊟ ⇌ ♣

Coedway

Old Hand & Diamond

On B4393
☎ (0743) 884379
11.30-11
Ansells Mild, Bitter; Draught Bass; Tetley Bitter Ⓗ
A plain exterior hides an immaculate, comfortable interior in this old pub of character: four rooms, incl. a restaurant, with oak beams and an inglenook in the bar. Occasional guest beers. Children welcome.
⌂ Q ⑧ ◖ ▮ ⊟ ⅋ ⚥ P

Cwmdu

Farmers Arms

On A479, 6 miles S of Talgarth
☎ (0874) 730464
11-3, 6-11
Draught Bass; Brains SA Ⓗ
Friendly, country pub; families welcome though no separate room. Large, wholesome meals are a speciality – if really hungry, choose the 'Cwmdu Challenge'. Guest beers.
⌂ Q ⑧ ◖ ▮ ⊟ ⚥ P

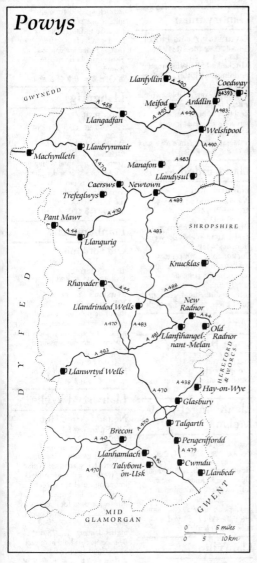

Arddlîn

Horseshoe

On A483/B4392
☎ (093 875) 318
12-11 (may close afternoons)
Draught Bass; Burtonwood Forshaw's; Marston's Pedigree Ⓗ
Plain but attractive pub on the main road, Offa's Dyke and the old canal. Children's adventure playground in the garden; table football in the bar. Two traditional ciders from Weston's.
⌂ ⇌ ⋈ ◖ ▮ ⊟ ♣ ◠ P

Brecon

Blue Boar Inn

The Watton (B4601, 400 yds from centre)
☎ (0874) 624848
11.30-3, 7-11 (11.30-11 Fri & Sat in summer)
Felinfoel Double Dragon; Whitbread Boddingtons Bitter Ⓗ
Pub with only one room, which acts as both bar and lounge, but offers comfortable seating and plenty of standing room. A large outdoor area includes play

Powys

Glasbury

Harp
On Hay road ☎ (049 74) 373
11–3, 6–11
**Robinson's Best Bitter;
Whitbread Flowers IPA,
Original** Ⓗ
Welcoming, riverside inn; a
17th-century ciderhouse.
Children welcomed, though no
special room.
🏨 Q 🍴 🅿️ ◑ 🍺 ♣ P

Maesllwch Arms Hotel
Off A438, on N side of Wye
Bridge ☎ (049 74) 226
11–11
Draught Bass Ⓗ
Informal hotel with a small,
cosy public bar; an ideal centre
for exploring the Wye Valley
and surrounding countryside.
Guest beers; Bulmers cider.
🏨 Q 🍴 🅿️ ◑ 🍺 ♣ ◔ P

Hay-on-Wye

Blue Boar
Castle Street
☎ (0497) 820884
11–3, 6–11
**Brains SA; Whitbread
Boddingtons Bitter, Flowers
IPA, Original** Ⓗ
Traditional pub next to the
main gate of the castle; an
inviting, wood-panelled public
bar and a small, intimate lounge.
A fine pub to sit and read the
books you may have unearthed
in the world-famous local
bookshops. Regular guest beers.
Eve meals in summer.
🏨 Q ◑ 🍺

Knucklas

Castle Inn
200 yds off B4355
☎ (0547) 528150
1–4, 7–11 (may extend)
Tetley Bitter Ⓗ
Large, village pub with friendly
hosts in a summer tourist area.
Walking parties arranged.
Newly installed en suite
accommodation.
🏨 🍴 🅿️ ◑ 🍺 Å ⇌ ♣

Llanbedr

Red Lion
☎ (0873) 810754
12–2.30, 6–11
**Felinfoel Cambrian, Double
Dragon; Wadworth Farmer's
Glory; Welsh Brewers
Worthington BB** Ⓗ
Friendly, country pub next to a
church, in the heart of the Black
Mountains. Families welcome,
though no separate room. Beers
vary. 🏨 Q 🍴 ◑ 🍺 Å ♣ P

Try also: Bear, Crickhowell

Llanbrynmair

Wynnstay Arms Hotel
On A470 ☎ (065 03) 431
11–3, 6–11
**Mitchell's ESB; Whitbread
Boddingtons Bitter, Flowers
IPA** Ⓗ
Well-kept, comfortable, two-bar,
village hotel with a pool room.
Real fires in both bars. Food is
served in the quiet lounge
(children welcome) or
restaurant. Beer range may vary.
🏨 Q 🍴 ◑ 🍺 ♣ P

Llandrindod Wells

Llanerch Inn
Waterloo Road
☎ (0597) 822086
11–2.30, 6–11
**Draught Bass; Robinson's
Best Bitter; Welsh Brewers
Hancock's HB** Ⓗ
Comfortable, 16th-century
coaching inn with low-beamed
ceilings and a large stone
hearth. Annual ale-tasting week
at the end of Aug. Occasional
guest beers. 🐴 🍴 🅿️ ◑ 🍺 ♣ P

Llandysul

Upper House
Off B4386
12–3 (not Wed), 6.30–11
Wood Special Ⓗ
Excellent, unspoilt, village local.
Quoits played. 🏨 🍴 🍺 ♣ P

Llanfihangel-nant-Melan

Red Lion
On A44 ☎ (054 421) 220
12–2 (2.30 summer), 6–11
Hook Norton Best Bitter Ⓗ
Quiet pub in Radnor Forest,
with a variety of comfortable
rooms. Convenient for holiday-
makers and hill-walkers. Quoits
and table skittles played.
🏨 🍴 🅿️ ◑ 🍺 ♣ P

Llanfyllin

Cain Valley Hotel
On A490 ☎ (069 184) 366
11–11
**Draught Bass; Marston's
Pedigree** Ⓗ
Historic coaching inn with an
original Jacobean staircase, two
attractive, wood-panelled
lounge bars and a basic public
bar with table football.
🏨 Q 🍴 ◑ 🍺 ♣ P

Llangadfan

Cann Office Hotel
On A458 ☎ (093 888) 202
12–2.30 (may extend), 6–11
**Marston's Burton Best Bitter,
Pedigree** (weekends &
summer) Ⓗ

Attractive and extremely
interesting, old posting inn on
the road to Dolgellau. Six
rooms and a large garden mean
that all tastes are catered for.
Fishing rights on the River
Banwy.
🏨 Q 🍴 🅿️ ◑ 🍺 Å ♣ P

Llangurig

Blue Bell
On A44 ☎ (055 15) 254
11–2.30, 6–11
**Whitbread Flowers
Original** Ⓗ
16th-century hotel with a fine
slate-floored bar and inglenook;
also a pool room, two dining
rooms and a family room. Book
for Sun lunch. Guest beer.
🏨 🍴 ◑ 🍺 Å ♣ P

Llanhamlach

Old Ford Inn
On A40, 3 miles E of Brecon
☎ (087 486) 220
11–3, 6–11 (11.30–2.30, 6.30–11
winter)
**Marston's Pedigree;
Whitbread Flowers IPA** Ⓗ
Roadside pub with a small
public bar but a spacious lounge
area. A very friendly pub where
a warm welcome is assured.
Magnificent display of over
150 old bottled beers.
Reasonably-priced range of
meals. 🍴 🅿️ ◑ 🍺 Å ♣

Llanwrtyd Wells

Neuadd Arms Hotel
The Square (A483)
☎ (059 13) 236
11.30–11 (may close afternoons)
**Felinfoel Double Dragon;
Greene King Abbot; Welsh
Brewers Worthington Dark** Ⓗ
Imposing hotel at the centre of
Britain's smallest town. Nearby
forests are used for events such
as a man *vs.* horse *vs.* mountain
bike race, bog snorkelling and
morris dancing. The Mid Wales
Beer Festival is held here each
Nov. Guest beers.
🏨 Q 🍴 ◑ 🍺 ⇌ ♣ P 🎿

Machynlleth

Dyfi Forester Inn
4 Doll Street (A487)
☎ (0654) 702004
11–3, 6–11 (11–11 Sat)
**Marston's Burton Best Bitter,
Pedigree, Owd Rodger** Ⓗ
Very friendly, town pub with an
attractive fireplace. Restaurant
downstairs. 🏨 🅿️ ◑ 🍺 ⇌ ♣ P

Manafon

Beehive
On B4390 ☎ (068 687) 244
12–3, 7–11
Banks's Mild, Bitter Ⓗ
Pleasant, well-run comfortable

pub with an unusual fireplace in the public bar. Children's play area at the rear.
🏠 🛏 🗘 ▶ 🍴 ♣ P

Meifod

Kings Head
On A495 ☎ (093 884) 256
11–3, 6–11
Burtonwood Best Bitter Ⓗ
Impressive, ivy-clad, stone-built inn in the centre of the village. Children admitted to the lounge for meals. 🛏 🗘 ▶ 🍴 🕭 ♣ P

New Radnor

Eagle Hotel
Broad Street (off A44)
☎ (054 421) 208
12–2, 7–11 (may extend summer; 11–11 Sat)
Draught Bass; Welsh Brewers Worthington BB Ⓗ
A traditional, wood-floored bar with a piano; a bright, comfortable lounge; a games room, and a restaurant and coffee shop. Spring Bank Holiday fundays with music and many ales. Popular with paragliding enthusiasts. Local farm perry sometimes available.
🏠 Q 🛏 🍴 ▶ 🍴 ♣ 🕭 P

Newtown

Buck Inn
High Street ☎ (0686) 622699
11–11 (11–4, 7–11 winter)
Draught Bass Ⓗ
Comfortable, town-centre pub. Live music Sun. Guest beers from independent breweries.
🛏 🕭 🍴 ♣

Grapes Hotel
Off A483 ☎ (0686) 625502
6 (12 Fri & Sat)–11
Ind Coope Burton Ale; Tetley Bitter Ⓗ
Friendly, wood-beamed hotel with a pool room at the rear. Occasional live music at weekends. Note: closed Mon–Thu lunchtimes.
🍴 🗘 ▶ 🍴 ♣

Pheasant
Market Street
☎ (0686) 625966
11–11
Burtonwood Mild, Best Bitter Ⓗ
Friendly, timbered, old pub with a separate games room. The public bar has a collection of unusual walking sticks.
🗓 🛏 🍴 🗘 ▶ 🕭 ♣

Sportsman
Severn Street
☎ (0686) 625885
11–2.30, 5–11
Ansells Mild; Ind Coope Burton Ale; Tetley Bitter Ⓗ
Comfortable, modernised, town-centre local, retaining its

original beams. Very popular, attracting a wide range of customers. Games area.
Q 🛏 🍴 ♣

Old Radnor

Harp Inn
1 mile W of A44/B4362 jct
☎ (054 421) 655
12–2.30 (not Tue), 7–11
Wood Special; Marston's Pedigree *or* Wood Wonderful Ⓗ
15th-century inn, beautifully restored by Landmark Trust: a slate-flagged floor, stone walls, a beamed ceiling, antique furniture and bric-a-brac inside; noisy geese and a memorable view of Radnor Forest outside. Families welcome. No eve meals Sun. Dining room has a no-smoking area.
🏠 Q 🛏 🍴 🗘 ▶ 🍴 ♣ P

Pant Mawr

Glansevern Arms
On A44, 4 miles W of Llangurig ☎ (055 15) 240
11–2, 6.30–11 (closed over Xmas/New Year)
Draught Bass Ⓗ
Two impeccable, quiet, comfortable bars in a hotel high up in the Wye Valley. Restaurant meals only; must book eves and Sun lunch; no food Sun eve. 🏠 Q 🍴 P

Pengenffordd

Castle Inn
On A479 ☎ (0874) 711353
11–3, 7–11
Wadworth 6X; Whitbread Boddingtons Bitter Ⓗ
Friendly, country local, popular with trekkers and walkers. Located on the summit of the mountain road between Talgarth and Crickhowell, with the highest hill fort in England and Wales, Castle Dinas, behind. Families welcome. Guest beers. 🏠 🛏 🍴 🗘 ▶ 🍴 ♣ 🕭 P

Rhayader

Cornhill Inn
West Street (B4518, Elan Valley road) ☎ (0597) 810869
11–3, 6–11 (may extend)
Hanby Drawwell; Marston's Pedigree; Mitchell's ESB; Wye Valley Hereford Supreme Ⓗ
Friendly, low-beamed, 400 year-old pub, reputedly with a resident female poltergeist. Guest beers. 🏠 🍴 ▶ 🍴 ♣ 🕭

Triangle Inn
Cwmdauddwr (off Bridge Street, B4518) ☎ (0597) 810537
11–2.30, 6.30–11
Draught Bass; Welsh Brewers Hancock's HB Ⓗ

Beautiful little, weatherboarded gem overlooking the River Wye. The ceilings are so low that customers have to stand in a hole in the floor to play darts! Vegetarian meals on request.
🛏 🗘 ▶ 🍴 ♣

Talgarth

Tower Hotel
The Square ☎ (0874) 711253
11–3, 7–11
Brains SA; Whitbread Boddingtons Bitter, Flowers IPA, Original Ⓗ
Popular, town-centre hotel that takes its name from the 14th-century Norman tower on the opposite side of the square of this small market town. An increasing range of well-kept ales, with regular guest beers.
🏠 🗓 🛏 🍴 🗘 ▶ P

Talybont-on-Usk

Star Inn
On B4558, ¾ mile off A40
☎ (087 487) 635
11–3, 6–11 (11–11 Sat)
Bullmastiff Ebony Dark, Son of a Bitch; Everards Tiger; Felinfoel Double Dragon; Greene King Abbot; Theakston Old Peculier Ⓗ
Very popular pub serving over 150 different real ales during the year, with at least 12 available at any one time. Large beer garden to the rear; live jazz band every Thu eve. The menu includes vegetarian and Indian dishes. Coach parties welcome.
🏠 🛏 🗘 ▶ 🍴 ♣ 🕭

Trefeglwys

Red Lion
On B4569 ☎ (055 16) 255
11.30–2.30, 6–11
Burtonwood Best Bitter Ⓗ
Excellent, village local with old village photographs displayed. Good reputation for bar meals.
🏠 🗘 ▶ 🍴 🗘 P

Welshpool

Talbot
High Street ☎ (0938) 553711
11–11 (may close afternoons)
Banks's Mild, Bitter Ⓔ
Little, two-bar, half-timbered local, handy for the bus stops and shops. Q 🛏 🗘 ▶ 🍴 🗘 ♣ P

Join CAMRA —
see page 480!

Borders

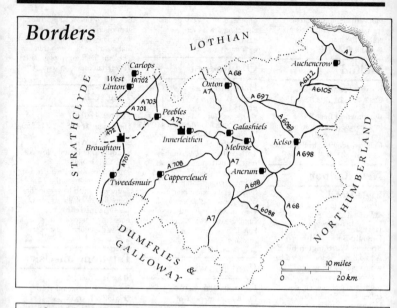

Borders

LOTHIAN

STRATHCLYDE

NORTHUMBERLAND

DUMFRIES & GALLOWAY

Carlops
West Linton
Peebles
Broughton
Tweedsmuir
Cappercleuch
Innerleithen
Galashiels
Melrose
Oxton
Ancrum
Kelso
Auchencrow

0   10 miles
0   20 km

🏠 **Broughton**, Broughton; **Traquair House**, Innerleithen

Ancrum

Cross Keys Inn
The Green (B6400, off A68 4
miles N of Jedburgh)
☎ (083 53) 344
6 (5 Fri)–11 (12 Thu & Fri; 11–12 Sat;
12.30–11 Sun; 11–11 Mon–Wed in
June–Aug)
Alloa Arrol's 80/- Ⓗ
Wonderfully unspoilt, stand-up,
village boozer with a friendly
welcome for locals and first-time
visitors alike. Restaurant
planned. Guest beer (two in
summer). 🏠 Q ⊛ ⊕ ♣ P

Auchencrow

Craw Inn
On B6438, off A1
☎ (089 07) 61253
12–2.30, 5 (6 winter)–11 (12.30–11.30
Sun)
**Draught Bass; Broughton
Greenmantle Ale, Special**
(summer) Ⓗ
Isolated gem with a two-
roomed bar reminiscent of an
English country pub. There is
also a lounge at the back.
Probably the only pub in
Scotland with its own putting
green. No eve meals Tue.
🏠 Q ⊛ ⊯ ◖ ▶ ⊕ ⊕ ♣ P

Cappercleuch

Tibbie Shiels Inn
St Mary's Loch (A708, S end of
loch)
☎ (0750) 42231
11 (12.30 Sun)–11 (closed Mon in
winter)

**Belhaven 80/-; Broughton
Greenmantle Ale** Ⓗ
Marvellous, isolated, lochside
howff on the Southern Upland
Way, popular with walkers and
motorised visitors. Water sports
and fishing available. Great
value meals.
🏠 Q ⊛ ⊯ ◖ ▶ ⊕ ▲ P

Carlops

Allan Ramsay Hotel
On A702
☎ (0968) 60258
11–12 (12.30–11 Sun)
**Belhaven 70/-; Tetley
Bitter** Ⓗ
Friendly, country inn with a
cosy log fire and a bare, stone-
flagged floor. The unusual
bartop is inset with hundreds of
old pennies. Meals available all
day, either in the bar or
restaurant. Guest beer.
🏠 ⊛ ⊯ ◖ ▶ ⅙ P

Galashiels

Cuddy Green
Green Street (off A7, near
cinema)
☎ (0896) 57667
11–11 (12 Thu–Sat; 12.30–2.30,
6.30–11 Sun)
Beer range varies Ⓗ
Large, one-room lounge with a
small bar area, but plenty of
seating, attracting a young
clientele. There is always a beer
from Theakston plus a guest
from the Nora Beer Agency. ◖ ▶

Innerleithen

Traquair Arms Hotel
Traquair Road (B709, off A72)
☎ (0896) 830229
11 (12.30 Sun)–11
**Broughton Greenmantle Ale;
Traquair House Bear Ale** Ⓗ
Family-run, 18th-century hotel
with a plush lounge bar,
warmed by a welcoming log
fire. Good, home-cooked food,
prepared from locally grown
produce, is available any time
until 9pm. Near Traquair House
brewery, Scotland's oldest
inhabited house. 🏠 Q ⊛ ⊯ ◖ ▶ P

Kelso

Black Swan Hotel
Horsemarket (off town square)
☎ (0573) 24563
11–11 (12 Fri & Sat)
Caledonian 80/- Ⓗ
Robust, wee public bar with
boisterous customers, and a
plusher lounge/dining area
which attracts a more upmarket
clientele who like muzak with
their pints. ⊯ ◖ ▶ ⊕ ♣

Red Lion Inn
Crawford Street (off town
square)
☎ (0573) 24817
11–12 (12.30–2.30, 6.30–11 Sun)
Tetley Bitter Ⓗ
Superb, traditional Borders
boozer with a surprisingly
ornate interior. It boasts a
splendid ceiling and a fine bar
back, topped with old casks.

The counter is made from a single piece of mahogany and is thought to be the longest in Scotland. Not to be missed.
🏠 🍴 ♣

Melrose

Burt's Hotel
Market Square (A6091)
☎ (089 682) 2285
11 (12.30 Sun)–2.30, 5 (6.30 Sun)–11
Belhaven 80/- Ⓐ
Upmarket hotel, renowned for its excellent cuisine, situated in the picturesque 18th-century town square. The comfortable lounge bar is usually busy for meals, so don't leave it too late if you want a seat. 🏠 Q 🛏 ◖ ▶ P

King's Arms Hotel
High Street (A6091)
☎ (089 682) 2143
11–2.30, 5–11 (12 Fri; 11–12 Sat; 12.30–11 Sun)
Broughton Greenmantle Ale Ⓐ
300 year-old former coaching inn, now a family-run hotel set in the heart of the Borders. The public bar is well frequented by locals who know their rugby. You *have* been warned!
🏠 🛏 ◖ ▶ 🍴 ♣

Oxton

Tower Hotel
Main Street (off A68)
☎ (057 85) 235
11 (12.30 Sun)–11 (12 Thu–Sat)
Broughton Greenmantle Ale Ⓗ
Friendly, country hotel and centre of village life. Note the fine stained-glass windows and the local landscape mural, painted by a former landlord. Even the pool table doesn't look out of place in this splendid hostelry. Children welcome in the lounge. 🏠 🛏 ◖ 🍴 ▲ ♣

Peebles

Kingsmuir Hotel
Springhill Road (off B7062, S of centre) ☎ (0721) 20151
11 (12.30 Sun)–11 (12 Fri & Sat)
Broughton Greenmantle Ale, 80/- (summer) Ⓗ
Friendly, family-run hotel which looks across parkland to the Tweed and the town centre. A fine menu complements the cask ale, which is available in the bar towards the rear of this 19th-century building. ⊛ 🛏 ◖ ▶ P

Tweedsmuir

Crook Inn
On A701, 1 mile N of Tweedsmuir
☎ (089 97) 272
12–11
Broughton Greenmantle Ale Ⓗ
Reputed to be the oldest licensed inn in Scotland. Dating from 1604, this is now a comfortable, modern hotel, yet retains many of its interesting, 30s features. 🏠 🛏 ◖ ▶ ♣ P

West Linton

Gordon Arms Hotel
Dolphinton Road (on A702)
☎ (0968) 60208
11 (12.30 Sun)–12
Alloa Arrol's 80/-; Tetley Bitter Ⓐ
Excellent public bar with a blazing fire and settles. An odd assortment of old phones, bottles and motoring paraphernalia provides topics for conversation. Take heed of the warning above the fruit machine!
🏠 ⊛ 🛏 ◖ ▶ 🍴 ♣ P

OPENING HOURS IN SCOTLAND

Generally, opening hours in Scotland are the same as in England and Wales, i.e. 11 am to 11 pm. However, as can be seen from the pub entries, extensions to these hours are widespread.

The granting of extensions has also been applied to Sunday, when standard opening time is 12–2.30 and 6.30–11. Scottish licensees can now request permission to stay open all day, and the pub entries show pubs which have been given this facility. However, this is a recent introduction and many pubs may still be feeling their way and assessing whether extended opening on Sunday is to their benefit. They may decide not to take up the option of staying open, even though they have the right to do so. Others may decide to give Sunday all-day opening a try during the currency of this guide.

Either way, it is probably best to telephone ahead – especially to isolated pubs – to avoid the disappointment of finding a pub closed, having made a special journey, or to discover new pubs which provide all-day drinking for visitors.

Central

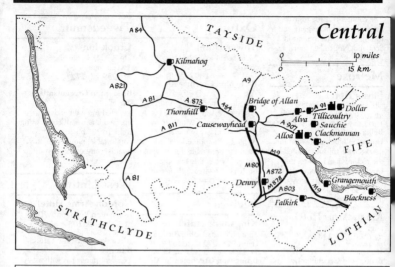

Harviestoun, *Dollar*; **Maclay**, *Alloa*

Alloa

Crams Bar
8 Candleriggs
☎ (0259) 722019
11–11 (12.30 Fri & Sat; 12.30–2.30,
7–11 Sun)
Maclay 80/-, Scotch Ale Ⓐ
Small, friendly, workingman's
bar in the heart of Alloa. Q

Ship Inn
Stripehead ☎ (0259) 722434
11–11 (1am Fri & Sat; 12.30–11 Sun)
Harviestoun 80/- Ⓗ
Workingman's bar where the
friendly locals find plenty to talk
about. ◖ ⊟

Alva

No. 5 Inn
Brook Street ☎ (0259) 60416
11–12 (11am Fri & Sat; 12.30–11 Sun)
Maclay 80/- Ⓐ
Attractive pub at the foot of the
Ochil Hills, where silver was
once mined. A former CAMRA
Forth Valley *Pub of the Year.*
Meals served Thu–Sun.
⊛ ◖ ◗ ⊟ ▲ P

Blackness

Blackness Inn
18 The Square (B903, off
A904) ☎ (0506) 834252
11–11 (11–2.30, 6.30–11 Sun)
**Alloa Arrol's 80/-; Ind
Coope Burton Ale** Ⓔ
Typical country inn, nicely
situated on the edge of the
River Forth, close to Blackness
Castle. A warm welcome is
assured, with real fires in both
bars and good, home-cooked
food. ⚏ ⊛ ⋈ ◖ ◗ ⊟

Bridge of Allan

Queen's Hotel
24 Henderson Street
☎ (0786) 833268
12–1 (incl. Sun)
Alloa Arrol's 80/- Ⓐ; **Tetley
Bitter** Ⓗ; **Younger IPA** Ⓐ
Long-established hotel: a
lounge bar, plus a TV room and
games room. The hotel also
boasts the only Mexican
restaurant in Central Scotland.
⌁ ⊛ ⋈ ◖ ◗ ⊜ ♣ P

Westerton Arms
34 Henderson Street
☎ (0786) 833659
11–12 (12.30–2.30, 7–11 Sun)
**Theakston Best Bitter;
McEwan 80/-** Ⓐ
Well-decorated, modern bar
with a feature fireplace. Good
quality and value food.
⚏ ⊛ ⋈ ◖ ⊟ ⊜ ⇌ ♣ P

Causewayhead

Birds & Bees
Easter Cornton Road
☎ (0786) 73663
11–1am (12 Mon; 12.30–2.30, 6.30–11
Sun)
Harviestoun Old Manor Ⓐ;
Tetley Bitter Ⓗ; **Younger
IPA** Ⓐ
Pub located in old farm
buildings, decorated with
designer-art, made from old
pieces of farm equipment. A
popular venue for petanque
players. ⊛ ◖ ◗ ⅋ ▲ ♣ P

Clackmannan

County Hotel
Main Street ☎ (0259) 722919

11–11 (12 Thu–Sat; 12.30–11 Sun)
Maclay 80/-, Scotch Ale Ⓐ
Village pub with a friendly
atmosphere. Pool room at the
rear. ⊟ ⅋ ♣

Denny

Royal Oak Hotel
169 Stirling Street
☎ (0324) 823768
11–2.30, 5–11 (12.30–2.30, 6.30–11
Sun)
Younger No. 3 Ⓐ
Pub which has been run by the
same family since 1925 and is
one of the few outlets for No. 3
in the area. Originally built in
1794 as a coaching inn.
Q ⋈ ◖ ◗ P

Dollar

King's Seat
19 Bridge Street
☎ (0259) 42515
11–2.30, 5–11 (12 Thu–Sat;
12.30–2.30, 6.30–11 Sun)
**Alloa Arrol's 80/-;
Caledonian 70/-; Ind Coope
Burton Ale** Ⓗ
Family pub offering well above
average standards of decor and
food. Q ◖ ◗ ⊜ ⊟ ▲

Strathallan Hotel
Chapel Place
☎ (0259) 42205
5–12 (11–1 Sat; 12.30–11 Sun)
**Harviestoun 70/-, 80/-, Old
Manor** Ⓗ
Harviestoun's brewery tap. A
popular pub in a central
location, with a very friendly
atmosphere. The interesting
collection of malt whiskies
makes an attractive display in
the main bar. ⊛ ⋈ ◖ ◗ ▲ ♣ P

Falkirk

Behind the Wall

14 Melville Street
☎ (0324) 33338
11–12 (12.45 Fri & Sat; 12.30–2.30,
6.30–11.30 Sun)
Whitbread Castle Eden Ale Ⓗ
Large, lively bar and bistro built
in an old Playtex bra factory.
The full range of meals includes
a vegetarian option. The toilets
are up two flights of stairs, so
beware. Large municipal car
park opposite. ⬗ ◖ ▮ ⇌

Rosebank

Main Street, Camelon
☎ (0324) 611842
11–11 (11.30 Fri & Sat; 12.30–2.30,
6.30–11 Sun)
Whitbread Castle Eden Ale Ⓗ
Part of the Beefeater chain,
opened in 1988 after a £1.5
million renovation of the former
Rosebank distillery bonded
warehouse. A Sun eve quiz is
very popular, as is reading the
comments in the visitors' book
in the foyer. Children well
catered for (typical Beefeater
fare). ◖ ▮ ⬕ ⬗ P

Grangemouth

Ship Inn

102 Newhouse Road
☎ (0324) 482206

11–2.30, 5.30–11 (11–11 Fri–Sun)
Maclay 80/- Ⓐ
Formerly called the 'New Ship';
a bar retaining its original
theme, with models and
pictures. ◖ ▮ P

Kilmahog

Lade Inn

At A84/A821 jct
☎ (0877) 30152
11–2.30, 5–11 (12.30–2.30, 6.30–11
Sun)
**Ruddles County; Webster's
Yorkshire Bitter, Choice** Ⓗ
Its location, at the foot of Ben
Ledi, is often described as truly
superb and the same can be said
of the pub/restaurant itself.
Owned by Canadians whose
son runs the Wellington mini-
brewery in Canada.
Q ⚲ ⬗ ⇔ ◖ ▮ ⬕ ⬗ Ⱥ P

Sauchie

Mansfield Arms

7 Main Street
☎ (0259) 722020
11–12 (1am Fri & Sat)
**Draught Bass; Harviestoun
70/-, 80/-; McEwan 80/-** Ⓐ
Former local CAMRA *Pub of the
Year*, run by the Gibson family,
with Mum cooking and the rest
of the family helping behind the

bars. A warm welcome is
extended to locals and visitors
alike. The main bar has a rare
Scottish atmosphere in which
you can imagine generations of
miners at play.
⬗ ◖ ▮ ⬕ ⬕ ♣ P

Thornhill

Crown Hotel

29 Main Street (A873,
Stirling–Aberfoyle road)
☎ (078 685) 217
11–2.30, 5–12 (12.30–2.30, 6.30–11
Sun)
McEwan 80/- Ⓐ
Coaching inn with low ceilings,
friendly locals and lots of bric-a-
brac on the walls.
Q ⇔ ⬕ ⬕ Ⱥ ♣ P

Tillicoultry

Woolpack

Glassford Square
☎ (0259) 50332
11–12 (1am Fri & Sat; 12.30–4,
6.30–11 Sun)
**Alloa Arrol's 80/-;
Caledonian 70/-; Ind Coope
Burton Ale** Ⓗ
Cosy, village pub with a low,
beamed ceiling. Ideally placed
for a drink after walking the
hills. Very friendly and warmly
welcoming. Q ⚲ ◖ ▮ ⬕ Ⱥ

'I tell you! No one's gonna take away my British identity!'

Dumfries & Galloway

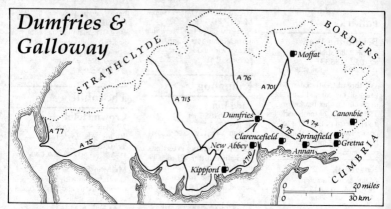

Dumfries &
Galloway

BORDERS
STRATHCLYDE
Moffat
A 76
A 701
A 713
Dumfries
Canonbie
A 77
Clarencefield Springfield
A 74
New Abbey
A 75
Gretna
Annan
A 75
A 710
Kippford
CUMBRIA

0   20 miles
0   30 km

Annan

Blue Bell
High Street ☎ (0461) 202385
11–11 (12 Thu–Sat; 12.30–11 Sun)
Theakston Best Bitter Ⓗ
Excellent, friendly, traditional
boozer with impressive wood-
panelling. Guest beer.
Q ☕ 🛏 🍴 ⚲ ♣

Canonbie

Riverside Inn
☎ (038 73) 71512
11–2.30, 6–11 (12 Fri; 11–12 Sat;
closed Sun lunch)
Yates Bitter Ⓗ
Charming, comfortable, country
inn, overlooking the River Esk.
Excellent food. Guest beer.
🛏 Q ☕ 🍴 🍺 P

Clarencefield

Farmers Inn
Main Street ☎ (0387) 87675
11–2.30, 6–11 (12 Fri; 11–12 Sat;
12.30–11 Sun; all day bank hols)
**Draught Bass ; Broughton
Greenmantle Ale ; Maclay
60/-** Ⓗ
Welcoming, 18th-century
coaching inn – one of many
frequented by Burns! Once a
temperance hotel.
🛏 ☕ 🛏 🍴 🍺 ⚲ ♣ P

Dumfries

Douglas Arms
Friars Vennel ☎ (0387) 56002
11–11 (12 Fri & Sat; 12.30–2.30,
6.30–11 Sun)
**Broughton Greenmantle Ale,
Old Jock ; Jennings
Cumberland Ale** Ⓗ
Grand, wee pub with a grand,
wee snug. The Broughton beers
may vary. 🍺 ♣

Globe Inn
High Street ☎ (0387) 52335
11–11 (12.30–2.30, 6.30–11 Sun in
winter)
**Belhaven 80/- ; McEwan
80/-** Ⓗ
17th-century howff, in a narrow

alley, a favourite of Burns.
Much Burns memorabilia ; a
superb, wood-panelled snug.
Good food (eve meals Thu–Sat
only). 🍴 ▶ ⚲

New Bazaar
Whitesands ☎ (0387) 68776
11–11 (12 Thu–Sat; 12.30–2.30,
6.30–11 Sun)
**Broughton Greenmantle Ale,
Special, Greenmantle 80/-,
Old Jock** Ⓗ
Marvellous, old bar with
Victorian fittings. Guest beer.
🛏 Q ☕ 🍴 🍺 ⚲

Ship Inn
97 St Michael Street
11–2.30, 5–11 (12.30–2.30, 6.30–11 Sun)
McEwan 70/-, 80/- Ⓐ
Cosy, two-roomed, olde-worlde
pub. Varied clientele ; friendly
atmosphere. Q ☕ 🍺 ♣

Station Hotel
(Somewhere Else Bar)
Lovers Walk ☎ (0387) 54316
11–2.30, 5–11 (11.45 Fri & Sat;
11.30–2.30, 5–11 Sun)
Draught Bass Ⓗ
Pleasant, café-style, basement
bar in an attractive, former
railway hotel. Wheelchair access
via hotel. ☕ 🛏 🍴 ▶ 🚻 ⚲

Tam O'Shanter
117 Queensberry Street
11–2.30, 5–11 (closed Sun)
**Draught Bass ; Caledonian
70/- ; McEwan 80/- ; Tetley
Bitter** Ⓐ
Excellent, traditional Scottish
bar with several wee rooms.
Q 🍺 ⚲ ♣

Gretna

Solway Lodge Hotel
Annan Road ☎ (0461) 38266
11–2.30, 5–11 (11–11 summer;
12–2.30, 6.30–11 Sun; 12–11 Sun in
summer)
**Broughton Special ; Tetley
Bitter** Ⓗ
Comfortable, friendly and
relaxing hotel in Britain's
wedding capital. Excellent value
meals. ☕ ☕ 🛏 🍴 ▶ 🚻 P

Kippford

Anchor Hotel
10.30–12 (10.30–2.30, 6–11 winter)
McEwan 80/- Ⓐ ; **Theakston
Best Bitter** Ⓗ
Wood-panelled pub with a
nautical theme. Overlooks the
harbour and hills beyond.
🛏 Q ☕ ☕ 🍴 ▶ 🍺 🛏 ♣ P

Moffat

Black Bull Bar
Station Road ☎ (0683) 20206
11–11 (11–12 Thu–Sat; 12.30–5,
6.30–11 Sun)
Theakston Best Bitter Ⓗ
Attractive, 16th-century inn
with Burns connections and
railway memorabilia. High teas
served. ☕ 🍴 ▶ 🍺

Star Hotel
High Street ☎ (0683) 20156
11–11 (11–2.30, 5–11 winter; 11–12
Fri, Sat & Sun all year)
Theakston Best Bitter Ⓗ
Welcoming, family-run
sandstone hotel with a relaxed
atmosphere. Real ale is in the
bar, but can be ordered from the
lounge. 🛏 🍴 ▶ 🍺 🛏 ♣

New Abbey

Criffel Inn
☎ (0387) 85305
11–2.30, 5.30–11 (12.30–2.30, 6.30–11
Sun)
Broughton Special Ⓐ
A traditional public bar in a
typical, Scottish, rural pub, in a
pleasant village near Sweetheart
Abbey. Eve meals till 7pm.
🛏 Q ☕ ☕ 🛏 🍴 ▶ 🍺 🛏 ♣ P

Springfield

Queens Head
Main Street ☎ (0461) 37173
12–2.30 (12.30–2.30 Sun), 7–11
McEwan 70/-, 80/- Ⓗ
Friendly, one-roomed, locals'
pub in a village adjoining
Gretna Green. ☕ ☕ ♣ P

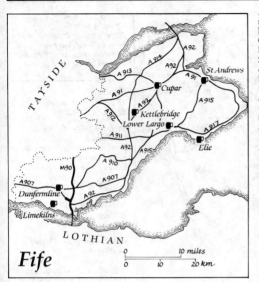

Fife

Cupar

Droukit Dug
43 Bonnygate (A91)
☎ (0334) 55862
11–12 (11–2.30, 6.30–12 Sun)
Ind Coope Burton Ale Ⓗ
Bistro-type, town-centre bar
with regular guest beers. ◖ ⇄

Dunfermline

Old Inn
13 Kirkgate ☎ (0383) 736652
11–11 (12.30–3, 6.30–11 Sun)
Theakston Best Bitter Ⓗ
Long, narrow bar with plenty of
atmosphere in the town's oldest
pub. The abbey and Pittencrief
Park are nearby. ♨ ◖ ⊟ ♿ ♣

Elie

Ship Inn
The Toft
11–12 (12.30–2.30, 6.30–11 Sun;
12.30–11 Sun in summer)

**Belhaven 80/-; Marston's
Pedigree** Ⓗ
Low-roofed pub with olde-
worlde charm and strong
nautical features, overlooking
the picturesque harbour.
Excellent beer garden with the
same view. ♨ Q ☙ ⊛ ⊟ ⚡

Kettlebridge

Kettlebridge Inn
4 Cupar Road
☎ (0337) 30232
11–2.30, 5–11 (11–11 Sat; 12.30–11
Sun)
**Ind Coope Burton Ale; Tetley
Bitter** Ⓗ
Pleasant and popular, village
local. Eve meals Thu–Sun only.
☙ ⇄ ◖ ⊟ ⚡

Limekilns

Ship Inn
Halkett's Hall (off A985)
☎ (0383) 872247

11–2.30, 5–11 (11–11.30 Sat; 12.30–11
Sun)
**Belhaven 80/-; Broughton
Greenmantle Ale; Courage
Directors** Ⓗ
Small, comfortably appointed,
one-roomed lounge bar.
Nautical bric-a-brac and fine
views over the Forth make this
a satisfying inn to visit. A warm
welcome greets locals and first
time visitors alike. ◖ ♿ ♣

Lower Largo

Railway Inn
1 Station Wynd (near harbour)
☎ (033 320) 239
11–12 (12.30–11 Sun)
Maclay 80/- Ⓗ
Cosy pub with strong nautical
features, set below the old
viaduct. ⊛ ⚡ ♣

St Andrews

Ardgowan Hotel
(Playfair Lounge)
2 Playfair Terrace
☎ (0334) 72970
12–2.30, 5–11.30 (12.30–2.30, 6.30–11
Sun)
**McEwan 80/-; Younger
No. 3** Ⓐ
Modern, basement lounge
displaying photos of old Fife.
Very popular for meals. No
rooms let in Jan. ⇄ ◖ ▶

Castle Tavern
23 South Castle Street
☎ (0334) 74977
11–11.30 (7–11.30 Sun)
**Broughton Greenmantle Ale;
Caledonian 80/-** Ⓐ
Pleasant and modernised pub
with George Younger mirrors
retained behind the bar.

Cellar Bar
32 Bell Street
☎ (0334) 77425
11–12 (4.30–11 Sun)
Belhaven 80/- Ⓗ
Popular bar below St Andrews
Wine Bar. Good food upstairs.
Regular guest beers. ◖ ▶ ⚡

The Symbols

♨	real fire	♿	easy wheelchair access
Q	quiet pub (at least one bar)	⚡	camping facilities at the pub or nearby
☙	indoor room for children	⇄	near British Rail station
⊛	garden or other outdoor drinking area	⊖	near Underground station
⇄	accommodation	♣	pub games
◖	lunchtime meals	⚲	real cider
▶	evening meals	P	pub car park
⊟	public bar	✗	no-smoking room or area

Grampian

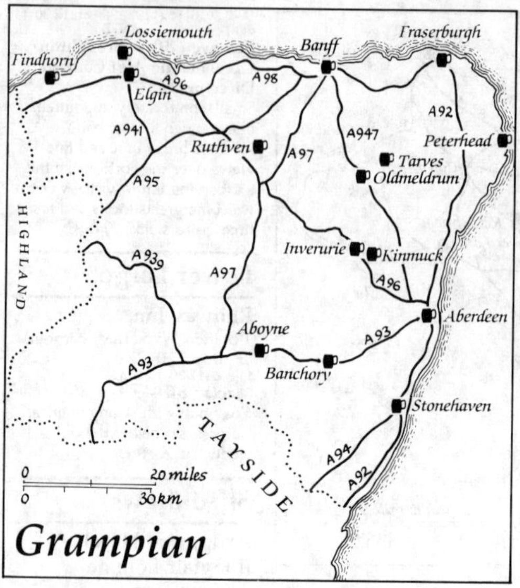

Aberdeen

Ale Cellar
114 Rosemount Viaduct
☎ (0224) 624700
10–9 (closed Sun)
Orkney Dark Island [H]
Off-licence stocking draught beer, plus a large range of British (especially Scottish) and other bottled beers. Guest beers.

Atholl Hotel
Kingsgate
☎ (0224) 323505
11–2.30, 5–11 (11.30 Fri & Sat; 12–2.30, 6.30–11 Sun)
Draught Bass [H]; McEwan 80/- [A]
Very comfortable West End hotel. Q 🛏 ◐ ◗ ♿ P

Betty Burkes
Langstane Place
☎ (0224) 210359
11–12 (6.30–11 Sun)
Ind Coope Burton Ale; Tetley Bitter [H]
Busy, city-centre bar with a very comfortable, attractively designed interior. Good selection of bottled beers.
◐ ◗ ≉

Blue Lamp
Gallowgate
☎ (0224) 647472
11–12 (12.30–2.30, 6.30–11 Sun)
McEwan 80/- [A]; Orkney Raven; Taylor Landlord; Theakston Best Bitter [H]; Younger No. 3 [A]
Pub with a small, dark but very comfortable bar and a large, stone-floored lounge. Free jukebox in both, with some gems among the old 45s in the public bar. ⊕ ♿ ≉ ♣

Camerons Inn
6 Little Belmont Street (by graveyard, off Union Street)
☎ (0224) 644487
11–12
Draught Bass; Belhaven 80/- [A]
Busy, city-centre pub, with an old-fashioned bar reflecting the bygone pub style. Well worth a visit. Good food. Q ◐ ◗ ⊕ ≉ ♣

Carriages
101 Crown Street (beneath Brentwood Hotel)
☎ (0224) 595440
11–3, 5–12 (6–12 Sun, closed Sun lunch)
Young's Special [H]
Comfortable basement bar with a highly recommended restaurant. It now offers draught Belgian beer, plus a guest beer. Free Bombay mix and nuts make it easy on the budget. Annual charity quiz league.
🛏 ◐ ◗ ≉ P

Ferryhill House Hotel
169 Bon Accord Street
☎ (0224) 590867
11–11 (11.30 Thu–Sat; 12.30–5, 6.30–11 Sun)
Broughton Greenmantle Ale; McEwan 80/- [A]; Orkney Raven [H]; Taylor Landlord [A]; Theakston Best Bitter [H]; Younger No. 3 [A]
Large lounge with a relaxed atmosphere; seating area outside in summer and a children's playground. A new function room is open to the public when not in use.
Q ☺ ❀ 🛏 ◐ ◗ ≉ P

Filthy McNasties
37 Summer Street
☎ (0224) 625588
11–12 (6.30–11 Sun)
Draught Bass [H]
Attractive, city-centre bar with wooden decor. Busy at weekends, with loud music, but pleasant during the day. Live band every Tue.

Globe
13 North Silver Street
☎ (0224) 624258
11–12 (11–11 Sun)
McEwan 80/-; Taylor Landlord [A]
Small, attractive, city bar, with a musical theme throughout. Boasts the best decorated toilets in town; a very comfortable pub. ◐ ◗ ≉

Moorings
2 Trinity Quay (opp. harbour)
☎ (0224) 587602
11–12 (12.30–11 Sun)
Caledonian 80/-; Orkney Skullsplitter [H]
Dark, narrow, city-centre pub with a host of electronic games. Weird and wonderful artwork on the walls, against a decor of red and black. A pub for rock/heavy metal fans. ≉

No. 10
10 Queens Terrace
☎ (0224) 631928
11–12 (12.30–11 Sun)
Courage Directors [H]; Tetley Bitter [A]
Modern café-bar, with brickwork and wood in evidence. ◐

Prince of Wales
St Nicholas Lane
☎ (0224) 640597
11–11 (12 Thu–Sat; 12.30–11 Sun)
Draught Bass; Caledonian 80/-; Theakston Old Peculier [H]; Younger No. 3 [A]
Homely atmosphere and wooden decor at the home of the local CAMRA branch. The best pub in the Aberdeen area and very busy. Ever-changing guest beers. Q ◐ ≉ ♣

Tap Room
22 Guild Street (opp. station)
☎ (0224) 589411
10–11 (closed Sun)
Caledonian 80/-; Orkney Raven [H]
Spacious, modern, city bar decorated in wood; good for darts players. Regular guest beers. ◐ ≉

Tilted Wig
55 Castle Street (opp. court house)
☎ (0224) 583248
12–12 (7–11 Sun)
Caledonian 80/-; Ind Coope Burton Ale; Tetley Bitter [H]
Busy, students', city-centre pub, its walls covered in pictures with a law theme/anecdotes; comfortable furnishings. ◐ ◗ ≉

Grampian

Aboyne

Charleston Hotel
Charleston Road
☎ (033 98) 86475
11–11 (12 Sat; 11–11 Sun)
Ind Coope Burton Ale Ⓐ
Popular, family-run hotel
offering a pleasant view from
the bar. Run by a very
hospitable licensee. Meals
served until 10.30pm.
Q ⊛ ⇔ ◖ 🏵 ◲ 🅰 P

Banchory

Scott Skinners
Station Road (A93, E of town)
☎ (033 02) 4393
11–2.30, 5–12 (11–12 Sat; 12.30–11 Sun)
Draught Bass Ⓗ
Small, friendly, locals' pub;
comfortable and warm. Three
guest beers and a games room.
Garden play area for children in
summer. ▲ Q ⊛ ◖ 🏵 ◲ 🅰 ♣ P

Tor-na-Coille Hotel
Inchmarlo Road (A93, W side
of town) ☎ (033 02) 2242
11.30–2.30, 5–11.30
Theakston Best Bitter Ⓗ
Hotel retaining all its Victorian
character, set in magnificent,
wooded surroundings. A very
relaxed and homely atmosphere
pervades, with plenty of
activities nearby. Croquet lawn
in the grounds.
▲ Q ⊛ ⇔ ◖ 🏵 ◲ 🅰 ♣ P

Banff

Ship Inn
7–8 Deveronside (by harbour)
☎ (026 12) 2620
10 (11 winter)–12 (12.30–11 Sun,
7–11 winter)
Theakston Best Bitter Ⓗ
Est. 1710, an original bar where
the movie *Local Hero* was partly
made, and which is designed as
clinker-built boat. A must for
passing yachtsmen. ▲ 🏵 P

Elgin

Thunderton House
Thunderton Place
☎ (0343) 548767
11–11 (12 Fri & Sat)
Draught Bass Ⓗ
Victorian-style restoration of an
historic building and former
temperance hotel. Reputed to be
a past (and present) haunt of
Bonnie Prince Charlie. Up to
three guest beers.
▲ ⇆ ◖ 🏵 ◲ ⇌

Findhorn

Crown & Anchor
Opp. old ferry pier
☎ (0309) 30243
11–11 (11.45 Fri & Sat; 12.30–11 Sun)
Draught Bass; Brakspear

Bitter; Courage Directors Ⓗ
Pub with a beautiful setting and
an excellent range of bottled
beers; perfection with scenery
thrown in. Three guest beers.
▲ ⇆ ⊛ ⇔ ◖ 🏵 ◲ 🅰 P

Fraserburgh

Crown Bar
45 Broad Street (opp. harbour,
up alley) ☎ (0346) 24941
11–11.30 (12.30–2.30, 6.30–11 Sun)
McEwan 80/- Ⓐ
One of the longest survivors in
the real ale desert. A basic,
friendly bar with a long,
wooden bar top and an unusual,
old Guinness fount. 🏵 ♣

Inverurie

Thainstone House
Hotel
Off A96, Aberdeen road
☎ (0467) 21643
11–11 (12.30–11 Sun)
Beer range varies Ⓗ
Imposing country house set
back from the main road; a
genteel atmosphere in a
popular, food-oriented
establishment. Guest ale.
▲ Q ⇆ ⊛ ⇔ ◖ 🏵 P

Kinmuck

Boars Head
Signed from B977 and B993
OS818199 ☎ (0224) 791235
11–2.30, 5–12 (12.30–2.30, 7–11 Sun)
Courage Directors;
Theakston Best Bitter Ⓗ
Previous national winner of
CAMRA *Pub of the Year* award.
Games night Fri; music Sat.
Always two additional ales on
tap, served from the cupboard.
Q 🏵 ♣ P

Lossiemouth

Clifton
Clifton Road
☎ (034 381) 2100
11–2.30, 5–11 (11–11.45 Fri & Sat)
McEwan 80/-; Theakston
Old Peculier Ⓗ
Comfortable bar opposite the
seafront. A popular spot for
local flyers. Guest beer.
Q ◖ 🏵 ◲ ♣ P

Oldmeldrum

Redgarth Lounge
Kirk Brae (signed E off A947,
Aberdeen–Banff road)
OS812273 ☎ (065 12) 2353
11–2.30, 5–11 (11.45 Fri & Sat;
12.30–2.30, 5.30–11 Sun)
Draught Bass Ⓗ
Popular, pleasant lounge bar
with a beer garden, enjoying a
magnificent, panoramic view.
Good value, fresh, home-cooked
food, incl. vegetarian. The
attentive host is a previous

---

national CAMRA *Pub of the
Year* winner, transforming a
new location. Ever-changing
good guest ales, and a house
beer (brewery not divulged).
Q ⊛ ◖ 🏵 ◲ ♣ P

Peterhead

Grange Inn
West Road (A950, Mintlaw
road from centre)
11–11.30 (12 Wed & Thu, 1 Fri & Sat;
12.30–11 Sun)
Tetley Bitter Ⓗ
A recently refurbished, nice,
open lounge and a small, plain
bar with barrel seats. It lacks the
usual bar ornaments, but the
landlord makes up for it.
Q ⊛ ♣ P

Ruthven

Borve Brew House
Off A96, between Huntly and
Keith ☎ (046 687) 373
11–11 (11.45 Fri & Sat; 12.30–2.30,
6.30–11 Sun)
Borve Ale, Elphinstone Ale Ⓗ
One-bar, one-stove, two-pump,
full mash brew pub in a rural,
converted school. Respectable,
superb-value brews by a master
brewer. If deserted call next
door! ▲ Q ◲ ♣ P

Stonehaven

Ship Inn
Shorehead
☎ (0569) 62617
11–12 (12.30–12 Sun)
McEwan 80/- Ⓐ
Warm and comfortable,
harbour-front pub, where the
lounge is dark and green in
colour – children are allowed if
they are eating. The public bar
has a Devanha Brewery mirror
and a huge crab and lobster on
the wall. Guest beers.
▲ Q ⊛ ⇔ ◖ 🏵 ◲ 🅰 ♣

Tarves

Globe Inn
Millbank (by B999)
OS865312 ☎ (065 15) 623
11–2.30, 5–12 (1 Fri; 11–11.45 Sat)
Broughton Greenmantle
Ale Ⓗ
Small, friendly, village pub with
a lively, compact bar and a
multi-purpose meals/pool
lounge adjacent. Guest beer.
▲ Q ⊛ ◖ 🏵 ◲ ♣ P

Join CAMRA —
see page 480!

371

Highland

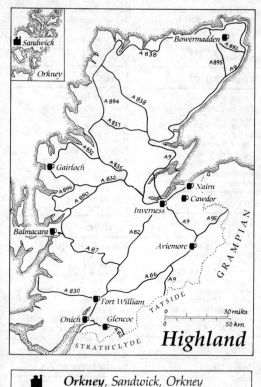

Orkney, Sandwick, Orkney

Aviemore

Winking Owl
Grampian Road
☎ (0479) 810841
11–11 (12 Fri, 11.45 Sat)
Alloa Arrol's 80/-; Tetley Bitter Ⓗ
Bar popular with the *apres-ski* crowd and tourists. Fine restaurant. ⌇ ◖◗ ▶ ≉ P

Balmacara

Balmacara Pub
On A87 OS806283
☎ (059 986) 283
11–2.30, 5–12 (11–12 Fri & Sat; 12.30–11 Sun)
McEwan 80/- Ⓐ
An essential stop for anyone visiting the far North West. The next real ale in any direction is more than 50 miles away.
⊛ ⋈ ◖◗ ▲ P

Bowermadden

Bower Inn
From Wick take A9 N, then A876 to Castletown for 11 miles
☎ (095 586) 292
11–2.30, 5–11 (12.30–2.30, 6.30–11 Sun)
Younger No. 3 Ⓐ

Originally an old country house set in the wilds of Caithness, on the north-western edge of the village. A friendly pub and an excellent restaurant with a nautical theme, run by a former submariner. ⌂ Q ⊛ ◖◗ ⊞ P

Cawdor

Cawdor Tavern
The Lane
☎ (066 77) 316
11–2.30, 5–11 (1am Fri; 11.45 Sat; 12.30–2.30, 6.30–11 Sun)
McEwan 80/- Ⓗ
Old coaching inn, set in a picturesque village on a back road from Inverness to Nairn. Close to the Culloden battlefield and the magnificent Cawdor Castle. ⌂ ⊛ ◖ ⊞ ▲ P

Fort William

Nevis Bank
Belford Road
☎ (0397) 705721
11–11 (1am Fri, 11.45 Sat; 12–11 Sun)
McEwan 80/-; Younger No. 3 Ⓐ
Plain public bar to the rear of the hotel, with a more comfortable lounge nearer the front. The best base camp for anyone heading up Ben Nevis

or the surrounding hills. Wheelchair access to the public bar only.
⌂ ⋈ ◖◗ ▶ ⊞ ⌖ ▲ ≉ ♣ P

Gairloch

Old Inn
The Harbour ☎ (0445) 2006
11–12 (11.30 Sat; 12.30–11 Sun)
Draught Bass; Belhaven 80/- Ⓗ
Old West Highland coaching inn, set by a footbridge in a quiet glen with views of loch and mountain. A warm and friendly, family-run, country inn. Occasional guest beer.
⌇ ⊛ ⋈ ◖◗ ⊞ ♣ P

Glencoe

Clachaig
On old Glencoe road, behind National Trust centre
☎ (085 52) 252
11–11 (12 Fri, 11.30 Sat; 12.30–11 Sun)
Alloa Arrol's 80/-; Ind Coope Burton Ale Ⓗ**; McEwan 80/-** Ⓐ**; Tetley Bitter; Theakston Best Bitter** Ⓗ**; Younger No. 3** Ⓐ
The biggest seller of real ale in the Highlands and the range is beginning to catch up with the quality. The public bar has been totally rebuilt but retains its former ambience – and what an ambience it is!
⌂ Q ⌖ ⊛ ⋈ ◖◗ ⊞ ⌖ ▲ P

Inverness

Clachnaharry Inn
High Street, Clachnaharry
☎ (0463) 239806
11–11 (11.45 Thu–Sat; 12.30–2.30, 6.30–11 Sun)
McEwan 80/- Ⓐ
Traditional coaching inn beside the sea lock of the Caledonian Canal and the single-track railway line. The lounge bar offers magnificent views across the Beauly Firth to the Black Isle. ⌂ ◖ ⊞ ♣

Gellions Hotel
10 Bridge Street (opp. the Town House)
☎ (0463) 233648
11–11 (1am Wed–Fri, 11.45 Sat; 12.30–11 Sun)
Caledonian 80/-; McEwan 80/-; Theakston Best Bitter Ⓐ
Small, town-centre hotel with a long established bar trade. Good beer in pleasant surroundings in the centre of town. No real ale in the public bar. ◖◗ ⊞ ▲ ≉

Glenmhor Hotel
10 Ness Bank (opp. cathedral)
☎ (0463) 234308
11–2.30, 5–11 (1am Thu & Fri, 11.45 Sat; 12.30–11 Sun)
Ind Coope Burton Ale Ⓗ

Busy, riverside hotel with a magnificent view of the cathedral. The popular public bar (selling cask beer) in the converted stables takes the name of 'Nicky Tams'.
🏠 🍴 🍺 ◐ ▶ 🍴 ☘ ⇌ P

Heathmount Hotel
Kingsmills Road (Crown area of town) ☎ (0463) 235877
11–11 (12.30 Thu & Fri, 11.30 Sat; 12.30–11 Sun)
McEwan 80/-; Younger No. 3 Ⓗ
Busy hotel lounge bar with distinctive decor and a friendly atmosphere. Excellent value, imaginative menu.
🍴 ◐ ▶ ⇌ ♣ P

Phoenix
108–110 Academy Street (near station) ☎ (0463) 233685
9am–11pm (1am Thu & Fri, 11.45 Sat; 12.30–2.30, 6.30–11 Sun)
Maclay 80/- Ⓗ
Lively, traditional horseshoe bar, complete with fresh sawdust and many interesting artefacts around the walls, including the pub's original beer engine (now in a glass case). Guest beer always available.
🍴 ◐ ▶ 🍺 ⇌

Nairn

Invernairne Hotel
Thurlow Road (between the links and the golf course)
☎ (0667) 52039
11–2.30, 5–11 (12 Mon & Sat, 1am Fri; 12.30–2.30, 6.30–11 Sun)
McEwan 80/- Ⓐ
Spacious lounge bar in a family-run hotel, a magnificent Victorian building right on the seashore. Note the impressive fireplace. Live jazz every Mon.
🏠 Q 🍴 🍴 ◐ ▶ 🍴 ⇌ P

Onich

Nether Lochaber Hotel
On sliproad to Corran–Ardgour ferry ☎ (085 53) 235
11–2.30, 5–11 (12.30–2.30, 6.30–11 Sun)
Draught Bass Ⓗ
Small, friendly bar (the 'Corran Bar') in an extension to a solid-looking hotel. The set of two, original handpumps is an absolute rarity in the Highlands, and they are actually in use. The dining room has a no-smoking area. Q 🍴 ◐ ▶ 🍴 P

FAMILY PUBS IN SCOTLAND

The law regarding children in pubs is different in Scotland from that in England and Wales. North of the border, licensees can apply for a 'children's certificate' to allow children into a pub, until eight in the evening, even if it has no designated family room.

This means that in the pub listings for Scotland, where the family room symbol is shown, it is quite possible that the pub has a children's certificate and that children are admitted to the main body of the pub (i.e. the bars) and not restricted to a family room as such.

For some licensees, obtaining a children's certificate has not been at all straightforward. The individual licensing authorities are able to make their own conditions concerning the granting of the certificates. In some cases, where they are obviously against the new law in principle, they have made the conditions so stringent, or difficult to fulfil, that many licensees have decided not to bother to apply, or given up in their attempt, which is obviously what the reluctant licensing authorities intended to happen.

Some of the authorities require, for example, that all electronic gaming machines are switched off whilst children are in the pub; that children's drinks are served only in plastic tumblers; that special nappy disposal bins are put in both ladies' *and* gents' toilets; and that half-price or children's menus *must* be available in pubs that offer food. Failing to conform to all the conditions imposed means that certificates will be refused. In Glasgow, for instance, only 19 out of 53 original applications were granted.

However, the licensing authorities in some areas are being more reasonable, especially in regions which rely heavily on tourist income, and where the livelihood of the local community is at stake.

Lothian

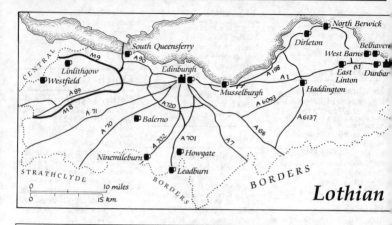

🏠 **Belhaven**, Dunbar; **Caledonian**, Edinburgh

Balerno

Grey Horse
22 Main Street (off A70)
☎ (031) 449 3092
11–2.30, 5–11 (closed Sun)
Belhaven 60/-, 80/- Ⓗ
Traditionally-run, wood-panelled gem in a village increasingly encroached upon by the city suburbs. Cheap beer. A busy local with a number of rare brewery mirrors. Q ♣ ♣

Belhaven

Mason's Arms
8 High Street (A1087, off A1, ½ mile W of Dunbar)
☎ (0368) 63700
11–2.30, 5–11 (closed Sun)
Belhaven 80/- Ⓗ
Friendly locals' bar just up the lane from the brewery in a hamlet on the outskirts of Dunbar. Lovely beaches nearby. Eve meals Thu–Sat.
🍴 ⊞ ≋ (Dunbar) ♣

Dirleton

Castle Inn
Off A198 ☎ (062 085) 221
11–2.30, 5–11 (12.30–11 Sun)
Caledonian 70/- Ⓐ
Attractive local, overlooking the village green and opposite the castle ruins. The bar, with a games room off, contains several fine mirrors. Good, tasty meals available daily in the bar and lounge. A handy base for the many nearby golf courses.
🏠 Q 🍴 ⊞ ♣ P

Dunbar

Bayswell Hotel
Bayswell Park (off Belhaven Rd)
☎ (0368) 62225

11–1am
Belhaven 80/- Ⓗ
Small lounge bar in a cliff-top country house hotel with impressive views across the Firth of Forth. 🛏 🍴 ◖ 🄳 ⅃ ≋ P

Craig-en-Gelt Hotel
Marine Road (off Belhaven Rd, on John Muir Clifftop Trail)
☎ (0368) 62287
12–2.30, 5.30–12 (12.30–2.30, 6.30–11 Sun)
Belhaven 80/- Ⓗ
Hotel on a clifftop, with fine views across the bay to the ruins of Dunbar Castle. A modern, comfortable lounge bar and restaurant, just a few minutes' walk from the town centre and harbour. Pool played.
Q 🍴 ◖ ≋ ♣

East Linton

Crown Hotel
27 Bridge Street (off A1)
☎ (0620) 860335
11–2.30, 5–11 (12 Thu & Sat, 1 Fri; 12.30–12 Sun)
Belhaven 80/- Ⓐ
Cosy, wood-panelled, locals' bar with a large lounge to the rear. A pair of rare Dudgeon & Co. windows remain as a reminder of the brewery's original name. Beware the keg 60/- and 70/-. Separate games room with a pool table. 🏠 🍴 ◖ ⊞ ♣

Drover's Inn
5 Bridge Street (off A1)
☎ (0620) 860298
11–2.30, 5–11 (12.30–11 Sun)
Draught Bass; Caledonian 80/-; Fuller's London Pride Ⓗ
Wood-panelled lounge with a marble-topped bar and a distinct 1930s atmosphere. The service is friendly and courteous, with a

bowl of fruit and mints provided for customers. A rare East Lothian outlet for Worthington White Shield.
🏠 Q 🍴 ◖ ⅃

Edinburgh

Bennet's Bar
1 Maxwell Street, Morningside (off Morningside Road, A702, 2 miles from Princes Street)
☎ (031) 447 1903
11–2.30, 5–11 (closed Sun)
Belhaven 70/-, 80/-; Caledonian Golden Promise Ⓐ
Long established, 1950s, beer-drinker's boozer at the foot of a Victorian tenement in central Morningside. Avoid the 60/- – it is *not* real ale. Q ⊞ ♣ ♣

Blue Lagoon
58 Angle Park Terrace (A70, 1½ miles from centre)
☎ (031) 337 9922
11–2.30, 5–11 (12 Mon, 12.45 Thu & Fri, 11.45 Sat; 12.30–11 Sun)
Alloa Arrol's 80/-; Caledonian 80/-; Ind Coope Burton Ale; Tetley Bitter Ⓐ
Cavernous lounge bar which tries hard not to look like a social club. Has rightly and successfully emerged from the shadow of its more famous neighbour, just along the street. Regular quiz nights. ⅃

Bow Bar
80 West Bow
☎ (031) 220 1823
11–11.15 (closed Sun)
Draught Bass; Caledonian Deuchars IPA, 80/-; Fuller's London Pride; Mitchell's Best Bitter; Taylor Landlord Ⓐ
A feast of brewery mirrors and wood, matched by efficient but firm service, typifies the best traditions of the Scottish public

bar in this award-winning paragon of pubs. Twelve cask ales, a vast range of malts and White Shield always available. Q ⬕ ⮀ (Waverley)

Cramond Inn

Cramond Glebe Road (off A90, towards Forth Road Bridge)
☎ (031) 336 2035
11–2.30, 5–11 (11–11 Sun & summer)
Samuel Smith OBB, Museum Ⓗ
Fine, old, village inn, popular with locals and day trippers alike. Dogs and children welcomed; fancy dress and charity parties organised in winter. Often packed out in summer. Near the remains of a Roman fort. ⓑ ♣ P

Drew Nicol's (Coppers)

19 Cockburn Street (next to Malt Shovel Inn)
☎ (031) 225 1441
11–2.30, 5–11 (11.45 Fri & Sat; closed Sun)
Ind Coope Burton Ale; Mitchell's Best Bitter; Tetley Bitter Ⓗ
One-room pub for discerning beer drinkers. Good range of guest beers and Worthington White Shield available.
⬕ ⮀ (Waverley)

Golden Rule

30 Yeaman Place, Fountainbridge
☎ (031) 229 3413
11–11 (12.30–2.30, 6.30–11 Sun)
Draught Bass; Caledonian 80/-; Harviestoun 70/-, 80/-, Old Manor; Orkney Raven Ⓗ
Recently renovated to a high standard, without becoming trendy; a friendly and comfortable bar, attracting discerning local and visiting clienteles. The bank of six handpumps is particularly attractive. Guest beer and White Shield available.
⬆ ◖ ▶ ⬕ ⮀ (Haymarket) ♣

Guildford Arms

1 West Register Street (E end of Princes Street, behind Wimpy)
☎ (031) 556 1023
11–11 (12 Fri & Sat: 12.30–2.30, 6.30–11 Sun)
Belhaven 80/-; Caledonian 80/-; Harviestoun 70/-, 80/-, Old Manor; Taylor Landlord Ⓗ
One of the city's finest interiors, with an unusual gallery alcove which overlooks the main bar. The famous ceiling is quite superb and there are interesting brewery mirrors, too. Close to bus and rail stations. Guest beers. ◖ ⮀ (Waverley)

Hampton Hotel

14 Corstorphine Road, Murrayfield (A8, opp. ice rink)
☎ (031) 337 1130

11–2.30, 5–11.30 (12.30–3, 6.30–11.30 Sun)
Belhaven 80/- Ⓐ
Family-run hotel with a split-level lounge bar. Often crowded with ice hockey and rugby fans. White Shield available. Limited parking. Q ⤤ ◖ P

Kay's Bar

39 Jamaica Street
☎ (031) 225 1858
11–11.45 (12.30–11 Sun)
Belhaven 80/-; Theakston Best Bitter Ⓗ
Cosy, convivial, comfortable and consistent New Town bar, tucked behind India Street and featuring clever and interesting bar furniture. Good, varied bar lunches. Guest beer.
⬛ Q ◖ ⮀ (Waverley)

Leith Oyster Bar

10 Burgess Street, Leith
☎ (031) 554 6294
12–1am
Marston's Pedigree Ⓗ
Historic building housing a comfortable lounge bar and restaurant. Over a dozen bottled beers from Belgium are available and the menu, with, for example, 'Dog's Breath Chilli', is, to say the least, interesting. Music Mon, Wed and Fri. Guest beer. ◖ ▶

Leslie's Bar

45 Ratcliffe Terrace
☎ (031) 667 5957
11–11 (12.30 Fri, 11.45 Sat; 12.30–2, 6.30–11 Sun)
Belhaven 80/-; Caledonian 70/-, 80/-; Harviestoun 80/- Ⓗ
A real gem of a Victorian pub, complete with a snob screen dividing the saloon from the public bar. The fine interior is somewhat marred by the unfortunate choice of decor but, architecturally, the pub remains one of the best in the city.
⬛ Q ⬕ ♣

Malt Shovel Inn

13 Cockburn Street (across Waverley Bridge, in Old Town)
☎ (031) 225 6843
12–11.45
Alloa Arrol's 80/-; Caledonian 70/-; Ind Coope Burton Ale; Tetley Bitter Ⓗ
Popular, Old Town lounge bar with a good atmosphere, an extensive choice of malt whiskies, and three, constantly-changing guest beers. Handy for bus and rail connections. Eve meals till 8pm.◖ ▶ ⮀ (Waverley)

Minders

114 Causewayside
12–12 (7–11 Sun)
Caledonian Deuchars IPA, 80/- Ⓗ
Busy, Southside lounge bar with three guest beers, attracting a good mix of clientele. ◖

Robbies Bar

367 Leith Walk (A900, ½ mile from Princes Street)
☎ (031) 554 6850
11–11.30 (12.30–4, 7–11 Sun)
Draught Bass; Caledonian Deuchars IPA, 80/-; Theakston XB Ⓗ
Well-run, traditional ale house with a lovely bank of original Woods & Cairns handpulls and a number of rare brewery and whisky mirrors. Three guest beers are always on tap, together with over 20 malt whiskies.
⬆ ⮀ (Waverley) ♣

St Vincent Bar

11 St Vincent Street, Stockbridge
☎ (031) 225 7447
11–2.30, 5–11 (11–11.45 Thu–Sat; 12.30–2.30, 7–11 Sun)
Alloa Arrol's 80/-; Caledonian 80/-; Maclay 80/-; Taylor Landlord; Tetley Bitter Ⓗ
Traditional bar with a superb gantry and many interesting wall decorations. Hospitable and cosy atmosphere. ◖

Southsider

3–5 West Richmond Street (near Surgeon's Hall, ½ mile from centre)
☎ (031) 667 2003
11–12 (12.30–2.30, 6.30–11 Sun)
Maclay 60/- Ⓗ**, 70/-, 80/-** Ⓐ**, Scotch Ale** Ⓗ
A long-established beer shop with a good mix of discerning drinkers. It has the best range of guest beers in the capital, together with a few bottled Belgian beers and Worthington White Shield. Good beer, good crack and the abuse from the assistant manager is worth going miles to endure. No food Sun.
Q ⬆ ◖ ⬕ ⮀ (Waverley) ♣

Stable Bar

Mortonhall Park, Frogston Road (off A720, near Fairmilehead)
☎ (031) 664 0773
11–12 (12.30–2.30, 6.30–11 Sun)
Caledonian 80/- Ⓗ
Characterful building housing a modern bar and serving the adjacent camping and caravan park. Interesting menu; the all-day meals are recommended. A well-run and friendly pub (children welcomed), but beware the lethal road humps on the driveway. Quizzes Fri.
⬛ ⓑ ◖ ▶ Ⓐ P

Todd's Tap

42 Bernard Street, Leith
☎ (031) 554 4122
12–12 (11 Mon–Wed, 11.30 Thu; 12.30–11 Sun)
Draught Bass; Belhaven 80/-; Ind Coope Burton Ale; Taylor Landlord; Tetley Bitter; Yates Bitter Ⓗ

Friendly, wee howff with a front bar and a back parlour with a warming fire. The unique collection of specially-commissioned photographs of extinct city breweries should not be missed. Guest beers.
🏠 Q ◐ 🍴

Haddington

Pheasant
72 Market Street (off A1)
☎ (062 082) 6342
11–11 (12 Thu–Sat; 11–2.30, 5–11 Tue)
Belhaven 80/-; Caledonian Deuchars IPA; Ind Coope Burton Ale; Tetley Bitter Ⓗ
Vibrant pub attracting young folk, especially at the weekend. The long bar snakes through from the games area to the lounge where Basil (surely a Norwegian Blue) holds court. Guest beer. ♣

Howgate

Old Howgate Inn
On A6094, near Penicuik
☎ (0968) 74244
11–2.30, 5–12 (11–12 Sat; 12.30–2.30, 6.30–11 Sun)
Belhaven 80/-; Broughton Special; Taylor Landlord Ⓗ
Once a coaching inn, dating from 1743, now a finely restored, cosy, wee pub and restaurant. Famous for its Danish open sandwiches; more traditional Scottish fare is also provided until 10pm.
🏠 Q ◐ ▮ P

Leadburn

Leadburn Inn
At A703/A701/A6094 jct, 3 miles S of Penicuik
☎ (0968) 72952
11–11.45 (12.30–11.45 Sun)
Caledonian 80/- Ⓗ
Large, food-oriented hostelry with 'meals on wheels' – an old railway coach turned into a restaurant. The public bar has two pot-bellied stoves and a picture window of the Pentland Hills; a conservatory links it to a plush lounge. Excellent menu.
🏠 Q 🍴 ▮ ◐ ▮ 🍴 ♣ P

Linlithgow

Four Marys
65 High Street
☎ (0506) 842171
12–2.30, 5–11 (12–2.30, 7–11 Sun)
Belhaven 70/-, 80/- Ⓗ
Attractive lounge bar with antique furniture and items reflecting the town's historic past. Good range of guest ales and a large choice of malt whiskies; twice-yearly beer festivals held. No food Sun eve. Children welcome in the rear lounge. 🍴 ◐ ▮ ≥

Red Lion
50 High Street
☎ (0506) 842348
11–11 (12 Thu–Sat; 12.30–11 Sun)
Ind Coope Burton Ale; Maclay 80/-; Tetley Bitter Ⓐ
Small, friendly bar, popular for pool and darts. Petanque piste in the garden area. Discounts for pensioners. ▮ ▮ ♣ 🍴

Musselburgh

Levenhall Arms
10 Ravensheugh Road (off A199 at roundabout near racecourse)
☎ (031) 665 3220
11–11 (1 Fri, 12 Sat; 12.30–2.30, 6.30–11 Sun)
Ind Coope Burton Ale Ⓗ
Characterful, roadside, locals' howff, attracting a good mix of clientele. A games room leads off the busy public bar, which has a horse racing theme. Regular sing-along Sat; music in the lounge Sun. ▮ ♣ P

Ninemileburn

Habbies Howe Hotel
Off A702
☎ (0968) 76969
12–11 (12.30–12 Sun)
Broughton Greenmantle Ale Ⓗ
A magic, wee, unspoilt howff, with settles, wood-panelling and a very rare (lager!) fount. A separate sitting/dining room leads through to a function suite where Fri folk nights are held.
🏠 Q ▮ ◐ ▮ ♣ P

North Berwick

Dalrymple Arms
Quality Street
☎ (0620) 2969
11–11 (12 Thu & Sat, 1 Fri; 12.30–11 Sun)
Draught Bass; Caledonian 80/- Ⓗ
Busy, locals' boozer in the middle of this seaside town, with a games/TV room at the rear. The cosy bar has an impressive range of 30 + malt whiskies and an unusual collection of Zippy cigarette lighters. Two guest beers.
🏠 ▮ 🍴 ≥ ♣

Nether Abbey Hotel
20 Dirleton Avenue (A198)
☎ (0620) 2802
11–3, 6–11 (1 Fri; 11–12 Sat; 11–11 Sun)
Caledonian 70/-, Merman XXX Ⓐ
Enterprising hotel which hosts its own beer festival each Feb. A haunt of the younger, affluent set in the eves; the bar, nonetheless, has retained a dartboard. A good place to stay. Guest beer. ▮ ◐ ▮ ≥ ♣ P

South Queensferry

Hawes Inn
Newhalls Road
☎ (031) 331 1990
11 (12.30 Sun)–11 (12 Fri)
Alloa Arrol's 80/-; Ind Coope Burton Ale Ⓐ
Fine country inn standing beneath the world's finest railway bridge. The bar is small and cosy and leads to a larger lounge which houses a food counter. Family room at the rear, with a huge Bernard's brewery mirror (worth seeing).
🏠 🍴 ▮ ◐ ▮ ≥ (Dalmeny) ♣ P

West Barns

Battleblent Hotel
Edinburgh Road (A1087, off A1, 1 mile W of Dunbar)
☎ (0368) 62234
11.30–2.30, 5–11 (1 Fri, 12 Sat; 12.30–2.30, 6.30–11 Sun)
Belhaven 80/- Ⓗ
Welcoming, country hotel set in more than two acres, overlooking the sands of Belhaven Bay; a cosy, Tudor-style lounge with an extensive range of malt whiskies. Excellent home-made meals complement the locally-brewed ale. Caravans welcome, but no tents.
🏠 🍴 ▮ ◐ ▮ 🍴 P

Westfield

Logievale Inn
Main Street
☎ (0506) 56088
11–2.30, 6.30–11 (11–11 Fri–Sun)
Caledonian 80/- Ⓐ
Converted cottages, making a bright, village local attractive to passing trade. Situated opposite a paper mill. Outdoor drinking area in summer.
🏠 ▮ ◐ ▮ 🍴 P

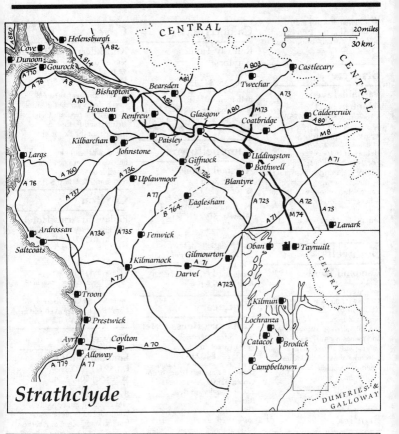

Strathclyde

🏭 *West Highland*, *Taynuilt*

Alloway

Belleisle House Hotel (Shanter Bar)
Belleisle Park (off Doonfoot Road, A719, S of Ayr)
☎ (0292) 42331
11–11 (11–6 winter)
Alloa Arrol's 80/- Ⓔ
The 19th hole; attached to a hotel located in a magnificent country park with two golf courses, gardens and a pets corner. Meals available in the hotel or cafeteria. Q ⇔ ⊕ ♣ P

Ardrossan

Boardwalk
17–19 Harbour Street
☎ (0294) 65675
11–12 (1am Thu–Sat)
McEwan 80/- Ⓐ
Comfortable bar, modernised in traditional style, close to the town centre and on the way to the Arran ferry. ◖ ⇌ (Town) ♣

Ayr

Chestnuts Hotel
52 Racecourse Road (A719, 1 mile from centre, near seafront)
☎ (0292) 264393
11–12 (12–12 Sun)
Draught Bass; Broughton Special; Theakston XB Ⓗ
Small lounge with a vaulted ceiling and a collection of over 300 water jugs. Excellent pub food. Children welcome.
▣ Q ❀ ⇔ ◖ ◗ ⇌ P

Geordies Byre
103 Main Street (old A79, N of centre and river)
☎ (0292) 264925
11–11 (12 Thu–Sat; 12.30–2.30, 6.30–11 Sun)
Broughton Special; Caledonian 80/- Ⓐ
Friendly public bar in the Newton end of town. The interesting rear lounge is full of Victorian bric-a-brac.
Q ⊕ ⇌ (Ayr/Newton)

Bearsden

Brae Bar (Burnbrae Hotel)
Milngavie Road (A81)
☎ (041) 942 5951
11–11 (11.45 Sat; 12.30–11 Sun; closed afternoons Mon–Thu, Jan–Feb)
McEwan 70/- Ⓐ; **Webster's Choice** Ⓗ
Friendly bar, with a thriving social scene, tucked away to the left and back of a modern hotel. Handy for the Allander Sports Centre and those keen to work off excessive fitness.
⇔ ◖ ⇌ (Hillfoot) P

Bishopton

Golf Inn
28–30 Old Greenock Road
☎ (0505) 862302
11–2.30, 5.30–11
Belhaven 80/-; Caledonian Golden Promise; Harviestoun Old Manor Ⓐ

Strathclyde

Traditional Scottish pub, established in the 19th century, and well stocked for off-sales. Q 🏠 P

Blantyre

Barnhill Tavern (Hoolets Nest)
113 Bardykes Road (B758, Low Blantyre–High Blantyre road)
☎ (0698) 821916
11–11.40 (12.30–2.30, 6.30–11 Sun)
Belhaven 80/- Ⓐ
Locals' pub with a splendid gantry and mirrors illustrating Scotland's brewing heritage. Large selection of owl artefacts – hence the local name for the pub, 'Hoolets Nest'. Quiet lounge. Children welcome at lunchtime. Q 🏠 🏠 ♣ P

Bothwell

Camphill Vaults
1–3 Main Street
☎ (0698) 853526
11–11.45 (12.30–11.45 Sun)
McEwan 80/- Ⓐ
Fine, traditional pub with separate alcoves, sitting rooms and games room. Traditional gantry with an excellent selection of malt whiskies. Children welcome in lounge until 9pm. A sitting room can be smoke-free if requested.
Q 🏠 🏠 ♣ P ⳤ

Brodick

Duncans Bar (Kingsley Hotel)
Shore Road ☎ (0770) 2531
11–2.30, 7–12 (closed eves Mon–Thu in winter; 11–1am summer, incl. Sun)
**McEwan 70/-, 80/-;
Theakston XB** Ⓗ
Large, friendly public bar, attached to the Kingsley Hotel, which has been owned by the Duncan family for half a century. The first real pint after getting off the ferry – or the last one before missing it! The garden has a children's play area. 🏠 🏠 🏠 ⑴ 🏠 P

Ormidale Hotel
Glencloy Road
☎ (0770) 2293
11 (4.30 Mon–Fri in winter)–1am (11–1am Sun)
McEwan 70/- Ⓐ
The pub that pioneered real ale on Arran and helped to make the island an oasis in the great beer desert of Western Scotland. The small and vibrant, traditional public bar has an adjoining glass-house which provides extra drinking space in summer. Accommodation and lunchtime meals only available in summer. 🏠 🏠 🏠 ⑴ ⑴ P

Caldercruix

Railway Tavern (Taylors)
67 Main Street
☎ (0236) 842429
11–11 (12.30–2.30, 6.30–11 Sun)
Belhaven 60/- Ⓐ
Busy, lively, village local. Note the large, rare brewery mirror and the tall founts. 🏠 🏠 🏠 ♣ P

Campbeltown

Ardsheil Hotel
Kilkerran Road
☎ (0586) 52133
11–1am (12.30–12 Sun)
Ind Coope Burton Ale Ⓗ;
McEwan 80/- Ⓐ; **Tetley
Bitter** Ⓗ
Well-run, friendly, family hotel on the outskirts of town on the outstandingly beautiful South Kintyre peninsula. Varied bar meals and à la carte restaurant.
🏠 Q 🏠 🏠 ⑴ ⑴ P

Castlecary

Castlecary House Hotel
Main Street (near railway viaduct over A80)
☎ (0324) 840233
11–11 (12.30–3.30, 6.30–11 Sun)
Draught Bass Ⓗ; **Broughton
Greenmantle Ale; Maclay
70/-; Theakston Best
Bitter** Ⓐ
This attractive, country hotel has offered real ales for many years in three separate drinking areas. A former winner of the *Pub of the Year* award from CAMRA Forth Valley.
Q 🏠 🏠 ⑴ ⑴ 🏠 🏠 P

Catacol

Catacol Bay Hotel
☎ (077 083) 231
11–2.30, 5–1 (11–1 Sat, Sun & summer)
Draught Bass Ⓗ
Small hotel in a hamlet looking across to Kintyre; a cosy lounge with an extension planned. Guest beers in summer. Try the pizzas. 🏠 🏠 🏠 ⑴ ⑴ P

Coatbridge

Carsons
4-6 Whifflet Street (near M8 jct on way into town)
☎ (0236) 22867
11–12 (12.30–12 Sun)
**Draught Bass; Broughton
Greenmantle Ale** Ⓗ
Modernised pub with polished wood throughout. Bas reliefs on the walls depict the pub and a brewery. The low-slung barrels can be a hazard! No food Sun; eve meals served until 6.30.
⑴ ⑴ 🏠 P

Cove

Knockderry Hotel
Shore Road (on B833)
☎ (043 684) 2283
11–11 (12 Thu, 1am Fri & Sat; 11–12 Sun)
Theakston Best Bitter Ⓗ
Converted Victorian mansion, displaying a pleasant blend of architectural features and situated on the Rosneath peninsula. The magnificent, wood-panelled lounge bar has fine views over Loch Long. Good food in bar and restaurant. 🏠 🏠 🏠 ⑴ ⑴ P

Coylton

Finlayson Arms Hotel
24 Hillhead (A70, 6 miles E of Ayr) ☎ (0292) 570298
11–2.30, 5–12 (1am Fri; 11–1am Sat; 12.30–12 Sun)
Broughton Special Ⓗ
Village inn with a very comfortable lounge. Excellent bar lunches; guest beers in summer; children welcome. Caravan Club approved site in the grounds. 🏠 🏠 ⑴ ⑴ 🏠 🏠 P

Darvel

Loudounhill Inn
On A71, E of Darvel
☎ (0560) 20275
11–12 (incl. Sun)
Belhaven 80/- Ⓗ
Old coaching inn opposite Loudoun Hill (a prominent landmark and scene of a battle in 1307). 🏠 Q 🏠 🏠 🏠 ⑴ ⑴ 🏠 P

Dunoon

Lorne Bar
249 Argyll Street
☎ (0369) 5064
11–12 (1am Fri & Sat; 12.30–12 Sun)
McEwan 80/- Ⓐ
Basic public bar that has resisted Americanisation. Meals are served in the smarter lounge. 🏠 Q ⑴ ⑴ 🏠 🏠 ≈ (Dunoon Ferry) ♣

Eaglesham

Cross Keys
2 Montgomery Street (B767)
11–11 (11.30 Thu, 12 Fri & Sat)
**Marston's Pedigree;
Whitbread Boddingtons
Bitter** Ⓗ
Traditional pub with a friendly atmosphere in a conservation village. Quiet lounge; excellent pub meals. ⑴ ⑴ 🏠

Fenwick

Kings Arms
89 Main Road (B7061, just off A77) ☎ (056 06) 276464
11–2.30, 5–11.30 (11–11.30 Fri & Sat; 12.30–2.30, 6.30–11 Sun)
Younger No. 3 Ⓐ

Traditional, Scottish village inn on the moorland edge. The white-painted exterior has a half-timbered, first-floor projection, a timber pillared porch and a stained-glass window. The interior has an 'olde-worlde' lounge and a separate snug (where children are welcome). Note the work of a local cartoonist on the walls.
★ ◐ ♣ P

Giffnock

Macdonald Hotel
Eastwood Toll (left at Whitecraigs Station)
11–11 (12 Thu–Sat; 12.30–5, 6.30–11 Sun)
Younger No. 3 Ⓐ
Comfortable bar in the corner of a large Thistle hotel. Separate pool room. Good value meals.
Q ⊷ ◐ ⇌ (Whitecraigs) P

Gilmourton

Bow Butts
½ mile from A71, Darvel–Strathaven road, 1 mile from Drumclog ☎ (0357) 40333
11–12 (12.30–11 Sun)
Belhaven 80/- Ⓗ
Small, cosy, traditional bar with a large, modern lounge attached (where children are welcomed). Excellent food, served Mon and Wed–Fri. Wed is also quiz night. ⚓ ★ ⊷ ◐ ▮ ᕦ ♣ P

Glasgow

Allison Arms
722 Pollokshaws Road (50 yds from station)
☎ (041) 423 1661
11–11 (12 Fri & Sat; 12.30–2.30, 6.30–11 Sun)
Belhaven 80/- Ⓐ
Basic, friendly local which attracts a varied clientele. Hosts some unusual events, as well as quiz nights.
◲ ⇌ (Queens Park) ♣

Babbity Bowster
16–18 Blackfriars Street (second left heading N from Glasgow Cross)
☎ (041) 552 5055
11–12 (12.30–12 Sun)
Maclay 70/-, 80/-, Porter Ⓐ
Very busy bar in the rejuvenated Merchant City area. Fast and friendly service.
⚓ Q ▦ ⊷ ◐ ▮ ⇌ (High St) ⊖ (Buchanan St) ↺

Blackfriars
36 Bell Street (Albion St jct)
☎ (041) 552 5924
11–12 (12.30–11 Sun)
Alloa Arrol's 80/- Ⓐ;
Belhaven 60/- Ⓗ; **Tetley Bitter** Ⓐ
Lively, Merchant City bar with a young clientele; spacious and modern, if a little spartan. Food

always available. Frequent live music downstairs. Two guest beers. ◐ ▮ ⇌ (High St/Argyle St) ⊖ (St Enoch)

Bon Accord
153 North Street (by M8, near Mitchell Library)
☎ (041) 248 4427
11–12 (12.30–2.30, 6.30–11 Sun)
Caledonian 70/-, Golden Promise; McEwan 80/-; Marston's Pedigree; Theakston Best Bitter, Old Peculier Ⓗ
Mock-traditional bar with a plush lounge at the rear. Usually four guest beers.
◐ ▮ ◲ ⇌ (Charing Cross)

Boswell Hotel
27 Mansionhouse Road, Langside (near Battlefield, behind geriatric units)
☎ (041) 632 9812
11–11 (12.30–2.30, 6.30–11 Sun)
Draught Bass; Belhaven 80/-; Caledonian 80/-, Golden Promise Ⓗ
Stone building, locally known as the 'Country Club', now renovated. The split-level lounge upstairs serves most of the beer, with a smaller public bar below. Six guest beers and one cider, as well as a large range of bottled Belgian beers. A house beer, Belhop, is an extra-hoppy, exclusive brew from Belhaven. Q ★ ▦ ⊷ ◐ ▮ ◲ ᕦ ⇌ (Langside) ♣ ↺ P ⅙

Brewery Tap
1055 Sauchiehall Street (5 mins' walk E of Partick Cross)
☎ (041) 339 8866
11–11 (12 Fri & Sat; 12.30–11 Sun)
Alloa Arrol's 80/- Ⓔ;
Belhaven 60/- Ⓐ;
Caledonian 70/-; Tetley Bitter Ⓔ
Pub with friendly bar staff, though the service can be slow. Occasional live music. Guest beer – different almost every day.
◐ ▮ ⇌ (Partick) ⊖ (Kelvinhall)

Findlays (Carruthers)
323 Hope Street (opp. Theatre Royal) ☎ (041) 333 9059
11–12 (12.30–11 Sun)
Belhaven 80/- Ⓗ
Split-level lounge bar decorated with ballet and theatrical photographs. Frequented by actors during intervals.
◐ ⇌ (Central/Queen St) ⊖ (Cowcaddens)

Horseshoe
17 Drury Street (near Central station) ☎ (041) 221 3051
11–12 (6.30–11 Sun)
Draught Bass Ⓗ; **Belhaven 80/-; Broughton Greenmantle 80/-; Caledonian 80/-; Maclay 80/-** Ⓐ

Large, city-centre pub with mirrors which make it appear even larger. Always busy but the central T-shaped bar allows ample room for service and bar stool customers.
◐ ▮ ⇌ (Central) ⊖ (St Enoch)

Tennents
191 Byres Road (Highburgh Road jct)
11–11 (12 Fri, 11.45 Sat; 12.30–2.30, 6.30–11 Sun)
Draught Bass; Broughton Greenmantle Ale; Caledonian 80/-, Golden Promise; Jennings Cumberland Ale; Maclay 80/- Ⓗ
Large bar recently redecorated in an incongruous but ignorable style. Fast and efficient service even at the busiest times.
◐ ▮ ◲ ⊖ (Hillhead)

Ubiquitous Chip
12 Ashton Lane (behind underground station)
☎ (041) 334 5007
11–11 (12 Fri & Sat; 12.30–11 Sun)
Caledonian 70/-, 80/- Ⓐ
Busy bar, looking down on one of Glasgow's best restaurants. Much favoured by the arts community. ⚓ Q ◐ ▮ ⊖ (Hillhead)

Victoria Bar
157–159 Bridgegate
☎ (041) 552 6040
11–12 (12.30–11 Sun)
Broughton Greenmantle Ale, Greenmantle 80/-; Maclay 70/-, Scotch Ale; Theakston Best Bitter Ⓐ
City-centre pub with a cosmopolitan clientele, incl. folkies, nautical students, intense actors and beer guide committees. Q ◲ ⇌ (Central/Queen St) ⊖ (St Enoch)

Gourock

Spinnaker Hotel
121 Albert Road (A8, coastal route) ☎ (0475) 33107
11.30–11.30 (11–12 Thu–Sat; 12.30–11 Sun)
Belhaven 80/- Ⓐ
Small hotel offering fine views of the Firth of Clyde. ᕦ ◐ ▮

Helensburgh

Teak 'n' Ash
82 West Princes Street (75 yds W of Colquhoun Square)
☎ (0436) 74287
11–12 (12.30–2.30, 6.30–11 Sun)
Broughton Greenmantle Ale Ⓐ
Popular, two-roomed, town-centre pub. The only working fount is in the public bar, but beer is also supplied to the comfortable lounge. Good value lunches (not served Sun). Regular beer competitions.
◐ ◲ ᕦ ⇌ (Central) ♣

Strathclyde

Houston

Cross Keys
Main Street ☎ (0505) 612209
11–12 (1am Fri, 11.45 Sat)
Theakston Best Bitter Ⓗ
A warm, friendly atmosphere in
a cosy bar. Pool room
downstairs and a separate
candle-lit restaurant. Bar snacks.
🏠 🍴 🌙 ▶ 🍺 ♣ P

Fox & Hounds
Main Street ☎ (0505) 612248
11–12 (11.45 Sat)
**Broughton Greenmantle 80/-;
McEwan 70/-** Ⓐ
Bar and a cosy lounge
downstairs; cocktail bar and a
restaurant upstairs, with real ale
in all bars. 🌙 ▶ 🍺 P

Johnstone

Coanes
26 High Street
☎ (0505) 22925
11–11 (12 Thu–Fri; 11.45 Sat; 6.30–11
Sun)
**Draught Bass; Broughton
Greenmantle Ale** Ⓗ;
**Caledonian Golden
Promise** Ⓐ; **Marston's
Pedigree; Whitbread
Boddingtons Bitter** Ⓗ
Cosy, town-centre pub with a
relaxed atmosphere and a recent
extension which has been
sympathetically designed. Bric-
a-brac above the bar includes
such gems as a 1962 *Eagle*
annual. Occasional guest ales.
No food Sun. 🌙 🍺 ≠ ♣

Kilbarchan

Trust Inn
8 Low Barrholm
☎ (050 57) 2401
5 (11 Thu–Sat)–12 (11.30–2.30, 7–11
Sun)
**Ind Coope Burton Ale; Tetley
Bitter** Ⓗ
Old, village pub in an old
weaving area. No food Sun. 🌙 ▶

Kilmarnock

Gordon's Lounge
17 Fowlds Street (opp. Tesco
on ring road)
☎ (0563) 42122
11–11 (12 Fri & Sat; 12.30–11 Sun)
Belhaven 80/- Ⓐ
Comfortable, town-centre
lounge, now with split-level
seating. Attracts a wide range of
customers, is deservedly
popular for its food and,
consequently, can be very busy
at lunchtimes. 🌙 ▶ ≠

Hunting Lodge
14–16 Glencairn Square (opp.
Safeway, S of centre)
☎ (0563) 22920
11–3, 5.30–11 (11–12 Sat, Sun &
summer)
Draught Bass; Broughton

Greenmantle Ale Ⓗ
Pub with an old oak-style
interior and hunting prints
around the walls. Friendly
atmosphere; children welcome.
Good food comes in generous
portions. 🍴 🌙 ▶ ♣ ✿

Kilmun

Coylet
Loch Eck (A815, 9 miles N of
Dunoon) ☎ (036 984) 426
11–2.30, 5–11 (12 Fri & Sat;
12.30–2.30, 6.30–11 Sun)
**McEwan 80/-; Younger
No. 3** Ⓐ
Remote, roadside pub
overlooking beautiful Loch Eck
in the heart of the Cowal
peninsula. Excellent food. The
water engine is no longer used;
it was built for urban use and
could not take the pressure of
the water off the mountain.
🏠 ♨ 🍴 🛏 🌙 ▶ ⚑ P

Lanark

Wallace Cave
11 Bloomgate ☎ (0555) 3662
11–2 (11.45 Sat; 12.30–2.30, 6.30–11
Sun)
Broughton Greenmantle Ale Ⓐ
Lively, 200 year-old pub in a
partly-listed building near the
bottom of the steep main street.
The name commemorates the
escape of the Scottish hero
William Wallace through the
tunnels under the pub. 🍺 ♿ ≠

Largs

Clachan
14 Bath Street (B7025, just off
A78) ☎ (0475) 672224
11–12 (1am Fri & Sat; 12.30–11 Sun)
Belhaven 80/- Ⓐ
Cheery and popular, single-bar
pub in a side-street just behind
the seafront. Very busy at
weekends with young people.
70/- is sometimes available.
🌙 ≠

Sheiling
144 Main Street (A78)
☎ (0475) 676171
11–12 (12.30–11 Sun)
Belhaven 80/- Ⓐ
Busy pub with a small lounge.
Photographs of Clyde shipping
adorn the walls of the public
bar. 🍺 ≠

Lochranza

Lochranza Hotel
☎ (077 083) 223
11–1am (11–2.30, 5–1 Nov–Mar, incl.
Sun)
McEwan 80/- Ⓗ
Family-run hotel on the shore of
the Loch. The basic public bar is
usually quiet, but livens up in
the evenings and on special
occasions. Beware of high tides
in the car park.
🏠 ♨ 🛏 🌙 ▶ 🍺 ⚑ P

Oban

Oban Inn
Stafford Street (400 yds from
station) ☎ (0631) 68284
11–1am
**McEwan 80/-; Younger
No. 3** Ⓐ
Busy, central pub in a terrace
overlooking the harbour. The
downstairs bar is always lively
and has a nautical decor; the
lounge upstairs has medieval
stained-glass panels. Real beer is
available in both rooms. Self-
catering flats to let. 🛏 🌙 🍺 ♣ ✿

Paisley

Bar Point
Wellmeadow Street
☎ (041) 889 5314
11–12 (11.45 Sat; 12.30–11 Sun)
Belhaven 80/- Ⓗ
Friendly pub with backgammon
and occasional live music.
🌙 ♣

Bruce Arms
59 High Street
☎ (041) 889 2367
11–12 (11.45 Sat; 11–11 Sun)
McEwan 80/- Ⓐ; **Theakston
Best Bitter** Ⓗ
Ordinary town pub frequented
by students. Lots of loud music.

Buddies
23 Broomlands Street (½ mile W
of Paisley Cross)
☎ (041) 889 5314
11–11 (12 Thu & Fri, 11.45 Sat;
12.30–2.30, 6.30–11 Sun)
Ind Coope Burton Ale Ⓗ
A friendly welcome (especially
from the gentle giant landlord)
in a fine, corner pub. Plays host
to golf and angling clubs; chess
played. 🌙 ♣ ✿

Chisholms
Shuttle Street
☎ (041) 889 6867
12–12 (1 Thu & Fri; 6–11 Sun)
**Broughton Greenmantle Ale;
Caledonian 80/-, Golden
Promise; Maclay 80/-** Ⓗ
Newly refurbished café-bar:
alcove style seating with a
raised floor for the restaurant
area; tiled bar top. Folk club and
pool bars; live music. Guest
beers. 🌙 ≠ (Gilmour St)

Hamiltons
2 Calside Road
11–11 (12 Fri, 11.45 Sat; 11–2.30,
6.30–11 Sun)
Draught Bass Ⓗ
Large, town pub with a passion
for loud musak. Quiz night
Mon. 🌙

Pats Bar
Left after Paisley College
☎ (041) 887 4768
11–12 (11–11 Sun)
**Ind Coope Burton Ale; Tetley
Bitter** Ⓗ

Popular, town-centre pub with a separate pasta restaurant – frequented by students during term-time and liable to get a bit boisterous.
◖ ▶ ⊕ ⇌ (Gilmour St)

R H Finlay's
33 Causeyside Street
☎ (041) 889 9036
11–12 (11.45 Sat; 6.30–11 Sun)
Draught Bass Ⓗ
Refurbished, traditional town pub. ◖ ⊕ & ⇌ (Gilmour St)

Samuel Brown's
16 Old Sneddon Street (left under bridge at Gilmour Street)
☎ (041) 889 2996
11–11 (12 Fri, 11.45 Sat)
McEwan 80/- Ⓗ
Under the station; a pub with a fine collection of old Paisley photographs. ⇌ (Gilmour St) ♣

Wee Howff
53 High Street
☎ (041) 889 2095
11–11 (11.30 Fri & Sat; closed Sun)
Alloa Arrol's 80/-; Ind Coope Burton Ale; Tetley Bitter Ⓗ
Traditional, Scottish town-centre bar with genuinely friendly staff. Guest beers.
⇌ (Gilmour St)

Prestwick

Golf Inn
154 Main Street (A79)
☎ (0292) 77616
11–12 (11 Tue, 12.30 Thu & Fri, 11.45 Sat; 12.30–2.30, 6.30–11 Sun)
Broughton Greenmantle Ale Ⓐ
Town-centre lounge bar with a family atmosphere at lunchtimes. Varied eve entertainment includes live music, discos, quiz nights and karaoke. Children welcome. Eve meals in summer only (book). ✪ ◖ ▶ & ⇌ ♣ P

Parkstone Hotel
Central Esplanade
☎ (0292) 77286
11–12.30 (1am Fri & Sat)
Belhaven 80/- Ⓗ
Popular seafront hotel with a lounge bar completely

redecorated and restyled in 1991. ▣ Q ✪ ⋈ ◖ ▶ ⇌ P

Renfrew

Ferry Inn
2 Clyde Street (by ferry slipway) ☎ (041) 886 2104
11–11 (12 Fri & Sat; 12.30–2.30, 6.30–11 Sun)
Belhaven 80/-; Marston's Pedigree Ⓗ
Friendly local with pictures of the heyday of Clyde ship-building around the walls. Occasionally ships pass on the Clyde and there are regular trips across the river to Glasgow. Bi-annual mini beer festival held.
▣ Q ▶ ♣ P

Saltcoats

Windy Ha'
31 Bradshaw Street, Saltcoats
☎ (0294) 63688
11–12 (12.30–4, 7–11 Sun)
Broughton Greenmantle Ale Ⓐ
Splendid, old-fashioned, Scots bar with a small snug at the back. The island bar is always surrounded by a variety of customers who make up strong teams for pool, darts, dominoes and football, including ladies teams. Prices are kept as low as possible. A good local. ⊕ ⇌ ♣

Taynuilt

Station Tap
Old Station ☎ (086 62) 246
11–2.30, 5–11 (11–11.30am summer; 12.30–2.30, 6.30–11 Sun)
West Highland Light, Heavy, Severe Ⓗ
Converted station waiting room attached to the West Highland Brewery (which is itself a converted ticket office!). Despite being only a few years old, it has the feel of a pub that has been around for centuries. Intensely friendly. ▣ ✪ & ⇌

Troon

Anchorage Hotel
149 Templehill (B749)

☎ (0292) 317448
11–12 (1am Fri & Sat)
Broughton Greenmantle Ale; Caledonian 80/-; Harviestoun 80/-; Ind Coope Burton Ale; Tetley Bitter; Theakston Best Bitter Ⓗ
Well situated for Troon marina with views of the Firth of Clyde and Arran. Children welcome until 9.30pm. Entertainment most nights; petanque court. Up to four guest beers.
▣ ⋈ ◖ ▶ & ⇌ ♣ P

Twechar

Quarry Inn
Main Street
☎ (0236) 821496
11–11 (1am Fri, 11.30 Sat; 12.30–11 Sun)
Maclay 60/-, 70/-, 80/- Ⓗ
Traditional local in a former mining village featuring coal-fired stoves and rare brewery mirrors on the oak-panelled walls. Small lounge. Petanque is played at the rear. Situated near the canal and Roman wall.
▣ Q ♣ P

Uddingston

Rowan Tree
60 Old Mill Road (next to Tunnock's bakery)
☎ (0698) 812678
11–11.45 (12.30–11.45 Sun)
Maclay 80/-, Scotch Ale Ⓐ
Public bar with two rooms off: one a lounge, the other a function room. Folk night on alternate Fris. Children welcome in lounge until 8pm.
▣ ◖ ⊕ & Å ⇌ ♣ P

Uplawmoor

Uplawmoor Hotel
66 Neilston Road
☎ (050 585) 565/566
11–11.30 (12 Thu, 12.30 Fri & Sat; 12.30–2.30, 6.30–11 Sun)
Theakston Best Bitter; Younger No. 3 Ⓗ
Large hotel in a small village. The home-made scotch eggs are a must. Bar staff very friendly.
⋈ ◖ ▶ P

&

Wheelchair Access

In appreciation of the difficulties faced by visitors with disabilities, we award the wheelchair symbol to those pubs which have adequate wheelchair access to the bars and WCs. We hope that more pubs will recognise the problems which face some visitors and that designers of new pubs will continue to address the issue in their plans.

Tayside

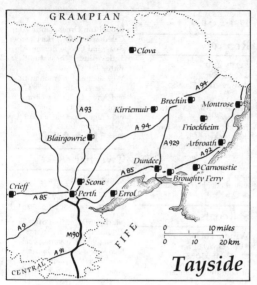

GRAMPIAN

Clova

Brechin • Montrose
Kirriemuir • A94
A93 Friockheim
A94 A929 Arbroath
Blairgowrie A92
Dundee • Carnoustie
A85 Broughty Ferry
Crieff • Scone
A85 Perth • Errol
A9
M90 FIFE
A91 CENTRAL

0   10 miles
0   10   20 km

Tayside

Pleasant, comfortable pub, offering reliable beer and good food. Children welcome in the bar and restaurant; playground outside.

Arbroath

Victoria
15 Catherine Street (near rail and bus stations)
☎ (0241) 74589
11–2.30, 5–11 (11–12 Fri & Sat)
Broughton Greenmantle Ale Ⓗ; **McEwan 80/-** Ⓐ; **Theakston Best Bitter** Ⓗ
Friendly, little pub. Watch the lounge through closed circuit TV in the bar.

Blairgowrie

Stormont Arms
Perth Street ☎ (0250) 3142
11–2.30, 5–11 (11–11.45 Fri & Sat; 12.30–2.30, 5.30–11 Sun)
Belhaven 80/- Ⓐ
Traditional, drinking-man's pub, with a friendly atmosphere. A favourite with local folk musicians who meet to play on Weds. Pavement drinking area. Very limited parking. Q ✿ Ⓐ P

Brechin

Dalhousie Bar
Market Street ☎ (035 62) 2096
11–11 (12–11 Sun)
Belhaven 80/- Ⓗ
Welcoming, if basic, bar where the owners and regulars have been instrumental in introducing cask beer to a previously ale-free area. Friendly atmosphere; original horseshoe bar. ♣

Broughty Ferry

Fishermans Tavern
12 Fort Street (by lifeboat station) ☎ (0382) 75941
11–12 (12.30–11 Sun)
Draught Bass; Belhaven 80/-; McEwan 80/-; Maclay 80/-; Theakston Best Bitter Ⓗ; **Younger No. 3** Ⓐ
Cosy, low-ceilinged pub – unique in Dundee – which is very popular. Guest beers vary.

Carnoustie

Morven Hotel
28 West Path (near High School) ☎ (0241) 52385
11–2.30, 4.30–12 (11–11 summer)
Theakston Best Bitter, XB Ⓗ
Small hotel on a hill with panoramic views. Guest beers; enthusiastic landlord. Well worth a visit.
Q ✿ ✿ ⋈ ◖ & Å ⇌ P

Try also: Glencoe Hotel, Links Parade (Maclay)

Clova

Clova Hotel
Glen Clova (B955 Kirriemuir road) ☎ (057 55) 222
11–11 (12.30–12 Sun)
Maclay 80/- Ⓗ
A popular haven for tourists, climbers and walkers. Occasional beer festivals. Beer is supplied on a guest basis and so will vary. ⚭ ✿ ✿ ⋈ ◖ ◗ Ⓐ Å P

Crieff

Oakbank Inn
Turret Bridge (left off A85 at first crossroads W of Crieff)
☎ (0764) 2420
12–2.30, 6–11 (11–11.45 Sat; 12.30–11 Sun)
Ind Coope Burton Ale Ⓗ

Dundee

Frews
117 Strathmartine Road (opp. Coldside library, near Dens Park) ☎ (0382) 810975
11–12 (12.30–4, 7–11 Sun)
Draught Bass Ⓗ
Busy, traditional pub with excellent, original features. Two lounges: one is an excellent example of provincial Art Deco.
Ⓐ ♣

McGonagalls
142–146 Perth Road (opp. art college) ☎ (0382) 22392
11–12
Belhaven 80/- Ⓐ; **Ind Coope Burton Ale** Ⓗ; **McEwan 70/-** Ⓗ, **80/-** Ⓐ
Busy, L-shaped bar run by a CAMRA stalwart. Frequent guest beers. Lounge downstairs.
◖ ⇌

Mercantile Bar
Commercial Street
☎ (0382) 25500
10–11 (12 Thu–Sat; 7–11 Sun)
Draught Bass; Ind Coope Burton Ale; McEwan 80/-; Maclay 80/-; Theakston Best Bitter Ⓗ; **Younger No. 3** Ⓐ
Victorian-style, split-level pub with separate drinking areas. Very busy at lunchtime. Eve meals Mon–Wed till 7pm and Thu–Sat till 8pm. Morning coffee from 10am.
◖ ◗ & ⇌ (Tay Bridge) ✗

Phoenix
103–105 Nethergate (near university)
☎ (0382) 200014
11–12
Draught Bass; Theakston Old Peculier Ⓗ
Popular, busy, city-centre pub with an enthusiastic landlord. Belgian beers are frequently available, as are regular guest beers. Backgammon played.
◖ ◗ ⇌ ♣

Royal Oak
167 Brook Street (off Hawkhill bypass) ☎ (0382) 29440
11–12
Ind Coope Burton Ale Ⓐ
Well maintained, friendly pub with a reputation for excellent food and good service. ⚭ ◖ ◗

Shakespeare
267 Hilltown
☎ (0382) 21454
11–12 (12.30–11 Sun)
Belhaven 80/- Ⓐ
Busy pub, handy for both Dundee football grounds. Ⓐ ♣

Swallow Hotel

Invergowrie (end of Kingsway)
☎ (0382) 641122
11–11
Ind Coope Burton Ale Ⓐ
Upmarket hotel on the outskirts
of the city which includes a
leisure club. Friendly staff.
Wheelchair WC.
Q ⛲ ⋈ ◖ ▶ & P

**Try also: Speedwell Bar
(Mennies)**, Perth Rd (Free)

Errol

Old Smiddy

The Cross
☎ (082 12) 888
11–2.30, 5–11 (11.45 Fri & Sat;
12.30–11 Sun; closed Mon)
Belhaven 80/- Ⓗ
A reproduction blacksmith's
forge (log-fired in winter)
enhances this cosy, country inn,
formerly the village smithy.
Reasonably priced menu, with
high tea, a Scottish speciality,
served on Sun.
🏛 ◖ ▶ & P

Friockheim

Star Inn

14 Gardyne Street (main street)
☎ (024 12) 248
11–2.30, 5–11 (11–11 summer;
12.30–11 Sun)
McEwan 80/- Ⓐ; **Theakston
Best Bitter; Younger No. 3** Ⓗ
Public and lounge bars with a
good, pub atmosphere,
encouraged by a low, beamed
ceiling. Guest beers.
🏛 Q ⛲ ⋈ ◖ ▶ ⬤ ♣

Kirriemuir

White Horse

1–3 Bellies Brae
☎ (0575) 73222
11–12 (12.30–12 Sun)
Belhaven 80/- Ⓗ
Pub recently refurbished in a
comfortable style, with a busy,
but pleasant, atmosphere.
Mainly frequented by a young
clientele; very busy at
weekends. Background music
played. Good selection of
bottled beers available. 🏛 &

Montrose

George Hotel

22 George Street (near police
station)
☎ (0674) 75050
11–11 (12–11 Sun)
**Marston's Pedigree;
Whitbread Boddingtons
Bitter** Ⓗ
An unexpected find in a
burgundy-velvet, hotel setting:
a family-run concern, with a
lounge bar, function suite and *à
la carte* restaurant. Good food.
The two regular beers are
supplemented by two guest
ales. ⋈ ◖ ▶ Å ⇌ P ⤬

Perth

Greyfriars

15 South Street
☎ (0738) 33036
11–3, 5–11 (11–11.45 Fri & Sat; closed
Mon eve)
**Ind Coope Burton Ale;
Orkney Raven, Dark Island** Ⓗ
Small, fuggy but friendly, city-
centre pub. Guest beers. Well
worth a visit. ◖ ▶ ⇌

King's Arms

7 George Street
☎ (0738) 29914
11–11.30 (11–12 Fri & Sat; closed
Sun)
Maclay 80/-, Scotch Ale Ⓗ
Recently resurrected old
favourite (formerly 'Hal o' the
Wynd'), now a lively pub with
a large portfolio of guest beers
and a selection of bottled
Belgian beers. The varied lunch
menu includes the famous red-
hot chilli. ◖ ⇌

Old Ship Inn

Skinnergate
☎ (0738) 24929
11–2.30, 5–11 (11–11 Fri & Sat; closed
Sun)
**Alloa Arrol's 80/-;
Caledonian 70/-** Ⓗ
The oldest pub in Perth,
established in 1665. Excellent
bar lunches in the upstairs
lounge (eve meals Sat only,
5–7.30pm). Q ◖ ▶ ⬤ ⇌ ♣

Scone

Scone Arms

Perth Road (A94, 2 miles NNE
of Perth)
☎ (0738) 51341
11–11 (11–11.45 Fri & Sat; 12.30–11
Sun)
Theakston Best Bitter, XB Ⓗ
Pub with a pine-panelled bar
and a games room. The
comfortable lounge has a
traditional atmosphere.
Renowned for its bar meals (eve
meals Fri and Sat only).
◖ ▶ ⬤ ♣ P

'Are you driving too?'

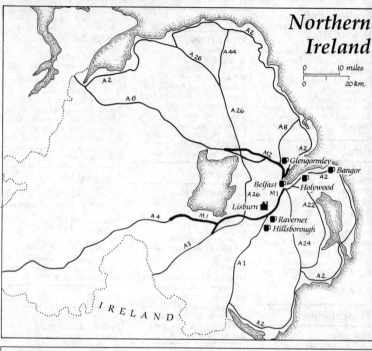

Northern Ireland

0   10 miles
0   20 km

A2, A26, A44, A2, A6, A26, A8, A2, M2, Glengormley, Bangor, A2, Belfast, Holywood, M1, A26, A22, Lisburn, Ravernet, Hillsborough, A4, M1, A3, A24, A1, A2, IRELAND, A2

🏭 **Hilden**, *Lisburn*

Bangor

Jenny Watts
High Street ☎ (0247) 270401
11–11 (1am Tue & Sat; 12–2.30,
7–10 Sun)
Worthington White Shield
Victorian-style lounge with
island bar, stone walls, old
bottles and whiskey mirrors. Can
get crowded late eves. Separate
restaurant.
Q 🏤 🅒 ▶ ♿ ≠ (NIR)

Belfast

Kings Head
829 Lisburn Road (A1),
Balmoral ☎ (0232) 667805
12–11 (7–10 Sun)
Hilden Ale 🅷
Comfortable series of bars of
different character, in two
Victorian semis with a later
conservatory. Beside Balmoral
station.
🏚 Q 🏤 🅒 🖰 ≠ (Balmoral NIR)

Kitchen Bar/Parlour Bar
18 Victoria Square/6 Telfair
Street ☎ (0232) 324901
11.30–11 (may close early; 12.30–2.30
Sun)
**Hilden Ale; Trough Wild
Boar** 🅷
Two long, narrow, inter-
connected, family-run bars of
inspiring and traditional
character in a city-centre

backwater. Super service;
legendary lunches; piano and
fiddles played. A gem.
Q 🅒 🖰 ≠ (Central NIR)

Linenhall
9 Clarence Street (opp. Ulster
Hall) ☎ (0232) 248458
12–11 (1am Fri; closed Sun)
Hilden Ale 🅷
Gregarious and cosmopolitan,
triangular public bar with a
sitting room to the rear, in
mellow brick and timber.
Frequently frenetic. Not to be
missed. 🅒 ▶ 🖰 ≠ (Botanic NIR)

Portside Inn
Dargan Road
11.30–11 (may close early Mon–Thu;
closed Sun)
Worthington White Shield
Modern building on the edge of
Dockside Ind. Estate; a lofty,
timber-lined bar and lounge.
Maritime memorabilia. 🅒 🖰 ♿ P

Glengormley

Crown & Shamrock
585 Antrim Road (A6)
11–11 (12.30–2.30, 7–10 Sun)
Worthington White Shield
Unspoilt, family-run, country
pub, with a low, panelled ceiling
to the plain, traditional bar and
intimate sitting room. An
institution. Occasional draught
beers. 🏚 Q 🏤 🖰 P

Hillsborough

Hillside
Main Street ☎ (0846) 682765
12–11 (12.30–2.30, 7–10 Sun)
Hilden Ale 🅷
Comfortable, stone-floored,
multi-cornered local. Excellent
bar snacks; renowned
restaurant. 🏚 Q 🏤 🅒 🖰 🖰

Holywood

Bear Tavern
High Street ☎ (023 17) 6837
11.30–11 (1am Fri & Sat; 12.30–2.30,
7–10 Sun)
Worthington White Shield
Long and narrow, new, lively
local of Victorian character.
Handsome, traditional interior:
sloping stone floor, inglenook,
tiles, mirrors and cosy corners.
Occasional draught beers.
🏚 🅒 🖰 ♿ ≠

Ravernet

Tidy Doffer
133 Ravernet Road (off A1)
☎ (0846) 689188
11.30–11 (12.30–2.30, 7–10 Sun)
Worthington White Shield
New, large, out-of-the-way,
tithe barn-style bar and 'monks
cell'-type sitting room, with a
thatched roof. Large linen-
making machines feature. Smart
restaurant. 🏚 Q 🏤 🏤 🅒 🖰 ♿ P

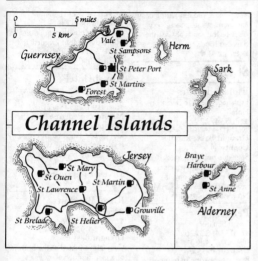

Channel Islands

🏰 *Guernsey, Randalls, St Peter Port*

Alderney

Braye Harbour

Moorings Hotel
Rue de Braye
☎ (048 182) 2421
11–midnight (12–2, 8–midnight Sun)
Guernsey Real Draught Bitter Ⓗ
Enterprising hotel with good bar snacks and separate restaurant. Large terrace overlooking Braye Bay. Shove-ha'penny board. ⌂ ⏸ ⇔ ⓓ ♣

St Anne

Coronation Inn
36 High Street
☎ (048 182) 2630
10–midnight (12–2, 8–midnight Sun)
Randalls Best Bitter Ⓖ
Unspoilt town local with a welcoming atmosphere.
⚓ Q ⊟ ♣

Guernsey

Forest

Deerhound Inn
Le Bourg
☎ (0481) 38585
11.30–2, 6–11.45 (12–2, 7–10.30 Sun for meals; closed Mon in winter)
Guernsey Real Draught Bitter Ⓗ
Welcoming, cosy country inn of character. Restaurant and bar meals. ⌂ ⏸ ⇔ ⓓ ⓖ P

St Martins

Captains Hotel
La Fosse
☎ (0481) 38990
11–11.30 (closed Sun)
Guernsey Real Draught Bitter Ⓗ
Attractive, L-shaped lounge bar boasting an impressive handpump. Separate restaurant upstairs. Shove-ha'penny board. ⏸ ⇔ ⓓ ♣ P

L'Auberge Divette
Jerbourg
☎ (0481) 38485
10.30–11 (closed Sun)
Guernsey LBA Mild, Real Draught Bitter Ⓗ
Local CAMRA *Pub of the Year* for 1990. An excellent country pub on a cliff-bound peninsula. Commands panoramic views from lounge and garden. Handy for the cliff paths. Bar billiards. No eve meals Thu.
⚓ ⌂ ⏸ ⓓ ⊟ ♣ P

St Peter Port

Britannia Inn
Trinity Square
☎ (0481) 721082
10.30–11 (closed Sun)
Guernsey LBA Mild, Real Draught Bitter Ⓗ
Small lounge bar in the old quarter of town which serves no keg bitter. Can get very smoky.

La Collinette Hotel
St Jacques
☎ (0481) 710331
12–2.30, 5–11.35 (closed Sun)

Guernsey Grizzly's Real Ale Ⓗ
Comfortable hotel lounge bar situated near Beau Sejour leisure centre. Grizzly's is exclusive to the hotel. Pool-side drinking area. ⌂ ⏸ ⇔ ⓓ ♣ P

Plough Inn
Vauvert
☎ (0481) 20599
10.30–2, 4.30–11 (closed Sun)
Guernsey LBA Mild Ⓗ
Traditional, multi-roomed local in the old quarter of town. Reputed to be the oldest pub in Guernsey. Pinball machine. ♣

Salerie Inn
Salerie Corner
☎ (0481) 724484
10.30–11 (closed Sun)
Guernsey LBA Mild, Real Draught Bitter Ⓗ
Plush lounge with a strong nautical theme, recently rebuilt and enlarged. Opposite public car park. ⚓ ⓓ

Ship & Crown
Esplanade
☎ (0481) 721368
10.30–11 (closed Sun)
Guernsey Real Draught Bitter Ⓗ
Busy town pub opposite the main marina for visiting yachts. Decorated with pictures of ships and local shipwrecks. ⓓ

Swan Inn
St Julians Avenue
☎ (0481) 28669
10.30–11 (closed Sun)
Guernsey Real Draught Bitter Ⓗ
Comfortable lounge bar retaining original features. Situated on the edge of the 'city' area. ⚓ ⓓ

Thomas de la Rue
Le Pollet
☎ (0481) 714990
10.30–11 (closed Sun)
Guernsey LBA Mild, Real Draught Bitter Ⓗ
Split-level lounge bar with view over harbour. The famous banknote printer set up business here in the 18th century. ⓓ

Try also: **Foresters Arms** (Guernsey)

St Sampsons

Pony Inn
Les Capelles
☎ (0481) 44374
10.30–11 (closed Sun)
Guernsey LBA Mild, Real Draught Bitter Ⓗ
Large and popular pub close to Guernsey Candles and Oatlands Craft Centre. Eve meals Fri and Sat only. ⏸ ⓓ ⓘ ⊟ ♣ P

385

Channel Islands

Vale

Hampshire Lodge
Rue Mainguy
☎ (0481) 57230
10.30–11 (12–2.30 Sun for meals only)
Guernsey LBA Mild Ⓗ
Busy local near the Bailiwick
Scout HQ, with separate
restaurant. Can get quite smoky.
❀ (Å ♣ P

Jersey

Grouville

Seymour Inn
La Rocque (on Gorey coast
road)
☎ (0534) 54558
11–11 (11–1, 4.30–11 Sun)
**Guernsey LBA Mild, Real
Draught Bitter** Ⓗ
Very smart and comfortable real
ale bar. Excellent, good-value
food (no meals Sun).
ை ⊱ ❀ (▶ ♣ P

St Brelade

La Pulente Hotel
La Pulente (extreme S end of
Five Mile Road)
☎ (0534) 41760
11–11 (11–1, 4.30–11 Sun)
Draught Bass Ⓗ
Unspoilt, local fisherman's bar
and cosy lounge at southern
end of St Ouens Bay,
overlooking the beach. A
superb place to view beautiful
sunsets. No meals Sun.
ை Q ❀ (⊟ ♣ P

Old Portelet Inn
Portelet Bay
☎ (0534) 41899
11–11 (11–1, 4.30–11 Sun)
**Draught Bass; Marston's
Pedigree** Ⓗ
17th century, timber-beamed
farmhouse in a superb position
above Portelet Bay beach. Four
separate bars; large children's
area (menu for them).
⊱ ❀ (▶ ♣ P

Smugglers Inn
Ouaisne Bay
☎ (0534) 41510
11–11 (11–1, 4.30–11 Sun)
Draught Bass Ⓗ

Welcoming old inn with a cosy
and warm atmosphere. Very
close to the sands at Ouaisne
Bay. No food Sun.
ை ⊱ (▶ ⊟ ♣

St Helier

Esplanade Bars
Esplanade (next to Swansons
Hotel)
☎ (0534) 22925
10–11 (11–1, 4.30–11 Sun)
**Draught Bass; Ruddles
County** Ⓗ
Spacious pub with a good
atmosphere that attracts a
mixed clientele. Long the
headquarters of local CAMRA.
No meals Sun. ⊱ (♣

Peirson
Royal Square
☎ (0534) 22726
10–11 (11–1, 4.30–11 Sun)
Draught Bass Ⓗ
Bustling, historic pub opposite
the States building in Royal
Square. Scars of the Battle of
Jersey are still visible on the
walls. No meals Sun. (⊟

St Lawrence

British Union Hotel
Main road (opp. parish church)
☎ (0534) 61070
10.30–11 (11–1, 4.30–11 Sun)
**Guernsey LBA Mild, Real
Draught Bitter** Ⓗ
Excellent, good-value food
lunchtime and eves in this
cheerful family-oriented pub
(children welcomed in both
lounges). Much frequented by
locals. No meals Mon eve or
Sun. ⊱ ❀ (▶ ⊟ ♣

St Martin

Anne Port Bay Hotel
Anne Port Bay (200 yds from
bay)
☎ (0534) 52058
11–2.30, 5–11 (11–1, 4.30–11 Sun)
**Draught Bass; Marston's
Pedigree** Ⓖ
Convivial and comfortable hotel
near the beach at Anne Port.
Snug bar. No lunches Sun.
Q ⋈ (P

Castle Green Hotel
Gorey (on hill overlooking
harbour)
☎ (0534) 53103

11–11 (11–1, 4.30–11 Sun)
Draught Bass Ⓖ
Popular pub with magnificent
views over Mont Orgueil
Castle and Gorey Harbour. No
meals Sun. (♣ ♣

Royal Hotel
Main road (opp. parish church)
☎ (0534) 56289
11–11 (11–1, 4.30–11 Sun)
Marston's Pedigree Ⓗ
Busy pub with a comfortable
lounge bar. Bar food or upstairs
restaurant available, with pew-
style seating (vegetarian dishes,
too). Excellent children's
adventure playground.
❀ (▶ ♣ P

Rozel Bay Inn
Rozel Bay
☎ (0534) 63438
11–11 (11–1, 4.30–11 Sun)
Draught Bass Ⓗ
Cosy pub situated at the bottom
of a picturesque valley in an
attractive fishing village. The
quaint harbour of Rozel is close
by. No meals Sun. ை ⊱ (⊟ P

St Mary

St Mary's Country
Hotel
Opp. parish church
☎ (0534) 81561
10–11 (11–1, 4.30–11 Sun)
Draught Bass Ⓗ
Superb country inn: extremely
comfortable and with every
facility. Extensive food menu
with daily specials. Excellent
children's room. No meals Sun;
eve meals Fri/Sat only.
ை Q ⊱ ❀ (▶ ⊟ ♣ P

Try also: **Les Fontaines
Tavern**, St John (Bass)

St Ouen

Le Moulin de Lecq
Greve de Lecq Bay (100 yds
from beach)
☎ (0534) 82818
11–11 (11–1, 4.30–11 Sun)
**Draught Bass; Guernsey LBA
Mild, Real Draught Bitter** Ⓗ
16th-century working watermill
close to the beach. Large
children's play area. Excellent
menu which includes local
specialities. Guest beers
available. ை Q ⊱ ❀ (▶ P

Å
Camping Facilities

Many pubs, particularly in tourist areas, are conveniently located close
to camp sites. Where a pub stands within one mile of a site we include
the tent symbol. Sometimes the pub itself offers camping facilities.

Isle of Man

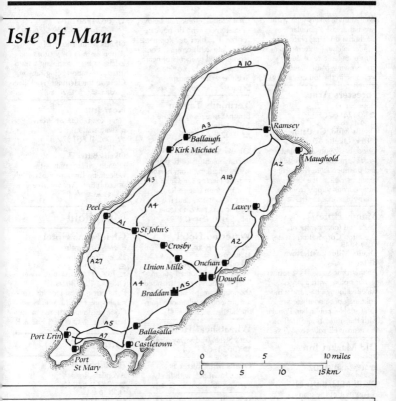

🏰 **Bushy's**, Braddan; **Isle of Man**, Douglas

Sunday hours on the Isle of Man are 12–1.30, 8–10

Ballasalla

Whitestone Inn
☎ (0624) 822334
12–10.45
Okells Bitter Ⓗ
Structurally unchanged during a recent period of refurbishment : a commodious lounge bar (for the yuppy and the well-heeled pensioner), and a comfortable public bar.
Ⓓ ⬰ ♿ ⇌ P

Try also: Rushen Abbey Hotel (Free)

Ballaugh

Raven Hotel
Main Road (on TT course at Ballaugh Bridge)
☎ (0624) 897272
12–10.45
Okells Bitter; Whitbread Castle Eden Ale Ⓗ
Popular pub with TT fans, set in the village of Ballaugh, in a rural area. Close to the wildlife park. Good pub atmosphere.
🏚 Q ⬰ Ⓓ ⛺ P

Castletown

Castle Arms (Glue Pot)
The Quay
☎ (0624) 824673
12–10.45
Okells Mild, Bitter Ⓗ
Small and comfortable pub right by the castle walls and close to the harbour. A *Beer Guide* regular, and deservedly so.
Q Ⓓ ▶ ⇌

Ducks Nest
Station Road
☎ (0624) 823282
12–10.45
Bushy's Best Bitter, Old Bushy Tail Ⓗ
Friendly pub right outside the steam railway station, recently purchased by Bushy's.
Q ⬰ ⇌ ♣ P

Union Hotel
In town centre
☎ (0624) 823214
11.30–10.45
Okells Mild, Castletown Bitter, Okells 45 Ⓗ
Substantial and comfortable, town-centre pub, the HQ of the

Castletown Ale Drinkers – a well-known local charitable organisation (New Year's Day sea-bathing a speciality).

Try also: George Hotel (Okells)

Crosby

Waggon & Horses (Halfway House)
Outside village, on Peel road
☎ (0624) 851291
11–10.45
Okells Mild, Bitter Ⓗ
Large, one-bar pub with a separate pool room. Good value lunchtime bar meal menu. Ⓓ P

Try also: Crosby Hotel (Okells)

Douglas

Bushy's Pub
Victoria Street (50 yds from sea terminal)
☎ (0624) 675139
12–10.30 (11 winter)
Bushy's Best Bitter, Old Bushy Tail, Piston Brew Ⓗ

Isle of Man

Well known, bikers' pub with two bar areas; a popular lunchtime drinking place. The regular evening entertainment is very popular. Site of Bushy's first brewing plant. Families welcome in the lounge. 🍴 ◖ ⊞

Foresters Arms
Hope Street
☎ (0624) 676509
11.30–10.45
Okells Mild, Castletown Bitter, Okells 45 Ⓗ
Good, basic pub and popular social venue for local residents and postmen from the sorting office, as well as the more adventurous yuppy from the nearby financial centre. 🍴 ⊞ ⇌

Manor Hotel
Willaston (near centre of Willaston Corporation Estate)
11.30–10.45
Okells Mild, Castletown Bitter Ⓗ
As the name suggests, a former manor house, with a large, panelled lounge bar, and a more utilitarian but nonetheless comfortable, public bar. Popular with the students and staff of the nearby FE college. 🍴 ◖ ⊞ P

Old Market Inn
Chapel Row
☎ (0624) 675202
11.30–10.45
Okells Mild, Bitter Ⓗ
A survivor of the many harbourside pubs in this area and the favourite of a substantial local clientele. Close to the bus station. Don't forget the low doorway to the gents. 🍴 ⊞ ⇌

Queen's Hotel
Queen's Promenade
☎ (0624) 675543
11.30–10.45
Okells Mild, Bitter, 45 Ⓗ
One of the few genuine Manx pubs to offer accommodation, the Queen's also affords excellent views of Douglas. The unique horse-tram service passes the front door. 🍴 ⊨ ◖ ⇌ (MER)

Rovers Return (Albion)
11 Church Street
☎ (0624) 676459
12–10.45
Bushy's Best Bitter, Old Bushy Tail Ⓗ
Small, back-street local, taken over and renamed by the developing Bushy's concern. Not easy to find, situated close to the police enquiry office and the Salvation Army citadel. Parking difficult. 🍴 ◖ ⇌

Saddle Inn
North Quay (halfway to steam railway station)
☎ (0624) 673161
11.30–10.45
Okells Mild, Bitter Ⓗ

Characterful, ethnic pub beloved of customers who do not care for the upmarket developments of the late 20th century. Local workers and residents of nearby corporation flats provide a lively evening atmosphere. Separate pool room. 🍴 ♣ ♠

Terminus Tavern
Strathallan Crescent (close to MER terminus)
☎ (0624) 624312
12 (earlier in summer)–10.45
Okells Mild, Bitter, 45 Ⓗ
A convenient place to pause whilst changing from horse-tram to electric car. Don't forget that the tram ride to Ramsey lasts 75 minutes, and the electric cars have no toilet facilities! ◖ ⇌ (MER)

Waterloo Hotel
Strand Street ☎ (0624) 676833
11.30–10.45
Okells Mild, Bitter Ⓗ
Modest, two-roomed pub in a busy and noisy, pedestrianised shopping street. Thick walls and a stout door insulate one from the hustle and bustle. ⊞

Wheatsheaf Hotel
Lord Street/Ridgeway Street
☎ (0624) 673144
11.30–10.45
Okells Mild, Bitter Ⓗ
Large, town pub with lively evening atmosphere. ⊞ ⇌

Woodbourne Hotel
Alexander Drive
☎ (0624) 676754
11.30–10.45
Okells Mild, Bitter, 45 Ⓗ
Substantial, brick-built edifice in up-town Douglas. Its major claim to fame (or notoriety) is the gents'-only bar (but ladies welcome elsewhere). ◖ ⊞

Try also: Albert Hotel, Chapel Row (Okells); **Old Curiosity Shop** (Derby Hotel), Castle St (Okells); **Ridgeway Hotel**, Ridgeway St (Okells)

Kirk Michael

Mitre Hotel
Main Road (500 yds from Glen Wyllin) ☎ (0624) 878244
12–10.30 (12–1.30, 8–10 Mon; 12–11 summer)
Okells Mild, Castletown Bitter Ⓗ
Village pub on the TT course, used mainly by locals but very popular with tourists during races (the Glen Wyllin campsite is within walking distance). 🍴 ◖ ♠ ♣ P

Laxey

Mines Tavern
Captains Hill (20 yds from railway; ½ mile from Laxey Wheel)

☎ (0624) 861484
12–2.30, 7–10.45 (12–10.45 Fri, Sat & summer)
Okells Mild, Bitter Ⓗ
A popular pub for visitors and locals, its bar resembling a tram (the tram station being nearby). Close to the Heritage Trail. Beer garden. ⊛ ◖ ▮ ⊞ ♠ P

New Inn
New Road (500 yds from railway station)
☎ (0624) 861077
12–10.45
Okells Bitter Ⓗ
Friendly, village pub with a welcoming landlord. Reasonably priced bitter. Well worth a visit. ⊛ ◖ ▮ ⇌ ♣ P

Maughold

Glen Mona Hotel
Glen Mona (main Laxey–Ramsey road)
☎ (0624) 861263
12–10.45 (12–2.30, 5–10.30 winter)
Okells Mild, Bitter Ⓗ
Pub with an ideal location: in a rural hamlet with scenic views. Good accommodation. On the bus route. 🍴 Q ⊛ ⊨ ◖ ▶ ⊞ ▮ P

Onchan

Archibald Knox
Avondale Road
☎ (0624) 620457
11.30–10.45
Okells Mild, Bitter, 45 Ⓗ
Pleasant, modern pub named after a well-known Manx artist, whose paintings are featured. A well-supported local, also popular with out-of-town drinkers. Opens 10am for tea/coffee and cakes, which are served all day. Well known for food. Q ⊛ ◖ ⊞ P

Try also: Liverpool Arms (Castletown)

Peel

Peel Castle
Market Place
☎ (0624) 842306
11–10.45
Okells Mild, Bitter Ⓗ
Pub which represents the current style of modernisation, with significant use of dark, polished wood, thick carpets and well-upholstered seating. ◖

Royal Hotel
Atholl Street (opp. bus garage)
11.30–10.45
Castletown Bitter Ⓗ
Large and often noisy public bar and a quieter, small front room. Note the unusual, venerable brewery advertising mirror. ⊞

Try also: Creek Inn (Okells); **Waterfall Hotel**, Glen Maye (Castletown)

Port Erin

Station Hotel
Station Road ☎ (0624) 832236
11–11
Okells Bitter, 45 Ⓗ
Large hotel in the middle of town: a lively public bar and a more sedate lounge. Very friendly atmosphere. One of the few pubs in the south of the island to offer accommodation. Separate restaurant.
⋈ ◖ ▮ ◖ ⇌ ♣ P

Try also: **Falcon's Nest** (Free)

Port St Mary

Albert Hotel
Athol Street (next to harbour)
☎ (0624) 832118
12–10.45
Okells Bitter Ⓗ
Excellent, traditional pub in a picturesque village. Friendly public bar, cosy lounge and separate pool room. ▮ Q ◖ P

Station Hotel
½ mile from centre, next to level crossing ☎ (0624) 832249
12–10.45
Okells Mild, Castletown Bitter Ⓗ

Large, imposing pub, handy for travellers on the steam railway, which runs just outside.
▮ Q ◖ ▮ ◖ ⇌ ♣ P

Ramsey

Central Hotel
Bowring Road (on TT course, opp. Parliament Square)
☎ (0624) 813177
11.30–10.45
Castletown Bitter Ⓗ
Popular, town-centre pub, well supported by TT enthusiasts. Large public car park nearby.
◖ ⇌

Royal George Hotel
Market Place
☎ (0624) 812146
11.30–10.45
Castletown Bitter, Okells 45 Ⓗ
The current café-bar style of the large lounge may suit some, particularly those seeking a lunchtime or evening meal from the substantial menu. Drinkers can adjourn to the public bar.
◖ ▮ ◖

Stanley Hotel
West Quay
☎ (0624) 812258

11.30–10.45
Castletown Bitter Ⓗ
Small and comfortable, quayside local. ▮ ◖

St John's

Tynwald Hill Inn
Opp. Tynwald Hill
☎ (0624) 801249
12–10.45
Okells Mild, Bitter Ⓗ
Conveniently situated close to the historic seat of Manx government, the Tynwald welcomes many holiday-makers, as well as a substantial number of locals. Good value bar meal menu. Large car park. ▮ ◖ ▮ P

Try also: **Central Hotel** (Castletown)

Union Mills

Railway Inn
Village centre
8–10.30 (closed Sat)
Castletown Bitter Ⓖ
Make a point of visiting this small, unspoilt, unmodernised, friendly, village local during its very limited opening hours (lunch opening only on Sun).
Q P

SERVING REAL ALE

Real ale should be served at a temperature of around 13 °C, 55 °F, cool enough for the beer to be refreshing but not so cold that it kills the flavour. Having its own natural carbonation, real ale needs no other fizz to give it life. It would be a pity, then, to use gas in order to simply force the beer to the point of sale. Unfortunately, some pubs do just this, taking perfectly good cask-conditioned beer and attaching a canister of CO_2 to push the beer from the cask to the bar. This method, known as top pressure, is taboo in CAMRA circles.

The most familiar means of dispensing real ale is through the beer engine, otherwise known as the handpump. By flexing biceps, the bar staff can draw a pint in a couple of pulls. Beware, though, of fake handpumps. These beer engine lookalikes serve no other purpose than to con the public into thinking that the keg product being served is in fact real. They are used for cider, too.

In the Midlands and the North, it's not unusual to find cask beer served by an electric pump. No extra gas is imparted: the pump simply saves the bar staff's muscles, but it's sometimes difficult to differentiate between the bar cowls of electrically-drawn cask beer and those of gas-driven keg. Ask the licensee or look for 'cask-conditioned' on the tap. In Scotland, although a system of using water pressure has mostly disappeared, the traditional Scottish air pump (using air not CO_2) remains popular.

Of course, the simplest way to serve beer anywhere is by gravity, by opening the tap on the cask and letting it pour out.

THE BREWERIES

Introduction by Iain Loe

Whilst much attention in the last few decades has been centred on the growth in lager sales in this country, British breweries have, nevertheless, shown a dogged determination to stick to an ale form of brewing. Although 50% of total beer sales (draught, canned, bottled, etc.) in Britain is now accounted for by lager, cask ale sales are rising. Interest in cask-conditioned beers is on the increase and there truly can be said to be a real ale revival going on. Breweries from the very largest, such as Allied and Bass, down to the smallest micro or home-brew pub are claiming that sales of cask beer are on the up.

The British brewing industry, despite receiving many kicks in recent years, is responding well to treatment. In the last year we have had the news of Greenall Whitley finally deciding to quit brewing and have its beer brewed by others. We've witnessed the pubs-for-breweries swap between Grand Metropolitan and Courage given the go-ahead, as well as seeing Bass close two breweries, the future of Cornish and Camerons put on the line and Hartleys assigned to brewing history by Robinson's. S&N similarly drew beer drinkers' contempt by its closure of Matthew Brown, despite promises to the contrary when the Blackburn brewery was taken over. But we have also seen many new breweries appear.

Another plus has been the *volte-face* in advertising philosophy. It is now no longer unusual to see a cask-conditioned beer promoted by one of the national breweries, and advertising spends of the order of £7 million are being made by the likes of Tetley and John Smith's. Furthermore, with the exception of Foster's (née Elders), the Australian owner of Courage, and Faxe of Denmark's investment in Cains, we have yet to see any major foreign brewer purchase a British ale brewery, though it seems only a matter of time before this happens.

NEW New to this year's *Guide* are several recent additions to the brewing ranks, not to mention two breweries closed by their previous owners but now re-opened by more enterprising people.

Tolly Cobbold's brewery in Ipswich was closed by owners Brent Walker in 1989, with production transferred hundreds of miles northward to the Camerons plant. However, a year later, a management buy-out succeeded in breathing new life into the brewery and it now supplies the Tolly pubs in East Anglia, as well as the free trade. And from the old Higsons brewery in Liverpool, unforgivably closed by Whitbread, real ale is once again flowing, thanks to Cains and its enterprising MD, Steve Holt.

Sadly, Barry Haslam of Miners Arms in Somerset has decided to give up production, although continuing to wholesale beers and run his two pubs. The brewery's beer brands are now being brewed by neighbour Mole's of Melksham. In Wales, the number of active breweries has this year been cut by nearly a third, with both Pembrokeshire's Own Ales and Sam Powell calling time.

STILL GOING STRONG Despite the concentration in the industry which has occurred over the years, it is comforting to acknowledge that there are still quite a few staunchly independent breweries who can claim to have been brewing for more than 100, 200 or even almost 300 years. Adnams in Southwold broke its century of brewing back in 1990, the same year as Harveys celebrated 200 years, and Shepherd Neame in the heart of the Kent countryside will notch up 300 years in 1998. Whether Shepherd Neame is the oldest working brewery in Britain is open to question, with London independent Young's claiming that brewing has been taking place on its Wandsworth site since the middle of the 17th century.

Hopefully, all these breweries will still be brewing when we come to compile the 1993 *Good Beer Guide*. Many have been increasing the size of their estates by buying pubs released by national brewers.

BREWING AT HOME Home-brew pubs, of which there were only a handful when CAMRA was founded back in 1971, continue to blossom. Although many, often because of lack of space, do not use a full mash but rely on malt extract, the quality of their ales is generally high.

Amongst the newcomers, Cumbria's Masons Arms, at Cartmel Fell, has long been known for its selection of bottled beers, including several from Belgium. Now, as well as more conventional ales, it brews a Damson Kriek-style beer. Meanwhile, David Bruce, creator of the Firkin chain, has bounced back with his new Hedgehog & Hogshead brew pubs.

Several brew pubs are now listed in the Independents section, as the majority of their production is now sold to the free trade. A notable example is the Hop Back Brewery, based at the Wyndham Arms in Salisbury, whose beers have already won CAMRA awards. The company has now acquired a second brew pub in Southampton, where it hopes to try out speciality beers. Worcester's Jolly Roger has also developed into a full-scale commercial operation and Isle of Man drinkers now enjoy more choice on the island, following the opening of Bushy's new brewery.

BIG BOYS The biggest of the country's brewers continue to close down breweries and transfer production of beers to other sites. Charrington IPA, the old London brew, has been forced to move home yet again, and now finds itself shifted to Bass's Cape Hill brewery, following the closure of the Springfield site. Whitbread continues to switch the production of its beers, too, and few of the beers now produced by the company have any connection with their original place of brewing. It is perhaps time for the introduction of a kind of *Appellation Controlée* for beer, to curb some of the more ridiculous attempts to replicate beers. Readers may be able to suggest a less vinous-sounding term which could be used to denote a beer that is still brewed in its birthplace.

As far as Allied is concerned, if you want to drink Tetley Bitter from Leeds, don't go to the North West, as the cask-conditioned Tetley's there will have come from the Tetley Walker plant in Warrington. The beers taste subtly different, but surely it would be better if they were clearly distinguished. Some people may prefer the Warrington taste to that from Leeds.

THE FUTURE

Real ale is still very alive and there does seem to be an increasing choice in the pubs that have not been closed or turned into holiday cottages or offices. But don't just be content to go for the most 'popular' brands, try, with the help of this guide, to seek out more unusual brews. Remember, your local national brewery tenant needs support if he is enterprising enough to stock a true guest beer to contrast with his well-known national brands.

Remember, also, that real ale doesn't have to come in casks; there is an increasing number of real ales in bottles. Bottle-conditioned beers such as Worthington White Shield and Guinness have long been available in pubs, but now several other breweries are also producing unpasteurised bottled beer.

Guinness has been synonymous with stout for many years, but Beamish and Murphy's now also vie for space on the bar counter. Sadly, none of these draught stouts is cask-conditioned, but, with the acknowledged demand for cask-conditioned beer, we may well see a wider availability of real stout in next year's *Guide*. Several micros already produce some.

USING THE BREWERIES SECTION

The following pages are your guide to all the breweries in the UK and the cask-conditioned beers they produce. It is divided into three parts: Independents, Nationals and Brew Pubs, and an index at the end enables you to locate specific brews.

Beers are listed in increasing gravity order and original gravities (OG) and alcohol by volume (ABV) figures are provided where obtainable. As gravities can vary across a range of figures from brew to brew, we give the average figure. For a beer with a range of 1040–1044, for instance, we quote an OG of 1042.

Tasting notes have been supplied by trained CAMRA tasting panels, who have tasted the beers in the area of the brewery, and further afield in the case of national beers. With many new beers appearing this year, we have been unable to methodically taste them all, and beers which have not been sampled are marked with an asterisk.

Iain Loe is CAMRA's Research Manager.

THE INDEPENDENTS

ADNAMS

ADNAMS

Adnams and Company PLC, Sole Bay Brewery, Southwold, Suffolk, IP18 6JW. Tel. (0502) 722424

East Anglia's famous seaside brewery which celebrated its centenary in 1990. Real ale is available in all its 69 pubs, as well as over 2,000 free trade outlets. Having expanded considerably into southern England, the brewery is now widening its horizons. About 84% of its beer goes into the free trade, half of which is sold outside the local trading area of Norfolk and Suffolk, using depots in Norwich, Maidstone and Heathrow, from where the Brewers Dray company distributes Wadworth, Everards and a small portfolio of other brands, as well as Adnams' own products. Looking for success in the export market and hoping to benefit from national brewery sell-offs by buying or leasing surplus pubs.

Mild

(OG 1034, ABV 3.2%) A fine dark mild, wholeheartedly malty with a suggestion of hops and fruit. A bitter finish with malt and a hint of hops.

Bitter

(OG 1036, ABV 3.6%) An excellent drinking beer; its hoppy aroma also has traces of malt and fruit. Hops and bitterness are prominent in the flavour, with a background of malt and fruit again. Dry, hoppy finish.

Old

(OG 1042, ABV 4.1%) A warm red/brown winter brew. The nose is a fine blend of malt, hops and fruit. The main body has a smooth maltiness with fruit, hops and roast undertones. Bittersweet and malty finish.

Extra

(OG 1043, ABV 4.3%) An amber beer, worth searching for. Its delicious fruity and bittersweet flavour is complemented by a hoppy aroma and a dry, slightly fruity finish. Due to be relaunched under a new name.

Broadside

(OG 1049, ABV 4.4%) A characterful beer with malt, hops and fruit in the aroma. The flavour is a well-balanced combination of malt, hops and fruit with a bittersweet tang. Dry finish with a trace of fruit.

Tally Ho*

(OG 1075, ABV 6.2%) A Christmas barley wine and a definite winter warmer. Fruit and malt abound in both the aroma and flavour, culminating in a delicious bittersweet aftertaste.

ALLIED BREWERIES

See page 455.

ALLOA

See Allied Breweries, page 455.

ANN STREET

Ann Street Brewery, Ann Street, St Helier, Jersey, CI. Tel. (0534) 31561

Brews no real ale but sells Guernsey Brewery beers in its pubs.

ANSELLS

See Allied Breweries, page 456.

ARCHERS

Archers Ales Ltd., Station Ind. Estate, London Street, Swindon, Wilts, SN1 5DG. Tel. (0793) 496789

A small brewery, set up in 1979, which has grown very successfully to supply roughly 120 free trade outlets from Oxford to Bath, plus four tied houses. Golden Bitter was relaunched in the winter of 1990, with a reduced gravity, and has been well received. ASB, meanwhile, is no longer brewed.

393

The Independents

Village Bitter	(OG 1035, ABV 3.5%) Dry and well-balanced, with a full body for its gravity. Malty and fruity on the nose, then a fresh, hoppy flavour with balancing malt, and a hoppy, fruity finish.
Best Bitter	(OG 1040, ABV 4%) Slightly sweeter and rounder than Village Bitter, with a malty, fruity aroma and a pronounced bitter finish.
Porter	(OG 1046, ABV 4.6%) A black beer with intense roast malt dominant on the tongue. The aroma is fruity and there is some sweetness on the palate, but the finish is pure roast grain.
Golden Bitter	(OG 1046, ABV 4.7%) A full-bodied, hoppy, straw-coloured brew with an underlying fruity sweetness. Very little aroma, but a strong bitter finish.
Headbanger*	(OG 1065, ABV 6.5%) Almost a barley wine in style, enjoying a full flavour. Sweet and powerful, with a pleasant, dry finish.

ARKELL'S	**Arkell's Brewery Ltd., Kingsdown, Swindon, Wilts, SN2 6RU. Tel. (0793) 823026**
ARKELL'S EST. BREWERY 1843	Family brewery, established in 1843 by a farmer whose great, great grandson, James Arkell, is the present MD. Real ale in 63 of its 68 tied houses, with one or two new properties acquired each year. Serves around 250 free trade outlets in the Thames Valley and London, including British Rail station buffets. In tied houses keg 3B is known as North Star Keg to avoid confusion with the real thing.
2B	(OG 1032, ABV 3.2%) Well-balanced, if slightly thin, malty/hoppy brew. The hop flavour is strong, but not overpowering, and remains during the aftertaste. A refreshing lunchtime pint.
3B	(OG 1040, ABV 4%) A pale brown brew with little aroma, but a balanced hoppy, grainy and sweetish palate, with traces of roast malt. The finish is hoppy with a fruity bitterness.
Mash Tun Mild	(OG 1040, ABV 4.2%) Brewed only in winter. An interesting, dark, strong mild bearing similarities to porter. Strong roast malt and hops are well balanced in the aroma and taste. The finish is hoppy, bitter and slightly fruity.
Kingsdown Ale	(OG 1052, ABV 5.2%) A strong and tasty, tawny/red beer with a fruity aroma, a malty, hoppy palate and a lingering, fruity bitterness.
Noel Ale*	(OG 1055, ABV 5.5%) The Christmas offering.

ASH VINE	**Ash Vine Brewery, The White Hart, Trudoxhill, Frome, Somerset, BA11 5DP. Tel. (0373) 84324**
ASH VINE BITTER	Set up in 1987, the brewery moved to the White Hart in January 1989 and bought a second tied house at the same time. Its growing free trade has been supplemented by a considerable wholesale distribution and Ash Vine beers can now be supped from Glasgow to Penzance. A new bitter, Challenger, was launched last year to fill the gap in strength between Bitter and Tanker.
Bitter	(OG 1039, ABV 3.8%) A light gold brew with a strong floral hop aroma with malt and fruit undertones. A powerful, bitter hoppiness dominates the taste and leads to a dry, hoppy finish which lasts. An excellent, unusual and distinctive brew.
Challenger*	(OG 1042, ABV 4.1%)
Tanker	(OG 1047, ABV 4.7%) A tawny-coloured beer with a well

The Independents

developed balance of malt, bitter hops, fruit and subtle sweetness. A hoppy aroma and a bitter, dry finish.

ASTON MANOR	**Aston Manor Brewery Company Ltd., 173 Thimblemill Lane, Aston, Birmingham, B7 5HS. Tel. (021) 328 4336**

Founded by ex-Ansells employees in 1983, Aston Manor moved very rapidly into the take-home trade, and discontinued brewing cask ale in 1986. Although this continues to be its major source of income, it did in fact resume brewing real ale in 1990 under contract to Chandler's Brewery Company Ltd. (one pub).

Dolly's Dark Mild — (OG 1031, ABV 3%) A roast and hop-flavoured mild with a hint of bitterness and sweetness. Dry, bitter finish.

JCB Bitter — (OG 1036, ABV 3.6%) Mid brown, hoppy and bitter beer with a sweet and bitter aftertaste.

Old Deadly's — (OG 1090, ABV 9%) A winter brew. A very strong, full-bodied beer, hoppy and fruity on the palate and in the aroma. The finish is warming, malty and bitter, with a hint of sweetness.

AYLESBURY (ABC) — See Allied Breweries, page 456.

BALLARD'S — **Ballard's Brewery Ltd., Unit C, The Old Sawmill, Nyewood, Rogate, Petersfield, Hants, GU31 5HA. Tel. (0730) 821362/821301**

Founded in 1980 at Cumbers Farm, Trotton, the brewery moved in 1985 to the Ballards pub (now the Elsted Inn) and has since relocated to Nyewood (West Sussex, despite the confusing postal address). Supplies 55 free trade outlets and has established a tradition of brewing Christmas ales with different names and appropriate gravities each year: Old Bounder (OG 1088) for 1988; Out to Lunch (OG 1089) for 1989, and Volcano (OG 1090) for 1990, etc.

Trotton Bitter — (OG 1036, ABV 3.5%) A well-flavoured session bitter, amber/tawny in colour. The good balance of malt and hops runs through from the aroma to the finish, with a slight fruitiness also present.

Best Bitter — (OG 1042, ABV 4.1%) Copper red, with a malty aroma. Indeed, a notably malty beer altogether, but well-hopped and with a satisfying finish.

Wassail — (OG 1060, ABV 5.8%) A strong, full-bodied, fruity beer with a predominance of malt throughout, but also an underlying hoppiness. Tawny/red in colour.

BANKS'S — **The Wolverhampton & Dudley Breweries PLC, Park Brewery, Lovatt Street, Wolverhampton, W. Midlands, WV1 4NY. Tel. (0902) 711811**

Wolverhampton & Dudley Breweries was formed in 1890 by the amalgamation of three local breweries. Hanson's (see entry) was acquired in 1943 and today the company is the largest surviving independent 'family brewers' in the country. Traditional ales are served in its entire tied estate of over 850 pubs, virtually all through electric, metered dispense. Extensive club trade in cask beer and over 2,000 free trade accounts.

Mild — (OG 1036, ABV 3.5%) The malty and hoppy aroma of this mid-brown beer leads on to a balanced, bittersweet taste of malt, roast and caramel. Malt and hops continue in the aftertaste.

The Independents

Bitter	(OG 1038, ABV 3.8%) Pale brown beer with a malty and hoppy aroma and a dry, bitter and malty taste.
	For Hanson's:
Hanson's Bitter	(OG 1035, ABV 3.4%) An aroma of malt and hops precedes a rather disappointing flavour. More hops evident in the finish.

BANKS & TAYLOR

Banks & Taylor Brewery Ltd., The Brewery, Shefford, Beds, SG17 5DZ. Tel. (0462) 815080

Founded in 1981 and now serving some 80 outlets in an expanding free trade in the Home Counties and East Anglia. Looking to add to its tied estate of 10 tied houses, and increase sales to national brewers' outlets. SOD is often sold under house names. The mild, the stout, 2XS and Black Bat are all new additions to the range.

Shefford Mild*	(OG 1035, ABV 3.5%) The new dark mild.
Shefford Bitter	(OG 1038, ABV 3.8%) A very drinkable, hoppy beer, with some malt and fruit flavours. Hoppy aroma and a bitter, hoppy aftertaste.
SPA	(OG 1041, ABV 4%) A well-balanced beer, sold as Eastcote Ale in one pub. Hops and malt are present throughout and there are hints of fruit in the aroma and taste. Dry, bitter aftertaste.
Edwin Taylor's Extra Stout*	(OG 1045, ABV 4.5%) A new bitter stout.
Shefford Old Strong (SOS)	(OG 1050, ABV 5%) A deceptively drinkable sweetish beer. A hoppy, malty aroma with hints of fruit leads to a well balanced taste of hops and malt. Sweetish, malty finish with discernible fruit.
Shefford Old Dark (SOD)	(OG 1050, ABV 5%) Dark, reddish-brown ale with similar characteristics to SOS, but with added caramel flavouring and often a greater fruity flavour.
2XS*	(OG 1058, ABV 5.8%)
Black Bat	(OG 1064, ABV 6.4%) A powerful sweet, fruity, malty beer. Fruit and malt dominate the aroma and aftertaste.

BARRON See Exe Valley, page 410.

BASS See page 458.

BATEMAN

George Bateman & Son Ltd., Salem Bridge Brewery, Mill Lane, Wainfleet, Skegness, Lincs, PE24 4JE. Tel. (0754) 880317

A family owned and run brewery whose XXXB was voted CAMRA's Champion Special Bitter four years running in the eighties. All but one of the 75 tied houses sell its 'Good Honest Ales' in traditional form. Serves 750 free trade outlets throughout much of England and Wales and has acquired pubs outside Lincolnshire, in Nottingham, Hull and Derby.

Dark Mild	(OG 1033, ABV 3%) A smooth, creamy palate with some roast and bitter flavours masking a degree of sweetness. The finish is hoppy and bitter. Happily, the beer is enjoying an increase in popularity.
XB	(OG 1036, ABV 3.8%) A refreshing, amber-coloured beer with a predominantly hoppy aroma and a dry and refreshing, bitter taste with a lingering, hoppy finish. Always available and popular in the tied estate, but overshadowed by its bigger brothers in the free trade.

The Independents

XXXB

(OG 1048, ABV 5%) Pale brown in colour with a malty aroma. A satisfying, smooth taste with hops and bitterness balanced by a malty presence. A worthy past winner of the Champion Beer of Britain award.

Victory Ale

(OG 1056, ABV 6%) For a beer of this strength, its taste is surprisingly light, lulling the unwary into a false sense of security. Malt, hops and bitterness combine to produce a full-bodied and well-balanced beer.

Winter Warmer

(OG 1058, ABV 6.2%) Made its first appearance at Christmas 1990 and has now become a regular winter feature. Strongly fruity throughout, with a malty balance, some roast and caramel, and a bitter finish.

BATHAM

Bathams (Delph) Ltd., Delph Brewery, Delph Road, Brierley Hill, W. Midlands, DY5 2TN. Tel. (0384) 77229

Hidden behind one of the Black Country's most famous pubs, the 'Bull & Bladder', this small family firm has managed to survive since 1877, brewing excellent beer for its eight pubs and the free trade, which now accounts for over 40% of its output. Looking to increase its tied estate in the future.

Mild Ale

(OG 1036.5, ABV 3.6%) Dark brown beer with an aroma of caramel. Caramel continues in the taste, but with balancing hop character. Sweet, hoppy finish.

Best Bitter

(OG 1043.5, ABV 4.3%) Sweet-tasting, but with bitterness and a long, dry finish. A straw-coloured beer with a flowery aroma.

XXX*

(OG 1063.5, ABV 6.5%) A Christmas ale which has replaced Delph Strong Ale.

BEER ENGINE

The Beer Engine, Newton St Cyres, Exeter, Devon, EX5 5AX. Tel. (0392) 851282

Successful brew pub now serving an expanding free trade. Stands next to the Barnstaple branch railway line. Owns one other pub, the Sleeper in Seaton. Occasionally produces a bottle-conditioned beer.

Rail Ale

(OG 1037, ABV 3.8%) Straw-coloured beer with a malty aroma and a hoppy/bitter flavour. Some bitterness in the aftertaste.

Piston Bitter

(OG 1044, ABV 4.3%) Mid brown in colour; a strong, malty, slightly fruity and bitter beer with a sweet aftertaste.

Sleeper Heavy

(OG 1055, ABV 5.5%) A pleasant, fruity, yet sweet-tasting beer which leaves its sweetness on the palate. Mid to dark brown in colour, with a strong, fruity aroma.

BELHAVEN

Belhaven Brewery Co. Ltd., Dunbar, Lothian, EH42 1RS. Tel. (0368) 62734

Scotland's oldest and most renowned independent brewery, which has had a turbulent history. It is now in the ownership of the London-based property and leisure group, Control Securities PLC, which continues to plan a major expansion of its pub estate throughout the UK. Roughly half of its 57 tied houses take real ale, which has won CAMRA local awards.

60/- Ale*

(OG 1032, ABV 2.9%) Dark and malty.

70/- Ale*

(OG 1035, ABV 3.6%) Light and hoppy.

80/- Ale*

(OG 1041, ABV 4.1%) Heavy, full-bodied ale.

90/- Ale*

(OG 1070, ABV 7.2%) An occasional, rich brew.

The Independents

BENSKINS See Allied Breweries, page 456.

BERROW **Berrow Brewery, Heron House, Coast Road, Berrow, Burnham-on-Sea, Somerset TA8 2QU.**
Tel. (0278) 751345

Founded in June 1982 and now supplying pubs and clubs locally, amounting to about 10 free trade outlets. Due to increasing demand, Topsy Turvy is now a more regular brew.

BBBB or 4Bs (OG 1038, ABV 3.8%) A pleasant, pale brown session beer, with a fruity aroma, a malty, fruity flavour and bitterness in the palate and finish.

Topsy Turvy (OG 1055, ABV 5.8%) An excellent, straw-coloured beer. Its aroma is of malt and hops, which are also evident in the taste, together with sweetness. The aftertaste is malty. Very easy to drink. Beware!

BIG END **Big End Brewery, 62a Otley Road, Harrogate, N. Yorks, HG2 0DP. Tel. (0423) 503299**

Established in August 1988 by CAMRA stalwart Bill Witty, with brewer Bernard Linley, and served up its first brew to the Great British Beer Festival at Leeds. Supplies two tied houses and around 40 free trade outlets in Yorkshire, Lancashire and Cleveland. Beware: Oliver John's Bitter is no longer brewed by Big End; the beer now sold under this name (at the former brew pub, the Golden Lion, Leyburn) is a new keg beer sold through a handpump.

Piston Bitter or Yorkshire Rose Bitter (OG 1038) A powerful hoppiness dominates the aroma and taste, balanced by some malt and a hint of fruitiness. Malt and hops persist into a bittersweet finish.

Old Lubrication (OG 1042) Dark brown beer, with roast malt in the nose. The taste is sweetish, with malt, fruit and hops, and a fruity aftertaste tinged with hops.

Monkey Wrench* (OG 1056)

BIG LAMP **Big Lamp Brewery Co. Ltd., 1 Summerhill Street, Newcastle upon Tyne, Tyne & Wear, NE4 6EJ.**
Tel. (091) 261 4227

Set up in 1982, now the longest-established independent real ale brewery in the North East. New ownership took over at the end of 1990. Supplies one tied house and an ever-changing free trade (about 15 outlets). Brewed Heroes Bitter for the Legendary Yorkshire Heroes chain for a while.

Bitter (OG 1038, ABV 3.8%) Now a lower gravity for this hoppy beer with fruitiness evident to some extent throughout. Pleasant, dryish finish.

Prince Bishop Ale (OG 1044, ABV 4.5%) Another gravity reduction, but still almost lager-coloured with a nicely balanced aroma and taste, and a hint of fruit. Pleasant finish.

Summerhill Stout* (OG 1044, ABV 4.5%)

Old Genie (OG 1070, ABV 8%) An occasional beer. A dark and strong, well-balanced ale, when well kept. Sweetness dominates the taste and aftertaste, although there are some roast and fruit elements in the aroma.

The Independents

Blackout   (OG 1100, ABV 10.5%) An occasional, rare beer. Extremely powerful and aptly-named. Usually brewed for CAMRA beer festivals.

BLACKAWTON   **Blackawton Brewery, Washbourne, Totnes, Devon, TQ9 7UF. Tel. (080 423) 339**

One of the earliest new small breweries, dating from 1977, and now the oldest brewery in Devon. Moved from the village of Blackawton to its present site in 1981 and changed ownership in 1988. Serves around 50 free trade outlets, having no pubs of its own. Prides itself on brewing from traditional ingredients with no additives.

Bitter   (OG 1037.5, ABV 3.8%) A bitter which is malty in its aroma and slightly fruity and malty in its taste.

Devon Gold*   (OG 1040.5, ABV 4.1%)

44 Special   (OG 1044.5, ABV 4.5%) Mid brown malty, slightly fruity-tasting beer with a hint of toffee. Malty aroma and aftertaste. Lacks hoppiness, but still enjoyable.

Headstrong*   (OG 1051.5, ABV 5.2%) Strong and full-bodied.

BODDINGTONS   See Whitbread, page 466.

BRAINS   **SA Brain & Co. Ltd., The Old Brewery, St Mary Street, Cardiff, S. Glamorgan, CF1 1SP. Tel. (0222) 399022**

A traditional brewery which has been in the Brain family since Samuel Brain bought the Old Brewery in 1882. Now the largest independent brewery in Wales, supplying cask-conditioned beer to all its 125 tied houses and a widespread free trade. The company has diversified in recent years with interests in hotel, tourism and leisure projects in Wales and the West Country. MA (OG 1035, ABV 3.5%) is only available at the Crown Hotel, Skewen.

Dark   (OG 1035, ABV 3.5%) A full-bodied dark brown mild with chocolate and fruit flavours and a rounded bittersweet finish.

Bitter   (OG 1035, ABV 3.7%) A distinctively bitter beer, pale, malty and very refreshing, with an intense, dry finish. Commonly known as 'Light'.

SA Best Bitter   (OG 1042, ABV 4.2%) A distinctively full-bodied malty beer; well-balanced, with a smooth and strong dry finish. This fine premium beer is affectionately known as 'Skull Attack'.

BRAKSPEAR   **WH Brakspear & Sons PLC, The Brewery, Henley-on-Thames, Oxfordshire, RG9 2BU. Tel. (0491) 573636**

Founded in 1779, this popular country brewery moved to its present site in 1896 when it became a limited company. It boasts many excellent, unspoilt pubs and all 117 tied houses serve traditional ales. Also supplies around 300 free trade outlets. Bitter is now widely available as a guest beer in the South.

XXX Mild   (OG 1030, ABV 2.8%) Thin beer with a red/brown colour and a sweet, malty, fruity aroma. The well-balanced taste of malt, hops and caramel has a faint bitterness, complemented by a sweet, fruity flavour, having hints of black cherries. The main characteristics extend through to the bittersweet finish.

Bitter   (OG 1035, ABV 3.4%) Amber in colour, with a good fruit, hop and malt nose. The initial taste of malt and the dry, well-hopped

The Independents

bitterness quickly dissolves into a predominantly bitter, sweet and fruity aftertaste that has a hint of pears.

Special (OG 1043, ABV 4%) Tawny/amber in colour, its good, well-balanced aroma has a hint of sweetness. The initial taste is moderately sweet and malty, but is quickly overpowered by the dry bitterness of the hops, bringing out a slightly sweet fruitiness with undertones of pears and apricots. A distinct, dry, malty finish.

Old Ale (OG 1043, ABV 4%) Red/brown with good body. The strong, fruity aroma is well complemented by malt, hops and roast caramel. Its pronounced taste of malt, with discernible sweet roast and caramel flavours, gives way to a fruitiness with hints of pears and apricots. The aftertaste is of bittersweet chocolate, even though chocolate malt is lacking.

BRITISH OAK **British Oak Brewery, Salop Street, Eve Hill, Dudley, W. Midlands, DY1 3AX. Tel. (0384) 236297**

Family run brew pub, set up in May 1988 and now supplying 20 free trade outlets, as well as a second pub of its own. Also produces traditional cider.

Castle Ruin* (OG 1038, ABV 3.9%) Available April-September; a light, straw-coloured session beer.

Eve'ill Bitter* (OG 1042, ABV 4.1%) Stronger, darker and more full-bodied than Castle Ruin.

Colonel Pickering's Porter* (OG 1046, ABV 4.4%) Not always available; sweet and creamy.

Dungeon Draught* (OG 1050, ABV 4.8%) A dark, distinctive, well-hopped, malty beer.

Old Jones* (OG 1060, ABV 5.5%) Available September-April; rich, dark and strong.

BROUGHTON **Broughton Brewery Ltd., Broughton, Peeblesshire, Borders, ML12 6HQ. Tel. (089 94) 345**

One of the most significant new breweries, set up in 1980 by former S&N executive David Younger. Broughton supplies its draught ales to some 200 free trade outlets in Scotland, as well as two tied houses in Dumfries. Bottled ales were introduced in 1982 and are now nationally distributed to supermarkets and major off-licence chains.

Greenmantle Ale (OG 1038, ABV 4%) Beer lacking aroma. Bittersweet in taste, with a hint of fruit, and a very dry finish.

Special Bitter (OG 1038, ABV 4%) A dry-hopped version of Greenmantle.

Greenmantle 80/- Ale (OG 1042, ABV 4.2%) Formerly known as Merlin's Ale; a distinctively-flavoured brew. Fruity and well-balanced, with a dry, hoppy finish.

Old Jock (OG 1069, ABV 6.7%) Strong, sweetish and fruity in the finish.

MATTHEW BROWN See Scottish & Newcastle, page 464.

BUCKLEY See Crown Buckley, page 407.

The Independents

BULLMASTIFF

Bullmastiff Brewery, 5 Anchor Way, Cogan, Penarth, S. Glamorgan, CF6 1SF. Tel. (0222) 702958

Small brewery set up in 1987 by a fanatical home-brewer. Supplies some 40 outlets locally, but not on a regular basis, so the beers are rather hard to find on the brewery's home patch. Much of the production is sold right across the country through wholesalers.

Bitter
(OG 1035) A pale brown beer with a distinctively bitter finish.

Ebony Dark
(OG 1042) As its name suggests, a very dark brown beer, offering a roast malt flavour and aroma. Very drinkable, with a rich, malty aftertaste.

Best Bitter
(OG 1043) A well-balanced, malty beer, light brown in colour, with a smooth, fruity finish.

Son of a Bitch
(OG 1062) Mid brown in colour, this is a full-bodied, notably hoppy, malty beer. A premium bitter with a bitter and distinctive aftertaste.

BUNCES

Bunces Brewery, The Old Mill, Netheravon, Salisbury, Wilts, SP4 9QB. Tel. (0980) 70631

Set up in 1984 on the Wiltshire Avon by Tony Bunce and his wife, this brewery continues to grow. Supplies cask-conditioned beers to around 40 free trade outlets within a radius of 50 miles. Visits to the listed brewery are welcomed with prior arrangement.

Vice Beer*
(OG 1033) A new wheat beer, introduced in summer 1991.

Benchmark
(OG 1035, ABV 3.4%) A pleasant, bitter ale of remarkable character, which maintains one's interest for a long time. The taste is malty, the aroma subtle and the very long finish is quite dry on the palate.

Best Bitter
(OG 1042, ABV 4.1%) A first-rate beer. The piquant aroma introduces a complex malty and bitter taste with a hint of fruit. Long, fresh, bitter aftertaste.

Old Smokey
(OG 1050, ABV 4.8%) A delightful, warming, dark winter ale, with a roasted malt taste and a hint of liquorice surrounding a developing bitter flavour. Very appealing to the eye.

BURTON BRIDGE

Burton Bridge Brewery, 24 Bridge Street, Burton upon Trent, Staffs, DE14 1SY. Tel. (0283) 510573

Established in 1982 by two former Ind Coope employees, Burton Bridge's one tied outlet stands at the front of the brewery. Last year, the adjoining premises were purchased to allow for brewery expansion and to give pub customers more elbow room. Supplies guest beers to around 300 outlets within a radius of 150 miles. Specialises in commemorative bottled beers. *Bottle-conditioned beer: Burton Porter (OG 1045, ABV 4.5%)* in pint bottles.

Summer Ale*
(OG 1038, ABV 3.8%) Summer beer.

XL Bitter
(OG 1040, ABV 4%) A golden/amber, malty drinking bitter, with a dry palate and finish. A faint hoppiness and fruitiness come through in the aroma and taste.

Bridge Bitter
(OG 1042, ABV 4.2%) Again, golden/amber in colour, robust and malty, with a hoppy and bitter palate and aftertaste. Malt and hops are both present throughout, but the dry, hoppy character dominates the finish. Some balancing fruitiness and sweetness.

The Independents

Burton Porter	(OG 1045, ABV 4.5%) A dark, ruby-red, sweetish porter. The malty, slightly fruity aroma is followed by a roast malt and fruit flavour, and a malty and fairly bitter finish.
Top Dog Stout*	(OG 1050, ABV 5%) A winter brew.
Burton Festival Ale	(OG 1055, ABV 5.5%) Strong, sweetish and full-bodied. The nose is malty and slightly hoppy, and the palate has similar characteristics, with a pronounced fruitiness. Copper-coloured; a little cloying and heavy.
Old Expensive*	(OG 1065, ABV 6.5%) Winter only; a dark, warming beer, also known as OX.

BURTONWOOD — **Burtonwood Brewery PLC, Burtonwood Village, Warrington, Cheshire, WA5 4PJ. Tel. (092 52) 25131**

A family-run public company, established in 1867, which has made significant changes in recent years. A new brewhouse was completed in 1990 and now supplies real ale to 205 of its 265 tied houses. Its free trade amounts to 400 outlets and Burtonwood is continuing to develop trading relationships with north-western pub groups.

Dark Mild	(OG 1032, ABV 3.1%) A smooth, dark brown, malty mild with a good roast flavour and some caramel and bitterness. Good dry finish. The balance of flavours changes with the age of the beer.
Best Bitter	(OG 1036, ABV 3.7%) A well-balanced, malty bitter, with good hoppiness. More fruity than last year. Bitter dry finish. Light, smooth and drinkable.
James Forshaw's Bitter	(OG 1038, ABV 4%) Slightly darker, more bitter and fruity than Best, this is Burtonwood's third attempt at a premium ale - but again it is premium in price rather than in gravity. Not really different enough from the bitter. Appears to be targeted at the guest ale market.

BURTS — **Burts Brewery Ltd., 119 High Street, Ventnor, Isle of Wight, P038 1LY. Tel. (0983) 852153**

Brewery founded in 1840 which seems to have hit troubled times of late. Has been selling off all its 11 pubs to generate capital and expand production, but the future of the brewery is uncertain, even though a working museum is being established. The Phillips family reluctantly relinquished control in July 1991.

LB Bitter*	(OG 1030, ABV 3.2%) A light bitter; Mild without the added caramel. A very rare find.
BMA Mild	(OG 1030, ABV 3.2%) A very dark, almost black beer, with a faint aroma of malt. Fairly thin, with a sweet, malt flavour and caramel detectable. Little hop character, but some malt and bitterness in the finish.
VPA	(OG 1040, ABV 3.9%) A malty drink with a hint of toffee, which also comes through in the aroma. The slightly grainy malt flavour leads to a dry, bitter finish. Lacks a distinct hoppiness. Red/brown in colour.
4X*	(OG 1040, ABV 3.9%) VPA with caramel. A winter brew.

BUSHY'S — **Bushy's Brewery, Mount Murray Brewing Co. Ltd., Mount Murray, Braddan, Isle of Man. Tel. (0624) 661244**

Former brew pub which has moved out of Douglas to a new central brewery. Now serves seven outlets (three tied houses) from its 40 barrel plant. A cask-conditioned stout is planned, as

The Independents

well as other celebration ales, all brewed to the stipulations of the Manx Brewers' Act of 1874.

Best Bitter (OG 1038) An aroma full of pale malt and hops introduces you to a beautifully hoppy, bitter beer. Despite the predominantly hop character, malt is also evident. Fresh and clean tasting.

Old Bushy Tail (OG 1045) An appealing reddish-brown beer with a pronounced hop and malt aroma, the malt tending towards treacle. Slightly sweet and malty on the palate, with distinct orangey tones. The full finish is malty and hoppy, with hints of toffee.

Piston Brew* (OG 1045) Available during the TT races only.

Christmas Ale* (OG 1060) The seasonal beer.

BUTCOMBE

Butcombe Brewery Ltd., Butcombe, Bristol, Avon, BS18 6XQ. Tel. (0275) 472240

One of the most successful of the new wave of breweries, set up in 1978 by a former Courage Western MD, Simon Whitmore. Has been brewing to virtual capacity since the MMC report - 10,000 barrels per year, but there are no plans to move premises in order to expand production. Real ale in its three houses (which are not tied) and in an extensive free trade, mostly around Avon and Somerset.

Bitter (OG 1039, ABV 4%) A pale brown-coloured beer with a pleasant, hoppy/bitter taste, some malt and occasional fruit. It has a hoppy, malty aroma and a bitter finish, which can be very drying. A crisp, refreshing beer.

BUTTERKNOWLE The Butterknowle Brewery Co., The Old School House, Lynesack, Butterknowle, Bishop Auckland, Co. Durham, DL13 5QF. Tel. (0388) 710109

Although the brewery only launched its first beer in August 1990, it has already firmly converted local palates to its beers, and demand is steadily increasing. Situated in the rambling Victorian buildings of the former Lynesack National School, Butterknowle reflects the area's mining history on its point of sale material. The beers are currently available at four outlets.

Bitter (OG 1036, ABV 3.6%) A good, hoppy, quaffing bitter, amber in colour with a malty aftertaste.

Festival Stout (OG 1038, ABV 3.6%) Originally brewed for the sixth Darlington Spring Festival; a beer with a roast, slightly smoky flavour, a hoppy aroma and a sweetish aftertaste.

Conciliation Ale (OG 1042, ABV 4.2%) Butterknowle's flagship brand: a proudly pure, full-flavoured premium ale, well-hopped in both aroma and palate, with some sweetness.

Black Diamond (OG 1050, ABV 4.8%) Actually dark brown in colour and styled as a porter, albeit a strong one. Dry flavoured, with a bitter finish.

High Force (OG 1060, ABV 6.2%) Smooth, unusually pale strong ale. Lots of hoppy fruitiness and good body.

CAINS

Robert Cain & Co. Ltd., Stanhope Street, Liverpool, Merseyside, L8 5XJ. Tel. (051) 709 8734

A resurrection on Merseyside. The Higsons brewery in Stanhope Street was closed by Whitbread in 1990, with all production transferred to Sheffield. The premises were taken on by GB Breweries, which concentrated on canned beer until producing its first draught ale to much acclaim in March 1991.

The Independents

The brewery has now reverted to the old name of Robert Cain, a brewery which owned the premises before Higsons. No tied houses, but a substantial free trade. Danish brewers Faxe took a financial stake in the company in summer 1991, but the future of ale production seems secure.

Traditional Bitter

(OG 1038) Darkish, malty, full-bodied and bitter, with a hint of roast malt and a little sulphur. Moderate hoppiness and a good bitter aftertaste. A well-balanced distinctive beer, a worthy successor to Higsons.

CALEDONIAN

The Caledonian Brewing Company Ltd., Slateford Road, Edinburgh, Lothian, EH11 1PH. Tel. (031) 337 1286

When Vaux closed the famous Lorimer & Clark brewery in May 1987, a management team acquired it. They now operate from the old brewery using the last three direct-fired open coppers in Britain - one of which is an original, dating back to 1869. No tied estate, but around 350 free trade outlets are supplied.

60/- Ale*

(OG 1032, ABV 3.2%) A flavoursome light ale.

70/- Ale*

(OG 1036, ABV 3.5%) Soft and malty in flavour.

R&D Deuchars IPA*

(OG 1038, ABV 3.8%) A well-hopped session beer, recently added to the range.

Porter*

(OG 1043, ABV 4.2%) Dry and nutty.

80/- Ale*

(OG 1043, ABV 4.2%) Malty and flavoursome, with hops well in evidence.

Golden Promise*

(OG 1048, ABV 4.6%) An organic beer.

Merman XXX*

(OG 1050, ABV 4.8%) Dark, sweetish heavy beer, based on a Victorian recipe.

Edinburgh Strong Ale or ESA*

(OG 1078, ABV 8%) Rich and deceptively strong.

CAMERONS

EST 1865

Camerons

Brent Walker Breweries Ltd., Lion Brewery, Hartlepool, Cleveland, TS24 7QS. Tel. (0429) 266666

A brewery whose future is uncertain, following the much-publicised financial difficulties of its parent company, Brent Walker. In 1989 Brent Walker took its first steps into the brewing industry by purchasing Camerons and Tolly Cobbold from the Barclay Bros hotel group. After a cash injection of 10 million at the Camerons Hartlepool brewery, production of the Tolly Cobbold ales was insensitively transferred north from its Ipswich base. However, a management buy-out of the Tolly Cobbold plant was announced in May 1990 and brewing is once more taking place at Ipswich (see Tolly Cobbold, page 447). Possibilities of a management buy-out exist for Camerons, though the worry is that Brent Walker will choose to sell the brewery to Allied and that could mean closure of the plant and the end of Camerons, as Allied still has spare capacity at its other breweries. Strongarm Premium has already been discontinued.

Traditional Bitter

(OG 1036, ABV 3.6%) A light beer with a good balance of malt and hops and a true bitter finish. An excellent session beer when in good form but quality does vary.

Strongarm

(OG 1040, ABV 3.9%) A pleasant medium-bodied ale with a lot of character. Darkish in colour, with a full, well-balanced flavour of malt and hops and a dry, bitter finish. Again, quality

The Independents

can vary and there is a trend in some pubs to serve it too cold to be appreciated.

CASTLETOWN	See Isle of Man Breweries, page 424.

CHARRINGTON	See Bass, page 459.

CHESTER'S	See Whitbread, page 467.

CHILTERN

The Chiltern Brewery, Nash Lee Road, Terrick, Aylesbury, Bucks, HP17 0TQ. Tel. (0296) 613647

Set up in 1980, and situated on a small farm, Chiltern specializes in an unusual range of beer-related products, eg beer mustards, Old Ale chutneys, cheeses and malt marmalade. These products are available from the brewery shop and also a dozen other retail outlets. The beer itself is supplied to five free trade outlets (no tied houses). *Bottle-conditioned beers: Three Hundred Old Ale (OG 1050, ABV 5%); Bodgers Barley Wine (OG 1080, ABV 7%)*

Chiltern Ale*	(OG 1036, ABV 3.3%) A distinctive, light bitter.
Beechwood Bitter*	(OG 1043, ABV 4%) Full-bodied and nutty.
Three Hundred Old Ale*	(OG 1050, ABV 5%)

CLARK'S

HB Clark & Co. (Successors) Ltd., Westgate Brewery, Wakefield, W. Yorks, WF2 9SW. Tel. (0924) 373328

Brewers and a drinks wholesale company, originally founded at the beginning of the century, which, after a chequered history, began brewing again in 1982. Within two months, Clark's Traditional Bitter was voted Best Bitter at the Great British Beer Festival in Leeds. The first of its four tied houses, Henry Boon's, named after one of the brewery's founders, was opened in premises next to the brewery the following year. Another 50 free trade outlets are supplied and the company also acts as real ale agents with a portfolio of 85 beers. Rams Revenge is the latest addition to the range, but HB and Garthwaite are no longer brewed. A mild is available (OG 1038, ABV 3.9%), but only at the Kings Arms in Heath.

Traditional Bitter	(OG 1038, ABV 4.1%) An amber-coloured standard bitter with a pleasing hoppy, fruity aroma. A fine hop flavour is predominant in the palate, with malt and fruit. A good, clean-tasting bitter with a long, hoppy finish.
Burglar Bill	(OG 1044, ABV 4.75%) Generally, a fuller version of the bitter. It has a richer malt taste and a fine, strong hop flavour, which leads to a good, malty and hoppy finish. Full-bodied.
Winter Warmer	(OG 1044, ABV 4.85%) A rich, slightly vinous, dark brown beer with a malty nose. Strong roast and malt flavours, with bitterness and underlying sweetness, and a malty and bitter aftertaste.
Ram's Revenge	(OG 1046, ABV 4.8%) A beer with a dark brown hue. Caramel is evident in both the aroma and taste, but with balancing hops and malt. The short, dry finish again has caramel.
Hammerhead	(OG 1056, ABV 5.95%) Rich malt in the mouth, but with hop flavour and bitterness to balance. The malty, hoppy aroma is faint, but the finish is long, malty and dry. A robust, strong bitter.

The Independents

COACH HOUSE

The Coach House Brewing Company Ltd., Wharf Street, Warrington, Cheshire. Tel. (0925) 232800

A brand new brewery, built in 1991 with Inn Brewing as the main contractor, and run mainly by ex-Greenall Whitley employees. Trading agreements have been made with Greenall Whitley as well as with Paramount PLC to take the beers, which will also be sold into the free trade. Brewing began in July, with a capacity of up to 300 barrels a week. Future plans include a town-centre pub.

Coachman's Best Bitter* (OG 1037, ABV 4.1%)

Innkeeper's Special Reserve* (OG 1045, ABV 5%)

CORNISH

Cornish Brewery Ltd., The Brewery, Redruth, Cornwall, TR15 1AT. Tel. (0209) 213591

Brewery founded in 1792 which now has new owners. Originally the Redruth Brewing Co., Cornish later became part of JA Devenish PLC. Devenish's old Weymouth brewery closed at the end of 1985, with all production transferred to Redruth, and a subsequent merger with Inn Leisure increased the size of its tied estate. After the Boddingtons group launched a hostile take-over bid in spring 1991, Devenish decided to opt out of brewing altogether when Whitbread offered a deal to supply beer to Devenish pubs. Although the future of the ales listed below is therefore in considerable doubt, in July 1991 it was announced that a management buy-out had saved the brewery and 30 jobs, so brewing will continue at Redruth.

JD Dry Hop Bitter (OG 1032, ABV 3%) There is very little aroma to this pale brown beer which has a hoppy, very bitter taste and a similarly bitter finish. A light, session beer.

Original Bitter (OG 1038, ABV 3.8%) Pale brown in colour and thin in aroma, with a bittersweet flavour which can vary. A slight bitter aftertaste.

Draught Steam Bitter (OG 1038, ABV 3.8%) A very variable beer which divides opinion: samples ranged from no flavour to strong and distinctive. The flagship of the Cornish brands.

Royal Wessex Bitter (OG 1042, ABV 4%) A golden, straw-coloured ale with no discernible aroma. There is some hoppiness amid a mainly bittersweet flavour and bitter aftertaste. Neither unpleasant nor distinctive. Sometimes sold as Vallence's Bitter.

COTLEIGH

Cotleigh Brewery, Ford Road, Wiveliscombe, Somerset, TA4 2RE. Tel. (0984) 24086

Continued growth has taken this brewery a long way from its first home - a stable block at Cotleigh Farmhouse in 1979. 1985 saw the completion of a purpose-built brewhouse and there was further expansion in 1991 with the purchase of adjoining premises and doubling of brewing capacity. Serves 80 outlets, mostly in Devon and Somerset, although the beers are also available across the country. Owns one pub, the Prince of Wales in Holcombe Rogus, Devon.

Nutcracker* (OG 1036) A dark mild, relaunched in summer 1991.

Harrier SPA (OG 1036, ABV 3.6%) A straw-coloured beer with a very

The Independents

hoppy aroma and flavour, and a hoppy, bitter finish. Plenty of flavour for a light, low gravity beer.

Tawny Bitter (OG 1040, ABV 3.8%) A mid brown-coloured, very consistent beer. A hoppy aroma, a hoppy but quite well-balanced flavour, and a hoppy, bitter finish. A classic.

Old Buzzard (OG 1048, ABV 4.8%) Dark ruby-red beer, tasting strongly of roast malt, balanced with hops. Roast malt again in the finish, with bitterness. Very drinkable once the taste is acquired.

Rebellion* (OG 1050, ABV 5%) An occasional brew.

Red Nose Reinbeer* (OG 1060, ABV 5.6%) A dark and warming Christmas brew.

COURAGE See page 461.

CROPTON **Cropton Brewery, New Inn, Cropton, Pickering, N. Yorks, Y018 8HH. Tel. (075 15) 330**

A former brew pub, established in 1984 at the New Inn, this brewery was expanded in 1988 to supply its additive-free beers to the local free trade and now sells to around 18 outlets.

Two Pints* (OG 1040, ABV 4%) Full-flavoured and distinctive.

Special Strong Bitter* (OG 1060, ABV 6.3%) A powerful winter ale.

CROUCH VALE **Crouch Vale Brewery Ltd., 12 Redhills Road, South Woodham Ferrers, Chelmsford, Essex, CM3 5UP. Tel. (0245) 322744**

Founded in 1981, Crouch Vale has a single tied house - the Cap & Feathers at Tillingham (a CAMRA Pub of the Year), as well as free trade business in Suffolk, Essex and Greater London (50 outlets). Sales have increased substantially and the future for the brewery looks bright. Plans include further upgrading of brewing equipment and the possible acquisition of an additional tied house.

Woodham IPA (OG 1035, ABV 3.5%) A pale session beer: dry and hoppy, with a faint balancing maltiness throughout.

Woodham Mild* (OG 1036, ABV 3.5%) A very occasional brew.

Best Bitter (OG 1039, ABV 4%) Pleasant, copper-coloured, hoppy bitter with some balancing maltiness and fruit on the tongue. Hoppy aftertaste.

Strong Anglian Special or SAS (OG 1048, ABV 5%) Copper in colour and full-bodied. Malty and strong tasting, with robust bitterness.

Essex Porter (OG 1050, ABV 5%) A black, bittersweet porter with a slight hint of blackberries.

Santa's Revenge* (OG 1055, ABV 6%) A Christmas ale, also sold throughout the year under house names. Despite its strength, it is dry and winey, not sweet.

Willie Warmer (OG 1060, ABV 6.5%) A fruity and well-flavoured, strong, dark and delicious, black ale.

CROWN BUCKLEY **Crown Buckley PLC, Pontyclun, Mid Glamorgan, CF7 9YG. Tel. (0443) 225453**

Buckley, the oldest brewery in Wales (estd. 1767) was taken over by Brodian in 1987. This failed to revitalise the ailing brewery which was bought out by Crown (the former United

The Independents

Clubs Brewery) in 1989 with Harp financial backing, merging the brewing interests and creating a total tied estate of 134 pubs. The company has since experienced another massive shake up and is now owned by Guinness. All beer production is carried out at the Llanelli (Buckley) site, where money is again being invested in equipment; kegging and bottling is done at Pontyclun, but one site seems almost certain to go in the end. Also has a major stake in Llanelli neighbours Felinfoel.

Buckley's Dark (OG 1034, ABV 3.4%) A very dark malty mild, fairly sweet with traces of chocolate and a nutty bitter finish. Difficult to find in good condition. Sometimes sold as Ansells Dark in S. Wales Allied houses.

Buckley's Best Bitter (OG 1037, ABV 3.8%) A well-balanced, fruity bitter which has a rather sweet, malty flavour and a pleasant, bitter finish.

Crown SBB (OG 1037, ABV 3.8%) Distinctively malty and clean tasting, with a pronounced bitter flavour and a rather dry aftertaste. A well-rounded beer which is not widely available.

Reverend James* (OG 1045, ABV 5%) A new flagship brew.

DARLEY See Wards, page 449.

DARLING'S See Longstone, page 427.

DAVENPORTS See Greenalls, page 415.

DENT **Dent Brewery, Hollins, Cowgill, Dent, Cumbria, LA10 5TQ. Tel. (058 75) 326**

Set up in a converted barn, this brewery started production in March 1990, using its own spring water. Has expanded from supplying just three pubs in Dentdale to 15 in the local area, as well as two tied houses.

Bitter* (OG 1036, ABV 3.6%)

Ramsbottom Strong Ale* (OG 1044, ABV 4.7%)

DEVENISH See Cornish, page 406.

DONNINGTON **Donnington Brewery, Stow-on-the-Wold, Glos, GL54 1EP. Tel. (0451) 30603**

It is a pity that Britain's most picturesque brewery, set in an old watermill alongside a lake, with water power still used for much of the machinery, is not open for visits. The mill in fact dates back to the 13th century, but only became a brewery in 1865, run by the Arkell family who still own it today. 15 tied houses, and a few free trade outlets, all serve beer on handpumps. Look out for the mild, available only in a few outlets.

XXX (OG 1036, ABV 3.5%) Thin in aroma, but flavoursome. More subtle than others in its class. Some fruit and traces of chocolate and liquorice in the taste, with a notably malty finish.

BB (OG 1036, ABV 3.5%) Again, little aroma, but a pleasing, bitter beer, with a good malt/hop balance. Not as distinctive as it used to be.

SBA (OG 1042, ABV 4%) Malt dominates over bitterness in the flavour of this premium bitter. Subtle, with just a hint of fruit and a dry, malty finish. Faintly malty aroma.

The Independents

EARL SOHAM **Earl Soham Brewery, The Victoria, Earl Soham, Wood-bridge, Suffolk, IP13 7RL. Tel. (072 882) 758**

Started in April 1985 to supply its own pub, the Victoria. Now owns a second pub, the Tram Depot in Cambridge.

Gannet Mild (OG 1033) Unusual ale, more like a light porter than a mild, given the bitter finish and roast flavours which compete with the underlying maltiness.

Victoria (OG 1037) A characterful, well-hopped malty beer whose best feature is the superbly tangy, hoppy aftertaste.

Albert Ale (OG 1045) Hops predominate in every aspect of this beer but especially in the finish which some will find glorious, others astringent. A truly extreme brew.

Old Cyril (OG 1060–76) The recipe for this winter only brew tends to change from batch to batch, but expect something rich, smooth and fruity with a bittersweet aftertaste. Sometimes sold as 'Jolabrugg'.

ELDRIDGE POPE **Eldridge, Pope & Co. PLC, Weymouth Avenue, Dorchester, Dorset, DT1 1QT. Tel. (0305) 251251**

Charles and Sarah Eldridge started the Green Dragon Brewery in Dorchester in 1837. By 1880, Edwin and Alfred Pope had bought into the company and it had moved to its present site, next to the railway, its first pubs situated along the line. The brewery is still run by the Pope family. Whilst Thomas Hardy's Ale is notable for being the strongest naturally-conditioned bottled beer, the award-winning draught beers are served using a cask breather device in many of the 190 tied houses. Those houses not using the device have been designated 'Traditional Ale Houses'. Free trade extends as far as London, Bristol and Exeter, serving a total of around 1000 outlets. *Bottle-conditioned beer: Thomas Hardy's Ale (OG 1125, ABV 12%)*

Dorchester Bitter (OG 1033, ABV 3.3%) A well-balanced session beer with a malt and hop flavour and aftertaste. Mainly malty aroma.

EP Best Bitter (OG 1036, ABV 3.8%) A bland mixture of malt and hops. Difficult to find in cask-conditioned form.

Thomas Hardy Country Bitter (OG 1040, ABV 4.2%) Mid brown beer which replaced IPA. Hops are dominant throughout, with bitterness coming through in the aftertaste.

Royal Oak (OG 1048, ABV 5%) Fruit and malt are prevalent in both aroma and taste. The flavour is balanced, with hops and some sweetness, and there is a fruity finish to this smooth, well-rounded brew.

ELGOOD'S **Elgood & Sons Ltd., North Brink Brewery, Wisbech, Cambs, PE13 1LN. Tel. (0945) 583160**

Elgood's is still proudly independent and the only brewery left in Cambridgeshire. From its classical Georgian, riverside premises (built in 1795 and acquired by Elgood's in 1878), it supplies all but two of its 51 tied houses with real ale. Also serves around 150 free trade outlets in East Anglia. *Bottle-conditioned beer: Winter Warmer (OG 1070, ABV 7.5%)* at Christmas only.

Bitter or EB (OG 1036, ABV 4.1%) A predominantly malty beer with traces of hop and fruit in both aroma and flavour. A bitter aftertaste with malt and some fruit.

The Independents

Greyhound Strong Bitter or GSB	(OG 1045, ABV 5.2%) On the verge of extinction; very few pubs sell this now. Malt is pronounced throughout, with traces of hops. Bitterness comes through in the aftertaste.
Winter Warmer*	(OG 1080, ABV 8.2%) A seasonal brew.

EVERARDS

Everards Brewery Ltd., Castle Acres, Narborough, Leicester, LE9 5BY. Tel. (0533) 630900

A small, family-owned brewery, which originated in Leicester in 1849, and moved back to the outskirts of the town in 1979 after a 50-year sojourn in Burton upon Trent. For several years, some of the beers continued to be brewed under licence at the Heritage brewery in Burton, but by mid 1990, expansion at the Castle Acres site was complete and now all beers are again brewed in Leicester. Most of its 130 tied houses sell real ale, many offering guest beers. Everards also supplies around 500 free trade outlets.

Mild	(OG 1033, ABV 3.1%) Satisfying, ruby-coloured beer, with an aroma of malt and fruit. Full-bodied malt flavour, with more than a hint of cherries. Long, malty finish.
Beacon Bitter	(OG 1036, ABV 3.8%) Light, golden beer with an aroma of hops and honey. The flavour balances malt and hops and the finish lingers.
Tiger Best Bitter	(OG 1041, ABV 4.2%) Copper-brown, with a malty, hoppy aroma and a soft, malty palate, with plenty of balancing hops and an underlying fruitiness. The finish is long, dry, hoppy and malty. A good, balanced, medium-bodied bitter.
Old Original	(OG 1050, ABV 5.2%) A beer with a smooth, distinctive palate and a faint, hoppy, fruity aroma. Dry, with malt and caramel flavours and some sweetness beneath. The finish is malty and sweetish; the colour is copper brown.
Old Bill Winter Warmer	(OG 1070, ABV 7.3%) Brewed Dec-Jan. A tawny/red winter ale with a sweet vinous character and an underlying hoppy flavour, which gives some balancing bitterness. The finish is sweet, with a fruity dryness and some malt.

EXE VALLEY

Exe Valley Brewery, Land Farm, Silverton, Exeter, Devon, EX5 4HF. Tel. (0392) 860406

A farm brewery, initiated as Barron Brewery, in an old barn in 1984, using the farm's own spring water. Production is at present 12 barrels a week, with two new beers added in 1990. These two new additions, Dob's Best Bitter and Exeter Old, are more or less dry-hopped versions of their stablemates, having similar OGs. Further expansion is planned and an increase in wholesale trade, now that owner Richard Barron has been joined by Guy Sheppard.

Bitter	(OG 1040, ABV 3.9%) Refreshing, slightly creamy, malty, pale brown bitter, with fruity and bittersweet undertones. Pleasant drinking.
Dob's Best Bitter	(OG 1041, ABV 4%) Mid brown, hoppy, yet fruity beer with a distinct bitter aftertaste. Fruity aroma.
Devon Glory	(OG 1047, ABV 4.7%) Mid brown and fruitily aromatic, with a sweet, fruity flavour and pleasantly sweet aftertaste.
Exeter Old Bitter	(OG 1048, ABV 4.8%) Red/brown-coloured, with a sweet, fruity taste, a fruity aroma and a malty aftertaste.

The Independents

EXMOOR

Exmoor Ales Ltd., Golden Hill Brewery, Wiveliscombe, Somerset, TA4 2NY. Tel. (0984) 23798

Somerset's largest brewery was founded in 1980 in the former West Country Brewing premises at Wiveliscombe, which had been closed in 1959. Supplies real ale to some 130 pubs in the region and over 350 nationwide via wholesalers. No houses of its own. Exmoor Dark has been discontinued, and in its place comes the stronger Exmoor Stag, which was also available during 1991 as the bottled (not bottle-conditioned) Centenary Ale, celebrating Somerset County Cricket Club's 100th birthday.

Exmoor Ale

(OG 1039, ABV 3.8%) Pale brown beer with a malty aroma and a malty, dry taste. Bitter and malty finish. Very drinkable.

Exmoor Gold

(OG 1045, ABV 4.5%) A yellow/golden colour, and a malty aroma and flavour, with slight sweetness and hoppiness. Sweet, malty finish.

Exmoor Stag

(OG 1050, ABV 5.2%) Pale brown in colour, with a malty taste and aroma, and a bitter finish. Slightly sweet. Very similar to Exmoor Ale and drinks as easily, so be warned!

FEDERATION

THE FEDERATION BREWERY

Northern Clubs Federation Brewery Ltd., Lancaster Road, Dunston Ind. Estate, Dunston, Tyne & Wear, NE11 9JR. Tel. (091) 460 9023

A co-operative, founded in 1919, which expanded to supply pubs and clubs through its own depots and wholesalers. This now accounts for the majority of the brewery's business, although it does have six tied houses, two of which take real ale. Only a very small proportion of the brewery's output is cask-conditioned.

Best Bitter

(OG 1036, ABV 3.6%) Very difficult to find, especially on top form, when it has a pleasant aroma, a bitter flavour and a well-balanced aftertaste, with a hint of fruit throughout. Drinks like an ordinary bitter.

Special Ale

(OG 1041, ABV 4%) Again, rare and variable, with malt and hop characteristics dominating. Some fruity undertones are detectable and maize is discernible throughout. A well-balanced finish.

FELINFOEL

The Felinfoel Brewery Co. Ltd., Farmers Row, Felinfoel, Llanelli, Dyfed, SA14 8LB. Tel. (0554) 773356/7

Despite Crown Buckley's sizeable stake, the Lewis family still have the major holding in this famous Welsh brewery and they are committed to independence. Runs 86 tenanted houses and serves an expanding free trade, which extends from Aberystwyth to Hereford and Bristol. Also acts as a wholesaler for other draught ales. A new beer, Cambrian Bitter, has been introduced as a mid range beer, whilst the gravity of Double Dragon has been upped from 1041.

Bitter

(OG 1033, ABV 3.2%) A very hoppy and moderately malty session beer. Pale brown in colour with a very refreshing, hoppy aftertaste. Now very difficult to find but worth the effort.

Cambrian Bitter*

(OG 1036, ABV 3.8%)

Double Dragon*

(OG 1048, ABV 5%)

FLOWERS

See Whitbread, page 467.

The Independents

FORBES

Forbes Ales, Unit 2, Harbour Road Ind. Estate, Oulton Broad, Lowestoft, Suffolk, NR32 3LZ.
Tel. (0502) 587905

Brewery set up in 1988, run by a brewer with a degree in sculpture. The beers are supplied to a couple of regular free trade outlets. Within the brewery itself there is now a function room and a museum. A bottling plant is planned and with it bottle-conditioned beers. The range of beers and their gravities are often changed and all the beers are brewed to be stronger than even their high gravity suggests.

Light Ale or IPA
(OG 1040, ABV 3.8%) Summer only. A yellow/gold-coloured beer which is definitely bitter, particularly in the aftertaste. This is balanced in the mouth by hoppiness and sweetness, with some sulphurous notes.

Brown Roy
(OG 1040) A real brown ale. There is a distinct fruitiness in the aroma, but it fades away in the flavour and aftertaste, to be pleasantly replaced by hoppy bitterness and malt.

Harvest Ale*
(OG 1044)

Northern Bitter
(OG 1045) An amber beer with a fruity aroma which belies the strong hoppy/bitter taste which lingers, together with some fruitiness. Decidedly drinkable for such a bitter beer.

Black Shuck
(OG 1052) Usually winter only. As its name suggests, a very black and intense stout. Roast malt bursts onto the nose and remains throughout, but there is also a strong hop presence and a bittersweet quality. The aftertaste is dry, with roast malt and hops.

Traditional or Boudecea*
(OG 1053.5)

Merrie Monarch
(OG 1069) A strong, dark brown beer with hops and malt in the nose. Roast malt and fruit are prominent on the tongue, followed by a malt in the finish, yet not without some balancing hops and bitterness.

FRANKLIN'S

Franklin's Brewery, Bilton Lane, Bilton, Harrogate, N. Yorks, HG1 4DH. Tel. (0423) 322345

A small brewery set up in 1980 behind the Gardeners Arms by Sean Franklin, but taken over in 1985 by Leeds CAMRA founder-member Tommy Thomas. Serves around 20 free trade outlets, but not the Gardeners.

Bitter
(OG 1038, ABV 4%) A tremendous, flowery, fruity nose leads into a full, balanced palate, which is still fruity and has hops and some malt contributing to a distinctive mix of flavours. The finish is sweet and hoppy, with some malt.

FREMLINS
See Whitbread, page 467.

FRIARY MEUX
See Allied Breweries, page 456.

FULLER'S

Fuller, Smith and Turner PLC, Griffin Brewery, Chiswick, London, W4 2QB. Tel. (081) 994 3691

One of the two surviving London independent brewers after the 1960s take-over spree. Has achieved its target of acquiring 200 pubs well in advance of the year 2000, with all but three serving real ale. Uses the CAMRA logo in advertisements for its cask beers; this is not surprising as they are regular CAMRA award-winners. An expanding free trade takes in about 500 outlets, with the brewery having a majority interest in Classic

The Independents

Ales (formerly West Country Products), a London real ale distributor. Brewery redevelopments are still progressing.

Chiswick Bitter   (OG 1034, ABV 3.5%) A distinctively hoppy beer when fresh, with strong maltiness and fruity characters. Finishes with a lasting, dry bitterness and a pleasing aftertaste. Champion Beer of Britain 1989.

London Pride   (OG 1040, ABV 4.1%) An excellent beer with a strong, malty base and a rich balance of well-developed hop flavours and a powerful bitterness.

Mr Harry*   (OG 1048, ABV 4.3%) An occasional brew.

ESB   (OG 1054, ABV 5.5%) A copper-red, strong, robust beer with great character. A full-bodied maltiness and a rich hoppiness are immediately evident and develop into a rich fruitiness with an underlying sweet fullness.

FURGUSONS   See Allied Breweries, page 455.

GALE'S   **George Gale & Co. Ltd., The Brewery, Horndean, Portsmouth, Hants, PO8 0DA. Tel. (0705) 571212**

Hampshire's major brewery, Gale's was originally founded in 1847 and has grown slowly and steadily over the years by means of small scale take-overs (and a dowry!), and now owns some attractive pubs. Its tied estate was increased by over 50 houses last year after bulk purchases from Allied and Whitbread, and all 150 of its tied houses serve real ale. To cope with the extra demand, much of Whitbread's old Faversham brewery equipment has also been purchased and moved to Horndean. Gale's also brews for Whitbread. *Bottle-conditioned beer*: Prize Old Ale (OG 1094, ABV 9%)

XXXL   (OG 1030, ABV 2.9%) A refreshing pale ale which is becoming harder to find. Has only a slight aroma, but the malt flavour leads to bitterness in the finish.

XXXD   (OG 1032, ABV 2.9%) A dark beer with ruby tints; sweet and caramelly, with a hint of plums. The dryish, grainy finish has a touch of bitterness.

BBB or Butser Brew Bitter   (OG 1036, ABV 3.6%) A variable, mid brown ale whose flavour has altered since the 1991 *GBG*. Now fairly sweet, but with some malt and hints of tangerine and plums. The finish is dryish, with some bitterness, and is sometimes cloying.

Best Bitter   (OG 1040, ABV 3.8%) Overall, malty and sweet, but hop character peeps through, together with some fruit (pears). Slight aroma (as with most Gale's beers); malty aftertaste.

5X   (OG 1044, ABV 4.2%) Available Oct–March. A very dark, fruity beer which appears to have lost the trace of Prize Old Ale it once had. Now has varying fruit flavours, with caramel and vanilla. The fruity finish has some bitterness.

HSB   (OG 1050, ABV 5%) A beer much changed since the 1991 *GBG*. This deep brown beer has an aroma of hops and vanilla, and a sweet middle period, with some malt, apples, pears and, sometimes, plums. Too sweet for many palates, but there is some hoppy bitterness in the finish.

Prize Old Ale*   (OG 1094, ABV 9%) Draught version of the bottle-conditioned beer, available in only a few outlets.

For Whitbread:

Pompey Royal   (OG 1043, ABV 4.5%) Now tastes more like it did when

413

originally brewed in Portsmouth. A strong, bitter finish follows a pear-flavoured, slightly sweet middle period. Pears also come through in the aroma of this mid brown beer.

**Wethered
Winter Royal**

(OG 1053, ABV 5.5%) Available Oct-March. A golden beer with hints of malt and fruit in the aroma. Very sweet and malty in the mouth, with banana fruit present. After this sweetness, the finish is bitter.

GIBBS MEW

GIBBS
MEW

Gibbs Mew PLC, Anchor Brewery, Milford Street, Salisbury, Wilts, SP1 2AR. Tel. (0722) 411911

A family concern which has been brewing in Salisbury since 1856. Its tied estate has grown considerably in the last ten years and real ale is supplied to almost all its 135 pubs. Extensive free trade in southern and south western England (over 200 outlets).

**Wiltshire
Traditional Bitter**

(OG 1036, ABV 3.5%) A pleasant enough flavour of malt and hops, but frankly bland and uninspiring. Dry finish.

**Timothy Chudley
Local Line**

(OG 1036, ABV 3.5%) A clean-tasting bitter to be savoured. Moderately-hopped and slightly fruity. An ideal lunchtime ale.

Premium Bitter

(OG 1042, ABV 4.2%) A truly bland and uninteresting beer. A small, corky taste and an overbearing sweetness are only tempered by bitterness in the aftertaste. Dwindling availability.

**Salisbury Best
Bitter**

(OG 1042, ABV 4.2%) A rather chewy, sweet ale, decidedly lacking in bitterness. The title 'Best' is somewhat misleading, but, all the same, it's a pleasant beer.

Bishop's Tipple

(OG 1066, ABV 6.5%) Weaker than the average barley wine, but not lacking in flavour. The full-bodied taste is marvellously malty with a kick that leaves the brain rather less clear than the beer.

GLENNY

**The Glenny Brewery Company, The Two Rivers Brewery, Station Lane, Witney, Oxfordshire, OX8 6BH.
Tel. (0993) 702574**

Set up in 1983 in part of the old Clinch's brewery, then moved to its own premises in 1987, from which it supplies around 60 free trade outlets. Its first brew was called Eagle Bitter, but the name was changed after a dispute with Charles Wells. The latest addition to the range is Dr Thirsty's Draught. The original owner, Paddy Glenny, emigrated to Canada in 1990.

Bitter

(OG 1036, ABV 3.7%) A pleasantly hoppy and malty, light brown session beer, with a roast malt and fruit aroma. Formerly known as Witney Bitter.

Wychwood Best

(OG 1044, ABV 4.2%) Mid brown, full-flavoured premium bitter. Moderately strong in hop and malt flavours, with pleasing, fruity overtones which last through to the aftertaste.

**Dr Thirsty's
Draught***

(ABV 5.2%)

Hobgoblin

(OG 1058, ABV 5.9%) Powerful, full-bodied, copper-red, well-balanced brew, reminiscent of a Bavarian style. Strong in roasted malt, with a moderate, hoppy bitterness and a slight fruity character.

GOACHER'S

P&DJ Goacher, Hayle Mill Cottages, Bockingford, Maidstone, Kent, ME15 6DT. Tel. (0622) 682112

Kent's most successful small independent brewer, set up in 1983 by Phil and Debbie Goacher, producing all-malt ales with

The Independents

Kentish hops for about 30 free trade outlets in the Maidstone area. Brewery is now installed in a nearby trading estate at Tovil, but the company address remains the same.

Maidstone Light (OG 1036) Pale golden brown bitter ale with a strong, hoppy aroma and aftertaste. A very hoppy and moderately malty session beer.

Maidstone Dark (OG 1040) Intensely bitter, balanced by a moderate maltiness with a complex aftertaste. Lighter in colour than it once was, but still darker than most bitters.

Maidstone Old* (OG 1066) Black, potent old ale, known locally as 1066. Winter only.

GOLDFINCH

Goldfinch Brewery (Tom Brown's Public House), 47 High East Street, Dorchester, Dorset, DT1 1HU. Tel. (0305) 264020

Former free house, now a brew pub, acting out a scene from Tom Brown's Schooldays. The brewery has been operating since 1987 in which time it has expanded from a one-barrel plant (still in operation), to a four-barrel plant and is still growing. Supplies an increasiing free trade.

Tom Brown's Best Bitter (OG 1039, ABV 4%) A pale-coloured bitter with a fruity nose. The taste is bittersweet, with malt, fruit and some hop. Complex aftertaste.

Flashman's Clout Strong Ale (OG 1043, ABV 4.5%) A beer with an attractive, honeyed aroma, and, again, a bittersweet taste with malt and fruit. Mid brown in colour, with a predominantly bitter finish.

GRAND METROPOLITAN

See Courage, page 461.

GREENALLS

GREENALLS

Greenalls Group PLC, Wilderspool, Warrington, Cheshire, WA4 6RH. Tel. (0925) 51234

Greenalls is now just a pub-owning group and no longer brews: so ends one of the most destructive eras in British brewing's history. After tearing the heart out of the Midlands brewing industry, Greenalls finally pulled out of brewing altogether in 1991. In the 1980s, Davenports, Simpkiss, Wem and Shipstone's all found themselves swallowed up by this voracious company, only for their breweries to be closed soon afterwards. When the end came, only Shipstone's Star Brewery in Nottingham and the original Warrington brewery remained. Greenalls beers are still on sale, though they are brewed by Allied at the Tetley Walker and Ind Coope breweries (see page 457). Admirably, some of the Warrington staff have branched out and formed their own micro-brewery, Coach House (see page 406). Meanwhile, the fight goes on to save the Star Brewery, though Greenalls, despite not wanting to brew there itself, seems intent on stopping any other would-be brewer from taking on the premises.

GREENE KING

Greene King PLC, Westgate Brewery, Bury St Edmunds, Suffolk, IP33 1QT. Tel. (0284) 763222

East Anglia's largest regional brewery, producing cask-conditioned beers at Bury; its Biggleswade brewery is now entirely given over to lager production. Closed the Rayments brewery at Furneux Pelham in 1987, but has appropriated the Rayments name for its new brew, Rayments Special Bitter, which is slightly sweeter than the other Greene King beers and which has replaced BBA. The future of XX Mild is, however, threatened by declining sales. Following the acquisition of 87 Allied pubs in 1990, the company's tied estate currently stands at 850 houses, all of which serve cask ale, with handpulls now replacing top pressure in most outlets (although a blanket of CO_2 and a cask breather are still sometimes applied). The brewery also serves an extensive free trade in the South East (around 2,000 outlets).

XX Mild

(OG 1032, ABV 3%) Like all Greene King beers, this dark brown ale is largely aroma-free. The taste is malty and well-rounded with a hint of blackcurrant and a degree of bitterness in the finish.

IPA

(OG 1036, ABV 3.6%) A fine, well-balanced brew when allowed to mature properly in the cask. However, it is sometimes served too young.

Rayments Special Bitter

(OG 1040, ABV 4%) Smooth, malty and distinctly sweet - more like a Scottish than an East Anglian brew.

Abbot Ale

(OG 1049, ABV 5%) A kaleidoscope of flavours holds together superbly on the tongue before giving way to a big, hoppy finish.

Winter Ale

(OG 1060, ABV 6%) Available November-January and usually served from polypins on the bar. A fine example of the old ale style: dark, malty and warming.

GUERNSEY

The Guernsey Brewery Co. (1920) Ltd., South Esplanade, St Peter Port, Guernsey, CI. Tel. (0481) 720143

One of two breweries on this Channel Isle, serving stronger than average real ales in 16 of their 32 tied houses. Free trade covers Alderney, Herm and Jersey. Originally opened as the London Brewery in 1856, the company underwent several name changes before 1920, when income tax was introduced and it became a Guernsey registered company. It has retained its name since then despite being taken over by Jersey's Ann Street Brewery (keg beer only) in 1988. Guernsey real ale is also available in selected Ann Street houses.

LBA Mild

(OG 1037, ABV 3.7%) Copper-red in colour, with a complex aroma of malt, hops, fruit and toffee. The rich, mellow flavour combines malt, fruit, hops and butterscotch. The finish has malt and hops. Full-flavoured and surprisingly dry.

Grizzly's Real Ale

(OG 1042) A brewery mix of mild and bitter, available in just one hotel (La Collinette at St Peter Port). Amber/tawny in colour, with an aroma of malt, fruit and toffee. Very malty on the palate and again in the finish. Full-bodied and satisfying.

Real Draught Bitter

(OG 1045, ABV 4.2%) Golden in colour, with a fine malt aroma. Malt and fruit are strong on the palate and the beer is quite dry for its strength. Excellent, dry, malt and hop finish.

GUINNESS

See page 463.

HADRIAN

Hadrian Brewery Ltd., Unit 7, Foundry Lane Ind. Estate, Byker, Newcastle upon Tyne, NE6 1LH. Tel. (091) 276 5302

Founded in 1987 by keen home-brewer Trevor Smith. Still increasing production to cope with demand – now supplying around 25 outlets, as far south as Leeds. About 30 barrels of

The Independents

this range of pure, adjunct-free beers are now produced each week, with further substantial expansion planned.

Gladiator Bitter (OG 1039, ABV 4%) A smooth, well-rounded, flavoursome pint, with a nicely balanced aroma, a hoppy/bitter taste, with some underlying fruitiness, and a well-balanced, dry finish.

Porter* (OG 1042, ABV 4.2%) A new addition to the range.

Centurion Best Bitter (OG 1045, ABV 4.5%) Excellently-balanced beer enjoying strong hops and malt presence, and a pleasing, hoppy finish.

Emperor Ale* (OG 1050, ABV 5%) An old ale.

Yule Fuel* (OG 1060, ABV 6%) The Christmas ale.

HALL & WOODHOUSE **Hall & Woodhouse Ltd., The Brewery, Blandford Forum, Dorset, DT11 9LS. Tel. (0258) 452141**

Founded as the Ansty Brewery in 1777 by Charles Hall, whose son, Robert, took Mr GEI Woodhouse into partnership in 1847. Now more usually known as 'Badger's', the brewery serves cask beer in all its 148 houses, although an increasing number now use cask breathers. Free trade to much of southern England (400 outlets), including London and Bedfordshire via wholesalers.

Badger Best Bitter (OG 1041, ABV 4%) The taste is strong in hop and bitterness, with a hint of malt and fruit. A hoppy finish with a bitter edge. A fine best bitter.

Tanglefoot (OG 1048, ABV 4.9%) An award-winning, straw-coloured beer with a full fruit character throughout. Malt is also present in the aroma and taste, whilst the finish is bittersweet. Dangerously drinkable.

HALLS See Allied Breweries, page 456.

HANBY **Hanby Ales, Unit C9, Wem Ind. Estate, Wem, Shropshire, SY4 5SD. Tel. (0939) 32432**

A brewing partnership which began operations in March 1989 and moved to new premises a year later. Started with a 25 barrel plant, now 50 barrels and capacity is being increased again. Nutcracker is now produced all year-round, and a mild has been added to the range. Serves about 40 outlets and the guest beer market.

Black Magic Mild* (OG 1033, ABV 3.3%)

Drawwell Bitter* (OG 1039, ABV 3.9%)

Treacleminer Bitter* (OG 1046, ABV 4.6%)

Nutcracker Bitter* (OG 1060, ABV 6%)

HANCOCK'S See Bass, page 460.

HANSON'S **Hanson's Brewery, High Street, Dudley, W. Midlands, DY1 1QR. Tel. (0902) 711811**

Victorian Black Country brewery with real ale in all 153 tied houses. The other half of Wolverhampton & Dudley Breweries (see Banks's, page 395). Hanson's Bitter is brewed by Banks's at Wolverhampton. Mild Ale, brewed in Dudley, is only available in cask-conditioned form.

The Independents

Bitter	(OG 1035, ABV 3.4%) See Banks's, page 396.
Mild Ale	(OG 1036, ABV 3.5%) Maltiness in the aroma and a balanced taste of malt, with caramel and roast malt flavours. A dry, hoppy and malty, smooth finish.

HARDINGTON

Hardington Brewery, Albany Buildings, Dean Lane, Bristol, Avon, BS3 1BT. Tel. (0272) 636194

HARDINGTON

New brewery totally unconnected with the old Somerset brewery of the same name. Began brewing in April 1991 and now serves some 25 outlets in Bristol and Somerset from a brewhouse hidden away at the end of a dark tunnel.

Traditional*	(OG 1038)
Best Bitter*	(OG 1042)
Jubilee*	(OG 1050)

HARDYS & HANSONS

Hardys & Hansons PLC, Kimberley Brewery, Nottingham, NG16 2NS. Tel. (0602) 383611

Hardys and Hansons were two competitive breweries on opposite sides of the road, sharing the same water supply, until a merger in 1930 produced the present company. Now Nottingham's last independent brewery, the company is controlled by descendants of the original Hardy and Hanson families. Noted for its good value beers, Kimberley Classic is the brewery's latest addition, launched in October 1990. Most of its 244 pubs serve real ale, but sadly, a tendency to use top pressure for dispense is still a feature of many managed houses.

Best Mild	(OG 1035, ABV 3.1%) A dark, sweetish mild, slightly malty. Can have fruity notes.
Best Bitter	(OG 1039, ABV 3.9%) Golden/straw-coloured, distinctive, faintly fruity beer. Subtle in aroma; malt is more prominent than hop character and balancing bitterness.
Kimberley Classic*	(OG 1047, ABV 4.8%) A light-coloured, deceptively strong beer.

HARTLEYS

Hartleys (Ulverston) Ltd., The Old Brewery, Ulverston, Cumbria, LA12 7HX. Tel. (0229) 53269

TRADITIONAL
Hartleys
DRAUGHT BEER

Another victim in a year of brewery closures. Hartleys, famous for its 'Beers from the Wood', was taken over in 1982 by Robinson's of Stockport who announced in June 1991 that brewing at Ulverston was to cease. Hartleys beers will now be brewed in Robinson's Unicorn brewery in Stockport, though the future of all the brands must be in doubt.

Mild	(OG 1031, ABV 2.9%) Very variable in quality, but a good pint is worth finding. Malty and bitter aroma, with a not-unpleasant hint of aniseed. Smooth, drinkable and well-balanced. The aftertaste is predominantly bitter but somewhat short-lived.
Bitter	(OG 1031, ABV 3%) Straw-coloured beer with little aroma. Thin and slightly bitter, with a lingering bitter aftertaste. Drunk more by visitors than by locals, who prefer the fuller-bodied XB.
Fellrunners	(OG 1035, ABV 3.3%) Very hard to find anywhere near the brewery; a little more popular in the Lake District. Darker and more malty than the bitter, with a pleasant hop character and a lasting, bitter aftertaste.
XB	(OG 1040, ABV 4%) The most commonly available, but least consistent, of all the brews. Pale brown in colour, with a hoppy

The Independents

and fruity aroma. Strong, bitter, faintly fruity and sweet flavour, with a lingering after-bitterness.

HARVEYS

Harvey & Son (Lewes) Ltd., Bridge Wharf Brewery, Cliffe High Street, Lewes, E. Sussex, BN7 2AH.
Tel. (0273) 480209

Traditional family brewery with real ale in all 33 tied pubs and about 300 free trade outlets in Sussex and Kent. Frequently produces commemorative beers - occasionally on draught.

XX Mild Ale

(OG 1030, ABV 3%) A pleasant, dark brew which is only just continuing to hold on. The aroma and taste are malty, with a roast flavour, and the palate is fruity and sweetish. The aftertaste is similar, with lingering malt. Well worth finding.

Pale Ale

(OG 1032, ABV 3.5%) A very well-hopped, refreshing brew. Hops are in the aroma and palate, with some fruit and sweetness. Hops in the finish, too, with some bitterness. A very good session beer.

Best Bitter

(OG 1038, ABV 4%) A fine example of a full-bodied southern bitter. Its hoppy aroma gives way to a fruity, sweetish palate. The complex aftertaste features hops, with some bitterness, yet with a lingering sweetness.

XXXX Old

(OG 1042, ABV 4.3%) Brewed October-May: rich and dark, with lively fruitiness and a caramelly flavour. Mellow and smooth, when on form.

Armada Ale

(OG 1046, ABV 4.5%) A well-hopped, strong bitter with a powerful finish.

Elizabethan*

(OG 1090, ABV 8.5%) Occasional. A silky-smooth barley wine.

HARVIESTOUN

Harviestoun Brewery Ltd., Dollarfield Farm, Dollar, Clackmannanshire, Central, FK14 7LX.
Tel. (025 94) 2141

A small craft brewery, built by hand in a 200 year-old stone byre, operating from a former dairy at the foot of the Ochil Hills, near Stirling. Started in 1985 and now brewing three beers regularly, plus a New Year ale every December (the OG changes for each year, so this year's will be 1092). A 1044 OG beer has also been available on a few occasions, and a new, custom-built brewing plant should soon treble capacity. Another recent development is the cracking of its own malt. Directly serves around 15 outlets in central Scotland.

Waverley Ale*

(OG 1037, ABV 3.7%)

80/-*

(OG 1041, ABV 4.1%)

Old Manor*

(OG 1050, ABV 5.4%) A dark beer with a roast malt flavour.

Nouveau*

(OG 1092, ABV 9.2%) A winter brew for the New Year.

HERITAGE

The Heritage Brewery Ltd., Anglesey Road, Burton upon Trent, Staffs, DE14 3PF. Tel. (0283) 69226

The brewing company of the Heritage Brewery Museum, based in the former Everards Tiger Brewery which was built in 1881 for Liverpool brewer Thomas Sykes. Heritage Bitter is distributed to the free trade by Lloyds (see page 427). Thomas Sykes Ale is the speciality brew, sold mostly in corked bottles for celebrations and commemorations, but also available on draught. The Lloyds connection may be developed further, with the Derbyshire brewery producing beers at the Museum.

419

The Independents

| Bitter* | (OG 1045, ABV 4.2%) |
| Thomas Sykes Ale* | (OG 1100, ABV 10%) |

| **HESKET NEWMARKET** | **Hesket Newmarket Brewery, Old Crown Barn, Hesket Newmarket, Cumbria, CA7 8JG. Tel. (069 98) 288** |

Brewery officially opened in 1988 by telex message from a regular, Chris Bonnington, from Kathmandu. It is situated in an attractive North Lakes village, in a barn behind the Old Crown Inn. Now supplies ten free trade outlets as well as the Old Crown, its only tied house. The summer beer, Wrynose, is no longer produced, but there may be a porter in the pipeline.

Blencathra Bitter*	(OG 1035, ABV 3.25%)
Skiddaw Special Bitter*	(OG 1035, ABV 3.25%)
Doris's 90th Birthday Ale*	(OG 1045, ABV 4.25%)
Old Carrock Strong Ale*	(OG 1060, 5.75%)

| **HIGHGATE** | See Bass, page 459. |

| **HIGSONS** | See Whitbread, page 467. |

| **HILDEN** | **Hilden Brewery, Hilden House, Lisburn, Co. Antrim. Tel. (0846) 663863** |

Mini brewery in a Georgian country house, set up in 1981 to counter the local all-keg Guinness/Bass duopoly. Presently the only real ale brewery in Northern Ireland, supplying eight regular free trade outlets and some pubs in England, with Hilden Ale possibly available soon in the Dublin area. The gravity of Special Reserve has been reduced from 1042 and a visitor centre has been planned.

| Hilden Ale | (OG 1039) An amber-coloured beer with an aroma of malt, hops and fruit. The balanced taste is slightly slanted towards hops, and hops are also prominent in the full, malty finish. Bitter and refreshing. |
| Special Reserve | (OG 1039) Dark red/brown in colour and superbly aromatic - full of dark malts, producing an aroma of liquorice and toffee. Malt, fruit and toffee on the palate, with a sweet, malty finish. Mellow and satisfying. |

| **HOLDEN'S** | **Holden's Brewery Ltd., Hopden Brewery, George Street, Woodsetton, Dudley, W. Midlands, DY1 4LN. Tel. (0902) 880051** |

One of the long-established family breweries of the Black Country, producing a good range of real ales for its 19 pubs and around 40 free trade customers. More tied houses are planned, as finances allow, and with the fourth generation of the Holden family now under tutelage, the future looks optimistic.

| Stout | (OG 1036, ABV 3.2%) A dark brown beer, with malt and roast in the aroma and flavour, and a faint, hoppy aftertaste. |
| Mild | (OG 1037, ABV 3.6%) A good, balanced beer, with malt, roast and hops. Slightly sweet, with a malty and hoppy aftertaste. |

420

The Independents

Bitter   (OG 1039, ABV 3.9%) A fine, hoppy and malty beer. The taste is pleasantly bitter and hoppy, and the finish is dry and bitter.

XB*   (OG 1041, ABV 4.1%) Often sold as a house beer, with each outlet giving it its own name.

Special Bitter   (OG 1051, ABV 4.9%) A strong and very flavoursome, pale brown, malty bitter, with a bitter and sweet aftertaste.

XL   (OG 1092, ABV 8.9%) An old ale, only available in December: very fruity and sweet; a very strong and warming beer.

HOLT   **Joseph Holt PLC, Derby Brewery, Empire Street, Cheetham, Manchester, M3 1JD. Tel. (061) 834 3285**

Not to be confused with Allied's Midlands company Holts (Holt, Plant & Deakin). A traditional family firm, established in 1849, it produces Britain's cheapest bitter. Real ale in all 100 tied houses, often delivered in hogsheads (54 gallon barrels) such is its enthusiastic following. Only one pub does not sell Mild. The fast-growing free trade to pubs and clubs currently stands at around 45 outlets.

Mild   (OG 1033, ABV 3.2%) Very dark beer. Good body, with a malty, fruity aroma and roast malt prominent in the taste. Strong in hoppiness and bitterness for a mild, reflected in the characteristic aftertaste.

Bitter   (OG 1039, ABV 4%) Pale brown in colour, with a strong hop aroma. Although balanced by malt and fruit, the uncompromising bitterness can be a shock to the unwary and extends into the aftertaste.

HOLTS   See Allied Breweries, page 455.

HOME   See Scottish & Newcastle, page 464.

HOOK NORTON   **The Hook Norton Brewery Co. Ltd., The Brewery, Hook Norton, Banbury, Oxon, OX15 5NY. Tel. (0608) 737210**

One of the most delightful traditional Victorian tower breweries in Britain, set on the fringe of a fine stone village. It retains much of its original plant and machinery, the showpiece being the 25 horsepower stationary steam engine which is still used to pump the Cotswold well water used for the beer. All its 33 country pubs serve real ale, and some 400 free trade outlets are also supplied.

Best Mild   (OG 1032, ABV 2.9%) A dark, red/brown mild with a malty aroma and a malty, sweetish taste, tinged with a faint hoppy balance. Malty in the aftertaste. Splendid and highly drinkable.

Best Bitter   (OG 1036, ABV 3.3%) An excellently-balanced, golden bitter. Malty and hoppy on the nose and in the mouth, with a hint of fruitiness. Dry, but with some balancing sweetness. A hoppy bitterness dominates the finish.

Old Hooky   (OG 1049, ABV 4.3%) An unusual, tawny beer with a strong fruity and grainy aroma and palate, balanced by a hint of hops. Full-bodied, with a bitter, fruity and malty aftertaste.

HOP BACK   **Hop Back Brewery, Wyndham Arms, 27 Estcourt Road, Salisbury, Wiltshire, SP1 3AS. Tel. (0722) 328594**

A brew pub, set up in May 1987 with a five barrel plant, producing award-winning beers. Acquired a second tied house in March 1991 where it is planning to try out 'speciality' brews.

The Independents

Currently produces around 30 barrels a week, some of which goes out to its 12 free trade customers.

GFB (OG 1035, ABV 3.5%) Golden, with the sort of light, refreshing quality which makes an ideal session ale. Mellow and fruity in flavour, with a caramel overtone. A hint of honey in the aroma, and a long, well-balanced finish.

Special or Flintnapper* (OG 1040, ABV 4%) A beer which has been given attention by the brewer after last year's poor rating, though the new brew has not yet been tasted.

Entire Stout* (OG 1044, ABV 4.5%)

Summer Lightning (OG 1050, ABV 5%) An extremely pleasurable, bitter, straw-coloured beer with a terrific, fresh, hoppy aroma and a well-rounded, malty, hoppy flavour with an intense bitterness, which leads to an excellent, long, dry finish.

HOSKINS **Hoskins Brewery PLC, Beaumanor Brewery, 133 Beaumanor Road, Leicester, LE4 5QE. Tel. (0533) 661122**

The smallest remaining pre-WWI brewery. Supplies real ale to all its 12 tied houses and offers a varied guest beer list. A pub-owning company is due to be launched under the Business Expansion Scheme, with 20 new houses planned.

Beaumanor Bitter (OG 1039, ABV 3.9%) A very drinkable and refreshing, amber-coloured beer with a thin yet satisfying texture. An aroma of hops and fruit leads on to a hoppy taste and then a long, malty finish.

Penn's Ale (OG 1045, ABV 4.3%) A full-bodied, easy-drinking beer, golden in colour and with a slightly fruity aroma. Rich, malty and well-balanced in flavour, followed by a clean, dry, crystal malt finish.

Premium (OG 1050, ABV 4.6%) Now only an occasional brew. A pale gold beer with fruit and toffee in the aroma, and fruit and some mustiness in the flavour. Slightly cloying, fruity finish.

Churchill's Pride (OG 1050, ABV 4.8%) A new brew which has become a regular at the expense of Premium.

Old Nigel (OG 1060, ABV 5.7%) Malt and hints of liquorice are present in the robust flavour of this winter beer. Fruity in aroma and sweet-tasting, with a lasting, pleasantly-fruity finish. Russet in colour.

HOSKINS & OLDFIELD **Hoskins & Oldfield Brewery Ltd., North Mills, Frog Island, Leicester, LE3 5DH. Tel. (0533) 532191**

Set up by two members of Leicester's famous brewing family, Philip and Stephen Hoskins, in 1984, after the sale of the old Hoskins Brewery. A wide range of beers is produced for a scattered free trade, but local availability is unfortunately limited. EXS is no longer brewed, but Heroes Bitter is produced for the Legendary Yorkshire Heroes chain.

HOB Mild (OG 1035) A dark ruby mild with a chocolate and coffee aroma, and a dry, stout-like flavour. Heavy and creamy, with a lasting, dry, malty finish.

HOB Bitter (OG 1041) Golden in colour, with an aroma of peardrops. Its flavour is fruity and hoppy, with a harsh, hoppy, but sweet aftertaste. Not the beer it was.

Little Matty* (OG 1041) A darker version of HOB Bitter.

The Independents

Tom Kelly's Stout	(OG 1043) A satisfying stout, dark in colour, with an attractive, golden, creamy head and an aroma of malt and fruit. The flavour is exceedingly bitter but malty and the finish is dry and chocolatey.
Old Navigation Ale	(OG 1071) Ruby/black beer, with an aroma reminiscent of sherry. Sweet and fruity, with a stout-like malt flavour.
Christmas Noggin	(OG 1100) Russet-coloured beer with a spicy, fruity aroma. The taste is of malt and fruit, and the finish balances malt and hops. Sweet but not cloying.
	For Legendary Yorkshire Heroes:
Heroes Bitter*	(OG 1037)

HP&D	See Allied Breweries, page 455.

SARAH HUGHES	**Sarah Hughes Brewery, Beacon Hotel, 129 Bilston Street, Sedgley, W. Midlands, DY3 1JE. Tel. (0902) 883380**

SARAH HUGHES BREWERY

Brewery re-opened after lying idle for 30 years, to serve the village pub and a few other outlets. Now produces for the free trade. A Victorian-style conservatory was opened in 1991 to act as a reception area for brewery visits (always welcome during regular opening hours). A bitter has been added since last year, and there are plans for bottling.

Sedgley Surprise*	(OG 1048, ABV 5%) A new bitter.
Original Dark Ruby Mild	(OG 1058, ABV 6%) A full-bodied and well-balanced, strong, malty and fruity beer. The aftertaste has malt, roast and quite sweet characteristics.

HULL	**Hull Brewery Company Ltd., 144–148 English Street, Hull, Humbs, HU3 2BT. Tel. (0482) 586365**

Resurrected in 1989 after a 15-year absence by two local businessmen, and designed by small brewing expert Peter Austin in an old fish smokehouse. The beer, which is brewed to the original recipe, is mostly sold on the Hull club scene, but also as a guest beer in a few pubs. Plans to develop its own small chain of local pubs.

Mild*	(OG 1033)

HYDES' ANVIL	**Hydes' Anvil Brewery Ltd., 46 Moss Lane West, Manchester, M15 5PH. Tel. (061) 226 1317**

Family-controlled traditional brewery, first established at the Crown Brewery, Audenshaw in Manchester in 1863 and on its present site since the turn of the century. It became the Anvil brewery in 1943 and is the smallest of the established Manchester breweries and the only one to produce more than one real mild. Cask ale in all its 49 tied houses and slowly expanding both its tied estate and its free trade.

Mild	(OG 1032, ABV 3.5%) A light, refreshing, slightly fruity drink with little aftertaste. Fruity aroma, with a hint of malt.
Dark Mild*	(OG 1034, ABV 3.5%) Light with added caramel.
Light	(OG 1034, ABV 3.7%) A lightly hopped session beer, complex in character, with malt dominating and a brief but dry finish. Available more in southern Manchester than Mild, and vice-versa in northern parts of the city.
Bitter	(OG 1036, ABV 3.8%) A good-flavoured bitter, with a malty

The Independents

nose, fruity background and a malty aftertaste. A hint of bitterness throughout.

Strong Ale

(OG 1080, ABV 8%) Rich and fruity in aroma and taste, rather drier than many strong ales. A fruity, yet dry finish. Brewed once a year in October, for distribution in December. Available to all outlets and the free trade in nine gallon casks. Not many landlords stock it, however.

IND COOPE See Allied Breweries, page 456.

ISLE OF MAN

Isle Of Man Breweries Ltd., Falcon Brewery, Douglas, Isle of Man. Tel. (0624) 661140

The island's major brewery, following the merger in 1986 of the Okell and Castletown breweries. Real ale is produced under the unique Manx Brewers' Act 1874 (permitted ingredients: malt, sugar and hops only). Operates from Okell's impressive Victorian tower brewhouse near the centre of Douglas. Sixty-three of its 66 tied houses sell real ale which is also supplied to 12 free trade outlets. Okells 45 Special Bitter was launched in April 1991.

Okells Mild

(OG 1034, ABV 3.4%) A genuine, well-brewed mild ale, with a fine aroma of hops and crystal malt. Reddish-brown in colour, this beer has a full malt flavour with surprising bitter, hop notes and a hint of blackcurrants and oranges. Full malty finish.

Okells Bitter

(OG 1035, ABV 3.7%) Golden, malty and superbly hoppy in aroma, with a hint of honey. Rich and malty on the tongue, with a wonderful, dry, malt and hop finish. A complex but rewarding beer.

Castletown Bitter

(OG 1035, ABV 3.8%) A really refreshing, pale golden beer, with an inviting aroma of malt, hops and citrus fruit. Full of hop bitterness, culminating in a clean, full, malt finish, with hops again detectable. A fine, bitter beer.

Okells 45 Special Bitter*

(OG 1045, ABV 4.5%)

JENNINGS

Jennings Bros PLC, Castle Brewery, Cockermouth, Cumbria, CA13 9NE. Tel. (0900) 823214

ESTD. 1828

Traditional brewery in the far North West, in business since 1828 and on the present site for over 100 years. Recent major expenditure in the fermenting and yeast rooms have helped maintain quality and resulted in the addition of two new beers, Cumberland Ale and Sneck Lifter, in the last two years. Real ale is supplied to 77 of its 85 tied houses, 120 free trade outlets, and increasingly throughout the UK via wholesalers.

Mild*

(OG 1031, ABV 3.1%) A dark, mellow mild.

Bitter

(OG 1035, ABV 3.4%) An excellent, distinctive, red/brown brew with a hoppy, malty aroma. A good, strong balance of grain and hops in the taste, with a moderate bitterness, developing into a lingering, dry, malty finish.

Cumberland Ale*

(OG 1040, ABV 3.8%)

Sneck Lifter*

(OG 1055, ABV 4.9%)

The Independents

JOLLY ROGER

Jolly Roger Brewery, 31–33 Friar Street, Worcester, WR1 2NA. Tel. (0905) 22222

Worcestershire's only brewery, established in 1982 as a brew pub. As demand outgrew the original site, a larger commercial brewery was developed in Friar Street in 1991. The brewery also operates as a museum, with organised groups welcome, and brews commemorative beers and occasional special ales, stouts and porters. Bottle-conditioned beers planned. Extensive free trade.

Jolly Roger Ale* (OG 1038) A golden-coloured beer.

Shipwrecked* (OG 1040) A dark bitter.

Goodness* (OG 1042) A stout.

Winter Wobbler* (OG 1092) The seasonal beer - a dark old English ale.

KING & BARNES

King & Barnes Ltd., The Horsham Brewery, 18 Bishopric, Horsham, W. Sussex, RH12 1QP. Tel. (0403) 69344

Independent family brewery, dating back almost 200 years and in the present premises since 1870. Originally run by the King family, it united with the Barnes family brewery in 1906. Its 'Fine Sussex Ales' are served in all 60 country houses. Extensive free trade mostly within a radius of 40 miles. A low alcohol keg beer, LA, has been served on handpull in recent years.

Mild (OG 1034, ABV 3.2%) A smooth, malty, dark brown mild, with a bittersweet finish and a fruity, malty aroma. Tends to be displaced by Old Ale in winter.

Sussex Bitter (OG 1034, ABV 3.5%) A splendid, hoppy, tawny-coloured bitter, with good malt balance and a dry finish. Can suffer from poor cellarmanship outside the tied estate.

Broadwood (OG 1040, ABV 4%) Pale brown with a faint malt aroma. A good marriage of malt and hops is present in the taste, with malt slightly dominating.

Old (OG 1046, ABV 4.1%) A classic, almost black old ale. A fruity, roast malt flavour, with some hops, leads to a bittersweet, malty finish. Lovely roast malt aroma. Available November-Easter.

Festive (OG 1050, ABV 4.8%) Tawny/red with a malty aroma. The flavour is fruity and malty, with a noticeable hop presence. Malt dominates the finish.

LARKINS

Larkins Brewery Ltd., Larkins Farm, Chiddingstone, Edenbridge, Kent, TN8 7BB. Tel. (0892) 870328

Started in 1986 with the purchase of the Royal Tunbridge Wells Brewery and moved to a converted barn at the owner's farm in Chiddingstone at the end of 1989, when an additional brewing copper and fermenter were acquired. Additive-free beers are brewed, partly using hops from the oast house next door. Supplies 60 free houses in the South East.

Traditional Bitter (OG 1035.5, ABV 3.4%) Tremendous bitterness, combined with a moderately hoppy taste, characterizes this pale brown beer, which has a hoppy aroma and aftertaste.

Sovereign Bitter (OG 1040, ABV 4%) A malty and slightly fruity, bitter ale, with a very malty finish. Copper-red in colour.

Best Bitter* (OG 1045.5, ABV 4.7%) The recipe of this beer has recently been changed, so no description is available.

The Independents

Porter Ale

(OG 1053, ABV 5.5%) Each taste and smell of this potent black beer reveals another facet of its character. An explosion of roasted malt, bitter and fruity flavours leaves a bittersweet aftertaste.

LEES

JW Lees & Co. (Brewers) Ltd., Greengate Brewery, PO Box 2, Middleton Junction, Manchester, M24 2AX. Tel. (061) 643 2487

One of Manchester's clutch of surviving family-owned, independent breweries, founded in 1828 by John Lees, a retired cotton manufacturer. The existing brewhouse dates from 1876 but has been expanded in recent years. Serves real ale in all 173 of its tied houses and clubs (mostly in northern Manchester). Free trade in the North West to about 100 outlets.

GB Mild

(OG 1032, ABV 3%) Malt and roast aroma, with a malty, fruity, sweet palate. Enjoys the characteristic dry, malty aftertaste unique to Lees beers. Low turnover in some outlets is a cause for concern.

Bitter

(OG 1038, ABV 4%) Pale beer with a malty, hoppy aroma and a distinctive, malty, dry and slightly metallic taste. Clean, dry Lees finish. The levels of malt, hops and bitterness can vary considerably.

Moonraker

(OG 1073, ABV 7.5%) Reddish-brown in colour, having a strong, malty, fruity aroma. The flavour is rich and sweet, with roast malt, and the finish is fruity yet dry. Only available in a handful of outlets.

LINFIT

Linfit Brewery, Sair Inn, Lane Top, Linthwaite, Huddersfield, W. Yorks, HD7 5SG. Tel. (0484) 842370

19th-century brew pub which recommenced brewing in 1982, producing an impressive range of ales for sale at the Sair and for free trade as far away as Manchester - now serves eight regular outlets. Occasional batches of bottled beers produced.

Mild

(OG 1032, ABV 3%) Roast malt dominates in this straightforward dark mild. Some hop aroma; slightly dry flavour. The finish is malty.

Bitter

(OG 1035, ABV 3.5%) Good session beer. A dry-hopped aroma leads to a clean-tasting, hoppy bitterness, balanced with some maltiness. The finish is well-balanced, too, but sometimes with intense bitterness.

Special

(OG 1041, ABV 4%) Dry-hopping again provides the aroma for this rich and mellow bitter. Very soft profile and character; fills the mouth with texture rather than taste. Clean, rounded finish.

English Guineas Stout

(OG 1050, ABV 5%) A fruity, roasted aroma preludes a smooth, roasted, chocolatey flavour which is bitter but not too dry. Excellent appearance; good, bitter finish.

Old Eli

(OG 1050, ABV 5%) Excellent, well-balanced premium bitter with a dry-hopped aroma and a fruity, bitter finish.

Leadboiler

(OG 1063, ABV 6%) Flowery and hoppy in aroma, with a very moreish, bitter and strong flavour which provides a soft mouthfeel. Well-balanced by a prominent maltiness; rounded, bitter finish.

Enoch's Hammer

(OG 1080, ABV 8%) Straw-coloured, vinous bitter with no pretentions about its strength or pedigree. A full, fruity aroma

The Independents

leads on to a smooth, alcoholic-tasting, hoppy, bitter taste, with an unexpectedly bitter finish.

Xmas Ale (OG 1082, ABV 8%) A hearty and warming ale. The flavour is strong in roasted malt, with some bitterness. Extremely vinous, with a slightly yeasty, metallic taste. Bitter finish. An adaption of Enoch's Hammer.

LLOYDS

Lloyds Country Beers, John Thompson Brewery, Ingleby, Derbyshire. Tel. (0332) 863426

Set up as a home-brew operation at an inn in 1977, Lloyds is now a separate business, serving around 60 free trade outlets. A new session bitter, Classic, was launched in 1990. Also distributes Heritage Bitter from the Heritage Brewery (see page 419), and there are plans for Lloyds to brew Heritage beers at the Burton brewery, whilst continuing in Derbyshire. There has been an upturn in sales and the future looks more promising for the brewery now than it has at any time.

Classic* (OG 1035, ABV 3.2%)

Derby Bitter or Country Bitter or JTS XXX* (OG 1043, ABV 4.2%) Full and fruity.

VIP (Very Important Pint)* (OG 1048, ABV 4.6%) Heavier, darker version of the bitter.

Skullcrusher* (OG 1067.5, ABV 6.8%) A heavy Christmas beer.

Overdraft* (OG 1070, ABV 7%)

LONGSTONE

Longstone Brewery, Station Road, Belford, Northumberland. Tel. (0668) 213031

After a year of difficulty in securing premises, this brewery finally got off the ground in 1991. It had been planned to call the company 'Darling's', but 'Longstone', the original name of the bitter, was adopted as the trading name instead.

Bitter* (OG 1039, ABV 4%)

LORIMER & CLARK See Vaux, page 448, and Caledonian Brewery, page 404.

McEWAN See Scottish & Newcastle, page 464.

MACLAY

Maclay & Co. Ltd., Thistle Brewery, Alloa, Clackmannanshire, Central, FK10 1ED. Tel. (0259) 723387

Founded in 1830 and still in family ownership, Maclay was one of just two independent breweries left in Scotland after the takeover typhoon swept through the country. Supplies real ale to 14 of its 25 houses and over 300 free trade outlets. Beer sphere containers (36-pint) are available for the take-home/party trade by arrangement. Scotch Ale is the latest addition to their beer range.

60/- Light Ale* (OG 1030, ABV 3.5%) A flavoursome, dark, session beer.

70/- SPA* (OG 1034, ABV 3.7%) A well-hopped, quenching beer.

80/- Export* (OG 1040, ABV 4%) Well-balanced and rich.

Porter* (OG 1040, ABV 4%) Dark and tasty.

Scotch Ale* (OG 1050, ABV 5%)

The Independents

McMULLEN

McMullen & Sons Ltd., The Hertford Brewery, 26 Old Cross, Hertford, SG14 1RD. Tel. (0992) 584911

Hertfordshire's oldest independent family brewery, built on the site of three wells, providing the water which adds to the characteristic flavour of McMullen's beers. Serves cask-conditioned beer in all but 10 of its 150 pubs in Hertfordshire, Essex and London, and in about 180 free trade outlets.

Original AK

(OG 1033, ABV 3.8%) A light bitter with a hoppy aroma. The malty, hoppy flavour is followed by an aftertaste which has bitterness, hoppiness and a touch of malt.

Country Best Bitter

(OG 1041, ABV 4.6%) A predominantly malty beer, although a bitter hoppiness can also be detected. The aroma has hops and malt, and there is a distinctive finish with bitterness, malt and hops.

Stronghart

(OG 1070, ABV 7%) A sweet, rich, dark beer; a single brew for the winter months. It has a malty aroma, with hints of hops and roast malt which carry through to the taste.

MALTON

Malton Brewery Co. Ltd., Crown Hotel, Wheelgate, Malton, N. Yorks, YO17 0HP. Tel. (0653) 697580

Small brewery, established in 1984 in a stable block at the rear of Malton's Crown Hotel. The racehorse Double Chance, the 1925 Grand National winner, was once stabled where the fermenting room now is, hence the name of the bitter. Now produces four regular, additive-free beers and occasional special beers, for the local free trade and countrywide distribution through beer agencies.

Pale Ale*

(OG 1034, ABV 3.5%) A light session beer.

Double Chance Bitter*

(OG 1038, ABV 4%) Well-hopped.

Pickwick's Porter*

(OG 1042, ABV 4.2%) A dry stout.

Owd Bob*

(OG 1055, ABV 5.8%) A dry, dark winter warmer.

MANSFIELD

Mansfield Brewery PLC, Littleworth, Mansfield, Notts, NG18 1AB. Tel. (0623) 25691

In the early 1970s, Mansfield's turned its back on cask beer, but, since its return to real ale production, it has been rewarded by steadily rising sales of three excellent traditional beers, with Riding Dark Mild holding its own in a declining sector of the market. One of the country's major regional brewers, Mansfield offers one or more of its real ales in most of its 340 tied houses. Substantial free trade, especially in East Midlands clubs, and a reciprocal trading arrangement with Charles Wells.

Riding Dark Mild

(OG 1035, ABV 3.1%) Dark brown in colour, with a hint of red. A predominantly chocolate malt taste and finish, with a dash of fruit, follows a pleasant, roast malt aroma.

Riding Traditional Bitter

(OG 1035, ABV 3.5%) Pale brown, with a malty, hoppy nose. A firm malt background is overlaid with a good bitter bite and hop flavours.

Old Baily

(OG 1045, ABV 4.5%) Resembles a Scotch heavy, but with a fine balance of hop, malt and fruit flavours. Dark copper-red in colour, with an aroma of malt and fruit.

The Independents

MARSTON MOOR	**Marston Moor Brewery, The Crown Inn, Kirk Hammerton, York, N. Yorks, YO5 8DD. Tel. (0423) 330341**

Small brewery set up in 1984, now brewing about 550 barrels a year, to supply the Crown and a scattered free trade.

Cromwell Bitter* — (OG 1037, ABV 3.7%) A distinctive, bitter beer.

Brewers Pride* — (OG 1042 ABV 4.2%) An amber-coloured, premium beer.

Porter* — (OG 1042, ABV 4.2%) A seasonal brew (November-May), ruby-coloured and stout-like.

Brewers Droop* — (OG 1050, ABV 5%) A potent, straw-coloured ale.

MARSTON'S — **Marston, Thompson & Evershed PLC, Shobnall Road, Burton upon Trent, Staffs, DE14 2BW. Tel. (0283) 31131**

One of Britain's great traditional breweries which, sadly, in 1984, its 150th year, took over the Border Brewery of Wrexham. It added to its tied estate again in 1990 by the purchase of 49 pubs from Ansells. Real ale is available in most of its 888 pubs, stretching from Cumbria to Hampshire, and the enormous free trade is helped by many Whitbread pubs stocking Pedigree Bitter. The only brewery still using the unique Burton Union system of fermentation for its stronger ales.

Border Mild — (OG 1031, ABV 3.1%) A thin, dark mild with negligible aroma, a slight malty flavour, with hints of caramel, sulphur and bitterness, and a faint, dry and malty finish.

Mercian Mild — (OG 1032, ABV 3.3%) A copper to dark brown beer, thin, but well balanced. Hints of roast malt and fruit in the taste, and a sweet, mild finish. A quaffing mild.

Border Exhibition — (OG 1034, ABV 3.5%) Originally a light mild when brewed in Wrexham, but now a thinnish, light, mid brown bitter with the typical Marston's sulphury taste.

Border Bitter — (OG 1034, ABV 3.6%) Thinnish, light session beer, pale brown in colour. The slight, well-balanced, malty, bitter taste, with hints of fruit and hop, is echoed in the aftertaste.

Burton Best Bitter — (OG 1036, ABV 3.7%) An amber/tawny session beer which can often be markedly sulphury in the aroma and taste. At its best, a splendid, subtle balance of malt, hops and fruit follows a faintly hoppy aroma and develops into a balanced, dry aftertaste.

Merrie Monk — (OG 1043, ABV 4.5%) A smooth, dark brew. Has a creamy, slightly sweet flavour, with traces of caramel, roast malt and fruit. Sweet, malty finish.

Pedigree Bitter — (OG 1043, ABV 4.5%) An amber, ubiquitous beer which can vary in character. When at its best, the taste balances grain and hops with a little fruitiness, and the finish is dry. A sulphury character can occasionally dominate.

Owd Rodger — (OG 1080, ABV 7.6%) A dark, ruby-red barley wine, with an intense fruity nose before a deep, winey, heavy fruit flavour, with malt and faint hops. The finish is dry and fruity (strawberries). Misunderstood, moreish and strong.

MAULDONS — **Mauldons Brewery, 7 Addison Road, Chilton Ind. Estate, Sudbury, Suffolk, CO10 6YW. Tel. (0787) 311055**

The head brewer at Watney's Mortlake plant revived the name of his former family brewery in 1982. Supplies over 150 free

The Independents

trade outlets in Suffolk, S. Norfolk, Essex, Cambridge and Hertfordshire, and provides house beers for local pubs (look out for names in pub descriptions). The beers are widespread, but worth seeking out.

FA Mild
(OG 1034, ABV 3.4%) A good balance between the initial malt and roast and the fruit and dryness in the aftertaste. Sadly, it is very hard to find this dark 'Fine Anglian' mild.

Golden Brown*
(OG 1034, ABV 3.4%)

Bitter
(OG 1037, ABV 3.8%) Malt and fruit are predominant throughout, with little balancing hop or bitterness.

Porter
(OG 1042, ABV 3.8%) A black beer with malt and roast flavours dominating. Some hop in the finish.

Old
(OG 1042, ABV 4%) Winter ale with a reddish brown appearance. The taste is complex, with fruit, malt, caramel, hop and bitterness all present.

Squires
(OG 1044, ABV 4.2%) A best bitter with a good, malty aroma. The taste is evenly balanced between malt and a hoppy bitterness.

Special
(OG 1045, ABV 4.2%) By far the most hoppy of Mauldons' beers, with a good, bitter finish. Some balancing malt.

Suffolk Punch
(OG 1050, ABV 4.8%) A full-bodied, strong bitter. The malt and fruit in the aroma are reflected in the taste and there is some hop character in the finish. Deep tawny/red in colour.

Black Adder
(OG 1055, ABV 5.3%) A dark, stout-like beer. Roast is very strong in the aroma and taste, but malt, hop and bitterness provide an excellent balance and a lingering finish. CAMRA's **Champion Beer of Britain** 1991.

Christmas Reserve
(OG 1065, ABV 6.6%) A sweet Christmas ale with malt and fruit. Typically for this type of ale, it has little bitterness. Fairly pale in colour for a strong beer, with red tints.

MILL

Mill Brewery, Unit 18c, Bradley Lane, Newton Abbot, Devon, TQ12 4JW. Tel. (0626) 63322

Founded in 1983 on the site of an old watermill and still aiming to expand. Special brews, based on Janner's Old Original, are often sold under local pub names, 'Janner' being the local term for a Devonian. Serves nine regular outlets and the free trade in southern Devon and Torbay.

Janner's Ale
(OG 1038) Pale brown-coloured, bland beer, without any discernible aroma. The flavour is bitter/hoppy and the aftertaste is also bitter, but it lacks balance.

Janner's Old Dark Ale*
(OG 1040) Now only an occasional brew.

Janner's Old Original
(OG 1045) A beer malty and sweet in character, with a slightly 'thick' consistency. Bitter finish.

Janner's Christmas Ale*
(OG 1050) The festive beer.

MINERS ARMS

Miners Arms Brewery, Westbury-sub-Mendip, Somerset, BA5 1HD. Tel. (0749) 870719

No longer brews. The beers are produced by Mole's (see page 432). Still has two tied houses.

The Independents

MITCHELL'S

Mitchell's of Lancaster (Brewers) Ltd., 11 Moor Lane, Lancaster, LA1 1QB. Tel. (0524) 60000

Lancaster's last independent brewery, wholly owned and run by direct descendants of William Mitchell. The brewing plant is very traditional: many of the casks are still wooden and all the beers are brewed with natural spring well water. With one exception, real ale is sold in all its 54 pubs and virtually countrywide in the free trade. In 1990 the company acquired Marsh Soft Drinks of Barrow-in-Furness and James Fletcher Wines of Cockermouth. Further expansion is planned.

Best Dark Mild — (OG 1033, ABV 3.2%) Black with ruby-red tints. Malty in aroma and taste, with a faint fruitiness. A smooth and highly drinkable mild.

Best Bitter — (OG 1035, ABV 3.6%) A golden bitter with a malty aroma and a superb, dry, malty flavour, with a faint balance of hops. A delicate bitter aftertaste usually demands more of the same.

ESB — (OG 1050, ABV 5%) Creamy in texture; malty in aroma. The flavour is also malty and fruity, with a hoppy finish.

Single Malt Winter Warmer — (OG 1064, ABV 7.5%) A seasonal brew, mid brown in colour and suggestive of malt whisky in aroma and flavour. Strongly malty throughout, with a subtle bittersweet, hoppy balance in the taste.

MITCHELLS & BUTLERS (M&B) — See Bass, page 459.

MOLE'S

Mole's Brewery (Cascade Drinks Ltd.), 5 Merlin Way, Bowerhill, Melksham, Wilts, SN12 6TJ. Tel. (0225) 704734

Established in 1982 by former Ushers brewer Roger Catte (the brewery name came from his nickname). Serves one tied house and over 50 outlets in Wiltshire and Avon, a poor area for free trade, as well as much of the country via beer agencies. Brews under contract for Miners Arms and acts as a distributor for other members of the Small Independent Brewers Association (SIBA).

IPA — (OG 1035, ABV 3.5%) A pale brown beer with a trace of maltiness in the aroma. A thin, malty, dry flavour, with little aftertaste.

Cask Bitter — (OG 1040, ABV 4%) A pale brown/golden-coloured beer with an aroma of malt, fruit and hops. The taste is malty, with some bitterness; the body is good, with a rounded finish of all the primary flavours. Not too bitter and a little dry.

Landlord's Choice — (OG 1045, ABV 4.5%) A copper-red beer with a malty aroma. The flavour, too, is malty and full-bodied, with hints of hops and banana. A strongly malty finish but with a dry bitterness which is long-lasting.

Brew 97 — (OG 1050, ABV 5%) A mid brown, full-bodied beer with a powerful, malty aroma. The strong flavour is sweet and malty, and the full aftertaste has malt and a dry bitterness. A rich, wonderfully warming, malty ale.

Xmas Ale — (OG 1064) A dark, red/brown beer with a noticeably complex aroma of fruit, roast malt, caramel and hops, and a similar, full-bodied, warming taste. It becomes bitter, dry and spicy towards the finish, which lasts well. Deserves to be brewed beyond the festive season.

The Independents

For Miners Arms:

Light*
(OG 1035, ABV 3.2%) Summer only.

Own Ale
(OG 1040, ABV 3.8%) Pale brown beer with a mostly malty, bitter taste, a malty aroma and a dry finish. Since being contract brewed, it has become noticeably sweeter and is more consistent. Can still be slightly lactic.

Guvnor's Special Brew
(OG 1048, ABV 4.8%) A golden, malty brew with a faint, hoppy aroma and a dry, slightly sour palate, with some citrus fruit. A dry, malty, lasting finish.

MOORHOUSE'S
Moorhouse's Brewery (Burnley) Ltd., 4 Moorhouse Street, Burnley, Lancs, BB11 5EN. Tel. (0282) 22864/416004

Long-established (1870) producer of hop bitters, which in 1979 began brewing traditional beer. Has since had several owners; the latest, Bill Parkinson, has invested in a new brewhouse to meet increased demand. His modern plant is complemented by traditional, turn-of-the-century equipment. Two tied houses and about 120 free trade outlets, all with real ale.

Black Cat Mild*
(OG 1034, ABV 3.4%)

Premier Bitter
(OG 1036, ABV 3.6%) A straw-coloured, clean-tasting bitter with a good balance of flavours and a distinctive, bitter finish. Refreshing.

Pendle Witches Brew
(OG 1050, ABV 5%) Fruit is prominent in the aroma, leading on to a full, malty taste with some of the sweetness more commonly associated with a higher gravity brew.

Owd Ale*
(OG 1065, ABV 6.4%) A winter brew.

MORLAND
Morland & Co. PLC, PO Box 5, Ock Street, Abingdon, Oxfordshire, OX14 5DD. Tel. (0235) 553377

Thames Valley brewery, established in 1711 with its own well. Handpumped ale is now in roughly 191 of the 205 tied houses, but this figure is liable to change, as Morland is sadly closing many low volume village pubs and concentrating on large town pubs, particularly those with catering facilities. In many of these outlets a cask-breather is used at the licensee's discretion. Real ale is also available in the club and free trade (around 400 outlets). A new beer, Old Speckled Hen, was launched last year and proved very popular, even though ridiculously highly priced in tied houses. It is a shame that it could not do more to maintain the quality of its present range.

Original Bitter
(OG 1035, ABV 4%) A light amber beer with malty, hoppy nose with a hint of fruitiness. The distinct, but lightish malt and hops carry over to the flavour and leave a sweet but dry, hoppy aftertaste.

Old Masters
(OG 1040, ABV 4.6%) A well-balanced tawny/amber beer with not outstandingly strong flavours. The initial aroma of malt and hops leads to a moderately malty, but dry and hoppy flavour, allowing a hint of fruit through with undertones of cherry which can be faintly sulphurous. Dry, bitter finish.

Old Speckled Hen
(OG 1050, ABV 5.2%) Morland's most distinctive beer, deep tawny/amber in colour. A well-balanced aroma of roasted malt and hops is complemented by a good hint of caramel. An initial sweet, malty, fruity, roast caramel taste soon allows the dry hop flavour through, leaving a well-balanced aftertaste.

The Independents

MORRELLS

1782
MORRELLS BREWERY
Oxford

Morrells Brewery Ltd., The Lion Brewery, St Thomas Street, Oxford, OX1 1LA. Tel. (0865) 792013

Owned and run by the Morrell family since 1782, this is Oxford's last surviving brewery. Totally committed to brewing, it produces one of the widest ranges of real ales in the country for all 131 of its mostly tenanted pubs, and has taken on the contract brewing of Whitbread's Strong Country Bitter. In summer 1991 the low-gravity light and dark milds were discontinued in favour of a stronger dark beer.

Bitter

(OG 1036, ABV 3.7%) Golden-yellow in colour and light in body, but not in flavour, with a good aroma of hops complemented by malt and fruitiness. The initial dry hop bitterness is well balanced by the flavour of malt which gives way to a nice, refreshing, slightly sweet fruitiness, with a hint of roast caramel. A bittersweet, hoppy finish.

Dark*

(OG 1036, ABV 3.7%)

Varsity

(OG 1041, ABV 4.3%) A tawny/amber beer. Malt, hops and fruit are the main features in aroma and taste, but are well balanced. The slightly sweet, malty, fruity start fades away to a distinctive, bittersweet finish.

Graduate

(OG 1048, ABV 5%) An intense malt and roast aroma is complemented by a moderate hoppiness in the taste. Pleasant, bitter finish. The gravity has reverted to 1048, from 1051.

College

(OG 1072, ABV 7.4%) Normally only available in winter.

For Whitbread:

Strong Country Bitter*

(OG 1037, ABV 3.9%)

NETHERGATE

NETHERGATE
FINE ALES

Nethergate Brewery Co. Ltd., 11-13 High Street, Clare, Suffolk, CO10 8NY. Tel. (0787) 277244

From the time it was set up, in 1986, until 1988, Nethergate only brewed one beer (winner of the Best Bitter award at the Cambridge CAMRA beer festival for three consecutive years). A second beer, Old Growler, was launched in late 1988 and is also an award-winner. Only traditional methods are used: no sugars, no colourings, no hop extracts and these beers are now available in roughly 100 outlets in Suffolk, Essex, Cambs and Herts. Casks IPA was originally brewed for a beer agency. Expansion is planned to double the brewing capacity.

Casks IPA

(OG 1035, ABV 3.6%) When first introduced in 1990 this was a bland, watery beer, but has now upgraded to an excellent session ale with a pronounced hoppiness on the palate.

Bitter

(OG 1040, ABV 4.1%) A dark beer whose enticingly hoppy fragrance leads into a flavour which balances lip-smacking hoppiness, true bitterness and smooth maltiness. A real beer drinker's beer.

Old Growler

(OG 1054, ABV 5.8%) A wonderfully complex dark ale whose bitter, roast initial taste is counterpoised by a rich, fruit and chocolate flavour before a long, hoppy finish. Based on an old London porter recipe.

NICHOLSON'S

See Allied Breweries, page 456.

The Independents

NIX WINCOTT

Nix Wincott Brewery, Three Fyshes Inn, Bridge Street, Turvey, Beds, MK43 8ER. Tel. (023 064) 264

Began brewing in 1987 when Two Henrys Bitter was immediately received by the local free trade and wholesalers. In a few years capacity was doubled. Winky's Winter Warmer is a new addition.

Two Henrys Bitter

(OG 1040, ABV 3.9%) Amber-coloured with malt and traces of fruit in the aroma. Well-balanced flavour with a bitter finish.

Old Nix

(OG 1058, ABV 5.5%) An overwhelming malty aroma, followed by a good balance of malt and fruit in the flavour, and then a complex aftertaste of malt, fruit and bitterness.

Winky's Winter Warmer*

(ABV 5.7%) A dark Christmas ale.

NORTH & EAST RIDING

North & East Riding Brewers Ltd., The Highlander, 15–16 Esplanade, South Cliff, Scarborough, N. Yorks. Tel. (0723) 365627

Now only brews for itself (see Brew Pubs: Highlander, page 469).

NORTH YORKSHIRE

THE NORTH YORKSHIRE BREWING COMPANY

North Yorkshire Brewing Co., 80–84 North Ormesby Road, Middlesbrough, Cleveland, TS4 2AG. Tel. (0642) 226224

A purpose-built brewery which began production in March 1990 and now supplies an expanding free trade, as well as its single tied house, the Tap & Barrel. No adjuncts in the beers. Has increased its range from just two to six beers.

Best Bitter

(OG 1036) Light and very refreshing. Surprisingly full-flavoured for a pale, low gravity beer. A complex, bittersweet mixture of malt, hops and fruit carries through into the aftertaste.

IPA or XXB

(OG 1040, ABV 4.2%) A pleasant, pale brown beer, fruity, malty and hoppy, but without the subtlety of Best Bitter and perhaps a little too sweet. The finish, however, is dry and hoppy.

Erimus Dark

(OG 1046) A dark, full-bodied, sweet brew with lots of roast malt and caramel, and an underlying hoppiness. At its best, it is very smooth indeed, with a tight, creamy head and a sweet, malty finish.

Flying Herbert

(OG 1048, ABV 5.2%) A refreshing, red/brown beer with a hoppy aroma. The flavour is a pleasant balance of roast malt and sweetness which predominates over the hops. The malty, bitter finish develops slowly.

Dizzy Dick

(OG 1080) A smooth, strong, dark, aromatic ale with an obvious bite, although too sweet for some. The very full, roast malt and caramel flavour has hints of fruit and toffee. The malty sweetness persists in the aftertaste.

NORWICH

See Courage, page 462.

OAK

Oak Brewing Company Ltd., Phoenix Brewery, Green Lane, Heywood, Gtr. Manchester, OL10 2EP. Tel. (0706) 627009

Brewery established in 1982, now supplying free trade from West Cheshire to West Yorkshire. The move to its new home in Heywood, from Ellesmere Port, was much delayed, but it took place in early summer 1991. The beers have not been tasted since the brewery move.

Hopwood Bitter* (OG 1034) A new brew from the new brewery.

Best Bitter (OG 1038) A tawny, hoppy session beer with some balancing malt in the aroma and taste. A strong, dry and hoppy finish.

Tyke Bitter* (OG 1042) Originally brewed for the West Riding Brewery (currently inoperative), but available throughout Oak's free trade.

Old Oak Ale (OG 1044) A well-balanced, brown beer with a multitude of mellow fruit flavours. Malt and hops balance the strong fruitiness in the aroma and taste, and the finish is malty, fruity and dry.

Extra Double Stout* (OG 1045) Trialled in the last year and may become permanent.

Double Dagger (OG 1050) A pale brown, malty brew, more pleasantly dry and light than its gravity would suggest. Moderately fruity throughout; a hoppy bitterness in the mouth balances the strong graininess.

Porter* (OG 1050) Now available all year round.

Wobbly Bob (OG 1060) A red/brown beer with a malty, fruity aroma. Strongly malty and fruity in flavour and quite hoppy, with the sweetness yielding to a dryness in the aftertaste.

OAKHILL **The Old Brewery, High Street, Oakhill, Bath, Avon, BA3 5AS. Tel. (0749) 840134**

A Somerset brewery, despite its Avon postal address, set up by a farmer in 1984 on the site of the original Oakhill brewery, built in 1767 and burnt down in 1925. Like its predecessor, the present Oakhill uses spring water from the outlying Mendip hills. Stout looks set to become a permanent fixture in the beer range. No tied houses, but roughly a hundred free trade outlets are supplied in Avon, Somerset, Dorset and Wiltshire, within a 35-mile radius.

Bitter (OG 1038, ABV 3.8%) Amber-coloured, with a hoppy, malty aroma. Hoppy and bitter in the mouth, with balancing malt. There is a similar balance in the strong finish. Can be sulphury.

Yeoman Ale (OG 1050, ABV 4.8%) A mid brown beer with a hoppy, malty aroma and a malty, fruity, bittersweet taste. The strong finish is fruity, hoppy and dry.

Draught Stout* (OG 1044, ABV 4%) At present, an occasional brew.

OKELL See Isle of Man Breweries, page 424.

OLDHAM See Whitbread, page 466.

OLD LUXTERS **Old Luxters Farm Brewery, Hambleden, Henley-on-Thames, Oxfordshire, RG9 6JW. Tel. (049 163) 330**

A brewery set up by David Ealand, owner and producer of Chiltern Valley Wines, with a three and a half barrel plant from Inn Brewing. The beer first appeared in May 1990 and is now available in five local free houses in the area. Plans for bottle-conditioned beers. Hambleden is in Buckinghamshire, despite the brewery's postal address.

Barn Ale (OG 1042.5) Predominantly malty, fruity and hoppy in taste and nose, and tawny/amber in colour. Fairly rich and strong in flavours: the initial, sharp, malty and fruity taste leaves a dry, bittersweet, fruity aftertaste, with hints of black cherry. Can be slightly sulphurous.

OLD MILL

Old Mill Brewery, Mill Street, Snaith, Goole, Humbs, DN14 9HS. Tel. (0405) 861813

Founded in 1983 by a former Wilson's production director, in a 200 year-old building which had previously served as a malt kiln and corn mill. 1991 saw the installation of new equipment to increase capacity to 300 barrels per week, and the opening of the company's ninth tied house (in Rotherham). Supplies real ale to all its tied houses and around 75 free trade customers, mostly within 40 miles.

Mild
(OG 1034, ABV 3.4%) A dark, red/brown beer, with roast and fruit aromas. Malt and bitter tastes follow, with a short, hoppy aftertaste. Seems to have lost body recently, but better than the average mild.

Bitter
(OG 1037, ABV 3.7%) A fresh, clean and hoppy, amber beer, with a malt and hop nose and a multi-layered grain and bitter taste. More malt in the aftertaste than previously, yet still dry. A classic bitter.

Bullion
(OG 1044, ABV 4.5%) Lots of taste in the mouth, as malt and hops follow a malty aroma. Dark amber in colour. Hints of fruit at every stage and a big, malt and bitter finish. A fine premium bitter.

ORKNEY

The Orkney Brewery, Quoyloo, Sandwick, Orkney, KW16 3LT. Tel. (0856) 84802

The Orkney's first brewery in living memory, set up in 1988 by former licensee Roger White. A real ale addict, he had to brew keg beer 'to appease local palates'. The original brew, Raven Ale, has now been joined by two more cask beers, and there are others in the pipeline. Bottle-conditioned beers are available to order. Serves the free trade in mainland Scotland and northern England.

Raven Ale
(OG 1038, ABV 3.8%) Still mainly keg (cask on mainland). Worth seeking out when in 'real' form. Smooth, mellow and malty, with a distinctive aroma and finish.

Dark Island*
(OG 1045, ABV 4.6%)

Skullsplitter *
(OG 1080, ABV 8.5%)

OTTER

Otter Brewery, Mathayes, Luppitt, near Honiton, Devon, EX14 0SA.

One of the country's newest breweries, opened in November 1990. So far, its ale, brewed with its own spring water and local malt, has been well received and brewing capacity is due for expansion. Currently supplies 18 free trade outlets, with an eye on markets in Devon, Somerset and Dorset.

Bitter*
(OG 1036, ABV 3.6%)

Otter Ale*
(OG 1044, ABV 4.4%)

PACKHORSE

The Packhorse Brewing Co., The Flour Mills, East Hill, Ashford, Kent, TN24 8PX. Tel. (0233) 638131

Brews no real ale. New brewery set up in 1991 to brew lagers to the German beer purity law.

The Independents

PALMERS

JC & RH Palmer Ltd., Old Brewery, West Bay Road, Bridport, Dorset, DT6 4JA. Tel. (0308) 22396

The only thatched brewery in the country, in a delightful seaside setting. Brewing has taken place in these former mill buildings since at least 1794, and the Palmer family have been here since the late 1880s. Cask-conditioned beer in all 65 tied houses, although top pressure and cask breathers are widely in use. About 40 direct free trade outlets.

Bridport Bitter or BB
(OG 1032, ABV 3.2%) A light beer with a hoppy aroma. A clean, hoppy taste with some bitterness and a bitter aftertaste.

IPA
(OG 1040, ABV 4.2%) A good balance of fruit, bitterness and hop in the taste, with malty undertones, leads to a predominantly bitter finish. A fruity aroma, with some hop.

Tally Ho!
(OG 1046, ABV 4.7%) A dark and complex brew with a malty aroma. The nutty taste is dominated by roast malt, balanced with some bitterness. Malty and bitter aftertaste. Difficult to find, especially in winter.

PARADISE

Paradise Brewery Ltd., Paradise Park, Hayle, Cornwall, TR27 4HY. Tel. (0736) 753365

Now only brews for its one pub (see Brew Pubs: Bird in Hand, page 468).

PARISH

Parish Brewery, The Old Brewery Inn, Somerby, Melton Mowbray, Leics. Tel. (066 477) 781

Brewery which started life at the Stag and Hounds, Burrough on the Hill and moved two miles to Somerby in May 1991 because of the need for greater capacity, following increased sales. Baz's Bonce Blower is the strongest draught beer available all year round in the UK. In addition to the Old Brewery Inn, Parish directly supplies half a dozen other outlets.

Mild*
(OG 1035, ABV 3.5%)

Special Bitter*
(OG 1038, ABV 3.8%)

Porter*
(OG 1048, ABV 5%)

Somerby Special*
(OG 1048, ABV 5%)

Poachers Ale*
(OG 1060, ABV 6.5%) Dark, sweet and malty.

Baz's Bonce Blower*
(OG 1110, ABV 14%) Rich, black and treacly.

PILGRIM

Pilgrim Brewery, West Street, Reigate, Surrey, RH2 9BL. Tel. (073 72) 22651

Surrey's only brewery, supplying real ale to London, Surrey, Kent and Sussex, as well as the Midlands and the North via wholesalers. Has formed Pilgrim Taverns to develop a tied estate.

Surrey Pale Ale or SPA
(OG 1037, ABV 3.7%) A well-balanced pale brown bitter with an underlying fruitiness. A good session beer.

XXXX Mild
(OG 1041, ABV 4%) Dark brown, with a malty flavour and pleasant fruitiness. A malty sweetness in the finish is balanced by a faint hoppiness which comes through.

Progress
(OG 1042, ABV 4%) Reddish-brown in colour, with a predominantly malty flavour and aroma. Whilst hops are evident in the taste, the beer is quite sweet.

The Independents

Talisman	(OG 1049, ABV 4.8%) Strong ale with a dark red colour, a fruity, malt flavour and a sweet finish. Available all year, but more common in winter.

PITFIELD	See Premier Ales, below, and Wiltshire, page 452.

PLASSEY   **Plassey Brewery, The Plassey, Eyton, Wrexham, Clwyd, LL13 0SP. Tel. (0978) 780277**

Brewery founded in 1985 and located in a prize-winning Edwardian farm building on the 250-acre Plassey site. The site also houses a touring caravan and leisure park, a craft centre and a licensed outlet for Plassey's ales. Farmhouse Bitter is now simply known as Plassey Bitter. The new beer, Cwrw Tudno ('St Tudno's beer'), was produced as a one-off for the Llandudno Beer Festival, but is now available on request. The brewery supplies about half a dozen pubs.

Bitter	(OG 1040, ABV 4%) Excellent, straw-coloured beer, well-hopped and bitter, with blackcurrant fruitiness. Light and refreshing. A little more malty than last year, but unfortunately difficult to come by.
Cwrw Tudno*	(OG 1047, ABV 5%)

PLYMPTON	See Allied Breweries, page 455.

POOLE   **Poole Brewery, 68 High Street, Poole, Dorset, BH15 1DA. Tel. (0202) 682345**

Brewery which opened in 1981 at different premises and which transferred all brewing to the present site in 1987. Supplies the Brewhouse pub and a dozen free trade outlets, but beer is kept under blanket pressure at the Brewhouse. An extension to the brewery has enabled bottling to be done on site and bottle-conditioned beers are planned.

Poole Best Bitter or Dolphin Best Bitter*	(OG 1038, ABV 4%) An amber-coloured, balanced bitter.
Bosun Bitter*	(OG 1043, ABV 4.5%) Amber and rich.

PREMIER   **Premier Ales Ltd., Stourbridge Estate, Mill Race Lane, Stourbridge, W. Midlands, DY8 1JN. Tel. (0384) 442040**

Originally a local free house chain, Premier began brewing in 1988. The company merged with Pitfield of London in 1989 and continues to brew the full range of Pitfield/Premier beers. However, as we went to press, the company announced that it was going into liquidation and so the future of the brewery is very much in doubt.

Pitfield Bitter*	(OG 1038, ABV 3.6%)
Old Merlin Mild	(OG 1038, ABV 3.6%) A dark brown beer with an emphasis on caramel and roast flavours. Sweet and malty aftertaste. Light and refreshing.
Knightly Bitter	(OG 1044, ABV 4.5%) A pale brown, malty-flavoured bitter. Quite hoppy and slightly sweet.
Pitfield Hoxton Heavy	(OG 1048, ABV 4.7%) A copper-red beer, quite hoppy in taste and aroma. Slightly sweet.
Pitfield Dark Star	(OG 1048, ABV 4.7%) A malt and roast-flavoured, black beer, slightly fruity, with a hop and bitter finish.

438

The Independents

Black Knight Stout	(OG 1050, ABV 5.2%) October-May only: a strong, black beer with a very malty and roasty taste, and a chocolatey, dry aftertaste.
Pitfield London Porter*	(OG 1058, ABV 5.5%) October-May only: a dark stout.
Maiden's Ruin	(OG 1075, ABV 7%) October-May only: a very strong, fruity beer with a sweet and malty taste and a very sweet aftertaste.

RANDALLS

Messrs RW Randall Ltd., Vauxlaurens Brewery, St Julian's Avenue, Guernsey, CI. Tel. (0481) 20134

Guernsey's smaller brewery, purchased by RH Randall in 1868. On his death in 1902, the brewery passed to his son, RW Randall, and successive generations have continued to run the business. Owns 20 houses, though most serve keg beer, meaning the following real ales are very difficult to find. The mild is so rarely seen that it is as good as discontinued.

Best Mild	(OG 1036) Copper-red, with a malty and fruity aroma and a hint of hops. The fruity character remains throughout, with a sweetish, malty undertone.
Best Bitter	(OG 1046) Amber in colour, with a malt and fruit aroma. Sweet and malty both on the palate and in the finish.

RANDALLS (JERSEY)

Randalls, Clare Street, St Helier, Jersey, CI. Tel. (0534) 73541

Brews no real ale but sells Bass and Marston's Pedigree in its pubs. No connection with Randalls of Guernsey.

RAYMENTS   See Greene King, page 415.

REEPHAM

Reepham Brewery, Unit 1, Collers Way, Reepham, Norfolk, NR10 4SW. Tel. (0603) 871091

Family brewery, founded in 1983 by a former Watney, Mann & Truman research engineer. The custom-built plant is housed in a small industrial unit. Supplies real ale to 30 outlets in Norfolk, and more extensively through wholesalers. Looking to develop its bottled trade. *Bottle-conditioned beer: Rapier Pale Ale (OG 1043, ABV 4.4%)*

LA Bitter*	(OG 1027, ABV 2%)
Granary Bitter	(OG 1038, ABV 3.9%) This amber-coloured beer is well balanced from aroma through to aftertaste, though malt is clearly evident on the palate. A good session beer.
Dark*	(OG 1040, ABV 4%) A strong mild.
Rapier Pale Ale	(OG 1043, ABV 4.4%) An even better-balanced beer than Granary. The pleasant aroma of hop, malt and fruit leads to a taste that is smooth, flavoursome and complex. Hoppy, malty and dry finish.
Smugglers Stout*	(OG 1045, ABV 4.4%) Available in winter.
Bircham Bitter	(OG 1046, ABV 4.6%) An amber/tawny beer with good body for its gravity. The fruity aroma precedes a complex, malty, hoppy palate, which also has a sweetness that dies away in the malty, dry finish. A winter brew.
Brewhouse*	(OG 1055, ABV 5.6%) A full-bodied bitter.

The Independents

RIDLEYS

TD Ridley & Sons Ltd., Hartford End Brewery, Chelmsford, Essex, CM3 1JZ. Tel. (0371) 820316

Brewery built by Thomas Dixon Ridley in 1842 on the banks of the River Chelmer in rural Essex. Brewing still takes place in the original buildings and some equipment dates from the brewery's earliest days. New offices were built at the side of the brewery in 1990, bringing all the business onto one site. Real ale is available in all its 64 houses and to an expanding free trade (over 300 outlets), at the lowest prices in the South East.

Mild
(OG 1034, ABV 3.4%) Formerly called XXX. Dark brown, with a powerful, hoppy and malty aroma. The palate is dry and hoppy, with underlying malt and caramel flavours, and a bitter finish. Very drinkable and all too rare.

IPA Bitter
(OG 1034, ABV 3.5%) A fine, amber bitter. A hoppy, faintly fruity nose leads into a strong, lingering, hoppy bitterness, with a little balancing malt. Delightful, dry aftertaste.

Christmas Ale*
(OG 1050, ABV 5.1%) The seasonal offering.

RINGWOOD

Ringwood Brewery Ltd., 138 Christchurch Road, Ringwood, Hants, BH24 3AP. Tel. (0425) 471177

Hampshire's first new brewery, founded in 1978 in an old bakery and now housed in attractive 18th-century buildings which formed part of the old Tunks' brewery in Ringwood. Famous for its award-winning Old Thumper, it has two tied houses and approximately 150 free trade accounts, from Weymouth to Chichester (plus one bar in Cherbourg).

Best Bitter
(OG 1038, ABV 4%) A golden brown, moreish beer, with flavours for all. The aroma has a hint of hops and leads to a malty sweetness, which becomes dry, with a hint of orange. Malt and bitterness in the finish.

XXXX Porter
(OG 1048, ABV 4.8%) Brewed October-March: a fine example of a porter. Dark ruby in colour, with a malty aroma, a middle period of balanced fruit, malt and bitterness, and a taste which lasts and lasts.

Fortyniner
(OG 1048, ABV 5%) A good premium beer, with malt and hops in good balance. The flavours slowly increase to fruity finish.

Old Thumper
(OG 1058, ABV 6%) A golden beer with a surprisingly bitter aftertaste, which follows a middle period tasting of a range of fruits. May be a little sweet for some.

ROBINSON'S

Frederic Robinson Ltd., Unicorn Brewery, Stockport, Cheshire, SK1 1JJ. Tel. (061) 480 6571

Major family brewery, founded in 1838, which took over Hartleys of Ulverston in 1982. All 323 tied houses (mainly concentrated in southern Manchester and Cheshire) sell real ale. Whereas Best Bitter is widely available, Bitter can be found in only about 20 outlets. Dark Best Mild is only provided on request and is essentially Best Mild with added caramel.

Best Mild
(OG 1032, ABV 3.3%) A pale brown, well-balanced beer, with a sweet aftertaste. A good, refreshing drink.

Dark Best Mild
(OG 1032, ABV 3.3%) Toffee/malt tasting, with a slight bitterness. Very quaffable, enjoying a fruity/malt aroma and a dry finish.

Bitter
(OG 1035, ABV 3.5%) Fresh-tasting, with an aniseed tinge.

The Independents

Characteristic aroma and a smooth but brief finish. Only available in 20 outlets.

Best Bitter (OG 1041, ABV 4.2%) A golden beer with a good, hoppy nose. A very well-balanced taste precedes a slight, bitter finish.

Old Tom (OG 1080, ABV 8.5%) A full-bodied, dark, fruity beer, similar in texture to a barley wine. The aroma is fruity and mouthwatering; the aftertaste is bittersweet. A beer to be respectfully sipped by a roaring winter fire.

ROBINWOOD

Robinwood Brewers & Vintners, Robinwood Brewery, Burnley Road, Todmorden, W. Yorks, OL14 8EX. Tel. (0706) 818160

Small brewery founded in 1988 and for a long time confused with the Staff of Life pub, which is run separately but which is now on the market to help fund brewery expansion. Growing free trade throughout West Yorkshire and Lancashire (about 80 outlets). IPA has been introduced in the last year, as has the occasionally-brewed Porter and an experimental 1050 OG beer. *Bottle-conditioned beer: Old Fart (OG 1060, ABV 6%)*

Best Bitter (OG 1036, ABV 4.1%) Beer with a faint, malty, fruity, sometimes yeasty aroma. The flavour is well-balanced, with a good, malty character which carries through to the finish (moderately bitter).

IPA* (OG 1040, ABV 4.2%)

Porter* (OG 1042) An occasional brew.

XB (OG 1046, ABV 4.7%) Both malt and hops come through in the aroma. The basic malty flavour is overtaken by bitterness and some chocolate. Good body; a malty/bitter finish, with burnt malt detectable at times.

Old Fart (OG 1060, ABV 6%) Dark brown in colour, with a fruity and slightly malty aroma. There is roasted malt in the vinous, sweet and fruity taste, with some caramel and hoppy bitterness coming through. The finish is malty and dry. Also available as Old XXXX Ale on request.

ROSS

Ross Brewing Company, 36 Gloucester Road, Bishopston, Bristol, Avon. Tel. (0272) 427923

Very small Bristol brewery, the first to brew beer with organic Soil Association barley. Plans are in hand to produce cask-conditioned beer but, at present, only bottle-conditioned beers are available. These are sold in pint bottles. The new brew, Saxon Strong Ale, is brewed to an authentic Saxon recipe, which includes honey, apple juice and borrage, as well as organic malt and hops. The beers are available in several pubs, restaurants and wine bars in the Avon area, and are wholesaled nationally. All are characterised by a certain yeastiness, which is not unpleasant.

Bottle-conditioned beers: Hartcliffe Bitter (OG 1045, ABV 4.5%) An amber/tawny-coloured, solidly malty, bitter beer. Good body, some hoppiness and a slightly sweet flavour. Bitter, malty aftertaste; *Clifton Dark Ale (OG 1045, ABV 4.5%)* A reddish-brown, full-bodied beer. There is a strong roast malt and bitter taste, and a lingering finish with some fruitiness. The aroma is malty. Very moreish; *Saxon Strong Ale (OG 1055, ABV 5.5%)* Unusual and distinctive. Golden brown in colour, with a light, fruity aroma. The taste is sweet but well-rounded and full-bodied, with a hint of honey and herbs. The finish is similar, with a trace of apples.

441

The Independents

ROYAL CLARENCE	**Royal Clarence, The Esplanade, Burnham-on-Sea, Somerset, TA8 1BQ. Tel. (0278) 783138**
	Seaside hotel brewery which also supplies the free trade. The new beer, Clarence Regent, was introduced in February 1991.
Clarence Pride	(OG 1036, ABV 3.6%) A pale brown beer with a hoppy/malty aroma, a hoppy, strongly bitter taste and a bitter, hoppy finish.
Clarence Regent*	(OG 1050, ABV 5%) A dark, brown/black winter brew.

RUDDLES	See Courage, page 462.

ST AUSTELL	**St Austell Brewery Co., 63 Trevarthian Road, St Austell, Cornwall, PL25 4BY. Tel. (0726) 74444**

Brewing company set up in 1861 by maltster and wine merchant Walter Hicks. It moved to the present site in 1893 and remains a popular family business, with many of Hicks's descendants employed in all areas of the company. 132 of the 135 tied houses serve traditional ale, with another 1,300 outlets in Cornwall and beyond supplied through the free trade.

Bosun's Bitter	(OG 1036, ABV 3.4%) A refreshing session beer, sweetish in aroma and bittersweet in flavour. Lingering, hoppy finish.
XXXX Mild	(OG 1039, ABV 3.6%) Little aroma, but a strong, malty, caramel-sweetish flavour is followed by a good, lingering aftertaste, which is sweet but with a fruity dryness. Very drinkable.
Tinners Ale	(OG 1039, ABV 3.7%) A deservedly-popular, golden beer with an appetising malt aroma and a good balance of malt and hops in the flavour. Lasting finish.
Hicks Special Draught or HSD	(OG 1051, ABV 5%) An aromatic, fruity, hoppy bitter which initially gives a sweet flavour and an aftertaste of pronounced bitterness, but which has a fully-rounded flavour.
Winter Warmer*	(OG 1060, ABV 6%)

SCOTTIES	**Scotties Brewery, Crown Hotel, 151 High Street, Lowestoft, Suffolk, NR32 1HR. Tel. (0502) 569592**

Brewery founded in June 1989 and now supplying beer to about half a dozen free trade outlets.

Scot's Golden Best Bitter	(OG 1038.5) A bitter hop flavour dominates this beer, but not overpoweringly, and mingles with a malty, fruity sweetness in the palate. A good lunchtime beer.
Blues and Bloater*	(OG 1039.5)
William French	(OG 1047) A full and beautifully balanced beer. A faint, malty aroma leads into a palate with strong malt and hop flavours, and considerable fruitiness. A full and balanced aftertaste, too.
Dark Oast	(OG 1047) A winter beer, red/brown in colour, with less body than its gravity would suggest. The taste has roast malt as its main characteristic, with hoppiness prominent in the aftertaste.

SCOTTISH & NEWCASTLE	See page 463.

SELBY	**Selby (Middlesbrough) Brewery Ltd., 131 Millgate, Selby, N. Yorks, YO8 0LL. Tel. (0757) 702826**
	Old family brewery that resumed brewing in 1972 after a gap

442

of 18 years and is now involved in wholesaling. Real ale is supplied to a few free trade outlets and the Brewery Tap off-licence in Selby, but not to the company's single tied house.

Best Bitter*	(OG 1039) Only available occasionally.
Old Tom*	(OG 1069, ABV 6.5%) A distinctive, strong ale.

SHEPHERD NEAME	**Shepherd Neame Ltd., 17 Court Street, Faversham, Kent, ME13 7AX. Tel. (0795) 532206**

A fine old brewery retaining many original features, with a visitor reception centre in a restored medieval hall. Believed to be the longest continuous brewer in the land, ever since 1698. The tied estate consists of 306 pubs, the majority selling real ale, which is brewed with only East Kent hops. Free trade runs to about 500 outlets, principally in Kent, Essex and London, although this figure includes a sizeable proportion of keg-only business. Some outlets dispense the beers using a low blanket pressure and the company, sadly, is giving active encouragement to other pubs to convert to this method.

Master Brew Bitter	(OG 1036, ABV 3.8%) A very distinctive bitter, mid brown in colour, with a very hoppy aroma. Well-balanced with a nicely aggressive bitter taste from its hops, leaving a hoppy/bitter finish, tinged with sweetness.
Best Bitter	(OG 1039, ABV 4%) Mid brown, with less marked characteristics than Bitter. However, the nose is very well balanced and the taste enjoys a malty, bitter smokiness. A malty, well-rounded finish.
Stock Ale	(OG 1039, ABV 4%) A dark brown winter brew. Malt and caramel are present in the aroma, and the beer is full of different flavours: malt, caramel and hops. Although never strong, it lacks body and seems to have become thinner in the last few years.
Spitfire Ale*	(OG 1044, ABV 5%) A commemorative brew (Battle of Britain) for the RAF Benevolent Fund's appeal.
Bishops Finger*	(OG 1052, ABV 5.4%). A well known bottled beer, introduced in cask-conditioned, draught form in November 1989.

SHIPSTONE'S	See Greenalls, page 415.

SMILES	**Smiles Brewing Co. Ltd., Colston Yard, Colston Street, Bristol, Avon, BS1 5BD. Tel. (0272) 297350**

Avon's first new brewer, established in 1977 and supplying real ale to around 200 outlets, including two tied houses, one leased pub and a new brewery tap. Old Vic has recently been revived.

Brewery Bitter	(OG 1037, ABV 3.7%) A golden/amber, light beer with plenty of flavour for its gravity. A good mix of malt, bitter, hops and fruitiness is followed by a pleasant, dry, malty aftertaste. Has a malty, hoppy aroma.
Best Bitter	(OG 1041, ABV 4.1%) A copper brown beer with malt, fruit and some hops in both nose and taste. A well rounded bitter with a dry, hoppy finish.
Exhibition	(OG 1051, ABV 5.2%) A deep red/brown-coloured beer, comprising a complex collection of rich flavours. There is a strong roast malt and fruit presence, with moderate hops and sweetness. Vinous, turning dry and bittersweet towards the finish.
Old Vic	(OG 1065, ABV 6.2%) An occasional winter brew. An excellent, dark brown, full-bodied strong ale, with a smooth,

443

The Independents

rich, warming sweetness and an unusual fruitiness. Has a malty, alcoholic aroma and a rich, spicy, bitter finish.

JOHN SMITH'S	See Courage, page 462.

SAMUEL SMITH

Samuel Smith Old Brewery (Tadcaster), Tadcaster, N. Yorks, LS24 9SB. Tel. (0937) 832225

Yorkshire's oldest and most traditional brewery, dating from 1758 and once owned by John Smith. Samuel Smith was John's brother and he inherited his business, along with another brother, William, when John died in 1879. William built the new John Smith's brewery in 1884 and the Old Brewery reverted to the late Samuel's heirs, who then proceeded with their own business. Although John Smith's is now Courage-owned, 'Sam's' remains firmly independent. Beers are brewed without the use of any adjuncts and all cask beer is fermented in Yorkshire stone squares and racked into wooden casks provided by the brewery's own cooperage. Real ale is served in the majority of its 200+ tied houses, which include 27 in London, representing good value for the capital. About 200 free trade outlets.

Old Brewery Bitter (OBB)

(OG 1037, ABV 3.8%) Beer with a malty predominance in the nose, which follows through into both the taste and the aftertaste, although this is underscored at all stages by a gentle hoppiness. Lots of flavour and body, complemented by an attractive amber colour.

Museum Ale

(OG 1048, ABV 5.2%) A fruity, amber, strong bitter. Malty, winey and sweetish in the mouth, with some bitterness in the aftertaste, though dominated throughout by fruitiness.

SPRINGFIELD	See Bass, page 459.

STOCKS

Stocks Brewery, The Hallcross, 33–34 Hall Gate, Doncaster, S. Yorks, DN1 3NL. Tel. (0302) 328213

Originated in December 1981 as a brew pub and now runs two other tied houses. Expanding free trade throughout the North, with Old Horizontal becoming particularly popular, especially in the Camerons Tap & Spile real ale pub chain.

Best Bitter

(OG 1037, ABV 3.6%) An ordinary session bitter, with a light aroma, a malty, bitter taste and a moderately dry, bitter aftertaste.

Select

(OG 1044, ABV 4.3%) A light beer in body, with little aroma. More malt in the mouth than before, but the same short, bitter taste and finish. Perhaps darker than it used to be, but still a mite disappointing.

48*

(OG 1048, ABV 4.8%) A golden-coloured beer, introduced in 1991.

Old Horizontal

(OG 1054, ABV 5%) A dark brown beer with red tints, this is the best Stocks brews by far. Can have fruit, roast and chocolate notes in the mouth, but malt is dominant. Hoppy aroma; dry and nutty finish. Sometimes thin for its gravity.

STONES	See Bass, page 460.

SUMMERSKILLS

Summerskills Brewery, Unit 15, Pomphlett Farm Ind. Estate, Billacombe, Plymouth, Devon, PL9 4BG. Tel. (0752) 481283

Brewery re-launched by new owners in October 1990 after

444

The Independents

lying dormant in its industrial estate site since 1985. Summerskills was initially set up in 1983 in a vineyard; now supplies 20 outlets in Devon, Cornwall, Wiltshire and South Wales, but has no houses of its own. The brewery logo comes from the ship's crest of HMS Bigbury Bay.

Best Bitter*	(OG 1042)
Drekly*	(OG 1046)
Old Rodent*	(OG 1050)

SUSSEX

Sussex Brewery, Main Road, Hermitage, Emsworth, W. Sussex, PO10 8AU. Tel. (024 33) 71533

Small, family-run brewery (formerly Hermitage Brewery), selling three brands to about eight local free trade customers and one tied house. However, production was suspended in summer 1991, owing to the poor financial climate.

Hermitage Best Bitter — (OG 1048) Subtly hoppy, with a moderately dry, hoppy finish.

Lumley Old Ale* — (OG 1058, ABV 5.8%) A dark, malty, winter beer.

Warrior Ale — (OG 1060) Moderately hoppy, with a slightly hoppy, fruity finish. Generally disappointing.

TAYLOR

Timothy Taylor & Co. Ltd., Knowle Spring Brewery, Keighley, W. Yorks, BD21 1AW. Tel. (0535) 603139

The fame of Timothy Taylor's prize-winning ales stretches far beyond West Yorkshire and the brewery's 29 pubs. Founded in 1858, it now offers one of the widest ranges of real ales, with Landlord the pride of the pack. A new brewhouse was phased in in spring 1991 and was immediately brewing to capacity. Extensive free trade.

Golden Best — (OG 1033, ABV 3.5%) A light, straw-coloured beer, with a faint hop and grain nose. The soft and smooth, malty taste is followed by a short bitter and malt finish. A quaffable light mild. Also sold as Bitter Ale.

Dark Mild — (OG 1033, ABV 3.5%) Golden Best with caramel, which can dominate the aroma and taste. Sweeter of late in both taste and finish. Not unpleasant.

Best Bitter — (OG 1037, ABV 4%) A golden, well-hopped bitter with a fresh, flowery aroma. The complex hop and grain taste has fruit notes and builds up to a distinctly dry, bitter finish. An underrated but very drinkable bitter.

Landlord — (OG 1042, ABV 4.3%) A distinctive, multi-layered and complex series of floral fragrances and mouth-filling fruit, hop and grain tastes. Strong hop and bitter finish. Still the top Taylor brand, but not always served to perfection.

Ram Tam (XXXX) — (OG 1043, ABV 4.3%) Landlord with too much caramel added. Sometimes the hops come through but usually there is just a burnt, cloying sweetness. Perhaps drier than it used to be, but it still lacks depth or character. A disappointing concoction.

Porter — (OG 1043, ABV 4.4%) Malt and caramel dominate both the nose and taste, but with some fruity notes. Less dark than it used to be and a lot less sweet. Much improved from last year.

TAYLOR WALKER

See Allied Breweries, page 456.

The Independents

TENNENT CALEDONIAN	See Bass, page 459.
JOSHUA TETLEY	See Allied Breweries, page 457.
TETLEY WALKER	See Allied Breweries, page 457.
THEAKSTON	See Scottish & Newcastle, page 465.

THOMPSON'S

Thompson's Brewery, 11 West Street, Ashburton, Devon, TQ13 7BD. Tel. (0364) 52478

Began brewing in 1981 for its own pub, the London Inn, but presently supplies about ten free trade outlets around Dartmoor and southern Devon, and is now looking to expand its estate.

Mild* (OG 1033, ABV 3.7%) An occasional brew.

Best Bitter (OG 1039, ABV 4.2%) A pleasant, hoppy brew, pale brown in colour, with a hoppy aroma, a bitter, slightly yeasty taste and a strong, bitter finish.

Celebration Porter* (OG 1040, ABV 4.2%) A new beer for the brewery's tenth birthday.

IPA (OG 1044, ABV 4.6%) A copper-red, well-balanced beer. The hoppy aroma is followed by a strong, bitter taste and finish.

Yuletide Tipple (OG 1050, ABV 5.2%) A fruity, copper-red beer, enjoying a distinctive contrast of roast and hop flavours, and a bitter finish. Hops and fruit in the aroma.

THWAITES

Daniel Thwaites PLC, PO Box 50, Star Brewery, Blackburn, Lancs, BB1 5BU. Tel. (0254) 54431

Traditional Lancashire brewery, founded by excise officer Daniel Thwaites in 1807. Still uses shire horse drays and, unusually, produces two milds. Thwaites ales have been regular CAMRA award-winners and are available in nearly all its 376 tied pubs, as well as some 600 free houses. Its managed pubs are run by the subsidiary Thwaites Inns and the brewery also operates hotels under the name of Shire Inns. Took over and closed Yates & Jackson's Lancaster brewery in 1984 and is currently seeking to expand its pub estate with purchases from Bass and other nationals.

Mild (OG 1031, ABV 3%) Dark brown/copper beer with a fine malty quality in both aroma and flavour. No perceptible finish.

Best Mild (OG 1033, ABV 3.2%) A rich, dark mild presenting a smooth, malty flavour and a pleasant, slightly bitter finish.

Bitter (OG 1036, ABV 3.4%) A gently-flavoured, clean-tasting bitter. Malt and hops lead into a full, lingering, bitter finish.

Daniel's Hammer* (OG 1050) A winter brew.

TITANIC

Titanic Brewery, 1 Dain Street, Middleport, Burslem, Stoke-on-Trent, Staffs, ST6 3LE. Tel. (0782) 823447

Named in honour of the Titanic's Captain Smith, who hailed from Stoke, this brewery continues to expand since resurfacing after ceasing trading in 1988. Over 100 free trade outlets are now supplied and larger brewing premises are being sought as a result. Having been suspended last year, the Best Bitter has

The Independents

now been relaunched as a seasonal beer. *Bottle-conditioned beer: Christmas Ale* (Wreckage matured for one year)

Best Bitter*   (OG 1036, ABV 3.6%) A summer beer.

Lifeboat Ale   (OG 1040, ABV 3.9%) A fruity and malty, red/brown, bitter beer, with a slight caramel character. The finish is dry and fruity. Almost like a strong dark mild.

Premium Bitter   (OG 1042, ABV 4.2%) A red/brown beer with a fruity aroma, a malty, fruity taste and aftertaste, and a lingering bitterness.

Captain Smith's Strong Ale   (OG 1050, ABV 5%) Another red/brown beer, but this one is hoppy and bitter with a balancing, malty sweetness. A hoppy aroma; a dry, malty finish. Highly drinkable.

Wreckage*   (OG 1080, ABV 7.6%) Available only at Christmas.

TOLLY COBBOLD   **Tollemache & Cobbold Brewery Ltd., Cliff Brewery, Ipswich, Suffolk, IP3 0AZ. Tel. (0473) 231723**

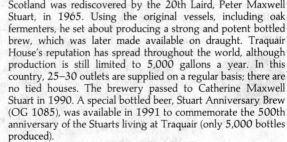

TOLLY·COBBOLD

A campaigning success story, this brewery was re-opened in 1990 after all production had been moved to Cleveland, following the Brent Walker takeover. A management buy-out has enabled all the old Tolly beers to be brewed in their proper home once again, with Brent Walker taking supplies for its East Anglian estate (the former Tolly pubs). A brewery museum is taking shape and a brewery tap is planned, though the new enterprise has no pubs of its own yet. Has introduced a special bottled 'Year Beer' (not bottle-conditioned), a tradition to be maintained every January as a way of recreating famous Tolly beers of the past. The 1991 offering was called Ipswich Pride.

Mild   (OG 1032, ABV 3.2%) A malty, dark mild with roasty notes and a hoppy finish to balance the malt. The aroma is mostly of malt. More full-bodied and roasty than the previous, inferior version from Hartlepool.

Bitter   (OG 1035, ABV 3.6%) A light-bodied session bitter. The gravity has been increased but the old Tolly maltiness has reappeared. Some hoppiness, mainly in the finish, but not a particularly bitter beer.

Original   (OG 1038, ABV 3.8%) Another beer with an increased gravity. Now has a more pronounced hoppy and bitter taste, with balancing maltiness. The finish is dry.

Old Strong   (OG 1047, ABV 4.6%) Available November-February. A dark winter ale with a good malt and roast aroma. These characteristics are also evident in the initial flavour, along with caramel. The finish is bittersweet, with a lasting dryness.

TRAQUAIR HOUSE   **Traquair House Brewery, Innerleithen, Peeblesshire, Borders, EH44 6PW. Tel. (0896) 830323**

The 200 year-old brewhouse in the oldest inhabited house in Scotland was rediscovered by the 20th Laird, Peter Maxwell Stuart, in 1965. Using the original vessels, including oak fermenters, he set about producing a strong and potent bottled brew, which was later made available on draught. Traquair House's reputation has spread throughout the world, although production is still limited to 5,000 gallons a year. In this country, 25–30 outlets are supplied on a regular basis; there are no tied houses. The brewery passed to Catherine Maxwell Stuart in 1990. A special bottled beer, Stuart Anniversary Brew (OG 1085), was available in 1991 to commemorate the 500th anniversary of the Stuarts living at Traquair (only 5,000 bottles produced).

The Independents

Bear Ale*	(OG 1050, ABV 5%) A strong draught ale.
Traquair House Ale*	(OG 1076.5, ABV 7%) Dark and potent.

TROUGH

Trough Brewery Ltd., Louisa Street, Idle, Bradford, W. Yorks, BD10 8NE. Tel. (0274) 613450

Established in 1980, Trough now serves four houses of its own (three tied) and a direct free trade of over 40 outlets, both pub and club. Remains firmly independent, yet does not shirk beneficial contact with larger concerns, such as the Camerons Tap & Spile chain. The beer range was increased when the company bought up the brewing plant of the defunct Gooseye Brewery of Keighley in 1989. All beers are now full mash brews and further expansion is expected.

Bitter	(OG 1036.5) Malty, with some balancing bitterness, but with a disappointing lack of hop flavour. A short, thinly malty finish. An amber-coloured, light session bitter.
Wild Boar	(OG 1041) A more malty bitter, but disappointingly light for its gravity. Has some balancing bitterness, but lacks hop character. Little aroma; poor, short finish of bittersweet malt.
Hogshead	(OG 1045.5) Beer with a predominantly full, malty taste, with fruity notes and sweetness. Lacks bitterness and hop flavour. Short, malty, sweet finish.

ULEY

Uley Brewery Ltd., The Old Brewery, Uley, Dursley, Glos, GL11 5TB. Tel. (0453) 860120

Brewing at Uley began in 1833, but the Old Brewery remained inactive for most of this century. Work commenced on restoring the premises in 1984 and Uley Brewery was reborn in 1985. The brewery has no pubs of its own but now serves over 30 free trade outlets in the surrounding Cotswolds area. No added sugar is used in the brewing process. Pig's Ear is only brewed to order.

Bitter or Hogshead or UB40	(OG 1040, ABV 4%) Copper-coloured beer with malt, hops and fruit in the aroma and a malty, fruity taste, underscored by a hoppy bitterness. The finish is dry, with a balance of hops and malt.
Old Spot Prize Ale	(OG 1050, ABV 5%) A fairly full-bodied, red/brown ale with a fruity aroma, a malty, fruity taste (with a hoppy bitterness), and a strong, balanced aftertaste.
Pig's Ear	(OG 1050, ABV 5%) A pale-coloured, light beer, deceptively strong. Notably bitter in flavour, with a hoppy, fruity aroma and a bitter finish.
Pigor Mortis	(OG 1058, ABV 5.7%) Another beer which belies its strength. No distinct aroma, but a sweet, smooth flavour, with hints of fruit and hops. Dry finish.

USHERS

See Courage, page 462.

VAUX

Vaux Breweries Ltd., The Brewery, Sunderland, Tyne & Wear, SR1 3AN. Tel. (091) 567 6277

First established in 1806 and now one of the country's largest regional brewers, Vaux remains firmly independent. Owns Wards of Sheffield, but sold off Lorimer & Clark in Edinburgh in 1987. Real ale is sold in 196 out of 493 tied houses (which include those run by Vaux Inns Ltd.) and is also provided to 10% of its 700 free trade customers. Sold its four London pubs in 1990 but, otherwise, is looking to increase its tied estate,

The Independents

buying pubs in Yorkshire and the North West from national brewers.

Lorimers Best Scotch
(OG 1036, ABV 3.6%) Dark, thin and with little aroma, but the roast malt flavour can shine through when the cellar temperature and pub turnover are right. Unfortunately, it is often served too cold. A replica of the original Scottish Scotch; today more of a mild?

Bitter*
(OG 1037, ABV 3.9%) Now back in production after having been discontinued.

Samson
(OG 1041, ABV 4.1%) Has a complex flavour, with malt and hops battling it out. Sometimes dryness and bitterness are the main taste characteristics; at other times the sweet notes dominate. Like other Vaux beers, low in aroma.

Double Maxim
(OG 1044, ABV 4.2%) A smooth, rich, brown ale, rarely found in draught form. Very malty throughout, with some roast. A slight, lingering fruitiness can be found in the aftertaste.

WADWORTH

Wadworth & Co. Ltd., Northgate Brewery, Devizes, Wilts, SN10 1JW. Tel. (0380) 723361

Delightful market town tower brewery set up in 1885 by Henry Wadworth. Solidly traditional, the brewery still employs its own cooper and runs horse-drawn drays. 6X is one of the South's most famous ales and is widely available in the free trade, whilst all 175 Wadworth tied houses sell real ale. Expansion is taking place at the old brewery to handle free trade demand, and new fermenting and collecting vessels are being installed, though the light, session beer, Devizes Bitter, was discontinued in spring 1990. Always keen to expand the tied estate.

Henry Wadworth IPA
(OG 1034, ABV 3.8%) A golden brown-coloured beer with a gentle, malty and slightly hoppy aroma, a good balance of flavours, with maltiness gradually dominating, and then a long-lasting aftertaste to match, eventually becoming biscuity. A good session beer, more pleasing than the popular 6X.

6X
(OG 1040, ABV 4.3%) Mid brown in colour, with a malty and fruity nose and some balancing hop character. The flavour is similar, with some bitterness and a lingering malty, but bitter finish. Full-bodied and distinctive.

Farmer's Glory
(OG 1046, ABV 4.5%) Can be delightfully hoppy and fruity, but is variable in flavour and conditioning. The aroma is of malt and it should have a dryish, hoppy aftertaste.

Old Timer
(OG 1055, ABV 5.8%) Available in winter only. A rich, copper-brown beer with a strong, fruity, malty aroma. The flavour is full-bodied and complete, with hints of butterscotch and peaches, beautifully balanced by a lasting, malty, dry finish. A classic beer.

PETER WALKER

See Allied Breweries, page 457.

WARDS

SH Ward & Co. Ltd., Sheaf Brewery, Ecclesall Road, Sheffield, S. Yorks, S11 8HZ. Tel. (0742) 755155

Brewery which celebrated its 150th birthday in 1990 but which became a subsidiary of Vaux of Sunderland in 1972. Since the closure of the neighbouring Thorne brewery in 1986, Wards has also produced Darley's beers. Real ale is available in 40% of the 200 or so Wards/Darley houses, and there is

The Independents

considerable free trade, including clubs. Still looking to increase its tied estate.

Mild
(OG 1032, ABV 3.2%) Formerly Darley Dark Mild. A light malt nose leads on to hints of fruit, chocolate and hop in the flavour, but these are overpowered by malt, which also dominates the finish. Can be sweet and thin.

Thorne Best Bitter
(OG 1037, ABV 3.9%) Little aroma, little character and short on taste. This is not the beer it used to be. Plain and undistinguished, with only hints of malt and bitterness. A session ale.

Sheffield Best Bitter
(OG 1038, ABV 4%) Notably malty aroma and taste, with an increasingly bitter balance. A clean and dry ale, with some hints of fruit. The malty aftertaste is edged with sweetness. Regaining some of its consistency but still varies widely.

Kirby Strong Beer
(OG 1045, ABV 5%) There are mixed reactions to this beer which seems to change recipe every brew. Can have a fine malt and bitter taste, with lingering fruit and sweetness, or can be cloying. Its colour varies, too. Usually pleasant.

WATNEY
See Courage, page 461.

WEBSTER'S
See Courage, page 463.

WELLS
Charles Wells Ltd., Havelock Street, Bedford, Beds, MK40 4LU. Tel. (0234) 272766

Successful family-owned brewery, established in 1876, which has a tied estate stretching from Lincolnshire to London. The bulk of the pubs, however, are centred around Bedford. Recently acquired 38 pubs from Bass. Cask beer is served in 339 of the 353 pubs and is supplied to 450 free trade outlets, but some tied houses use CO_2 in the dispense and over half apply cask breathers. Allows guest beers from other independents in its tied pubs.

Eagle Bitter
(OG 1035, ABV 3.6%) Amber/tawny beer presenting a pronounced hoppy aroma, with some malt and fruit. There is a clean, hoppy bitterness in the flavour and a bitter and faintly fruity finish.

Bombardier
(OG 1042, ABV 4.2%) Becoming quite rare these days. Pale brown in colour, but not pale in character. A mainly hoppy flavour is complemented by a complex aroma of malt, hops, fruit and sulphur. A clean, bitter finish with some fruit.

WELSH BREWERS
See Bass, page 460.

WEM
See Greenalls, page 415.

WEST COAST
West Coast Brewery Co. Ltd., Kings Arms Hotel, 4a Helmshore Walk, Chorlton-on-Medlock, Manchester, M13 9TH. Tel. (061) 273 1053

Successful brewery on the premises of the Kings Arms, providing beer for this outlet and a growing free trade. Founded by Brendan Dobbin who ran the Hilden Brewery for some years and who now also works as a small-scale brewing consultant. Sierra Nevada Pale Ale has been renamed Yakima Grande Pale Ale, North County Mild has been discontinued, a new porter has been added and one-off brews are frequent.

Dobbin's Dark Mild
(OG 1032, ABV 3%) Very full-flavoured for its gravity; dark and rather fruity.

The Independents

Dobbin's Best Bitter	(OG 1038, ABV 4%) A pale beer with malt, hops and fruit in the aroma. Fresh, clean taste - hoppy and bitter, with some malt and a dry finish.
Dobbin's Guiltless Stout	(OG 1039, ABV 4%) Very dark in colour, with roast malt predominant in the smell and taste. A long, dry aftertaste.
Dobbin's Yakima Grande Porter*	(OG 1050, ABV 5.5%) Rich, mellow and dark, brewed with the same American hops as the Pale Ale below.
Dobbin's Yakima Grande Pale Ale	(OG 1050, ABV 6%) A pale beer with a strong, hoppy nose. Hops are also very evident in the flavour. A well-attenuated beer, making it strong and very dry.
Dobbin's Extra Special Bitter	(OG 1060, ABV 7%) A powerful, mid brown beer with a strong, complex aroma, malt and hops on the tongue (with sweetish, fruity undertones), and a full, predominantly bitter, hoppy finish.

WEST HIGHLAND	**West Highland Brewers, Old Station Brewery, Taynuilt, Argyllshire, Strathclyde, PA35 1JB. Tel. (086 62) 246**
	Brewery set up in November 1989 in listed buildings, part of an active British Rail station. Serves a regular free trade and wholesalers, as well as a brewery tap.
Highland Light*	(OG 1034)
Highland Heavy*	(OG 1038)
Highland Severe*	(OG 1052)

WETHERED	See Whitbread, page 467.

WHITBREAD	See page 465.

WHITBY'S	**Whitby's Own Brewery Ltd., St Hilda's, The Ropery, Whitby, N. Yorks, YO22 4ET. Tel. (0947) 605914**
	Brewery set up in 1988 in a former workhouse in this famous Yorkshire fishing port, though there are plans to move to larger premises. Free trade (mostly as guest beers) extends from Newcastle upon Tyne to Huddersfield and takes in 25–30 outlets, but Whitby's has no pubs of its own. Force Nine is a regular award-winner.
Little Waster*	(OG 1036)
Merryman's Mild*	(OG 1036)
Ammonite	(OG 1038, ABV 3.8%) A light, refreshing beer, pleasant and fruity, with a hoppy aftertaste. Difficult to track down, but well worth the effort.
Woblle	(OG 1045, ABV 4.5%) A copper-red, full-bodied, malty bitter, with a burnt roast flavour and a dry, hoppy finish.
Force Nine	(OG 1055, ABV 5.5%) Strong and dark, with a well-balanced blend of contrasting flavours: sweet and fruity, dry and malty, with a strong, bitter finish. A beer of the winter ale type, excellent in its class.
Demon	(OG 1066, ABV 6.6%) Available only in winter. A full-bodied and well-balanced strong ale, less smooth than Force Nine, with an obvious bite and a strong finish. First brewed in 1989 to celebrate the brewery's first birthday. Not easy to find.

The Independents

WICKWAR

The Wickwar Brewing Company, The Old Cider Mill, Station Road, Wickwar, Avon, GL12 8NB. Tel. (0454) 294168

A brewery set up by two Courage multiple tenants, Brian Rides and Ray Penny, in an old cider mill, originally the site of Arnold, Perrett & Co. Ltd. brewery. The first beer was produced on 1 May 1990 and the brewery is now operating full-time. The beers are available in the founders' four pubs, as well as 25 other outlets. Produced 'Victory' (OG 1044) ale in the aftermath of the Gulf War.

Cooper's WPA* (OG 1036, ABV 3.5%) First brewed in May 1991.

Brand Oak Bitter (OG 1039, ABV 4.2%) A tasty balance of hops, malt and fruits come through in the aroma and in the initially subtle finish, which later asserts a lasting, malty, bitter hoppiness. Full of character; very moreish. Known locally as 'BOB'.

Olde Merryford Ale (OG 1049, ABV 5.1%) A copper-brown, well-balanced beer. Full-flavoured, with a fruity, bitter, dry finish and a hoppy, fruity aroma.

WILSON'S See Courage, page 463.

WILTSHIRE

Wiltshire Brewery Co. PLC, Stonehenge Brewery, Church Street, Tisbury, Wilts, SP3 6NH. Tel. (0747) 870666

Operating from a former workhouse, which became a brewery in 1868, the Wiltshire Brewery Company was set up in 1985 and is now quoted on the USM. It runs 31 pubs, all serving cask beer, and bought Ma Pardoe's brew pub (Old Swan, Netherton: see page 470) from Hoskins in 1989, to use as a West Midlands base. Ma Pardoe's has since been sold and the mild is now brewed at Tisbury. Ever-keen to progress, Wiltshire also acquired the Pitfield Brewery name, although all Pitfield beers are still brewed by Premier Ales (see page 438). Wiltshire supplies about 100 free trade outlets. *Bottle-conditioned beers*: Stonehenge Real Ginger Beer (OG *1059.5, ABV 6%*); *Stonehenge Exhibition Ale (ABV 8%)*

Ma Pardoe's Mild* (ABV 3.6%)

Stonehenge Best Bitter (OG 1041, ABV 4.1%) Rather unusual, lollipop-tasting ale which will suit those with a sweet tooth. Lacks the bitterness of a more conventional beer of this gravity, but a slowly-released, subtle hop aroma adds interest.

Old Grumble* (OG 1049, ABV 5%)

Old Devil Strong Ale (OG 1059, ABV 5.9%) Full-bodied ale with a multi-dimensional taste. Various flavours also follow in the aftertaste, permitting the alcohol to arrive unannounced. Beware!

Stonehenge Exhibition Ale* (OG 1084, ABV 8%) Only available in cask form in winter.

WOOD

The Wood Brewery Ltd., Wistanstow, Craven Arms, Shropshire, SY7 8DG. Tel. (0588) 672523

Village brewery founded by the Wood family in 1980 which, after early successes, suffered trading difficulties in the 1980s. With new market conditions, Wood is hoping to expand and produce 100 barrels a week. It still has just the one tied house, the adjacent Plough Inn, but now supplies 60 free trade outlets. Specialises in producing commemorative bottled beers.

The Independents

Parish Bitter*	(OG 1040, ABV 3.75%) A light, refreshing bitter.
Special Bitter*	(OG 1043, ABV 4%) A full-flavoured, sweetish beer.
Wonderful Bitter*	(OG 1050, ABV 4.75%) Strong and dark.
Christmas Cracker*	(OG 1060, ABV 6%) A dark winter warmer.

WOODFORDE'S   **Woodforde's Norfolk Ales, Broadland Brewery, Woodbastwick, Norwich, Norfolk, NR13 6SW.
Tel. (0603) 720353**

Founded in late 1980 in Norwich to bring much-needed choice to a long Watney-dominated region. Moved to a converted farm complex in the picturesque Broadland village of Woodbastwick in 1989. No tied houses but 225 free trade outlets in Norfolk, Suffolk and Lincolnshire.

Mardler's Mild*	(OG 1036, ABV 3.6%)
Broadsman Bitter	(OG 1036, ABV 3.7%) Good balance throughout, with a bitter hop character and hints of a sweet toffeeness on the palate. A very moreish, refreshing session beer which ought to be on sale more than it is.
Wherry Best Bitter	(OG 1039, ABV 4%) This award-winning, amber beer has a distinctly hoppy nose and a well-balanced palate with pronounced bitterness and, usually, a flowery hop character. A long-lasting, satisfying, bitter aftertaste.
Norfolk Porter	(OG 1042, ABV 4.3%) Light-tasting for a beer of its strength and colour, this red/brown beer has a fruity aroma, fleshed out with roast malt and hops. The taste is well balanced, with roast malt and hops; the aftertaste is mainly bitter.
Old Bram*	(OG 1044, ABV 4.5%) A roasty, medium dark, winter beer.
Phoenix XXX	(OG 1047, ABV 4.9%) Interesting and drinkable. The taste is balanced and complex, and follows a deceptively fruity nose, before giving way to a full and bitter aftertaste.
Norfolk Nog	(OG 1049, ABV 5.1%) A full-bodied red/brown beer with plenty of flavour and aroma. Roast malt balances the sweeter components of the palate. A very good, dark winter brew.
Baldric	(OG 1052, ABV 5.5%) The hops and fruit in the aroma are carried through to the palate where they mix with malt and hop bitterness. A dryish aftertaste rounds off this very drinkable, tasty beer. Not as sweet as many beers of this strength.
Headcracker	(OG 1069, ABV 7.5%) A well-balanced, pale brown beer with a fruity and bitter aftertaste. There is a strong presence of toffee in both the aroma and palate. Not too sweet for a beer of this strength and body.

WORTHINGTON   See Bass, page 460.

WYE VALLEY   **Wye Valley Brewery, 69 St Owen Street, Hereford, HR1 2JQ. Tel. (0432) 274968**

Herefordshire brewery, established in 1985 and now expanding steadily into the local free trade. From one beer initially, a portfolio of four ales is now available. Runs one tied house (Barrels in Hereford) and supplies 20 other outlets.

Hereford Bitter	(OG 1036) Very little nose, but a crisp, dry and truly bitter taste, with a balancing malt flavour. The initial bitter aftertaste mellows to a pleasant, lingering malt.

The Independents

Hereford Pale Ale or HPA

(OG 1040) Has a distinctive colour of old pine and a malty nose. On the tongue, the beer is malty, with some balancing bitterness and a hint of sweetness. Good, dry finish.

Hereford Supreme

(OG 1043) This rich, copper-red beer has a good malty, fruity aroma. In the complex variety of flavours, the malt, fruit and bitterness are distinctive. The finish has bitterness but can be cloyingly malty.

Brew 69

(OG 1055) A pale beer which disguises its strength. Has a well-balanced flavour and finish, without the sweetness which normally characterizes beer of this strength.

YATES

Yates Brewery, Ghyll Farm, Westnewton, Aspatria, Cumbria, CA5 3NX. Tel. (069 73) 21081

Small, traditional brewery set up in 1986 by Peter and Carol Yates in an old farm building on their smallholding, which itself used to be a brew pub. Probably the only brewery in the country with a herd of pedigree goats. Directly serves 18 free trade outlets and brewing capacity has now more than doubled to 33 barrels a week.

Bitter

(OG 1035, ABV 3.9%) A fruity, bitter, straw-coloured ale with malt and hops in the aroma and a long, bitter aftertaste.

Premium

(OG 1048, ABV 5.2%) Available at Christmas and a few other times of the year. Straw-coloured, with a strong aroma of malt and hops, and full-flavoured, with a slight toffee taste. The malty aftertaste becomes strongly bitter.

Best Cellar

(OG 1052, ABV 5.3%) Brewed only in winter. An excellent, red/brown beer with a fruity aroma and a sweet, malty flavour, contrasted by a hoppy bitterness. The finish is a bittersweet balance, with grain and some hops.

YOUNGER

See Scottish & Newcastle, page 464.

YOUNG'S

Young & Co. PLC, Ram Brewery, High Street, Wandsworth, London, SW18 4JD. Tel. (081) 870 0141

One of the most warmly regarded breweries in the country, which stood alone against the keg tide in the capital in the early 1970s. Some of the award-winning beers are still delivered by horse-drawn drays. Much brewery redevelopment has taken place in the last 10–15 years and further plans include the acquisition of more tied houses. At present, all 155 houses take real ale, and the company supplies around 600 free trade outlets, mostly within the M25 ring, though its presence is rapidly extending westward. Special is regularly seen as a guest beer in Courage pubs.

Bitter

(OG 1036, ABV 3.7%) A light and distinctive bitter with well-balanced malt and hop characters. A strong bitterness is followed by a delightfully astringent and hoppy aftertaste.

Special

(OG 1046, ABV 4.8%) A strong, full-flavoured, bitter beer with a powerful hoppiness and a malty aroma. Hops persist in the aftertaste, with a rich fruitiness and lasting fullness.

Winter Warmer

(OG 1055, ABV 5%) A dark brown ale with a malty, fruity aroma, a sweet and fruity flavour, with roast malt and some balancing bitterness, and a bittersweet finish, including some lingering malt.

THE NATIONALS

ALLIED BREWERIES

Head Office: 107 Station Street, Burton upon Trent, Staffs, DE14 1BZ. Tel. (0283) 31111

Part of the food and retailing group, Allied-Lyons, this brewing conglomerate dates from 1961 and the merger of Ansells, Tetley Walker and Ind Coope. The number of trading companies under the umbrella has been reduced in recent years, and the retail and production sides have been split in many cases. The company currently controls over 6000 pubs, but it has been selling off packages to regional and local brewers, as well as to pub chains, subsequent to the legislation which followed the MMC report into the brewing industry in 1989. Allied claims to be committed to brewing, though there has been much speculation of a link with Whitbread. It has also been in discussions about leasing pubs and supplying beer to troubled Brent Walker – a deal which would inevitably mean the closure of the Camerons brewery. In the meantime, Allied has already begun to fill out its excess brewing capacity with the contract brewing of Greenalls beers at Warrington and Burton. Also runs a keg beer brewery at Romford, and a lager plant in Wrexham.

ALLOA

Alloa Brewery Company Ltd., Whins Road, Alloa, Clackmannanshire, Central, FK10 3RB. Tel. (0259) 723539

Allied's Scottish arm, established in 1810, which was taken over by Archibald Arrol in 1866. It fell to Ind Coope & Allsopp's in 1951, becoming part of Allied in the 1961 merger. Took over Drybroughs from Watney in 1987. Deleted Arrol's 70/- in 1989, which was replaced in pubs by Tetley Bitter. Takes Maclay 70/- and 80/- as a guest beer in its pubs throughout Scotland, and Caledonian 70/- and 80/- in the Edinburgh area. Real ale in only 92 of its 358 tied houses.

Arrol's 80/-*

(OG 1042, ABV 4.2%) A full-flavoured beer with dry hop character.

FURGUSONS

Furgusons Plympton Brewery, Valley Road, Plympton, Plymouth, Devon, PL7 3LQ. Tel. (0752) 330171

Set up in Halls' Plympton depot in 1984, this brewery now offers three ales of its own for sale in all its 32 pubs and a south-western free trade (about 50 accounts).

Dartmoor Best Bitter

(OG 1038, ABV 3.7%) Mid brown, with a moderately hoppy palate and a restrained, dry, malty finish. Rather thin and a thirst-quenching session beer, but not a best bitter.

Dartmoor Strong*

(OG 1044, ABV 4.5%) Light-coloured, but full-bodied bitter.

Cockleroaster

(OG 1062, ABV 6.5%) A powerful, golden beer with a strong, near perfect mix of malt and hop flavours, and a fruity note which dominates the aroma. Not overpowering, but distinctive, with a good, hoppy finish.

HP&D

Holt, Plant & Deakin Ltd., Dudley Road, Wolverhampton, W. Midlands, WV2 3AF. Tel. (0902) 450504

Trades under the name of Holts, but do not confuse it with Manchester's Joseph Holt brewery. A Black Country company set up in 1984 and now running 47 traditional pubs, all serving real ale. Mild and Bitter are brewed by Tetley Walker in Warrington; Downfall and Progress are brewed at the address

The Nationals

above, as is most of the Entire output, though some is still produced at the old brewery in Oldbury. Some occasional, one-off brews.

Mild   (OG 1036, ABV 3.4%) See Tetley Walker, page 458.

Bitter   (OG 1036, ABV 3.4%) See Tetley Walker, page 458.

Entire   (OG 1043, ABV 4.4%) A malty and hoppy beer, dry tasting.

Plant's Progress*   (OG 1060, ABV 6.2%)

Deakin's Downfall*   (OG 1060, ABV 6.4%) A winter ale.

IND COOPE   Ind Coope Burton Brewery Ltd., 107 Station Street, Burton upon Trent, Staffs, DE14 1BZ. Tel. (0283) 31111

The major brewery in the Allied group which resulted from the merger of the adjoining Allsopp's and Ind Coope breweries in 1934. It is currently benefiting from a £30 million investment programme and now has a capacity of two and a half million barrels a year. Altogether, it brews eight real ales for the South and the Midlands, providing beer for the Ansells, Ind Coope Retail, Taylor Walker and Nicholson's trading divisions (real ale in roughly two-thirds of all pubs). Ansells is Allied's Midlands and Wales wing, operating some 1,600 pubs; Ind Coope Retail controls over 1,400 pubs in the Home Counties, those formerly owned by Aylesbury Brewery, Benskins, Friary Meux and Halls, whose names are still used on pub livery and signs. With the exception of Halls (whose Harvest Bitter has bitten the dust in the last year), the old brewery names are still used on the beers brewed here in Burton. Taylor Walker runs 685 pubs and restaurant-pubs in London (including the Muswell's and Exchanges chains), whilst Nicholson's operates 35 upmarket pubs in the capital. Again, Taylor Walker Best Bitter, and a new Nicholson's Best Bitter, are brewed in Burton. All these 'local' beers are derived from two mashes: ABC, Friary and Taylor Walker from one, Benskins and Nicholson's from the other. Ind Coope Burton Brewery also brews Lumphammer (OG 1039) under contract for the Worcestershire-based Little Pub Co. chain.

For Ind Coope Retail:

ABC Best Bitter*   (OG 1036, ABV 3.5%) A light, refreshing bitter, owing much of its character to dry hopping.

Friary Meux Best Bitter   (OG 1036, ABV 3.5%) Malt just dominates over hops in the aroma and flavour of this tawny beer. A strange, fruity flavour lurks in the background.

Benskins Best Bitter   (OG 1037, ABV 3.5%) A hoppy aroma, taste and finish. Can be a bit thin on occasions, when any malt and fruit flavours are lost. Otherwise, it's a pleasant, suppable pint.

Burton Ale   (OG 1048, ABV 4.8%) Full of hop and malt flavours with hints of fruit and sweetness. It has a hoppy, malty aroma with a faint smell of fruit, and a bitter, hoppy finish. *Champion Beer of Britain* in 1990.

For Ansells:

Ansells Mild   (OG 1035.5, ABV 3.2%) A malty, dark brown beer with a roast and caramel flavour, and a slightly sweet aftertaste. Occasionally known as 'Dark'.

Ansells Bitter   (OG 1037, ABV 3.5%) A very hoppy and bitter, pale brown beer, with malt and a touch of sweetness.

The Nationals

For Taylor Walker and Nicholson's:

Taylor Walker Best Bitter* (OG 1036, ABV 3.5%) Light, malty bitter.

Nicholson's Best Bitter* (OG 1037, ABV 3.5%)

For Greenalls:

Shipstone's Mild* (OG 1034, ABV 3.6%)

Davenports Best Mild* (OG 1035, ABV 3.2%)

Shipstone's Bitter* (OG 1037, ABV 4%)

Davenports Traditional Bitter* (OG 1038, ABV 3.9%)

JOSHUA TETLEY Joshua Tetley & Son Ltd., PO Box 142, The Brewery, Leeds, W. Yorks, LS1 1QG. Tel. (0532) 435282

Yorkshire's best-known brewery, founded in 1822 by maltster Joshua Tetley and now owning 962 pubs, 93% of which serve cask beer. The brewery site now covers 20 acres and includes a new brewhouse, opened in May 1989 to handle the increased demand for Tetley Bitter, which is now available nationally and is Allied's biggest selling cask beer. The success of Bitter across the country owes much to the specially developed dispense system which recreates the famous Yorkshire tight, creamy head. The brewery, admirably, has also been promoting Mild, through a successful 'Master of Mild' cellarman scheme. It should be noted that versions of both Mild and Bitter are brewed at the Tetley Walker plant in Warrington, with no point of origin declared on the pump clips.

Mild (OG 1032, ABV 3.2%) Red/brown in colour, with a light hint of malt and hops in the aroma. A rounded taste of malt and caramel follows, with balancing bitterness, then a generally dry finish. A smooth, satisfying mild.

Bitter (OG 1036, ABV 3.6%) An amber-coloured standard bitter with an inviting, hoppy aroma. A good, refreshing, smooth balance of hop flavour, bitterness and grain in the mouth, finishing with a long, dry aftertaste.

TETLEY WALKER Tetley Walker Ltd., Dallam Lane, Warrington, Cheshire, WA2 7NU. Tel. (0925) 31231

Brewery founded by the Walker family in 1852 which merged with Joshua Tetley in 1960. Now brews for the Tetley Walker, Peter Walker, HP&D and Greenalls companies. Of the Tetley Walker 275 tied houses, 173 sell real ale. Peter Walker's 91 tied houses in the Merseyside, Wigan and Bolton areas all serve cask beer. For HP&D and Greenalls see respective entries. The versions of Tetley Mild and Bitter produced here are not differentiated from the Leeds brews at the point of sale. But, in the pub listings, we state Tetley Walker instead of Tetley when we are aware that the beer comes from Warrington and not Leeds.

Tetley Dark Mild (OG 1032, ABV 2.9%) A dark, malty mild with some caramel and fruit. A slight bitter finish. Not as consistent as last year and has a tendency to being rather thin and tasteless.

457

The Nationals

Tetley Mild (OG 1032, ABV 3.15%) A smooth, malty mild with some fruitiness and bitter notes. The aftertaste is malty, with a little dryness. Less sweet than last year; a refreshing, darkish mild.

Walker Mild (OG 1032, ABV 2.9%) Smooth, dark mild with fruit and caramel, which dominates hints of roast malt and bitterness. The malty aftertaste quickly gives way to a faint dryness.

Walker Bitter (OG 1033, ABV 3.3%) A light, refreshing, well-balanced bitter. Fruitiness dominates the hop flavour and the aftertaste is fairly bitter. Drinks more like a light mild than a bitter.

Walker Best Bitter (OG 1036, ABV 3.3%) A bitter beer with a dry finish. Not as hoppy as last year. The bitterness is sometimes astringent and can overwhelm the other flavours.

Tetley Bitter (OG 1036, ABV 3.6%) A fruity session beer with a dry finish. Bitterness tends to dominate malt and hop flavours. Sharp, clean-tasting and popular.

Walker Winter Warmer (OG 1060, ABV 5.8%) A smooth, dark and sweet winter ale, with a strong, fruity flavour, balanced to some degree by a bitter taste and the dry character of the finish. Improves with age as sweetness declines and other flavours emerge. At its best, it is dangerously drinkable.

For HP&D:

HP&D Mild (OG 1036, ABV 3.4%) Light and thin-bodied. A beer with faint malt and caramel in its taste.

HP&D Bitter (OG 1036, ABV 3.4%) Pale brown in colour, slightly sweet and hoppy, but lacking in character.

For Greenalls:

Greenalls Mild (OG 1032, ABV 3.1%) A dark, malty mild with a faint malt and fruit aroma. Hints of caramel, roast, fruit and bitterness come through in the taste. Like the Greenalls-brewed product, good when on form but let down by a tendency to being thin and bland.

Greenalls Bitter (OG 1036, ABV 3.8%) A well-balanced beer which is quite fruity and well hopped, with a good, dry finish. Less bitter and more malty than when Greenalls brewed it; it is now much improved and is arguably the best beer to come out of Tetley Walker's brewery.

Thomas Greenall's Original Bitter (OG 1045, ABV 4.4%) In the early days of this new brew, astringent bitterness dominated malt and hop flavours; it was fairly fruity and a little sweet. However, recent samples have been sweeter, offsetting the bitterness, and more full-flavoured. Still quite thin for the gravity and not an improvement on the Greenalls-brewed version.

BASS

Head Office: 66 Chiltern Street, London, W1M 1PR. Tel. (071) 486 4440

The UK's largest brewer is now experiencing major internal restructuring in the aftermath of the MMC report into the brewing industry. Having decided to stay in brewing, it has begun to sell or release from the tie thousands of pubs, in order to meet the requirements of the new legislation. The pubs and retail sections of Bass have been formed into separate companies

The Nationals

from its brewing division (which has its head office in Burton), with Bass Inns & Taverns, Charrington and Welsh Brewers operating nearly 7,000 pubs, over 4,000 selling real ale. Unique amongst the big brewers, Bass had not closed a brewery for many years, until the announcement in May 1991 that the Springfield Brewery at Wolverhampton (together with the keg beer plant at Preston Brook) were to end operations. Heavy promotion of Worthington Best Bitter from Cardiff and Stones Best Bitter from Sheffield sounded the death knell for the brewery and Springfield Bitter is now to be brewed at Cape Hill, alongside Springfield's other cask beer, Charrington IPA, which is on the move yet again. If the fierce marketing of Bass's national brands continues, the future of Springfield Bitter, even in its new home, must be in doubt. Bass's remaining 11 brewing centres include keg-only plants at Belfast, Alton, Glasgow and Edinburgh (now that Tennent's 80/- has been discontinued). Its cask beer breweries are listed below.

BURTON

Bass Brewers Ltd., 137 High Street, Burton upon Trent, Staffs, DE14 1JZ Tel. (0283) 511000

The original home of Bass, producing one of Britain's most famous ales, available throughout its estate and the free trade. Production of the bottle-conditioned White Shield has been transferred to the Hope Brewery, Sheffield.

Draught Bass

(OG 1043, ABV 4.4%) Formerly one of Britain's classic beers, this tawny ale can vary widely in character, depending on its age. A fruity and malty aroma and taste are balanced by an underlying hoppy dryness when at its best, though the palate is usually sweetish. The finish is bittersweet, with some lingering malt. Often served too green, but, when it's good, it's still a classic pint.

CAPE HILL

Cape Hill Brewery, PO Box 27, Birmingham, B16 0PQ. Tel. (021) 558 1481

The head office of the Mitchells & Butlers (M&B) trading division and one of the largest cask beer production centres in the country. Much of M&B's real ale sales are in the Walsall, Wolverhampton and Cannock areas.

M&B Mild

(OG 1035, ABV 3.4%) A dark mild with a faint malt and roast aroma. Roast and caramel in the flavour, then a slightly hoppy and dry, sweet finish.

M&B Springfield Bitter*

(OG 1036, ABV 3.5%)

M&B Brew XI

(OG 1040, ABV 4.1%) A pale brown beer with a slightly sweet, hoppy and bitter taste, with a faint bitter and dry aftertaste.

For Charrington:

Charrington IPA*

(OG 1039, ABV 3.6%)

HIGHGATE

Highgate Brewery, Sandymount Road, Walsall, WS1 3AP. Tel. (0922) 23168

Built in 1895 and now a listed building, the Highgate Brewery is the smallest in the Bass group and has remained unchanged for many years. The future of the resurrected Highgate Old is still in some doubt.

459

The Nationals

M&B Highgate Mild
(OG 1035.5, ABV 3.2%) Dark brown beer, very malty in aroma and taste. Well-balanced and smooth with roast malt and a hint of bitterness.

M&B Highgate Old Ale*
(OG 1055.7, ABV 5.2%) Winter only.

TOWER
Tower Brewery, Wetherby Road, Tadcaster, N. Yorks, LS24 9SD. Tel. (0937) 832361

Together with the Cannon Brewery, serves Bass's northern outlets.

Light
(OG 1031, ABV 3.3%) An amber-coloured mild: a lightly-flavoured blend of malt, sweetness and bitterness. At its best, has a delicate, pleasing, flowery taste, but can too often be bland. A disappointing, short, sweetish finish and little aroma.

Mild XXXX
(OG 1031, ABV 3.3%) A pleasant, smooth, dark brown mild with a faint aroma of caramel, which leads to a smooth, caramelly, rich taste, with complementing sweetness and underlying bitterness. A good, long, satisfying, caramel-sweet finish. Difficult to find in cask-conditioned form.

Special Bitter
(OG 1035, ABV 3.7%) Certainly not special. Pale brown in hue, with little aroma. The generally bland taste has sweetness, malt and a slight bitterness. The poor, short, sweet and dryish finish can be cloying. Unexciting.

CANNON
Bass Brewing (Sheffield) Ltd., Cannon Brewery, Rutland Road, Sheffield, S. Yorks, S3 8BE. Tel. (0742) 293313

Stones Best Bitter
(OG 1038, ABV 4.1%) A golden/straw-coloured beer with malt, hop and fruit aromas. On the tongue, there is delicate malt, with a refreshing, bitter hoppiness. The strong hop and malt finish leaves a clean glow. Tends to be served too green, but, on the whole, it is an underrated cask brand.

HOPE
Bass Brewing (Sheffield) Ltd., Hope Brewery, Claywheels Lane, Wadsley Bridge, Sheffield, S. Yorks, S6 1NB. Tel. (0742) 349433

Bass's specialist bottled beer brewery. *Bottle-conditioned beer: Worthington White Shield* (OG 1051, ABV 5.6%) In a new home, but still much under-promoted for a beer of its quality.

CARDIFF
Bass Brewing (Cardiff) Ltd., Crawshay Street, Cardiff, CF1 1TR. Tel. (0222) 233071

The Hancock's brewery (founded in 1884) which was taken over by Bass Charrington in 1968 and serves Welsh Brewers, its South Wales trading division. Supplies an extensive free trade, with real ale now becoming more prominent in valleys pubs. However, as was feared, Hancock's Pale Ale (PA) was discontinued early in 1991.

Worthington Dark
(OG 1033, ABV 3.3%) Dark brown in colour, with some maltiness in the taste and a sweet finish. Difficult to find in some areas, but popular in West Glamorgan.

Hancock's HB
(OG 1037, ABV 3.8%) A slightly malty bitter, with a bittersweet aftertaste. A bitter lacking in character.

Worthington BB
(OG 1037, ABV 3.8%) A fairly malty, light-coloured beer, with a somewhat bitter finish. A pleasant drinking beer.

The Nationals

COURAGE

Head Office: Ashby House, Bridge Street, Staines, Middlesex, TW18 4XH. Tel. (0784) 466199

Despite the MMC findings that it was 'against the public interest', after a certain prevarication by the Secretary of State for Trade and Industry, the pubs-for-breweries swap between Courage (now a division of the Foster's Brewing Group) and Grand Metropolitan (formerly Watney's breweries) was given the go-ahead. The result of this effort at dodging the recommendations of the 1989 MMC report into the brewing industry is as follows:

– Courage has taken over all Grand Met's breweries – the Ruddles, Ushers and Webster & Wilson's real ale plants, and the keg beer factory at Mortlake. Together with its existing breweries in Bristol and Tadcaster, and the keg beer plant at Reading, this gives the company control of 20% of all beer production in Britain.

– Courage pubs (4,910) and around three-quarters of Grand Met pubs (3,540) have been taken under the umbrella of a new jointly-owned company known as Inntrepreneur Estates. These outlets are tied to taking beer from Courage for seven years, although, in compliance with the 1989 legislation, 1,100 will be sold off and a further 2,470 must be freed from the tie before November 1992.

– Grand Met still operates 990 pubs of its own, as well as leasing back 550 from Inntrepreneur. These pubs are tied to Courage for four years.

What this means is less competition in the brewing industry, and that, for the beer drinker, does not bode well in terms of choice and pricing, if past experience is anything to go by. Will the Inntrepreneur pubs really have a free hand in seven years' time? Or will the Foster's boardroom influence see the same beers signed up again? And in the meantime, what ration-alisation will take place? It is hard to foresee Foster's wishing to continue marketing two 'Yorkshire Bitters', for instance, so it's likely one (probably Webster's) will disappear.

BRISTOL	Bristol Brewery, Counterslip, Bristol, Avon, BS1 6EX. Tel. (0272) 297222

The former Georges brewery, which, until the take-over of Ushers, was Courage's only real ale brewery in the South, following the closure of traditional breweries in London, Reading and Plymouth. Growing demand for cask beer has resulted in expansion at this plant in recent years, with Best and Directors very well promoted nationally and Bitter Ale neglected somewhat but now making more of a comeback.

Bitter Ale	(OG 1031, ABV 3.2%) A pale, light-bodied bitter, with a delicately hoppy, bitter, malty taste. A dry bitter finish and a hoppy aroma.
Best Bitter	(OG 1039, ABV 4%) A pale brown bitter with a good balance of bitter hops, grainy malt (sometimes fruit), and a slight sweetness. The aroma is malty and hoppy; the finish is bitter and malty.
Directors	(OG 1046, ABV 4.8%) A fine, well-balanced, red/brown malty ale, with ample malt, hops and fruit in the nose. The strong, malty, dry, hoppy taste has a faint fruitiness, and develops into a bitter, dry finish. All too often served below par.

The Nationals

RUDDLES

Ruddles Brewery Ltd., Burley Road, Langham, Oakham, Rutland, Leicestershire, LE15 7JD. Tel. (0572) 756911

Britain's most famous real ale brewers, founded in 1858, taken over by Grand Met in 1986 and now in the Foster's portfolio. Its beers are national brands and widely promoted.

Best Bitter

(OG 1037, ABV 3.8%) Thin, with a faint, fruity, malty nose leading into an astringent bitter palate, with little discernible malt or hop presence.

County

(OG 1050, ABV 5%) Copper-coloured, with a fruity, malty aroma and taste; sweetish on the tongue, but with a dry, malty aftertaste. Pleasant, but nothing like the County of old. Markedly lacking in hoppiness for a bitter of this gravity.

JOHN SMITH'S

John Smith's Tadcaster Brewery Ltd., Tadcaster, N. Yorks, LS24 9SA. Tel. (0937) 832091

A business founded at the Old Brewery in 1758 and taken over by John Smith (brother of Samuel Smith, see page 444) in 1847. The present brewery was built in 1884 and became part of the Courage empire in 1970. John Smith's Bitter is now probably Courage's best known ale, thanks to extensive television advertising since its re-emergence in traditional form in 1984. A massive £7 million was earmarked for commercials in 1991, strengthening doubts about the future of Webster's Yorkshire Bitter. The John Smith's trading division runs 1418 houses, of which over 916 sell cask beer, and serves an enormous free trade. *Bottle-conditioned beer*: *Imperial Russian Stout* (*OG 1098*), a famous export beer which is now only rarely brewed.

Bitter

(OG 1036, ABV 3.8%) Copper-coloured beer with a pleasant mix of hops and malt in the nose. In the taste maltiness comes through more strongly, with the hops taking over in the finish. The brewer's quality control for this beer is excellent. Known as John Smith's Yorkshire Bitter outside the county.

Magnet

(OG 1040, ABV 4%) Copper-amber, with a fruity, malty nose, a nutty, grainy palate and balancing fruit and hops. Outstandingly long and dry finish, with lingering malt. A very palatable best bitter.

USHERS

Ushers Brewery Ltd., Parade House, Trowbridge, Wiltshire, BA14 8JY. Tel. (0225) 763171

Founded in 1824, this was Grand Met's West Country brewery, with a trading area extending from Lands End to Oxford. The Watney/Grand Met era saw the disappearance of beers like Pale Ale and Founders Bitter, in favour of the mass-advertised Webster's and Ruddles County. Its future is still in considerable doubt; it is now on the market, along with 434 pubs, but a management buy-out is a probability, giving the West Country another Independent.

Best Bitter

(OG 1038, ABV 3.6%) A thin, disappointing tawny beer with a faint, but balanced, aroma and some bitter hop character and grainy sweetness in the taste, which can be metallic. Brief, slightly sharp, dry, bitter finish.

Bullard's Old

(OG 1057) A dark brown winter ale brewed in small quantities for East Anglia – a relic of the Norwich brewery closed by Watney. The fruity aroma is followed by a robust, fruity, malty taste and a good bitter finish.

The Nationals

FOUNTAIN HEAD

Courage Brewing (North) Ltd., Fountain Head Brewery, Ovenden Wood, Halifax, West Yorks, HX2 0TL. Tel. (0422) 357188

The original Samuel Webster brewery, merged by Watney in 1985 with Wilson's of Manchester, a move which saw the closure of Wilson's own brewery.

Wilson's Original Mild

(OG 1032, ABV 3%) A malty and fruity aroma leads on to a predominantly malty/caramel flavour, with some bitterness. Thin in body. The aftertaste is slightly malty and bittersweet. Outlets still declining in number.

Webster's Green Label Best

(OG 1034, ABV 3.4%) A faint, hoppy aroma, with a little fruitiness at times. Some sweetness in the malty taste, and a bitter finish. A boy's bitter.

Webster's Yorkshire Bitter

(OG 1037, ABV 3.8%) A disappointing beer with a faintly malty and fruity aroma (sometimes metallic). Often very bland in taste to offend no-one. If you are lucky it can have a good, fresh, hoppy-bitter flavour and finish (but very rare!).

Wilson's Original Bitter

(OG 1037, ABV 3.8%) A fairly thin, golden beer with a malty and fruity aroma and a flowery hop flavour, which can be very bitter at times. Malty overtones in taste and finish. Number of outlets slowly declining.

Webster's Choice

(OG 1044, ABV 4.6%) Well-balanced bitter with little aroma or flavour, but with a strong hoppy/bitter finish which is sometimes intense. Not available in many outlets; drink it while you can (Ruddles County or Courage Directors poised to take over)!

GUINNESS

Head Office: Guinness Brewing GB, Park Royal Brewery, London, NW10 7RR. Tel. (081) 965 7700

The brewer of the most famous of stouts has breweries scattered around the world, with Guinness also brewed under licence in many countries. Sadly, an excellent and stronger, bottle-conditioned export version, brewed in Dublin and once sold as Triple XXX, is no longer available in the UK. All Draught Guinness sold in the UK is keg; in Ireland Draught Guinness (OG 1038, brewed at Arthur Guinness, St James's Gate, Dublin 8) is not pasteurised but is served with gas pressure. Draught Guinness in a can is again pasteurised and produces the tight, creamy head by use of a small plastic sparkler at the bottom of the can. *Bottle-conditioned beer: Original (OG 1042)*, formerly known as Guinness Extra Stout. Available in bottle-conditioned form only from pubs and bars, except in Scotland where all Guinness is pasteurised. All non-returnable bottles and cans from supermarkets and off-licences throughout Britain are also pasteurised.

SCOTTISH & NEWCASTLE

Head Office: Scottish & Newcastle Breweries PLC, Abbey Brewery, Holyrood Road, Edinburgh, Lothian. Tel. (031) 556 2591

The 1960 merger between Scottish Brewers Ltd. and Newcastle Breweries Ltd. has had a major influence on the British brewing industry. It may not be officially classed as a 'National', because it does not own more than 2,000 pubs, but S&N is a giant

463

The Nationals

brewer in every other way. Its massive free trade presence (particularly through McEwan and Theakston brands) ensures that its influence is significant. This has not been highlighted better than in the last ten years. In this time, S&N acquired Matthew Brown of Blackburn, after two previous bids for the brewery had been quashed by the MMC. Despite having declared in 1985 that the Blackburn brewery and its Theakston subsidiary at Masham were 'sacrosanct' – a pledge which swayed the MMC in its decision to allow the take-over to progress, brewing at Matthew Brown was brought to a halt early in 1991. There has been great investment at Masham, but how long does 'sacrosanct' mean for Theakston, especially when the bulk of its beers is already produced at Newcastle? In the meantime, beers bearing the Matthew Brown name are being supplied by Home in Nottingham, though this also seems a temporary measure, a transitory phase before the name of Matthew Brown disappears from brewing altogether, thanks to S&N. The company now has only five breweries, including a keg beer plant in Manchester.

FOUNTAIN	Fountain Brewery, Fountainbridge, Edinburgh, Lothian, EH3 9YY. Tel (031) 229 9377

The Scottish production centre, formerly the home of William McEwan & Co. Ltd, founded in 1856. Its beers are sold under two separate names – McEwan and Younger, depending on the trading area, but such is the promotion of Theakston products that the futures of 70/- and No. 3 are in doubt.

McEwan 70/- or Younger Scotch*	(OG 1037, ABV 3.7%) A well-balanced, sweetish brew, becoming more and more rare.
McEwan 80/- or Younger IPA*	(OG 1042, ABV 4.5%) Malty and sweet-flavoured, with some graininess and a dry finish.
Younger No. 3*	(OG 1043, ABV 4.5%) Rich and dark.

TYNE	Tyne Brewery, Gallowgate, Newcastle upon Tyne, Tyne & Wear, NE99 1RA. Tel. (091) 232 5091

The production centre of Newcastle Breweries Ltd., formed in 1890 as an amalgamation of five local breweries. In recent years it brewed no cask beer, until most of Theakston's production was transferred here (see Theakston, page 465). No indication is given at the point of sale that Theakston beers are brewed in Newcastle. Has a cask-conditioned ale cellar for training licensees and has opened a new visitor centre.

Theakston Best Bitter	(OG 1038, ABV 3.8%)
Theakston XB	(OG 1044, ABV 4.5%)
Theakston Old Peculier	(OG 1057, ABV 5.6%)

HOME	Home Brewery PLC, Mansfield Road, Daybrook, Nottingham, NG5 6BU. Tel. (0602) 269741

Founded in 1875 and acquired by S&N in 1986, Home's tied estate offers real ale in 180 of its 400 pubs. Extensive free trade in the Midlands and the North. Now brews the beers from the closed Matthew Brown brewery in Blackburn and these are still sold in 184 of the 403 Matthew Brown pubs in the North West, although their future is far from certain.

The Nationals

Matthew Brown Mild*	(OG 1031, ABV 3.1%)
Matthew Brown Bitter*	(OG 1035, ABV 3.5%)
Home Mild	(OG 1036, ABV 3.6%) A notably malty, dark beer, with little aroma. Chocolate and liquorice in the flavour, and an unusually bitter finish for a mild. Slightly acidic and fruity.
Home Bitter	(OG 1038, ABV 3.8%) Again low in aroma. The flavour balances malt and hops well, with a smooth, initial taste and a lingering, dry, bitter finish. Golden/copper in colour.

THEAKSTON   T&R Theakston Ltd., Wellgarth, Masham, Ripon, N. Yorks, HG4 4DX. Tel. (0765) 689544

Company formed in 1827 which built this brewery in 1875. Became part of S&N when its parent company, Matthew Brown, was swallowed up. More than £1 million has been spent on this brewery in the last few years, reflecting the 'national' status its brews have been given by S&N. Theakston itself runs just ten tied houses, but the free trade is enormous. Despite the expensive refit, the brewery has not been able to cope with demand and most of Theakston's beers are now brewed in Newcastle, but the consumer is never told when this is the case. Not even in Masham are you guaranteed a pint of original Theakston's. A visitor centre is open to the public from May to October: ring for an appointment. Meanwhile, family member Paul Theakston has plans to start his own independent brewery in Masham.

Best Bitter	(OG 1038, ABV 3.8%) A delicate, straw-coloured beer with a hoppy and fruity nose. There is sharp hoppiness in the flavour, with some hints of malt and fruit, and the finish is dry and lasting.
XB	(OG 1044, ABV 4.5%) An impressive aroma of hops and malt, with a hint of fruit, precedes a well-balanced taste where hops slightly outweigh other elements, including vine fruits. The finish is very dry and slightly unexpected. A well-made beer.
Old Peculier	(OG 1057, ABV 5.6%) Almost as black as sin, but with a copper-red showing through and an aroma filled with malt and fruit. The flavours are complex, but roast malt and butterscotch stand out, with a gentle, hoppy bitterness and some fruit. The lasting aftertaste reveals that hops play a major part in the making of this rich, full-bodied beer.

WHITBREAD

Head Office: The Whitbread Beer Company, Porter Tun House, Capability Green, Luton, Beds, LU1 3LS. Tel. (0582) 391166

A name once famous for brewing (founded 1742) which has now become infamous for tactless brewery closures. In 1981 Whitbread operated 16 breweries across Britain. Such has been its butchery that, apart from keg beer factories in Magor (South Wales) and Samlesbury (Lancashire), only the four real ale breweries listed below are still in existence and one of these, Boddingtons, was only taken over in 1989. The most recent mutilation of its empire came in January 1990, with the closure of Fremlins in Faversham and Higsons in Liverpool, hot on the heels of the demise of Wethered in Marlow, Chester's in Salford and Strong's in Romsey. Cynically, the beers made famous by

The Nationals

these interesting breweries are still being marketed, even though they are no longer brewed at their original home. Two giant cask beer production centres have grown up at Cheltenham and Sheffield, churning out once-crafted beers in large quantities, many of them appearing misleadingly as 'guests' on the guest beer list offered to Whitbread licensees. In May 1991, Whitbread announced that it had reached an agreement with Devenish for the supply of Whitbread beers to Devenish pubs – a move which put the Cornish Brewery at Redruth in jeopardy. What's the next stop on the Whitbread Tour of Destruction? Let's hope there are no more closures, though the future of Castle Eden looks highly precarious.

BODDINGTONS Boddingtons Brewery, PO Box 331, Strangeways, Manchester, M60 3EL. Tel. (061) 831 7881

Brewery established in 1778 whose Bitter has long been one of Britain's best-known traditional beers. Whitbread, well aware of this, took over the Strangeways brewery to buy up the name, with the Boddingtons company happy to retire to pub owning, amongst other enterprises, having already assisted in the dismantling of the North West's brewing heritage by the take-over and closure of Oldham Brewery. Now Whitbread is pushing Boddingtons relentlessly across the country, but never indicating at the point of sale that it is now a Whitbread beer. So far Boddingtons Mild and the Oldham beers survive, but for how long?

OB Mild (OG 1032, ABV 3%) Copper-red in colour, with a malty aroma. A smooth caramel and fruit flavour follows, then a dry, malty aftertaste. Being replaced by Chester's Mild in some of its traditional outlets.

Boddingtons Mild (OG 1032, ABV 3%) A sweet, dark, thin mild, with a caramel and malt flavour and a malty, fruity aftertaste. Number of outlets still in decline.

Boddingtons Bitter (OG 1034, ABV 3.8%) A pale beer in which good hoppiness and bitterness are often spoiled by a rather cloying sweetness. The same characteristic is apparent in the aftertaste.

OB Bitter (OG 1037, ABV 3.8%) Pale beer with an aroma of malt. The flavour is malty and bitter, with a bittersweet tinge and a dry, malty finish.

CASTLE EDEN The Brewery, PO Box 13, Castle Eden, Hartlepool, Cleveland, TS27 4SX. Tel. (0429) 836431

Originally attached to a 17th-century coaching inn, the old Nimmo's brewery was purchased by Whitbread in 1963 and now appears vulnerable to the giant's axe, especially in the light of recent redundancies, including the loss of the head brewer. It primarily produces Castle Eden Ale, the low-alcohol White Label and lagers now being moved elsewhere. Future plans involve bringing in production of Trophy or keg Scotch Bitter, for local consumption, alongside keg Campbells 70/- and 80/-, for the Scottish market.

Castle Eden Ale (OG 1040, ABV 4.2%) A characteristically sweet north eastern beer, with a hoppy aroma and a nutty flavour. Possibly the most full-flavoured of the remaining Whitbread ales – probably too good to last. Sadly rare in its native territory.

CHELTENHAM The Brewery, Monson Avenue, Cheltenham, Gloucestershire, GL50 4EL. Tel. (0242) 521401

The Nritten

The Nationals

Brewery established in 1888, the former home of West Country Breweries Ltd. and now the centre of Whitbread's cask ale production in the South. Interestingly, though, the latest trend is to contract out the brewing of some beers: Strong Country Bitter to Morrells, Winter Royal and Pompey Royal to Gale's and, most recently, Wethered Bitter to McMullen.

West Country Pale Ale (WCPA) — (OG 1030, ABV 3%) Hoppy in aroma, but not as distinctive as it used to be. Light, refreshing and hoppy, with a clean, dry finish.

Fremlins Bitter* — (OG 1035, ABV 3.5%)

Wethered Bitter* — (OG 1035, ABV 3.6%) Now to be brewed at McMullen.

Flowers IPA — (OG 1036, ABV 3.6%) Pale brown, with little aroma, perhaps a faint maltiness. Moderately dry taste and finish, but no discernible hoppiness. Thin and uninspiring.

Best Bitter* — (OG 1036) Also available in keg form.

Strong Country Bitter — (OG 1037, ABV 3.9%) See Morrells, page 433.

Pompey Royal — (OG 1043, ABV 4.5%) See Gale's, page 413.

Flowers Original — (OG 1044, ABV 4.5%) Hoppy aroma and hops in the taste, with some malt and a hint of fruit. A notably bitter finish.

Wethered Winter Royal — (OG 1053, ABV 5.5%) Available October–March. See Gale's, page 414.

SHEFFIELD — Exchange Brewery, Bridge Street, Sheffield, S. Yorks, S3 8NL. Tel. (0742) 761101

Whitbread's remaining Yorkshire brewery, once the base of Tennant Brothers Ltd. Now brews beers for sale under the Chester's, Bentley's and Higsons dead breweries' names. Complete refurbishment of the centre of the brewhouse is in hand.

Higsons Mild — (OG 1032, ABV 3.2%) A thin, caramel-tasting, dark mild with hints of roast malt and bitterness. Some 'papery' notes and a dryish aftertaste. Lacks the distinctive character of the old Liverpool-brewed mild.

Chester's Best Mild — (OG 1032, ABV 3.5%) An almost black beer with a faint, malty, fruity nose and a palate dominated by caramel, with some malt and fruit. A sweetish, malty finish. Not the beer which once bore the name.

Chester's Best Bitter — (OG 1033, ABV 3.6%) Pale in colour and character. Little discernible aroma; a bitter taste, but with little malt or hop flavour, and a faint, malty, dry finish. Insipid, harsh and uninteresting.

Trophy — (OG 1036, ABV 3.8%) A thin, pale brown beer with a light malt aroma and a moderately sweetish, malty taste. Occasional bitter hints in the aftertaste. Can be refreshing but tends to be one-dimensional and tired.

Higsons Bitter — (OG 1037, ABV 3.8%) A fruity bitter with a harsh, artificial bitterness which subsumes any malt and hop taste. Again 'papery' notes, and a dry 'papery' aftertaste. Nothing like the 'Higgies' of old and a good example of the futility of matching brews.

Bentley's Yorkshire Bitter — (ABV 3.8%) A resurrection of an old brewery name (closed by Whitbread in 1972) to jump on the Yorkshire Bitter bandwagon.

BREW PUBS

ABINGTON PARK BREWERY CO.
Wellingborough Road, Northampton, NN1 4EY.
Tel. (0604) 31240
Cobblers Ale (OG 1037)
Dark (OG 1044)
Extra (OG 1047)
Batsman (OG 1050)
Celebration (OG 1052)
Headspinner (OG 1060)
One of the Clifton Inns in-house breweries. Stores beer in cellar tanks under a cover of CO_2. Four or five beers are available at any time, with Cobblers and Extra the mainstays.

ALE HOUSE
79 Raglan Road, Leeds, W. Yorks, LS2 9DZ.
Tel. (0532) 455447
Meek and Mild (OG 1031)
Monster Mash (OG 1042)
XB (OG 1045)
No. 9 (OG 1046)
Simon's Super Stout (OG 1046)
Brainstormer (OG 1055)
White Rose Ale (OG 1064)
Bye Bye Bitter (OG 1079)
Housewarmer (OG 1079) Brewed at Christmas.
Real ale off-licence next to Leeds University.

ALFORD ARMS
Frithsden, Hemel Hempstead, Herts, HP1 3DD.
Tel. (0442) 864480
Cherry Pickers (ABV 3.4%)
Pickled Squirrel (ABV 4.5%)
Whitbread's first brew pub, founded in 1981, using malt extract. Has experienced staffing and technical problems in the past year, resulting in only one brew in eight months. However, its brewing future now looks rosier.

ALL NATIONS (Mrs Lewis's)
Coalport Road, Madeley, Telford, Shropshire, TF7 5DP. Tel. (0952) 585747
Pale Ale (OG 1032)
One of four brew pubs left before the new wave arrived. The others are the Blue Anchor, Old Swan and Three Tuns. Still known as Mrs Lewis's, the inn has been in the same family since 1934 and has been brewing for 200 years.

ANCIENT DRUIDS
Napier Street, Cambridge, CB1 1HR.
Tel. (0223) 324514
Midsummer Mild (OG 1035, ABV 3.2%) Summer only.
Kite Bitter (OG 1040, ABV 4.1%)
Druid's Special (OG 1047, ABV 4.7%)
Merlin (OG 1055, ABV 6%)
Frostbiter (OG 1065, ABV 6.7%) Winter only.
Charles Wells brew pub. Uses malt extract.

BIRD IN HAND
Paradise Brewery Ltd., Paradise Park, Hayle, Cornwall, TR27 4HY. Tel. (0736) 753365
Bitter (OG 1040)
Artists Ale (OG 1055)
Victory Ale (OG 1070) Winter only.
Unusual brewery in a bird park, which now only brews for the Bird in Hand.

BLACK HORSE & RAINBOW
Berry Street, Liverpool, Merseyside, L1 9DS.
Tel. (051) 709 5055
Rainbow Bitter (OG 1039)
Black Horse (OG 1045)
Opened in summer 1990. Brews occasional stronger beers. Uses cellar tanks with a blanket of CO_2.

BLUE ANCHOR
50 Coinagehall Street, Helston, Cornwall.
Tel. (0326) 562821
Medium (OG 1050)
Best (OG 1053)
Special (OG 1066)
Extra Special (OG 1076) Brewed in winter and for Easter.
Historic thatched brew pub, originating as a monks' resting place in the 15th century. Produces powerful ales known locally as 'Spingo' beers.

BORVE BREW HOUSE
Ruthven, by Huntly, Grampian, AB5 4SR.
Tel. (046 687) 343
Borve Ale (OG 1040, ABV 3.7%)
Elphinstone Ale (OG 1053, ABV 5%)
Extra Strong (OG 1085, ABV 10%)
Moved from its original site on the Isle of Lewis in 1989 to a former school on the mainland. Extra Strong is matured in oak; Elphinstone Ale began life as a special commission for the 500th anniversary of Aberdeen in 1989. Both casks and cellar tanks are used for storage.

DUKE OF NORFOLK BREWERY
202–204 Westbourne Grove, London, W11.
Tel. (071) 229 3551
Broads Bitter (OG 1043)
Norfolk Best (OG 1047)
Dynamite (OG 1054)
Clifton Inns brew pub which began production in November 1989. Beer, brewed from whole malt with no adjuncts, is either cask-conditioned in the usual way or stored in cellar tanks fitted with a breather. Also produces Christmas ale and provides cask ales for a couple of other London pubs.

FAT CAT
Kelham Island Brewery, 23 Alma Street, Sheffield, S. Yorks, S3 8SA.
Bitter (OG 1038, ABV 4%)
Celebration (OG 1044, ABV 4.5%)
Full mash brewery which opened in 1990, using equipment purchased from the Oxford Brewery and Bakehouse. Hopes to produce vegetarian beer.

FELLOWS, MORTON & CLAYTON BREWHOUSE COMPANY
54 Canal Street, Nottingham, NG1 7EH.
Tel. (0602) 506795
Samuel Fellows Bitter (OG 1040, ABV 4%)
Matthew Clayton's (OG 1048, ABV 4.6%)
Easter XXXtra (OG 1055, ABV 5.4%) Seasonal.
Abraham Morton's New Year Nectar (OG 1060, ABV 6%) Seasonal.
Founded in 1980 as a Whitbread malt extract brew pub, the new tenants are hoping to negotiate a lease free of the Whitbread tie and to re-site the brewery, bringing in full mash brewing at the same time.

Brew Pubs

FIRST IN, LAST OUT
St Clements Brewery, 14–15 High Street, Old Town, Hastings, E. Sussex, TN34 3EY.
Tel. (0424) 425079
Crofters (OG 1038)
Cardinal (OG 1045)
Established in 1985.

FLAMINGO BREWERY COMPANY
88 London Road, Kingston upon Thames, KT2 6PX.
Tel. (081) 541 3717
Fairfield Bitter (OG 1037)
Royal Charter (OG 1044)
Coronation (OG 1059)
Once a David Bruce pub, now owned by Saxon Inns. Malt extract used and some cellar tanks.

FOX & HOUNDS
Barley Brewery, Barley, Royston, Herts, SG8 8HU.
Tel. (0763) 848459
Old Dragon (OG 1038)
Flamethrower (OG 1049)
Early member of the pub brewing revival, using a 19th-century brewhouse. New equipment has recently been installed.

FOX & HOUNDS
Stottesdon, Shropshire, DY14 8TZ.
Tel. (074 632) 222
Woody Woodward's Wonder Water or Woody's Bitter (OG 1037)
Dasher's Draught (OG 1040)
Hound's Bitter (OG 1044)
Millward's Mega Mild (OG 1046)
Winter Ale (OG 1070)
Also supplies some other pubs.

FOX & NEWT
9 Burley Street, Leeds, W. Yorks, LS3 1LD.
Tel. (0532) 432612
Burley Bitter (OG 1036, ABV 3.8%)
Old Willow (OG 1046, ABV 4.6%)
Kirkstall Ruin (OG 1066, 6.5%) A winter beer.
A Whitbread malt extract pub, opened in 1982.

FROG & PARROT
Division Street, Sheffield, S. Yorks, S1 4GF.
Tel. (0742) 721280
Old Croak Ale (OG 1035)
Reckless Bitter (OG 1046)
Roger's Conqueror (OG 1066)
Roger & Out (OG 1125)
Whitbread malt extract brew pub. Roger & Out is listed in the *Guinness Book of Records* as the world's strongest beer in terms of alcoholic content.

GREYHOUND BREWERY COMPANY
151 Greyhound Lane, Streatham Common, London, SW16 5NJ. Tel. (081) 677 9962
XXXP Mild (OG 1036, ABV 3.6%)
Special Ale (OG 1038, ABV 3.8%)
Streatham Strong (OG 1048, ABV 4.9%)
Streatham Dynamite (OG 1056, ABV 5.5%)
A Clifton Inns brew pub, set up in 1984. XXXP is the only traditional mild brewed in London, though blanket pressure is used in the cellar tanks.

HAND IN HAND
Kemptown Brewery Company Ltd., 33 Upper St James's Street, Kemptown, Brighton, E. Sussex, BN2 1JN. Tel. (0273) 602521

Mild (OG 1035, ABV 3.5%)
Bitter (OG 1041, ABV 4%)
Celebrated Staggering Ale (OG 1050, ABV 5%)
Staggering in the Dark (SID) (OG 1052, ABV 5.1%)
Old Grumpy (OG 1065, ABV 6%) Winter only.
Full mash brewery started in November 1989, taking the name of the old Kemptown Brewery, 500 yards away. Specially constructed behind the pub in the 'tower' tradition. Some free trade supplied.

HEDGEHOG & HOGSHEAD
100 Goldstone Villas, Hove, E. Sussex, BN3 3RX.
Tel. (0273) 733660
Brighton Breezy Bitter (OG 1045)
Hogbolter (OG 1060)
Prickletickler (OG 1075) An occasional brew.
The first of David Bruce's new ventures, which opened in July 1990. Blanket pressure used.

HEDGEHOG & HOGSHEAD
163 University Road, Highfield, Southampton, Hampshire, SO2 1TS. Tel. (0703) 581124
Belcher's Best Bitter (OG 1045)
Hogbolter (OG 1060)
Prickletickler (OG 1075) An occasional brew.
Slay Belles (OG 1080) The Christmas beer.
The second in the new chain. Blanket pressure used.

HIGHLANDER
North & East Riding Brewers Ltd., 15–16 Esplanade, South Cliff, Scarborough, N. Yorks.
Tel. (0723) 365627
EXB (OG 1038)
Mild (OG 1040)
Thistle Bitter (OG 1042)
68 (OG 1046)
Brewery set up behind a Victorian hotel, which used to sell its 'William Clark' Scotch-style beers to the free trade, but now only brews for itself.

JOLLY ROGER
88 St Owen Street, Hereford, HR1 2QD.
Tel. (0432) 274998
Quaff Ale (OG 1038)
Blackbeard (OG 1043)
Old Hereford Bull (OG 1050)
An off-shoot of the well-established Worcester Jolly Roger. The bar takes the shape of a galleon.

JOLLY ROGER BREWERY AND TAP
50 Lowesmoor, Worcester, WR1 2SG.
Tel. (0905) 21540
Quaff Ale (OG 1038)
Severn Bore Special (OG 1048)
Old Lowesmoor (OG 1058)
Winter Wobbler (OG 1092) The seasonal brew.
Set up in 1982 and grew to the point where it was supplying around 50 other outlets before a separate commercial brewery was opened (see Independents). Occasional one-off beers.

LASS O'GOWRIE
Charles Street, Manchester, M1 7DB.
Tel. (061) 273 6932
LOG 35 (OG 1035)
LOG 42 (OG 1042)
Centurion (OG 1052)
Graduation (OG 1056)
A Whitbread malt extract brew pub, opened in 1983. Beer is stored in cellar tanks without CO_2.

Brew Pubs

MARISCO TAVERN
Lundy Island Brewery, Lundy Island, Bristol
Channel, EX39 2LY. Tel. (0237) 431831
Mild (OG 1035) Summer only.
Pale Ale (OG 1044)
Old Light Bitter (OG 1055)
Beers produced using Lundy water and no additives.

MARKET PORTER
9 Stoney Street, Borough Market, London, SE1
9AA. Tel. (071) 407 2495
Bitter (OG 1038)
Special (OG 1048)
Malt extract brew pub.

MASONS ARMS
Lakeland Brewery Company, Strawberry Bank,
Cartmel Fell, Grange-over-Sands, Cumbria, LA11
6NW. Tel. (044 88) 486
Amazon Bitter (OG 1038)
Captain Flint (OG 1040) Occasional.
Great Northern (OG 1047)
Big Six (OG 1066)
Famous pub which began brewing in May 1990.
Beer names are based on books by local author
Arthur Ransome. *Bottle-conditioned beer*: *Damson
Beer* (*ABV* 9%) – made from the pub's own
damsons to a Kriek recipe and available in the
spring.

MINERVA
Nelson Street, Hull, Humbs, HU1 1XE.
Tel. (0482) 26909
Pilots Pride (OG 1039)
Joshua Tetley full mash brew pub, set up in 1983
and storing its beer under blanket pressure in both
casks and cellar tanks. Brews occasional specials.

MIN PIN INN
North Cornwall Brewers, Tintagel Brewery,
Tregatta, Tintagel, Cornwall, PL34 0DX.
Tel. (0840) 770241
Legend Bitter (OG 1036)
Brown Willy (OG 1052.5)
Converted farmhouse with possibly the only
entirely female-operated brewery in the country.
Malt extract used; beers only produced in summer.

OLD SWAN (Ma Pardoe's)
Halesowen Road, Netherton, Dudley, W. Midlands,
DY2 1BT. Tel. (0384) 253075
Ma Pardoe's Home-Brew (OG 1035, ABV 3.3%)
One of the great institutions of Black Country
drinking which was taken over by Wiltshire
Brewery in 1989. Has undergone a technical
overhaul in the last year and, consequently, did not
brew for a time. Ma Pardoe's Mild is now produced
at the Wiltshire brewery in Tisbury even though the
brewery no longer owns the pub.

ORANGE BREWERY
37–39 Pimlico Road, London, SW1W 8NE.
Tel. (071) 730 5984
Pimlico Light (OG 1032, ABV 3%)
SW1 (OG 1040, ABV 3.6%)
Pimlico Porter (OG 1046, ABV 4.1%)
SW2 (OG 1050, ABV 4.6%)
Stout (OG 1058, ABV 5.5%)
Clifton Inns' first in-house brewery, opened in 1983.
The full mash brews are kept with a cask breather,

except for the Stout which is under mixed gas
pressure. Brews a host of seasonal beers.

PLOUGH INN
Bodicote Brewery, Bodicote, Banbury, Oxfordshire,
OX15 4BZ. Tel. (0295) 262327
Bitter (OG 1035)
Old English Porter (OG 1045)
No. 9 (OG 1045)
Triple X (OG 1050) The Christmas ale.
Brewery founded in 1982; pub has been in the
same hands for 34 years. Brews for some free trade.

REINDEER FREEHOUSE & BREWERY
10 Dereham Road, Norwich, Norfolk, NR2 4AY.
Tel. (0603) 666821
Bill's Bevy (OG 1037, ABV 4%)
Moild (OG 1037, ABV 4%)
Bitter (OG 1047, ABV 5%)
Red Nose (OG 1057, ABV 6%)
Sanity Claus (OG 1067, ABV 6%) Christmas.
Sledgehammer (OG 1067, ABV 6%) Christmas.
Brewery opened in May 1987. Beer is stored in
cellar tanks under blanket pressure.

RISING SUN INN
Knowle Bank Road, Shraley Brook, Audley, Stoke-
on-Trent, Staffs, ST7 8DS. Tel. (0782) 720600
Sunlight (OG 1036) Summer only.
Rising (OG 1040, ABV 3.9%)
Setting (OG 1045, ABV 4.4%)
Sun Stroke (OG 1056, ABV 5.6%)
Total Eclipse (OG 1072, ABV 6.5%)
Solar Flare (OG 1100, ABV 9.7%) Winter only.
Pub which began brewing in June 1990.

ROSE STREET BREWERY
Rose Street, Edinburgh, Lothian, EH2.
Tel. (031) 220 1227
Auld Reekie 80/- (OG 1043, ABV 4%)
Auld Reekie 90/- (OG 1057.5, ABV 5%+)
Scotland's first brew pub, founded in 1983, run by
Alloa Brewery and now supplying seven other
outlets. Malt extract used.

**ROYAL INN & HORSEBRIDGE
BREWERY**
Horsebridge, Tavistock, Devon, PL19 8PJ.
Tel. (082 287) 214
Tamar (OG 1039, ABV 3.9%)
Horsebridge Best (OG 1045, ABV 4.4%)
Right Royal (OG 1050) Special occasions only.
Heller (OG 1060, ABV 5.8%)
15th-century country pub, once a nunnery, which
began brewing in 1981.

SADDLE INN
Featherstone Brewery, Main Street, Twyford,
Melton Mowbray, Leicestershire, LE14 2HU.
Tel. (0664) 840237
Best Bitter (OG 1040)
Extra Special Bitter (OG 1055)
New brew pub which also produces a handpulled
lager. Supplies one other pub.

STEAM PACKET INN
Racca Green, Knottingley, Pontefract, W. Yorks.
Tel. (0977) 677266
Mellor's Gamekeeper (OG 1037)
New brew pub with other beers planned.

Brew Pubs

TALLY HO COUNTRY INN & BREWERY
14 Market Street, Hatherleigh, Devon, EX20 3JN.
Tel. (0837) 810306
Potboiler's Brew (OG 1036)
Tarka's Tipple (OG 1044)
Nutters (OG 1050)
Janni Jollop (OG 1064) Winter only.
Full mash brew pub, established 1990.

THREE TUNS BREWERY
Salop Street, Bishop's Castle, Shropshire, SY9 5AL.
Tel. (0588) 638797
Mild (OG 1035)
XXX (OG 1040)
Steamer (OG 1045)
Old Scrooge (OG 1054) Winter only.
Historic brew pub which first obtained a brewing licence in 1642. The tower brewery was built in 1888 and is still in use.

WATERLOO ARMS
101 Waterloo Road, Freemantle, Southampton, Hampshire.
New brew pub owned by Hop Back brewery, opened in May 1991. Beers have initially been supplied by Hop Back.

WILLY'S
17 High Cliff Road, Cleethorpes, Humbs, DN35 8RQ. Tel. (0472) 602145
Original Bitter (OG 1038, ABV 3.9%)
Festival Bitter (OG 1038, ABV 3.9%) An occasional brew.
Coxswains Special Bitter (OG 1049, ABV 5%)
Old Groyne (OG 1060, ABV 6.2%)
Brewery opened in May 1989. Another outlet, SWIGS, was bought in December 1989.

YORKSHIRE GREY
2 Theobalds Road, London, WC1X 8PN.
Tel. (071) 405 2519
City Bitter (OG 1032)
Headline Bitter (OG 1037)
Holborn Best (OG 1047)
Regiment Bitter (OG 1056)
Clifton Inns brew pub. CO_2 blanket on cellar tanks.

THE FIRKIN PUBS
This highly successful chain of brew pubs was initiated by David Bruce in 1979. In 1988 he sold all the pubs to Midsummer Leisure, later European Leisure, who, in turn, sold them to Stakis Leisure in September 1990, the same month as a new pub, Manchester's Flea & Firkin, was opened. Not all the Firkin pubs now brew; some are supplied by the others, so only the actual brew pubs are listed here. All the brews are full mash beers, but most of the pubs use cellar tanks for storage, with the beer kept under a blanket of CO_2.

FALCON & FIRKIN
360 Victoria Park Road, Hackney, London, E9 7BT.
Tel. (081) 985 0693
Victoria Amber Mild (OG 1037, ABV 3.7%) Usually only in winter.
Falcon (OG 1038, ABV 3.7%)
Hackney (OG 1043, ABV 4.4%)
Dogbolter (OG 1059, ABV 6%)

Slaybells (OG 1072, ABV 7.5%) A Christmas brew. The largest of the Firkin breweries.

FERRET & FIRKIN
114 Lots Road, Chelsea, London, SW10 0RJ.
Tel. (071) 352 6645
Ferret Ale (OG 1044, ABV 4.6%)
Dogbolter (OG 1059, ABV 6%)
'The Ferret & Firkin in the Balloon up the Creek', as it is properly known. Opened in 1983.

FLAMINGO & FIRKIN
Becket Street, Derby, DE1 1HT. Tel. (0332) 45948
Special Stout (OG 1042)
Tom Becket (OG 1043)
Dogbolter (OG 1059)
Slaybells (OG 1070) A Christmas beer.
Established in 1988.

FLEA & FIRKIN
137 Grosvenor Street, Manchester, M1 7DZ.
Tel. (061) 274 3682
Scratch (OG 1036)
Grosvenor (OG 1043)
Dogbolter (OG 1059)
The newest Firkin, already expanded.

FLOUNDER & FIRKIN
54 Holloway Road, London, N7 8JL.
Tel. (071) 609 9574
Bruce's Mild (OG 1036)
Fish T'ale (OG 1036)
Whale Ale (OG 1044)
Ginger Tom (OG 1050) Summer only.
Bruce's Stout (OG 1050)
Dogbolter (OG 1059)
Opened in 1985. Ginger Tom is a ginger beer.

FOX & FIRKIN
316 Lewisham High Street, London, SE13.
Tel. (081) 690 8925
Fox Bitter (OG 1044)
Dogbolter (OG 1059)
Opened in 1980. Special brews for the Firkin chain are produced here. Vixen Bitter (OG 1036) is occasionally brewed for the Fox at the Falcon & Firkin.

GOOSE & FIRKIN
47–48 Borough Road, London, SE1.
Tel. (071) 403 3590
Borough Bitter (OG 1044)
Dogbolter (OG 1059)
The first of the Firkin pubs, still using malt extract in its small cellar brewery. Goose Bitter (OG 1036) is brewed at the Falcon & Firkin.

PHOENIX & FIRKIN
5 Windsor Walk, Camberwell, London, SE5 8BB.
Tel. (071) 701 8282
Rail Ale (OG 1037)
Phoenix Bitter (OG 1044)
Midnight Express Stout (OG 1051)
Dogbolter (OG 1059)
An award-winning reconstruction of the burnt-out Denmark Hill railway station, opened in 1984. Midnight Express is cask-conditioned (no blanket).

THE BEERS INDEX

The Beers Index is your reference to those beers not always remembered by their brewery prefix. Adnams Mild, for example, will clearly be found under Adnams in the Breweries Section and therefore this and other such easy-to-locate beers have not been included here. But if you want to find out more about Abbot Ale, for instance, then this index will tell you that it is brewed by Greene King and more information can be found on page 416.

CAMRA BOOKS AND PRODUCTS

A full list of CAMRA books, local guides and products is available on request. Here is just a selection – all prices include post and packing. Tear out or copy this form for ease of ordering; use the blank line for any books not listed, which have been described on previous pages.

	Quantity	Price each	Amount
National Guides CAMRA Guide to Good Pub Food (new edition)		£7.99	
The Best Pubs for Families		£4.95	
Good Cider Guide		£5.95	
Beer, Bed & Breakfast		£6.99	
Regional Guides (£1 off cover price) The Best Pubs in... Devon & Cornwall		£3.95	
East Anglia		£3.95	
Lakeland		£2.95	
London		£3.95	
North Wales		£3.95	
Yorkshire		£3.95	
Other Titles CAMRA Guide to Home Brewing		£4.99	
Bedside Book of Beer		£6.99	
21st Birthday Book		£6.99	
Other Products 21st Birthday Tie		£5.95	
CAMRA Tie		£5.50	
PVC Protective Cover for the *Good Beer Guide*		£2.50	
PLUS:		£	
		Total	£

Please send to CAMRA Ltd., 34 Alma Road, St Albans, Herts, AL1 3BW (cheques made payable to CAMRA Ltd. must accompany all orders). Allow three weeks for delivery. To place a credit card order, phone (0727) 867201.

Name	
Address	
	Post Code

HAVE YOUR SAY

Suggestions for pubs to be included or excluded

All pubs are surveyed by the local branches of CAMRA. If you would like to draw their attention to a pub already featured, or any you think should be featured, please fill in the form below and send it to the address indicated. We also welcome letters, if readers feel strongly about pub entries. Readers contributions are much appreciated.

Pub Name:

Address:

Reason for recommendation/criticism:

Pub Name:

Address:

Reason for recommendation/criticism:

Your name and address:

Please send to: GBG, CAMRA Ltd., 34 Alma Road, St Albans, Herts, AL1 3BW.

INSTRUCTION TO YOUR BANK
TO PAY DIRECT DEBITS

Please complete parts 1 to 4 to instruct your bank to make payments directly from your account.

Return the form to Campaign for Real Ale Limited, 34 Alma Road, St Albans, Herts, AL1 3BW.

To the Manager

Bank

1 Please write the full postal address of your bank branch in the box.

2 Name(s) of account-holder(s)

Address

Post Code

3 Account number

Banks may refuse to accept instructions to pay direct debits from some types of account.

Direct debit instructions should only be addressed to banks in the United Kingdom.

CAMRA Computer Membership No. (for office use only)

| 0 | 0 | | | | | |

Originator's Identification No.

| 9 | 2 | 6 | 1 | 2 | 9 |

4 Your instruction to the bank, and signature.
* I instruct you to pay direct debits from my account at the request of Campaign for Real Ale Limited.
* The amounts are variable and are to be debited annually.
* I understand that Campaign for Real Ale Limited may change the amount only after giving me prior notice.
* PLEASE CANCEL ALL PREVIOUS STANDING ORDER INSTRUCTIONS IN FAVOUR OF CAMPAIGN FOR REAL ALE LIMITED.
* I will inform the bank in writing if I wish to cancel this instruction.
* I understand that if any direct debit is paid which breaks the terms of this instruction, the bank will make a refund.

Signature(s)

Date

JOIN CAMRA NOW
TRIAL MEMBERSHIP – FREE FOR THREE MONTHS

Once dubbed 'the most successful consumer organisation in Europe', CAMRA has always been known for its forceful campaigning on the issues of beer and pubs. But CAMRA is far more than just a pressure group. Yes, we attack brewery closures, lobby Parliament, organise rallies and applaud the praiseworthy, but we also have a lot of fun.

As a CAMRA member, you can attend local branch meetings. These often arrange brewery trips and other social outings, but they also determine the entries for the *Good Beer Guide*. If you feel strongly about a pub in your area and want to have your say, join now and speak up at the next selection meeting.

As a CAMRA member, you receive generous discounts on all CAMRA books and products, including the *Good Beer Guide*. You also receive the monthly *What's Brewing* newspaper, bringing you all the latest on the pub scene.

As a CAMRA member, you can vote at the annual Conference, help dictate policy, nominate beers for the *Champion Beer of Britain* awards and gain free or reduced rate admission to our many beer festivals across the country.

So why not give it a try, at no cost to yourself? The three month trial membership entitles you to:

★ the next three copies of *What's Brewing*
★ the information-packed Member's Handbook
★ the full range of product discounts
★ a CAMRA membership card, entitling you to beer festival reductions

All you have to do is fill in the direct debit form overleaf and sign the application form below. If after three months you do not wish to continue your membership, simply write to us, returning your membership card, and you will owe nothing.

On the other hand, if you do not wish to take advantage of this offer, but still want to join, just fill in the application form and send it with a cheque for your first year's subscription. Do not fill in the direct debit form. For payment by credit card, phone the membership secretary on (0727) 867201.

Full membership £10; Joint husband/wife membership £12; Life membership £100/£120
Please delete as appropriate:
I/We wish to take advantage of the trial membership, and have completed the instructions overleaf.
I/We wish to become members of CAMRA.
I/We agree to abide by the memorandum and articles of association of the company.
I/We enclose a cheque/p.o. for £   (payable to CAMRA Ltd.)

Name(s)

Address

Signature(s)

CAMRA Ltd., 34 Alma Road, St Albans, Herts, AL1 3BW.